Introducing a wider variety of tools
than ever before,
to help your students learn.

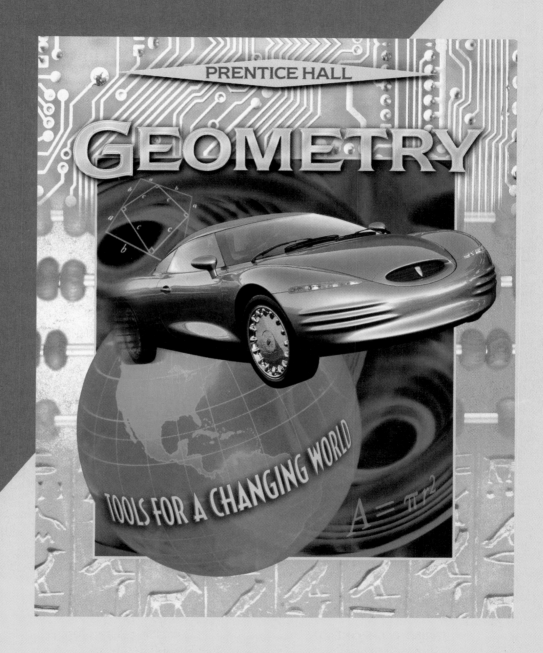

PRENTICE HALL

GEOMETRY

TOOLS FOR A CHANGING WORLD

$A = \pi r^2$

Prentice Hall's all-new Math Series provides you with more Motivation and Management Tools than any other program.

Our world is constantly changing. Recently in math, teachers are being asked to respond to a variety of new learning styles and to deal with multiple classroom environments. Prentice Hall's all-new Math Series—*Algebra, Geometry, and Advanced Algebra: Tools for a Changing World* ©1998—has been developed specifically to help teachers manage these key changes, and many others. We do it through more worked-out examples, better ties to the real world, more small group work, and accessible technology. Finally, a math series that can motivate today's student, cover the basic skills, support the NCTM guidelines, and ultimately lead to success.

Geometry: Tools for a Changing World

▼ Geometry and algebra reinforce each other through multiple tie-ins. Now, you're able to keep algebra alive in your classroom as well as reach a wider variety of learners.

▼ Inductive and deductive reasoning are introduced early. Students progress gradually from informal arguments to more formal presentations of proof.

▼ Coordinate and transformational geometry are interwoven *throughout* the text.

▼ Hands-on activities, at point of use, allow students to discover geometric concepts and make the mathematics their own.

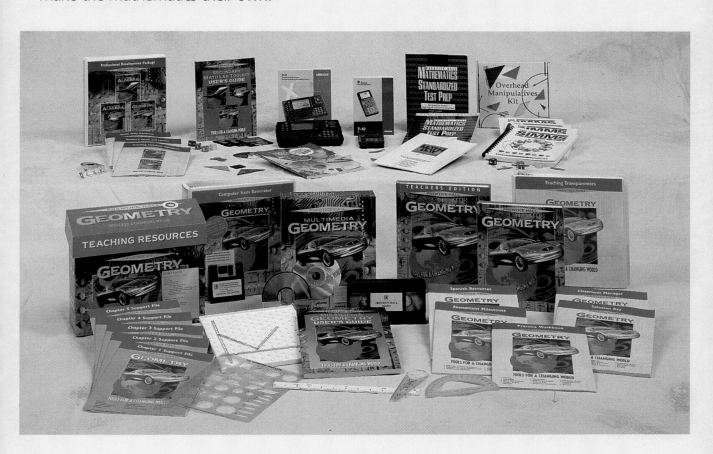

TECHNOLOGY COMPONENTS:
Video Field Trips
Graphing Calculator Handbook
Calculator-Based Laboratory™
   Activities (CBL™)
Graphing Calculator TI-83 10-Pack
Graphing Calculator TI-92 10-Pack
Computer Item Generator
   with Dial-A-Test™
Secondary Math Lab Toolkit™
Multimedia Algebra CD-ROM
Multimedia Advanced Algebra
   CD-ROM
Multimedia Geometry CD-ROM
Resource Pro™ CD-ROM

TABLE OF CONTENTS ON NEXT PAGE

PRENTICE HALL MATH

GEOMETRY © 1998

ALGEBRA © 1998

ADVANCED ALGEBRA © 1998

PRENTICE HALL

GEOMETRY

AUTHORS

Laurie E. Bass

Art Johnson

Basia Rinesmith Hall

Dorothy F. Wood

Contributing Author

Simone W. Bess

Algebra Authors

Allan Bellman

Theodore J. Gardella

Sadie Chavis Bragg

Bettye C. Hall

Suzanne H. Chapin

William G. Handlin, Sr.

Edward Manfre

TOOLS FOR A CHANGING WORLD

PRENTICE HALL
Needham, Massachusetts
Upper Saddle River, New Jersey

REVIEWERS

Series Reviewers

James Gates, Ed.D.
Executive Director Emeritus, National Council of Teachers of Mathematics
Reston, Virginia

Vinetta Jones, Ph.D.
National Director, Equity 2000, The College Board, New York, New York

Geometry

Sandra Argüelles Daire
Miami Senior High School
Miami, Florida

Priscilla P. Donkle
South Central High School
Union Mills, Indiana

Tom Muchlinski, Ph.D.
Wayzata High School
Plymouth, Minnesota

Bonnie Walker
Texas ASCD
Houston, Texas

Karen Doyle Walton, Ed.D.
Allentown College of
Saint Francis de Sales
Center Valley, Pennsylvania

Algebra

John J. Brady III
Hume-Fogg High School
Nashville, Tennessee

Elias P. Rodriguez
Leander Junior High School
Leander, Texas

Dorothy S. Strong, Ed.D.
Chicago Public Schools
Chicago, Illinois

Art W. Wilson, Ed.D.
Abraham Lincoln High School
Denver, Colorado

Advanced Algebra

Eleanor Boehner
Methacton High School
Norristown, Pennsylvania

Laura Price Cobb
Dallas Public Schools
Dallas, Texas

William Earl, Ed.D.
Formerly Mathematics
Education Specialist
Utah State Office of Education
Salt Lake City, Utah

Robin Levine Rubinstein
Shorewood High School
Shoreline, Washington

Staff Credits

The people who made up the Geometry team—representing editorial, design, marketing, page production, manufacturing, technology, electronic publishing, and advertising and promotion—and their managers are listed below. Bold type denotes core team members.

Alison Anholt-White, Jackie Zidek Bedoya, Barbara A. Bertell, Bruce Bond, Ellen Brown, Judith D. Buice, Kathy Carter, Kerri Caruso, **Linda M. Coffey**, **Noralie V. Cox**, Sheila DeFazio, Edward de Leon, Christine Deliee, Gabriella Della Corte, Robert G. Dunn, Barbara Flockhart, Audra Floyd, David Graham, Maria Green, Bridget A. Hadley, Joanne Hudson, Vanessa Hunnibell, Mimi Jigarjian, **Linda D. Johnson**, Elizabeth A. Jordan, Russell Lappa, **Catherine Martin-Hetmansky**, Eve Melnechuk, Cindy A. Noftle, Caroline M. Power, Roger E. Powers, Martha G. Smith, Kira Thaler, Robin Tiano, Christina Trinchero, Stuart Wallace, Cynthia A. Weedel, **Jeff Weidenaar**, **Pearl B. Weinstein**, Mary Jane Wolfe, Stewart Wood, David Zarowin

We would like to give special thanks to our National Math Consultants, Ann F. Bell, Patricia M. Cominsky, and Brenda Underwood, for all their help in developing this program.

PRENTICE HALL
Simon & Schuster Education Group
A VIACOM COMPANY

ISBN: 0-13-411067-6

2 3 4 5 6 7 8 9 10   03 02 01 00 99 98 97

Geometry Authors

Laurie E. Bass is a classroom teacher at the Fieldston School in Riverdale, New York. Ms. Bass has a wide base of teaching experience, ranging from grades 6 and 7 through Advanced Placement Calculus. She also has been a contributing writer of a number of publications, including software-based activities for the Algebra 1 classroom. One of her areas of special interest is geometric exploration on the computer. Chapters 2, 7, 9

Basia Rinesmith Hall, Department Chairperson at Alief Hastings High School, Alief Independent School District in Alief, Texas, is a 1992 winner of the Presidential Award for Excellence in Mathematics Teaching. Ms. Hall was a member of the NCTM Professional Teaching Standards Review Committee, served on the writing committee of the Texas Essential Knowledge Skills (TEKS), and is President of the Texas Council of Teachers of Mathematics (1996–1998). Chapters 3, 8, 11

Art Johnson, Ed.D., is a classroom teacher in Nashua High School, Nashua, New Hampshire. Dr. Johnson is a frequent speaker and workshop leader and the recipient of a number of awards, including the Tandy Prize for Teaching Excellence in 1995 and a 1992 Presidential Award for Excellence in Mathematics Teaching. He was profiled by the Disney Corporation in the American Teacher of the Year Program. Chapters 1, 6, 10

Dorothy F. Wood, formerly with the Kern High School District in Bakersfield, California, is an active member of the California Mathematics Council and a frequent presenter at their conferences. She is also a leader of middle and high school staff-development workshops sponsored by schools, districts, and county offices. As Teacher Leader and Evaluator, she serves numerous schools in the California Department of Education Mathematics Demonstration Program. Chapters 4, 5, 12

Contributing Author

Simone W. Bess, Ed.D., Adjunct Mathematics Instructor at the University of Cincinnati and Cincinnati State Technical and Community College, came to mathematics education through a career in engineering at General Electric Aircraft Engines. She is a frequent speaker at professional meetings around the country, and has special interests in integrating diversity in the classroom and supporting girls and women in mathematics careers. Dr. Bess has also been active in coordinating a number of NSF-funded programs for minority students, K–12.

Algebra & Advanced Algebra Authors

Allan Bellman
Watkins Mill High School
Gaithersburg, Maryland

Sadie Chavis Bragg, Ed.D.
The City University of New York
New York, New York

Suzanne H. Chapin, Ed.D.
Boston University
Boston, Massachusetts

Theodore Gardella
Formerly, Bloomfield Public Schools
Bloomfield Hills, Michigan

Bettye C. Hall
Formerly, Unified School District
Houston, Texas

William G. Handlin, Sr.
Spring Woods High School
Houston, Texas

Edward Manfre
Albuquerque, New Mexico

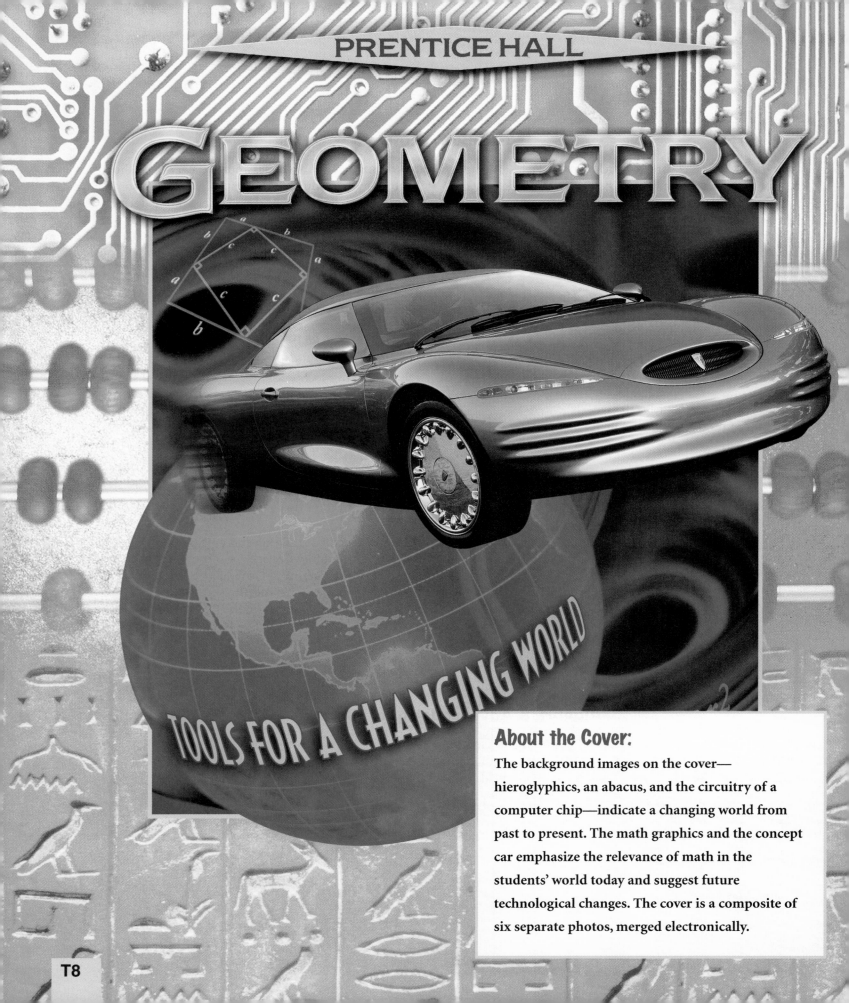

PRENTICE HALL

GEOMETRY

TOOLS FOR A CHANGING WORLD

About the Cover:

The background images on the cover—hieroglyphics, an abacus, and the circuitry of a computer chip—indicate a changing world from past to present. The math graphics and the concept car emphasize the relevance of math in the students' world today and suggest future technological changes. The cover is a composite of six separate photos, merged electronically.

GEOMETRY
TOOLS FOR A CHANGING WORLD

CONTENTS

Geometry Contents

The "To the Student" pages help students understand how they learn and how the textbook relates to their daily lives. The Skills Handbook provides an in-text tutorial of skills that students may need to review. Extra Practice pages for each chapter contain additional exercises correlated to each lesson. The Glossary/Study Guide provides not only a definition and a page reference but also an example of each vocabulary term.

Tools of Geometry

Connections and Applications

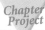

Chapter Project *On Folded Wings*
The Art of Origami

Students develop inductive and deductive reasoning skills as they learn the basics of geometry. They make and test conjectures about mathematical and real-world patterns. They draw and measure two- and three-dimensional figures. As they build their geometric vocabulary, they write and test their own definitions. Chapter 1 also introduces coordinate geometry, which is stranded throughout the text.

2 Investigating Geometric Figures

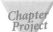
Through hands-on activities, students investigate properties of the basic figures of geometry — triangles, quadrilaterals and other polygons, as well as circles. They use hands-on materials to explore congruency and similarity, concepts that are revisited throughout the text. Students apply their algebra skills as they study parallel and perpendicular lines in the coordinate plane.

CHAPTER 3 · Transformations: Shapes in Motion

Chapter Project

Frieze Frames
Analyzing and Creating Frieze Patterns

Students expand their hands-on study of congruence and similarity by discovering the properties of reflections, translations, rotations, glide reflections, and dilations. The relevance of transformations is emphasized through real-world applications and works of art. In the rest of the course, students revisit transformations in a variety of contexts.

CHAPTER
4
Triangle Relationships

 Connections and Applications

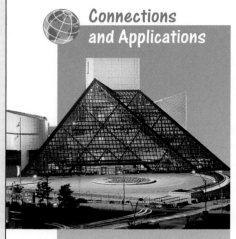

. . . and More!

Chapter Project   *Puzzling Pieces*
Solving and Writing Logic Puzzles

 x   Contents

Students are exposed to deductive argument in informal, real-life situations and in mathematical settings related to properties of triangles. As students improve their reasoning skills, the groundwork is laid for later, more in-depth work with proof.

5 Measuring in the Plane

Connections and Applications

. . . and More!

Chapter Project **And Sew On**
Planning and Designing a Quilt

xi

Using a variety of investigative tools, students discover formulas for the areas of polygons and circles, and apply them to solve real-world problems. Students study area-based proofs of the Pythagorean Theorem — which are more visual and convincing than the traditional proofs. Finally, they use algebra to deduce the properties of 30°-60°-90° and 45°-45°-90° triangles.

CHAPTER 6 Measuring in Space

Connections and Applications

xii

Students develop and improve their spatial visualization and reasoning skills with three-dimensional figures. They begin by drawing nets of solids. Using area formulas of plane figures as a starting point, students develop the formulas for surface area and volume of prisms, cylinders, pyramids, cones, and spheres. The last lesson provides an opportunity for students to review concepts from Chapters 5 and 6 in the context of geometric probability.

Reasoning and Parallel Lines

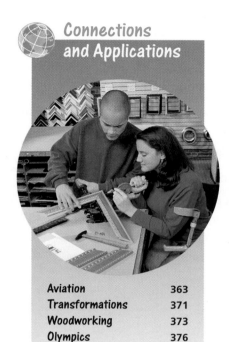

Connections and Applications

... and More!

Chapter Project **Network News**
Analyzing and Designing Networks

Students investigate properties of parallel lines and write deductive arguments to justify their conclusions. They apply properties of parallel lines to real-world situations, constructions, and drawing in one- and two-point perspective. Finally, they explore spherical geometry (in which no parallel lines exist!) and contrast it with Euclidean geometry.

CHAPTER 8 Proving Triangles Congruent

Connections and Applications

Chapter Project **Tri Tri Again**
Using Triangles to Build Bridges

Building on the strong foundation of congruency established in earlier chapters, students use manipulatives and technology to discover conditions that ensure congruent triangles. A gradual introduction to proof provides students with the confidence and the solid conceptual understanding they need to write well-reasoned deductive arguments.

T18

Connections and Applications

... and More!

Chapter Project

Go Fly a Kite
Designing and Constructing a Kite

Students apply what they have learned about triangles to develop properties of parallelograms, trapezoids, and kites. They continue to develop their mathematical reasoning abilities and their algebraic skills by learning to write coordinate proofs.

CHAPTER

10 Similarity

 Connections and Applications

. . . and More!

 Chapter Project

Fractals Forever
Investigating Self-similarity and Fractals

xvi

Similarity is an important strand throughout the text. In Chapter 2, students learned that two figures are similar if they have the same shape but not necessarily the same size. In Chapter 3, they studied similarity from another perspective, dilations. Now, in addition to learning how to prove triangles similar, students apply similarity to study fractals, scale drawings, and the connections between areas and volumes of similar figures.

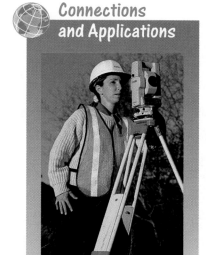

Connections and Applications

Chapter Project

Measure for Measure
Measuring Distance Indirectly

Right-triangle trigonometry comes alive with a variety of connections to the real world. Lessons on vectors provide an interesting and relevant context for application of trigonometric ratios. Connections to area involve more applications of trigonometry and simultaneously review significant concepts.

Connections
and Applications

Chapter Project **Go For a Spin**
Using Circles in Art

Students study circles from an algebraic point of view by writing equations of circles in the coordinate plane. They use compasses, protractors, MIRAs™, and software to make conjectures about circles, chords, tangents, and secants, and then write well-constructed justifications in a variety of formats — two-column proofs, paragraph proofs, flow proofs, and coordinate proofs.

PRENTICE HALL MATH

"After reviewing all of the chapters, I believe I can say that you have done an excellent job interpreting the NCTM Standards, both the process standards as well as the content standards."

James Gates, Ed.D.
Executive Director Emeritus
National Council of Teachers of Mathematics

"I am glad to see that the Prentice Hall textbook will contain information that will answer the most popular questions asked by students: When and where are we going to use this? and Do I really have to know this?"

Elias P. Rodriguez
Mathematics Teacher
Leander, Texas

"The Prentice Hall book was fun, and I learned a lot! I had trouble reading our old book's examples. The examples in the Prentice Hall book were much easier to understand. I learn more by using the examples, and this helped a lot! My grades went up this quarter."

Heidi S.
Field-test student

"The chapter was very well organized and it had a lot of review. This review is very precise and covers all I needed to know. All textbooks should have this kind of review."

Ali A.
Field-test student

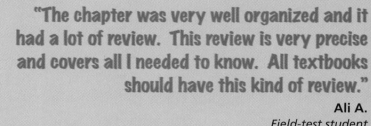

Teachers and students across the country helped Prentice Hall develop this program. They identified the teaching tools that you can use to motivate students and manage instruction. We would like to hear from you. Write us at Prentice Hall Math, 160 Gould Street, Needham, MA 02194, or visit us on the Internet at http://www.phschool.com.

Why did we name our program "Tools for a Changing World"?

Because you've said

...not all **STUDENTS** have the same learning style;

...not all **TEACHERS** have the same teaching style;

...and no two **CLASSROOM** environments are the same.

It is for these reasons that we offer you a <u>wide variety of teaching tools</u> to help you M<small>OTIVATE</small> your students and M<small>ANAGE</small> instruction.

TOOLS FOR A CHANGING WORLD

brings together the widest variety of Teaching Tools.

Using these tools, Prentice Hall Math helps you address the *motivation* and *management* issues you've told us are foremost on your mind.

✔	Motivating Students	*See page* **T26**
✔	Integrating Technology	*See page* **T28**
✔	Assessing Students' Learning	*See page* **T29**
✔	Managing Time Constraints	*See page* **T30**
✔	Pacing the Course	*See page* **T31**
✔	Growing Professionally	*See page* **T32**

Motivating Students

How can I motivate students to *want* to learn math?

BY USING ANY OR ALL OF THESE RESOURCES.	Where do I look?	
The Relating to the Real World completely worked-out Examples and practice exercises show students just how often math is used in their lives today and in the future.	Student Edition	
Chapter Projects are long-term projects that provide a real-world connection to the math content of the chapter.	Student Edition	
Video Field Trips support the chapter projects or other real-world connections for each chapter in the Student Edition.	Video Field Trips	
Suggestions for Connecting to the Students' World provide opportunities for discussing how students apply math in their lives.	Teacher's Edition	
Connecting to Prior Knowledge sections show students how new math concepts are related to material previously learned.	Teacher's Edition	
The Student Manipulatives Kit engages students in a hands-on experience when discovering and connecting math concepts.	Student Manipulatives Kit	
Multimedia Math Labs combine animation, graphics, video, and Math Tools in chapter-long Math Labs to spark the students' interest in the mathematics of each chapter.	Multimedia Math Labs	
Secondary Math Lab Toolkit™ gives you and students software-based Integrated Math Labs with Math Tools for exploration.	Secondary Math Lab Toolkit™	
Prentice Hall's Internet Home Page offers a special section on Math, including projects of the month, exciting links, and a calendar of events.	Internet http://www .phschool.com	

How can I help *all* students become lifelong learners?

BY USING ANY OR ALL OF THESE RESOURCES.	Where do I look?
In Work Together explorations students use a variety of tools, including algebra, technology, and manipulatives, to discover geometric concepts. In these activities students learn to work cooperatively, just as they will in the workplace.	Student Edition
Think and Discuss interactive questions offer students opportunities to communicate with their peers by practicing their listening, thinking, talking, and writing skills.	Student Edition
ESL and Diversity suggestions help reach students of various backgrounds to make their math experience fulfilling.	Teacher's Edition
Learning Styles sections provide suggestions for teaching concepts to students of different learning styles (tactile, auditory, kinesthetic, visual).	Teacher's Edition
Alternative Activities offer students of varying learning styles another way of understanding the lesson concepts.	Teaching Resources
Spanish Resources help students whose first language is Spanish to understand and apply concepts.	Teaching Resources
Study Skills Handbook offers students tips for successful studying that can be applied to other subject areas.	Teaching Resources
Secondary Math Lab Toolkit™ gives students the opportunity to integrate software into their learning, just as they will be using technology in most jobs.	Secondary Math Lab Toolkit™

Skills Practice · Assessment Options · Students' Experiences · Technology Options · **Teaching Tools** · Real World Contexts · Interactive Questioning · Group Work

PRENTICE HALL MATH

Helping you manage
the widest variety of motivational tools to

Reach All Students

What technology tools are available for me to use?

USE ANY OR ALL OF THESE RESOURCES.	Where do I look?
The Student Edition assumes the use of scientific calculators and incorporates investigations that use geometry software to explore and develop geometric concepts.	Student Edition
A Technology Options side column correlates all the technology components available in the program to each lesson.	Teacher's Edition
Graphing Calculator Handbook provides step-by-step instructions to guide students using a variety of calculators as they work on topics in some Student Edition lessons.	Graphing Calculator Handbook
Calculator-Based Laboratory™ Activities takes advantage of powerful CBL™ equipment and provides activities that relate to the math concepts in the Student Edition.	CBL Activities
Multimedia Math Labs feature CD-ROM–based Labs with QuickTime™ movies, animations, and the Secondary Math Lab Toolkit™ — all keyed to the program objectives.	Multimedia Math Labs
Secondary Math Lab Toolkit™ gives you and students software-based Integrated Math Labs with Math Tools for exploration.	Secondary Math Lab Toolkit™
Prentice Hall's Internet Home Page offers a special section on Math, including projects of the month, exciting links, and a calendar of events.	Internet http://www.phschool.com
The Resource Pro™ CD-ROM package helps you to plan by including many of the supplemental materials in an easy-to-access format.	Resource Pro™

Technology Options

Teaching Tools

Skills Practice

Assessment Options

Students' Experiences

Group Work

Interactive Questioning

Real World Contexts

PRENTICE HALL MATH

Helping you manage the many and varied options for

Using Technology

Where do I look for options to evaluate students' success?

USE ANY OR ALL OF THESE RESOURCES.	Where do I look?
Think and Discuss sections with their interactive questions and **Try This** practice exercises offer ongoing assessment as lessons are developed.	Student Edition
Preparing for Standardized Tests provides practice with open-ended, multiple-choice, and free-response questions and allows teachers to assess students' learning of the math concepts.	Student Edition and Teaching Resources
Alternative Assessment includes Self-Assessment sections, Portfolio activities, Journal questions, and Chapter Assessments in a variety of testing formats.	Student Edition and Teaching Resources
Lesson Quizzes offer you yet another opportunity to assess students' understanding of the lesson concepts.	Teacher's Edition and Transparencies
The **Interactive Student Tutorial** CD-ROM provides electronic self-tests for students as they prepare for exams and includes on-screen hints, lesson/lab tutorials, and instant scoring	Interactive Student Tutorial
Computer Item Generator enables you to customize assessment for individual needs.	Computer Item Generator with Dial-A-Test™
Chapter Project and Scoring Rubric helps students understand what is expected of them as they work on the chapter projects in the Student Edition.	Teaching Resources
Cumulative Assessment offers the option of long-term assessments (mid-book, second-half-of-book, end-of-book).	Teaching Resources

PRENTICE HALL MATH

Helping you manage
the many and varied options for

Assessing Learning

How can I free up my time for teaching?

BY USING ANY OR ALL OF THESE RESOURCES.

	Where do I look?
Work Together activities in the lesson itself provide cooperative group work without having to supplement the textbook.	Student Edition
Lessons divided into **Parts,** with titles announcing each new math concept, break the lesson into manageable sections.	Student Edition
Assignment Options that correlate to the lesson parts in the Student Edition offer you a quick and handy assignment, no matter how much of the lesson you cover during a class period.	Teacher's Edition
Chapter Support Files are organized chapter-by-chapter to keep the shuffling of booklets to a minimum and to help you easily find the resources you need.	Teacher's Edition
Classroom Manager pulls together Lesson Planners and Chapter Organizers that streamline your planning time.	Classroom Manager
Transparencies provide clear visual support to facilitate instruction and learning.	Transparencies
Computer Item Generator is a data bank of test items that allows you to quickly customize practice and assessment.	Computer Item Generator with Dial-A-Test™
Resource Pro™ is a CD-ROM–based package, containing supplemental materials and planning tools, that enables you to customize each lesson quickly and easily.	Resource Pro™

PRENTICE HALL MATH

Helping you manage your time!

TEACHING SUPPORT

How can I cover my objectives while accommodating different schedules?

BY USING THE FOLLOWING COURSE PACING GUIDE.

This chart is provided merely as a guide to help you customize your course. To accommodate flexible scheduling, many lessons are subdivided into parts. In your Teacher's Edition, these parts are indicated in red by the symbol ▼. The Assignment Options in each lesson indicate the practice exercises in the Student Edition that correspond to the parts of each lesson.

	Chapter 1 (8 lessons)	Chapter 2 (7 lessons)	Chapter 3 (7 lessons)	Chapter 4 (8 lessons)	Chapter 5 (8 lessons)	Chapter 6 (8 lessons)
Traditional Class Periods (40–45 minutes)	18	17	14	15	16	17
Block Scheduling Class Periods (90 minutes)	9	7	7	8	9	8

	Chapter 7 (5 lessons)	Chapter 8 (5 lessons)	Chapter 9 (6 lessons)	Chapter 10 (6 lessons)	Chapter 11 (6 lessons)	Chapter 12 (6 lessons)	TOTALS
Traditional Class Periods (40–45 minutes)	8	12	10	12	9	12	160
Block Scheduling Class Periods (90 minutes)	4	6	5	6	5	6	80

AND BY USING THIS PACING RESOURCE.

Where do I look?

Detailed **Chapter Pacing Options** precede each chapter and give you lesson-by-lesson pacing suggestions for that specific chapter.

Teacher's Edition

How can I find ideas and materials that will help me grow professionally?

BY TAKING ADVANTAGE OF SOME OR ALL OF THESE ACTIVITIES.

	Where do I look?
Lesson-specific or chapter-specific Teaching Notes at point of use offer you professional support.	Teacher's Edition
Professional Development Package offers you all the training tools necessary for customized professional development.	Professional Development Package
The Prentice Hall Internet Home Page provides, among other things, a calendar of professional events and a variety of links to other sites on the Web that offer content ideas as well as growth opportunities.	Internet http://www .phschool.com
Prentice Hall Summer Seminars, focusing on math issues and technology, bring together math educators and experts for a variety of interactive and hands-on sessions.	Watch your mail for special flyers.
Prentice Hall Consultant Workshops offer you experiences during in-service training to learn about specific math issues.	Contact your local Prentice Hall sales representative.

TEACHING SUPPORT

PRENTICE HALL MATH

Helping you manage the many and varied options for effective

Professional Development

PRENTICE HALL

GEOMETRY

Prentice Hall dedicates
this mathematics program
to all mathematics educators
and their students.

PRENTICE HALL
Needham, Massachusetts
Upper Saddle River, New Jersey

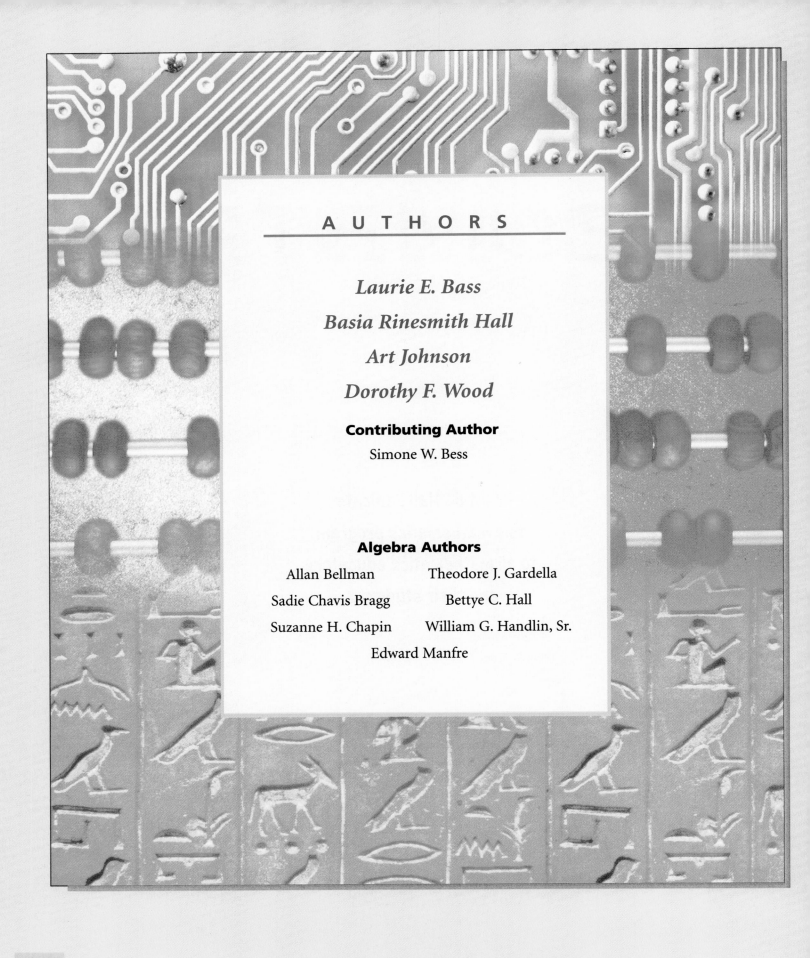

AUTHORS

Laurie E. Bass

Basia Rinesmith Hall

Art Johnson

Dorothy F. Wood

Contributing Author

Simone W. Bess

Algebra Authors

Allan Bellman   Theodore J. Gardella

Sadie Chavis Bragg   Bettye C. Hall

Suzanne H. Chapin   William G. Handlin, Sr.

Edward Manfre

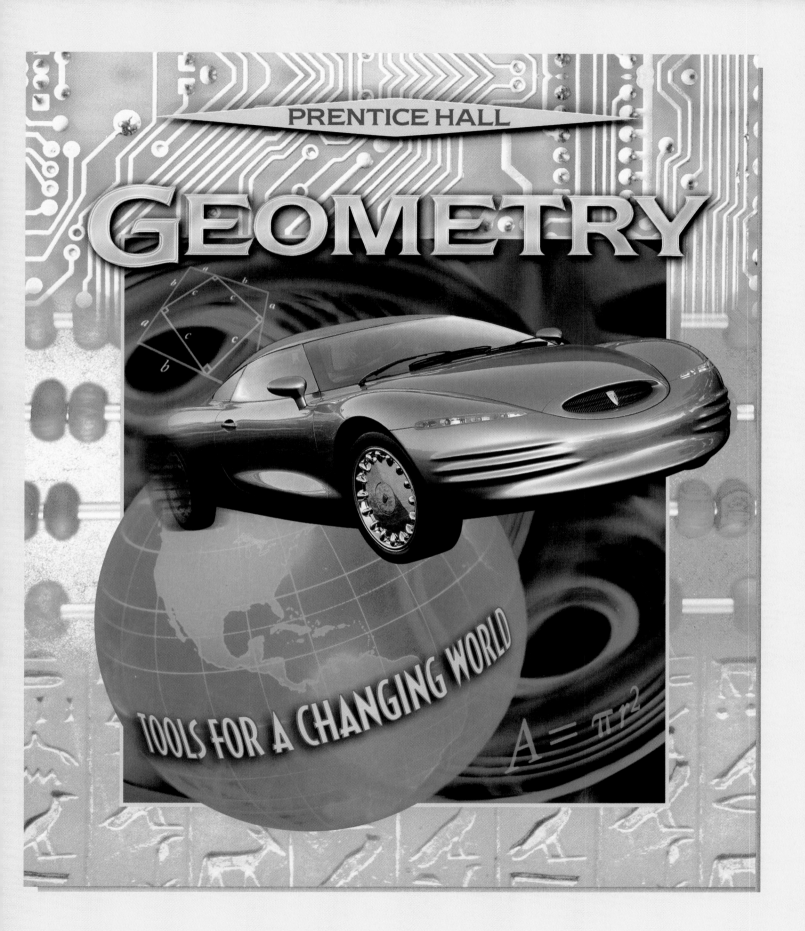

PRENTICE HALL

GEOMETRY

TOOLS FOR A CHANGING WORLD

$$A = \pi r^2$$

Authors, Geometry

Laurie E. Bass
The Fieldston School
Riverdale, New York

Basia Rinesmith Hall
Alief Hastings High School
Alief Independent School District
Alief, Texas

Art Johnson, Ed.D.
Nashua High School
Nashua, New Hampshire

Dorothy F. Wood
Formerly, Kern High School District
Bakersfield, California

Contributing Author
Simone W. Bess, Ed.D.
University of Cincinnati
College of Education
Cincinnati, Ohio

Authors, Algebra & Advanced Algebra

Allan Bellman
Watkins Mill High School
Gaithersburg, Maryland

Sadie Chavis Bragg, Ed.D.
Borough of Manhattan
Community College
The City University of New York
New York, New York

Suzanne H. Chapin, Ed.D.
Boston University
Boston, Massachusetts

Theodore J. Gardella
Formerly, Bloomfield Hills Public Schools
Bloomfield Hills, Michigan

Bettye C. Hall
Mathematics Consultant
Houston, Texas

William G. Handlin, Sr.
Spring Woods High School
Houston, Texas

Edward Manfre
Mathematics Consultant
Albuquerque, New Mexico

PRENTICE HALL
Simon & Schuster Education Group
A VIACOM COMPANY

Copyright ©1998 by Prentice-Hall, Inc., a Viacom Company, Upper Saddle River, New Jersey 07458. All rights reserved. No part of this book may be reproduced or transmitted in any form or by any means, electronic or mechanical, including photocopying, recording, or by any information storage and retrieval system, without permission in writing from the publisher.

Printed in the United States of America.

ISBN: 0-13-416785-6

2 3 4 5 6 7 8 9 10   04 03 02 01 00 99 98 97

REVIEWERS

Series Reviewers

James Gates, Ed.D.
Executive Director Emeritus, National Council of Teachers of Mathematics, Reston, Virginia

Vinetta Jones, Ph.D.
National Director, EQUITY 2000, The College Board, New York, New York

Geometry

Sandra Argüelles Daire
Miami Senior High School
Miami, Florida

Priscilla P. Donkle
South Central High School
Union Mills, Indiana

Tom Muchlinski, Ph.D.
Wayzata High School
Plymouth, Minnesota

Bonnie Walker
Texas ASCD
Houston, Texas

Karen Doyle Walton, Ed.D.
Allentown College of
   Saint Francis de Sales
Center Valley, Pennsylvania

Algebra

John J. Brady III
Hume-Fogg High School
Nashville, Tennessee

Elias P. Rodriguez
Leander Junior High School
Leander, Texas

Dorothy S. Strong, Ed.D.
Chicago Public Schools
Chicago, Illinois

Art W. Wilson, Ed.D.
Abraham Lincoln High School
Denver, Colorado

Advanced Algebra

Eleanor Boehner
Methacton High School
Norristown, Pennsylvania

Laura Price Cobb
Dallas Public Schools
Dallas, Texas

William Earl, Ed.D.
Formerly Mathematics
   Education Specialist
Utah State Office of Education
Salt Lake City, Utah

Robin Levine Rubinstein
Shorewood High School
Shoreline, Washington

Staff Credits

The people who made up the *Geometry* team — representing editorial, design, marketing, page production, editorial services, production, manufacturing, technology, electronic publishing, and advertising and promotion — and their managers are listed below. Bold type denotes core team members.

Alison Anholt-White, Jackie Zidek Bedoya, Barbara A. Bertell, Bruce Bond, Ellen Brown, Judith D. Buice, Kathy Carter, Kerri Caruso, **Linda M. Coffey, Noralie V. Cox,** Sheila DeFazio, Edward de Leon, Christine Deliee, Gabriella Della Corte, Robert G. Dunn, Barbara Flockhart, Audra Floyd, David Graham, Maria Green, Bridget A. Hadley, Joanne Hudson, Vanessa Hunnibell, Mimi Jigarjian, **Linda D. Johnson,** Elizabeth A. Jordan, Russell Lappa, **Catherine Martin-Hetmansky,** Eve Melnechuk, Cindy A. Noftle, Caroline M. Power, Roger E. Powers, Martha G. Smith, Kira Thaler, Robin Tiano, Christina Trinchero, Stuart Wallace, Cynthia A. Weedel, **Jeff Weidenaar, Pearl B. Weinstein,** Mary Jane Wolfe, Stewart Wood, David Zarowin

To the Student

Students like you helped Prentice Hall develop this program. They identified tools you can use to help you learn now in this course and beyond. In this special "To the Student" section and throughout this program, you will find the **tools you need to help you succeed.** We'd like to hear how these tools work for you. Write us at Prentice Hall Mathematics, 160 Gould Street, Needham, MA 02194 or visit us at http://www.phschool.com.

"… Instead of problem after problem of pointless numbers, we should have a chance to think and to truly understand what we are doing. I personally think that we all should be taught this way."

Chris, Grade 9
Carson City, NV

"… I learn mathematics best when I draw a diagram or make a graph that helps show what the problem is that I will solve."

Amy, Grade 11
Columbia, SC

"… I like to review what I learn as I go, rather than cramming the night before a test."

Ali, Grade 10
St. Paul, MN

Use this "To the Student" section to help students understand how they learn. It also shows how this textbook relates what they experience daily to the math they're learning and will need in the workplace of the future.

LEARN About Learning!

What comes to your mind when you hear the word **style**? Maybe it's hair style, or style of dress, or walking style. Have you ever thought about your learning style? Just like your hair or your clothes or your walk, everybody has a learning style that they like best because it works best for them. Look around you now. What do you see? Different styles … some like yours, some different from yours. That's the way it is with learning styles, too.

What's Your Best Learning Style?

I understand math concepts best when I...

☐ A. Read about them.

☐ B. Look at and make illustrations, graphs, and charts that show them.

☐ C. Draw sketches or handle manipulatives to explore them.

☐ D. Listen to someone explain them.

When I study, I learn more when I...

☐ A. Review my notes and the textbook.

☐ B. Study any graphs, charts, diagrams, or other illustrations.

☐ C. Write ideas on note cards; then study the ideas.

☐ D. Explain what I know to another person.

When I collaborate with a group, I am most comfortable when I...

☐ A. Take notes.

☐ B. Make visuals for display.

☐ C. Demonstrate what I know to others.

☐ D. Give presentations to other groups or the whole class.

Look for a pattern in your responses.
  "A" responses suggest that you learn best by reading;
  "B" responses indicate a visual learning style;
  "C" responses suggest a tactile, or hands-on, learning style;
  "D" responses signal that you probably learn best by listening and talking about what you are learning.

Students determine their dominant learning style by taking this quick and easy survey.

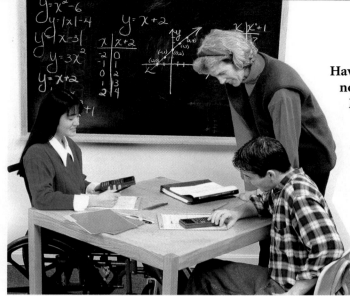

Having a preferred learning style does not limit you to using just that one. Most people learn by using a combination of learning styles. You'll be amazed by the ways that knowing more about yourself and how you learn will help you be successful — not only successful in mathematics, but successful in all your subject areas. When you know how you learn best, you will be well equipped to enter the work place.

Use this chart to help you strengthen your different learning styles.

Learning Style	Learning Tips
Learning by *reading*	✳ Schedule time to read each day. ✳ Carry a book or magazine to read during wait time. ✳ Read what you like to read—it's OK not to finish a book.
Learning by using *visual* cues	✳ Visualize a problem situation. ✳ Graph solutions to problems. ✳ Let technology, such as computers and calculators, help you.
Learning by using *hands-on* exploration	✳ Make sketches when solving a problem. ✳ Use objects to help you solve problems. ✳ Rely on technology as a tool for exploration and discovery.
Learning by *listening and talking*	✳ Volunteer to give presentations. ✳ Explain your ideas to a friend. ✳ Listen intently to what others are saying.

Most important, believe in yourself and your ability to learn!

What you do now...	What you do in this course...	What you do in the work place...
Learn best by using a particular learning style . . .	**Example 1** **Example 2** **Relating to the Real World** 🌐	*Choose a career that you enjoy because it is natural for you.*

Note the diagram at the bottom of the page that connects instructional methods utilized throughout the program with what students experience today and in their future.

Help Teamwork Work for YOU!

Each of us works with other people on teams throughout our lives. What's your job? Your job on a team, that is. Maybe you play center on your basketball team, maybe you count votes for your school elections, perhaps you help decorate the gym for a school function, or maybe you help make scenery for a community play. From relay races to doing your part of the job in the work place, teamwork is required for success.

TEAMWORK CHECKLIST

☑ **Break apart the large task into smaller tasks, which become the responsibility of individual group members.**

☑ **Treat the differences in group members as a benefit.**

☑ **Try to listen attentively when others speak.**

☑ **Stay focused on the task at hand and the goal to be accomplished.**

☑ **Vary the tasks you do in each group and participate.**

☑ **Recognize your own and others' learning styles.**

☑ **Offer your ideas and suggestions.**

☑ **Be socially responsible and act in a respectful way.**

What you do now...	What you do in this course...	What you do in the work place...
Play on a team, decorate the gym, or perform in the band...	WORK TOGETHER	*Collaborate with coworkers on projects.*

Both teachers and students can reference this handy Teamwork Checklist while students are working in pairs or in small groups.

T42

It's All COMMUNICATION

We communicate in songs. We communicate in letters. We communicate with our body movements. We communicate on the phone. We communicate in cyberspace. It's all talking about ideas and sharing what you know. It's the same in mathematics — we communicate by reading, writing, talking, and listening. Whether we are working together on a project or studying with a friend for a test, we are communicating.

Ways to Communicate What You Know and Are Able to Do

✔ Explain to others how you solve a problem.

✔ Listen carefully to others.

✔ Use mathematical language in your writing in other subjects.

✔ Pay attention to the headings in textbooks — they are signposts that help you.

✔ Think about videos and audiotapes as ways to communicate mathematical ideas.

✔ Be on the lookout for mathematics when you read, watch television, or see a movie.

✔ Communicate with others by using bulletin boards and chat rooms found on the Internet.

What you do now...

Teach a young relative a sport...

What you do in this course...

THINK AND DISCUSS

What you do in the work place...

Written and verbal communication at work.

Build communication skills with these hints on how students can communicate more effectively with their teachers and their classmates.

Solving PROBLEMS — a SKILL You USE Every DAY

Problem solving is a skill — a skill that you probably use without even knowing it. When you think critically in social studies to draw conclusions about pollution and its stress on the environment, or when a mechanic listens to symptoms of trouble and logically determines the cause, you are both using a mathematical problem-solving skill. Problem solving also involves logical reasoning, wise decision making, and reflecting on our solutions.

Tips for Problem Solving

Recognize that there is more than one way to solve most problems.

When solving a word problem, read it, decide what to do, make a plan, look back at the problem, and revise your answer.

Experiment with various solution methods.

Understand that it is just as important to know how to solve a problem as it is to actually solve it.

Be aware of times you are using mathematics to solve problems that do not involve computation, such as when you reason to make a wise decision.

What you do now...	What you do in this course...	What you do in the work place...
Make decisions based on changing conditions, such as weather...	PROBLEM SOLVING	*Synchronize the timing of traffic lights to enhance traffic flow.*

Establish problem solving success by helping students understand that there isn't always one answer to or one way of solving a problem.

Studying for the TEST — Whatever It May Be

SATs, ACTs, chapter tests, and weekly quizzes — they all test what you know and are able to do. Have you ever thought about **how** you can take these tests to your advantage? You are evaluated now in your classes and you will be evaluated when you hold a job.

Pointers for Gaining Points

◆ Study as you progress through a chapter, instead of cramming for a test.

◆ Recognize when you are lost and seek help before a test.

◆ Review important theorems and postulates when studying for a test, and recognize how they relate to each other.

◆ Study for a test with a friend or study group.

◆ Take a practice test.

◆ Think of mnemonic devices to help you, such as Please Excuse My Dear Aunt Sally, which is one way to remember order of operations (parentheses, exponents, multiply, divide, add, subtract).

◆ Reread test questions before answering them.

◆ Check to see if your answer is reasonable.

◆ Think positively and visualize yourself doing well on the test.

◆ Relax during the test… there is nothing there that you have not seen before.

What you do now...	What you do in this course...	What you do in the work place...
Study notes in preparation for tests and quizzes...	SELF ASSESSMENT ▶ **How am I doing?** *Exercises* ON YOUR OWN *Exercises* CHECKPOINT	*Prepare for and participate in a job interview.*

These test-taking strategies highlight techniques that students can use to prepare for various assessments leading to success.

To accommodate flexible scheduling, some lessons are divided into parts. Assignment Options are given in the Lesson Planning Options for each lesson.

PACING OPTIONS

This chart suggests pacing only for the core lessons and their parts, and it is provided merely as a possible guide. It will help you determine how much time you have in your schedule to cover other features, such as the Chapter Project, Math Toolboxes, Wrap Up, and Assessment.

	1 Class Period	1 Class Period	1 Class Period	1 Class Period	1 Class Period	1 Class Period	1 Class Period	1 Class Period	1 Class Period
Traditional (40–45 min class periods)	1-1	1-2 **1**	1-2 **2**	1-3	1-4 **1**	1-4 **2**	1-5 **1**	1-5 **2**	1-6 **1**
Block Scheduling (90 min class periods)	1-1	1-2 **1 2**	1-3	1-4 **1 2**	1-5 **1 2**	1-6 **1 2**	1-7 **1 2**	1-8	

What Students Will Learn and Why

In this chapter, students learn some of the basic terms and postulates of geometry and become familiar with the tools they will use as they study this subject. They use patterns and inductive reasoning to make conjectures. They learn the meaning of point, line, and plane; how segments and rays are related to lines; how to recognize parallel lines and parallel planes; and how to find the length of a segment and the measure of an angle. Students learn what makes a good definition in geometry and how to use a compass and straightedge to perform some basic constructions. They use deductive reasoning to solve problems and test conjectures. Finally, students learn to find distance and midpoints of segments in the coordinate plane.

Discussing the Chapter/Building on Experience

The concept map below relates chapter topics to real-world applications. You and your class may wish to add to the map or develop maps of your own. The center oval describes the topic of the chapter. The next level displays topics within the lessons. The outer ovals reflect applications of the content. As you and your class build a concept map, invite students to discuss applications with which they are familiar.

1 Class Period	1 Class Period	1 Class Period	1 Class Period	1 Class Period	1 Class Period	1 Class Period	1 Class Period	1 Class Period	1 Class Period	1 Class Period
1-6 ▽2	1-7 ▽1	1-7 ▽2	1-8							

Interactive Questioning Tips

A question is interactive when there is "give and take" between the questioner (teacher or student) and the respondent. In Think and Discuss or when a critical thinking question is asked, it is important to encourage students to explain their answers in detail. Encouraging students to explain their answers promotes active participation and stimulates higher levels of thought. These two elements are essential in developing high-level thinking skills. For example, in Lesson 1-4, Question 5, students are asked to explain why they think absolute value is used to express the distance between two points. Allow students time to compose their answer mentally.

Skills Practice

Every lesson provides skill practice with Try This exercises, Exercises On Your Own, and Exercises Mixed Review. The Student Edition includes Checkpoints (pp. 31, 52) and Preparing for Standardized Tests (p. 65). In the Teacher's Edition, the Lesson Planning Options section for each lesson lists Prerequisite Skills students should know for that lesson. At the back of the Student Edition is the Skills Handbook—mini-lessons on math your students may need to review. The Chapter Support File for Chapter 1 in the Teaching Resources box includes two Practice worksheets per lesson, a worksheet for two Checkpoints, and worksheets for Cumulative Review and Standardized Test Preparation.

Diverse Learning and Teaching Styles

In your Teacher's Edition, you will find suggestions as to how you can help students complete mathematical tasks in Chapter 1 by reinforcing various learning styles. Here are some examples.

- **Visual learning** use inductive reasoning relying on visual cues (p.7), remember abbreviations by observing the visual representations of a segment, ray, and line (p. 18), benefit from drawings (p. 51)

- **Tactile learning** use index cards to illustrate two planes that intersect on horizontal and vertical lines (p. 14), investigate properties of a Mobius band (p. 36), discuss and perform each step of Construction 1 (p. 40)

- **Auditory learning** take turns explaining the Protractor Postulate to partners (p. 27)

- **Kinesthetic learning** move outdoors to observe and record real-world examples of ways two lines can be related (p. 21)

Alternative Activity for Lesson 1-4

for use with Segment Additions and Angle Addition Postulates, uses geometry software to find the lengths of segments and the measures of angles.

Alternative Activity for Lesson 1-5

for use with definitions presented in the student text, uses geometry software to explore the meaning of the terms *angle bisector* and *perpendicular*.

Alternative Activity for Lesson 1-7

for use with the Work Together, uses dynamic geometry software to explore angles formed by intersecting lines.

Cooperative Learning Tips

When used effectively, cooperative learning can help students develop interpersonal skills, learn to perform specific roles in a group, and learn to carry out specific responsibilities. The components of Chapter 1 provide a range of cooperative learning opportunities.

- In the Student Edition, the **Work Together** parts of lessons are specifically designed for cooperative learning activities.

- In the Teacher's Edition, you will find helpful hints for addressing diverse learning styles (see page C for Chapter 1). For every lesson, you will find a **Reteaching Activity**, which may involve cooperative learning.

Materials and Manipulatives

The authors expect all students to use scientific calculators. Calculator use is integrated throughout the course.

- colored pencils (1-3)
- compass (1-6)
- graph paper (1-3, 1-8)
- protractor (1-4)
- ruler (1-2, 1-6, 1-8)
- tape (1-3)
- tracing paper (1-6, 1-8)

TECHNOLOGY OPTIONS

Technology Tools		Chapter Project	1-1	1-2	1-3	1-4	1-5	1-6	1-7	1-8
Calculator		Assumed that students have scientific calculators at any time.								
Software	Secondary Math Lab Toolkit™		✔	✔	✔	✔	✔	✔	✔	✔
	Integrated Math Lab					✔				✔
	Computer Item Generator		✔	✔	✔	✔	✔	✔	✔	✔
	Student Edition					✔		✔ᵀ		
Video	Video Field Trip	✔								
CD-ROM	Multimedia Geometry Lab			✔	✔	✔		✔		
Internet		See the Prentice Hall site. (http://www.phschool.com)								

✔ᵀ indicates Math Toolbox.

The Prentice Hall Geometry program offers you a rich variety of technology options. Be assured that all these options are provided as a means of enriching the program and are not essential for the successful completion of the course.

Assessment Options

The Prentice Hall Geometry Program provides you with many options. From these options, you may choose instructional materials and techniques appropriate for your students, or those necessary to meet your district's curriculum requirements. As the chart indicates, the program also supports your teaching efforts by offering you many choices for assessment.

ASSESSMENT OPTIONS

Assessment Support Materials	Chapter Project	1-1	1-2	1-3	1-4	1-5	1-6	1-7	1-8	Chapter End
Chapter Project	▲■	▲■		▲■	▲■		▲■			▲■
Checkpoints			■		▲■●			▲■●		
Self-Assessment										
Writing Assignment		▲	▲■	▲■	▲■●	▲■	▲	▲●	▲	●▲
Chapter Assessment										▲●
Alternative Assessment		■	■	■	■	■	■	■	■	●■
Cumulative Review										●
Standardized Test Prep		▲■	▲■	▲		▲■		▲■		▲●
Computer Item Generator	Can be used to create custom-made practice or assessment at any time.									

▲ = Student Edition   ■ = Teacher's Edition   ● = Teaching Resources

Checkpoints

Alternative Assessment

Chapter Assessment

Available in both Form A and Form B

Making the Right Connections

Mathematics is imbedded in nearly every walk of life. The National Council of Teachers of Mathematics (NCTM) encourages educators to recognize these connections and to emphasize them for the purpose of better educating students for success in life and in a global economy. The **Connections** chart below highlights these connections for Chapter 1.

CONNECTIONS

Lesson	Interdisciplinary Connections	Career Prep	Other Real World Connections	Math Integration	NCTM Standards
Chapter Project	Art	Graphic Design			Problem Solving Connections
1-1	History	Manufacturing Communications	Marathon Running Fitness Transportation	Algebra	Reasoning Communication Problem Solving
1-2	Astronomy		Navigation Magic	Probability Coordinate Geometry	Communication Problem Solving
1-3	Chemistry Language Arts	Engineering	Navigation	Coordinate Geometry	Communications Problem Solving
1-4	Art	Cartography	Flower Arranging Ski Jumping Travel Mile Markers Billiards	Coordinate Geometry Algebra	Algebra Communication Problem Solving
1-5	Language Arts	Cabinet making		Algebra Coordinate Geometry Geometry in 3 Dimensions	Connections Algebra Communication Problem Solving
1-6	Art	Engineering			Communication Problem Solving
1-7		Medicine Carpentry Auto Repair	Parking Restrictions	Algebra Coordinate Geometry	Reasoning Communication Algebra Problem Solving Structure
1-8	Astronomy		Transportation Communications	Algebra Geometry in 3 Dimensions	Coordinate Geometry Algebra Communication Problem Solving

CONNECTING TO PRIOR LEARNING Have students brainstorm geometric topics with which they are already familiar. Encourage them to think of gecmetry topics or properties they have studied in courses such as history, art, science, or algebra.

CULTURAL CONNECTIONS Origami is closely associated with Japan, but paper folding is also used in other countries, such as Germany, Spain, South America, England, and the United States. Paper foldings are used for decorations, ceremonial purposes, and to teach math and function design. Ask students to describe objects they have constructed by folding paper.

INTERDISCIPLINARY CONNECTIONS Origami originated in the Orient and may have been derived from an older tradition of cloth folding. Ask students to describe other ancient art forms and their origins, such as sand painting.

ABOUT THE PROJECT Using paper-folding techniques throughout the chapter helps students explore geometric patterns in a fun way. The Find Out questions in this chapter will give students practice making models and using the language of geometry to describe them.

Technology Options

Prentice Hall Technology

 Video
• Video Field Trip 1, "Rising Sun," a look at Japanese culture

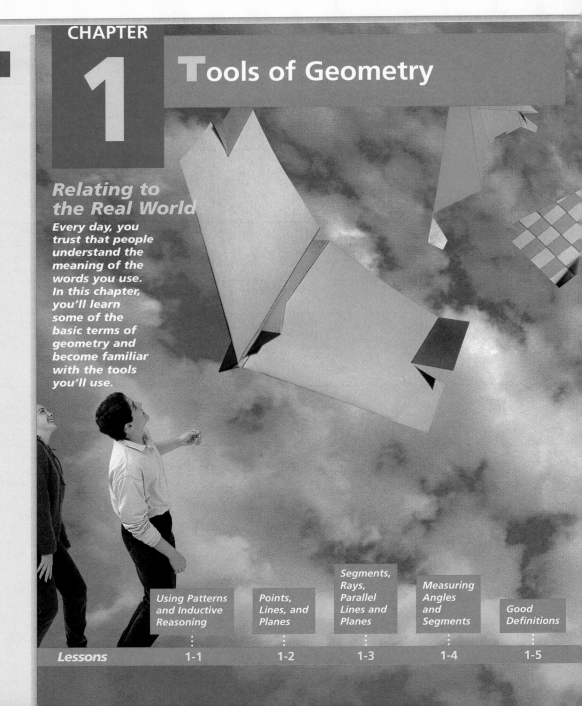

CHAPTER **1** **T**ools of Geometry

Relating to the Real World

Every day, you trust that people understand the meaning of the words you use. In this chapter, you'll learn some of the basic terms of geometry and become familiar with the tools you'll use.

Using Patterns and Inductive Reasoning	Points, Lines, and Planes	Segments, Rays, Parallel Lines and Planes	Measuring Angles and Segments	Good Definitions
Lessons 1-1	1-2	1-3	1-4	1-5

PROJECT NOTEBOOK Encourage students to keep all project-related materials in a separate folder or notebook. **See Chapter Project and Scoring Rubric in Chapter Support File.**

- Assign students to work with a partner or a small group. Have them make paper airplanes using sheets of paper.
- Ask each team to explain to the class how they made their airplane. Make a list of any math-related terms students use in their descriptions.

TRACKING THE PROJECT You may wish to have students read Finishing the Chapter Project on page 58 to help them get an overview of the project. Set benchmark deadlines for students to show their work in progress.

CHAPTER PROJECT

On Folded Wings

Some people look at a plain sheet of paper and see the hidden form of a swan or a seashell waiting to be revealed. Almost magically, with a few meticulous folds, an origami artist can produce startling replicas of animals, flowers, buildings, vehicles, and even people. The ancient art of paper folding has come to us from Japan, where it has thrived since at least the twelfth century. As a child, every time you made a paper airplane or a paper hat, you were practicing the art of origami.

In this chapter project, you will use paper folding to explore geometric patterns. You will make origami models, and then use the language of geometry to tell others how to make them.

To help you complete the project:

▼ **p. 10** *Find Out by Doing*
▼ **p. 22** *Find Out by Creating*
▼ **p. 31** *Find Out by Researching*
▼ **p. 44** *Find Out by Writing*
▼ **p. 58** *Finishing the Project*

Basic Constructions | *Using Deductive Reasoning* | *The Coordinate Plane*

1-6 | 1-7 | 1-8

▼ Project Resources

 Teaching Resources
Chapter Support File, Ch. 1
- Chapter Project Manager and Scoring Rubric

Transparencies
21

▼ Using the Rubric

Sharing the scoring rubric for the project with your students will alert them to your expectations before they begin work on the project.

As students complete each Find Out question in the chapter, you may wish to have them evaluate their own work or a partner's work, based on the scoring rubric. Students should have the opportunity to revise their work after it has been reviewed.

CONNECTING TO PRIOR KNOWLEDGE Ask students about price trends over the past five years in items such as sneakers or movie tickets. Ask them if they can predict the price a year from now and five years from now based on what prices have done in the past. Have them discuss their reasoning.

WORK TOGETHER

ERROR ALERT! Students counting the number of paths to each intersection on Longwood Avenue may count paths that are not the shortest paths. **Remediation:** Emphasize that students should count only the shortest paths to each intersection. Illustrate a type of path that should not be counted as shown here.

Lesson Planning Options

Prerequisite Skills

- Performing operations with real numbers
- Recognizing basic geometric figures

Assignment Options for Exercises On Your Own

Core 1–34, 36
Extension 35, 37–40

Use Mixed Review to maintain skills.

Resources

 Student Edition
Skills Handbook, pp. 648, 649
Extra Practice, p. 634
Glossary/Study Guide

 Teacher's Edition
Chapter Support File, Ch. 1
- Practice 1-1 (two worksheets)
- Reteaching 1-1
Classroom Manager 1-1
Glossary, Spanish Resources

 Transparencies
3, 14, 20, 22, 26, 27

What You'll Learn
- Using inductive reasoning to make conjectures

...And Why
To sharpen your ability to reason inductively, a powerful tool used in mathematics and in making everyday decisions

PROBLEM SOLVING HINT
Copy the diagram. Find the number of ways to reach each intersection. Look for a number pattern.

Who? The pattern of numbers you discovered in the Work Together is known as Pascal's Triangle, after the French mathematician Blaise Pascal (1623–1662).

Connections 🌐 Manufacturing ... and more

1-1 Using Patterns and Inductive Reasoning

WORK TOGETHER

The shortest path from the school to Longwood Avenue is six blocks long. One path is shown below in red.

Work with a group to answer the following questions.

1. How many different six-block paths can you take from the school to Longwood Avenue? **64**

2. How many of these paths will end at the corner directly across from the movie theater? **20**

Have students counting the number of paths to each intersection look at each row of numbers in the Problem Solving Hint. Ask them what patterns they observe and how each row relates to the previous row.

ALGEBRA Questions 3 and 4 You may want to have students write algebraic expressions to represent the patterns. (The pattern in Question 3 can be represented by $2n$ for $n = 1, 2, 3, \ldots$, and the pattern in Question 4 can be represented by $3(2^n)$ for $n = 0, 1, 2, 3, \ldots$).

Example 1 Relating to the Real World

ALTERNATIVE METHOD Another way to see that the number of small-wheeled skateboards is decreasing by about 3 each month is to find the difference between the number of small-wheeled skateboards in consecutive months. The differences are 3, 4, 3, 3. These differences are all 3 or close to 3, so it is reasonable to predict 3 fewer skateboards in June.

CRITICAL THINKING Discuss with students whether they think this pattern will continue and, if so, for how long. Ask them if it is reasonable to assume that in 15 months from May the company will produce no small-wheeled skateboards.

THINK AND DISCUSS

To answer the questions in the Work Together, you used inductive reasoning. **Inductive reasoning** is a type of reasoning that allows you to reach conclusions based on a pattern of specific examples or past events. Mathematicians have made many discoveries using inductive reasoning.

3. **a.** Find the next two terms in this sequence: 2, 4, 6, 8, . . . **10, 12**
   b. Describe the pattern you observed.
   Add 2 to each term to get the next term.
4. **a.** Find the next two terms in this sequence: 3, 6, 12, 24, . . . **48, 96**
   b. Describe the pattern you observed.
   Multiply each term by 2 to get the next term.
5. **a.** Find the next two terms in this sequence: 1, 2, 4, 5, 10, 11, 22, . . . **23, 46**
   b. Describe the pattern you observed.
   Add 1, then double; add 1, then double; and so on.

A conclusion reached by using inductive reasoning is sometimes called a **conjecture.** For each sequence above, you found the next term by first finding a pattern, and then using the pattern to make a conjecture about the next term. Inductive reasoning from patterns is a powerful thinking process you will use throughout the year in geometry.

6. **Try This** Describe the next term in this sequence.

a circle around a triangle around a circle around a triangle

Example 1 Relating to the Real World

Manufacturing A skateboard shop finds that for five consecutive months sales of skateboards with small wheels (39 mm to 48 mm in diameter) decreased.

January: 58   February: 55   March: 51   April: 48   May: 45

Skateboards Sold

Use inductive reasoning to make a conjecture about the number of small-wheeled skateboards the shop will sell in June.

As the graph at the left shows, the number of small-wheeled skateboards is decreasing by about 3 skateboards each month. The skateboard shop can predict about 42 small-wheeled skateboards will be sold in June.

Not every conjecture or conclusion found by inductive reasoning is correct. The next problem illustrates the limitations of inductive reasoning.

Additional Examples

FOR EXAMPLE 1

Refer to Example 1. If the numbers of small-wheeled skateboards per month from January to May were 34, 38, 43, 47, 51, make a conjecture about the number of small-wheeled skateboards produced in June.
About 55

Discussion: *Do you think the number of small-wheeled skateboards will keep increasing?*

FOR EXAMPLE 2

Explain why the following conjecture is or is not true. "The number of units in the perimeter of a rectangle is greater than the number of square units in its area." **No; for example, a square with a 7-in. side has a perimeter of 28 in. and an area of 49 in.^{2}**

FOR EXAMPLE 3

Use inductive reasoning to find the sum of the first 20 positive even numbers starting with 2. **420**

Discussion: *What pattern did you observe?*

Example 2 ···········

Have students note that the points on the circle are not equally spaced. You may want to have students investigate what happens when the six points are equally spaced. (The center region "disappears" because its vertices form a straight angle leaving only 30 regions.)

EXTENSION Goldbach's Conjecture states that if *n* is an even number greater than 2, then there are always two prime numbers whose sum is *n*. For example, when $n = 4$, $2 + 2 = 4$ and when $n = 10$, $7 + 3 = 10$. If you have block scheduling or an extended period, you may wish to have students test Goldbach's conjecture for the first 20 even numbers greater than 2. Ask them if each sum is unique.

Example 3 ···········

Question 8 Before answering this question, have students use a calculator to confirm that the sum of the first 20 odd numbers is 400.

MAKING CONNECTIONS An elementary school teacher in Germany in the late eighteenth century assigned students the task of adding the numbers 1 through 100. One of her students, Karl Friedrich Gauss, later to become a famous mathematician, used a pattern to find the sum almost immediately. He noticed that there are 50 pairs of numbers who sums are each 101: 50(101) = 5050.

Technology Options

For Exercises 23–24, students may use drawing software. For Exercise 38, students may graph the points using a graphing calculator or graphing software.

Prentice Hall Technology

 Software
- Secondary Math Lab Toolkit™
- Computer Item Generator 1-1

 Internet
- See the Prentice Hall site. (http://www.phschool.com)

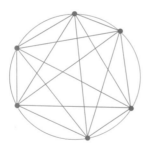

Example 2 ···········

If six points on a circle are joined by as many segments as possible, how many nonoverlapping regions will the segments determine?

The table at the right shows the data for 2, 3, 4, and 5 points. The number of regions appears to double at each stage. Inductive reasoning would predict that there are 32 regions for 6 points on the circle. And yet, as the diagram at the left shows, there are only 31 regions formed. In this case, the conjecture is incorrect.

Points	Regions
2	2
3	4
4	8
5	16

Because the conjectures arrived at by inductive reasoning are not always true, you should verify them if possible.

7. Try This Candace examined five different examples and came up with this **conjecture:** "If any two positive numbers are multiplied, their product is always greater than either of the two numbers." Is her **conjecture** correct? Explain why or why not.

No; for example, $\frac{1}{2} \times \frac{1}{2} = \frac{1}{4}$.

Sometimes you can use inductive reasoning to solve a problem that at first does not seem to have any pattern.

Example 3 ···········

Use inductive reasoning to find the sum of the first 20 odd numbers.

Find the first few sums. Notice that each sum is a perfect square.

1	=	1	=	1^2
$1 + 3$	=	4	=	2^2
$1 + 3 + 5$	=	9	=	3^2
$1 + 3 + 5 + 7$	=	16	=	4^2

Reasoning inductively, you would expect that the sum of the first 20 odd numbers would be 20^2, or 400.

 8. Try This What is your **conjecture** for the sum of the first 30 odd numbers? Use your calculator to verify your **conjecture.** 30^2, or 900

6

Exercises ON YOUR OWN

CRITICAL THINKING Exercises 1–12 Ask students whether any of the sequences end.

Exercises 7 and 8 You may want to provide a hint that the letters may be abbreviations for words.

WRITING Exercise 13 Discuss students' responses. Students may describe the same pattern in more than one way.

ESL VISUAL LEARNING Exercises 17–22 These problems rely on visual cues and require a minimum of verbal cues. They may prove helpful in assessing ESL students' ability to use inductive reasoning to continue patterns.

Exercises 23–24 Students may think in terms of line segments instead of lines, which is acceptable at this point in the text. The distinction will be clarified in Lesson 1-3. You may need to define the word *parallel*. Use objects in the classroom as illustrations, such as the opposite edges of a book, the top and bottom of a bulletin board, or the rows of ceiling tiles.

Exercises ON YOUR OWN

Find the next two terms in each sequence.

1. 5, 10, 20, 40, . . . 80, 160

2. 3, 33, 333, 3333, . . . 33333, 333333

3. 1, −1, 2, −2, 3, . . . −3, 4

4. $1, \frac{1}{2}, \frac{1}{4}, \frac{1}{8}, \ldots$ $\frac{1}{16}, \frac{1}{32}$

5. 15, 12, 9, 6, . . . 3, 0

6. 81, 27, 9, 3, . . . $1, \frac{1}{3}$

7. O, T, T, F, F, S, S, E, . . . N, T

8. J, F, M, A, M, . . . J, J

9. 1, 2, 6, 24, 120, . . . 720, 5040

10. 1, 2, 4, 7, 11, 16, 22, . . . 29, 37

11. $1, \frac{1}{4}, \frac{1}{9}, \frac{1}{16}, \frac{1}{25}, \ldots$ $\frac{1}{36}, \frac{1}{49}$

12. $1, \frac{1}{2}, \frac{1}{3}, \frac{1}{4}, \ldots$ $\frac{1}{5}, \frac{1}{6}$

13. Writing Choose two of the sequences in Exercises 9–12 and describe the pattern. See margin.

14. Deano has started working out regularly. When he first started exercising he could do 10 push-ups. After the first month he could do 14 push-ups. After the second month he could do 19, and after the third month he could do 25. How many push-ups would you **predict** he will be able to do after the fifth month of working out? Are you absolutely sure about your prediction? Why or why not?
40; no; he may not be able to continue the pattern indefinitely.

15. Alexa rides a bus to school. On the first day the trip to school took 25 minutes. On the second day the trip took 24 minutes. On the third day the trip took 26 minutes. On the fourth day the trip took 25 minutes. What **conjecture** would you make? The trip takes about 25 min.

16. History Leonardo of Pisa (c. 1175–c. 1258) was born in Italy and educated in North Africa. He was one of the the first Europeans to use modern numerals instead of Roman numerals. He is also known for the Fibonacci Sequence: 1, 1, 2, 3, 5, 8, 13, ... Find the next three terms. 21, 34, 55

Draw the next figure in each sequence. 17–22. See margin.

17. **18.** **19.**

20. **21.** **22.**

23. Draw two parallel lines on your paper. Locate four points on the paper an equal distance from both lines. Describe the figure you would get if you continued to locate points an equal distance from both lines.
a line parallel to the first two and midway between them

24. Draw a line on your paper. Locate four points on the paper that are each 1 in. from the line. Describe the figure you would get if you continued to locate points that are 1 in. from the line.
two lines on either side of the original line and 1 in. away from it

TECHNOLOGY HINT
Exercises 23 and 24 could be done using geometry software.

pages 7–10 On Your Own

13. Answers may vary. Sample:
(9) Start with 1. Multiply by 2. Multiply the result by 3. Multiply the result by 4, and so on.
(10) Start with 1. Add 1. Add 2 to the result. Add 3 to the result. Add 4 to the result, and so on.
(11) The value of each term is $\frac{1}{n^2}$, where n is the term number.
(12) The value of each term is $\frac{1}{n}$, where n is the term number.

17. **18.**

19. **20.**

21. **22.**

26. It's correct for numbers greater than 1, and for negative numbers. But $0^2 = 0$, $1^2 = 1$, and $\left(\frac{1}{2}\right)^2 = \frac{1}{4}$.

27a.

There will be about 15,000 radio stations.

b. Answers may vary. Sample: Very confident; the number of radio stations seems to have increased at a steady rate for 40 years.

25. For the past four years Paulo has grown 2 in. every year. He is now 16 years old and is 5 ft 10 in. tall. He figures that when he is 22 years old he will be 6 ft 10 in. tall. What would you tell Paulo about his **conjecture?** It's possible but not likely. As he grows older, his rate of growth will slow down and eventually stop.

26. After testing her idea with eight different numbers, Jean stated the following **conjecture:** "The square of a number is always greater than the number you started with." What would you tell Jean about her **conjecture?** See margin.

27. a. *Communications* The number of radio stations in the United States is increasing. The table shows the number of radio stations for a 40-year period. Make a line graph of the data. Use the graph and inductive reasoning to make a **conjecture** about the number of radio stations in the United States by the year 2010.

    b. How confident are you about your conjecture? Explain.
       a–b. See margin.

Radio Stations	
1950	2,773
1960	4,133
1970	6,760
1980	8,566
1990	10,819

📊 **Find the next term in each sequence. Check your answer with a calculator.**

28. $12345679 \times 9 = 111111111$
    $12345679 \times 18 = 222222222$
    $12345679 \times 27 = 333333333$
    $12345679 \times 36 = 444444444$
    $12345679 \times 45 = ?$ 555555555

29. $1 \times 1 = 1$
    $11 \times 11 = 121$
    $111 \times 111 = 12321$
    $1111 \times 1111 = 1234321$
    $11111 \times 11111 = ?$ 123454321

30. *Open-ended* Write two different sequences that begin with the same two numbers. Answers may vary. Sample: 1, 2, 4, 8, 16, . . . and 1, 2, 3, 4, 5, . . .

31. *Weather* The temperature in degrees Fahrenheit determines how fast a cricket chirps. If you heard 20 cricket chirps in 14 seconds, what do you think the temperature would be? 75°

Chirps per 14 s	
5 chirps	45°
10 chirps	55°
15 chirps	65°

32. a. A *triangular number* can be represented by a triangular arrangement of dots. The first two triangular numbers are 1 and 3. What are the next three triangular numbers? 6, 10, 15
    b. What is the tenth triangular number? 55
    c. *Algebra* Which of the following expressions represents the *n*th triangular number? C

       A. $n(n + 1)$ B. $n(n - 2)$ C. $\frac{n(n + 1)}{2}$ D. $\frac{n(n - 1)}{2}$

33. a. The first two *square numbers* are 1 and 4. Draw diagrams to represent the next two square numbers. See right.
    b. What is the twentieth square number? Describe the pattern.
    c. *Algebra* Write an algebraic expression in terms of *n* for the *n*th square number. n^2

       b. 20^2, or 400; the sequence is the squares of successive counting numbers.

8

34. **History** Nicomachus of Gerasa first described *pentagonal numbers* in *Introductio arithmetica* about A.D. 100. The first three pentagonal numbers are shown. Draw a diagram to represent the next pentagonal number. See margin.

1   5   12

34.

22

The Race to the Finish Line

Top female runners have been improving about twice as quickly as the fastest men, a new study says. If this pattern continues, women may soon outrun men in competition!

The study is based on world records collected at 10-year intervals, starting in 1905 for men. Reliable women's records were not kept until the 1920s. Women's marathon records date only from 1955.

If the trend continues, the top female and male runners in races ranging from 200 m to 1500 m might attain the same speeds sometime between 2015 and 2055. The rapid improvement in women's marathon records suggests that the marathon record for women will equal that of men even more quickly—perhaps by 2005.

Women's speeds may have improved so quickly because many more women started running competitively in recent decades, according to a professor of anatomy who studies locomotion and gait. This increase in the talent pool of female runners has improved the chance of finding better runners.

35. a. What conclusions were reached in the study mentioned in the newspaper clipping? a–c. See margin.
b. How was inductive reasoning used to reach the conclusions?
c. Explain why the conclusion that women may soon be outrunning men may be incorrect. For which race is the conclusion most suspect? For what reason?

36. **Standardized Test Prep** Which of the following can be a term in the sequence 1, 3, 7, 15, 31, . . . ? D
A. 32   **B.** 47   **C.** 55   **D.** 127   **E.** 128

37. a. *Leap years* have 366 days. 1984, 1988, 1992, 1996, and 2000 are consecutive leap years. Make a **conjecture** about leap years.
b. Which of the following years do you think will be leap years? 2010, 2020, 2100, 2400
a–c. See margin.
c. **Research** Find out if your **conjecture** for part (a) and your answer for part (b) are correct. How are leap years determined?

38. a. **Coordinate Geometry** Graph the following points:

$A(1, 5)$	$B(2, 2)$	$C(2, 8)$	$D(3, 1)$
$E(3, 9)$	$F(6, 0)$	$G(6, 10)$	$H(7, -1)$
$I(7, 11)$	$J(9, 1)$	$K(9, 9)$	$L(10, 2)$
$M(10, 8)$	$N(11, 5)$	See margin.	

b. Which of the points do not fit the same pattern as the others? *H* and *I*
c. Describe the figure you would get if you continued graphing points that fit the pattern. a circle

February   1996

35a. Women may soon outrun men in running competitions.

b. The conclusion was based on continuing the trend shown in past records.

c. The conclusions are based on fairly recent records for women, and those rates of improvement may not continue. The conclusion about the marathon is most suspect because records date only from 1955.

37a. Answers may vary. Sample: Leap years are divisible by 4.

b. Answers may vary. Sample: 2020, 2100, 2400

c. Leap years are divisible by 4 except years ending in 00, which are leap years only if they are divisble by 400.

38a.

> **QUICK REVIEW**
>
> The first coordinate is the *x*-coordinate. The second coordinate is the *y*-coordinate.

ESL **Exercise 39** Review the meaning of *power*, *base*, and *exponent*.

Chapter Project **FIND OUT BY DOING** Each student should have a paper square that is at least 6 in. by 6 in. Make sure students read an entire set of directions before beginning the activity. Suggest that they use a ruler to crease their folds so that when they unfold the paper, they can see the creases. Remind students to keep their Find Out exercise work in one place, so they can complete the chapter project at the end of the chapter.

GETTING READY FOR LESSON 1-2 This exercise prepares students for Lesson 1-2 in which they study points and lines.

Wrap Up

THE BIG IDEA Ask students: *Describe how patterns are used to make conjectures. List some of the limitations of making conjectures using patterns.*

RETEACHING ACTIVITY Students use coins to investigate three-dimensional patterns. (Reteaching worksheet 1-1)

Exercises **MIXED REVIEW**

Exercises 41–52 Students review graphing ordered pairs in the coordinate plane.

Lesson Quiz

Lesson Quiz is also available in Transparencies.

For Exercises 1–2, find the next three terms in the sequence.

1. 96, 92, 88, 84, ... **80, 76, 72**

2.

3. What is the last digit of 4^{25}? **4**

---

39. What is the last digit of 2^{85}? Make a table of values and use inductive reasoning. **2**

40. Patterns How many different squares are there in this 5-by-5 grid? **55**

Chapter Project **Find Out by Doing**

Most origami creations are made by folding square paper. You can create patterns while you practice paper folding.

• Carefully fold a square piece of paper four times as shown.

• Unfold the paper after each fold. Count the number of non-overlapping triangles formed. Record your results in a table like the one below.

Fold	1st	2nd	3rd	4th
No. of △s	2	■	■	■

4; 8; 16

• Make a fifth fold. How many triangles are formed? How many triangles do you think will be formed after a sixth fold? Extend the table and describe the number pattern.
32; 64; mult. by 2

• Keep this origami creation for use in upcoming project activities.

QUICK REVIEW

$2^3 = 2 \times 2 \times 2$

PROBLEM SOLVING HINT
Look at 1-by-1, 2-by-2, and 3-by-3 grids. Count squares and look for a pattern.

Exercises **MIXED REVIEW**

Graph the following points. **41–52. See back of book.**

41. $Y(-5, -8)$ **42.** $B(7, -10)$ **43.** $M(9, 12)$ **44.** $Q(-3, 2)$ **45.** $G(-6, 0)$ **46.** $F(-4, -5)$

47. $C(-7, 10)$ **48.** $N(0, -5)$ **49.** $R(4, 8)$ **50.** $H(-4, -9)$ **51.** $W(2, -5)$ **52.** $T(0, 4)$

53. a. In Exercises 41–52, which points are in the fourth quadrant? **B and W**
  b. Which points are on the *y*-axis? **N and T**

Getting Ready for Lesson 1-2

54. Copy the diagram at the right. Draw as many different lines as you can to connect pairs of points.

10

Math ToolboX — Algebra Review

Transparencies 5

Probability

Before Lesson 1-2

Probability ranges from 0, an impossible event, to 1, a certain event. You can find the probability of an event using this formula.

$$P(\text{event}) = \frac{\text{number of favorable outcomes}}{\text{number of possible outcomes}}$$

Example 1

What is the probability of answering correctly a four-option multiple choice question if you pick an answer at random?

There are 4 possible outcomes. One of them is correct. The probability of getting the correct answer is $\frac{1}{4}$.

Example 2

Find the probability that a point picked at random from the graph at the right is in the first quadrant.

List the possible outcomes: *A, B, C, D, E, F, G, H, I, J.*
There are 10 outcomes.

List the favorable outcomes: *C* and *D.*
There are 2 favorable outcomes.

The probability of a point picked at random being in the first quadrant is $\frac{2}{10} = \frac{1}{5}$.

Use the graph from Example 2 to find each probability. Assume points are picked at random.

1. $P(\text{the point is in the fourth quadrant})$ $\frac{3}{10}$

2. $P(\text{the point is on an axis})$ $\frac{3}{10}$

3. $P(\text{the point is at the origin})$ 0

4. $P(\text{the point has a } y\text{-coordinate of 2})$ $\frac{1}{5}$

5. $P(\text{the point has an } x\text{-coordinate less than 4})$ $\frac{9}{10}$

6. $P(\text{the point is on the } x\text{-axis})$ $\frac{1}{5}$

7. $P(\text{the point is to the right of the } y\text{-axis})$ $\frac{3}{5}$

8. $P(\text{the point has an } x\text{-coordinate of 1})$ $\frac{3}{10}$

9. $P(\text{the point is on the } y\text{-axis})$ $\frac{1}{10}$

10. $P(\text{the point is below the } x\text{-axis})$ $\frac{2}{5}$

11. $P(\text{the point has a } y\text{-coordinate greater than 1})$ $\frac{2}{5}$

12. $P(\text{the point is in the third quadrant})$ $\frac{1}{10}$

Use the spinner at the right. Find each probability.

13. $P(\text{blue})$ $\frac{1}{3}$

14. $P(\text{red})$ $\frac{1}{3}$

15. $P(\text{yellow or red})$ $\frac{2}{3}$

16. $P(\text{purple})$ 0

17. $P(\text{blue or red})$ $\frac{2}{3}$

18. $P(\text{yellow or red or blue})$ 1

PROBLEM OF THE DAY

How many numbers in the set 100, 101, 102, 103, ..., 999 do not contain the digits 2, 5, 7, or 8? **180**

Problem of the Day is also available in Transparencies.

CONNECTING TO PRIOR KNOWLEDGE Ask students if they have ever viewed a constellation. Most will be familiar with the Big Dipper. See if students can sketch the Big Dipper. Ask: "How many stars are in the Big Dipper? How many lines are used to connect the stars to form the Big Dipper?"

Have each student complete Question 1. Then have a different person in each group draw the diagrams with four points, five points, and six points. Have groups discuss whether or not the number of lines depends on where the dots are placed on the circle.

MAKING CONNECTIONS The same constellation can have different names depending on how the points are connected. For example, in Scotland the stars in the Big Dipper are connected to form the Plow.

Lesson Planning Options

Prerequisite Skills

- Graphing points in the coordinate plane
- Finding the probability that an event will occur

Assignment Options for Exercises On Your Own

To provide flexible scheduling, this lesson can be subdivided into parts.

▼1 **Core** 1–26, 43–46
  Extension 48

▼2 **Core** 27, 29–39, 47
  Extension 28, 40–42

Use Mixed Review to maintain skills.

Resources

 Student Edition

Skills Handbook, pp. 659, 665, 667
Extra Practice, p. 634
Glossary/Study Guide

■ **Teaching Resources**

Chapter Support File, Ch. 1
- Practice 1-2 (two worksheets)
- Reteaching 1-2
Classroom Manager 1-2
Glossary, Spanish Resources

 Transparencies
20, 22

12

Connections 🌐 Astronomy . . . and more

What You'll Learn
- Understanding basic terms of geometry
- Understanding basic postulates of geometry

...And Why
To lay the foundation for your study of geometry

What You'll Need
- ruler

1-2 Points, Lines, and Planes

WORK TOGETHER

Many constellations are named after animals and mythological figures. It takes some imagination to connect the points representing the stars so that the result is a recognizable figure such as Leo the Lion. There are many different ways to connect the points. How many different lines could be used to connect all ten points?

Ten major stars make up the constellation called Leo the Lion.

Work in groups of three. Make a table and look for a pattern to answer the following questions.

1. Put three points on a circle. Now connect the three points with as many lines as possible. How many lines do you need? **3**

2. Put four points on another circle. How many lines can you draw connecting four points? **6**

3. Repeat for five points on a circle and then for six points. How many lines can you draw to connect the points? **five points:10; six points:15**

4. Use inductive reasoning to tell how many lines you could draw to connect the ten points of the constellation Leo the Lion. **45**

THINK AND DISCUSS

Basic Terms **Part 1**

Since stars are so far away, they appear quite small to us. We think of them as points even though they are actually quite large. In geometry a **point** has no size. You can think of it as a location. A point is represented by a small dot and is named by a capital letter. All geometric figures are made up of points. **Space** is the set of all points.

P •
point *P*

5. *Open-ended* Name something in your classroom that is a physical representation of a point. **Answers may vary. Sample: the corner of the room where the walls meet the ceiling.**

$\overrightarrow{AB}$ (or $\overrightarrow{BA}$)

t

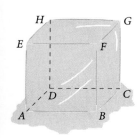

Pensacola

R

St. Petersburg

S

Ft. Lauderdale W

The points representing the three towns on this map are collinear.

You can think of a **line** as a series of points that extends in two directions without end. You can name a line by two points on the line, such as $\overleftrightarrow{AB}$ (read "line AB"). Another way to name a line is with a single lowercase letter, such as line t.

6. *Open-ended* Describe some physical representations of lines in the real world. **Answers may vary. Samples: edge of a table, clothesline, grout between square tiles**

7. *Critical Thinking* Why do you think arrowheads are used when drawing a line or naming a line such as $\overleftrightarrow{AB}$? **to show the line continues in both directions without end**

8. **Try This** Name the line at the left in as many ways as possible. $\overleftrightarrow{RS}$, $\overleftrightarrow{RW}$, $\overleftrightarrow{SW}$, $\overleftrightarrow{SR}$, $\overleftrightarrow{WR}$, $\overleftrightarrow{WS}$

Points that lie on a line are **collinear.**

collinear points   noncollinear points

A **plane** is a flat surface that extends in all directions without end. It has no thickness.

9. *Open-ended* Name three objects in your classroom that represent planes. **Answers may vary. Samples: walls, floors, desktops**

You can name a plane either by a single capital letter or by naming at least three noncollinear points in the plane.

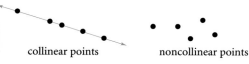

plane P plane ABC

In the diagram, each surface of the ice cube is part of a plane.

10. How many planes are suggested by the surfaces of the ice cube? **6**

11. **Try This** Name the plane represented by the front of the ice cube in several different ways. **Answers may vary. Samples: plane AEF, plane AEB, plane $ABFE$**

Points and lines in the same plane are **coplanar.**

12. **Try This** Name a point that is coplanar with the given points.
   a. E, F, G **H**
   b. B, C, G **F**
   c. A, D, E **H**
   d. D, C, G **H**

13. **Try This** Name two lines that are coplanar with $\overleftrightarrow{AB}$ and $\overleftrightarrow{DC}$. $\overleftrightarrow{AC}$, $\overleftrightarrow{BD}$, $\overleftrightarrow{AD}$, $\overleftrightarrow{BC}$

H, G, E, F, D, C, A, B (ice cube diagram)

13

TACTILE LEARNING Postulate 1-3 Have students illustrate this postulate by using two index cards or two pieces of stiff paper each cut halfway across. Have them manipulate the cards to illustrate two planes that intersect in a horizontal line and two planes that intersect in a vertical line.

Postulate 1-4 Have students illustrate this postulate using three pencil tips to balance a piece of cardboard. They should discover that the cardboard is balanced as long as the pencils are not in a straight line.

CRITICAL THINKING Ask students to explain why a kitchen stool with three legs does not wobble even if the legs are different lengths. Ask them how the seat might appear if the legs are different lengths. Have them support their explanations with diagrams.

14

Part 2 **Basic Postulates**

A **postulate** is an accepted statement of fact. You used some of the following geometry postulates in algebra. For example, when you graphed an equation such as $y = -2x + 8$, you began by plotting two points and then you drew the line through those two points.

| **Postulate 1-1** | Through any two points there is exactly one line. |

Line t is the only line that passes through points A and B.

In algebra, one way to solve the following system of equations is to graph the two equations.

$$y = -2x + 8$$
$$y = 3x - 7$$

As the graph shows, the two lines intersect at a single point, $(3, 2)$. The solution to the system of equations is $x = 3$, $y = 2$. This illustrates the following postulate.

| **Postulate 1-2** | If two lines intersect, then they intersect in exactly one point. |

14. **Open-ended** Describe two planes in your classroom that intersect. Also describe the intersection of the planes. Answers may vary. Sample: Two adjacent walls intersect in a line.

| **Postulate 1-3** | If two planes intersect, then they intersect in a line. |

Plane RST and plane STW intersect in $\overleftrightarrow{ST}$.

15. a. **Try This** What is the intersection of plane $HGFE$ and plane $BCGF$? $\overleftrightarrow{FG}$
  b. What is the intersection of plane AEF and plane BCG? $\overleftrightarrow{BF}$

A three-legged stool will always be stable, as long as the feet of the stool don't lie on a line. This illustrates the following postulate.

| **Postulate 1-4** | Through any three noncollinear points there is exactly one plane. |

Some students may have trouble visualizing planes other than those formed by the sides of the box. If possible, use a clear box such as a plastic food storage container and a piece of stiff paper to show plane *EBCH*.

Exercises 1–12 Students may want to construct the diagram using a piece of cardboard as plane *M* and a pencil as $\overleftrightarrow{AC}$.

Exercise 11 Ask students to describe the ways in which a line and a plane can intersect.

Exercises 13–26 Have physical models available. Kleenex® Brand Boutique® tissue boxes work well, but students can use about any box-shaped object.

Who? Euclid is known for compiling all the geometry of his time into postulates and theorems. His masterwork *The Elements* (about 300 B.C.) is the basis for geometry books today.

Example

Are points *E*, *H*, *B*, and *C* coplanar?
Are points *E*, *H*, *F*, and *B* coplanar?

Yes, the plane that contains the three noncollinear points *E*, *H*, and *B* also contains *C*.

No, points *E*, *H*, and *F* lie in exactly one plane, which doesn't contain *B*.

Exercises   ON YOUR OWN

Are the points collinear?

1. *A*, *D*, *E* no   **2.** *B*, *C*, *D* yes   **3.** *B*, *C*, *F* no   **4.** *A*, *E*, *C* yes   **5.** *F*, *B*, *D* no

Are the points coplanar?

6. *B*, *C*, *D*, *F* yes   **7.** *A*, *C*, *D*, *F* no   **8.** *B*, *D*, *E*, *F* no   **9.** *A*, *C*, *E*, *F* yes

10. Name plane *M* in another way. Answers may vary. Sample: plane *BCF*

11. What is the intersection of plane *M* and $\overleftrightarrow{AE}$? C

12. What is the intersection of $\overleftrightarrow{AE}$ and $\overleftrightarrow{BD}$? C

** Exs. 1 – 12**

Are the following coplanar?

13. *Q*, *V*, *R* yes   **14.** *X*, *V*, *R* yes   **15.** *U*, *V*, *W*, *S* no

16. *W*, *V*, *Q*, *T* yes   **17.** point *X*, $\overleftrightarrow{QT}$ yes   **18.** $\overleftrightarrow{RS}$, point *X* yes

19. $\overleftrightarrow{XW}$, $\overleftrightarrow{UV}$ yes   **20.** $\overleftrightarrow{UX}$, $\overleftrightarrow{WS}$ no   **21.** $\overleftrightarrow{UV}$, $\overleftrightarrow{WS}$ no

22. What is the intersection of plane *QRST* and plane *RSWV*? $\overleftrightarrow{RS}$

23. What is the intersection of $\overleftrightarrow{UV}$ and plane *QTXU*? U

24. Name three lines that intersect at point *S*. Answers may vary. Sample: $\overleftrightarrow{RS}$, $\overleftrightarrow{WS}$, $\overleftrightarrow{TS}$

25. Name two planes that intersect at $\overleftrightarrow{TS}$. Answers may vary. Sample: plane *XWST* and plane *UVST*

26. Name another point that is in the same plane as points *Q*, *T*, and *W*. V

Exs. 13 – 26

RESEARCH Exercise 28 Numerous translations of Euclid's *The Elements* exist. However, they may be too sophisticated for some students. Have students read about Euclid in an encyclopedia and look for material on the Internet.

STANDARDIZED TEST TIP Exercise 31 The key word in this question is "not." A common error is to choose the first acceptable name without observing that four of the five names are acceptable.

ALTERNATIVE ASSESSMENT Exercise 32 This exercise can be used to assess students' understanding of Postulate 1-4. Students observe that given a line and a point not on the line, they can find three noncollinear points by choosing any two points on the line and the point not on the line. These three points determine exactly one plane.

ESL Exercises 34–39 These exercises reinforce the vocabulary in this lesson. Have students work with partners to discuss any unclear terms. Clarify the meanings of the terms "all," "some," and "none."

PROBABILITY Exercise 41a Suggest that students list the possible ways to choose three points from four given (*ABC*, *ABD*, *ACD*, *BCD*), then check to see which of the ways lie in a line.

CONNECTING TO STUDENTS' WORLD Football quarterbacks also use Postulates 1-1 and 1-2 to determine where to throw a pass to a receiver. If you have block scheduling or an extended period, you may wish to take students outside to investigate this application.

pages 15–17 On Your Own

27. The ends of the 3 legs define points that will determine a plane that provides a stable base for the instruments regardless of the unevenness of the terrain.

28. Answers may vary. Sample: Euclid of Alexandria wrote *The Elements* about 300 B.C., and it has gone through about 1000 editions.

29. An infinite number; infinitely many planes can intersect in one line.

30. Postulate 1-1: Through any 2 points there is exactly 1 line.

47. Answers may vary. Sample: a flat roof, an inclined roof and the standing wall that bears their weight

27. **Writing** Surveyors and photographers use a *tripod*, or three-legged stand, for their instruments. Use one of the postulates to explain why. **See margin.**

28. **Research** Find out more about Euclid's book *The Elements*. What made it such a significant book? Where did Euclid get his information? **See margin.**

29. How many planes contain three collinear points? Explain. **See margin.**

30. Which postulate is sometimes stated as "Two points determine a line"? **See margin.**

31. **Standardized Test Prep** Which of the following is *not* an acceptable name for the plane shown? **C**
    A. plane *RSZ*
    B. plane *RSWZ*
    C. plane *WSZ*
    D. plane *RSTW*
    E. plane *STZ*

32. How many planes contain each line and point?
    a. $\overleftrightarrow{EF}$ and point Q 1   b. $\overleftrightarrow{PH}$ and point E 1
    c. $\overleftrightarrow{FG}$ and point P 1   d. $\overleftrightarrow{EP}$ and point G 1
    e. Use inductive reasoning. What do you think is true of a line and a point not on the line? **Through a line and a point not on that line there is exactly 1 plane.**

33. **Logical Reasoning** Suppose two lines intersect. How many planes do you think contain both lines? Use the diagram at the right to explain your answer. **1; points A, B, and C are points on the 2 lines and these 3 points are noncollinear, so exactly 1 plane contains them.**

Complete with *always*, *sometimes*, or *never* to make a true statement.

34. Intersecting lines are __?__ coplanar. **always**

35. Two planes __?__ intersect in exactly one point. **never**

36. Three points are __?__ coplanar. **always**

37. A line and a point not on the line are __?__ coplanar. **always**

38. Four points are __?__ coplanar. **sometimes**

39. Two lines __?__ meet in more than one point. **never**

Probability Given points A, B, C, and D as shown, solve each problem.

40. Two points are picked at random. Find P(they are collinear). 1

41. Three points are picked at random.
    a. Find P(they are collinear). $\frac{1}{4}$ b. Find P(they are coplanar). 1

OPEN-ENDED Exercise 47 Emphasize that the three planes need to intersect in a line and not just a point. For example, two walls that meet at a corner and the ceiling are contained in planes that intersect at a point. Three pages of a book (that is fanned out) are contained in planes that intersect in a line.

MAKING CONNECTIONS Exercise 48 When you are crossing a street in a crosswalk, the letters in the word STOP painted on the street for automobiles appear long and narrow. A driver from an approaching car views the letters at an angle so they appear normal.

GETTING READY FOR LESSON 1-3 These exercises prepare students for the definition of *skew lines*.

Wrap Up

THE BIG IDEA Ask students: *Describe the similarities, differences, and connections between lines and planes.*

RETEACHING ACTIVITY Students use the basic definitions and postulates to identify points, lines, and planes on figures. (Reteaching worksheet 1-2)

Exercises   MIXED REVIEW

Exercises 49–52 Students review evaluating variable expressions for given values.

42. Navigation Rescue teams use the principles in Postulates 1-1 and 1-2 to determine the location of a distress signal. In the diagram, a ship at point *A* receives a signal from the northeast. A ship at point *B* receives the same signal from due west. Trace the diagram and find the location of the distress signal. Explain how the two postulates help to find the location of the distress signal.   **See below.**

Coordinate Geometry **Are the points collinear? Graph them to find out.**

43. $(1, 1), (4, 4), (-3, -3)$ collinear   **44.** $(2, 4), (4, 6), (0, 2)$ collinear

45. $(0, 0), (8, 10), (4, 6)$ noncollinear   **46.** $(0, 0), (0, 3), (0, -10)$ collinear

47. Open-ended Give an example from your classroom or your home of three planes intersecting in one line.   **See margin p. 16.**

48. Optical Illusions The diagram at the right is an optical illusion. Which points are collinear, *A*, *B*, *C* or *A*, *B*, *D*? Are you sure? Use a ruler to check your answer.   **A, B, D**

42. Let *D* be the location of the distress signal. By Postulate 1-1, *A* and *D* determine a line, and *B* and *D* determine another. By Postulate 1-2, the two lines intersect in exactly one point, *D*.

Exercises   MIXED REVIEW

Algebra **Evaluate each expression for the given values.**

49. $a^2 + b^2$ for $a = 3$ and $b = -5$ 34   **50.** $\frac{1}{2}bh$ for $b = 8$ and $h = 11$ 44

51. $2\ell + 2w$ for $\ell = 3$ and $w = 7$ 20   **52.** $b^2 - 4ac$ for $a = 2, b = 5,$ and $c = 1$ 17

53. Patterns What is the last digit of 3^{45}? Make a table and use inductive reasoning. Explain the pattern.   3

For more practice with evaluating expressions, see Skills Handbook page 659.

Getting Ready for Lesson 1-3

Will the lines intersect or not?

54. no   **55.** yes   **56.** no   **57.** no

Lesson Quiz

Lesson Quiz is also available in Transparencies.

1. Are the points *A*, *D*, and *C* collinear?   No

2. Are the points *A*, *B*, *C*, and *E* coplanar?   No

3. Are $\overleftrightarrow{DH}$ and *E* coplanar?   Yes

4. Are $\overleftrightarrow{AB}$ and $\overleftrightarrow{CG}$ coplanar?   No

THINK AND DISCUSS

PROBLEM OF THE DAY

Find the letter that is the 276th entry in the following sequence: G, L, G, L, L, G, L, L, L, G, L, L, L, L, G, L, L, … **G**

Problem of the Day is also available in Transparencies.

CONNECTING TO PRIOR KNOWLEDGE Ask students to describe real-world examples of parallel lines. Examples may include lane dividers, rows of crops, streets on a map, railroad tracks, and so on. Ask them to describe the characteristics of these lines.

THINK AND DISCUSS

In geometry, betweenness implies collinearity. For example, $\overline{AB}$ contains all the points between A and B that lie on the same line as A and B.

VISUAL LEARNING Students can remember the meaning of the abbreviations $\overline{AB}$, $\overrightarrow{AB}$, and $\overleftrightarrow{AB}$ by observing that visual representations of a segment, ray, and line, respectively, are —, →, ↔ .

Lesson Planning Options

Prerequisite Skills

• Understanding of points, lines, and planes

Assignment Options for Exercises On Your Own

Core 1–34, 37, 39
Extension 35–36, 38

Use Mixed Review to maintain skills.

Resources

 Student Edition

Extra Practice, p. 634
Glossary/Study Guide

 Teaching Resources

Chapter Support File, Ch. 1
• Practice 1-3 (two worksheets)
• Reteaching 1-3
Classroom Manager 1-3
Glossary, Spanish Resources

 Transparencies
23, 28

18

What You'll Learn

• Relating segments and rays to lines
• Recognizing parallel lines and parallel planes

...And Why

To provide a vocabulary of terms needed for communicating in geometry

What You'll Need

graph paper, colored pencils, tape

A ray in geometry is named after the rays of the sun.

1-3 Segments, Rays, Parallel Lines and Planes

THINK AND DISCUSS

Many geometric figures, such as squares and angles, use only the parts lines called segments and rays.

A **segment** is the part of a line consisting of two *endpoints* and all points between them.

A **ray** is the part of a line consisti one *endpoint* and all the points of line on one side of the endpoint.

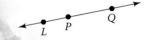

segment AB   ray YX
A   B   X   Y
endpoint $\overline{AB}$ endpoint $\overrightarrow{YX}$ endp

Yes; the segments have the same endpoints and contain the sam points between the

1. Is $\overline{AB}$ the same as $\overline{BA}$? Explain.

2. Is $\overrightarrow{YX}$ the same as $\overrightarrow{XY}$? Explain. **No, they have different endpoi and continue in opposite directions.**

3. How is a ray like a line? How is a ray different from a line?
A ray extends forever in one direction, while a line extends forever in both directions.

Opposite rays are two collinear rays with the same endpoint. Opposi rays always form a line.

Answers may vary. Sample: $\overrightarrow{LP}$, $\overrightarrow{PQ}$, $\overrightarrow{PL}$, $\overrightarrow{QL}$

4. **a.** Name four different rays in the figure below.
   b. Name two opposite rays. $\overrightarrow{PL}$ and $\overrightarrow{PQ}$

L   P   Q

Lines that do not intersect may or may not be coplanar. **Parallel lines** coplanar lines that do not intersect. Segments and rays are parallel if t lie in parallel lines.

You can use arrowheads to show parallel lines.

Read "is parallel to."

$\ell \parallel n$ $\overrightarrow{AB} \parallel \overrightarrow{EF}$

MAKING CONNECTIONS Air traffic controllers keep eastbound and westbound airplanes from colliding by having them cruise at different altitudes. The airplanes thus pass each other in parallel planes.

5. Name all the segments shown at the left that are parallel to:
   a. $\overline{DC}$
   $\overline{AB}, \overline{GH}, \overline{JI}$
   b. $\overline{GJ}$
   $\overline{AD}, \overline{EF}, \overline{BC}, \overline{HI}$
   c. $\overline{AE}$
   $\overline{DF}$

Skew lines do not lie in the same plane. They are neither parallel nor intersecting.

$\overleftrightarrow{AB}$ and $\overleftrightarrow{HI}$ are skew.

Parallel planes are planes that do not intersect.

plane $ABCD \parallel$ plane $GHIJ$

6. Name some other pairs of skew lines in the diagram at the left. Answers may vary.
   Sample: $\overleftrightarrow{AB}$ and $\overleftrightarrow{GJ}$, $\overleftrightarrow{AB}$ and $\overleftrightarrow{DJ}$

7. Name two more pairs of parallel planes.
   plane $ABHG \parallel$ plane $DCIJ$, plane $ADJG \parallel BCIH$

A box diagram is a good way to represent parallel lines and segments, skew lines, and parallel planes. Some other ways to draw planes are shown below.

8. Which pairs of planes shown above are parallel? Which are intersecting? *A and B, C and D; E and F, G and H*

Example

Draw planes A and B intersecting in $\overleftrightarrow{FG}$.

Using graph paper will help you draw parallel lines and representations of planes.

Step 1   Step 2   Step 3

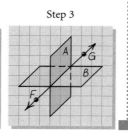

9. **Try This** Use graph paper and colored pencils to draw pairs of parallel and intersecting planes like those above Question 8.
   Check students' work.

ALTERNATIVE ASSESSMENT This activity can help you assess students' understanding of parallel lines, skew lines, and parallel planes. It may help students to tape a piece of paper with the appropriate vertex labeled on it to each corner of the stack of books. Have students take turns recording answers to Questions 10–12.

Exercises 9–12 Students may need a ruler or straightedge. Some may prefer to use graph paper, although this is not necessary.

ESL Exercises 21-30 These exercises reinforce the meanings of the new vocabulary taught in this lesson as well as "always," "sometimes," and "never." You may want to have students work with partners to discuss unfamiliar terms.

Technology Options

Exercises 9–12 can be sketched using drawing software. For Exercises 21–30, students may investigate the different cases using geometry software.

Prentice Hall Technology

Software
• Secondary Math Lab Toolkit™
• Computer Item Generator 1-3

CD-ROM
• Multimedia Geometry Lab 1

Internet
• See the Prentice Hall site.
(http://www.phschool.com)

20

Work in pairs to answer these questions about the lines and planes determined by the surfaces of a rectangular solid.

Stack your geometry books to form a rectangular solid. Label the vertices *P, Q, R, S, T, U, V,* and *W.* Identify each of the following.

10. three pairs of parallel planes   See below.

11. all lines that are parallel to $\overleftrightarrow{PQ}$ $\overleftrightarrow{TU}$, $\overleftrightarrow{SR}$, $\overleftrightarrow{VW}$

12. all lines that are skew to $\overleftrightarrow{PQ}$ $\overleftrightarrow{TW}$, $\overleftrightarrow{UV}$, $\overleftrightarrow{SW}$, $\overleftrightarrow{RV}$

10. plane *PQR* and plane *TUV*, plane *PQU* and plane *SRV*, plane *PST* and plane *QRV*

Name all the segments that are parallel to the given segment.

1. $\overline{AC}$ $\overline{DF}$ **2.** $\overline{EF}$ $\overline{BC}$ **3.** $\overline{AD}$ $\overline{CF}$, $\overline{BE}$

4. Name all the lines that form a pair of skew lines with $\overleftrightarrow{AD}$.

5. Name a pair of parallel planes. $\overleftrightarrow{BC}$, $\overleftrightarrow{EF}$
plane *ABC* and plane *DEF*

Exs. 1–5

Use the line at the right for Exercises 6–8.   6a. $\overrightarrow{TW}$ and $\overrightarrow{TS}$ or $\overrightarrow{TW}$ and $\overrightarrow{TR}$

6. a. Name a pair of opposite rays with point *T* as endpoint.
   b. Name another pair of opposite rays. $\overrightarrow{SR}$ and $\overrightarrow{ST}$

7. Name all the segments shown.   or $\overrightarrow{SR}$ and $\overrightarrow{SW}$

8. Name $\overrightarrow{RT}$ two other ways. $\overline{RS}$, $\overline{RT}$, $\overline{RW}$, $\overline{ST}$, $\overline{SW}$, $\overline{TW}$ **Exs. 6–8**
$\overrightarrow{RS}$, $\overrightarrow{RW}$

Make a separate sketch for each of the following.

9. Draw three parallel lines *a, t,* and *q.*

10. Draw parallel planes *A* and *B.*

11. Draw $\overleftrightarrow{AB}$, $\overleftrightarrow{CD}$, and $\overleftrightarrow{EF}$ so that $\overleftrightarrow{AB} \parallel \overleftrightarrow{CD}$, $\overleftrightarrow{AB}$ and $\overleftrightarrow{EF}$ are skew, and $\overleftrightarrow{CD}$ and $\overleftrightarrow{EF}$ are skew.   See margin p. 21.

12. Draw planes *C* and *D,* intersecting in $\overleftrightarrow{XY}$.   See margin p. 21.

9.

10.

Write *true* or *false.*

13. $\overleftrightarrow{CB} \parallel \overleftrightarrow{GF}$ false

14. $\overleftrightarrow{ED} \parallel \overleftrightarrow{HG}$ false

15. plane *AED* $\parallel$ plane *FGH*

16. plane *ABH* $\parallel$ plane *CDF*

17. $\overleftrightarrow{AB}$ and $\overleftrightarrow{HG}$ are skew lines.   true

18. $\overleftrightarrow{AE}$ and $\overleftrightarrow{BC}$ are skew lines.   false

19. $\overleftrightarrow{CF}$ and $\overleftrightarrow{AI}$ are skew lines.   true

20. $\overleftrightarrow{CF}$ and $\overleftrightarrow{AJ}$ are skew lines.   false

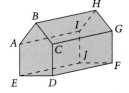

KINESTHETIC LEARNING Exercise 31 If you have block scheduling or an extended period, take students outside and ask them to find and record examples for each of the different ways that two lines can be related.

MAKING CONNECTIONS Exercise 32 Because Earth's axis is at a 23.4° tilt, any plane that cuts through the center of the earth and its two poles is at a 23.4° angle to Earth's horizontal orbital plane. The tilt in the earth alternately tips the North and South poles toward the Sun, which causes the seasons.

CRITICAL THINKING Exercise 35 Students may want to construct the described situation using index cards or other sturdy paper.

RESEARCH Exercise 36 Students should be able to find this information in a chemistry book or encyclopedia. You may wish to ask the science department in your school for three-dimensional models of atoms for students to examine.

Complete with *always*, *sometimes*, or *never* to make a true statement.

21. $\overrightarrow{AB}$ and $\overrightarrow{BA}$ are __?__ the same ray. **never**

22. $\overrightarrow{AB}$ and $\overrightarrow{AC}$ are __?__ the same ray. **sometimes**

23. $\overline{AX}$ and $\overline{XA}$ are __?__ the same segment. **always**

24. $\overleftrightarrow{TQ}$ and $\overleftrightarrow{QT}$ are __?__ the same line. **always**

25. Two parallel lines are __?__ coplanar. **always**

26. Skew lines are __?__ coplanar. **never**

27. Opposite rays __?__ form a line. **always**

28. Two lines in the same plane are __?__ parallel. **sometimes**

29. Two planes that do not intersect are __?__ parallel. **always**

30. Two lines that lie in parallel planes are __?__ parallel. **sometimes**

31. Writing **Summarize** the different ways that two lines may be related. Give examples from the real world that illustrate the relationships. **See margin.**

32. Navigation North and south are directions on a compass that are on opposite rays. Name two other pairs of compass directions that are on opposite rays. **Answers may vary. Sample: NW and SE**

33. Coordinate Geometry $\overrightarrow{AB}$ has endpoint $A(2, 3)$ and goes through $B(4, 6)$. Give some possible coordinates for point C so that $\overrightarrow{AB}$ and $\overrightarrow{AC}$ will be opposite rays. Graph your answer. **See margin.**

34. Inductive Reasoning Draw a diagram similar to the one shown.
Step 1: Draw $\overline{AU}$ and $\overline{BT}$. Label their intersection point as X.
Step 2: Draw $\overline{AV}$ and $\overline{CT}$. Label their intersection point as Y.
Step 3: Draw $\overline{BV}$ and $\overline{CU}$. Label their intersection point as Z.
Make a **conjecture** about points X, Y, and Z. **They are collinear.**

35. Critical Thinking Suppose two parallel planes A and B are each intersected by a third plane C. What do you think will be true of the intersection of planes A and C and the intersection of planes B and C? Give an example in your classroom. **See margin.**

36. Research In diamond, each carbon atom bonds to four other carbon atoms in a three-dimensional network. In graphite, each carbon atom bonds to three other carbon atoms in the same plane. The "sheets" or planes of graphite are parallel. Find out how these structures affect the properties of diamond and graphite. **Answers may vary. Sample: The diamond structure makes it tough, strong, hard and durable. The graphite structure makes it soft and slippery.**

Directions are printed on a compass card, a circle divided into 32 equally-spaced compass points.

---

11.   **12.**

31. Lines can be coplanar or skew. If they are coplanar, they can be parallel or intersecting.

Answers may vary. Sample: Skew lines—vapor trails of a north-bound jet and a west-bound jet at different altitudes, Parallel lines—train tracks, Intersecting lines—two edges of a roof that meet at the peak

33.

Answers may vary. Samples: $(0, 0)$, $(-2, -3)$, and $(-4, -6)$.

35. The lines of intersection are parallel. Answers will vary. Sample: the ceiling and floor intersect a wall in two parallel lines.

WRITING Exercise 38 Have students give examples of how *skew* can be used in nonmathematical sentences.

Chapter Project **FIND OUT BY CREATING** Have students work in groups. Provide each student with several paper squares and a paper lunch bag in which they can store their origami figures. Allow time for students to share their figures with other groups.

Exercises   MIXED REVIEW

Exercises 40–42 Students use inductive reasoning to determine terms in a pattern.

Exercises 43–45 Students review the symbols for geometric figures.

GETTING READY FOR LESSON 1-4 By reviewing absolute value and inequalities, these exercises prepare students to find the lengths of line segments.

 JOURNAL Suggest that students sketch their examples and label the geometric terms they illustrate.

Wrap Up

THE BIG IDEA Ask students: *Explain how two planes can be related and how two lines in those planes can be related.*

RETEACHING ACTIVITY Students identify different pairs of skew, parallel, and intersecting lines. (Reteaching worksheet 1-4)

Lesson Quiz

1. Name a line that forms a pair of skew lines with $\overleftrightarrow{EH}$.
Sample: $\overleftrightarrow{AB}$, $\overleftrightarrow{DC}$, $\overleftrightarrow{CG}$, $\overleftrightarrow{BF}$

2. Name a pair of parallel planes.
Answers may vary. Sample: Planes AEF and DHG, ADH and BCG, EFG and ABC

3. Name a line that forms a pair of parallel lines with $\overleftrightarrow{CG}$.
$\overleftrightarrow{BF}$, $\overleftrightarrow{DH}$, or $\overleftrightarrow{AE}$

22

---

37. *Open-ended* List four pairs of parallel planes in your classroom. Answers may vary. Sample: ceiling and floor, desktop and floor, front wall and back wall, two side walls

38. *Writing* The term *skew* is from a Middle English word meaning "to escape." Explain why this might be an appropriate origin for the word that names skew lines.
Sample: Skew lines cannot be "contained" by one plane. Therefore, they have "escaped" a plane.

39. *Standardized Test Prep* Which statement(s) can be true about three planes? E
  I. They intersect in a line.   **II.** They intersect in a point.   **III.** They have no points in common.
  A. I only   **B.** II only   **C.** I and II only   **D.** I and III only   **E.** I, II, and III

Chapter Project **Find Out by Creating**

Some artists create origami by experimenting. They fold and unfold a piece of paper until they see a resemblance to the real world. Take your folded square from the Find Out question on page 10 (or make a new one). Use the existing creases to construct the dog and the flower pictured at the right. Now try to create your own origami with a fresh square of paper. Check students' work.

Exercises   MIXED REVIEW

Find the next two terms in each sequence.

40. 0.1, 0.12, 0.123, 0.1234, . . .
0.12345, 0.123456

41. $-1, -2, -4, -7, -11, -16, . . .$
$-22, -29$

42. AB, BC, CD, DE, EF, . . .
FG, GH

State the ways you can name each geometric figure.

43. a line by two points on the line or with a single lower-case letter

44. a point with a capital letter

45. a plane See margin p. 23.

46. *Logical Reasoning* Raven made the following **conjecture**: "When you subtract a number from a given number, the answer is always smaller than the given number." Is her **conjecture** correct? Explain.
No; her statement is true only when the number being subtracted is greater than zero.

Getting Ready for Lesson 1-4

Simplify each expression.

47. $|-6|$ 6
48. $|3.5|$ 3.5
49. $|7 - 10|$ 3
50. $|-4 - 2|$ 6
51. $|8 - 5|$ 3
52. $|4 + 1|$ 5
53. $|-3 + 12|$ 9
54. $|-21 + 6|$ 15
55. $|-11 - (-2)|$ 9

Graph each inequality on a number line.   56–64. See margin p. 23.

56. $t > 6$
57. $9 \leq m$
58. $w < -4$
59. $5 > s$
60. $p \leq 7$
61. $-1.5 \geq b$
62. $x \geq -3$
63. $0 < q$
64. $-5 \leq v < -2$

FOR YOUR JOURNAL
Choose five geometric terms from this lesson. Describe real-world examples of each.

In this chapter, students solve linear equations to find the lengths of segments, the measures of angles, and the coordinates of points. This toolbox reviews the basic skills for solving linear equations including combining like terms and isolating all the variables on one side of the equation.

Example 1

Make sure students understand why $a - b = a + (-b)$ and how the Distributive Property is applied.

Example 2

ERROR ALERT! Students may lose track of signs when moving variables and constants to opposite sides of the equals sign. **Remediation:** Encourage students to perform one step at a time, first moving the variables to one side, then moving the constants to the other side. It may be helpful for some students to write out each step instead of performing some only mentally. Also, remind students to check their answer in the original equation.

ALTERNATE ASSESSMENT You can use Exercises 2–3 to evaluate students' understanding of combining like terms and Exercises 1 and 4 to evaluate students' understanding of isolating the variable on one side.

Math ToolboX — Algebra Review

Solving Linear Equations

Before Lesson 1-4

Sometimes you need to combine like terms when you are solving linear equations.

Example 1

Solve $(5x + 8) - (2x - 9) = 38$.

$(5x + 8) + (-1)(2x - 9) = 38$	$-(2x - 9) = (-1)(2x - 9)$
$5x + 8 - 2x + 9 = 38$	Use the Distributive Property.
$3x + 17 = 38$	Simplify.
$3x = 21$	Subtract 17 from each side.
$x = 7$	Divide each side by 3.

When you are solving equations with variables on both sides, first get all the variables on the same side of the equation.

Example 2

Solve $4x - 9 = 7x - 15$.

$4x - 9 = 7x - 15$	
$-9 = 3x - 15$	Subtract $4x$ from each side.
$6 = 3x$	Add 15 to each side.
$2 = x$	Divide each side by 3.

Solve.

1. $5x + 10 - 6x + 3 = 6 - 2x - 2$ -9

2. $(6a - 54) - (5a + 27) = 23$ 104

3. $(2 + 4y) - (y + 9) = 26$ 11

4. $7t - 8t + 4 = 5t - 2$ 1

5. $(9k + 30) - (4k + 10) = 100$ 16

6. $6x + 17 = 9x + 2$ 5

7. $(3x + 10) - 5x = 6x - 50$ $\frac{15}{2}$

8. $(3y - 5) + (5y + 20) = 135$ 15

9. $10n + 12 = 14n - 12$ 6

10. $13c + 40 = 9c - 20 + c$ -20

11. $(4w - 28) + (11w + 13) = 180$ 13

12. $7f + 16 = 3f + 48$ 8

13. $(7a + 3) + (-a - 5) = -16$ $-\frac{7}{3}$

14. $3x - 35 = 9x - 59$ 4

15. $7y + 44 = 12y + 11$ $\frac{33}{5}$

16. $(11x - 37) + (5x + 59) = 54$ 2

17. $(7t - 21) + (t + 4) = 15$ 4

18. $(5w + 24) + (2w + 13) = 156$ 17

---

page 22 Mixed Review

45. with the word *plane* followed either by a single capital letter or the names of at least 3 noncollinear points in the plane

56. $-2\ 0\ 2\ 4\ 6\ 8$

57. $7\quad 9\quad 11$

58. $-6\ -4\ -2$

59. $2\quad 4\quad 6$

60. $6\quad 8\quad 10$

61. $-4\ -2\quad 0$

62. $-6\ -4\ -2$

63. $-2\quad 0\quad 2$

64. $-6\ -4\ -2$

WORK TOGETHER

PROBLEM OF THE DAY

What is the least number of line segments you can draw end to end to connect the nine dots on the grid? **4**

Problem of the Day is also available in Transparencies.

CONNECTING TO PRIOR KNOWLEDGE Ask students if they have ever seen "mile" markers on the side of a highway. Ask them if the numbers on the "mile" markers increased or decreased as they went along. Discuss what the markers mean.

WORK TOGETHER

Students may need help reading the map. Help them identify mileage markers and different routes. Discuss the map symbols and what they represent.

MAKING CONNECTIONS The task of a cartographer or map maker has been simplified by the development of modern technological devices. Satellites can now take pictures of the earth which computers can project onto flat surfaces. Cartographers have easy access to biological, geological, and atmospheric tables which have been gathered and stored in computer data banks.

Lesson Planning Options

Prerequisite Skills

- Finding absolute value
- Solving one-variable equations

Assignment Options for Exercises On Your Own

To provide flexible scheduling, this lesson can be subdivided into parts.

▼ **Core** 1–14, 24
Extension 27–28

▼ **Core** 15–23, 32–36
Extension 25–26, 29–31

Use Mixed Review to maintain skills.

Resources

 Student Edition

Skills Handbook, pp. 652, 659, 663
Extra Practice, p. 634
Glossary/Study Guide

Teaching Resources

Chapter Support File, Ch. 1
- Practice 1-4 (two worksheets)
- Reteaching 1-4
- Alternative Activity 1-4
Classroom Manager 1-4
Glossary, Spanish Resources

 Transparencies
4, 12, 23

24

What You'll Learn
- Finding the length of a segment and the measure of an angle

...And Why
To understand the building blocks of many geometric figures

What You'll Need
protractor

Connections Travel . . . and more

1-4 **M**easuring Angles and Segments

WORK TOGETHER

Your family is traveling on Interstate 80 through Nebraska. You entered the highway at mileage marker 126. You decided to drive as far as you could before stopping for breakfast within $1\frac{1}{2}$ hours. Assume that on the highway you drive at an average speed of 60 mi/h. Work with a partner to answer these questions.

1. How far will you travel in $1\frac{1}{2}$ hours? **90 mi**

2. a. At what mileage marker will you exit to get breakfast? **211 or 38**
  b. Is there another possible answer for the mileage marker? **38 or 211**

3. Suppose you are traveling east on I-80, starting at mileage marker 126. Not counting side trips for sightseeing, you travel 111 mi on I-80 before you exit for a campground. **increase**
  a. Do mileage markers increase or decrease from west to east?
  b. What mileage marker is at your exit? **237**

4. Does the *direction* you travel affect the *distance* you travel? **No**

Ruler Postulate Point out that the length of a segment is denoted by writing the endpoints without a bar over them. Remind students that the vertical bars around $a - b$ indicate absolute value.

Example 1

You may need to review the definition of absolute value. Have students check the solution using a number line.

Point out, on diagrams, how tick marks are used to show congruent segments.

CRITICAL THINKING Ask students why $\overline{AB} = \overline{CD}$ would not be correct.

Part 1 Measuring Segments

If you picture straightening out the map of Interstate 80, you will have a model for a number line. The mileage markers represent *coordinates*.

Postulate 1-5
Ruler Postulate

The points of a line can be put into a one-to-one correspondence with the real numbers so that the distance between any two points is the absolute value of the difference of the corresponding numbers.

the length of $\overline{AB}$

$$AB = |a - b|$$

coordinate of A coordinate of B

5. **Critical Thinking** Why do you think that absolute value is used to express the distance between two points?
Distance is a positive number.

Example 1

PROBLEM SOLVING HINT

Draw a diagram.

Find QS if the coordinate of Q is -3 and the coordinate of S is 21.

$$QS = |-3 - 21| = |-24| = 24$$

6. Suppose you subtracted -3 from 21 in Example 1. Would you get the same result? Why or why not? Yes; $|-3 - 21| = 24 = |21 - (-3)|$

7. **Try This** Find AB if the coordinate of point A is -8, and the coordinate of point B is 11.   19

Two segments with the same length are **congruent** ($\cong$). In other words, if $AB = CD$, then $\overline{AB} \cong \overline{CD}$. You can use these statements interchangeably. Segments can be marked alike to show that they are congruent.

2 cm
A B A B

$\longrightarrow$ $AB = CD$ $\longrightarrow$ $\overline{AB} \cong \overline{CD}$

2 cm
C D C D

8. **a. Try This** Name two segments that are congruent. $\overline{AB}, \overline{BC}$
 b. Name a second pair of congruent segments. $\overline{CD}, \overline{DE}$

Additional Examples

FOR EXAMPLE 1 ....

Find BC if the coordinate of B is -12 and the coordinate of C is -5. **7**

Discussion: *How can you check your answer?*

FOR EXAMPLE 2 ....

Refer to the diagram in Example 2. If $DT = 85$, find the value of x. Then find DS and ST.   **$x = 21$, $DS = 34$, $ST = 51$**

Discussion: *What postulate do you use to solve this problem?*

Example 2

This problem is solved in two steps: finding the value of *x* and then evaluating the expressions for *DS* and *ST*.

Question 11 When naming angles with three letters, the vertex should be the middle letter. For example ∠*COD* and ∠*DOC* describe the same angle but ∠*DCO* does not.

ERROR ALERT! Students whose experiences with measurement have been primarily measuring distances might assume that the measure of an angle is related to the "lengths" of the rays drawn. **Remediation:** Reinforce that the measure of an angle measures the opening of the angle. Also remind students that the rays drawn are just representations and that rays extend infinitely in one direction.

Technology Options

For Exercise 21, students may draw and measure angles using geometry software. For Exercise 30, students may replicate the activity using geometry software.

Prentice Hall Technology

Software
- Secondary Math Lab Toolkit™
- Integrated Math Lab 23
- Computer Item Generator 1-4

CD-ROM
- Multimedia Geometry Lab 1

Internet
- See the Prentice Hall site. (http://www.phschool.com)

26

If three points *A*, *B*, and *C* are collinear and *B* is between *A* and *C*, then *AB* + *BC* = *AC*.

Example 2

Algebra If *DT* = 60, find the value of *x*. Then find *DS* and *ST*.

$DS + ST = DT$	Segment Addition Postulate
$(2x - 8) + (3x - 12) = 60$	Substitution
$5x - 20 = 60$	Simplify.
$5x = 80$	Add 20 to each side.
$x = 16$	Divide each side by 5.

$DS = 2x - 8 = 2(16) - 8 = 24$

$ST = 3x - 12 = 3(16) - 12 = 36$

For more practice with solving linear equations, see Skills Handbook, page 663.

9. Explain how to check the answers in Example 2. **Substitute numbers to see that** *DS* + *ST* = *DT*. **24 + 36** ≟ **60, 60 = 60** ✔

10. a. Try This *EG* = 100. Find the value of *x*. **15**
   b. Find *EF* and *FG*. **40; 60**

$4x - 20$ $2x + 30$
E   *F*   *G*

Part 2 Measuring Angles

An **angle** (∠) is formed by two rays (called *sides* of the angle) with the same endpoint (called the *vertex* of the angle). You can name an angle several ways.

∠*A*   ∠1   ∠*TBQ*

11. a. Name ∠1 two other ways. ∠*AEC*, ∠*CEA*
   b. Name ∠*CED* two other ways.
   c. Would it be correct to refer to any of the angles at the right as ∠*E*? Why or why not?

b. ∠2, ∠*DEC*
c. No; there are 3 angles shown with *E* as their vertex.

Angles are measured in *degrees*. The *measure* of ∠*A* is written as *m*∠*A*.

$$m\angle A = 80$$

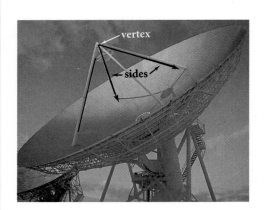
vertex
sides

When you use a *protractor* to measure angles you are applying the following postulate.

Postulate 1-7
Protractor Postulate

Let $\overrightarrow{OA}$ and $\overrightarrow{OB}$ be opposite rays in a plane. $\overrightarrow{OA}$, $\overrightarrow{OB}$ and all the rays with endpoint O that can be drawn on one side of $\overleftrightarrow{AB}$ can be paired with the real numbers from 0 to 180 in such a way that:

a. $\overrightarrow{OA}$ is paired with 0 and $\overrightarrow{OB}$ is paired with 180.

b. If $\overrightarrow{OC}$ is paired with x and $\overrightarrow{OD}$ is paired with y, then $m\angle COD = |x - y|$.

Answers may vary slightly.

12. Try This Use a protractor to find the measure of each angle.

a. $m\angle AOC$
35

b. $m\angle EOB$
75

c. $m\angle DOF$
80

d. $m\angle COE$
70

13. Try This Use a protractor to draw a 105° angle.
Check students' work.

You can classify angles according to their measures.

This symbol indicates a right angle.

Acute	Right	Obtuse	Straight
$0 < x < 90$	$x = 90$	$90 < x < 180$	$x = 180$

27

ESTIMATION Question 14 Students can use a corner of a piece of paper (90° angle) to help them estimate the measure of an angle. When students measure the angles with a protractor, allow up to about 2° of variation.

Angle Addition Postulate A point is in the interior of an angle if it does not lie on the sides of the angle and lies on a segment whose endpoints are on the sides of the angle. Since a straight angle has no interior, the angle addition postulate for straight angles is stated separately.

Exercises 1–4 Students may want to copy the number line and fill in the other coordinates along the scale. These problems can be completed by counting the units between the numbers on the number line or by taking the absolute value of the difference between the coordinates of the endpoints.

14. Estimate the measure of each angle. Then use a protractor to find the measure. **Estimates may vary slightly.**

a.
120

b.
45

c.
90

15. Classify each angle in Exercise 14 as *acute, obtuse,* or *right.*
obtuse   acute   right

Angles with the same measure are **congruent.** In other words, if $m\angle 1 = m\angle 2$, then $\angle 1 \cong \angle 2$. You can use these statements interchangeably. Angles can be marked alike to show that they are congruent.

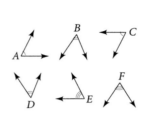

16. Name the congruent angles shown at the left.
$\angle A \cong \angle C, \angle B \cong \angle D, \angle E \cong \angle F$

The Angle Addition Postulate is very similar to the Segment Addition Postulate. Notice that it has a special case for straight angles.

Postulate 1-8 Angle Addition Postulate	If point *B* is in the interior of $\angle AOC$, then $m\angle AOB + m\angle BOC = m\angle AOC$. If $\angle AOC$ is a straight angle, then $m\angle AOB + m\angle BOC = 180$.

17. a. $m\angle RST = 50$ and $m\angle RSW = 125$.
What is $m\angle TSW$? **75**

    b. $m\angle DEG = 145$.
What is $m\angle GEF$? **35**

Complete each equation.

1. $AC = \blacksquare$ 9   **2.** $BD = \blacksquare$ 9   **3.** $AD = \blacksquare$ 11   **4.** $BE = \blacksquare$ 13

Exs. 1–10

Write *true* or *false.*

5. $\overline{AB} \cong \overline{ED}$ false   **6.** $BD < CD$ false   **7.** $AC + BD = AD$ false   **8.** $AC + CD = AD$
                                                                                                true

9. Name two pairs of congruent segments. $\overline{AB} \cong \overline{CD}, \overline{AC} \cong \overline{BD}$

10. $EG = 5$. Find the coordinate of point *G*. Is there another possibility? **2; 12**

28

ALTERNATIVE ASSESSMENT Exercises 11–12, 15–16 These exercises help you assess students' understanding of the Segment Addition Postulate and both cases of the Angle Addition Postulate. Have students compare answers with partners.

ALGEBRA Exercises 13–14 Some students will stop after they find the value of *x*. Remind them to find the values of *RS* and *ST*.

CONNECTING TO STUDENTS' WORLD Exercise 17 Have students write their first names using block letters. Then have them count the number of acute, right, and obtuse angles suggested by the letters.

ESL Exercises 20 and 26 Reinforce the meanings of the new vocabulary taught in this lesson as well as the English words that may be unfamiliar such as *ski-jumping*, *billiards*, and *shot*. You may want to have students work with partners to discuss unfamiliar terms.

EXTENSION Exercise 24 Have students graph all possible locations of point *B*.

Use the figure at the right for Exercises 11–14.

R   S   T

11. If $RS = 15$ and $ST = 9$, then $RT = $ ■.   24

12. If $ST = 15$ and $RT = 40$, then $RS = $ ■.   25

13. Algebra If $RS = 3x + 1$, $ST = 2x - 2$, and $RT = 64$, find the value of *x*. Then find *RS* and *ST*. 13; 40; 24

14. Algebra If $RS = 8y + 4$, $ST = 4y + 8$, and $RT = 15y - 9$, find the value of *y*. Then find *RS* and *ST*. 7; 60; 36

Use the figure at the right for Exercises 15–17.

15. If $m\angle MQV = 90$ and $m\angle VQP = 35$, what is $m\angle MQP$? 125

16. If $m\angle MVQ = 55$, what is $m\angle QVP$? 125

Answers may vary. Samples:

17. Judging by appearance, name each of the following.
 a. two acute angles $\angle QVM$, $\angle PVN$
 b. two obtuse angles $\angle QVP$, $\angle MVN$
 c. two right angles $\angle MQV$, $\angle QNP$

18. Without using your protractor, sketch angles with the following measures. Then use your protractor to see how close you are.
 a. 30   **b.** 60   **c.** 120
 Check students' work.

19. Open-ended The mileage markers on highways are an example of a numbering system that resembles a number line. Give another example.
 Answers may vary. Sample: tape measure

20. Ski Jumping This ski jumper is using a new style of jumping. The skis are at an angle rather than parallel. Measure the angle formed by the two skis.
 about 43°

Estimation **Estimate the measure of each angle. Then use a protractor to measure it. Classify each angle.** 21–23. Estimates may vary slightly.

21.   **22.**   **23.**

60; acute   90; right   135; obtuse

24. Coordinate Geometry $AB = 12$. Point *A* has coordinates $(3, 0)$. Give four possible locations for point *B*.
 (15, 0), (−9, 0), (3, 12), (3, −12)

25. Open-ended Name two times when the hands of a clock
 a. form an acute angle.   **b.** form a right angle.
 c. form an obtuse angle.   **d.** form a straight angle.
 Answers may vary. Sample: a. 1:00, 2:00 b. 3:00, 9:00

26. Billiards In billiards, the cue ball must bounce off three cushions on every shot. If there is no spin on the shot, $\angle 1$ and $\angle 2$ will be congruent. Find the measures of $\angle 1$ and $\angle 2$. 30; 30

25c. 4:00, 5:00 d. 6:00, about 9:16

Checkpoint   page 31

4. (1) Each term is 2.5 greater than the preceding term.
   (2) Each term is the same as the preceding term with the next consecutive digit added at the end.
   (3) Each term is −3 times the preceding term.

27. **Algebra** If $AD = 12$ and $AC = 4y - 36$, find the value of y. **15**

28. **Algebra** If $ED = x + 4$ and $DB = 3x - 8$, find EB. **20**

29. **Writing** The word "acute" can mean *sharp* in conversational English. Explain why this meaning describes an acute angle.
    The two rays come together to form a sharp point at the vertex.

30. **Technology** Leon constructed an angle. Then he constructed a ray from the vertex of the angle to a point in the interior of the angle. He measured all the angles formed. Then he moved the interior ray.

a. The sum of the measures of the 2 smaller angles remains 105.

a. **Patterns** What patterns do you observe? **See above right.**
b. What postulate does this support? **Angle Addition Postulate**

31. **Golf Fun** Copy the diagram. (1) Estimate the distance in centimeters from the tee to the hole. Estimate the angle in degrees from the tee to the hole. (2) Use a ruler and protractor to plot your estimate. This is stroke 1. Add a penalty stroke if you land in the sand or the water. (3) Continue until you are at most 0.5 cm from the hole marked by the flag. What was your score? **Check students' work.**

Algebra Solve for x.

32. $m\angle AOC = 7x - 2$, $m\angle AOB = 2x + 8$, $m\angle BOC = 3x + 14$ **12**

33. $m\angle AOB = 4x - 2$, $m\angle BOC = 5x + 10$, $m\angle COD = 2x + 14$ **8**

34. $m\angle AOB = 28$, $m\angle BOC = 3x - 2$, $m\angle AOD = 6x$ **18**

35. $m\angle AOB = 4x + 3$, $m\angle BOC = 7x$, $m\angle AOD = 16x - 1$ **7**

36. **Decorating** Japanese flower arranging makes precise use of angles to create a mood. A vertical stem is matched with 0. Other stems are matched with numbers from 0 to 90 in both directions from the vertical. What numbers would the flowers shown be paired with on a standard protractor?
    45 or 135; 75 or 105; 15 or 165

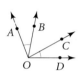

30

THE BIG IDEA Ask students: *Summarize the Ruler Postulate and the Protractor Postulate in your own words.*

RETEACHING ACTIVITY Students measure and classify angles found on a five-pointed star. (Reteaching worksheet 1-4)

In this Checkpoint, your students will assess their own progress on Lessons 1-1 to 1-4.

Exercise 14 Make sure students use three letters to name the angles.

Chapter Project   *Find Out by Researching*

Choose one of the origami creations pictured on pages 2 and 3. Find a book that contains directions for making the figure, and follow the directions to make your favorite origami creation.

Exercises   MIXED REVIEW

Find the next term in each sequence.

37. 5, 10, 15, 20, . . . 25

38. 5, 25, 125, 625, . . . 3,125

39. 14, 18, 22, 26, . . . 30

Complete each statement.

40. Three points are always __?__ . coplanar

41. Intersecting lines are always __?__ . coplanar

42. Two intersecting planes intersect in a __?__ . line

43. Two points are always __?__ . collinear

44. A 24-cm segment is divided into two segments. One segment is three times as long as the other. Find the lengths of both segments. 6 cm and 18 cm

Getting Ready for Lesson 1-5

Sketch each figure.

45. $\overline{CD}$

46. $\overrightarrow{GH}$

47. $\overleftrightarrow{AB}$

48. line *m*

Exercises   CHECKPOINT

Find the next two terms in each sequence.

1. 19, 21.5, 24, 26.5, . . . 29, 31.5

2. 3.4, 3.45, 3.456, 3.4567, . . . 3.45678, 3.456789

3. −2, 6, −18, 54, . . . −162, 486

4. Writing Describe the pattern of the sequences in Exercises 1–3. See margin p. 30.

Are the following coplanar?

5. *A, E, F, B* yes

6. *F, C, B, H* no

7. $\overleftrightarrow{DC}$, point *E* yes

8. *D, G, B* yes

9. $\overleftrightarrow{GC}, \overleftrightarrow{BC}$ yes

10. What is the intersection of plane *EFGH* and $\overleftrightarrow{DH}$? *H*

11. Name all the segments parallel to $\overline{HG}$. $\overline{DC}, \overline{EF}, \overline{AB}$

12. Name two skew lines. Sample: $\overleftrightarrow{AB}$ and $\overleftrightarrow{EH}$

13. Name two parallel planes.
Sample: plane *ABFE* ∥ plane *DCGH* or plane *HEFG* ∥ plane *ABCD* Exs. 5–15

14. Name an acute, an obtuse, and a right angle. Sample: ∠*EAB*; ∠*AEF*; ∠*EHG*

15. Algebra If *AB* = 4*x* + 5 and *DC* = 3*x* + 8, find *AB*. 17

Lesson Quiz

Lesson Quiz is also available in Transparencies.

1. If *XY* = 7 and *XZ* = 19, then find *YZ*. 12

2. If *m*∠*XYS* = 50 and *m*∠*XYT* = 130, find *m*∠*SYT*. 80

3. Name an acute angle.
∠*XYS*, ∠*SYT*, or ∠*TYZ*

4. Use a protractor to draw an obtuse angle. Label its measure.
Answers will vary. Sample:

135°

31

CONNECTING TO PRIOR KNOWLEDGE Ask students to share experiences about using directions to assemble something or following instructions for a recipe. Ask them what was most important about how the directions were written.

WORK TOGETHER

Question 2 Students should describe what a polyglob *is* and not what it *is not.*

EXTENSION Questions 1–2 Have students think of an object and a name for the object, and then draw pictures of what the object is and what it is not. The pictures should be almost alike. State the name and have other students come up with the definition.

Lesson Planning Options

Prerequisite Skills

- Solving one-variable equations
- Graphing on number lines and coordinate planes

Assignment Options for Exercises On Your Own

To provide flexible scheduling, this lesson can be subdivided into parts.

1. **Core** 1–8, 29–40
   Extension 44

2. **Core** 9–28, 45–54
   Extension 41–43, 55

Use Mixed Review to maintain skills.

Resources

 Student Edition

Skills Handbook, pp. 663, 665
Extra Practice, p. 634
Glossary/Study Guide

 Teaching Resources

Chapter Support File, Ch. 1
- Practice 1-5 (two worksheets)
- Reteaching 1-5
- Alternative Activity 1-5
Classroom Manager 1-5
Glossary, Spanish Resources

 Transparencies
24, 29

32

What You'll Learn

- Identifying a good definition
- Understanding the meaning of terms like *bisector* and *perpendicular*

...And Why

To sharpen a skill that is a key to communicating

1-5 Good Definitions

WORK TOGETHER

Work with a partner to identify what makes a figure a *polyglob*.

Polyglobs

Not Polyglobs

1. Which figures above are polyglobs? **b**

2. Describe what a polyglob is.
   Answers may vary. Sample: a figure with three fingers and three solid dots

THINK AND DISCUSS

Part 1

Properties of Good Definitions

In geometry we start with undefined terms such as *point, line,* and *plane* whose meanings we understand intuitively. Then we use those terms to define other terms such as *collinear points.*

A good definition can help you identify or classify an object. A good definition has several important components.

✔ A good definition uses clearly understood terms. The terms should be commonly understood or previously defined.

✔ A good definition is precise. Good definitions avoid words such as *large, sort of,* and *some.*

✔ A good definition states what the term *is,* rather than what it is not. A poor definition of *big* is "Big is the opposite of small."

The geometry we are studying is called Euclidean geometry. There are other types of geometry that establish relationships among points, lines, and planes differently. For example, in spherical geometry, a "point" is a point on a sphere while a "line" is a great circle (the circle formed when a plane intersects a sphere through its center).

MAKING CONNECTIONS The earliest examples of dictionaries are from classical Greece, many being glossaries of difficult terms in Homer's poems. The first general dictionary was compiled by Marcus Verrius Flaccus about 20 B.C.

Example 1 Relating to the Real World

Point out to students that while a counterexample can show a definition is wrong, an example cannot show that a definition is acceptable.

Question 6 Check that students recognize that a segment bisector can be a ray, line, or line segment of any length that intersects the given segment at its midpoint.

A **midpoint** of a segment is a point that divides a segment into two congruent segments.

3. What previously defined terms are used in the definition of *midpoint*?
segment, congruent
A good definition is *reversible*.

If $\overline{AM} \cong \overline{MB}$, then M is the midpoint of $\overline{AB}$.

If N is the midpoint of $\overline{CD}$, then $\overline{CN} \cong \overline{ND}$.

4. a. If $\angle A$ is a right angle, what is the measure of $\angle A$? 90
b. If $m\angle B = 90$, classify $\angle B$. $\angle B$ is a right angle.

Notice that you can use the definition of a right angle to justify your answer to each part of question 4.

One way to test a definition is to look for a *counterexample* that shows that the definition is wrong.

Example 1 Relating to the Real World

Language Arts Is the following an acceptable definition? Explain.

An airplane is a vehicle that flies.

The definition is not acceptable because a helicopter is also a vehicle that flies, and a helicopter is not an airplane.

5. **Try This** Is the following an acceptable definition? Explain.

A square is a figure with four right angles.
No; a figure with four right angles may be a rectangle that is not a square.

Part 2 Bisectors

6. Answers may vary. Sample a segment bisector is a line, segment, or ray that intersects the midpoint of a given segment.

6. Study the diagrams below and write a definition of a *segment bisector*.

Segment bisectors   Not segment bisectors

Perpendicular lines are two lines that intersect to form right angles. The symbol ⊥ is read as "is perpendicular to." In the diagram at the right, $\overleftrightarrow{AB} \perp \overleftrightarrow{CD}$.

QUICK REVIEW

A right angle is an angle whose measure is 90.

Additional Examples

FOR EXAMPLE 1

Explain why the following statement is or is not acceptable as a definition. Soccer is a game played with a ball.
No; there are many games played with a ball.

Discussion: *How can you make this definition acceptable?*

FOR EXAMPLE 2

Refer to the diagram in Example 2. $\overrightarrow{KN}$ bisects $\angle JKL$. $m\angle JKN = 4x + 7$ and $m\angle NKL = 5x - 5$. Solve for x and find $m\angle JKN$.
$x = 12$, $m\angle JKN = 55$

Discussion: *What definition are you using to solve this problem?*

33

Exercises 56–61 Students review properties of rays and angles.

GETTING READY FOR LESSON 1-6 These exercises prepare students to construct bisectors of segments and angles.

Wrap Up

THE BIG IDEA Ask students: *Describe the three types of bisectors discussed in this lesson.*

RETEACHING ACTIVITY Students investigate line segments and angles by folding paper. (Reteaching worksheet 1-5)

Geometry at Work

For further information about the training and skills necessary for woodworking, contact your local artisan guild, technical schools, or community colleges.

Encourage students to investigate these topics:

- the training necessary to become a skilled woodworker
- the math and computer skills used by woodworkers
- the type of businesses or contractors that hire woodworkers

Lesson Quiz

Lesson Quiz is also available in Transparencies.

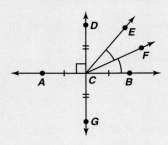

1. If $AC = 7$, then find AB. **14**

2. __?__ is the angle bisector of __?__. $\overleftrightarrow{CF}, \angle BCE$

3. $m\angle ACG =$ __?__ **90**

4. $CG = 2x + 2$, $DC = 5x - 1$. Find x and CG. $x = 1$, $CG = 4$

Exercises   MIXED REVIEW

Use the diagram at the right for Exercises 56–60.

56. Find each measure.

   a. $m\angle AOC$ 80 **b.** $m\angle AOD$ 125

   c. $m\angle DOB$ 65 **d.** $m\angle BOE$ 90

57. Name an obtuse angle.
   Sample: $\angle AOD$

58. Name an acute angle.
   Sample: $\angle AOB$

59. Name a right angle.
   $\angle BOE$

60. Name all the rays.
   $\overrightarrow{OA}$, $\overrightarrow{OB}$, $\overrightarrow{OC}$, $\overrightarrow{OD}$, $\overrightarrow{OE}$

61. Draw opposite rays $\overrightarrow{RS}$ and $\overrightarrow{RW}$. Find RS if $SW = 8$ and $RW = 5$. 3

Getting Ready For Lesson 1-6

62. $\overleftrightarrow{AX}$ is the perpendicular bisector of $\overline{QS}$ at point M. Name two congruent segments. $\overline{QM} \cong \overline{MS}$

63. $\overrightarrow{PT}$ is the bisector of $\angle APR$. Name two congruent angles. $\angle APT \cong \angle TPR$

64. $\overrightarrow{OR}$ is the bisector of right $\angle TOS$. Find $m\angle TOR$. 45

Geometry at Work

Cabinetmaker

Cabinetmakers make not only cabinets but all types of wooden furniture. The artistry of cabinetmaking can be seen in the beauty and uniqueness of the finest doors, shelves, and tables. The craft of the profession is in knowing which types of wood and tools to use, and how to use them.

The carpenter's square is one of the most useful of the cabinetmaker's tools. It can be applied to a variety of measuring tasks. The figure shows how to use a carpenter's square to bisect $\angle O$.

First, mark equal lengths OA and OC on the sides of the angle. Then position the square so that $AB = BC$ to locate point B. Finally, draw $\overrightarrow{OB}$. $\overrightarrow{OB}$ bisects $\angle O$.

Mini Project: Make a carpenter's square out of cardboard. Mark the edges in equal intervals as shown in the figure. Draw a line segment. Then demonstrate how you can use the square to draw the perpendicular bisector of the segment. See margin p. 37.

CONNECTING TO PRIOR KNOWLEDGE Ask students to use a ruler and a protractor to draw a segment 5 cm long and a 50° angle. Then have them use the ruler and protractor to draw bisectors of the segment and the angle.

WORK TOGETHER

Have students work in pairs to draw segments of different lengths and angles of different measures. Suggest one student draw an acute angle and the other an obtuse angle.

THINK AND DISCUSS

Students may not understand the difference between *drawing* and *constructing.* Emphasize that when drawing, a ruler and protractor can be used. In constructions, only a compass and straightedge can be used.

What You'll Learn

- Using a compass and straightedge to construct congruent angles and congruent segments
- Using a compass and straightedge to bisect segments and angles

...And Why

To lay the foundation for more complex constructions you will use in later chapters

What You'll Need

ruler, compass, tracing paper

Connections **Art . . . and more**

1-6 Basic Constructions

WORK TOGETHER

Use a ruler to draw a segment on tracing paper. Fold the paper so that one endpoint lies on the other endpoint. Unfold the paper and compare your result with a partner's.

1. What kinds of angles are formed by the segment and the fold line?
   right angles
2. What is the relationship between the original segment and the segments determined by the fold line?
   The original segment is twice as long.
3. What geometric term best describes the fold line?
   perpendicular bisector

Draw an angle on tracing paper. Fold the paper so that one side of the angle lies on the other side and the fold line goes through the vertex of the angle.

4. What geometric term best describes the fold line?
   angle bisector

THINK AND DISCUSS

Part 1 *Constructing Congruent Segments and Angles*

Another method for creating the bisectors you made in the Work Together is by construction. A **construction** uses a straightedge and a compass to make geometric figures. A **straightedge** is a ruler with no markings on it. (You may use a ruler as a straightedge, but you have to ignore the markings.) A **compass** is a geometric tool used to draw circles and parts of circles called arcs.

The four basic constructions involve constructing congruent segments and angles as well as constructing bisectors of segments and angles.

Lesson Planning Options

Prerequisite Skills

- Using a compass
- Recognizing congruence

Assignment Options for Exercises On Your Own

To provide flexible scheduling, this lesson can be subdivided into parts.

1 **Core** 1, 4–11
Extension 18

2 **Core** 2, 3, 12–17
Extension 19

Use Mixed Review to maintain skills.

Resources

 Student Edition
Extra Practice, p. 634
Glossary/Study Guide

 Teaching Resources
Chapter Support File, Ch. 1
- Practice 1-6 (two worksheets)
- Reteaching 1-6
Classroom Manager 1-6
Glossary, Spanish Resources

 Transparencies
24

MAKING CONNECTIONS Napoleon Bonaparte (1769–1821), a famous emperor of France, is also credited with the following theorem: If three triangles with equal side lengths are constructed off the sides of *any* triangle, then the centers of the circles which circumscribe each triangle are vertices of another triangle with equal side lengths.

TACTILE LEARNING **Construction 1** Illustrate each step of the construction on the board or using an overhead projector. Have students work in pairs to discuss and perform each step.

DIVERSITY Some students may not be physically able to use a compass and straightedge. Have students work in pairs and share the responsibilities for reading and following the instructions.

ERROR ALERT! Some students may squeeze the compass too hard and change its setting; some compasses may "slip" by themselves. **Remediation:** Have students check the compass opening after using it to draw an arc. If their "squeeze" is too strong, suggest a better way to hold the compass. If it slips, try to fix it yourself or give the student a different compass.

Additional Examples

FOR EXAMPLE ....

Use the segments given in the example. Construct a triangle whose sides have lengths *a*, *a*, and *b*.

Discussion: *One student constructs a segment with length* a *first and another student constructs a segment with length* b *first. Will their resulting triangles be different?*

Construction 1
Congruent Segments

Construct a segment congruent to a given segment.

Given: $\overline{AB}$

A ———————— B

Step 1
Draw a ray with endpoint C.

C ————————→

Step 2
Open the compass to the length of $\overline{AB}$.

Step 3
With the same compass setting, put the compass point on C. Draw an arc that intersects the ray. Label the point of intersection D.
$\overline{CD} \cong \overline{AB}$

Construction 2
Congruent Angles

Construct an angle congruent to a given angle.

Given: $\angle A$

Step 1
Draw a ray with endpoint S.

S •————————→

Step 2
With the compass point on point A, draw an arc that intersects the sides of $\angle A$. Label the points of intersection B and C.

Step 3
With the same compass setting, put the compass point on point S. Draw an arc that intersects the ray at point R.

Step 4
Open the compass to the length of $\overline{BC}$. Keeping the same compass setting, put the compass point on R. Draw an arc to determine point T.

Step 5
Draw $\overrightarrow{ST}$.
$\angle S \cong \angle A$

You can use these constructions to construct different geometric figures.

5. **Try This** Draw angles like ∠*X* and ∠*Y*. Then construct ∠*Z* so that $m\angle Z = m\angle X + m\angle Y$. See margin p. 42.
6. Describe how you would construct an angle, ∠*D*, so that $m\angle D = m\angle X - m\angle Y$.

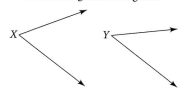

You can use a compass and straightedge to construct triangles with sides of specific lengths.

Example

Construct a triangle whose sides have the given lengths.

Step 1
Use Construction 1 to construct $\overline{RS}$ with length *a*.

Step 2
Open the compass to the length *b*. Put the compass point on *R* and draw an arc.

Step 3
Open the compass to the length *c*. Put the compass point on *S* and draw an arc. Be sure the two arcs intersect. Label the intersection of the arcs as point *T*.

Step 4
Draw segments from point *T* to both *R* and *S*.

7. **Try This** Draw $\overline{XY}$. Then construct a triangle with three sides the length of $\overline{XY}$. See below.

Part 2 Constructing Perpendicular Bisectors and Angle Bisectors

The next two constructions will show you how to bisect segments and bisect angles. These constructions and Construction 2 are based on *congruent triangles*. You will see *why* the constructions work in future chapters.

7.

Technology Options

Exercises 1–12 may be completed using the *construct* and *draw* tools in geometry software.

Prentice Hall Technology

Software
• Secondary Math Lab Toolkit™
• Computer Item Generator 1-6

CD-ROM
• Multimedia Geometry Lab 1

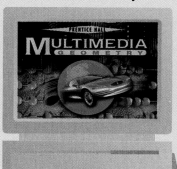

Internet
• See the Prentice Hall site. (http://www.phschool.com)

Construction 3 As students read Step 1, emphasize that the opening of the compass needs to be greater than half the length of the segment. Have students tell why. Then make sure students draw their arcs large enough so that they intersect.

Question 8 This construction requires that students use both Construction 3 and Construction 4. Have students work in small groups or with a partner first to plan their steps, then to construct the angle.

ALTERNATIVE ASSESSMENT Exercises 1–9 A selection of these exercises can be used to assess students' ability to construct segments and angles. Emphasize that students carefully follow each step of the construction as described in the lesson and ask them to leave all construction marks on their figures.

CRITICAL THINKING Exercise 12 Students must recognize that $45 = \frac{1}{2}(90)$ and $135 = 45 + 90$, then construct a 90° angle by constructing a perpendicular bisector of a segment. Realizing that they must construct a segment in order to begin will be a difficult first step for some.

---

pages 39–42   Think and Discuss

5.

pages 43-44   On Your Own

1.

2.   3.

Construction 3
Perpendicular Bisector

Construct the perpendicular bisector of a segment.

Given: $\overline{AB}$

Who? In 1672 Danish mathematician Georg Mohr showed that all constructions that use a compass and a straightedge can be done using only a compass.

Step 1
Put the compass point on point A and draw an arc. Be sure the opening is greater than $\frac{1}{2}AB$. Keep the same compass setting for Step 2.

Step 2
Put the compass point on point B and draw an arc. Label the points where the two arcs intersect as X and Y.

Step 3
Draw $\overleftrightarrow{XY}$. Label the intersection of $\overline{AB}$ and $\overleftrightarrow{XY}$ as point M.

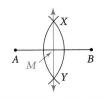

$\overleftrightarrow{XY}$ is the perpendicular bisector of $\overline{AB}$. Point M is the midpoint of $\overline{AB}$.

You can use Construction 3 to divide any segment into fourths or eighths.

Construction 4
Angle Bisector

Construct the bisector of an angle.

Given: $\angle A$

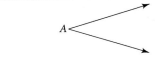

Step 1
Put the compass point on vertex A. Draw an arc that intersects the sides of $\angle A$. Label the points of intersection B and C.

Step 2
Put the compass point on point C and draw an arc. Keep the same compass setting and repeat with point B. Be sure the arcs intersect. Label the point where the two arcs intersect as point X.

Step 3
Draw $\overrightarrow{AX}$.

$\overrightarrow{AX}$ is the angle bisector of $\angle CAB$.

8. Construct a ⊥ bisector of a segment to form a right angle and then bisect that angle.

8. Describe how you could construct a 45° angle.

42

Exercises ON YOUR OWN

Draw a diagram similar to the given one. Then do the construction. 1–3. See margin p. 42.

1. Construct $\overline{XY}$ congruent to $\overline{AB}$. Check your work with a ruler.

2. Construct the perpendicular bisector of $\overline{AB}$. Check your work with a ruler and a protractor.

3. Construct the angle bisector of $\angle C$. Check your work with a protractor.
   4–11. See margin.

4. Construct $\overline{DE}$ so that $DE = TR + PB$.

5. Construct $\overline{QS}$ so that $QS = TR - PB$.

6. Construct $\overline{XY}$ so that $XY = 2TR$.

7. Construct $\angle B$ so that $m\angle B = m\angle 1 + m\angle 2$.

8. Construct $\angle C$ so that $m\angle C = m\angle 1 - m\angle 2$.

9. Construct $\angle D$ so that $m\angle D = 2m\angle 2$.

10. Draw an angle that is about 120°. Then construct a congruent angle.

11. Use a ruler to draw two segments that are 4 cm and 5 cm long. Then construct a triangle with sides 4 cm, 4 cm, and 5 cm long.

12. **a.** Construct a 45° angle. See right.
    b. Construct a 135° angle. See part (a). $180° - 45° = 135°$

13. **Writing** Describe how to construct the midpoint of a segment. Construct a ⊥ bisector. Its intersection with the segment is the midpoint of the segment.

14. **Open-ended** Which method do you prefer for bisecting an angle— paper folding or construction with compass and straightedge? Why?
    Answers may vary. Sample: compass and straightedge; it is more precise.

15. **Patterns** Draw a large triangle with three acute angles. Construct the angle bisectors of all three angles of the triangle. What is true about the intersection of the three angle bisectors? Repeat for another triangle that has an obtuse angle. Make a **conjecture** about the three angle bisectors of any triangle.
    The angle bisectors of the 3 angles of any triangle intersect in a single point.

16. **Patterns** Draw a large triangle with three acute angles. Construct the perpendicular bisectors of all three sides. What is true about the intersection of the three perpendicular bisectors? Repeat for another triangle that has an obtuse angle. Make a **conjecture** about the three perpendicular bisectors of the sides of any triangle. The ⊥ bisectors of the 3 sides of any triangle intersect in a single point.

17. **a.** Draw a segment, $\overline{AB}$. Construct a triangle whose sides are all congruent to $\overline{AB}$.
    b. Measure the angles of the triangle. 60
    c. **Writing** Describe how to construct a 60° angle and a 30° angle.
    Construct a 60° angle by constructing an equilateral triangle. Bisect one of the angles to construct a 30° angle.

sample:

A   B

A   B

C

1   2

4.

TR   PB
D   E

5.

TR
Q S PB

6.

TR   TR
X   Y

7.

$m\angle 1 + m\angle 2$
1   2
B

8.

$m\angle 1 - m\angle 2$
2
C

9.

D

10.

120°
A   B

11.
4 cm   4 cm
5 cm

12a.

45°

44

18. Art You can create intricate designs using your compass. Follow these directions to design a *daisy wheel*. **a–d. Check students' work.**

   a. Construct a circle. Keeping the same compass setting, put the compass point on the circle and construct an arc. The endpoints of the arc should be on the circle.

   b. Keeping the same compass setting, put the compass point on each endpoint of the first arc and draw two new arcs.

   c. Continue to make arcs around the circle from the new endpoints of arcs until you get a six-petal daisy wheel.

   d. Personalize your daisy wheel by decorating it.

19. a. Use your compass to draw a circle. Locate three points A, B, and C on the circle.   **a–b. Answers may vary. See margin p. 45 for samples.**

   b. Construct the perpendicular bisectors of $\overline{AB}$ and $\overline{BC}$.

   c. Critical Thinking Label the intersection of the two perpendicular bisectors as point O. Describe point O. **Point O is the center of the circle.**

Exercises   MIXED REVIEW

Use the number line at the right to find the length of each segment.

20. $\overline{AC}$ 12   **21.** $\overline{AD}$ 16   **22.** $\overline{CD}$ 4   **23.** $\overline{BC}$ 8

24. Make a sketch of three planes intersecting at one point. **Answers may vary. Sample:**

Getting Ready For Lesson 1-7

25. Find the value of x. 50

26. Find the value of y. 35

27. Find the value of z. 45

In this toolbox, students extend their understanding of constructions by using geometry software to investigate the difference between *draw* and *construct* tools. The software enables students to see that constructions are dependent upon the initial figure (segment, angle, triangle, etc.).

Investigate

Students will see that, using the *construction* tool, a perpendicular bisector to a segment will remain a perpendicular bisector to that segment no matter how that segment is changed. However, when a line is drawn perpendicular to a segment using the *draw* tool, as the segment is changed, the relationship between the line and the segment also changes.

ERROR ALERT! Some students may not be familiar with how to draw or construct using geometry software. **Remediation:** Allow students time to explore the tools before beginning this activity. Pair students more familiar with the software with students who are less familiar.

ADDITIONAL PROBLEM Draw a segment with endpoints *A* and *B*. Construct △*ABC* with three sides of length *AB*. Then draw △*XYZ*. Drag the vertices until *XY* = *YZ* = *ZX*. Manipulate both triangles and observe the side lengths. Are the sides always congruent in △*ABC*? yes in △*XYZ*? no

---

Exploring Constructions

◄ After Lesson 1-6

Points, lines, and figures are created in geometry software using *draw* or *construct* tools. A figure created by *draw* has no constraints. When the figure is manipulated it moves or changes size freely. A figure created by *construct* is dependent upon an existing object. When you manipulate the existing object, the *construct* object moves or resizes similarly.

In this activity you will explore the difference between *draw* and *construct*. Before you begin, familiarize yourself with your software's tools.

Construct   Check students' work.

- Draw $\overline{AB}$ and construct perpendicular bisector $\overleftrightarrow{DC}$.

- Draw $\overleftrightarrow{EF}$ and construct *G*, any point on $\overleftrightarrow{EF}$. Draw $\overleftrightarrow{HG}$. Find *EG*, *GF*, and *m∠HGF*. Attempt to drag *G* so that *EG* = *GF*. Attempt to drag *H* so that *m∠HGF* = 90. Were you able to draw the perpendicular bisector of $\overline{EF}$? Explain.

Investigate

- Drag *A* and *B*. Observe *AC*, *CB*, and *m∠DCB*. Is $\overleftrightarrow{DC}$ always the perpendicular bisector of $\overline{AB}$ no matter how you manipulate the figure? yes

- Drag *E* and *F*. Observe *EG*, *GF*, and *m∠HGF*. How is the relationship between $\overleftrightarrow{EF}$ and $\overleftrightarrow{HG}$ different from the relationship between $\overline{AB}$ and $\overleftrightarrow{DC}$?
  $\overleftrightarrow{HG}$ intersects $\overline{EF}$, but it is not the perpendicular bisector of $\overline{EF}$.

Summarize

Write a description of the general difference between *draw* and *construct*. Use your description to explain why the relationship between $\overleftrightarrow{EF}$ and $\overleftrightarrow{HG}$ differs from the relationship between $\overline{AB}$ and $\overleftrightarrow{DC}$.   See margin.

$\overrightarrow{KM}$ is always the angle bisector of ∠*JKL*.

$\overrightarrow{OQ}$ is not always the bisector of ∠*NOP*.

Extend

Draw ∠*JKL* and construct its angle bisector, $\overrightarrow{KM}$. Draw ∠*NOP*. Draw $\overrightarrow{OQ}$ in the interior of ∠*NOP*. Drag *Q* until *m∠NOQ* = *m∠QOP*. Manipulate both figures and observe the different angle measures. Is $\overrightarrow{KM}$ always the angle bisector of ∠*JKL*? Is $\overrightarrow{OQ}$ always the angle bisector of ∠*NOP*?

Materials and Manipulatives

- Geometry software

pages 43–44 On Your Own

19a–b. Answers may vary. Sample:

Math Toolbox   page 45

SUMMARIZE

A figure created by *draw* has no constraints. A figure created by *construct* is dependent upon an existing object. Since $\overleftrightarrow{DC}$ was constructed as the ⊥ bisector of $\overline{AB}$, it remains the ⊥ bisector through any manipulation. Since point *G* was constructed on $\overline{EF}$, the only restriction on $\overleftrightarrow{HG}$ during any manipulation is that it must contain point *G* which has to be on $\overline{EF}$.

PROBLEM OF THE DAY

If $a * b = ab - 1$ and $a \wedge b = \frac{(a + b)}{2}$, then find
$2 * [(5 \wedge 3) \wedge (8 * 1)]$. **10**

Problem of the Day is also available in Transparencies.

CONNECTING TO PRIOR KNOWLEDGE Have students recall any properties of equality from algebra they can remember. Display the equations $y + 4 = 20$ and $\frac{x}{2} = 20$. Ask students what conclusions they can make about x and y and the reasons for their conclusions.

DIVERSITY Discuss with students jobs that require people to use deductive reasoning. Try to include a variety of occupations that use different skills and require different educational backgrounds.

AUDITORY LEARNING Have students take turns explaining the properties of equality to a partner. With each explanation, have the student give an example of the property using real numbers.

Lesson Planning Options

Prerequisite Skills

- Understanding the properties of equality from algebra
- Solving one-variable equations

Assignment Options for Exercises On Your Own

To provide flexible scheduling, this lesson can be subdivided into parts.

▼ **Core** 1–10, 29–31
Extension 34–38

▼ **Core** 11–28
Extension 32–33

Use Mixed Review to maintain skills.

Resources

📖 **Student Edition**

Skills Handbook, p. 650
Extra Practice, p. 634
Glossary/Study Guide

🗂 **Teaching Resources**

Chapter Support File, Ch. 1
- Practice 1-7 (two worksheets)
- Reteaching 1-7
- Alternative Activity 1-7
Classroom Manager 1-7
Glossary, Spanish Resources

Transparencies
20, 25

What You'll Learn

- Using deductive reasoning to solve problems and verify conjectures
- Understanding how certain angle pairs are related

...And Why

To reach valid conclusions in geometry and in life

What You'll Need

- tracing paper

Connections 🌐 **Auto Repair . . . and more**

1-7 Using Deductive Reasoning

THINK AND DISCUSS

Part 1

Connecting Algebra and Geometry

Deductive reasoning is a process of reasoning logically from given facts to a conclusion. If the given facts are true, deductive reasoning always produces a valid conclusion.

1. **Try This** Maria's parents tell her she can go to the mall with her friends if she finishes her homework. Maria shows her parents her completed homework. What conclusion can you make?
She can go to the mall.

Many people use deductive reasoning in their jobs. A physician diagnosing a patient's illness uses deductive reasoning. A mechanic trying to determine what is wrong with a car uses deductive reasoning. A carpenter uses deductive reasoning to determine what materials are needed at a work site.

Do you remember these Properties of Equality and Real Numbers from algebra?

Properties of Equality and Real Numbers

Addition Property	If $a = b$, then $a + c = b + c$.
Subtraction Property	If $a = b$, then $a - c = b - c$.
Multiplication Property	If $a = b$, then $a \cdot c = b \cdot c$.
Division Property	If $a = b$, then $\frac{a}{c} = \frac{b}{c}$ ($c \neq 0$).
Substitution Property	If $a = b$, then b can replace a in any expression.
Distributive Property	$a(b + c) = ab + ac$

Example 1 ·····

Point out that the justification for the first step comes from geometry. Once variables are substituted, each justification comes from algebra.

Question 2 The reflexive, symmetric, and transitive properties can also be used to describe verbal relationships. For example, "is a cousin of" is symmetric (only), "is shorter than" is transitive (only), and "has the same first name as" is reflexive, symmetric, and transitive. Students may enjoy stating and classifying other verbal relationships.

WORK TOGETHER

ALTERNATIVE METHOD Have students place a piece of tracing paper over the intersecting angles and shade ∠1. Then with their pencil point on the point of intersection of the lines, have them rotate the tracing paper slowly about the point of intersection until the shaded area is over ∠2. Students can repeat this activity with ∠3 and ∠4.

You may not realize it, but you use deductive reasoning every time you solve an equation.

Example 1 ·····

Algebra $m\angle AOC = 140$. Solve for x and justify each step.

$m\angle AOB + m\angle BOC = m\angle AOC$	Angle Addition Postulate
$x + (2x + 20) = 140$	Substitution
$3x = 120$	Subtraction Property of Equality
$x = 40$	Division Property of Equality

These properties of congruence follow from the properties of equality.

QUICK REVIEW

Properties of Equality
Reflexive Property
$a = a$
Symmetric Property
If $a = b$, then $b = a$.
Transitive Property
If $a = b$ and $b = c$, then $a = c$.

Properties of Congruence

Reflexive Property	$\overline{AB} \cong \overline{AB}$
	$\angle A \cong \angle A$
Symmetric Property	If $\overline{AB} \cong \overline{CD}$, then $\overline{CD} \cong \overline{AB}$.
	If $\angle A \cong \angle B$, then $\angle B \cong \angle A$.
Transitive Property	If $\overline{AB} \cong \overline{CD}$ and $\overline{CD} \cong \overline{EF}$, then $\overline{AB} \cong \overline{EF}$.
	If $\angle A \cong \angle B$ and $\angle B \cong \angle C$, then $\angle A \cong \angle C$.

2. Try This Name the property of equality or congruence illustrated.
a. $\angle K \cong \angle K$
b. If $2x - 8 = 10$, then $2x = 18$.
c. If $\overline{RS} \cong \overline{TW}$ and $\overline{TW} \cong \overline{PQ}$, then $\overline{RS} \cong \overline{PQ}$.
d. If $m\angle A = m\angle B$, then $m\angle B = m\angle A$.

a. Reflexive Property of ≅
b. Addition Property of =
c. Transitive Property of ≅
d. Symmetric Property of =

Part 2

WORK TOGETHER

Draw two intersecting lines. Number the angles as shown.

3. Fold the sides of ∠1 onto ∠2. What do you notice?   ∠1 ≅ ∠2

4. Fold the sides of ∠3 onto ∠4. What do you notice?   ∠3 ≅ ∠4

5. Compare your results with those of others in your group. Make a **conjecture** about the angles formed by two intersecting lines.
When 2 lines intersect, the angles across from each other are ≅.

Additional Examples

FOR EXAMPLE 1 ·····

Refer to the diagram in Example 1. $m\angle AOB = 40$, $m\angle BOC = 3x + 15$, and $m\angle AOC = 4x - 15$. Solve for x and justify each step.

$m\angle AOB + m\angle BOC = m\angle AOC$
(Angle Addition Postulate)

$40 + 3x + 15 = 4x - 15$
(Substitution)

$3x + 70 = 4x$
(Addition Property of Equality)

$70 = x$
(Subtraction Property of Equality)

FOR EXAMPLE 2 ·····

Refer to the diagram in Example 2. If $m\angle 1 = 150$, find the measures of ∠2 and ∠3.   150; 30

Students may remember vertical angles from Exercise 34 in Lesson 1-5. You might want to suggest that the term "vertical" is used because the angles share the same vertex, although not all angles that share the same vertex are vertical angles.

The illustrations show that complementary and supplementary angles can be adjacent or nonadjacent. You may want to use a triangle with angle measures 90, 60 and 30 and a quadrilateral with angle measures 70, 70, 110, and 110 to show that complementary and supplementary angles can share a side.

ERROR ALERT! Students may mistakenly think that three angles whose measures have a sum of 90 or 180 are complementary or supplementary, respectively. **Remediation:** Reinforce that the terms *complementary* and *supplementary* are used to describe relationships between two angles.

ESL Students may want to create flash cards writing the terms *vertical angles, adjacent angles, complementary angles,* and *supplementary angles* on one side and the definitions along with diagrams on the other.

Technology Options

For Exercise 19, students may use geometry software to plot points *A*, *O*, and *X*, then pick point *B* and measure ∠*BOA* and ∠*AOX*.

Prentice Hall Technology

 Software
• Secondary Math Lab Toolkit™
• Computer Item Generator 1-7

 Internet
• See the Prentice Hall site. (http://www.phschool.com)

6a. Answers may vary.
Samples: ∠*CFD* and
∠*CFB*, ∠*BFC* and ∠*BFA*

Angle Pairs

In the Work Together you made a conjecture about a pair of angles that has a special name, *vertical angles.* You will learn about several important angle pairs in this lesson.

vertical angles

two angles whose sides are opposite rays

adjacent angles

a common side and a common vertex but no common interior points

complementary angles

two angles, the sum of whose measures is 90

supplementary angles

two angles, the sum of whose measures is 180

6. a. Name two pairs of adjacent angles in the photo at the left. **See below left.**

  b. Name two pairs of supplementary angles.
  Answers may vary. Samples: ∠*AFB* and ∠*BFE*, ∠*EFD* and ∠*DFA*

In the Work Together you used inductive reasoning to make a conjecture. Now, based on what you know, you can use deductive reasoning to show that your conjecture is always true.

Theorem 1-1 Vertical Angles Theorem	Vertical angles are congruent.

Example 2

Write a convincing argument that the Vertical Angles Theorem is true.

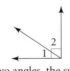

You are given that ∠1 and ∠2 are vertical angles. You must show that ∠1 ≅ ∠2.

By the Angle Addition Postulate,
$m\angle 1 + m\angle 3 = 180$ and $m\angle 2 + m\angle 3 = 180$.
By substitution, $m\angle 1 + m\angle 3 = m\angle 2 + m\angle 3$. Subtract $m\angle 3$ from each side, and you get $m\angle 1 = m\angle 2$, or ∠1 ≅ ∠2.

48

Example 2

Example 3

ALGEBRA Help students understand that the process of writing a convincing argument is similar to the process students use for problem solving. They should first read the question, then consider what information they are given, what they are trying to prove, and what relationships they can use to prove it.

CRITICAL THINKING Have students explain why it can be concluded that $m\angle 1 + m\angle 2 = m\angle 3 + m\angle 2$.

You may want to review the marks used to indicate congruent segments and angles, right angles, perpendicular lines, and parallel lines.

A convincing argument that uses deductive reasoning is also called a *proof*. A conjecture that is proven is a **theorem.** The Vertical Angles Theorem is actually a special case of the following theorem.

Theorem 1-2
Congruent Supplements Theorem

If two angles are supplements of congruent angles (or of the same angle), then the two angles are congruent.

Example 3

Write a convincing argument that supplements of the same angle are congruent.

Given: $\angle 1$ and $\angle 2$ are supplementary.
$\angle 3$ and $\angle 2$ are supplementary.
Prove: $\angle 1 \cong \angle 3$

Because $\angle 1$ and $\angle 2$ are supplementary, $m\angle 1 + m\angle 2 = 180$.
Because $\angle 3$ and $\angle 2$ are supplementary, $m\angle 3 + m\angle 2 = 180$.
So $m\angle 1 + m\angle 2 = m\angle 3 + m\angle 2$.
Therefore, $m\angle 1 = m\angle 3$, and $\angle 1 \cong \angle 3$. ∎

7. Try This An argument is convincing only if any reasons that are not stated are clearly understood. What is the reason that $m\angle 1 = m\angle 3$?
Subtraction Prop. of =
The next theorem is much like the Congruent Supplements Theorem.

Theorem 1-3
Congruent Complements Theorem

If two angles are complements of congruent angles (or of the same angle), then the two angles are congruent.

As you will see in Chapter 4, a proof may take many different forms. The format of a proof is not important. Logical use of deductive reasoning is.

You can draw certain conclusions directly from diagrams. You can conclude that angles are
▪ vertical angles
▪ adjacent angles
▪ adjacent supplementary angles.

Unless there are marks that give this information, you cannot assume that
▪ angles or segments are congruent
▪ an angle is a right angle
▪ lines are perpendicular or parallel.

8. What can you conclude? Explain. a–c. See margin.

a.
b.
c.

pages 48–49 Think and Discuss

8a. $\angle 1 \cong \angle 2$ as they are marked. From the Angle Add. Post., $\angle 3$ and $\angle 1$ as well as $\angle 4$ and $\angle 2$ are supplements. $\angle 3 \cong \angle 4$ by the Congruent Supplements Thm.

b. $\overline{TW} \cong \overline{WV}$ as they are marked congruent. $\overline{PQ}$ bisects $\overline{TV}$ by definition of segment bisector.

c. $\angle RSW$ is a right angle and $\angle WSZ \cong \angle ZST$ because of markings. $\angle WST$ is a right angle by def. of $\perp$ lines. $m\angle RSW = 90$ by def. of right angle. $m\angle WSZ = m\angle ZST = 45$ because they are $\cong$ and the sum of their measures is 90.

pages 50–52 On Your Own

26. $m\angle DOA = 55$ as vert. angles are $\cong$. $m\angle DOB = m\angle AOC = 125$ as these are supplements of $\angle BOC$.

27. $\angle EIG$ and $\angle FIH$ are right angles by the markings. $\angle EIF \cong \angle GIH$ because they are complements of the same angle.

28. $\angle JPK \cong \angle JPM$ by the markings. Also by the Angle Add. Post., $\angle JPK$ and $\angle KPL$ are supplements and $\angle JPM$ and $\angle MPL$ are supplements. $\angle KPL \cong \angle MPL$ as supplements of $\cong$ angles are $\cong$.

32. Because $\angle 1$ and $\angle 2$ are complementary, $m\angle 1 + m\angle 2 = 90$. Because $\angle 3$ and $\angle 2$ are complementary, $m\angle 3 + m\angle 2 = 90$. So $m\angle 1 + m\angle 2 = m\angle 3 + m\angle 2$ by Substitution. Therefore, $m\angle 1 = m\angle 3$, and $\angle 1 \cong \angle 3$.

33. Because $\angle 1$ and $\angle 2$ are supplementary, $m\angle 1 + m\angle 2 = 180$. Because $\angle 3$ and $\angle 4$ are supplementary, $m\angle 3 + m\angle 4 = 180$. So, $m\angle 1 + m\angle 2 = m\angle 3 + m\angle 4$. Because $\angle 2 \cong \angle 4$, $m\angle 2 = m\angle 4$. Thus, by Subtraction Prop. of =, $m\angle 1 = m\angle 3$ and $\angle 1 \cong \angle 3$.

Exercises ON YOUR OWN

Name the property that justifies each statement.

1. $\angle Z \cong \angle Z$ Reflexive Prop. of $\cong$

2. If $12x = 84$, then $x = 7$.   Division Prop. of =

3. If $\overline{ST} \cong \overline{QR}$, then $\overline{QR} \cong \overline{ST}$. Symmetric Prop. of $\cong$

4. If $3x + 14 = 80$, then $3x = 66$. Subtraction Prop. of =

5. If $2x + y = 5$ and $x = y$, then $2x + x = 5$. Substitution Prop.

6. If $AB - BC = 12$, then $AB = 12 + BC$. Add. Prop. of =

7. If $m\angle A = 15$, then $3m\angle A = 45$. Mult. Prop. of =

8. $QR = QR$ Reflexive Prop. of =

9. If $\angle 1 \cong \angle 2$ and $\angle 2 \cong \angle 3$, then $\angle 1 \cong \angle 3$. Trans. Prop. of $\cong$

10. $2(3x + 5) = 6x + 10$ Dist. Prop.

11. **Writing** How is a theorem different from a postulate? A theorem can be proven; a postulate is assumed to be true.

12. **Open-ended** Give an example of vertical angles in your home. Answers may vary. Sample: scissors or salad tongs

Algebra Find the values of the variables.

13. 9

14. $x = 25$; $y = 105$

15. 18

16. 15

17. 10

18. 11

19. **a.** *Coordinate Geometry* $\angle AOX$ contains points $A(1, 3)$, $O(0, 0)$, and $X(4, 0)$. Find the coordinates of a point B so that $\angle BOA$ and $\angle AOX$ are adjacent complementary angles. B can be any point on the positive y-axis, for example, (0, 5).

   b. Find the coordinates of a point C so that $\overrightarrow{OC}$ is a side of a different angle that is adjacent to and complementary to $\angle AOX$. Answers may vary. Sample: (3, −1)

   c. $\angle DOE$ contains points $D(2, 3)$, $O(0, 0)$, and $E(5, 1)$. Find the coordinates of a point F so that $\overrightarrow{OF}$ is a side of an angle that is adjacent to and supplementary to $\angle DOE$. Answers may vary. Sample: (−5, −1)

20. *Algebra* $\angle A$ and $\angle B$ are supplementary angles. $m\angle A = 3x + 12$ and $m\angle B = 2x - 22$. Find the measures of both angles. $m\angle A = 126$; $m\angle B = 54$

21. *Algebra* Solve for x and y. $x = 14$; $y = 15$

50

22. *Standardized Test Prep* In the diagrams at the right, which is greater, x or y? **y**

23. *Critical Thinking* If possible, find the measures of the angles described. If it is not possible, explain why.
    a. congruent adjacent supplementary angles   **90**
    b. congruent adjacent complementary angles   **45**
    c. congruent vertical angles   **Not possible; all vertical angles are ≅.**

24. *Algebra* The measure of a supplement of ∠1 is six times the measure of a complement of ∠1. Find the measures of ∠1, its supplement, and its complement.   **m∠1 = 72; supplement, 108; complement, 18**

25. One angle is twice as large as its complement. Find the measures of both angles. **30 and 60**

What can you conclude about the angles in each diagram? Justify your answers. 26–28. See margin p. 50.

26.

27.

28.
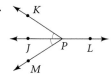

Give a reason for each step.

29. 3x − 15 = 105
    3x = 120
    x = 40
    Add. Prop. of =; Div. Prop. of =;

30. 12y + 24 = 96
    12y = 72
    y = 6
    Subtr. Prop. of =; Div. Prop. of =

31. $\frac{1}{2}x − 5 = 10$
    $2(\frac{1}{2}x − 5) = 20$
    x − 10 = 20
    x = 30
    Mult. Prop. of =;
    Distr. Prop.;
    Add. Prop. of =

32. *Preparing for Proof* Write a convincing argument that complements of the same angle are congruent.

    Given: ∠1 and ∠2 are complementary.
    ∠3 and ∠2 are complementary.
    Prove: ∠1 ≅ ∠3 See margin p. 50.

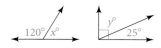

33. *Preparing for Proof* Write a convincing argument that supplements of congruent angles are congruent.

    Given: ∠1 and ∠2 are supplementary.
    ∠3 and ∠4 are supplementary.
    ∠2 ≅ ∠4
    Prove: ∠1 ≅ ∠3 See margin p. 50.

PROBLEM SOLVING HINT

Let x = m∠1. Then 180 − x = measure of its supplement, and 90 − x = measure of its complement.

51

Exercises 39–41 Have students label and name the points, rays, and lines.

GETTING READY FOR LESSON 1-8 These exercises prepare students for using the distance formula in Lesson 1-8.

Wrap Up

THE BIG IDEA Ask students: *Describe the difference between inductive and deductive reasoning. Give examples to support your answer.*

RETEACHING ACTIVITY Students are given the statements of an argument out of order. They must rearrange the statements in the correct order. (Reteaching worksheet 1-7)

In this Checkpoint, your students will assess their own progress on Lessons 1-5 to 1-7.

Exercise 2 Students will need a protractor and a compass.

Exercise 3 Students will need a protractor.

Lesson Quiz

Lesson Quiz is also available in Transparencies.

1. Name the property of congruence that justifies the following statement. If $\overline{QR} \cong \overline{OP}$, then $\overline{OP} \cong \overline{QR}$. **Symmetric Property**

2. The measures of two complementary angles are $3x + 4$ and $5x + 6$. Find x. **$x = 10$**

3. The measures of two vertical angles are $4x - 10$ and $2x + 8$. Find the measures of the angles. **26**

4. Write a convincing argument why the complements of congruent angles are congruent. Given: $\angle 1$ and $\angle 2$ are complements, $\angle 3$ and $\angle 4$ are complements, $\angle 2 \cong \angle 4$ Prove: $\angle 1 \cong \angle 3$.
See back of book.

52

Use the cartoon and deductive reasoning to answer *yes* or *no*. Explain any *no*.

34. Could a person with a red car park here on Tuesday at 10:00 A.M? **No; red cars may not park.**

35. Could a man with a beard park here on Monday at 10:30 A.M.? **No; guys with beards may not park on Mon.**

36. Could a woman with a wig park here on Saturday at 10:00 A.M.? **yes**

37. Could a person with a blue car park here on Tuesday at 9:05 A.M.? **No; parking is not allowed from 6:49 A.M. to 9:11 A.M. on Tues.**

38. Could a person with a convertible with leather seats park here on Sunday at 6:00 P.M.? **yes**

Sketch each of the following. 39–41. See margin p. 51.

39. three collinear points

40. two intersecting rays

41. two perpendicular lines

42. Find the next three terms in the sequence: $1, 1, \frac{1}{2}, \frac{1}{3}, \frac{1}{5}, \frac{1}{8}, \ldots$
$\frac{1}{13}, \frac{1}{21}, \frac{1}{34}$

Getting Ready for Lesson 1-8

Calculator **Find the square root of each number to the nearest tenth.**

43. 25 **5**   44. 17 **4.1**   45. 123 **11.1**

46. 48 **6.9**   47. 96 **9.8**   48. 1023 **32.0**

SELF ASSESSMENT

FOR YOUR JOURNAL

Give examples of your use of deductive and inductive reasoning in the last month.

1. Writing What are the components of a good definition? **A good definition states precisely what a term is, using commonly understood or previously defined terms.**

2. a. Use a protractor to draw $\angle R$ with measure 78.
   b. Construct an angle whose measure is $2 \cdot m\angle R$.
   c. Construct an angle whose measure is $\frac{1}{2} \cdot m\angle R$.
   a–c. See margin p. 51.

3. Open-ended Use a protractor to draw a pair of adjacent complementary angles. Then draw another pair of complementary angles that are *not* adjacent. **See margin p. 51.**

4. Standardized Test Prep If $-6 \leq x \leq 1$ is graphed on a number line, its graph is which of the following? **C**
   A. 7 points   B. 8 points   C. a segment   D. a line   E. a ray

PROBLEM OF THE DAY

A rectangle measures 10 units by 15 units and is tiled with unit-square tiles. How many tiles are crossed by one diagonal of the rectangle? **20**

Problem of the Day is also available in Transparencies.

CONNECTING TO PRIOR KNOWLEDGE Discuss with students types of maps they have seen such as world maps, globes, state maps, local maps, subway maps, bike and hiking paths, and elevation maps.

WORK TOGETHER

You may need to review with students how to use a scale to find distances on a map.

CONNECTING TO STUDENTS' WORLD Have students bring in local maps and develop a coordinate system and scale. Then have them find the coordinates of two locations on a diagonal street and find the distance between the two locations using the distance formula.

What You'll Learn

- Finding the distance between two points in a coordinate plane
- Finding the coordinates of the midpoint of a segment in a coordinate plane

...And Why

To improve skills such as map reading

What You'll Need

tracing paper, ruler, graph paper

Scale in Miles 1 in. ≈ 0.4 mi.

0.0 — 0.4

0.0 — 0.5

Scale in Kilometers 1 in. ≈ 0.5 km

Connections Transportation ... and more

1-8 The Coordinate Plane

WORK TOGETHER

Much of New York City is laid out in a rectangular grid, as shown in this map. Most of the streets in the grid are either parallel or perpendicular.

Yvonne's family is on the corner of 44th Street and 7th Avenue. They plan to walk to Madison Square Park at 23rd Street and 5th Avenue. There are several possible routes they can take.

Work with your group. Trace the routes on the map and answer the following questions.

1. Yvonne's father wants to walk east on 44th Street until they reach 5th Avenue. He then plans to walk south on 5th Avenue to Madison Square Park. About how long is his route? **1.4 mi**

2. Yvonne's mother wants to walk south on 7th Avenue until they reach 23rd Street. She then plans to walk east on 23rd Street to Madison Square Park. About how long is her route? **1.4 mi**

3. Yvonne notices on the map that Broadway cuts across the grid of streets and leads to Madison Square Park. She suggests walking all the way on Broadway. About how long is her route? **1.1 mi**

4. Whose route is the shortest? Why? **4. Yvonne's; the shortest distance between two points is a straight line.**

5. Whose route is the longest? Why?

5. Yvonne's mother's and father's routes are the same length; both paths have a turn in them.

Lesson Planning Options

Prerequisite Skills

- Finding distance on a number line
- Using a calculator to find square roots

Assignment Options for Exercises On Your Own

Core 1–25, 27–31
Extension 26, 32–33

Use Mixed Review to maintain skills.

Resources

 Student Edition

Skills Handbook, p. 659
Extra Practice, p. 634
Glossary/Study Guide

 Teaching Resources

Chapter Support File, Ch. 1
- Practice 1-8 (two worksheets)
- Reteaching 1-8
Classroom Manager 1-8
Glossary, Spanish Resources

 Transparencies
5, 25

53

Students were shown distance on a number line in Lesson 1-4. Show how vertical and horizontal segments not on the axes can be thought of as part of a number line.

Some students may be familiar with the distance formula from algebra. Some may also be familiar with the Pythagorean Theorem from which the distance formula is derived. The Pythagorean Theorem is presented in Lesson 5-3.

Example 1   Relating to the Real World 🌐 ·················

CRITICAL THINKING As students read the problem, discuss how the directions can be used to plot points on a coordinate grid. Help students understand that the distance formula is used to find the solution because the two locations do not lie on the same vertical or horizontal line.

Additional Examples

FOR EXAMPLE 1 ·····························

Refer to the diagram for Example 1. Symphony Station is 1 mi east and 2 mi north of City Plaza and Elm Station is 3 mi west and 6 mi south of City Plaza. How far is Symphony Station from Elm Station?

Let $(x_1, y_1) = (1, 2)$ and $(x_2, y_2) = (-3, -6)$.

$d = \sqrt{(1 - (-3))^2 + (2 - (-6))^2}$

$= \sqrt{16 + 64} = \sqrt{80} \approx 8.9$

about 8.9 mi

FOR EXAMPLE 2 ·····························

Find the coordinates of the midpoint of $\overline{AB}$ with endpoints $A(2, 3)$ and $B(-5, 7)$. **(−1.5, 5)**

Discussion: *Does it matter which point is chosen as (x_1, y_1)?*

You can think of a point as a dot, and a line as a series of points. In coordinate geometry you can describe a point with an ordered pair (x, y) and a line with an equation $y = mx + b$.

QUICK REVIEW

The x- and y-axes divide the coordinate plane into four quadrants.

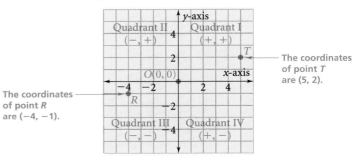

The coordinates of point R are $(-4, -1)$.

The coordinates of point T are $(5, 2)$.

Finding the distance between two points is easy if the points lie on a horizontal or a vertical line.

6. Try This Find AB and CD in the graph at the left. **4; 5**

To find the distance between two points that are not on the same horizontal or vertical line, you can use the Distance Formula.

The Distance Formula

The distance d between two points $A(x_1, y_1)$ and $B(x_2, y_2)$ is

$$d = \sqrt{(x_2 - x_1)^2 + (y_2 - y_1)^2}.$$

Example 1   Relating to the Real World 🌐 ·············

Transportation Luisa takes the subway from Oak Station to Jackson Station each morning. Oak Station is 1 mi west and 2 mi south of City Plaza. Jackson Station is 2 mi east and 4 mi north of City Plaza. How far does she travel by subway?

Let (x_1, y_1) and (x_2, y_2) represent Oak and Jackson, respectively. Then, $x_1 = -1$, $x_2 = 2$, $y_1 = -2$, and $y_2 = 4$.

$d = \sqrt{(x_2 - x_1)^2 + (y_2 - y_1)^2}$ Use the Distance Formula.

$d = \sqrt{(2 - (-1))^2 + (4 - (-2))^2}$ Substitute.

$d = \sqrt{3^2 + 6^2}$ Simplify.

$d = \sqrt{9 + 36} = \sqrt{45}$

45 ✓ *6.7082039*   Use your calculator.

Luisa travels about 6.7 mi by subway.

54

ERROR ALERT! Question 8 Students using calculators must make sure that the correct order of operations is used.
Remediation: Give students enough time to practice using the distance formula. They will need to use memory or parentheses keys. By working in groups, students can check each other's work.

EXTENSION Question 11 Have students work in groups to generalize the diagram by finding coordinates for R, M_1, and M_2 when S has coordinates (x_1, y_1) and T has coordinates (x_2, y_2).

Example 2

VISUAL LEARNING Have students check the results by graphing the segment and midpoint on a coordinate plane.

---

7. In Example 1 suppose you let (x_1, y_1) be $(2, 4)$ and (x_2, y_2) be $(-1, -2)$. Would you get the same result? Why or why not? **See below.**

8. *Calculator* Find the length of $\overline{AB}$ with endpoints $A(1, -3)$ and $B(-4, 4)$ to the nearest tenth. **8.6**

You know how to find the midpoint of a segment on a number line. Now you will use a similar process to find the midpoint of a segment in the coordinate plane.

Graph $\overline{TS}$ with endpoints $T(4, 3)$ and $S(8, 5)$.

Let $\overline{TR}$ be a horizontal segment and $\overline{SR}$ be a vertical segment. Add the coordinates to your drawing as you answer these questions.

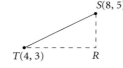

9. What are the coordinates of point R? **(8, 3)**

10. **a.** What are the coordinates of M_1, the midpoint of $\overline{TR}$? **(6, 3)**

   b. What are the coordinates of M_2, the midpoint of $\overline{SR}$? **(8, 4)**

11. What are the coordinates of M, the midpoint of $\overline{TS}$? **(6, 4)**

This specific case shows you how the Midpoint Formula was developed.

The system of longitude and latitude lines on Earth is a type of coordinate system.

The Midpoint Formula

The coordinates of the midpoint M of $\overline{AB}$ with endpoints $A(x_1, y_1)$ and $B(x_2, y_2)$ are the following:

$$M = \left(\frac{x_1 + x_2}{2}, \frac{y_1 + y_2}{2} \right)$$

QUICK REVIEW

$\frac{x_1 + x_2}{2}$ is the *arithmetic mean* of x_1 and x_2. Another word for arithmetic mean is *average*.

Example 2

Find the coordinates of the midpoint M of $\overline{QS}$ with endpoints $Q(3, 5)$ and $S(7, -9)$.

Let $x_1 = 3$, $x_2 = 7$, $y_1 = 5$, and $y_2 = -9$.

x-coordinate of $M = \frac{x_1 + x_2}{2} = \frac{3 + 7}{2} = \frac{10}{2} = 5$

y-coordinate of $M = \frac{y_1 + y_2}{2} = \frac{5 + (-9)}{2} = \frac{-4}{2} = -2$

The coordinates of point M are $(5, -2)$.

12. **Try This** Find the coordinates of the midpoint of $\overline{AB}$ with endpoints $A(2, -5)$ and $B(6, 13)$. **(4, 4)**

7. Yes; the differences between coordinates have opposite signs from those in Example 1, but when you square them, the result is the same.

Technology Options

In Exercises 7–15, students may write a program on a computer or graphing calculator that will calculate the distance between two points when their coordinates are entered.

Prentice Hall Technology

Software
- Secondary Math Lab Toolkit™
- Integrated Math Lab 24
- Computer Item Generator 1-8

Internet
- See the Prentice Hall site. (http://www.phschool.com)

55

Exercises 16–21 Encourage students to graph the segment and midpoint to check that each answer is reasonable.

Exercise 23 Have students discuss their methods for finding the solution. Possible methods include: using the formula to write and solve two equations, or reading the results from a graph, checking, and revising if necessary.

ALTERNATIVE ASSESSMENT **Exercises 29–31** These exercises can help you assess students' ability to use the midpoint and distance formulas. Students should carefully determine the coordinates of each endpoint. They can use the graphs to estimate the midpoints and distances to check that their answers are reasonable.

ESL **VISUAL LEARNING** **Exercise 33** Before students begin this problem, you may want to display a model of a three-dimensional coordinate system and discuss which directions are *positive* and *negative* on each axis.

pages 56–57 On Your Own

1–6.

26a. **D(3, 6) or D(−5, 2)**

b. **exactly one point E(−5, 2)**

c. **G(1, 0) or G(−1, 4)**

d. **H(3, 4) or H(2, 6)**

33b.

R(4, 5, 9)

Graph each point in the same coordinate plane. 1–6. See margin.

1. $A(5, -3)$ **2.** $B(-3, 0)$ **3.** $C(6, 2)$ **4.** $D(-6, 2)$ **5.** $E(-4, 3)$ **6.** $F(0, 5)$

Choose **Use mental math, pencil and paper, or a calculator to find the distance between the points to the nearest tenth.**

7. $J(2, -1), K(2, 5)$ 6   **8.** $L(10, 14), M(-8, 14)$ 18   **9.** $N(-11, -11), P(-11, -3)$ 8

10. $A(0, 3), B(0, 12)$ 9   **11.** $C(12, 6), D(-8, 18)$ 23.3   **12.** $E(6, -2), F(-2, 4)$ 10

13. $Q(12, -12), T(5, 12)$ 25   **14.** $R(0, 5), S(12, 3)$ 12.2   **15.** $X(-3, -4), Y(5, 5)$ 12.0

Find the coordinates of the midpoint of $\overline{HX}$.

16. $H(0, 0), X(8, 4)$ (4, 2)   **17.** $H(-1, 3), X(7, -1)$ (3, 1)   **18.** $H(13, 8), X(-6, -6)$ $\left(\frac{7}{2}, 1\right)$

19. $H(7, 10), X(5, -8)$ (6, 1)   **20.** $H(-6.3, 5.2), X(1.8, -1)$ (−2.25, 2.1)   **21.** $H\left(5\frac{1}{2}, -4\frac{3}{4}\right), X\left(2\frac{1}{4}, -1\frac{1}{4}\right)$ $\left(3\frac{7}{8}, -3\right)$

22. The midpoint of $\overline{QS}$ is the origin. Point Q is located in Quadrant II. What quadrant contains point S? IV

23. $M(5, 12)$ is the midpoint of $\overline{AB}$. The coordinates of point A are (2, 6). What are the coordinates of point B? **(8, 18)**

24. The midpoint of $\overline{QT}$ has coordinates (3, −4). The coordinates of point Q are (2, 3). What are the coordinates of point T? (4, −11)

25. The coordinates of A, B, C, and D are given at the right. Graph the points and draw the segments connecting them in order. Are the lengths of the sides of ABCD the same? Explain.
No; $AD = AB \approx 4.2, DC = CB \approx 3.2$.

$A(-6, 2)$ $B(-3, 5)$
$C(-6, 6)$ $D(-9, 5)$

26. *Open-ended* Graph $A(-2, 1)$ and $B(2, 3)$. Draw $\overleftrightarrow{AB}$. For each point described, give two sets of possible coordinates if they exist. Otherwise write "exactly one point" and give the coordinates.

a. point D so that $\overleftrightarrow{CD}$ contains $C(-1, 4)$ and is parallel to $\overleftrightarrow{AB}$

b. point E so that $\overleftrightarrow{AE}$ is parallel to $\overleftrightarrow{BC}$, $\overleftrightarrow{BC}$ contains $C(-1, 4)$, and $\overleftrightarrow{EC}$ is parallel to $\overleftrightarrow{AB}$

c. point G so that $\overleftrightarrow{FG}$ contains $F(0, 2)$ and is perpendicular to $\overleftrightarrow{AB}$

d. point H so that $\overleftrightarrow{HJ}$ contains $J(4, 2)$ and is perpendicular to $\overleftrightarrow{AB}$

26a–d. Answers may vary. See margin for samples.

27. *Writing* Why do you think that some cities are designed with a rectangular grid instead of a triangular grid or some other shape?
See above right.

27. Answers may vary. Sample: for convenience in specifying and locating addresses

28. Graph the points $A(2, 1), B(6, -1), C(8, 7)$, and $D(4, 9)$. Draw quadrilateral ABCD. Use the Midpoint Formula to determine the midpoints of $\overline{AC}$ and $\overline{BD}$. What do you notice?
Midpoint of $\overline{AC}$, (5, 4); midpoint of $\overline{BD}$, (5, 4); they are the same.

56

Exercises 34–39 Have students draw complementary and supplementary angles. If such an angle cannot be drawn, have students explain why.

 PORTFOLIO Share with students the criteria you will use to assess their work in portfolios, as well as how you plan to use the results. Students should understand how the rubrics assess their work, how each piece in the portfolio counts, and how the scores they get in their portfolios will affect their overall evaluation.

Wrap Up

THE BIG IDEA Ask students: *Draw a triangle on the coordinate plane and find the length and midpoint of each side.*

RETEACHING ACTIVITY Students find the lengths of sides of a triangle in the coordinate plane by using the distance formula. (Reteaching worksheet 1-8)

For each graph, find (a) the length of $\overline{AB}$ to the nearest tenth and (b) the coordinates of the midpoint of $\overline{AB}$. **29–31. See below.**

29.   **30.**   **31.**

32. Communications Long-distance rates for telephone calls are determined mainly by the distance between the two ends of the call. To determine these distances, long-distance telephone companies have divided North America into a grid, with each unit equaling $\sqrt{0.1}$ mile. The distance between two customers is then determined by using the Distance Formula. The coordinates for certain customers in several cities are listed. Find the distance between customers in the following cities:

a. Boston and San Francisco   about 2,690 mi
b. Houston and Chicago   about 934 mi
c. Denver and New Orleans   about 1,077 mi

San Francisco (8719, 8492)
Chicago (3439, 5985)
New Orleans (2637, 8482)
Denver (5899, 7501)
Los Angeles (7878, 9213)
Houston (3537, 8936)
Boston (1248, 4422)

33. Geometry in 3 Dimensions You can use three coordinates (x, y, z) to locate points in three dimensions. Point P has coordinates $(3, -3, 5)$.
a. Give the coordinates of points A, B, C, D, E, F, and G.   See below.
b. Draw three axes like those shown. Then graph $R(4, 5, 9)$.   See margin p. 56.

33a. $A(0, 0, 0)$, $B(3, 0, 0)$, $C(3, -3, 0)$, $D(0, -3, 0)$ $E(0, 0,5)$, $F(3, 0, 5)$, $G(0, -3, 5)$

Find the measure of the complement and supplement of each angle, if possible.

34. $m\angle B = 56$ **35.** $m\angle R = 18$ **36.** $m\angle D = 179$
  34; 124   72; 162
37. $m\angle P = 23.5$ **38.** $m\angle T = 108$ **39.** $m\angle E = 78$
  66.5; 156.5   not possible; 72   12; 102
40. The length of $\overline{AC}$ is 45. If $AB = x + 8$ and $BC = 3x - 3$, find the value of x.   10
  36. not possible; 1

 PORTFOLIO

For your portfolio, select one or two items from your work for this chapter. Here are some possibilities.
• corrected work
• an origami creation
• a journal entry
Explain why you have included each selection you make.

29a. 19.2   30a. 10.8   31a. 5.4
  b. (−1.5, 0)   b. (3, −4)   b. (−1, 0.5)

Name_____ Class_____ Date_____
Reteaching 1-8
Name_____ Class_____ Date_____
Practice 1-8
Name_____ Class_____ Date_____
Practice 1-8
Mixed Exercises
Graph each point in the coordinate plane.
  1. $A(-2, 5)$ 2. $B(5, -2)$ 3. $C(0, 6)$ 4. $D(-4, 0)$ 5. $E(-4, -2)$
Find the distance between each pair of points.
  6. $L(-4, 11), M(-5, 4)$ 7. $N(1, 0), P(3, 8)$
  8. $Q(10, 10), R(10, -2)$ 9. $S(0, 5), T(0, -3)$
  10. $U(11, 0), V(-1, 0)$ 11. $W(2, 7), X(1, 2)$
Find the coordinates of the midpoint of each segment.
The coordinates of the endpoints are given.
  12. $A(6, 7), B(4, 3)$ 13. $C(-1, 5), D(2, -5)$
  14. $E(14, -2), F(7, -8)$ 15. $O(0, 0), G(-5, 12)$
  16. $H(2.8, 1.1), I(-3.4, 5.7)$ 17. $J(2\frac12, -\frac12), K(3\frac14, -1)$
  18. The midpoint of $\overline{AB}$ is (1, 2). The coordinates of A are $(-3, 6)$.
    Find the coordinates of B.
  19. The midpoint of $\overline{CD}$ is (4, 11). The coordinates of D are (4, 12).
    Find the coordinates of C.
  20. The midpoint of $\overline{EF}$ is $(-3, 7)$. The coordinates of E are $(-4, 5)$.
    Find the coordinates of F.
  21. Graph the points $A(2, 1), B(2, -5), C(-4, -5),$ and $D(-4, 1)$.
    Draw the segments connecting $A, B, C,$ and D in order.
    Are the lengths of the sides of $ABCD$ the same? Explain.
  22. A crow flies to a point that is 1 mile east and 20 miles south. How far
    does the crow fly?
Quadrilateral PQSR has coordinates as follows:
$P(0, 0), Q(-1, 4), R(8, 2)$ and $S(7, 6)$.
  23. Sketch quadrilateral PQSR.
  24. What is the perimeter of PQSR?
  25. What is the midpoint of $\overline{QR}$?

Lesson Quiz

Lesson Quiz is also available in Transparencies.

1. Find the distance between $K(5, -6)$ and $L(3, 4)$ to the nearest tenth.   10.2

2. Find the coordinates of the midpoint of the segment with endpoints $E(3, 7)$ and $F(-2, -1)$. (0.5, 3)

3. The midpoint of $\overline{AB}$ has coordinates (3, 4). Point A has coordinates $(-3, -2)$. Find the coordinates of point B.   (9, 10)

Finishing the Chapter Project

PROJECT DAY You may wish to plan a project day on which students share their completed projects. Encourage groups to explain their processes as well as their products.

PROJECT NOTEBOOK Have students review their project work and bring their notebooks up to date.

- Have students review their figures, the methods for creating them, and the vocabulary used in writing their instructions.
- Ask groups to share the origami figure that is their favorite. Also ask them what they found most difficult about creating origami figures and what they found most difficult about writing the directions.

SCORING RUBRIC

3 Student's origami figures are created correctly. Instructions are neat and well-organized. Geometry vocabulary is used accurately and appropriately.

2 Student's origami figures are created correctly with few minor flaws. Directions are neat and organized. Geometry vocabulary is used fairly accurately and appropriately and with few inaccuracies.

1 Student's origami figures contain several flaws. Directions are not well organized. Geometry vocabulary is used infrequently.

0 Major elements are incomplete or missing.

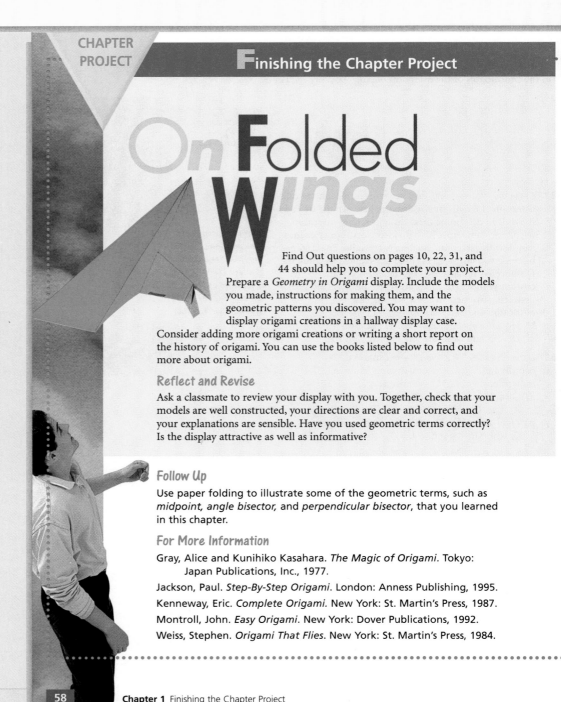

CHAPTER PROJECT

Finishing the Chapter Project

On Folded Wings

Find Out questions on pages 10, 22, 31, and 44 should help you to complete your project. Prepare a *Geometry in Origami* display. Include the models you made, instructions for making them, and the geometric patterns you discovered. You may want to display origami creations in a hallway display case.
Consider adding more origami creations or writing a short report on the history of origami. You can use the books listed below to find out more about origami.

Reflect and Revise

Ask a classmate to review your display with you. Together, check that your models are well constructed, your directions are clear and correct, and your explanations are sensible. Have you used geometric terms correctly? Is the display attractive as well as informative?

Follow Up

Use paper folding to illustrate some of the geometric terms, such as *midpoint, angle bisector,* and *perpendicular bisector*, that you learned in this chapter.

For More Information

Gray, Alice and Kunihiko Kasahara. *The Magic of Origami*. Tokyo: Japan Publications, Inc., 1977.

Jackson, Paul. *Step-By-Step Origami*. London: Anness Publishing, 1995.

Kenneway, Eric. *Complete Origami*. New York: St. Martin's Press, 1987.

Montroll, John. *Easy Origami*. New York: Dover Publications, 1992.

Weiss, Stephen. *Origami That Flies*. New York: St. Martin's Press, 1984.

Wrap Up

---

1 Wrap Up

Resources

📖 **Student Edition**
Extra Practice, p. 634
Glossary/Study Guide

■ **Teaching Resources**
Student Skills Handbook
Glossary, Spanish Resources

Key Terms

acute angle (p. 27)
adjacent angles (p. 48)
angle (p. 26)
angle bisector (p. 34)
collinear (p. 13)
compass (p. 39)
complementary
  angles (p. 48)
congruent angles (p. 28)
congruent segments (p. 25)
conjecture (p. 5)
construction (p. 39)
coordinate (p. 25)
coplanar (p. 13)
deductive reasoning (p. 46)
inductive reasoning (p. 5)
line (p. 13)

measure of an angle (p. 26)
midpoint (p. 33)
obtuse angle (p. 27)
opposite rays (p. 18)
parallel lines (p. 18)
parallel planes (p. 19)
perpendicular
  bisector (p. 34)
perpendicular lines (p. 33)
plane (p. 13)
point (p. 12)
postulate (p. 14)
proof (p. 49)
quadrant (p. 54)
ray (p. 18)
right angle (p. 27)
segment (p. 18)

segment bisector (p. 33)
skew lines (p. 19)
space (p. 12)
straight angle (p. 27)
straightedge (p. 39)
supplementary angles (p. 48)
theorem (p. 49)
vertical angles (p. 48)

How am I doing?

• State three ideas from this chapter that you think are important. Explain your choices.
• Describe three types of mathematical statements.

Using Patterns and Inductive Reasoning   1-1

You use **inductive reasoning** when you make conclusions from specific examples or patterns. You can use inductive reasoning to make conjectures. A **conjecture** describes a conclusion reached from observations or inductive reasoning. Because conjectures are not always valid, you should verify them if possible.

Find the next two terms of each sequence and describe the pattern.

1. $1, 5, 9, 13, \ldots$ **17, 21**   **2.** $1, 3, 7, 15, 31, \ldots$ **63, 127**

3. $\frac{1}{2}, \frac{2}{3}, \frac{3}{4}, \frac{4}{5}, \ldots$ $\frac{5}{6}, \frac{6}{7}$ **4.** $0, 1, -2, 3, -4, \ldots$ **5, −6**

5. Draw the next figure in the sequence.

6. a. *Calculator* Find the last two digits of $76^2, 76^4, 276^2$, and 376^3. **76**
   b. Make a **conjecture** about powers of numbers whose last two digits are 76.   The last two digits will always be 76.

1. Add 4 to the previous term to get the next term.

2. Add consecutively increasing powers of 2 to the previous term to get the next term.

3. Add 1 to numerator and denominator of the preceding term to get the next term.

4. Write the sequence of whole numbers and then change the signs of the even whole numbers.

59

Basic Concepts   1-2, 1-3

Points that lie on a line are **collinear**. Points and lines in the same plane are **coplanar**.

Two coplanar lines that do not intersect are **parallel**. Two lines in space that are not parallel and do not intersect are **skew**. Two planes that do not intersect are **parallel**.

Segments and **rays** are parts of lines.

7. *Critical Thinking* Explain why the postulate "Through any three noncollinear points there is exactly one plane" applies only to noncollinear points.   **If the points were collinear, an infinite number of planes would pass through them.**

Use the figure to answer Exercises 8–13. 8–13. Answers may vary. Samples are given.

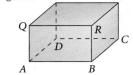

8. Name two intersecting lines.
   $\overleftrightarrow{QR}$ and $\overleftrightarrow{RS}$
9. Name a pair of skew lines.
   $\overleftrightarrow{QR}$ and $\overleftrightarrow{SC}$
10. Name three noncollinear points.
    Q, R, and *S*
11. Name four noncoplanar points.
    Q, R, S, C
12. Name a pair of parallel planes.
    plane *QRST* and plane *ABCD*
13. Name three lines that intersect at *D*.
    $\overleftrightarrow{AD}$, $\overleftrightarrow{CD}$, $\overleftrightarrow{TD}$

Complete with *always, sometimes,* or *never* to make a true statement

14. A line and a point are _?_ coplanar. **always**
15. Two segments are _?_ coplanar. **sometimes**
16. Skew lines are _?_ coplanar. **never**
17. Opposite rays _?_ have the same endpoint. **always**
18. Two points are _?_ collinear. **always**
19. Parallel lines are _?_ skew. **never**

Angles, Segments, and Deductive Reasoning   1-4, 1-7

Segments with the same length are **congruent**. An **angle** is formed by two rays with the same endpoint. Angles are measured in degrees. Angles with the same measure are **congruent**.

Deductive reasoning is the process of reasoning logically from given facts to a conclusion. If the given facts are true, deductive reasoning always produces a valid conclusion.

Special relationships exist between certain angle pairs. For example, vertical angles are congruent. The sum of the measures of a pair of **complementary angles** is 90. The sum of the measures of a pair of **supplementary angles** is 180.

20. *Open-ended* Describe a real-world situation where you use deductive reasoning.

21. Find possible coordinates of point *Q* on the number line so that *PQ* = 5.
    3 or −7

20. Answers may vary. Sample: You want to use your own money to buy a bicycle that costs $320. You have $275. You cannot buy the bike.

60

Exercises 22–24 You may want to have students describe what definitions and postulates they used in solving each problem.

Exercises 25–27 Students' conclusions should be about properties of the figure. Students do not need to find angle measures or segment lengths.

ALGEBRA Exercise 30 Students can check their answers by evaluating the variable expressions for *BE* and *EK* to see whether they are equal.

Algebra Find the value of each variable in the diagrams below.

22.
18

$(3y + 20)°$ $(5y - 16)°$

23.
31

$(3x + 31)°$ $(2x - 6)°$

24.
20

$90°$
$(k + 10)°$
$(3k)°$

What can you conclude from each diagram? Justify your answers. 25–27. See margin.

25.
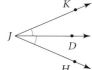
K
J
D
H

26. A   B   C   D

27.

2 3 4
1

Wrap Up   pages 59–62

25. $m\angle KJD + m\angle DJH = m\angle KJH$ by the Angle Add. Post.;
$m\angle KJD = m\angle DJH$ by the markings; $\overrightarrow{JD}$ bisects $\angle KJH$ by the definition of angle bisector.

26. *AB* = *CD* by the markings; *AC* = *BD* by the Seg. Add. Post.

27. $\angle 1 \cong \angle 4$ by the markings; $\angle 1 \cong \angle 2$ and $\angle 3 \cong \angle 4$ because vert. angles are $\cong$; $\angle 2 \cong \angle 3$ by the Trans. Prop. of $\cong$.

Good Definitions   1-5

A good definition is precise. A good definition uses terms that have been previously defined or are commonly accepted.

The **midpoint** of a segment divides a segment into two congruent segments. **Perpendicular lines** intersect at right angles. A **perpendicular bisector** of a segment is perpendicular to a segment at its midpoint. An **angle bisector** divides an angle into two congruent angles.

28. Writing Rico defines a book as something you read. Explain what's wrong with this definition. Write a good definition for the word *book*. See below.

29. Critical Thinking In the diagram at the right, $\overleftrightarrow{LJ}$ is the perpendicular bisector of $\overline{BK}$. Is $\overleftrightarrow{BK}$ necessarily the perpendicular bisector of $\overline{LJ}$? Explain.   See below.

L
B E   K
J

30. Algebra In the diagram at right, point *E* is the midpoint of $\overline{BK}$, $BE = 3y - 2$, and $EK = 2y + 1$. Find the value of *y*. **3**

31. Find the coordinate of the midpoint of $\overline{GH}$. **1**

G   H
−4 −3 −2 −1 0 1 2 3 4 5 6

32. Standardized Test Prep In which figure is the $m\angle 1$ *not* equal to 60? **D**

A. 70° 1 50°   **B.** 30° 1   **C.** 1 60°   **D.** 40° 1   **E.** 1 120°

28. Something you read could be a newspaper or traffic sign. A book is a collection of printed pages permanently bound together along one edge. It is usually longer than a magazine.

29. No; $\overleftrightarrow{BK}$ may not bisect $\overline{LJ}$.

WRITING Exercise 35 Encourage students to check their descriptions by performing the construction.

ALTERNATIVE ASSESSMENT Exercises 36–41 Have students connect the points in these exercises to form a plane figure Then have them find the length and midpoint of each segment they draw.

Remind students that the new mathematical terms in this chapter are defined in the Glossary/Study Guide in the back of the book.

Getting Ready For Chapter 2

Students may work these exercises independently or in small groups. The skills previewed will help prepare students to investigate polygons.

33.

34a–b.

36–41.

44a.

Basic Constructions
1-6

A **construction** is the process of making geometric figures using a **straightedge** and **compass**.

33. Use a protractor to draw a 72° angle. Then construct a congruent angle. **See margin.**

34. a. Construct $\overline{AB} \cong \overline{PQ}$.
   b. Construct the perpendicular bisector of $\overline{AB}$. **a–b. See margin.**

P •———————————• Q

35. Writing Describe how to construct a 45° angle.
   Construct a ⊥ bisector to a segment. Then bisect one of the resulting right angles.

The Coordinate Plane
1-8

The **x-axis** and the **y-axis** intersect at the **origin** $(0, 0)$ and determine a **coordinate plane**. You can find the coordinates of the midpoint M of $\overline{AB}$ with endpoints $A(x_1, y_1)$ and $B(x_2, y_2)$ using the **Midpoint Formula**.

$$M = \left(\frac{x_1 + x_2}{2}, \frac{y_1 + y_2}{2}\right)$$

You can find the distance d between points $A(x_1, y_1)$ and $B(x_2, y_2)$ using the **Distance Formula**.

$$d = \sqrt{(x_2 - x_1)^2 + (y_2 - y_1)^2}$$

Graph each point in the same coordinate plane. 36–41. See margin.

36. $A(-1, 5)$ **37.** $B(0, 4)$ **38.** $C(-1, -1)$ **39.** $D(6, 2)$ **40.** $E(-7, 0)$ **41.** $F(3, -4)$

42. $\overline{GH}$ has endpoints $G(-3, 2)$ and $H(3, -2)$. Find the coordinates of the midpoint of $\overline{GH}$. **(0, 0)**

43. Calculator Find the distance between points $B(4, -3)$ and $D(3, 0)$ to the nearest tenth. **3.2**

Getting Ready for..
CHAPTER
2

44. a. Graph points $A(-1, 3)$, $B(-1, 6)$, and $C(4, 3)$ in the same coordinate plane and connect them to form a triangle. **See margin.**
   b. Choose Use pencil and paper, mental math, or a calculator to find the lengths of the three sides of the triangle.
   c. List the sides in order from longest to shortest. $AB = 3$, $AC = 5$, $BC \approx 5.8$
   $\overline{BC}, \overline{AC}, \overline{AB}$

Name a real-world object that has the given geometric shape. 45–49. Samples are given.

45. triangle
   yield sign

46. circle
   clock

47. rhombus
   quadrilaterals
   in a chain
   link fence

48. cylinder
   soup can

49. cube
   child's
   building
   block

62

Assessment

ENHANCED MULTIPLE CHOICE QUESTIONS are more complex than traditional multiple choice questions, which assess only one skill. Enhanced multiple choice questions assess the processes that students use, as well as the end results. The questions are written so that students use more than one strategy to solve the problem. Using multiple strategies is encouraged by the National Council of Teachers of Mathematics (NCTM). **Exercises 10 and 36** are enhanced multiple choice questions.

FREE RESPONSE QUESTIONS do not give answer choices. Some exercises have more than one possible answer. Students need to give only one correct response. **Exercises 1–4, 6–9, 11–21, 23–35, and 37–45** are free response questions.

WRITING EXERCISES allow students to describe how they think about and understand the concepts they have learned. **Exercise 22** is a writing exercise.

OPEN-ENDED PROBLEMS allow for more than one solution. Students must construct their own responses instead of choosing from possible answers. The student responses will help you determine the depth of their understanding and any possible areas of difficulty. **Exercise 5** is an open-ended problem.

---

1 Assessment

Find the next two terms in each sequence.

1. $8, -4, 2, -1, \ldots$ $\frac{1}{2}, -\frac{1}{4}$

2. $0, 2, 4, 6, 8, \ldots$ $10, 12$

3.

4.

5. **Open-ended** Write two different sequences whose first three terms are 1, 2, 4. Describe each pattern.   **See margin.**

Use the figure to answer Exercises 6–10.

6. Name three collinear points.   **A, B, C**

7. Name four coplanar points.
   A, B, C, D (or A, B, C, E)

8. Name four noncoplanar points.
   See margin.

9. What is the intersection of $\overleftrightarrow{AC}$ and plane Q?   **B**

10. How many planes contain each line and point?

    a. $\overleftrightarrow{BD}$ and point A **1** b. $\overleftrightarrow{AB}$ and point C

    c. $\overleftrightarrow{BE}$ and point C **1** d. $\overleftrightarrow{BD}$ and point E **1**
    10b. infinitely many

Is the definition of the term in red acceptable? If not, write a good definition. **11–12. See margin.**

11. A pencil is a writing instrument.

12. Vertical angles are angles that are congruent.

13. Complementary angles are angles that form a right angle. **No; complementary angles are two angles the sum of whose measures is 90.**

Complete with *always, sometimes,* or *never* to make each statement true.

14. $\overleftrightarrow{LJ}$ and $\overrightarrow{TJ}$ are __?__ opposite rays.   **never**

15. Four points are __?__ coplanar.   **sometimes**

16. Skew lines are __?__ noncoplanar.   **always**

17. Two lines that lie in parallel planes are __?__ parallel.   **sometimes**

18. The intersection of two planes is __?__ a point. **never**

19. Algebra $JK = 48$. Find the value of x.   **10**

Algebra **Use the figure to find the values of the variables in Exercises 20 and 21.**

20. $m\angle BDK = 3x + 4, m\angle JDR = 5x - 10$ **7**

21. $m\angle BDJ = 7y + 2, m\angle JDR = 2y + 7$ **9**

22. Writing Why is it useful to have more than one way of naming an angle? **See margin.**

Name the property of equality or congruence that justifies each statement.
Transitive Prop. of =
23. If $UV = KL$ and $KL = 6$, then $UV = 6$.

24. If $m\angle 1 + m\angle 2 = m\angle 4 + m\angle 2$, then $m\angle 1 = m\angle 4$.   **Subtr. Prop. of =**

25. $\angle ABC \cong \angle ABC$ **Refl. Prop. of $\cong$**

26. If $\frac{1}{2}m\angle D = 45$, then $m\angle D = 90$.
    Mult. Prop. of =

27. If $\angle DEF \cong \angle HJK$, then $\angle HJK \cong \angle DEF$.
    Symm. Prop. of $\cong$

33.

42. $m\angle VNM = 62$ because vert. angles are $\cong$.
$m\angle LNV = m\angle PNM = 118$ because both angles are supplementary to $\angle LNP$.

45.

60°

Preparing for Standardized Tests
page 65

14. Inductive reasoning uses observations to make reasonable conjectures. Deductive reasoning is the process of reasoning logically from given facts to a conclusion.

Use the figure to complete Exercises 28–32.

28. $\overline{VW}$ is the __?__ of $\overline{AY}$.   perp. bisector

29. $EW + EV = \blacksquare$ VW

30. If $EY = 3.5$, then $AY = \blacksquare$.   7

31. $\frac{1}{2}\blacksquare = AE$ AY

32. $\blacksquare$ is the midpoint of $\blacksquare$. E; $\overline{AY}$

33. Construct a triangle whose sides have the given lengths.   See margin.

Algebra Use the figure to complete Exercises 34 and 35. $\overrightarrow{AE}$ bisects $\angle DAC$. Find the values of the variables.

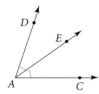

34. $m\angle DAE = 4y + 4$, $m\angle CAE = 6y - 12$ 8

35. $m\angle CAE = 6c - 12$, $m\angle DAC = 72$ 8

36. **Standardized Test Prep** The measure of an angle is $2z$. What is the measure of its supplement?   **E**
   A. $90 - 2z$
   B. 180
   C. $2z$
   D. $2z - 180$
   E. $180 - 2z$

---

37. Find the measure of each angle.

   a. $\angle CDM$ 135   **b.** $\angle KDM$ 135
   c. $\angle JDK$ 180   **d.** $\angle JDM$ 45
   e. $\angle CDB$ 180   **f.** $\angle CDK$ 90

Use the graph to complete Exercises 38–41.

38–40. See below.
38. Find the coordinates of each labeled point.

39. Find the coordinates of the midpoint of $\overline{EH}$.

40. Find the coordinates of the midpoint of $\overline{AF}$.

41. Find the length of each segment to the nearest tenth.
   a. $\overline{AC}$ 5.8   **b.** $\overline{BH}$ 4.0
   c. $\overline{GB}$ 5.0   **d.** $\overline{AF}$ 9.4

What can you conclude from each diagram? Justify your answers. 42. See margin.

42.

L 62° P
N
V M

43.

E F
B C D

See below.

44. The coordinates of the midpoint of $\overline{RS}$ are $(-1, 1)$. The coordinates of R are $(3, 3)$. What are the coordinates of S? $(-5, -1)$

45. Use a protractor to draw a 60° angle. Then construct its bisector.   See margin.

38. $A(-3, 3)$, $B(2, 0)$, $C(0, -2)$, $D(-4, 1)$, $E(2, 3)$, $F(5, -2)$, $G(-2, -3)$, $H(-2, 0)$

39. $\left(0, \frac{3}{2}\right)$ **40.** $\left(1, \frac{1}{2}\right)$

43. $\angle BCE \cong \angle DCF$ by the markings and thus $\angle BCF \cong \angle ECD$ by the Angle Add. Post.

Standardized tests, such as those administered for state assessment, the SAT, or the ACT, include regular math questions, quantitative comparison questions, open-ended problems, and free response questions (which the SAT calls *grid-ins*).

MULTIPLE CHOICE QUESTIONS are followed by five answer choices, one of which is correct. **Exercises 1–7** are multiple choice questions.

QUANTITATIVE COMPARISON QUESTIONS ask students to compare two quantities. **Exercises 8–11** are quantitative comparison questions.

FREE RESPONSE QUESTIONS do not give answer choices. Students must provide one correct answer on their own. **Exercise 13 and 14** are free response questions.

OPEN-ENDED PROBLEMS allow for more than one solution. Students must construct their own responses instead of choosing a single answer. The responses students give will help you determine the depth of their understanding and what difficulties, if any, they are experiencing. **Exercise 12** is an open-ended problem.

STANDARDIZED TEST TIP Exercise 6 Students often make subtraction errors with the distance formula. The answer choices include answers that are results of common errors. Students should check their work carefully and not assume their answers are correct just because they appear as possible choices.

For Exercises 1–7, choose the correct letter.

1. The intersection of two planes is
A. a point. **B.** a ray. **C.** a segment.
D. a line. **E.** none of the above   D

2. Estimate $m\angle BCD$.   B

A. 25 **B.** 55 **C.** 85
D. 105 **E.** 125

3. Which is the next figure in the sequence?   E

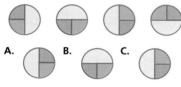

A. **B.** **C.**

D. **E.** none of the above

4. Find the values of x and y.   C

$(2y - 30)°$
$(2x - 20)°$ $(x + 10)°$

A. $x = 40, y = 140$ **B.** $x = 10, y = 170$
C. $x = 30, y = 85$ **D.** $x = 30, y = 90$
E. none of the above

5. Two right angles can be   E
I. vertical. **II.** adjacent.
III. complementary. **IV.** supplementary.

A. I and II **B.** II and III **C.** III and IV
D. I and IV **E.** I, II, and IV

6. Find the distance between $A(4, -5)$ and $B(-2, 1)$ to the nearest tenth.   A
A. 8.5 **B.** 7.2 **C.** 6.7 **D.** 6.3 **E.** 4.5

7. Which point lies the farthest from the origin?
A. $(0, -7)$ **B.** $(-3, 8)$ **C.** $(-4, -3)$
D. $(5, 1)$ **E.** $(-6, 0)$ B

For Exercises 8–11, compare the boxed quantity in Column A with the boxed quantity in Column B. Choose the best answer.

A. The quantity in Column A is greater.
B. The quantity in Column B is greater.
C. The two quantities are equal.
D. The relationship cannot be determined on the basis of the information supplied.

Column A	Column B

$\overline{MV}$ bisects $\overline{NW}$.

8. $m\angle MEN$ | $m\angle VEW$ C

9. $m\angle MEW$ | $m\angle VEW$ D

10. EW | EN C

11. EM | EV D

12. *Open-ended* Write the measures of three noncongruent acute angles. Find the complement and supplement of each.
See below left.

13. Find the coordinates of the midpoint of $\overline{CD}$ with endpoints $C(5, 7)$ and $D(10, -3)$. $\left(\dfrac{15}{2}, 2\right)$

14. *Writing* Explain the difference between inductive and deductive reasoning.
See margin p. 64.

12. Answers may vary. Sample: angle measure 10 — comp. 80, supp. 170; angle measure 25 — comp. 65, supp. 155; angle measure 63 — comp. 27, supp. 117

Resources

Teaching Resources
Chapter Support File, Ch. 1
• Standardized Test Practice
• Cumulative Review

Teacher's Edition
See also p. 2E for assessment options

Investigating Geometric Figures

To accommodate flexible scheduling, some lessons are divided into parts. Assignment Options are given in the Lesson Planning Options for each lesson.

2-1 Triangles (pp. 68–74)

Part ▼**1** The Triangle Angle-Sum Theorem

Part ▼**2** Exterior Angles of a Triangle

Key Terms: acute, corollary, equiangular, equilateral, exterior angle, isosceles, obtuse, remote interior angles, right, scalene

2-2 Polygons (pp. 76–81)

Part ▼**1** Polygons and Interior Angles

Part ▼**2** Exterior Angles

Key Terms: concave, convex, equiangular polygon, equilateral polygon, polygon, regular polygon

2-3 Parallel and Perpendicular Lines in the Coordinate Plane (pp. 83–88)

Part ▼**1** Slope and Graphing Lines

Part ▼**2** Parallel and Perpendicular Lines

2-4 Classifying Quadrilaterals (pp. 90–95)

Key Terms: isosceles trapezoid, kite, parallelogram, rectangle, rhombus, square, trapezoid

2-5 Circles (pp. 96–101)

Part ▼**1** Parts of a Circle

Part ▼**2** Central Angles and Arcs

Key Terms: adjacent arcs, circle, central angle, diameter, major arc, minor arc, radius, semicircle

2-6 Congruent and Similar Figures (pp. 102–108)

Part ▼**1** Congruent Figures

Part ▼**2** Similar Polygons

Key Terms: congruent circles, congruent polygons, similarity ratio, similar

2-7 Isometric and Orthographic Drawings (pp. 109–115)

Part ▼**1** Isometric Drawings

Part ▼**2** Orthographic Drawings

Key Terms: foundation drawing, isometric drawing, orthographic drawing

PACING OPTIONS

This chart suggests pacing only for the core lessons and their parts, and it is provided merely as a possible guide. It will help you determine how much time you have in your schedule to cover other features, such as the Chapter Project, Math Toolboxes, Wrap Up, and Assessment.

	1 Class Period	1 Class Period	1 Class Period	1 Class Period	1 Class Period	1 Class Period	1 Class Period	1 Class Period	1 Class Period
Traditional (40–45 min class periods)	2-1 ▼1	2-1 ▼2	2-2 ▼1	2-2 ▼2	2-3 ▼1	2-3 ▼2	2-4	2-5 ▼1	2-5 ▼2
Block Scheduling (90 min class periods)	2-1 ▼1 ▼2	2-2 ▼1 ▼2	2-3 ▼1 ▼2	2-4	2-5 ▼1 ▼2	2-6 ▼1 ▼2	2-7 ▼1 ▼2		

What Students Will Learn and Why

In this chapter, students expand on their understanding of basic geometric concepts by investigating shapes that occur often in everyday life: polygons, lines, and circles. Students classify triangles and other polygons, and they connect geometry to algebra by relating *parallel* and *perpendicular* to the concept of *slope*. They explore angles and arcs of a circle and apply those ideas to circle graphs. They learn about congruence and similarity, and they draw three-dimensional figures using isometric and orthographic drawings, which are important in design and engineering.

Discussing the Chapter/Building on Experience

The concept map below relates chapter topics to real-world applications. You and your class may wish to add to the map or develop maps of your own. The center oval describes the topic of the chapter. The next level displays topics within the lessons. The outer ovals reflect applications of the content. As you and your class build a concept map, invite students to discuss applications with which they are familiar.

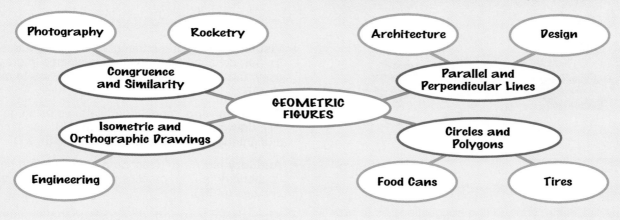

1 Class Period	1 Class Period	1 Class Period	1 Class Period	1 Class Period	1 Class Period	1 Class Period	1 Class Period	1 Class Period	1 Class Period	1 Class Period
2-6 ▼1	2-6 ▼2	2-7 ▼1	2-7 ▼2							

Interactive Questioning Tips

A question is interactive when there is "give and take" between the questioner (teacher or student) and the respondent. In Think and Discuss or when a critical thinking question is asked, it is important to encourage students to analyze the question throughly before attempting an answer. For example, in Lesson 2-4, Example 2, students are asked to explain how they know that a certain quadrilateral is not a square. Students must analyze the parts of the question—what are the characteristics of a quadrilateral; what are the characteristics of a square; how do these characteristics compare or contrast.

Skills Practice

Every lesson provides skill practice with Try This exercises, Exercises On Your Own, and Exercises Mixed Review. The Student Edition includes Checkpoints (pp. 88, 108) and Cumulative Review (p. 121). In the Teacher's Edition, the Lesson Planning Options section for each lesson lists Prerequisite Skills students should know for that lesson. At the back of the Student Edition is the Skills Handbook—mini-lessons on math your students may need to review. The Chapter Support File for Chapter 2 in the Teaching Resources box includes two Practice worksheets per lesson, a worksheet for two Checkpoints, and worksheets for Cumulative Review and Standardized Test Preparation.

Diverse Learning and Teaching Styles

In your Teacher's Edition, you will find suggestions as to how you can help students complete mathematical tasks in Chapter 2 by reinforcing various learning styles. Here are some examples.

- **Visual learning** trace triangles and cut out interior angles (p. 69), describe the appearance of lines in graphs (p. 83), copy and color circles to illustrate answers to exercises (p. 99)

- **Tactile learning** model quadrilaterals using geoboards (p. 91), draw answers to exercises (p. 95), use a compass and straightedge to draw and label a circle (p. 97)

- **Auditory learning** describe a triangle using new vocabulary (p. 71), practice naming polygons, sides, and vertices (p. 77)

- **Kinesthetic learning** demonstrate that the sum of the exterior angles of a polygon is 360° (p.78), demonstrate why a circle is 360° (p. 98), draw different views of real-world objects (p. 113)

Alternative Activity for Lesson 2-1

for use with the Work Together and Example 1, uses geometry software to draw triangles and measure angles.

Alternative Activity for Lesson 2-2

for use with the Work Together and Example 3, uses geometry software to draw polygons, change the shapes, and find the sum of the angle measures.

Alternative Activity for Lesson 2-5

for use with Part 2, uses geometry softwar to draw circles and angles and arcs.

Cooperative Learning Tips

When used effectively, cooperative learning can help students develop interpersonal skills, learn to perform specific roles in a group, and learn to carry out specific responsibilities. The components of Chapter 2 provide a range of cooperative learning opportunities.

- In the Student Edition, the **Work Together** parts of lessons are specifically designed for cooperative learning activities.

- In the Teacher's Edition, you will find helpful hints for addressing diverse learning styles (see page C for Chapter 2). For every lesson, you will find a **Reteaching Activity**, which may involve cooperative learning.

Materials and Manipulatives

The authors expect all students to use scientific calculators. Calculator use is integrated throughout the course.

- cardboard (2-4)
- centimeter ruler (2-6)
- compass (2-5)
- cubes (2-7)
- graph paper (2-3, 2-7)
- graphing calculator (2-3)
- isometric dot paper (2-7)
- protractor (2-1, 2-5, 2-6)
- ruler (2-3)
- scissors (2-1, 2-4, 2-5, 2-6)
- straightedge (2-7)
- toothpicks (2-4)

TECHNOLOGY OPTIONS

Technology Tools		Chapter Project	2-1	2-2	2-3	2-4	2-5	2-6	2-7
Calculator		Assumed that students have scientific calculators at any time.							
Software	Secondary Math Lab Toolkit™		✔	✔	✔	✔	✔	✔	✔
	Integrated Math Lab				✔			✔	
	Computer Item Generator		✔	✔	✔	✔	✔	✔	✔
	Student Edition			✔T	✔T				
Video	Video Field Trip	✔							
CD-ROM	Multimedia Geometry Lab		✔	✔		✔	✔		
Internet		See the Prentice Hall site. (http://www.phschool.com)							

✔T indicates Math Toolbox.

The Prentice Hall Geometry program offers you a rich variety of technology options. Be assured that all these options are provided as a means of enriching the program and are not essential for the successful completion of the course.

Assessment Options

The Prentice Hall Geometry Program provides you with many options. From these options, you may choose instructional materials and techniques appropriate for your students, or those necessary to meet your district's curriculum requirements. As the chart indicates, the program also supports your teaching efforts by offering you many choices for assessment.

ASSESSMENT OPTIONS

Assessment Support Materials	Chapter Project	2-1	2-2	2-3	2-4	2-5	2-6	2-7	Chapter End
Chapter Project	▲■●	▲■	▲■		▲■		▲■	▲■	▲■
Checkpoints				▲■●			▲■●		
Self-Assessment				▲■		▲■		▲■	▲■
Writing Assignment		▲	▲■	▲■	▲■●	▲■	▲	▲■	●
Chapter Assessment									▲●
Alternative Assessment	■	■	■	■	■	■	■	■	●■
Cumulative Review									●▲■
Standardized Test Prep	▲■		▲■				▲■		▲■●
Computer Item Generator	Can be used to create custom-made practice or assessment at any time.								

▲ = Student Edition   ■ = Teacher's Edition   ● = Teaching Resources

Checkpoints

Alternative Assessment

Chapter Assessment

Available in both Form A and Form B

Making the Right Connections

Mathematics is imbedded in nearly every walk of life. The National Council of Teachers of Mathematics (NCTM) encourages educators to recognize these connections and to emphasize them for the purpose of better educating students for success in life and in a global economy. The **Connections** chart below highlights these connections for Chapter 2.

CONNECTIONS

Lesson	Interdisciplinary Connections	Career Prep	Other Real World Connections	Math Integration	NCTM Standards
Chapter Project	History				Problem Solving Communication Algebra Logical Reasoning
2-1	Music	Construction Design	Furniture Design Grand Piano Weaving	Algebra Spherical Geometry Probability	Problem Solving Communication Algebra Logical Reasoning
2-2	Drama	Industry Marketing	Manufacturing Design Theater-in-the-Round	Probability Data Analysis	Problem Solving Communication Algebra Logical Reasoning
2-3	Writing	Architecture	Building Cycling Lines of Longitude	Data Analysis Algebra Mental Math	Problem Solving Communication Algebra Logical Reasoning
2-4	Art History Science	Industry	Cubism	Algebra	Problem Solving Communication Algebra Logical Reasoning
2-5	Economics Computer Science	Marketing Research	Printing Travel Amusement Parks Satellites	Algebra Statistics	Problem Solving Communication Algebra Logical Reasoning
2-6	Art	Science	Photography Rocketry	Fractals	Problem Solving Communication Algebra Logical Reasoning
2-7	Writing Design	Industrial Design Engineering	Movies Building	Probability	Problem Solving Communication Algebra Logical Reasoning

CONNECTING TO PRIOR LEARNING Ask students for examples of geometric shapes they can see in the classroom or outside the window. Discuss why certain objects may be the shape they are. For example, ask: *Why is a cup or glass round? Why does cereal come in rectangular boxes? Why are roofs triangular-shaped?*

CULTURAL CONNECTIONS The ancient Chinese game of tangrams is classified as a "packing problem." The object of such puzzles is to "pack" a number of pieces into a specified shape or container. Ask students if they have ever played the "15-puzzle," the goal of which is to arrange square tiles numbered 1–15 in increasing order in a 4-by-4 square tray.

INTERDISCIPLINARY CONNECTIONS Computers can be programmed "to play" games such as nim and tic-tac-toe. Because no perfect strategy is known for chess, a computer can be programmed to play skillfully but, as of yet, has not been able to win consistently against chess champions. Students may want to research the success of chess-playing computers.

Technology Options

Prentice Hall Technology

Video
Video Field Trip 2, "Mazed and Confused," a visit to a topiary maze

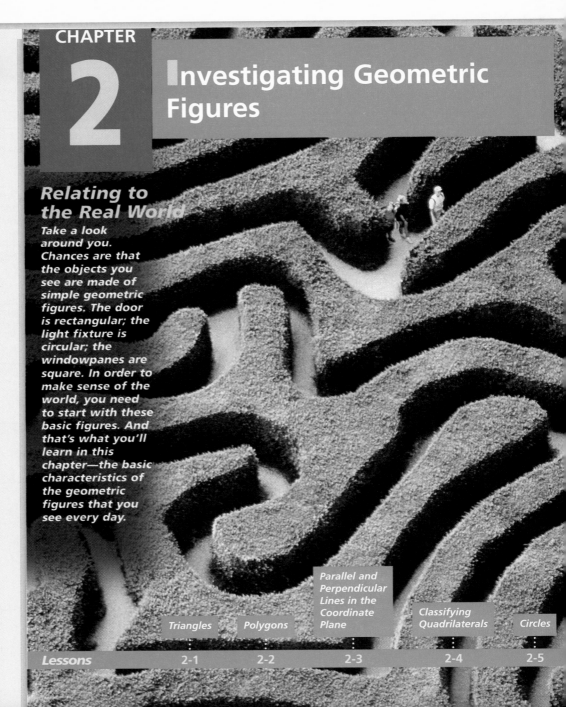

CHAPTER

2 ▌Investigating Geometric Figures

Relating to the Real World

Take a look around you. Chances are that the objects you see are made of simple geometric figures. The door is rectangular; the light fixture is circular; the windowpanes are square. In order to make sense of the world, you need to start with these basic figures. And that's what you'll learn in this chapter—the basic characteristics of the geometric figures that you see every day.

Lessons	2-1	2-2	2-3	2-4	2-5
	Triangles	Polygons	Parallel and Perpendicular Lines in the Coordinate Plane	Classifying Quadrilaterals	Circles

ABOUT THE PROJECT The Chapter Project gives students an opportunity to manipulate geometric figures by creating and solving shape puzzles in order to see how the figures relate to each other. In the Find Out questions found throughout the chapter, students create tangram pieces and use them to form triangles, quadrilaterals, pentagons, and hexagons. Students then create pentominoes and use them to make rectangles. Students also create Soma pieces, three-dimensional figures made out of cubes.

Launching the Project

PROJECT NOTEBOOK Encourage students to keep all project-related materials in a separate folder or notebook. **See Chapter Project and Scoring Rubric in Chapter Support File.**

- Ask students to give examples of games they have played that involve geometric shapes (e.g., checkers, Chinese checkers, Jenga®).
- Have students create magic squares by placing the numbers 1–9 in the squares of a 3-by-3 grid so that all the rows, columns, and diagonals have the same sum.
- Have students cut a paper square along its two diagonals. Then have them describe shapes they can make with two, three, and four pieces.

TRACKING THE PROJECT You may wish to have students read Finishing the Project on page 116 to help them get an overview of the project. Set benchmark deadlines for students to show their work in progress.

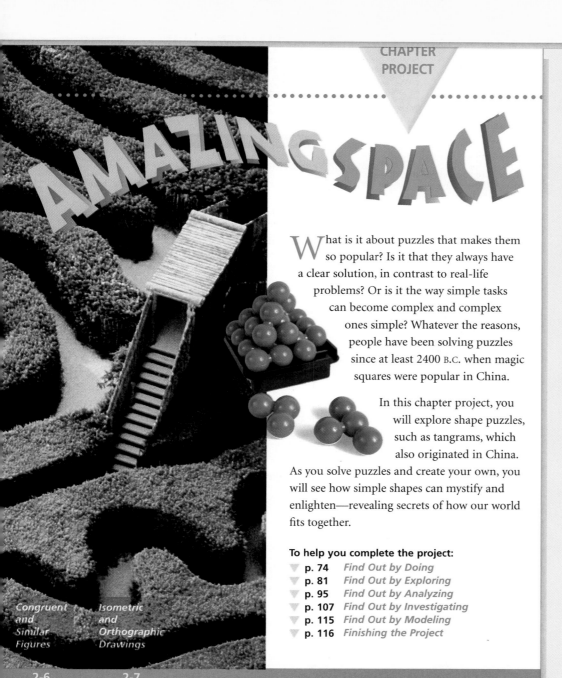

CHAPTER PROJECT

AMAZING SPACE

What is it about puzzles that makes them so popular? Is it that they always have a clear solution, in contrast to real-life problems? Or is it the way simple tasks can become complex and complex ones simple? Whatever the reasons, people have been solving puzzles since at least 2400 B.C. when magic squares were popular in China.

In this chapter project, you will explore shape puzzles, such as tangrams, which also originated in China. As you solve puzzles and create your own, you will see how simple shapes can mystify and enlighten—revealing secrets of how our world fits together.

To help you complete the project:

▽ **p. 74** *Find Out by Doing*
▽ **p. 81** *Find Out by Exploring*
▽ **p. 95** *Find Out by Analyzing*
▽ **p. 107** *Find Out by Investigating*
▽ **p. 115** *Find Out by Modeling*
▽ **p. 116** *Finishing the Project*

Congruent and Similar Figures

Isometric and Orthographic Drawings

2-6   2-7

▼ Project Resources

Teaching Resources
Chapter Support File, Ch. 2
- Chapter Project Manager and Scoring Rubric

Transparencies
30

▼ Using the Rubric

Sharing the scoring rubric for the project with your students will alert them to your expectations before they begin work on the project.

As students complete each Find Out question in the chapter, you may wish to have them evaluate their own work or a partner's work based on the scoring rubric. Students should have the opportunity to revise their work after it has been reviewed.

Name _____ Class _____ Date _____
Chapter Project Manager
Chapter 2 Puzzling Pieces

67

PROBLEM OF THE DAY

The area of one tangram piece is given. Find the total area of all seven pieces.

16 square units

←1 sq unit

Problem of the Day is also available in Transparencies.

CONNECTING TO PRIOR KNOWLEDGE Ask students to draw one triangle with three sides of equal length, one with two sides of equal length, and one with no sides of equal length. Then have them classify each angle of the triangles.

WORK TOGETHER

ALTERNATIVE METHOD Use geometry software to construct a triangle and measure its angles. Use the calculator function of the software to find the sum of the measures of the angles. The sum will be about 180. Have students drag any vertex of the triangle and observe the change in angle measures as well as the constancy of their sum.

Have students draw triangles beginning with any size angle so they can see that the sum is independent of the different types of angles used.

Lesson Planning Options

Prerequisite Skills

• Solving one-variable equations
• Recognizing supplementary and vertical angles

Assignment Options for Exercises On Your Own

To provide flexible scheduling, this lesson can be subdivided into parts.

 Core 10–17, 21–22, 25–28
Extension 29

 Core 1–9, 18–20, 23
Extension 24, 30–34

Use Mixed Review to maintain skills.

Resources

📖 **Student Edition**

Skills Handbook, p. 652
Extra Practice, p. 635
Glossary/Study Guide

📦 **Teaching Resources**

Chapter Support File, Ch. 2
• Practice 2-1 (two worksheets)
• Reteaching 2-1
• Alternative Activity 2-1
Classroom Manager 2-1
Glossary, Spanish Resources

 Transparencies
31, 35, 36

What You'll Learn

• Finding the measures of angles of a triangle
• Classifying triangles

...And Why

To increase your knowledge of triangles, the simplest polygons used in the design of furniture, buildings, and bridges

What You'll Need

• scissors
• protractor

🖥 **TECHNOLOGY HINT**

The Work Together could be done using geometry software.

1. The three angles form a straight angle.
2. The sum of measures of angles of a triangle is 180.

Connections 🌐 **Furniture Design . . . and more**

2-1 Triangles

WORK TOGETHER

Work in a group to explore the angle measures of triangles.

▪ Have each member of your group draw and cut out a large triangle.
▪ Number the angles and tear them off.
▪ Place the three angles adjacent to each other to form one angle.

1. Compare your results with group members. Describe your observations.
   See left.
2. Make a **conjecture** about the sum of the measures of the angles of a triangle.
   See left.

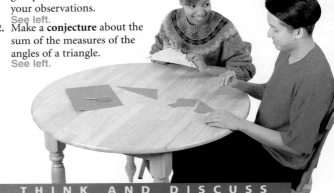

THINK AND DISCUSS

Part 1 The Triangle Angle-Sum Theorem

The Work Together demonstrates the following theorem that you will prove in Chapter 7.

Theorem 2-1
Triangle Angle-Sum Theorem

The sum of the measures of the angles of a triangle is 180.

$$m\angle A + m\angle B + m\angle C = 180$$

3. **Try This** Find the measure of each numbered angle.

a.
80
1
35° 65°

b.
118 26°
2 36°

c.
32 58°
3

ERROR ALERT! Question 3 Some students may be confused by the three numbers in the triangle thinking that they are all angle measures. **Remediation:** Point out that the numbers 1, 2, and 3 are used to name the angles and are not measures.

Question 5b Some students may recognize that $x = y$ because the angles are vertical angles and thus congruent. Others may use the Congruent Supplements Theorem to explain why $x = y$.

ESL To help students remember the meaning of *remote interior angle,* use the word remote in other contexts, such as a remote island or a television remote control.

VISUAL LEARNING Question 6 You may want to have students trace their triangles first, then cut out two remote interior angles. Arranging the cut-outs on their original drawings may help students see more clearly the relationship between the exterior angle and the remote interior angles.

Example 1

Discuss with students other ways to find the values of *y* and *z*. For example, *z* can be found by setting the sum of the angle measures of △*FGH* equal to 180 and solving for *z*. Once *z* is found, set the sum of the angle measures of △*JGH* equal to 180 and solve for *y*.

Example 1

Find the values of x, y, and z.

To find the value of x, use △*FJG*.

$65 + 39 + x = 180$	Triangle Angle-Sum Theorem
$104 + x = 180$	Simplify.
$x = 76$	Subtract 104 from each side.

To find the value of y, look at ∠*FJH*. It is a straight angle.

$m\angle GJF + m\angle GJH = 180$	Angle Addition Postulate
$76 + y = 180$	Substitution
$y = 104$	Subtract 76 from each side.

To find the value of z, use △*GJH*.

$104 + 21 + z = 180$	Triangle Angle-Sum Theorem
$125 + z = 180$	Simplify the left side.
$z = 55$	Subtract 125 from each side.

PROBLEM SOLVING

Look Back Check your answers by finding the sum of the measures of the angles in each triangle.

4. $m\angle F + m\angle FGH + m\angle H$
$= 180;$
$65 + (39 + 21) + z = 180;$
$z = 55$

4. Critical Thinking Describe how you could use △*FGH* instead of △*GJH* to find the value of z. **See left.**

5. Try This Find the values of x and y.

a.
$x = 50; y = 20$

b.
$x = 56; y = 56$

Part 2 Exterior Angles of a Triangle

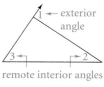
remote interior angles

An **exterior angle** of a polygon is an angle formed by a side and an extension of a side. For each exterior angle of a triangle, the two non-adjacent interior angles are called its **remote interior angles.**

∠2 and ∠3 cover ∠1 without overlapping.

6. a. Manipulatives Draw and label a large triangle like the one shown at the left. Cut out the two remote interior angles and place them on the exterior angle as shown. What do you observe?

b. Make a **conjecture** about the measure of an exterior angle of a triangle. **The measure of an exterior angle of a triangle = the sum of the measures of its 2 remote interior angles.**

Your **conjecture** in Question 6 is the basis of the following theorem, which you will justify in Exercise 32.

Additional Examples

FOR EXAMPLE 1

Find the values of x, y, and z.
$x = 30, y = 70, z = 20$

Discussion: *Is it possible to find z without knowing the value of x? without knowing the value of y?*

FOR EXAMPLE 2

Refer to the diagram in Example 2. If $m\angle NGL = 30$ and $m\angle GNL = 110$, find $m\angle 1$. **140**

Discussion: *Can you think of other real-world examples similar to Example 2?*

Exterior Angle Theorem Exercise 32 provides an opportunity for students to complete a proof of this theorem.

Question 7 You may want to have students find the measures of all six exterior angles of each triangle. Point out that the angle formed by the extensions of two sides is not an exterior angle.

Example 2 **Relating to the Real World**
Discuss with students the greatest and least possible measures of ∠1 and what the chair would look like when ∠1 has these measures.

For Exercises 5–8, students may draw the triangles using a drawing program or geometry software. For Exercise 34b, students may create their designs using a drawing program or geometry software.

Prentice Hall Technology

 Software
- Secondary Math Lab Toolkit™
- Computer Item Generator 2-1

 CD-ROM
- Multimedia Geometry Lab 2

 Internet
- See the Prentice Hall site. (http://www.phschool.com)

70

Theorem 2-2
Exterior Angle Theorem

The measure of each exterior angle of a triangle equals the sum of the measures of its two remote interior angles.

$$m\angle 1 = m\angle 2 + m\angle 3$$

7. Try This Find the measure of each numbered exterior angle.

a.
70 40° 1 30°

b.
113 2 70° 43°

c.
90 45° 45° 3

A **corollary** is a statement that follows directly from a theorem. The following statement is a corollary to the Exterior Angle Theorem.

Corollary to Theorem 2-2

The measure of an exterior angle of a triangle is greater than the measure of either of its remote interior angles.

$$m\angle 1 > m\angle 2 \text{ and } m\angle 1 > m\angle 3$$

8. Use what you know from the Exterior Angle Theorem to explain why this corollary makes sense. *m∠1 = m∠2 + m∠3.* **All the measures are pos. numbers so m∠1 > m∠2 and > m∠3.**

Example 2 **Relating to the Real World**

Furniture Design The lounge chair has different settings that change the angle between the seat and the back. Find the angle at which the chair in the diagram at the left is reclining.

$m\angle 1 = m\angle LGN + m\angle GNL$	Exterior Angle Theorem
$m\angle 1 = 56 + 78$	Substitution
$m\angle 1 = 134$	Simplify.

The chair is reclining at a 134° angle.

9. Explain how you could have found *m∠1* without using the Exterior Angle Theorem. **See below.**

10. Try This You change the setting on the chair so that *m∠NGL = 90* and *m∠ GNL = 45*. Find the angle at which the chair is reclining. **135°**

9. Use the Triangle Angle-Sum Thm. to find m∠NLG. Then subtract m∠NLG from 180.

AUDITORY LEARNING Working with a partner, have one student describe a triangle using the vocabulary presented on page 71. The other student should sketch the triangle. Then have students switch roles and repeat the activity.

Question 11c At this point in the text, students do not know that equilateral implies equiangular. However, students will easily discover through drawing that an obtuse equilateral triangle is impossible.

Exercises 5–8 You may want students to label angle measures and side lengths in their triangles.

LOGICAL REASONING Exercise 9 Students can use a sketch to illustrate their answers but justifications should be based on definitions, postulates, theorems, and corollaries.

Exercises 1–4 Students should measure the sides and angles carefully. They can check for angle-measurement error by finding the sum of the three angle measures.

Classifying Triangles

In Chapter 1, you classified an angle by its measure. You can classify a triangle by its sides and by its angles.

equilateral
all sides congruent

isosceles
at least two sides congruent

scalene
no sides congruent

equiangular
all angles congruent

acute
all angles acute

right
one right angle

obtuse
one obtuse angle

11. Try This Draw and label a triangle to fit each description. If no triangle can be drawn, write *not possible* and explain.
 a. acute scalene **b.** right isosceles
 c. obtuse equilateral **d.** acute isosceles
 a–d. See margin.

Use a protractor and a centimeter ruler to measure the sides and angles of each triangle. Classify each triangle by its sides and angles.

1.

2.

3.

4.

acute isosceles   equiangular equilateral   right scalene   obtuse isosceles

Sketch a triangle to fit each description. If no triangle can be drawn, write *not possible* and explain. 5, 7–8. See margin for samples.

5. obtuse scalene **6.** right equilateral **7.** acute equilateral **8.** obtuse isosceles
        Not possible; an equilateral triangle is acute.

9. a. *Logical Reasoning* What is the measure of each angle of an equilateral triangle? **Justify** your reasoning.   60; the sum of measures is 180 and the 3 measures are =.
 b. What is the sum of the measures of the acute angles of a right triangle? **Justify** your reasoning.   90; the sum of measures is 180 and the measure of the 3rd angle is 90.

---

pages 68–71   Think and Discuss
11a. Sample: **b.** Sample:

c. Not possible; an equilateral triangle is acute.

d. Sample:

pages 71–74   On Your Own
5.   **7.**

8.

---

23. Yes; no; every equilateral △ has three ≅ sides, so at least 2 sides are always ≅; in an isosceles △ 2 sides are ≅ but they need not be ≅ to the 3rd side.

26. Answers may vary. Sample: The ratio of the angle measures of an isosceles right triangle is 1:1:2. The ratio of the length of the sides is not 1:1:2.

Choose Use paper and pencil, mental math, or a calculator to find the values of the variables.

10.
30   117°   x°   33°

11.
115.5   128.5°   s°   13°

12.
52.5   75°   x°

13.
t = 60; w = 60
w°   t°   30°

14.
x = 38;
y = 36;
z = 90
y° x°   54°   z°   52°

15.
83.1   52.2°   44.7°   w°

16.
y = 88;
z = 92
45°   z° y°   47°

17.
e°   d°   32°   c°   b°   55°   a°
a = 67;
b = 58; c = 125;
d = 23; e = 90

Use the figure at the right for Exercises 18–20.

18. Find m∠3 if m∠5 = 130 and m∠4 = 70. **60**

19. Find m∠1 if m∠5 = 142 and m∠4 = 65. **103**

20. Find m∠2 if m∠3 = 125 and m∠4 = 23. **32**

5   2   4   3   1

21. **Standardized Test Prep** The measures of the angles of a triangle are shown below. In which case is *x not* an integer? **C**
    A. *x*, 2*x*, 3*x*   B. *x*, 3*x*, 5*x*   C. *x*, 3*x*, 4*x*   D. *x*, 4*x*, 7*x*   E. 2*x*, 3*x*, 4*x*

22. The measure of one angle of a triangle is 115. The other two angles are congruent. Find their measures. **32.5**

23. **Writing** Is every equilateral triangle isosceles? Is every isosceles triangle equilateral? Explain. **See margin.**

24. **Algebra** A right triangle has acute angles whose measures are in the ratio 1 : 2. Find the measures of these angles. (*Hint:* Let *x* and 2*x* represent the angle measures.) **30, 60**

25. **Music** The top of a grand piano is held open by props of varying lengths, depending upon the desired volume of the music. The longest prop makes an angle of 57° with the piano. What is the angle of opening between the piano and its top? **33°**

26. **Critical Thinking** Rosa makes the following claim: The ratio of the lengths of the three sides of a triangle equals the ratio of the three angle measures. Give examples to support her claim or one counterexample to disprove it. **See margin.**

57°

72

ALGEBRA Exercise 30 You may want to remind students to look at the hint for Exercise 24.

PROBABILITY Exercise 31 Students will need to have answered Exercise 9a correctly to solve this problem.

LOGICAL REASONING Exercise 32 You may want students to rewrite the Exterior Angle Theorem followed by the completed statements a–d.

Exercise 33 You may need to review with students how to solve equations of the form $\sqrt{x} = a$.

OPEN-ENDED Exercise 34b Students may want to color their designs and display them in the classroom.

Algebra **Find the measures of the angles of each triangle. Classify each triangle by its angles.**

27. 37, 78, 65; acute

$(2x + 4)°$

$(2x - 9)°$ $x°$

28. 35, 55; right

$(8x - 1)°$

$(4x + 7)°$

29. *Geometry on a Sphere* Suppose you were measuring the angles of a triangle on a globe. The meridians of longitude pass through both poles and are perpendicular to the equator. Will the sum of the measures of the angles of this triangle be equal to, greater than, or less than 180? Explain.   > 180; measures of both angles at the equator = 90 and the angle at the pole has pos. measure.

30. a. *Algebra* The ratio of the angle measures in △BCR is 2 : 3 : 4. Find the angle measures.   40, 60, 80
b. What type of triangle is △BCR?   acute

31. a. *Probability* Find the probability that a triangle is equiangular if the measure of each of its angles is a multiple of 30. $\frac{1}{3}$
b. Find the probability that a triangle is equiangular if the measure of each of its angles is a multiple of 20. $\frac{1}{7}$

PROBLEM SOLVING HINT
Make a table showing all possibilities.

32. *Logical Reasoning* Complete the following statements to **justify** the Exterior Angle Theorem.
a. By the Angle Addition Postulate, $m\angle 1 + m\angle 4 = $ ■.   180
b. By the Triangle Angle-Sum Theorem, $m\angle 2 + m\angle 3 + m\angle 4 = $ ■.   180
c. By the __?__ Property, $m\angle 1 + m\angle 4 = m\angle 2 + m\angle 3 + m\angle 4$.   Substitution
d. By the __?__ Property of Equality, $m\angle 1 = m\angle 2 + m\angle 3$.   Subtraction

33. The measures of the angles of △RST are $\sqrt{x}$, $2\sqrt{x}$, and $3\sqrt{x}$.
a. Find the value of x and the measures of the angles.   900; 30, 60, 90
b. What type of triangle is △RST?   right

34. *Weaving* Patricia Tsinnie, a Navajo weaver, often uses isosceles triangles in her designs.   34a–b. Check students' work.
a. Trace the design shown below. Then use a colored pencil to outline isosceles triangles used in the design.
b. *Open-ended* Make a repeated design of your own that uses isosceles triangles.

73

FIND OUT BY DOING After students make a set of tans, they may want to trace the pieces onto poster board and store them in a plastic bag for future use. Remind students to keep their Find Out exercise work in one place so they can complete the Chapter Project.

Wrap Up

THE BIG IDEA Ask students: *Describe how triangles are classified.*

RETEACHING ACTIVITY Students use theorems to find missing angle measures in a rectangle, then classify the triangles they find. (Reteaching worksheet 2-1)

Exercises   MIXED REVIEW

Exercise 39 Make sure students read the problem carefully and do not assume that $\angle AOC$ is a right angle.

GETTING READY FOR LESSON 2-2 These exercises prepare students to find the sum of the measures of the angles of a polygon.

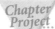

Lesson Quiz

Lesson Quiz is also available in Transparencies.

1. Find the value of *x*. **40**

2. Find the value of *y*. **140**

3. Classify △*AED* by its sides and angles. **right scalene**

4. Draw an isosceles triangle.
   Check students' work.

74

Find Out by Doing

The *tangram,* known in China as the *ch'i-ch'iao t'u,* meaning "ingenious seven-piece plan," is one of the oldest manipulative puzzles. You can use paper folding to make your own tangram.

• Fold a square sheet of paper in half four times and then unfold it. Draw the segments shown to form seven tangram pieces, called *tans.*

• Cut out the seven tans.

How many of the tans are triangles? Form other triangles by placing tans together. Make a sketch of each. Classify each triangle by its sides and angles. Can you make one triangle using all seven tans?

5; all triangles are right isosceles; yes

Exercises   MIXED REVIEW

Draw the next figure in each sequence.

35.

36.

▦ **Find the length of $\overline{WZ}$ to the nearest tenth.**

37. *W*(8, −2) and *Z*(2, 6) **10.0**

38. *W*(−4.5, 1.2) and *Z*(3.5, −2.8) **8.9**

39. In the figure, $m\angle AOB = 3x + 20$, $m\angle BOC = x + 32$, and $m\angle AOC = 80$. Find the value of *x*. **7**

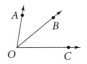

Getting Ready for Lesson 2-2

Find (a) the measure of each angle of quadrilateral *ABCD,* and (b) the sum of the measures of the angles of quadrilateral *ABCD.*

40.

41.

42.

40a. 77, 87, 131, 65
b. 360

41a. 60, 120, 60, 120
b. 360

42a. 90, 140, 60, 70
b. 360

Students use geometry software to explore the exterior angles of a polygon. The software enables students to manipulate the polygon while observing that the sum of the exterior angles remains the same. The Polygon Exterior Angle-Sum Theorem is formally presented in Lesson 2-2.

Construct

ERROR ALERT! Students may extend each side of the polygon in more than one direction. **Remediation:** Make sure students extend each side in only one direction so that there is only one exterior angle at each vertex.

Investigate

Remind students what it means for a polygon to be convex.

Conjecture

Students may want to compare their results with others, before making their conjectures.

Extend

If possible, have students use software to decrease the size of the polygon as shown in the diagrams.

ADDITIONAL PROBLEM Have students repeat the *Construct* and *Investigate* activities with other polygons to verify their conjectures.

Math ToolboX — Technology

Exploring the Exterior Angles of a Polygon

With Lesson 2-2

Work in pairs or small groups.

Construct

Use geometry software. Construct a convex polygon. Extend each side as shown. To measure the exterior angles you will need to mark a point on each ray.

> Check students' work.

Investigate

- Measure each exterior angle.

- Calculate the sum of the measures of the exterior angles.   360

- Manipulate the polygon, making sure it remains convex. Observe the sum of the measures of the exterior angles.

Conjecture

- Write a conjecture about the sum of the measures of the exterior angles (one at each vertex) of a convex polygon.
  > The sum of measures of the exterior angles of a polygon is always 360.
- Test your conjecture with another polygon.

Extend

The figures below show a polygon that is decreasing in size until finally it "disappears." Describe how these figures could be used as a justification for your conjecture.

> When the polygon "disappears," the angles become adjacent. The sum of their measures is 360.

Materials and Manipulatives

- Geometry software

Transparencies
13

PROBLEM OF THE DAY

How many isosceles triangles are in the diagram? 60

Problem of the Day is also available in Transparencies.

ESL Begin by drawing some familiar examples of polygons such as triangles, squares, and regular pentagons. Then sketch figures that are not polygons and discuss why they are not polygons.

Students may wonder why the 11-gon is not in the list of polygons. An 11-gon, also called an undecagon, is not very common. Also point out that *n*-gon is the term used when the number of sides is not known.

CONNECTING TO PRIOR KNOWLEDGE Ask students to list words beginning with the prefixes *tri-*, *quad-*, *pent-*, and *oct-*. Examples include triathlon, quadriplegic, pentameter, and octopus. Discuss the meanings of the words and prefixes.

Lesson Planning Options

Prerequisite Skills

- Applying the Triangle Angle-Sum Theorem
- Solving one-variable equations

Assignment Options for Exercises On Your Own

To provide flexible scheduling, this lesson can be subdivided into parts.

1 **Core** 1–9, 28–29
Extension 27, 30

2 **Core** 10–17, 19–26
Extension 18

Use Mixed Review to maintain skills.

Resources

 Student Edition

Skills Handbook, p. 656
Extra Practice, p. 635
Glossary/Study Guide

 Teaching Resources

Chapter Support File, Ch. 2
- Practice 2-2 (two worksheets)
- Reteaching 2-2
- Alternative Activity 2-2
Classroom Manager 2-2
Glossary, Spanish Resources

 Transparencies
13, 31

What You'll Learn
- Classifying polygons
- Finding the sum of the measures of the interior and exterior angles of polygons

...And Why

To increase your understanding of polygons, which are found in art and nature as well as in manufactured products

Polygon	Number of Sides
triangle	3
quadrilateral	4
pentagon	5
hexagon	6
heptagon	7
octagon	8
nonagon	9
decagon	10
dodecagon	12
n-gon	*n*

QUICK REVIEW

A diagonal of a polygon is a segment that connects two nonconsecutive vertices.

Connections **Manufacturing . . . and more**

2-2 **P**olygons

THINK AND DISCUSS

Part 1

Polygons and Interior Angles

Walking around a city, you can see polygons in buildings, windows, and traffic signs. The grillwork in the photo is a combination of different polygons that form a pleasing pattern.

A **polygon** is a closed plane figure with at least three sides. The sides intersect only at their endpoints and no adjacent sides are collinear. To identify a polygon, start at any vertex and list the other vertices consecutively.

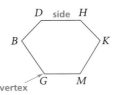

polygon *DHKMGB*

sides: $\overline{DH}, \overline{HK}, \overline{KM}, \overline{MG}, \overline{GB}, \overline{BD}$
vertices: *D, H, K, M, G, B*
angles: $\angle D, \angle H, \angle K, \angle M, \angle G, \angle B$

You can classify polygons by the number of sides. The most common polygons are listed at the left.

A polygon is **convex** if no diagonal contains points outside the polygon.

A polygon is **concave** if a diagonal contains points outside the polygon.

In this textbook, the term *polygon* refers to a convex polygon unless otherwise stated.

1. *Open-ended* Draw a convex and a concave octagon. Draw diagonals and explain why one octagon is convex and the other is concave.
   See back of book.

AUDITORY LEARNING Using the polygons on page 76, have students practice naming polygons, sides, and vertices. You may want to point out that the vertex they start with does not matter but that naming the vertices consecutively does.

WORK TOGETHER

VISUAL LEARNING After students have sketched the polygons, have them use shading to indicate the interior angles. After dividing the polygons into triangles, have them use a different color shading for all the angles in each triangle. This will help convince students that the sum of the measures of the angles of the triangles equals the sum of the measures of the interior angles of the polygon.

Polygon Interior Angle-Sum Theorem Remind students that if they ever forget the formula given in this theorem, they can always use the method from the Work Together to find the sum of the measures of the angles.

Question 3 Point out to students that using the Polygon Interior Angle-Sum Theorem takes less than drawing the polygons and their diagonals.

Example 1

ESTIMATION To check that the answer is reasonable, have students estimate that the sum of $m\angle T$, $m\angle R$, $m\angle V$, and $m\angle M$ which is about 400, so $m\angle Y$ should be about 140.

WORK TOGETHER

You can use triangles and the Triangle Angle-Sum Theorem to find the measures of the interior angles of a polygon. Work with a partner. Record your data in a table like the one shown below.

- Sketch polygons with 4, 5, 6, 7, and 8 sides.

- Divide each polygon into triangles by drawing all the diagonals from one vertex.

- Multiply the number of triangles by 180 to find the sum of the measures of the interior angles of each polygon.

2. **Inductive Reasoning** Look for a pattern in the table. Write a rule for finding the sum of the measures of the interior angles of a polygon with n sides. **See margin p. 79.**

Polygon	Number of Sides	Number of Triangles Formed	Sum of the Interior Angle Measures
⬜	4	▪	▪ • 180 = ▪

THINK AND DISCUSS

The results of the Work Together suggest the following theorem.

Theorem 2-3
Polygon Interior Angle-Sum Theorem

The sum of the measures of the interior angles of an n-gon is $(n - 2)180$.

3. **Try This** Find the sum of the measures of the interior angles of each polygon.
   a. 15-gon **2340**
   b. 20-gon **3240**
   c. decagon **1440**
   d. dodecagon **1800**

Example 1

Find $m\angle Y$ in *TVYMR*.

Use the Polygon Interior Angle-Sum Theorem for $n = 5$.

$m\angle T + m\angle V + m\angle Y + m\angle M + m\angle R = (5 - 2)180$
$90 + 90 + m\angle Y + 90 + 135 = 540$
$m\angle Y + 405 = 540$
$m\angle Y = 135$

Additional Examples

FOR EXAMPLE 1

If $m\angle B = m\angle D$, find $m\angle B$ in *ABCD*.
$m\angle A + m\angle B + m\angle C + m\angle D =$
$(4 - 2)180$

$100 + m\angle B + 40 + m\angle D$	$= 360$
$m\angle B + m\angle D + 140$	$= 360$
$m\angle B + m\angle D$	$= 220$
$2m\angle B$	$= 220$
$m\angle B$	$= 110$

Discussion: *What theorem did you apply to find $m\angle B$?*

FOR EXAMPLE 2

Find the measures of an interior and an exterior angle of a regular hexagon. **Measure of one exterior angle = 60; measure of one interior angle = 120.**

Discussion: *Which method did you use? Why?*

77

Question 4 The Toolbox on page 75 provides a direct way for students to investigate the sum of the exterior angles of a polygon using geometry software.

ALTERNATIVE METHOD Have students draw a polygon with one exterior angle at each vertex. Then have them cut out the exterior angles and tape the vertices together. Ask students to make a conjecture about the sum of the exterior angles of a polygon based on their taped figures.

KINESTHETIC LEARNING Use masking tape to make a large polygon on the floor showing one exterior angle at each vertex. Have students start at one vertex and walk around the polygon in the direction of the exterior angles. When the students return to the starting point, they have made five turns totaling 360°.

Technology Options

For Exercises 5–8, students may use geometry software to draw the polygons. For Exercise 27, students may use a graphing calculator or other graphing software to draw the scatter plot.

Prenetice Hall Technology

 Software
- Secondary Math Lab Toolkit™
- Computer Item Generator 2-2

 CD-ROM
- Multimedia Geometry Lab 2

 Internet
- See the Prentice Hall site. (http://www.phschool.com)

78

Part 2 **Exterior Angles**

Technology The figures below show one exterior angle drawn at each vertex of each polygon.

4. a. Find the sum of the measures of the exterior angles (one at each vertex) of each polygon. 360; 360; 360

b. Make a conjecture about the sum of the measures of the exterior angles (one at each vertex) of a polygon.

The sum of measures of exterior angles of a polygon is 360.

This inductive reasoning leads to the following theorem.

Theorem 2-4
Polygon Exterior Angle-Sum Theorem

The sum of the measures of the exterior angles of a polygon, one at each vertex, is 360.

An **equilateral polygon** has all sides congruent. An **equiangular polygon** has all angles congruent. A **regular polygon** is equilateral and equiangular.

Example 2

Find the measure of an interior angle and an exterior angle of a regular octagon.

Method 1: Find the measure of an interior angle first.

Sum of the measures of the interior angles =
$(8 - 2)180 = 1080$

- Measure of one interior angle = $\frac{1080}{8} = 135$
- Measure of its adjacent exterior angle = $180 - 135 = 45$

Method 2: Find the measure of an exterior angle first.

Sum of the measures of the exterior angles = 360

- Measure of one exterior angle = $\frac{360}{8} = 45$
- Measure of its adjacent interior angle = $180 - 45 = 135$

5. Try This Find the measure of an interior angle and an exterior angle of a regular dodecagon. 150; 30

Regular Octagon

Example 2

Two methods are presented for finding the solution. Take time to discuss both methods and why each works.

Question 5 You may want to provide students with a visual model of a regular dodecagon. Use the method described in Exercises 5–8 to prepare one in advance on a transparency.

Example 3 Relating to the Real World

Help students see that the four right triangles are congruent. Also emphasize that ∠1 is an exterior angle but ∠2 is not, and check that they understand why.

Exercises ON YOUR OWN

MAKING CONNECTIONS Exercises 1–4 A diamond cutter uses diamonds to cut another diamond so that the flat surfaces of the diamond are polygons. Some of the more popular cuts are the "brilliant cut," "oval cut," "marquise cut," and "pear cut."

Exercises 5–8 These exercises provide a good opportunity for students to work in groups. Students should draw a point on a piece of paper, then use two protractors to form a circle.

Example 3 Relating to the Real World

Manufacturing Mindco, a toy manufacturer, is packaging a Chinese checkers game. The game consists of colored pegs and a regular hexagonal wooden board. Mindco is packaging the game in a rectangular box using four right triangles made of foam. Find the measures of the acute angles of each foam triangle.

∠1 is an exterior angle of a regular hexagon.

Find $m\angle 1$ and then use the Triangle Angle-Sum Theorem to find $m\angle 2$.

$6 \cdot m\angle 1 = 360$	Sum of the measures of the exterior ∠s of a polygon = 360.
$m\angle 1 = 60$	Divide each side by 6.
$m\angle 1 + m\angle 2 + 90 = 180$	Triangle Angle-Sum Thm.
$60 + m\angle 2 + 90 = 180$	Substitution
$m\angle 2 + 150 = 180$	Simplify.
$m\angle 2 = 30$	Subtract 150 from each side.

The measures of the acute angles of each foam triangle are 60 and 30.

page 77 Work Together

2.	4	2	2 • 180 = 360
	5	3	3 • 180 = 540
	6	4	4 • 180 = 720
	7	5	5 • 180 = 900
	8	6	6 • 180 = 1080

The sum of measures of interior angles of an n-gon is $(n - 2) \cdot 180$.

pages 79–81 On Your Own

5.   6.

7.   8.

Exercises ON YOUR OWN

Classify each polygon by its number of sides. Identify which polygons are convex and which are concave.

1.
convex dodecagon

2.
concave decagon

3.
convex octagon

4.
concave pentagon

Draw each regular polygon.

Sample: dodecagon   5–8. See margin.

Draw a circle. Use a protractor to locate 12 points equidistant around a circle. (These points will be located every 30 degrees around a circle, since 360° ÷ 12 = 30°.) Connect these points to form a regular dodecagon.

5. triangle   6. quadrilateral

7. pentagon   8. hexagon

27a. (20, 162), (40, 171), (60, 174), (80, 175.5), (100, 176.4), (120, 177), (140, 177.4), (160, 177.8), (180, 178), (200, 178.2)

b.

c. very close to 180
d. No; a regular polygon with all straight angles would have all its vertices on a straight line.

29a.

b.

9. *Design* A theater-in-the-round is constructed so that the audience surrounds the stage. Such theaters are not always circular in shape, however. Classify the theater-in-the-round shown in the diagram below the photo, by the number of sides. Find the measure of each numbered angle.
   octagon; $m\angle 1 = 135$; $m\angle 2 = 45$

Find the measure of an interior angle and an exterior angle for each regular polygon. $\frac{180y - 360}{y}$; $\frac{360}{y}$

10. pentagon   11. nonagon   12. 18-gon   13. y-gon
    108; 72   140; 40   160; 20

The measure of an exterior angle of a regular polygon is given. Find the number of sides.

14. 72 5   15. 36 10   16. 18 20   17. x $\frac{360}{x}$

18. *Writing* Keach said that he drew a regular polygon and measured one of its interior angles. He got 130°. Explain to him why this is impossible. **Answers may vary. Sample: The measure of the exterior angle is 50. Then the polygon must have $\frac{360}{50}$ sides. But this number is not an integer.**

Choose **Use pencil and paper, mental math, or a calculator to find the values of the variables.**

19. 102   20. 145   21.   22. 103

$y = 103; z = 70$

23. $x = 69;$ $w = 111$ 24. 60   25. 113   26. $w = 72;$ $x = 59; y = 49;$ $z = 121$

a–d. See margin.

27. a. *Calculator* Find the measure of an interior angle of a regular n-gon for $n = 20, 40, 60, 80, \ldots 200$. Record your results as ordered pairs (n, measure of each interior angle).
     b. Show your results on a graph like the one at the right.
     c. *Data Analysis* What predictions would you make about the measure of an interior angle of a regular 1000-gon?
     d. Is there a regular n-gon with an interior angle of 180°? Explain.

28. *Probability* Find the probability that the measure of an interior angle of a regular n-gon is a positive integer if n is an integer and $3 \leq n \leq 12.\frac{4}{5}$

80

GETTING READY FOR LESSON 2-3 These exercises provide practice evaluating the slope formula, which prepares students to work with slopes of parallel and perpendicular lines.

Wrap Up

THE BIG IDEA Ask students: *Restate the Polygon Interior Angle-Sum Theorem and the Polygon Exterior Angle-Sum Theorem and give an example illustrating each.*

RETEACHING ACTIVITY Students apply the Polygon Interior Angle-Sum and Polygon Exterior Angle-Sum Theorems to find the measures of interior and exterior angles of polygons. (Reteaching worksheet 2-2)

Exercises MIXED REVIEW

Exercises 35–37 You may also want students to classify each triangle according to its angle measures.

Exercise 37 Students should first solve for *x* using the Angle Addition Postulate. Then have them share their methods for finding *y*.

---

29. **a.** *Open-ended* Sketch a quadrilateral that is not equiangular. a–b. See margin p. 80.
    b. Sketch an equiangular quadrilateral that is not regular.

30. *Critical Thinking* Laura suggests another way to find the sum of the measures of the interior angles of an *n*-gon. She picks an interior point of the figure, draws segments to each vertex, counts the number of triangles, multiplies by 180, then subtracts 360. Does her method work? Explain.   Yes; the sum of measures of angles at the interior point is 360. The sum of angle measures of all the triangles is 180*n*. 180*n* − 360 = (*n* − 2) • 180

Chapter Project *Find Out by Exploring*

In 1942, two mathematicians at the University of Chekiang in China proved that only 13 convex polygons could be formed by using all 7 tans. They were able to form 1 triangle, 6 quadrilaterals, 2 pentagons, and 4 hexagons. Try to make these using your set of tans. Make a sketch of each figure. See back of book.

Exercises MIXED REVIEW

Identify the following.
31. a pair of opposite rays $\overrightarrow{RT}$ and $\overrightarrow{RK}$
32. two right angles   ∠*BRT* and ∠*BRK*
33. a pair of supplementary angles   34. a pair of complementary angles

Answers may vary. Sample: ∠*BRT* and ∠*BRK*   34. ∠*BRM* and ∠*MRK*

Choose Use paper and pencil, mental math, or a calculator to find the values of the variables.

35.
    35°   (*y* − 16)°
    3*y*°
    40.25

36.
    27.5
    (*x* + 23)° (*x* + 12)°

37.
    (2*y* − 1)°
    x°(*x* − 28)° *y*°
    x = 104; *y* = 35

38. The measure of an angle is one-third the measure of its supplement. Find the measures of the angles. 45 and 135

39. The measure of an angle is four times the measure of its complement. Find the measures of the angles. 72 and 18

Getting Ready for Lesson 2-3

Find $\frac{y_2 - y_1}{x_2 - x_1}$.

40. $(x_1, y_1) = (3, 5)$ and $(x_2, y_2) = (1, 4)$ $\frac{1}{2}$ 41. $(x_1, y_1) = (-2, 6)$ and $(x_2, y_2) = (3, 1)$ −1

42. $(x_1, y_1) = (1, -8)$ and $(x_2, y_2) = (1, 2)$ undefined 43. $(x_1, y_1) = (-5, 3)$ and $(x_2, y_2) = (1, 3)$ 0

Lesson Quiz

Lesson Quiz is also available in Transparencies.

1. Classify the polygon. heptagon

2. Find the sum of the measures of the interior angles. 900

3. Find *x*. 65

Students use graphing calculators to explore equations of lines and make conjectures about how the values of *m* and *b* in *y* = *mx* + *b* affect the graph of the line. In the Extend, students explore the slopes of parallel and perpendicular lines. These topics will be addressed formally in Lesson 2-3.

The graphing calculator enables students to graph many lines quickly so they can easily view how lines vary as the values of *m* and *b* vary.

ERROR ALERT! Students' graphing calculators may not have a zoom feature to use to create a square window.
Remediation: Have students consult the owner's manual to set the origin in the center of the viewing window.

Investigate

Students may wonder about equations of the form *y* = *x* − *b*. Help them see that every equation of that form can be rewritten as *y* = *x* + (−*b*).

Conjecture

Students can test their conjectures by graphing equations of the form *y* = *mx* + *b*.

ADDITIONAL PROBLEM Ask students to find a pair of equations whose graphs are parallel and cross the *y*-axis two units apart. Then ask students to find a pair of equations whose graphs are perpendicular and intersect at (0, 2).

Materials and Manipulatives

• Graphing calculator

 Transparencies
5, 8, 9, 10

Investigate

The value of *m* affects the steepness of the line.

Changing the value of *b* shifts the line vertically.

Conjecture

Answers may vary. Samples: A line with pos. value of *m* goes from the lower left to the upper right. The greater the abs. value of *m* the steeper the line. For neg. values of *b*, the line shifts down by the number of units = to the abs. value of *b*. The line passes through the origin if *b* = 0.

Extend

The lines are ∥; the values of *m* are =; lines with equations that have = values of *m* are ∥.

Exploring Equations of Lines

With Lesson 2-3

Work in pairs or small groups. To make sure that the viewing grid on your graphing calculator screen is square, press ZOOM 5 .

Investigate See margin.

■ Use your graphing calculator to graph the lines *y* = *x*, *y* = 2*x*, and *y* = 3*x*. Experiment with other equations of lines in the form *y* = *mx*. Substitute fractions and negative numbers for *m*. How does the value of *m* affect the graph of a line?

■ Graph the lines *y* = *x* + 1, *y* = *x* + 2, and *y* = *x* + 3. Experiment with other equations of lines in the form *y* = *x* + *b*. Substitute fractions and negative numbers for *b*. How does the value of *b* affect the graph of a line?

Conjecture See margin.

When you graph an equation in the form *y* = *mx* + *b*, how do the values of *m* and *b* affect the graph of the line? List all your **conjectures**.

Extend

■ Graph the lines $y = -\frac{2}{3}x$, $y = -\frac{2}{3}x + 3$, and $y = -\frac{2}{3}x - 2$. What appears to be true of these lines? How are the values of *m* related? Make a **conjecture** about the graphs of equations of lines where the values of *m* are the same. Test your **conjecture** by graphing several equations of lines where the values of *m* are the same. See margin.

■ Graph each pair of lines:

   a. $y = \frac{1}{2}x, y = -2x$ a–c. See back of book.
   b. $y = \frac{3}{4}x, y = -\frac{4}{3}x$
   c. $y = 5x, y = -\frac{1}{5}x$

What appears to be true of these lines? For each pair, how are the values of *m* related? Make a **conjecture** about the graphs of equations of lines where the product of the values of *m* is −1. Test your **conjecture** by graphing several pairs of equations of lines where the product of the values of *m* is −1.

PROBLEM OF THE DAY

Find the sum of the measures of the angles shown. **2880**

Problem of the Day is also available in Transparencies.

CONNECTING TO PRIOR KNOWLEDGE Have students make a table of values to graph $y = -\frac{1}{2}x + 5$ and $y = 2x - 1$. Ask them how the lines appear to be related.

VISUAL LEARNING Have students describe the appearance of the lines in each of the four graphs. Emphasize that a line with a positive slope rises *from left to right* and a line with a negative slope falls from *left to right*.

Question 1 Students will often confuse the slope of a vertical line with the slope of a horizontal line. You may need to review that $\frac{0}{1} = 0$ and $\frac{1}{0}$ is undefined. Then, for the horizontal and vertical lines shown in the diagram, have students choose two pairs of points on each and try to apply the slope formula.

MENTAL MATH Question 2b Students should be able to answer this question based on the graphs from part a.

What You'll Learn

- Graphing lines in the coordinate plane
- Recognizing parallel and perpendicular lines by their slopes

...And Why

To familiarize yourself with parallel and perpendicular lines, which are essential to the construction of houses, furniture, and machinery

What You'll Need

graph paper, ruler

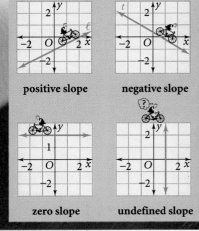

positive slope   negative slope

zero slope   undefined slope

Connections **Architecture . . . and more**

2-3 Parallel and Perpendicular Lines in the Coordinate Plane

T H I N K   A N D   D I S C U S S

Part 1 Slope and Graphing Lines

In everyday life the word *slope* refers to the steepness of a mountain, the grade of a road, or the pitch of a roof. In algebra, the *slope* of a line is the ratio of the vertical change to the horizontal change between any two points on a line.

Lesson Planning Options

Prerequisite Skills

- Recognizing that division by zero is undefined
- Recognizing equations of vertical and horizontal lines

Assignment Options for Exercises On Your Own

To provide flexible scheduling, this lesson can be subdivided into parts.

▼ **Core** 1–3, 23
   Extension 26, 29

▼ **Core** 4–22, 24–25
   Extension 27–28

Use Mixed Review to maintain skills.

Resources

Student Edition
Skills Handbook, pp. 656, 664, 665
Extra Practice, p. 635
Glossary/Study Guide

Teaching Resources
Chapter Support File, Ch. 2
- Practice 2-3 (two worksheets)
- Reteaching 2-3
Classroom Manager 2-3
Glossary, Spanish Resources

Transparencies
5, 8, 9, 10, 32

QUICK REVIEW

Slope $= \dfrac{\text{vertical change (rise)}}{\text{horizontal change (run)}}$

$m = \dfrac{y_2 - y_1}{x_2 - x_1}$

1. a. Use $\dfrac{\text{vertical change}}{\text{horizontal change}}$ to find the slopes of line ℓ and line t shown above. $\frac{1}{2}; -\frac{2}{3}$ **b. The vertical change is 0.**
   b. Explain why the slope of a horizontal line is zero.
   c. Explain why the slope of a vertical line is undefined.
   The horizontal change is 0. Division by 0 is undefined.

2. Try This Use these pairs of points to answer parts (a)–(c).
   $R(-3, -4), S(5, -4)$ **a. See back of** $C(-2, 2), D(4, -2)$
   $K(-3, 3), T(-3, 1)$ **book.** $P(3, 0), Y(0, -5)$
   a. Graph and label a line that contains each pair of points.
   b. Mental Math Decide whether the slope of each line is positive, negative, zero, or undefined. 0; neg.; undef.; pos.
   c. Find the slope of each line.   0; $-\frac{2}{3}$; undefined; $\frac{5}{3}$

83

Example 1

Help students see that another point on the line can be found by moving three units up and four units right from (4, 5) or by moving three units down and four units left from (0, 2).

ERROR ALERT! **Question 3** Students sometimes plot the *y*-intercept on the *x*-axis. **Remediation:** Explain that the *y*-intercept is the *y*-coordinate where the line crosses the *y*-axis. The coordinates of this point are (0, *b*).

Question 4 Point out that the slope of $-\frac{1}{2}$ is equivalent to $\frac{-1}{2}$ or $\frac{1}{-2}$ but not $\frac{-1}{-2}$. Have students use a graph to show why this is true.

The Math Toolbox on page 82 provides an alternative activity for exploring the slopes of parallel and perpendicular lines using a graphing calculator.

Question 5a Students may be unsure as to which points on a line to use when finding the slope. Help them see that the slope of a line does not depend on which points on the line they choose to use.

Question 6 Students may have difficulty seeing pairs of perpendicular lines other than vertical and horizontal lines. Students may want to use a protractor to confirm that the perpendicular lines shown in the graph intersect at a 90° angle.

Additional Examples

FOR EXAMPLE 1

Graph the line $y = -x + 3$.

Discussion: *Describe two ways to move from one point on the line to another while staying in the coordinate plane.*

FOR EXAMPLE 2

Find the slope of the line perpendicular to $y = \frac{1}{2}x - 5$. -2

Discussion: *How many lines are perpendicular to $y = \frac{1}{2}x - 5$? How many of those lines pass through $(0, -5)$?*

QUICK REVIEW

The slope-intercept form of a linear equation is

$y = mx + b$.

slope   y-intercept

You can graph a line by starting at a given point and using the slope of the line to plot another point.

Example 1

Graph the line $y = \frac{3}{4}x + 2$.

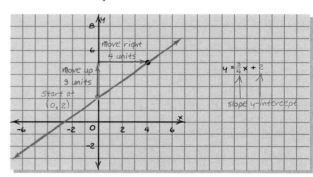

3. **Try This** Use the slope and *y*-intercept to graph each line.
   a. $y = 3x - 4$ b. $y = \frac{1}{2}x + 3$ c. $y = -2x - 1$.
                           See back of book.
4. Describe how you would graph a line with a slope of $-\frac{1}{2}$ and a *y*-intercept of 0. **Start at the *y*-intercept, graph a point (0, 0). Then go down 1 unit and to the right 2 units and graph a 2nd point (2, −1). Draw the line through the 2 points.**

WORK TOGETHER

Part 2 Work in a group to explore the slopes of parallel and perpendicular lines in a coordinate plane.

5. a. Find the slopes of both parallel lines shown in the first graph at the left. **1; 1**
   b. Have each member draw a pair of nonvertical parallel lines on graph paper and find the slopes of both lines. **Check students' work.**
   c. Compare your results with group members. Make a **conjecture** about the slopes of parallel lines. **Slopes of ∥ lines are =.**

6. a. Find the slopes of both perpendicular lines shown in the second graph at the left. $\frac{1}{2}; -2$
   b. Have each member draw a line on graph paper. (Do not use a vertical or horizontal line.) Then use a corner of the paper to draw a line perpendicular to it. Find the slopes of both lines. Find the product of the slopes. **Check students' work.**
   c. Compare your results with group members. Make a **conjecture** about the product of the slopes of two perpendicular lines. **The product of slopes of ⊥ lines is −1.**

84

Discuss with students how the algebraic properties of parallel and perpendicular lines connect algebra and geometry. While the relationship between the lines does not depend on coordinates (i.e., take away the coordinates and the lines would still be parallel or perpendicular), the coordinates give mathematicians a numerical way to describe the relationship.

EXTENSION You may want students to research René Descartes, the first mathematician to introduce coordinates into the study of geometry.

Questions 7 and 8 You may want to review equations of vertical lines ($x = a$) and equations of horizontal lines ($y = c$).

Example 2

One method for finding the slope of a line perpendicular to $y = -3x + 4$ is to solve the equation $-3 \cdot m = -1$ as presented in the text. Another method is to take the negative reciprocal of -3, $-\left(\frac{1}{-3}\right) = \frac{1}{3}$. If students use this second method, caution them to find the *negative* reciprocal and not just the reciprocal of the given slope.

Question 11 This question demonstrates that perpendicularity in a plane is not a transitive relationship. In other words, $t \perp k$ and $k \perp s$ implies $t \parallel s$, *not* $t \perp s$.

THINK AND DISCUSS

Parallel and Perpendicular Lines

Your observations in the Work Together are summarized below.

7. No 2 lines are $\parallel$; (b) and (c) are $\perp$.

8a.

Slopes of Parallel and Perpendicular Lines

The slopes of nonvertical parallel lines are equal. Two lines with the same slope are parallel. Vertical lines are parallel.

The product of the slopes of two perpendicular lines, neither of which is vertical, is -1. If the product of the slopes of the two lines is -1, then the lines are perpendicular. A horizontal and a vertical line are perpendicular.

7. Try This Which of these lines are parallel? Which are perpendicular?
  a. $y = 2x + 1$ **b.** $y = -x$ **c.** $y = x - 4$
  d. $y = \frac{1}{2}$ **e.** $y = -2x + 3$ See above left.

8. a. Graph $y = 5$, $y = -1$, and $x = -4$. See above left.
  b. Which lines are parallel? Which are perpendicular?
  $y = 5$ and $y = -1$ are $\parallel$; $x = -4$ is $\perp$ to the other 2.

Example 2

Find the slope of a line perpendicular to $y = -3x + 4$.

The slope of line $y = -3x + 4$ is -3.
Let m be the slope of the perpendicular line.

$-3 \cdot m = -1$ The product of the slopes is -1.
$m = \frac{1}{3}$ Divide each side by -3.

Sample: $y = -3x - 12$

9. Open-ended Give an equation of a line parallel to $y = -3x + 4$.

Architecture There are parallel and perpendicular lines in the photo at the left.

10. If line $k \parallel$ line ℓ and line $r \parallel$ line ℓ, what is the relationship between lines k and r? $k \parallel r$

11. If line $t \perp$ line k and line $s \perp$ line k, what is the relationship between lines t and s? $t \parallel s$

Questions 10 and 11 demonstrate the following theorems.

Theorem 2-5   Two lines parallel to a third line are parallel to each other.

Theorem 2-6   In a plane, two lines perpendicular to a third line are parallel to each other.

Technology Options

For Exercises 12–19, students may use a graphing software to draw each pair of lines. For Exercise 29, students may use a graphing software to draw the scatter plot.

Prentice Hall Technology

 Software
  • Secondary Math Lab Toolkit™
  • Integrated Math Lab 25
  • Computer Item Generator 2-3

Internet
  • See the Prentice Hall site. (http://www.phschool.com)

MENTAL MATH Exercise 1 Students should be able to answer this question visually, without finding the slopes.

WRITING Exercise 3 Students may want to support their explanations with real-world examples of zero slope and no slope.

ALTERNATIVE ASSESSMENT Exercises 4–9 These exercises can help you assess students' understanding of the relationship between slopes of parallel and perpendicular lines.

STANDARDIZED TEST TIP Exercise 20 Suggest that it might be helpful to rewrite the equations in the slope-intercept form $y = mx + b$ by solving for y.

---

pages 86–87   On Your Own

21a, c.   22a, c.

23. **Answers may vary. Sample: Yes; the ramp cannot be straight, but it can have 3 turns between 4 straight parts so the total length is at least 36 ft.**

25.

a. $\overleftrightarrow{AB} \perp \overleftrightarrow{FB}, \overleftrightarrow{BC} \perp \overleftrightarrow{FB}, \overleftrightarrow{AB} \perp \overleftrightarrow{BC}$

b. $\overleftrightarrow{AB} \perp \overleftrightarrow{BC}, \overleftrightarrow{BC} \perp \overleftrightarrow{CG}, \overleftrightarrow{AB}$ **and** $\overleftrightarrow{CG}$ **are skew lines.**

---

1. Identify the slope of each line in the graph as positive, negative, zero, or undefined. **k: pos.; ℓ: neg.; s: 0; t: undef.**

2. a. What is the slope of the x-axis? Explain. **0**
   b. What is the slope of the y-axis? Explain. **Undefined**

3. Writing A classmate claims that having no slope and having a slope of 0 are the same. Is your classmate right? Explain. **No; lines with no slope are vert. Lines with slope 0 are horizontal.**

11. **No; the slopes of the sides are $\frac{3}{5}, -\frac{5}{8}$, and $-\frac{8}{3}$. No 2 sides are ⊥.**

📓 Choose **Use pencil and paper, mental math, or a calculator to find the slopes of $\overleftrightarrow{AB}$ and $\overleftrightarrow{CD}$. Then determine if the lines are parallel, perpendicular, or neither.**   undef.; undef.; ∥   undef.; 0; ⊥

4. $A(-1, \frac{1}{2}), B(-1, 2), C(3, 7), D(3, -1)$

5. $A(-2, 3), B(-2, 5), C(1, 4), D(2, 4)$

6. $A(2, 4), B(5, 4), C(3, 2), D(0, 8)$ **0; −2; neither**

7. $A(-3, 2), B(5, 1), C(2, 7), D(1, -1)$ $-\frac{1}{8}$; 8; ⊥

8. $A(1, -3), B(3, 2), C(4, 5), D(2, 0)$ $\frac{5}{2}; \frac{5}{2}$ **parallel**

9. $A(4.5, 5), B(2, 5), C(1.5, -2), D(3, -2)$ **0; 0; parallel**

10. Use slope to show that the opposite sides of hexagon *RSTUVW* are parallel. **See right.**

11. Use slope to determine whether a triangle with vertices (3, 2), (8, 5), and (0, 10) is a right triangle. Explain. **See above right.**

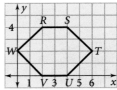

10. **Slope of $\overline{WR}$ and $\overline{TU}$ is 1; slope of $\overline{RS}$ and $\overline{UV}$ is 0; slope of $\overline{ST}$ and $\overline{VW}$ is −1. Lines with = slope are ∥.**

Sketch each pair of lines. Tell whether they are parallel, perpendicular, or neither.

    neither   perpendicular   parallel

12. $y = 5x - 4$ 13. $y = \frac{1}{3}x - 1$ 14. $x = -2$ 15. $y = -4$

    $x = 2$ $y = -3x + 5$ $x = 0$ $y = \frac{1}{4}$ **parallel**

16. $y = 2.5x + 1$ 17. $y = x - \frac{1}{2}$ 18. $y = \frac{3}{4}x - 2$ 19. $y = -7$

    $y = 2.5$ $y = x + 1$ $y = -2$ $x = -5$

    neither   parallel   neither   perpendicular

20. Standardized Test Prep Which of the lines is *not* parallel to the line $y = -\frac{2}{3}x + 8$? **D**

    A. $2x + 3y = 1$ **B.** $4x = 3 - 6y$ **C.** $x = -1.5y$ **D.** $24 = 2x - 3y$ **E.** $9y = -6x - 2$

21. a. Sketch vertical line *t* containing (−5, 2). **See margin.**
   b. Write an equation for line *t*. $x = -5$
   c. On the same graph, sketch horizontal line *s* containing (−5, 2). **See margin.**
   d. Write an equation for line *s*. $y = 2$
   e. What is the relationship between line *t* and line *s*? Explain.   **The lines are ⊥; a horizontal line is always ⊥ to a vertical line.**

22. a. Sketch line *w* perpendicular to $y = 5$, and containing (1, 4). **See margin.**
   b. Write an equation for line *w*. $x = 1$
   c. On the same graph, sketch line *r* parallel to $y = 5$, and containing (1, 4). **See margin.**
   d. Write an equation for line *r*. $y = 4$
   e. What is the relationship between line *r* and line *w*? Explain.   **The lines are ⊥; a line with slope 0 is ⊥ to a line with undefined slope.**

DIVERSITY Exercise 23 Students may have seen ramps that "zig-zag" toward an entrance rather than approach it directly. Discuss why the ramp was made that way. Help students see that a slope of $\frac{1}{12}$ means that the ramp rises one foot for every twelve feet measured horizontally.

OPEN-ENDED Exercise 24 It may help students to begin with a diagram.

GEOMETRY ON A SPHERE Exercise 27 This exercise demonstrates how relationships between lines in Euclidean geometry can be different from those in non-Euclidean geometries.

23. **Building** A law concerning wheelchair accessibility states that the slope of a ramp must be no greater than $\frac{1}{12}$. A local civic center plans to install a ramp. The height from the pavement to the main entrance is 3 ft and the distance from the sidewalk to the building is 10 ft. Is it possible for the center to design a ramp that complies with this law? Explain. **See margin p. 86.**

24. **a.** *Open-ended* Find the equations of two lines perpendicular to line $y = 3x - 2$. **Sample:** $y = -\frac{1}{3}x + 1$, $y = -\frac{1}{3}x - 3$
   b. Find the equations of two lines parallel to line $y = 3x - 2$. **Sample:** $y = 3x + 1$, $y = 3x$

25. *Manipulatives* Use straws, toothpicks, or pencils.
   a. *Geometry in 3 Dimensions* Show how two lines that are each perpendicular to a third line can be perpendicular to each other. **a–b. See margin p. 86.**
   b. Show how two lines that are each perpendicular to a third line can be skew to each other.

26. **a.** Graph the points $A(1, 7)$, $B(2, 5)$, and $C(5, -1)$.
   b. What appears to be the relationship between these three points? **They are collinear.**
   c. Find the slopes of $\overleftrightarrow{AB}$, $\overleftrightarrow{BC}$, and $\overleftrightarrow{AC}$. **−2;−2;−2**
   d. *Logical Reasoning* Use part (c) to **justify** your answer to part (b).

26a,d. See margin.

27. *Geometry on a Sphere* Suppose you are investigating "lines" on a globe. The lines pass through both poles and are perpendicular to the equator. Are the lines of longitude "parallel" to each other? Explain. **Answers may vary. Sample: No; the "lines" intersect twice.**

28. **a.** Sketch line c with a slope -5 and line f with slope $\frac{1}{5}$. **28a–b. See margin.**
   b. On the same graph, sketch line w perpendicular to line f.
   c. What is the relationship between line c and line w? Explain. **$c \parallel w$; in a plane, 2 lines $\perp$ to a 3rd are $\parallel$.**

29. **a.** *Calculator* Find the slopes of each line containing the origin and $(\frac{1}{n}, 10)$ for $n = 1, 2, 3, \ldots 10$. Record your results as ordered pairs (n, slope).
   b. Show your results on a graph like the one shown.
   c. *Data Analysis* What predictions can you make about the slope of the line when $n = 100$?
   d. *Critical Thinking* Do you think that the slope will get infinitely large? Explain your reasoning.

29a–d. See margin.

Slope

26a.

d. Since $\overleftrightarrow{AB}$ and $\overleftrightarrow{BC}$ have the same slope and are not ∥, they must be the same line. Therefore A, B, and C must be collinear.

28a–b.

29a. **(1, 10), (2, 20), (3, 30), (4, 40), (5, 50), (6, 60), (7, 70), (8, 80), (9, 90), (10, 100)**

b.

c. The slope is 1000.

d. Sample: Yes; you can make the slope as steep as you want, but it will never be vertical.

87

Exercises · MIXED REVIEW

Exercises 31–32 Students review the meanings of complementary and supplementary angles.

Exercise 33 You may want to suggest students let x and $3x$ represent the measures of acute angles.

GETTING READY FOR LESSON 2-4 These exercises prepare students for classifying quadrilaterals.

Wrap Up

THE BIG IDEA Ask students: *Given the line $y = -4x + 5$, write an equation of a line parallel to it and an equation of a line perpendicular to it. Explain your methods. How are the lines you found related?*

RETEACHING ACTIVITY Students find the slopes of lines parallel and perpendicular to a given line. (Reteaching worksheet 2-3)

Exercises · CHECKPOINT

In this Checkpoint, your students will assess their own progress on Lessons 2-1 to 2-3.

Exercises 10–13 Students can graph the lines to check their answers.

OPEN-ENDED Exercise 14 Students may want to start with a graph and then write the equation.

Lesson Quiz

Lesson Quiz is also available in Transparencies.

1. Graph the line $y = -\frac{2}{3}x + 2$. **See back of book.**

Determine whether the lines are parallel, perpendicular, or neither.

2. $y = -\frac{1}{2}x + 5$ $y = 2x - 3$
perpendicular

3. $y = -5$ $y = 3$ **parallel**

4. $\overleftrightarrow{AC}$ and $\overleftrightarrow{EG}$, given $A(3, 2)$, $C(5, 6)$, $E(-1, 4)$, and $G(-2, 2)$ **parallel**

Exercises · MIXED REVIEW

Use the diagram for the Exercises 30–32.

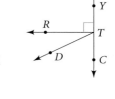

30. Name an acute angle, an obtuse angle, a right angle, and a straight angle.
$\angle RTD$ or $\angle CTD$; $\angle DTY$; $\angle RTY$ or $\angle RTC$; $\angle CTY$

31. Find $m\angle DTR$ when $m\angle CTD = 64.5$. **25.5**

32. Find the value of x when $m\angle CTD = x + 32$ and $m\angle DTY = 3x + 20$. Then find the measures of both angles. **32; 64 and 116**

33. The measure of one acute angle of a right triangle is three times the measure of the other acute angle. Find the measures of the angles. **22.5 and 67.5**

Getting Ready for Lesson 2-4
In each quadrilateral below, name any sides that appear to be parallel.

 FOR YOUR JOURNAL
Describe real-world examples of parallel and perpendicular lines that you see on the way to school.

34.

$\overline{AD}$ and $\overline{BC}$

35.

$\overline{FG}$ and $\overline{EH}$, $\overline{EF}$ and $\overline{GH}$

Exercises · CHECKPOINT

Draw each figure. Mark congruent sides and angles. 1–8. See margin p. 89.

1. equilateral triangle **2.** isosceles triangle **3.** right triangle **4.** acute triangle

5. obtuse triangle **6.** regular octagon **7.** concave decagon **8.** convex nonagon

9. *Writing* Describe two methods you can use to find the measure of each interior angle of a regular polygon. **(1) Divide 360 by n to find the exterior angle measure. Subtract the result from 180. (2) Multiply 180 by $n - 2$ and divide the result by n.**

Find the slope of lines $\overleftrightarrow{RS}$ and $\overleftrightarrow{TV}$. Then determine if $\overleftrightarrow{RS}$ and $\overleftrightarrow{TV}$ are *parallel, perpendicular,* or *neither.* 10. $-\frac{2}{5}$; $\frac{5}{2}$; perpendicular 11. 1; -1; perpendicular

10. $R(-2, 6)$, $S(3, 4)$, $T(2, 5)$, $V(0, 0)$ **11.** $R(6, -1)$, $S(7, 0)$, $T(3, -4)$, $V(0, -1)$

12. $R(9, 1)$, $S(5, 6)$, $T(3, 8)$, $V(-2, 4)$ **13.** $R(5, -7)$, $S(-4, -9)$, $T(6, 2)$, $V(-3, 0)$
$-\frac{5}{4}$; $\frac{4}{5}$; perpendicular $\frac{2}{9}$; $\frac{2}{9}$ parallel

14. a. *Open-ended* Write an equation of a nonvertical line with a y-intercept of 2. **Sample: $y = 3x + 2$**

  b. Write an equation of a line perpendicular to this line having the same y-intercept. **For sample in part (a): $y = -\frac{1}{3}x + 2$**

88

Math ToolboX — Algebra Review

Transparencies 5, 8, 9

Writing Linear Equations

When you know the slope of a line and a point on it, you can use the slope-intercept form of a line to write a linear equation.

Example 1

Write an equation of a line that has a slope of $\frac{1}{4}$ and contains the point $R(8, -3)$.

$y = mx + b$	Use the slope-intercept form.
$-3 = \frac{1}{4}(8) + b$	Substitute the slope and the x- and y-coordinates of the point.
$-3 = 2 + b$	Simplify.
$-5 = b$	Solve for b.

The equation of the line is $y = \frac{1}{4}x - 5$.

You can also use the slope-intercept form of a linear equation when you know the coordinates of two points on the line.

Example 2

Write an equation of a line containing $A(9, -2)$ and $B(3, 4)$.

$m = \frac{y_2 - y_1}{x_2 - x_1}$	Use the formula to find the slope.
$m = \frac{4 - (-2)}{3 - 9} = -1$	Substitute the coordinates of both points.
$y = -1x + b$	Substitute −1 for m in y = mx + b.
$4 = -1(3) + b$	Substitute the coordinates of one of the points and solve for b.
$7 = b$	

The equation of the line is $y = -1x + 7$ or $y = -x + 7$.

Write an equation of the line with the given slope, and containing point T.

1. $m = 3, T(0, 5)$ **2.** $m = \frac{2}{3}, T(-6, -1)$ **3.** $m = -\frac{1}{2}, T(4, -8)$ **4.** $m = 1, T(-1, 3)$

5. $m = -\frac{5}{4}, T(4, 3)$ **6.** $m = -1, T(-1, -8)$ **7.** $m = \frac{3}{2}, T(4, 4)$ **8.** $m = \frac{3}{4}, T(-12, -9)$

Write an equation of the line containing points C and D.

9. $C(9, -2), D(3, 4)$ **10.** $C(2, 1), D(-2, 3)$ **11.** $C(0, 3), D(-5, 0)$ **12.** $C(-5, 0), D(-2, 1)$

13. $C(2, 0), D(3, 5)$ **14.** $C(3, -1), D(2, -3)$ **15.** $C(0, 0), D(8, -2)$ **16.** $C(-8, 3), D(4, -6)$

After Lesson 2-3

1. $y = 3x + 5$
2. $y = \frac{2}{3}x + 3$
3. $y = -\frac{1}{2}x - 6$
4. $y = x + 4$
5. $y = -\frac{5}{4}x + 8$
6. $y = -x - 9$
7. $y = \frac{3}{2}x - 2$
8. $y = \frac{3}{4}x$
9. $y = -x + 7$
10. $y = -\frac{1}{2}x + 2$
11. $y = \frac{3}{5}x + 3$
12. $y = \frac{1}{3}x + \frac{5}{3}$
13. $y = 5x - 10$
14. $y = 2x - 7$
15. $y = -\frac{1}{4}x$
16. $y = -\frac{3}{4}x - 3$

Checkpoint   page 88

1.   2.   3.

4.   5.

6.   7.

8.

PROBLEM OF THE DAY

Each angle has a measure of 60. Find the number of equilateral triangles in this picture. **48**

Problem of the Day is also available in Transparencies.

CONNECTING TO PRIOR KNOWLEDGE Have students review the sum of the measures of the interior angles of a quadrilateral. Have them find the measure of one interior angle of a *regular* quadrilateral.

WORK TOGETHER

In this activity, students explore the properties of quadrilaterals before formal definitions are presented. Students should use graph paper for their sketches.

ERROR ALERT! Students may assume that all the quadrilaterals they draw can be classified by one of the special names given at the top of the page. **Remediation:** Draw examples of quadrilaterals that cannot be classified with the special names given. Explain that the best name for such a figure is quadrilateral.

Lesson Planning Options

Prerequisite Skills

- Using the distance formula
- Finding slope

Assignment Options for Exercises On Your Own

Core 1–27
Extension 28–31

Use Mixed Review to maintain skills.

Resources

 Student Edition

Skills Handbook, pp. 664, 665
Extra Practice, p. 635
Glossary/Study Guide

 Teaching Resources

Chapter Support File, Ch. 2
- Practice 2-4 (two worksheets)
- Reteaching 2-4
Classroom Manager 2-4
Glossary, Spanish Resources

 Transparencies
32, 37, 38

90

What You'll Learn
- Defining and classifying special types of quadrilaterals

...And Why
To learn about the most commonly used polygons in buildings, architecture, and design

What You'll Need
- toothpicks

4: rhombus, square
5: isos. trapezoid
6: parallelogram, rectangle, kite
7: isos. trapezoid, trapezoid
8: square, rectangle, rhombus, kite, parallelogram, isos. trapezoid

2b. 2 opposite sides are ∥ and the other 2 are not.

c. Opposite sides are ∥. Opposite sides are ≅.

Connections 🌐 Kites . . . and more

2-4 Classifying Quadrilaterals

WORK TOGETHER

Some quadrilaterals have special names.

parallelogram   rectangle   rhombus

square   kite   trapezoid   isosceles trapezoid

Work in a group to build all the different quadrilaterals that you can using 4, 5, 6, 7, and 8 toothpicks. Each toothpick represents a side or a part of a side. Sketch and name each quadrilateral you form. Two examples are shown at the left.

1. Which quadrilaterals can you build with an even number of toothpicks? with an odd number of toothpicks? Explain.

even: parallelogram, rectangle, rhombus, square, kite, isos. trapezoid
odd: trapezoid, isos. trapezoid

THINK AND DISCUSS

As you made quadrilaterals out of toothpicks, you probably noticed some of the properties of special quadrilaterals. 2–3. Answers may vary. Samples are given.

2. What appears to be true about the sides of the following quadrilaterals?
   a. rhombus   **b.** trapezoid   **c.** parallelogram **d.** kite
   a. All sides are ≅. Opposite sides are parallel.

3. What appears to be true about the angles of a rectangle and a square?
   All the angles are rt. angles.

2d. 2 adj. sides are ≅ and the other 2 adj. sides are ≅.

As you discuss the definitions of special quadrilaterals with students, you may want to review how to mark figures to indicate parallel lines, congruent sides, and right angles.

ESL **TACTILE LEARNING** Have students model the quadrilaterals using geoboards. As they create a figure have them pronounce its name aloud. Check students' pronunciation of *isosceles*, *trapezoid,* and *rhombus*.

Example 1

LOGICAL REASONING Question 5 Before students answer this question, display a Venn diagram showing the relationships between triangles, isosceles triangles, and equilateral triangles. Review how the diagram illustrates the relationships among these triangles.

You can use characteristics of special quadrilaterals to define them.

Special Quadrilaterals

A **parallelogram** is a quadrilateral with both pairs of opposite sides parallel. In Chapter 9, you will prove that both pairs of opposite sides are also congruent. The symbol for a parallelogram is ▱.

A **rhombus** is a parallelogram with four congruent sides.

A **rectangle** is a parallelogram with four right angles.

A **square** is a parallelogram with four congruent sides and four right angles.

A **kite** is a quadrilateral with two pairs of adjacent sides congruent and no opposite sides congruent.

A **trapezoid** is a quadrilateral with exactly one pair of parallel sides.

An **isosceles trapezoid** is a trapezoid whose nonparallel sides are congruent.

Additional Examples

FOR EXAMPLE 1 ....

 Judging by appearance, name the quadrilateral in as many ways as possible.
quadrilateral, parallelogram, rhombus

Discussion: *Can you draw a different quadrilateral that has the same relationships among its sides and angles?*

FOR EXAMPLE 2 ....

Given $C(1, 2)$, $D(5, 2)$, $E(7, -2)$, and $F(-1, -2)$, determine the most precise name for quadrilateral *CDEF*. isosceles trapezoid

Discussion: *Explain why CDEF is not a parallelogram.*

FOR EXAMPLE 3 ....

Refer to the diagram in Example 3. If $KT = x + 4$, $KB = 2x + 4$, $JB = y - 4$, and $JT = 2x$, find the values of x and y. $x = 4$, $y = 16$

Example 1

Judging by appearance, name *DEFG* in as many ways as possible.

It is a quadrilateral because it has four sides.

It is a parallelogram because both pairs of opposite sides are parallel.

It is a rectangle because it has four right angles.

4. Which name do you think gives the most information about *DEFG*? Explain. Sample: Rectangle; a rectangle is a parallelogram and a quadrilateral.

5. *Logical Reasoning* Which Venn diagram at the left shows the relationship between rectangles and squares? Explain. Sample: 1st diagram; all squares are rectangles, but not all rectangles are squares.

EXTENSION If you have block scheduling or an extended class period, have students use magazines and newspapers to find real-world examples of each type of special quadrilateral. Then have them use these examples to create a poster or mobile of the diagram on page 92.

ALTERNATIVE METHOD Have pairs of students draw ten different special quadrilaterals on index cards, one per card, labeling each quadrilateral with its most precise name. One student should sort the ten cards into two piles according to a certain characteristic. For example, the two piles might be quadrilaterals that have right angles and quadrilaterals that do not. The partner then tries to determine what property the student used to make the two piles.

Technology Options

The diagram below shows the relationships among special quadrilaterals.

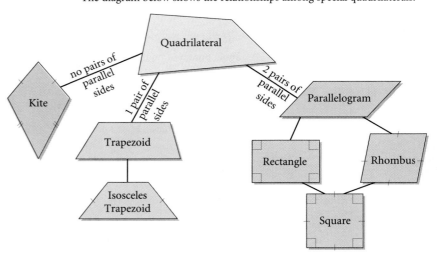

You can use the definitions of special quadrilaterals and what you know about slope and distance to classify a quadrilateral.

Example 2

Determine the most precise name for quadrilateral *LMNP*.

Find the slope of each side.

slope of $\overline{LM} = \frac{3-2}{3-1} = \frac{1}{2}$ slope of $\overline{NP} = \frac{2-1}{5-3} = \frac{1}{2}$

slope of $\overline{MN} = \frac{3-2}{3-5} = -\frac{1}{2}$ slope of $\overline{LP} = \frac{2-1}{1-3} = -\frac{1}{2}$

Both pairs of opposite sides are parallel, so *LMNP* is a parallelogram.

Now use the Distance Formula to see if any of the sides are congruent.

$$LM = \sqrt{(3-1)^2 + (3-2)^2} = \sqrt{5}$$
$$MN = \sqrt{(3-5)^2 + (3-2)^2} = \sqrt{5}$$
$$NP = \sqrt{(5-3)^2 + (2-1)^2} = \sqrt{5}$$
$$LP = \sqrt{(1-3)^2 + (2-1)^2} = \sqrt{5}$$

All sides are congruent, so *LMNP* is a rhombus.

For practice with radicals, see Skills Handbook, page 660.

6. Explain how you know that *LMNP* is *not* a square. The product of slopes of adjacent sides is not −1, so the sides are not ⊥.

7. Try This Determine the most precise name for quadrilateral *ABCD* with vertices *A*(0, 4), *B*(3, 0), *C*(0, −4), *D*(−3, 0). rhombus

Example 2 ·······································

Example 3 ··

Help students understand that both pairs of opposite sides are parallel because the lines containing the sides have the same slope.

Have students discuss a plan for solving this problem. Use the fact that $KB = JB$ to find x. Substitute the value of x to find KT, then use the fact that $KT = JT$ to find y.

ERROR ALERT! Question 6 Students may erroneously say $\frac{-1}{2} \times \frac{1}{2} = -1$ and mistakenly claim that *LMNP is* a square.
Remediation: Review how to multiply fractions.

Question 7 Make sure students can distinguish between a kite and a parallelogram.

Exercises   ON YOUR OWN

MAKING CONNECTIONS Exercises 1–4 A pantograph is made of four rods held together by pins to form a loose-jointed parallelogram. This mechanical instrument is used by drafters to enlarge or reduce a drawing.

You can use the definitions of special quadrilaterals to find lengths of sides of objects like kites.

Example 3 ··

Find the values of the variables in the kite at the left.

$KB = JB$	Definition of kite
$3x - 5 = 2x + 4$	Substitution
$x - 5 = 4$	Subtract $2x$ from each side.
$x = 9$	Add 5 to each side.
$KT = x + 6, KT = 15$	Substitute 9 for x.
$KT = JT$	Definition of kite
$15 = 2y + 5$	Substitution
$10 = 2y$	Subtract 5 from each side.
$5 = y$	Divide each side by 2.

8. What are the lengths of the longer sides of the kite? **22**

9. What types of triangles are formed when you draw diagonal $\overline{KJ}$?
   isosceles

10. What types of triangles are formed when you draw diagonal $\overline{BT}$?
    scalene

Exercises   ON YOUR OWN

Judging by appearance, name each quadrilateral in as many ways as possible.

1.
2.
3.
4.

See right.   parallelogram   trapezoid   parallelogram, rhombus

1. parallelogram, rhombus, rectangle, square

Copy the Venn diagram. Show the relationships of special quadrilaterals by adding the labels *Rectangles, Rhombuses,* and *Trapezoids.* Then use the diagram to decide whether each statement is true or false.

5. All squares are rectangles. **true**

6. A trapezoid is a parallelogram. **false**

7. A rhombus can be a kite. **false**

8. Some parallelograms are squares. **true**

9. A quadrilateral is a parallelogram. **false**

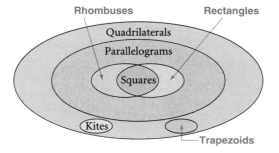

Rhombuses   Rectangles
Quadrilaterals
Parallelograms
Squares
Kites
Trapezoids

93

CONNECTING TO STUDENTS' WORLD Exercise 10 Students may want to create their own artwork. Suggest that students draw everyday objects such as flowers, animals, or people using geometric shapes.

ALTERNATIVE ASSESSMENT Exercises 11–13 These exercises can help you assess students' understanding of the properties of the special quadrilaterals.

Exercise 20 Lead students to observe the fold lines on the unfolded parallelogram and conjecture that the diagonals of a parallelogram bisect each other. Students will study this and other properties of parallelograms in Chapter 9.

pages 93–95 On Your Own

11.   12.

13.

14. **Sample:** A rhombus has 4 ≅ sides. A kite has 2 pairs of ≅ sides. Opp. sides of a rhombus are ∥. Opp. sides of a kite are not ∥.

15a. **Sample:**

Find Out By Analyzing

10. **Art** Inspired by Cubists like Pablo Picasso, American artist Charles Demuth created *My Egypt*. Identify the geometric figures in this oil painting. List all the special quadrilaterals you see.
rectangle, square, trapezoid

Draw each figure on graph paper. 11–14. See margin.

11. parallelogram that is neither a rectangle nor a rhombus

12. trapezoid with a right angle

13. rhombus that is not a square

14. **Writing** Describe the difference between a rhombus and a kite.

15. **a. Open-ended** Graph and label points $K(-3, 0)$, $L(0, 2)$, and $M(3, 0)$. Find possible coordinates for point N so that *KLMN* is a kite. See margin.
    b. Explain why there is more than one possible fourth vertex. All points on the negative *y*-axis are equidistant from *K* and *M*.

Coordinate Geometry Graph and label each quadrilateral with the given vertices. Use slope and/or the Distance Formula to determine the most precise name for each figure.

16. $A(3, 5)$, $B(7, 6)$, $C(6, 2)$, $D(2, 1)$ rhombus

17. $W(-1, 1)$, $X(0, 2)$, $Y(1, 1)$, $Z(0, -2)$ kite

18. $J(2, 1)$, $K(5, 4)$, $L(7, 2)$, $M(2, -3)$ trapezoid

19. $R(-2, -3)$, $S(4, 0)$, $T(3, 2)$, $V(-3, -1)$ rectangle

20. **Paper Folding** Fold a rectangular piece of paper in half horizontally and then vertically. Draw and then cut along the line connecting the two corners containing a fold. What quadrilateral do you find when you unfold the paper? Explain. Rhombus; the sides of the quadrilateral are ≅ because they come from the same cut.

Name all special quadrilaterals that satisfy the given conditions. Make a sketch to support your answer.

21. exactly one pair of congruent sides some isos. trapezoids, some trapezoids

22. two pairs of parallel sides parallelogram, rhombus, rectangle, square

23. four right angles rectangle, square

24. adjacent sides that are congruent kite, some trapezoids, rhombus, square

Algebra Find the values of the variables and the lengths of the sides.

25. kite *ABCD*

$x = 11; y = 21; 13, 13, 15, 15$

26. isosceles trapezoid *DEFG*

15; 11, 20, 11, 31

27. rhombus *HIJK*

$b = 9; r = 5; 6, 6, 6, 6$

TACTILE LEARNING Exercises 28–31 Students may want to draw their answers and cover them with a piece of paper to check that the part remaining uncovered matches the sketch in the text.

Chapter Project **FIND OUT BY ANALYZING** Have students draw their pentominoes on grid paper and then glue them to poster board and keep the set for the Find Out investigation in Lesson 2-6. Emphasize that students check carefully that the pentominoes they make are all different.

Exercises   MIXED REVIEW

Exercise 34 Students apply what they know about angles of a triangle to find measures of angles formed by three intersecting lines.

GETTING READY FOR LESSON 2-5 These exercises prepare students for measuring central angles and arcs.

Wrap Up

THE BIG IDEA Ask students: *Define each type of special quadrilateral and give a real-world example for each.*

RETEACHING ACTIVITY Students draw quadrilaterals with certain characteristics, then name them in as many ways as possible. (Reteaching worksheet 2-4)

Part of each quadrilateral is covered. Name all special quadrilaterals that each could be. Explain each choice.

28.
parallelogram, rectangle, trapezoid

29.
parallelogram, kite, rhombus, trapezoid, isos. trapezoid

30.
kite, parallelogram, rhombus, trapezoid, isos. trapezoid

31.
parallelogram, rectangle, square, kite, trapezoid

Chapter Project **Find Out by Analyzing**

You can create another geometric puzzle, called *pentominoes*, by joining five unit squares. Each square shares a side with at least one other square.

These are pentominoes.   These are not pentominoes.

- There are twelve different pentominoes. Sketch the other ten pentominoes on graph paper.   See margin p. 94.
- Make a set of pentominoes out of cardboard. Use any three pentominoes to form a 3 x 5 rectangle. Find and record as many solutions as you can. See margin p. 94.

Exercises   MIXED REVIEW

Use a calculator to find *TR* to the nearest tenth.

32. $T(3, 7)$, $R(6, -2)$ 9.5   **33.** $T(-8, 4)$, $R(0, 2)$ 8.2

34. a. Find $m\angle 5$ if $m\angle 7 = 103$ and $m\angle 2 = 48$. 55
   b. Find $m\angle 1$ if $m\angle 7 = 110$ and $m\angle 6 = 153$. 97
   c. Find $m\angle 9$ if $m\angle 3 = 138$ and $m\angle 5 = 51$. 93

35. a. Sketch the line perpendicular to $x = 2$ containing the point $(3, -1)$.
   b. Sketch the line parallel to $x = 2$ containing the point $(3, -1)$.

35a.

b.

Getting Ready for Lesson 2-5

Estimate the percent of the circle that is shaded.

36.
25%

37.
33%

38.
50%

39.
75%

40.
67%

Name_____ Class_____ Date_____
Reteaching 2-4

Name_____ Class_____ Date_____
Practice 2-4

Name_____ Class_____ Date_____
Practice 2-4
Mixed Exercises

Lesson Quiz

Lesson Quiz is also available in Transparencies.

1. Given $G(2, 4)$, $H(6, 4)$, $I(0, -2)$, and $J(4, -2)$, determine the most precise name for quadrilateral *GHIJ*. **parallelogram**

2. Find the lengths of the sides of the isosceles trapezoid. **11, 8, 11, and 12**
$g + 2$
$g + 5$ $2g - 1$
12

3. Draw a parallelogram that has right angles but is not a square.
Students should draw a rectangle so that the length does not equal the width.

95

PROBLEM OF THE DAY

How many squares are in the figure? **7**

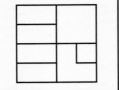

Problem of the Day is also available in Transparencies.

CONNECTING TO PRIOR KNOWLEDGE Discuss with students what the measurements mean in the following phrases: 10-in. pizza, 14-in. tire, and 6-ft round table.

WORK TOGETHER

To prevent students from reading the definition of circle given in the textbook, have students cover the page under the Work Together activity with their notebooks.

ERROR ALERT! Students often think that a circle includes its interior. **Remediation:** Make sure students' definitions clearly define only those points equidistant from the center of the circle.

Lesson Planning Options

Prerequisite Skills

- Using the midpoint and distance formulas
- Finding percents

Assignment Options for Exercises On Your Own

To provide flexible scheduling, this lesson can be subdivided into parts.

1 **Core** 10–20, 22–27
Extension 48

2 **Core** 1–9, 21, 28–38, 40–47
Extension 39, 49–50

Use Mixed Review to maintain skills.

Resources

 Student Edition

Skills Handbook, p. 657
Extra Practice, p. 635
Glossary/Study Guide

Teaching Resources

Chapter Support File, Ch. 2
- Practice 2-5 (two worksheets)
- Reteaching 2-5
- Alternative Activity 2-5
- Classroom Manager 2-5
- Glossary, Spanish Resources

 Transparencies
4, 12, 33

Connections ● Amusement Parks . . . *and more*

What You'll Learn

- Measuring central angles and arcs of circles.
- Displaying data in a circle graph.

...And Why

To learn about a geometric figure at the heart of the design of many things, including amusement park rides, satellite orbits, and circle graphs

What You'll Need

- compass
- protractor

2-5 Circles

WORK TOGETHER

circles   not circles

Have each person in your group write a definition of a circle. Exchange papers. Examine the definition you receive. Try to find a counterexample. Continue until your group has agreed on a definition of a circle.

THINK AND DISCUSS

Part 1 **Parts of a Circle**

A **circle** is the set of all points in a plane *equidistant* from a given point, called the center. You name a circle by its center. Circle $P(\odot P)$ is shown.

A **radius** is a segment that has one endpoint at the center and the other endpoint on the circle. $\overline{PC}$ is a radius. $\overline{PA}$ and $\overline{PB}$ are also radii.

A **diameter** is a segment that contains the center of the circle and has both endpoints on the circle. $\overline{AB}$ is a diameter.

QUICK REVIEW

The length r of a radius is *the radius* of a circle. The length d of a diameter is *the diameter* of a circle. $d = 2r$

1. **Amusement Parks** The Scream Weaver at Paramount's Carowinds, North Carolina, is a gondola ride with a diameter of 13.1 m. Find the length of each arm. **6.55 m**

2. Complete: The center of a circle is the __?__ of a diameter. **midpoint**

Question 1 Refer students to the Quick Review which explains the relationship between the point-set and measurement concepts of diameter and radius.

Example 1

Students may be accustomed to seeing a diameter of a circle drawn horizontally. Students can convince themselves that $\overline{AB}$ is the diameter by tracing the circle and $\overline{AB}$, then folding the

paper along $\overline{AB}$. They should see that the two halves of the circle are the same so $\overline{AB}$ must go through the center.

Question 3 When students find the radius, make sure that they find the distance between the center and one of the endpoints and not between the two endpoints.

Example 2 Relating to the Real World

You may need to review how to find percents. Make sure students understand how to use the percent key on their calculators or how to change percents to decimals or fractions. Also remind them that "of" implies multiplication.

Students may want to add the angle measures to see that they total 360.

Example 1

Coordinate Geometry $\overline{AB}$ is a diameter of the circle. Find the coordinates of the center and the radius of the circle.

The center P of the circle is the midpoint of the diameter.

$$P = \left(\frac{-3 + 5}{2}, \frac{2 + 4}{2}\right) \quad \text{Use the Midpoint Formula.}$$

$$P = (1, 3) \quad \text{Simplify.}$$

The radius is the distance from the center to any point on the circle.

$$PB = \sqrt{(1 - 5)^2 + (3 - 4)^2} \quad \text{Use the Distance Formula.}$$

$$PB = \sqrt{(-4)^2 + (-1)^2} \quad \text{Simplify.}$$

$$PB = \sqrt{16 + 1} = \sqrt{17}$$

The center of the circle is $(1, 3)$. The radius is $\sqrt{17}$.

For practice with radicals, see Skills Handbook, page 660.

3. Try This Find the coordinates of the center and the radius of a circle with diameter $\overline{AB}$ whose endpoints are $A(1, 3)$ and $B(7, -5)$. $(4, -1)$; 5

Part 2 Central Angles and Arcs

You often see circle graphs in newspapers and magazines. When you make a circle graph you have to find the measure of each wedge, or central angle. A **central angle** is an angle whose vertex is the center of the circle.

Example 2 Relating to the Real World

How Do You Spend Your Day?

To learn how people really spend their time, a market research firm studied the hour-by-hour activities of more than 3,000 people. The participants were between 18 and 90 years old.

Each participant was sent a 24-h recording sheet every March for 3 years from 1992 to 1994. The study found that people spend most of their time sleeping, working, and watching television.

Source: *The New York Times*

Statistics Find the measure of each central angle in the circle graph.

Since there are 360 degrees in a circle, multiply each percent by 360 to find the measure of each central angle in the circle graph.

Sleep: 31% of 360 = 111.6
Food: 9% of 360 = 32.4
Work: 20% of 360 = 72

Must Do: 7% of 360 = 25.2
Entertainment: 18% of 360 = 64.8
Other: 15% of 360 = 54

Additional Examples

FOR EXAMPLE 1

A diameter of a circle has endpoints $A(-3, -2)$ and $B(1, 4)$. Find the coordinates of the center and the radius. $(-1, 1)$, $\sqrt{13}$

Discussion: *Describe two ways to find the length of the radius?*

FOR EXAMPLE 3

Find the measure of each arc.

a. $\overarc{MN}$ 60
b. $\overarc{LM}$ 50
c. $\overarc{KLM}$ 120
d. $\overarc{LKN}$ 250

Discussion: *Name two other major arcs.*

KINESTHETIC LEARNING If you have block scheduling or an extended class period, take students outside to demonstrate why a circle is 360°. Have students draw coordinate axes in the dirt. Standing at the "origin," a student can act as a human compass by using a meter stick extended at arm's length and touching the ground. Without changing the angle between the arm and the body, have the student slowly rotate around the origin tracing a circle in the dirt. They should see that they moved through four 90° quadrants or 360°. Students can use a similar method to draw arcs of different measures.

Have students practice naming the three types of arcs — semicircles, minor arcs, and major arcs — using the appropriate number of points and the appropriate symbols.

Example 3

Point out that the number written inside of the circle indicates the angle measure and the number written outside the circle indicates the arc measure.

Question 6 Make sure students can locate the center of their circle. Suggest that they mark it in order to know where to center the protractor.

What? Geosynchronous satellites stay above the same point on Earth's equator. They orbit Earth in a near-circular path every 24 hours at a distance 42,000 km from the Earth's center. The radius of Earth is about 6000 km. How far above Earth's surface are these satellites?
36,000 km

An *arc* is a part of a circle. There are three types of arcs: a *semicircle*, a *minor arc*, and a *major arc*.

  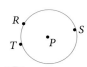

$\overparen{TRS}$ is a semicircle. $\overparen{RS}$ is a minor arc. $\overparen{RTS}$ is a major arc.
$m\overparen{TRS} = 180$ $m\overparen{RS} = m\angle RPS$ $m\overparen{RTS} = 360 - m\overparen{RS}$

A **semicircle** is half a circle. The measure of a semicircle is 180. A **minor arc** is shorter than a semicircle. The measure of a minor arc is the measure of its corresponding central angle. A **major arc** is longer than a semicircle. The measure of a major arc is 360 minus the measure of its related minor arc.

4. *Critical Thinking* What kind of arcs can you name with only two points? What kind of arcs must you name with three points? Why?
   See margin p. 99.

Adjacent arcs are two arcs in the same circle that have exactly one point in common. You can add the measures of adjacent arcs just as you can add the measures of adjacent angles.

Arc Addition Postulate

The measure of the arc formed by two adjacent arcs is the sum of the measures of the two arcs.
$$m\overparen{ABC} = m\overparen{AB} + m\overparen{BC}$$

Example 3

Find the measure of each arc.

a. $\overparen{BC}$ b. $\overparen{BD}$ c. $\overparen{ABC}$ d. $\overparen{AB}$ e. $\overparen{BAD}$

a. $m\overparen{BC} = m\angle BOC = 32$
b. $m\overparen{BD} = 32 + 58 = 90$ $m\overparen{BD} = m\overparen{BC} + m\overparen{CD}$
c. $m\overparen{ABC} = 180$ $\overparen{ABC}$ is a semicircle.
d. $m\overparen{AB} = 180 - 32 = 148$
e. $m\overparen{BAD} = 360 - m\overparen{BD}$
   $= 360 - 90 = 270$

6b. Draw a circle with the same center and a greater radius. The arc on that circle with the same central angle is a longer arc with measure 75.

5. **Try This** Find $m\angle COD$, $m\overparen{CDA}$, and $m\overparen{AD}$. **58; 180; 122**

6. a. Use a compass to draw a circle. Then use a protractor to draw $\overparen{JK}$ with measure 75. **Check students' work.**
   b. Explain how to draw a longer arc that has a measure of 75.
      See left.

98

Exercises ON YOUR OWN

1–4, 6–8. Answers may vary. Samples are given.

Identify the following in ⊙O.

1. two minor arcs $\overset{\frown}{BC}, \overset{\frown}{CD}$ **2.** two major arcs $\overset{\frown}{BDF}, \overset{\frown}{CFD}$ **3.** two semicircles $\overset{\frown}{BCE}, \overset{\frown}{BFE}$

4. three radii $\overline{OB}, \overline{OD}, \overline{OF}$ **5.** two diameters $\overline{BE}, \overline{CF}$ **6.** a pair of adjacent arcs $\overset{\frown}{BC}, \overset{\frown}{CD}$

7. an acute central angle ∠BOC **8.** an obtuse central angle ∠COE **9.** a pair of congruent angles ∠BOC, ∠EOF

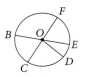

Find the diameter of a circle with the given radius.

10. 20 ft 40 ft **11.** 5 cm 10 cm **12.** $3\frac{1}{2}$m 7 m **13.** $6\sqrt{2}$ in. $12\sqrt{2}$ in. **14.** r mi $2r$ mi

Find the radius of a circle with the given diameter.

15. 13 cm 6.5 cm **16.** 10.5 m 5.25 m **17.** $5\sqrt{3}$ in. $\frac{5\sqrt{3}}{2}$ in. **18.** $\frac{1}{3}$ ft $\frac{1}{6}$ ft **19.** d km $\frac{d}{2}$ km

20. Printing Newspaper companies use offset presses to print. The paper passes between cylinders. The radius of each large cylinder is 7 in. Find *PR* in the diagram. 28 in.

21. Paper Folding Use a compass to make a circle. Cut out the circle and use paper folding to form 90°, 45°, and 135° central angles. Check students' work.

Coordinate Geometry Find the coordinates of the center and the radius of each circle with diameter $\overline{AB}$.

(0, 0); 5
22. $A(3, 4), B(-3, -4)$

(−2, 5); $\sqrt{5}$
23. $A(0, 4), B(-4, 6)$

(0.5, 4); 6.5
24. $A(-2, -2), B(3, 10)$

(−1, 4); $\sqrt{10}$
25. $A(2, 3), B(-4, 5)$

(−3, 2); 5
26. $A(-6, -2), B(0, 6)$

(3, −4.5); 8.5
27. $A(-1, -12), B(7, 3)$

Find the measure of each arc in ⊙P.

28. $\overset{\frown}{TC}$ 128 **29.** $\overset{\frown}{TBD}$ 180 **30.** $\overset{\frown}{BTC}$ 218

31. $\overset{\frown}{CD}$ 52 **32.** $\overset{\frown}{CBD}$ 308 **33.** $\overset{\frown}{TCD}$ 180

34. $\overset{\frown}{TDC}$ 232 **35.** $\overset{\frown}{TB}$ 90 **36.** $\overset{\frown}{BC}$ 142

37. Use a compass to draw ⊙A. Then use a protractor to draw $\overset{\frown}{XY}$ with measure 105. Check students' work.

38. Statistics Americans throw out more than 150 million tons of garbage each year. The circle graph shows the percent of different materials found in a typical city trash collection. a, c. See margin.

a. Find the measure of the central angle for each category (rounded to the nearest whole number).

b. Find the sum of the measures of these angles. 360

c. Writing Explain why the sum might not equal 360.

Yard Waste 16% Other 9% Paper and Paperboard 38% Food Waste 7% Wood 6% Plastics 9% Metals 8% Glass 7%

Source: *The American Almanac*

ALGEBRA Exercise 45 Help students understand why $m\widehat{PQ} = m\widehat{SR}$.

RESEARCH Exercise 48 Students can use an encyclopedia. Have them look up both "Zulu" and "Africa."

DIVERSITY Exercise 49 This problem provides a good opportunity to discuss customs and traditions of different nationalities and how they affect what a person does in a 24-h period.

CONNECTING TO STUDENTS' WORLD Exercise 50 Have students conduct a survey in school of who uses the Internet and display the data in a circle graph.

Exercises **MIXED REVIEW**

JOURNAL To get students started, ask them what circular objects they used at breakfast or to get to school.

50.

Who Is Using the Internet?

- 55+ 3%
- refused to answer 2%
- 44-54 15%
- 18-24 20%
- 35-44 25%
- 25-29 20%
- 30-34 15%

page 101   Mixed Review

56.

39. a. How many degrees does a minute hand move in 1 minute? in 5 minutes? in 20 minutes?
  b. How many degrees does an hour hand move in 5 minutes? in 10 minutes? in 20 minutes?
  c. What is the measure of the angle formed by the hands of the clock at 8:25?   102.5
    a. 6°; 30°; 120°   **b.** 2.5°; 5°; 10°

Find each indicated measure for $\odot O$.

40. a. $m\angle EOF$ 70
  b. $m\widehat{EJH}$ 180
  c. $m\widehat{FH}$ 110
  d. $m\angle FOG$ 55
  e. $m\widehat{JEG}$ 235
  f. $m\widehat{HFJ}$ 290

41. a. $m\widehat{TR}$ 90
  b. $m\angle COD$ 30
  c. $m\widehat{BT}$ 145
  d. $m\widehat{BR}$ 125
  e. $m\widehat{BTR}$ 235
  f. $m\widehat{TRB}$ 215

42. a. $m\angle LOM$ 45
  b. $m\widehat{QP}$ 45
  c. $m\widehat{PMQ}$ 315
  d. $m\angle QOL$ 135
  e. $m\widehat{QLP}$ 315

43. a. $m\angle KOV$ 80
  b. $m\widehat{KZ}$ 100
  c. $m\angle SOW$ 150
  d. $m\widehat{YVK}$ 210
  e. $m\widehat{WSZ}$ 280

Algebra Find $m\widehat{PQ}$ in $\odot A$.

44. 38

45. 160
  $(3y - 5)°$
  $(2y + 50)°$

46. 140
  $(x + 40)°$ P
  $(3x + 20)°$
  $(2x + 60)°$ Q

47. Travel Five streets come together at a traffic circle. Vehicles travel counterclockwise around the circle. Use arc measure to give directions to someone who wants to get to East Street from Neponset Street.   **Stay in the circle for a 220° arc before exiting.**

48. Research Describe the traditional life of the Zulus of South Africa. Find out how they use circles when building and designing their villages.   **Check students' work.**

100

49. Open-ended Make a circle graph showing how you spend a 24-hour weekday.
Check students' work.

50. Statistics In 1995, O'Reilly & Associates surveyed people 18 and older in the United States to find out "Who's Using the Internet?" The table shows Internet users by age groups. (Of those surveyed, 2% refused to answer.) Display the data in a circle graph.
See margin p. 100.

Who's Using the Internet?

Age	% of Surveyed Internet Users	Age	% of Surveyed Internet Users
18–24 years	20%	35–44 years	25%
25–29 years	20%	44–54 years	15%
30–34 years	15%	55+ years	3%

Source: *U.S. News & World Report*

Exercises   MIXED REVIEW

Find the values of the variables.

51. 95

$(c + 23)°$ $c°$ $(c + 52)°$

52. 135

80°
100°
$x°$ $x°$

53.

$t°$
$y°$
$t = 120; y = 60$

54.

80°   111°
$w°$ $d°$
$d = 101; w = 79$

55. Find the measure of an angle that is 16° less than its complement.
37

Getting Ready for Lesson 2-6

56. The diagram below at the left shows a 4-by-4 square on graph paper. You can divide the square into two identical pieces by cutting along grid lines. One way to do this is to make a vertical or a horizontal line. Another way is shown below at the right. Find the four other ways of doing this.   See margin p. 100.

101

CONNECTING TO PRIOR KNOWLEDGE Discuss with students examples of scale models with which they are familiar, such as doll houses, matchbox cars, and model airplanes. Also compare objects such as utensils for infants and adults and chairs and desks in elementary and high schools.

THINK AND DISCUSS

ERROR ALERT! Students may think that $\angle X$ corresponds to $\angle Q$, $\angle B$ to $\angle Y$, etc. because they are in the same relative positions on the two figures. **Remediation:** Make sure students can identify corresponding parts. Students can trace and cut out one of the figures and place it on top of the other figure so that corresponding parts "match."

Example 1 Relating to the Real World

Point out that there is more than one way to show a congruence correspondence. For example, the congruence of the fins can be expressed as $SPACE \cong DTRWB$ or $SECAP \cong DBWRT$.

Lesson Planning Options

Prerequisite Skills

- Writing and solving proportions
- Finding perimeter

Assignment Options for Exercises On Your Own

To provide flexible scheduling, this lesson can be subdivided into parts.

Resources

 Student Edition

Skills Handbook, pp. 661, 662
Extra Practice, p. 635
Glossary/Study Guide

 Teaching Resources

Chapter Support File, Ch. 2
- Practice 2-6 (two worksheets)
- Reteaching 2-6
Classroom Manager 2-6
Glossary, Spanish Resources

 Transparencies
1, 33

What You'll Learn

- Measuring congruent and similar figures
- Using properties of congruence and similarity

...And Why

To model real-world situations, such as mass production and photography

What You'll Need

- scissors
- protractor
- centimeter ruler

Connections Rocketry ... and more

2-6 Congruent and Similar Figures

THINK AND DISCUSS

Part 1

Congruent Figures

Congruent figures have exactly the same size and shape. When two figures are congruent you can slide, flip, or turn one so that it fits exactly on the other one.

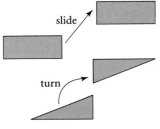

Congruent circles have congruent radii. **Congruent polygons** have congruent corresponding parts. The matching angles and sides of congruent polygons are called *corresponding parts*. Matching vertices are *corresponding vertices*. When you name congruent polygons, always list corresponding vertices in the same order.

C corresponds to R.
$\angle B$ corresponds to $\angle Q$.
$\overline{AX}$ corresponds to $\overline{PY}$.
$ACBX \cong PRQY$

Example 1 Relating to the Real World

Rocketry The fins of the rocket are congruent pentagons. Find $m\angle B$.

Because the fins are congruent, $\angle B \cong \angle E$. So you can find $m\angle B$ by first finding $m\angle E$.

By the Polygon Interior Angle-Sum Theorem, you know that the sum of the measures of the interior angles of pentagon $SPACE$ is $(5 - 2)180$, or 540.

$$m\angle S + m\angle P + m\angle A + m\angle C + m\angle E = 540$$
$$88 + 90 + 90 + 132 + m\angle E = 540$$
$$400 + m\angle E = 540$$
$$m\angle E = 140$$

So $m\angle E = m\angle B = 140$.

Example 2 ⋯⋯⋯⋯⋯⋯⋯⋯⋯⋯

$\triangle TJD \cong \triangle RCF$. List congruent corresponding parts.

$\overline{TJ} \cong \overline{RC}$ $\overline{JD} \cong \overline{CF}$ $\overline{DT} \cong \overline{FR}$

$\angle T \cong \angle R$ $\angle J \cong \angle C$ $\angle D \cong \angle F$

1. Try This $\triangle WYS \cong \triangle MKV$. List congruent corresponding parts.
Part
$\overline{WY} \cong \overline{MK}$; $\overline{YS} \cong \overline{KV}$; $\overline{SW} \cong \overline{VM}$; $\angle W \cong \angle M$; $\angle Y \cong \angle K$; $\angle S \cong \angle V$

2 **Similar Polygons**

QUICK REVIEW

Corresponding sides are *proportional* if the ratios of their lengths are equal.

Two figures that have the same shape but not necessarily the same size are similar (~). Two polygons are **similar** if (1) corresponding angles are congruent and (2) corresponding sides are proportional. The ratio of the lengths of corresponding sides is the **similarity ratio.**

Example 3 ⋯⋯⋯⋯⋯⋯⋯⋯⋯⋯

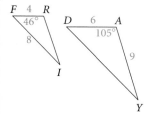

$\triangle FRI \sim \triangle DAY$. Find:

a. the similarity ratio   b. $m\angle R$ c. RI

a. Since $\overline{FR}$ and $\overline{DA}$ are corresponding sides, the similarity ratio is $\frac{FR}{DA} = \frac{4}{6} = \frac{2}{3}$.

b. $\angle R$ corresponds to $\angle A$, so $m\angle R = m\angle A$. $m\angle A = 105$, so $m\angle R = 105$.

PROBLEM SOLVING

Look Back Describe how you could use the similarity ratio to solve for *RI*.

Multiply *AY* by the similarity ratio.

c. Write a proportion to solve for RI.

$\frac{FR}{DA} = \frac{RI}{AY}$

$\frac{4}{6} = \frac{RI}{9}$ Substitution

$36 = 6 \cdot RI$ Use cross-products.

$6 = RI$ Divide each side by 6.

2. Try This Find DY and $m\angle D$.   12; 46

3. a. Find the perimeter of $\triangle FRI$.   18
   b. Find the perimeter of $\triangle DAY$.   27
   c. What is the ratio of the perimeter of $\triangle FRI$ to the perimeter of $\triangle DAY$? $\frac{2}{3}$

d. The ratio of perimeters of similar figures = the similarity ratio.

   d. Compare your answer to part (c) to the similarity ratio. Make a **conjecture** about the ratio of the perimeters of similar figures.
   e. Test your **conjecture** by drawing and measuring other pairs of similar polygons.   Check students' work.

4. *Critical Thinking* What type of similar figures have a similarity ratio of 1?   congruent figures

103

Example 4   **Relating to the Real World** ·············

It may help students to write the proportions in words first.

$$\frac{\text{width of photo}}{\text{width of poster}} = \frac{\text{length of photo}}{\text{length of poster}}$$

CRITICAL THINKING Question 6 Review with students the methods for checking whether a proportion is true, such as checking for equal cross products and simplifying both sides to the same fraction.

Have students use the tans they created in Lesson 2-1, or provide a tangram handout for the students to cut. Students should keep track of their responses by sketching the figures and labeling the sketches with the pieces used.

Technology Options

For Exercise 29, students may use geometry software to create fractal designs.

Prentice Hall Technology

 Software
- Secondary Math Lab Toolkit™
- Integrated Math Lab 26
- Computer Item Generator 2-6

Internet
- See the Prentice Hall site. (http://www.phschool.com)

Example 4   **Relating to the Real World** ·············

Photography You want to enlarge a photo that is 4 in. tall and 6 in. wide into a poster. The poster will be 24 in. wide. How tall will it be?

$$\frac{6}{24} = \frac{4}{x}$$ Write a proportion.

$6 \cdot x = 24 \cdot 4$ Use cross-products.

$x = 16$ Divide each side by 6.

The poster will be 16 in. tall.

5. What is the similarity ratio of the photo to the poster? $\frac{1}{4}$

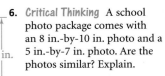

6. **Critical Thinking** A school photo package comes with an 8 in.-by-10 in. photo and a 5 in.-by-7 in. photo. Are the photos similar? Explain.

   No, $\frac{8}{5} \neq \frac{10}{7}$.

Trace the diagram and cut out the seven pieces. (Or use the tans you made in Lesson 2-1.)

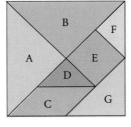

7. Which pieces are congruent?   A and B, D and F

8. Which pieces are similar? (Check that all pairs of corresponding angles are congruent and that corresponding sides are proportional.)
   A, B, D, F, G

9. Find other congruent and similar pairs by placing pieces together. Record your answers.   See margin p. 105.

Here are some examples:

congruent   similar

      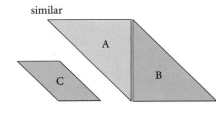

104

Exercise 1 Students may want to trace and cut out the figures to manipulate them.

Exercises 2–10 Students can identify the corresponding parts using the name of the figures or using the sketches. Encourage students to use the method they prefer.

Exercises 25–26 Some students may want to sketch congruent quadrilaterals and label the vertices.

Exercises O N Y O U R O W N

1. Identify the pairs of triangles that appear to be congruent. **A and H, B and G, C and E, F and D**

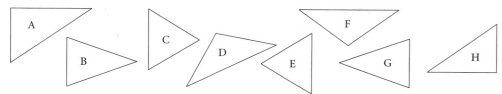

$\triangle LMC \cong \triangle BJK$. **Complete the congruence statements.**

2. $\overline{LC} \cong$ ▨ **BK**   **3.** $\overline{KJ} \cong$ ▨ **CM**   **4.** $\overline{JB} \cong$ ▨ **ML**

5. $\angle L \cong$ ▨ **∠B**   **6.** $\angle K \cong$ ▨ **∠C**   **7.** $\angle M \cong$ ▨ **∠J**

8. $\triangle CML \cong$ ▨   **9.** $\triangle KBJ \cong$ ▨   **10.** $\triangle MLC \cong$ ▨
     △KJB   **△CLM**   **△JBK**

JDRT ~ JHYX. **Complete the proportions and congruence statements.**

11. $\dfrac{JD}{JH} = \dfrac{DR}{\text{▨}}$ **HY**   **12.** $\dfrac{RT}{YX} = \dfrac{\text{▨}}{JX}$ **JT**   **13.** $\dfrac{\text{▨}}{DR} = \dfrac{YX}{RT}$ **HY**

14. $\angle D \cong$ ▨ **∠JHY**   **15.** $\angle Y \cong$ ▨ **∠R**   **16.** $\angle T \cong$ ▨
                                                                              ∠YXJ

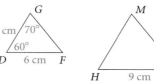

$\triangle DFG \sim \triangle HKM$. **Use the diagram to find the following.**

17. the similarity ratio of $\triangle DFG$ to $\triangle HKM$ $\frac{2}{3}$

18. the similarity ratio of $\triangle HKM$ to $\triangle DFG$ $\frac{3}{2}$

19. $m\angle F$ **50**   **20.** $m\angle K$ **50**   **21.** $m\angle M$ **70**

22. $\dfrac{DF}{HK}$ $\frac{2}{3}$ **23.** HM **7.5 cm**   **24.** GF **5.6 cm**

In Exercises 25–27, POLY ≅ SIDE.
25–26. See below.
25. List four pairs of congruent angles.

26. List four pairs of congruent sides.

27. Complete the congruence statements.
   a. $OLYP \cong$ ▨   **b.** $DESI \cong$ ▨
      IDES   **LYPO**

28. **Art** An art class is painting a mural for a spring festival. The students are working from a diagram that is 48 in. long and 36 in. high. Find the length of the mural if its height is to be 12 ft. **16 ft**

25. $\angle P \cong \angle S$; $\angle O \cong \angle I$; $\angle L \cong \angle D$; $\angle Y \cong \angle E$
26. $\overline{PO} \cong \overline{SI}$; $\overline{OL} \cong \overline{ID}$; $\overline{LY} \cong \overline{DE}$; $\overline{YP} \cong \overline{ES}$

page 104   Work Together
   9. Samples:

congruent

similar

RESEARCH Exercise 29 Students can find information on fractals in an encyclopedia. They may also want to research Georg Cantor and Benoit Mandelbrot. Numerous books are also available at the library that describe fractals in nature.

ALTERNATIVE ASSESSMENT Exercises 32–34 These exercises can help you to assess students' ability to identify congruent figures by how they list corresponding vertices.

STANDARDIZED TEST TIP Exercise 38 Once students see that *H* corresponds with *C*, have them visualize possible locations for *H*.

pages 105–107   On Your Own

30a. Sample:

$\frac{8}{3}, \frac{8}{3}$

b. Yes; all the angles are ≅ and the lengths of the corresp. sides have = ratios.

c. Sample:

$\frac{3}{2}, \frac{1}{2}$

d. Answers may vary. Sample: No; all the angles are ≅, but the ratios of the lengths of the corresp. sides need not be =.

e. All squares are similar; not all rectangles are similar; the lengths of corresp. sides of any 2 squares have = ratios and the corresp. angles are ≅; the lengths of corresp. sides of 2 rectangles need not have = ratios. Use diagrams for parts (a) and (c).

29. Research A *fractal* is a self-similar geometric pattern. It is made up of parts that are similar to the object itself. A good example of this is a fern frond. Break off any leaflet and the leaflet looks like a small fern frond. Investigate fractals and **summarize** your findings.   Check students' work.

30. a. Draw two different-sized squares on graph paper. Find the ratio of each pair of corresponding sides.
  b. Are these squares similar? Explain.
  c. Draw two different-sized rectangles on graph paper. Find the ratio of each pair of corresponding sides.
  d. Are these rectangles similar? Explain.
  e. Writing Are all squares similar? Are all rectangles similar? Explain. Sketch pictures to support your conclusion.
  a–e. See margin.

31. Critical Thinking Kimi claims that all circles are similar. Is she right? Explain.   Yes; the ratios of radii, diameters, and circumferences of 2 circles are =.

Write a congruence statement for each pair of triangles.

32.

△BJY ≅ △HXC

33.

E is the midpoint of $\overline{CD}$.
△BEC ≅ △AED

34.

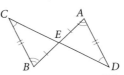

$\overrightarrow{TK}$ bisects ∠PTR.
△KPT ≅ △KRT

📱 **Choose** Use pencil and paper, mental math, or a calculator to find the values of the variables.

35.

△ABC ≅ △KLM
t = 2 in.; *x* = 15

36.

△WLJ ∼ △QBV
x = 60; *y* = 25

37.

△PRQ ∼ △SRT
2.3 cm

38. Standardized Test Prep △KJH is congruent to the triangle shown. Which of these *cannot* be the coordinates of point *H*? **E**

  A. (5, 0)   **B.** (5, 4)   **C.** (6, 4)
  D. (6, 0)   **E.** (7, 0)

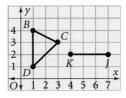

106

---

39. When you make an enlargement on a copy machine, the enlargement is similar to the original. You are making an enlargement of △ABC. Suppose you choose the 120% enlargement setting. This means that the similarity ratio of the enlargement to the original is $\frac{120}{100}$, or $\frac{6}{5}$.

   a. Find the lengths of the sides of the enlargement. **7.2 cm; 9.6 cm; 12 cm**
   b. Find the measures of the angles of the enlargement. **53; 90; 37**
   c. Suppose you use the 150% setting. Find the lengths of the sides of the triangle. **9 cm; 12 cm; 15 cm**

The triangles are similar. Find the similarity ratio of the first to the second.

40. $\frac{2}{1}$

41. $\frac{3}{4}$

42. $\frac{3}{1}$

43. a. **Photography** Is an 8 in.-by-10 in. photograph similar to a 16 in.-by 20 in. photograph? Explain. **yes;** $\frac{8}{16} = \frac{10}{20}$
   b. Is a 4 in.-by-5 in. photograph similar to a 5 in.-by-7 in. photograph? Explain. **no;** $\frac{4}{5} \neq \frac{5}{7}$

44. **Standardized Test Prep** The circle shown is congruent to a circle with center $P(1, -4)$. Which of these *cannot* be the coordinates of a point on ⊙P? **D**
   A. $(-1, -2)$ B. $(-1, -6)$ C. $(3, -2)$ D. $(3, -4)$ E. $(3, -6)$

45. **Open-ended** Draw two quadrilaterals that have sides in the ratio 2 : 1 and yet are not similar. **See sample at right.**

rhombus

square

---

page 108 Mixed Review

46.

47.

Trapezoid; slope of $\overline{BT}$ = slope of $\overline{AS}$.

Trapezoid; slope of $\overline{AB} \neq$ slope of $\overline{ST}$.

Checkpoint page 108

14.   15.

16.

Exercises MIXED REVIEW

JOURNAL Have students review what it means for a polygon to be regular.

Exercise 46 Students will need a compass and straightedge to construct a perpendicular bisector of a segment.

GETTING READY FOR LESSON 2-7 These exercises prepare students for drawing orthographic views of objects.

Wrap Up

THE BIG IDEA Ask students: *What is the difference between congruence and similarity?*

Exercises CHECKPOINT

In this Checkpoint, your students will assess their own progress on Lessons 2-4 to 2-6.

Exercises 1–4 Make sure students find the radius and not the diameter.

MENTAL MATH Exercise 17 Students can eliminate some of the answer choices by sketching the quadrilateral.

Lesson Quiz

Lesson Quiz is also available in Transparencies.

For Exercises 1–2, △*CAT* ≅ △*DOG*.

1. List the congruent corresponding parts. $\overline{CA} \cong \overline{DO}$, $\overline{AT} \cong \overline{OG}$, $\overline{TC} \cong \overline{GD}$, $\angle C \cong \angle D$, $\angle A \cong \angle O$, $\angle T \cong \angle G$

2. If $m\angle C = 90$, and $m\angle A = 40$, find $m\angle G$. **50**

For Questions 3–4, *AEGH* ~ *XZLM*, *EG* = 3, *GH* = 6, *ZL* = 1.

3. Find the similarity ratio. **3**

4. Find *LM*. **2**

Exercises MIXED REVIEW

46. *Constructions* Draw a 3-in. segment. Construct the perpendicular bisector of that segment. Check your work with a ruler and a protractor. **See margin p. 107.**

47. *Coordinate Geometry* Connect $A(3, 3)$, $B(5, 5)$, $T(9, 1)$, and $S(9, -3)$ in order. What type of quadrilateral is *ABTS*? Explain. **See margin p. 107.**

48. $M(-1, 0)$ is the midpoint of $\overline{AB}$. The coordinates of *A* are $(5, 1)$. Find the coordinates of *B*. **(−7, −1)**

49. What is the measure of each interior angle of a regular 18-gon? **160**

FOR YOUR JOURNAL

Are all regular pentagons similar? Are all regular hexagons similar? Make a conjecture about regular polygons and similarity. Justify your reasoning.

Getting Ready for Lesson 2-7

Imagine you are looking down at each of these figures from above. Describe the geometric figure you see.

50.

a circle

51.

a rectangle

52.

a rectangle

Exercises CHECKPOINT

Find the center and radius of each circle with diameter $\overline{AB}$.

1. $A(4, 1)$, $B(7, 5)$
(5.5, 3); 2.5

2. $A(0, 8)$, $B(3, 6)$
$(1.5, 7); \frac{\sqrt{13}}{2}$

3. $A(-3, 9)$, $B(4, -2)$
$(0.5, 3.5); \frac{\sqrt{170}}{2}$

4. $A(-2, -5)$, $B(-8, 4)$
$(-5, -0.5); \frac{\sqrt{117}}{2}$

Find the measure of each arc or angle in ⊙*A*.

5. $\angle WAX$ 65

6. $\overset{\frown}{RX}$ 90

7. $\angle SAR$ 25

8. $\overset{\frown}{TRW}$ 245

9. $\angle TAW$ 115

10. $\overset{\frown}{RT}$ 90

11. $\overset{\frown}{SR}$ 25

12. $\overset{\frown}{XST}$ 180

13. $\overset{\frown}{STW}$ 180

Draw a pair of figures to fit each description. **14–16. See margin p. 107.**

14. congruent right triangles

15. similar pentagons

16. similar rectangles

17. What is the most precise name for a quadrilateral with vertices at $(3, 5)$, $(-1, 4)$, $(7, 4)$, and $(3, -5)$? **A**
   A. kite   **B.** rectangle   **C.** parallelogram   **D.** rhombus   **E.** trapezoid

CONNECTING TO PRIOR KNOWLEDGE Have students create a scale drawing of the classroom or a room in their home. Have them include objects like furniture, appliances, and fixtures. Discuss how they represented three-dimensional objects. Did they draw the objects from a front view, side view, or top view?

THINK AND DISCUSS

(ESL) VISUAL LEARNING Give real-world examples of one-dimensional (i.e., a decimal point, a dot on an i or j, a period), two dimensional (i.e., images in a photograph or painting, your signature), and three-dimensional objects.

Make sure students have plenty of isometric dot paper and graph paper to use throughout this lesson.

DIVERSITY Because of poor visualization and drawing skills, some students may have great difficulty with this lesson. Provide many practice examples and opportunities to improve visual and drawing skills to remedy these difficulties.

What You'll Learn
• Drawing isometric and orthographic views of objects

...And Why
To practice a skill used in industries of all sorts

What You'll Need
• isometric dot paper
• graph paper
• straightedge
• cubes

Connections • **Animation . . . and more**

2-7 Isometric and Orthographic Drawings

THINK AND DISCUSS

Part 1 Isometric Drawings

The figures that you've studied so far in this chapter have been two-dimensional. The *faces* of three-dimensional figures are two-dimensional. Many types of industries use two-dimensional drawings of three-dimensional objects. The makers of some animated cartoons for example, use computers to create *wire-frame models* of three-dimensional characters. These wire-frame images—basically complicated stick figures—are made up of polygons.

The wire frame model of the insect's leg is made up of polygons. Notice how they are joined to give the illusion of a curved surface.

The computer forms the final image by adding a "skin" to the wire-frame and then lighting the figure.

One way to show a three-dimensional object is with an isometric drawing. An **isometric drawing** shows a corner view. It shows three sides of an object in a single drawing. Here are two examples.

Lesson Planning Options

Prerequisite Skills
• Drawing different views of a cube

Assignment Options for Exercises On Your Own

To provide flexible scheduling, this lesson can be subdivided into parts.

1 **Core** 1–8 (a), 16
Extension 12–15

2 **Core** 1–8 (b), 9–11, 17–24
Extension 25

Use Mixed Review to maintain skills.

Resources

Student Edition
Extra Practice, p. 635
Glossary/Study Guide

Teaching Resources
Chapter Support File, Ch. 2
• Practice 2-7 (two worksheets)
• Reteaching 2-7
Classroom Manager 2-7
Glossary, Spanish Resources
Chapter Support File, Ch. 11

Transparencies
6, 34

109

Example 1

Students may want to begin by first creating isometric drawings of one cube, then two cubes, then the figure in Example 1. Some may find it easier to draw all the edges of each cube, then erase the edges that are hidden.

Question 1 If wooden or plastic cubes are not available, students may use sugar cubes.

MAKING CONNECTIONS As of 1996, the Sears Tower in Chicago was the tallest office building in the world. The national headquarters for Sears, Roebuck, and Company, it was built between August, 1970, and May, 1973. It contains 110 floors, 104 elevators, and 16,100 windows.

Example 2

Some students may find it easier to create the foundation drawing in the same orientation as the isometric drawing.

Additional Examples

FOR EXAMPLE 1

Use four cubes to make a structure that has three cubes in the bottom layer and one cube in the center of the top layer. Create an isometric drawing of the cube structure.

FOR EXAMPLE 2

Create a foundation drawing for the figure in Additional Example 1.

front

FOR EXAMPLE 3

Create an orthographic drawing for the figure in Additional Example 1.

front   top   right

You can use isometric dot paper to draw cube structures.

Example 1

Create an isometric drawing of the cube structure at the left.

Step 1   Step 2   Step 3

1. Try This Build a structure using 4 cubes. Create an isometric drawing of your structure. **Check students' work.**

Another way to show some types of three-dimensional objects is with a foundation drawing. A **foundation drawing** shows the base of a structure and the height of each part. The diagram at the right is a foundation drawing of the Sears Tower in Chicago.

54	67	54
67	98	67
41	98	41

The Sears Tower is made up of nine sections. The numbers tell how many stories tall each section is.

Example 2

Create a foundation drawing for the isometric drawing below.

Isometric Drawing

Foundation Drawing

2. a. How many cubes are needed to make the structure in Example 2? 9
b. Which drawing did you use to answer part (a), the foundation drawing or the isometric drawing? Why? **Foundation; the total number of cubes is the sum of the numbers in each square.**

Point out that for consistency, an orthographic drawing should show the front, top, and right side views.

MAKING CONNECTIONS It was not until the former Soviet Union sent a space probe around the moon in 1959 that any view of the moon, other than a front view, had been seen.

Example 3

ERROR ALERT! Students may think that the right view in the orthographic drawing of the first isometric drawing should show three faces, not two. **Remediation:** Students should draw the view they see when the figure is at eye level. It may help students to build the second figure with cubes and view it from the front, top, and right side.

OPEN-ENDED Question 3 Suggest that students choose objects they can stand over to see the top view and raise to eye level to view the front and right side.

Part 2 Orthographic Drawings

A third way to show three-dimensional figures is with an orthographic drawing. An **orthographic drawing** shows a top view, front view, and right-side view. Here is an example.

Isometric Drawing   Front   Top   Right

Example 3

Create an orthographic drawing for each isometric drawing at the left.

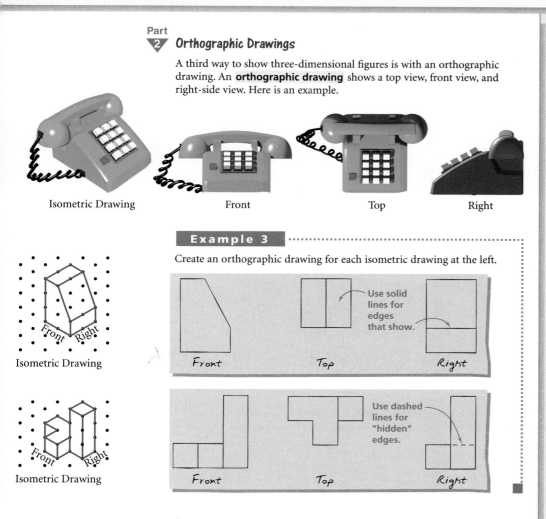

Isometric Drawing

Isometric Drawing

Use solid lines for edges that show.

Use dashed lines for "hidden" edges.

Front   Top   Right

Front   Top   Right

3. *Open-ended* Choose a simple object in your classroom. Make an orthographic drawing showing three views. **Check students' work.**

4. a. *Manipulatives* Build a cube structure for the foundation drawing at the left. Then create an isometric drawing for the structure.
   b. Create an orthographic drawing showing a top view, front view, and right-side view. **a–b. See back of book.**

3	
2	1

Front   Right

Technology Options

Prentice Hall Technology

Software
• Secondary Math Lab Toolkit™
• Computer Item Generator 2-7

Internet
• See the Prentice Hall site.
(http://www.phschool.com)

111

W O R K   T O G E T H E R

Some students may be able to complete these steps more quickly than others. Carefully arrange groups so that students can work at their own pace and so that one students does not do all the work.

Exercises   O N   Y O U R   O W N

Exercises 1–8 Students may want to use cubes before drawing the figures.

pages 112–115 On Your Own

1a.

1	1
1	1
1	1

front / right

b.

front, right, top

2a.

3
2
1

front / right

b.

front top right

3a.

3	2
1	1
1	

front / right

b.

front top right

4a.

	2	2
3	2	1

front / right

b.

front top right

W O R K   T O G E T H E R

Step 1: Work in a group to build a structure using 12 cubes. Label the sides of the structure *Front, Back, Right,* and *Left.*

Step 2: Have each member of your group use graph paper to create a foundation drawing of the structure. Then use isometric dot paper to create an isometric drawing. In both drawings, label the sides.

Step 3: Trade isometric drawings with another group. Use their drawings to re-create their structure. Use the other group's foundation drawings to check that you built their structure correctly.

Step 4: Repeat Steps 1–3, substituting orthographic drawings for the isometric drawings in Steps 2 and 3.

Front   *Right*

Exercises   O N   Y O U R   O W N

For each figure, (a) create a foundation drawing, and (b) create an orthographic drawing.   1–4. See margin.

1.   *Front Right*

2. *Front Right*

3. *Front Right*

4. *Front Right*

For each foundation plan, (a) create an isometric drawing on dot paper, and (b) create an orthographic drawing.   5–6. See margin p. 113.   7–8. See back of book.

5.

3	3
2	1

Front / Right

6.

1	2	3
	2	1

Front / Right

7.

1		
3	2	
3	2	1

Front / Right

8.

4	3
2	
2	

Front / Right

a–c. See back of book.

9. **a.** *Open-ended* Create an isometric drawing of a figure that can be constructed using 8 cubes.
   b. Create an orthographic drawing of this structure.
   c. Create a foundation plan for the figure.

112

Read the comic strip and complete Exercises 10 and 11.

SHOE by Jeff MacNelly

10. What type of drawing that you've studied in this lesson is a "bird's-eye view"?   **orthographic top view**

11. Writing Photographs of the Washington Monument are typically not taken from a bird's-eye view. Describe a situation in which you would want a photo showing a bird's-eye view.   **Sample: You need a photograph to make a topographic map of the area.**

Cross Sections Imagine cutting straight through an orange. The *cross section* will always be a circle. Describe the cross section in each diagram.

Sample:

This cross section of a cylinder is a rectangle. The width of the rectangle is the diameter of the circular base of the cylinder. The length of the rectangle is the height of the cylinder.

12.

square

13.

triangle

14.

regular hexagon with a hexagonal hole

15.

isosceles triangle

16. Probability Jake makes a structure using 27 wooden cubes. He paints four of the faces blue and leaves the top and bottom unpainted. Then he takes the structure apart and places the cubes in a bag. Leah closes her eyes, reaches into the bag, and pulls out a cube.
   a. What is the probability that the cube is unpainted? $\frac{1}{9}$
   b. What is the probability that two of its faces are blue? $\frac{4}{9}$
   c. What is the probability that only one of its faces is blue? $\frac{4}{9}$

5a.

b.

front   top   right

6a.

b.

front   right

top

21. front right top

22. front top right

23. front top right

24. front right top

Match each isometric drawing with the correct orthographic drawing.

17. B   18. A 19. D 20. C

A. Right Top Front

B. Right Top Front

C. Right Top Front

D. Right Top Front

Create an orthographic drawing for each isometric drawing.   21–24. See margin.

21. 22. 23. 24.

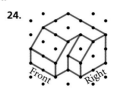

25. **Engineering** Engineers use an *engineering layout* to describe structures. A complete layout includes three orthographic views and an isometric view. Make a complete engineering layout for the foundation plan.   See back of book.

4	3	2
3	2	1
2	1	

Right
Front

Top   Isometric   Front   Right

Engineering Layout

THE BIG IDEA Ask students: *Describe the difference between an isometric and an orthographic drawing. Which type of drawing do you think best describes an object? Explain.*

RETEACHING ACTIVITY Students create isometric and orthographic drawings of objects. (Reteaching worksheet 3-7)

Geometry at Work

For further information about the training and skills necessary to be a industrial designer, contact accredited institutions that offer industrial design degrees such as Arizona State University, or the Massachusetts College of Art.

You can also contact the CORE Industrial Design Network on the Internet at http://www.core77.com.

Encourage students to investigate these topics:

- the training necessary to become an industrial designer
- the math and computer skills used by industrial designers
- the types of industries that hire interior designers

In the Mini Project, student should specify whether their drawing shows the right shoe or the left shoe.

Chapter Project *Find Out by Modeling*

Soma is a three-dimensional puzzle made of unit cubes. All Soma pieces consist of 3 or 4 unit cubes. Each cube shares a face with at least one other cube. Every Soma piece must contain at least two cubes, which meet to form a 90° dihedral angle. (A *dihedral angle* is an angle formed by two planes.) There are exactly seven Soma pieces, and all are different. The photograph shows two Soma pieces.

- Build a set of Soma pieces by gluing cubes together.
- Draw the other five Soma pieces on isometric dot paper.
- Use all seven Soma pieces to build a cube.

See back of book.

Exercises **MIXED REVIEW**

Find the length of each segment with the given endpoints. Then find the coordinates of the midpoint of each segment.

26. $A(4, 6)$ and $B(2, 9)$
$\sqrt{13}$; (3, 7.5)

27. $G(-3, -1)$ and $H(1, 2)$
5; (−1, 0.5)

28. Use slope to determine whether points $A(0, 1)$, $B(-3, -2)$, and $C(4, 5)$ are collinear.
The slopes are 1, 1, and 1; the points are collinear.

Draw a diagram that illustrates each concept.

29. adjacent angles

30. perpendicular bisector

29–30. See back of book.

Geometry at Work

Industrial Designer

Industrial designers work on two-dimensional surfaces to develop products that have three-dimensional appeal to consumers. They use computer-aided design (CAD) software to create two-dimensional screen images and manipulate them for three-dimensional effects. Fashion designers use CAD to study their creations on electronic human forms from various angles and distances.

Mini Project: Design an athletic shoe. Use an engineering layout to display your design. Include three orthographic views and an isometric view.

Lesson Quiz

Lesson Quiz is also available in Transparencies.

	2	1	right
2	1		
front			

1. Create an isometric drawing for the foundation plan. See back of book.

2. Create an orthographic drawing for the foundation plan. See back of book.

3. Create a foundation plan for the figure given below. See back of book.

Finishing the Chapter Project

PROJECT DAY You may wish to plan a project day on which students share their completed projects. Encourage groups to explain their process as well as their product.

PROJECT NOTEBOOK Have students review their project work and bring their notebooks up to date.

- Have students review the tangram pieces, pentominoes, and Soma pieces they created for the project. Also have them review the figures they created using these objects.

- Ask students to share any insights they found in completing the project, such as patterns they discovered. Also, ask which figures students found easy to make and which were more difficult.

SCORING RUBRIC

3 Student's models are created correctly and the instructions for making them are accurate. The display is clear, organized, and uses geometric terms correctly.

2 Student's models are created correctly and most of the instructions for making them are accurate. The display is clear, organized, and uses geometric terms with only minor errors.

1 Student's models are created with minor errors. The instructions have minor flaws. The display is organized but geometric terms are used improperly or unclearly.

0 Major elements are incomplete or missing.

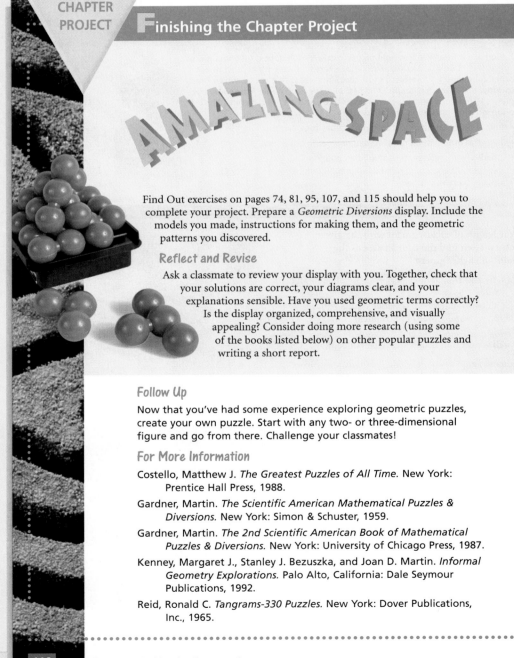

CHAPTER PROJECT

Finishing the Chapter Project

AMAZING SPACE

Find Out exercises on pages 74, 81, 95, 107, and 115 should help you to complete your project. Prepare a *Geometric Diversions* display. Include the models you made, instructions for making them, and the geometric patterns you discovered.

Reflect and Revise

Ask a classmate to review your display with you. Together, check that your solutions are correct, your diagrams clear, and your explanations sensible. Have you used geometric terms correctly? Is the display organized, comprehensive, and visually appealing? Consider doing more research (using some of the books listed below) on other popular puzzles and writing a short report.

Follow Up

Now that you've had some experience exploring geometric puzzles, create your own puzzle. Start with any two- or three-dimensional figure and go from there. Challenge your classmates!

For More Information

Costello, Matthew J. *The Greatest Puzzles of All Time.* New York: Prentice Hall Press, 1988.

Gardner, Martin. *The Scientific American Mathematical Puzzles & Diversions.* New York: Simon & Schuster, 1959.

Gardner, Martin. *The 2nd Scientific American Book of Mathematical Puzzles & Diversions.* New York: University of Chicago Press, 1987.

Kenney, Margaret J., Stanley J. Bezuszka, and Joan D. Martin. *Informal Geometry Explorations.* Palo Alto, California: Dale Seymour Publications, 1992.

Reid, Ronald C. *Tangrams-330 Puzzles.* New York: Dover Publications, Inc., 1965.

Wrap Up

 HOW AM I DOING? Have students work in small groups. Ask each group to make a short presentation describing the geometric figures presented in the chapter. Each presentation must include a visual aid and a sample problem.

KEY TERMS The numbers in parentheses direct students to the pages where the terms (or symbols) are used or defined. Students should be able to (1) write a simple explanation of each term, (2) illustrate the term with a diagram, or (3) show an example that uses the term.

Exercises 1–4 Make sure students find the values of the variables *and* classify each triangle.

STANDARDIZED TEST TIP Exercise 5 Make sure that students do not conclude that a triangle is not obtuse if they find $x < 90$.

---

2 Wrap Up

Key Terms

acute triangle (p. 71)
adjacent arcs (p. 98)
circle (p. 96)
central angle (p. 97)
concave (p. 76)
congruent circles (p. 102)
congruent polygons (p. 102)
convex (p. 76)
corollary (p. 70)
diameter (p. 96)
equiangular polygon (p. 78)
equiangular triangle (p. 71)
equilateral polygon (p. 78)
equilateral triangle (p. 71)
exterior angle (p. 69)
foundation drawing (p. 110)

isometric drawing (p. 109)
isosceles trapezoid (p. 91)
isosceles triangle (p. 71)
kite (p. 91)
major arc (p. 98)
minor arc (p. 98)
obtuse triangle (p. 71)
orthographic drawing
  (p. 111)
parallelogram (p. 91)
polygon (p. 76)
radius (p. 96)
rectangle (p. 91)
regular polygon (p. 78)
remote interior angle (p. 69)
rhombus (p. 91)

right triangle (p. 71)
scalene triangle (p. 71)
semicircle (p. 98)
similar polygons (p. 103)
similarity ratio (p. 103)
square (p. 91)
trapezoid (p. 91)

How am I doing?

• State three ideas from this chapter that you think are important. Explain your choices.
• Describe different ways of classifying triangles and quadrilaterals.

Resources

📖 **Student Edition**
Extra Practice, p. 635
Glossary/Study Guide

📦 **Teaching Resources**
Study Skills Handbook
Glossary, Spanish Resources

Triangles   2-1

The sum of the measures of the angles of a triangle is 180. The measure of each **exterior angle** of a triangle equals the sum of the measures of its two **remote interior angles,** and is therefore greater than the measure of either remote interior angle.

You can classify triangles according to their sides and angles.

Find the values of the variables. Then classify each triangle by its sides and angles.

$x = 45$; $y = 45$; isosceles; right

1.

$x°$, $78°$, $41°$

61; scalene acute

2.

110°, 35°, $x°$

35; isosceles obtuse

3.

60°, $x°$, $y°$ 120°

$x = 60$; $y = 60$; equilateral; equiangular

4.

$x°$, $y°$ 135°

5. Standardized Test Prep The measures of the angles of different triangles are shown below. Which triangle is obtuse? **D**

A. $x + 10$, $x - 20$, $x + 25$ **B.** x, $2x$, $3x$
C. $20x + 10$, $30x - 2$, $7x + 1$ **D.** $10x - 3$, $14x - 20$, $x + 3$
E. none of the above

117

Wrap Up   pages 117–119

29.

Polygons and Classifying Quadrilaterals   2-2, 2-4

A **polygon** is a closed plane figure with at least three sides. A polygon is **convex** if no diagonal contains points outside the polygon. Otherwise, it is **concave**. A **regular polygon** is equilateral and equiangular.

The sum of the measures of the interior angles of an *n*-gon is $(n - 2)180$. The sum of the measures of the exterior angles (one at each vertex) of an *n*-gon is 360.

Quadrilaterals have four sides. Some quadrilaterals have special names.

Find the measure of each interior angle and exterior angle for each regular polygon.

6. a hexagon
120; 60

7. an octagon
135; 45

8. a decagon
144; 36

9. a 24-gon
165; 15

Algebra Find the values of the variables and the lengths of the sides.

10. isosceles trapezoid *ABCD*

A 2x − 2 *B*

2x − 7   x + 1

D   *C*
x − 1

8; 14, 9, 7, 9

11. kite *KLMN*

L
m + 3   m + 2t
K   *M*
3m − 5   t + 9
N

m = 4; t = 5; 7, 14, 14, 7

12. rhombus *PQRS*

P
4a + 2   2a + 2b
S   *Q*
6a   3a + b + 1
R

a = 1; b = 2; 6, 6, 6, 6

Parallel and Perpendicular Lines in the Coordinate Plane   2-3

The slopes of two nonvertical parallel lines are equal. Two lines parallel to a third line are parallel to each other.

The product of the slopes of two nonvertical perpendicular lines is −1. In a plane, two lines perpendicular to a third line are parallel to each other.

Find the slopes of $\overleftrightarrow{AB}$ and $\overleftrightarrow{CD}$. Then determine if the lines are parallel, perpendicular, or neither.
5; 3; neither

13. $A(-1, -4), B(2, 11), C(1, 1), D(4, 10)$

4; 4; parallel

14. $A(2, 10), B(-1, -2), C(3, 7), D(0, -5)$

15. $A(-3, 3), B(0, 2), C(1, 3), D(-2, -6)$
$-\frac{1}{3}$; 3; perpendicular

16. $A(-1, 3), B(6, 10), C(-6, 0), D(4, 10)$
1; 1; parallel

Circles   2-5

A **circle** is the set of all points in a plane equidistant from one point called the center. The measure of a minor arc is the measure of its corresponding central angle. The measure of a major arc is 360 minus the measure of its related minor arc. **Adjacent arcs** have exactly one point in common.

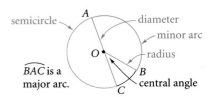

$\overset{\frown}{BAC}$ is a major arc.

Exercises 17–20 Students can find the radius by finding the length of the segment between the center and one of the points on the circle or by finding the length of the diameter and dividing by 2.

OPEN-ENDED Exercise 29 Students may want to draw two circles of different sizes and use the method given on page 79 to draw two rectangular hexagons.

Remind students that the new mathematical terms in this chapter are defined in the Glossary/Students Guide in the back of the book.

Getting Ready for Chapter 3

Students may work these exercises independently or in small groups. The skills previewed will help prepare students for working with transformations.

Find the coordinates of the center and the radius of each circle with diameter $\overline{AB}$.

17. $A(4, 0)$, $B(4, 6)$
(4, 3); 3

18. $A(2, -3)$, $B(0, 1)$
(1, −1); $\sqrt{5}$

19. $A(-4, -5)$, $B(2, -1)$
(−1, −3); $\sqrt{13}$

20. $A(7, 2)$, $B(4, 8)$
(5.5, 5); $\frac{3\sqrt{5}}{2}$

Find each measure.

21. $m\angle APD$ 30

22. $m\widehat{AC}$ 120

23. $m\widehat{ABD}$ 330

24. $m\angle CPA$ 120

Congruent and Similar Figures   2-6

Congruent polygons have congruent corresponding parts. **Similar polygons** have congruent corresponding angles and proportional corresponding sides. The ratio of the lengths of corresponding sides is the **similarity ratio**.

$RSTUV \cong KLMNO$. **Complete each congruence statement.**

25. $\overline{TS} \cong$ ■ $\overline{ML}$

26. $\angle N \cong$ ■ $\angle U$

27. $\overline{LM} \cong$ ■ $\overline{ST}$

28. $VUTSR \cong$ ■
ONMLK

29. *Open-ended* Sketch a pair of similar hexagons.
See p. 118 for sample.

Isometric and Orthographic Drawings   2-7

There are different ways to make two-dimensional drawings of three-dimensional objects. An **isometric drawing** shows three sides of an object in one drawing. A **foundation drawing** shows the bottom of a structure and the height of each part. An **orthographic drawing** shows the top, front, and right-side view of an object.

30. Use the isometric drawing at the right. a–b. See margin.
   a. Make an orthographic drawing.
   b. Make a foundation drawing.

31. *Writing* Describe a situation in which an orthographic drawing is useful. **An orthographic drawing is useful when parts of the object obscure each other in isometric view.**

Getting Ready for ....► CHAPTER 3

Draw a pair of figures to fit each description.   32–37. See margin.

32. similar acute triangles with similarity ratio $\frac{1}{2}$

33. similar quadrilaterals with similarity ratio $\frac{3}{4}$

Draw each figure. Then draw a line dividing the figure in half.

34. regular octagon   **35.** rectangle   **36.** isosceles trapezoid   **37.** kite

119

ENHANCED MULTIPLE CHOICE QUESTIONS are more complex than traditional multiple choice questions, which assess only one skill. Enhanced multiple choice questions assess the processes that students use, as well as the end results. The questions are written so that students use more than one strategy to solve the problem. Using multiple strategies is encouraged by the National Council of Teachers of Mathematics (NCTM). **Exercise 25** is an enhanced multiple choice question.

FREE RESPONSE QUESTIONS do not give answer choices. Some exercises have more than one possible answer. Students need to give only one correct response. **Exercises 1–6, 8–14, 16–24 and 26–27** are free response questions.

WRITING EXERCISES allow students to describe how they think about and understand the concepts they have learned. **Exercise 7** is a writing exercise.

OPEN-ENDED PROBLEMS allow for more than one solution. Students must construct their own responses instead of choosing from possible answers. The student responses will help you determine the depth of their understanding and any possible areas of difficulty. **Exercise 15** is an open-ended problem.

Resources

 Teaching Resources

Chapter Support File, Ch. 2
- Chapter Assessment, Forms A and B
- Alternative Assessment
Chapter Assessment, Spanish Resources

 Teacher's Edition

See also p. 66E for assessment options

 Software

Computer Item Generator

Assessment   page 120

7. If no diagonal contains points outside the polygon, then it is convex. If not, then it is concave.

15a. Sample: (0, 0), (2, 2), (4, 0), (2, −2)
b. Sample: (2, 3), (5, −1), (4, −3), (1, 1)
c. Sample: (1, 2), (4, 8), (5, 0), (8, 6)
d. Sample: (0, 5), (5, 0), (5, 2), (2, 5)

Use a protractor and a centimeter ruler to classify each triangle by its angles and sides.

1.

acute isosceles

2.
obtuse scalene

Algebra Find the values of the variables.

3. 40
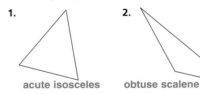

4. $x = 55; y = 70$

5. 109

6. $x = 85; y = 100; z = 100$

7. **Writing** Explain how you can determine if a polygon is concave or convex.
See margin.

Sketch each pair of lines. Tell whether they are *parallel, perpendicular,* **or** *neither.*

8. perpendicular
$y = 4x + 7$
$y = -\frac{1}{4}x - 3$

9. parallel
$y = 3x - 4$
$y = 3x + 1$

10. $y = x + 5$
$y = -5x - 1$
neither

11. $y = x - 6$
$y = -x + 2$
perpendicular

Coordinate Geometry Graph quadrilateral $ABCD$. Then determine the most precise name for each figure.

12. $A(1, 2), B(11, 2), C(7, 5), D(4, 5)$ trapezoid

13. $A(3, -2), B(5, 4), C(3, 6), D(1, 4)$ kite

14. $A(1, -4), B(1, 1), C(-2, 2), D(-2, -3)$ parallelogram

---

15. *Open-ended* Write the coordinates of four points that determine each figure.
a. square
b. parallelogram
c. rectangle
d. trapezoid
a–d. See margin.

Find the radius of a circle with the given diameter.

16. 6 ft
3 ft
17. 5.1 m
2.55 m
18. $4\sqrt{5}$ in.
$2\sqrt{5}$ in.

Find each measure for $\odot P$.

19. $m\angle BPC$ 40

20. $m\widehat{AB}$ 50

21. $m\widehat{ADC}$ 270

22. $m\widehat{ADB}$ 310

Find the values of the variables for each pair of similar figures.

23.

$x = 42; y = 138; z = 9$

24.

$x = 50; y = 3$

25. *Standardized Test Prep* What is the measure of each exterior angle of a regular 12-gon? **B**

A. 150 **B.** 30 **C.** 300 **D.** 210 **E.** 36
26–27. See back of book.

Use the figure below for Exercises 26 and 27.

26. Create an isometric drawing.

27. Create an orthographic drawing.

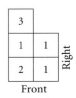
Front

120

Cumulative Review

Item	Review Topic	Chapter
1	Classifying Quadrilaterals	2
2	Planes	1
3, 12	Parallel and Perpendicular Lines in the Coordinate Plane	2
4	Circles	2
5	Measuring Angles	1
6	Triangles	2

Item	Review Topic	Chapter
7, 11	Coordinate Plane	1
8	Using Patterns	1
9	Deductive Reasoning	1
10	Polygons	2
13	Isometric Drawings	2
14	Basic Constructions	1

2 Cumulative Review

For Exercises 1–10, choose the correct letter.

1. What is a name for the quadrilateral below? **D**

   I. square   **II.** rectangle
  III. rhombus   **IV.** parallelogram
  A. I only   **B.** IV only   **C.** I and II
  D. II and IV   **E.** I and III

2. Which can be the intersection of three distinct planes? **C**
   I. a point   **II.** a line
  III. a plane   **IV.** a ray
  A. I only   **B.** II only   **C.** I and II
  D. II and IV   **E.** I, II, and III

3. Which line is parallel to $y = 3x - 2$? **E**
  A. $y = \frac{1}{3}x + 5$ **B.** $y = 3$
  C. $y = -3x + 1$ **D.** $y = -\frac{1}{3}x - 4$
  E. none of the above

4. Find the diameter of a circle with radius $6\sqrt{5}$. **A**
  A. $12\sqrt{5}$ **B.** $6\sqrt{10}$ **C.** $3\sqrt{5}$
  D. $6\sqrt{2.5}$ **E.** none of the above

5. What is $m\angle CDF$? **C**

  A. 18   **B.** 274   **C.** 86   **D.** 94
  E. cannot be determined from the information given

6. $\triangle ABC$ is obtuse. Two vertices of the triangle are $A(3, 4)$ and $B(-1, 1)$. What could be the coordinates of point C? **A**
  A. $(-1, -3)$ **B.** $(3, 1)$ **C.** $(0, 0)$
  D. $(-1, 4)$ **E.** none of the above

7. What is the length of the segment with endpoints at $A(1, 7)$ and $B(-3, -1)$? **B**
  A. 8   **B.** $4\sqrt{5}$ **C.** 40   **D.** $2\sqrt{10}$ **E.** $\sqrt{5}$

8. What is the next number in the pattern $1, -4, 9, -16 \ldots$? **D**
  A. -25 **B.** -5 **C.** 5   **D.** 25   **E.** 35

Compare the boxed quantity in Column A with the boxed quantity in Column B. Choose the best answer.

A. The quantity in Column A is greater.

B. The quantity in Column B is greater.

C. The two quantities are equal.

D. The relationship cannot be determined on the basis of the information supplied.

Column A	Column B

$\angle A$ is a supplement of $\angle B$.

9.

$m\angle A$	$m\angle B$	**D**

10.

the measure of each interior angle of a regular hexagon	the measure of each exterior angle of a regular octagon	**A**

Find each answer.

11. What are the coordinates of the midpoint of $\overline{CD}$ with endpoints $C(5, 3)$ and $D(0, -7)$? **(2.5, -2)**

12. *Open-ended* Write an equation of a line perpendicular to the line $y = 6x + 4$.
                    Sample: $y = -\frac{1}{6}x - 2$

13. Create an isometric drawing for this foundation plan. **See back of book.**

Front   Right

14. Draw an angle. Then construct another angle congruent to the first. **Check students' work.**

Resources

Teaching Resources

Chapter Support File, Ch. 2
- Cumulative Review
- Standardized Test Practice

Teacher's Edition

See also p. 66E for assessment options

Transformations: Shapes in Motion

To accommodate flexible scheduling, some lessons are divided into parts.
Assignment Options are given in the Lesson Planning Options for each lesson.

3-1   Reflections (pp. 124–130)

Part **1** An Introduction to Transformations
Part **2** Reflections

Key Terms: image, isometry, maps, orientation, preimage, prime notation, reflection, transformation

3-2   Translations (pp. 132–137)

Key Terms: composition, frieze pattern, strip pattern, translation

3-3   Rotations (pp. 138–143)

Key Terms: rotation

3-4   Compositions of Reflections (pp. 144–150)

Part **1** Compositions of Two Reflections
Part **2** Compositions of Three Reflections

Key Terms: glide reflection

3-5   Symmetry (pp. 152–158)

Part **1** Reflectional Symmetry
Part **2** Rotational Symmetry

Key Terms: half-turn, line symmetry, point symmetry, reflectional symmetry, rotational symmetry, symmetry

3-6   Tessellations (pp. 159–165)

Part **1** Identifying Figures that Tessellate
Part **2** Tessellations and Symmetry

Key Terms: glide reflectional symmetry, pure tessellation, tessellation, tilings, translational symmetry

3-7   Dilations (pp. 166–172)

Key Terms: dilation, enlargement, reduction, scalar multiplication, scale factor, similarity transformation

PACING OPTIONS

This chart suggests pacing only for the core lessons and their parts, and it is
provided merely as a possible guide. It will help you determine how much
time you have in your schedule to cover other features, such as the Chapter
Project, Math Toolboxes, Wrap Up, and Assessment.

	1 Class Period	1 Class Period	1 Class Period	1 Class Period	1 Class Period	1 Class Period	1 Class Period	1 Class Period	1 Class Period
Traditional (40–45 min class periods)	3-1 **1**	3-1 **2**	3-2	3-3	3-4 **1**	3-4 **2**	3-5 **1**	3-5 **2**	3-6 **1**
Block Scheduling (90 min class periods)	3-1 **1** **2**	3-2	3-3	3-4 **1** **2**	3-5 **1** **2**	3-6 **1** **2**	3-7		

What Students Will Learn and Why

In this chapter, students learn to describe changes in shape and size with transformational geometry and how to recognize isometries. They identify and describe reflections, translations, and rotations. They learn how composition of reflections are related to other isometries. They learn how to identify glide reflections, symmetries, and figures that tessellate. Finally, students learn how to locate dilation images of figures. The principles presented in the chapter have applications in many diverse fields such as science, architecture, music, and history.

Discussing the Chapter/Building on Experience

The concept map below relates chapter topics to real-world applications. You and your class may wish to add to the map or develop maps of your own. The center oval describes the topic of the chapter. The next level displays topics within the lessons. The outer ovals reflect applications of the content. As you and your class build a concept map, invite students to discuss applications with which they are familiar.

1 Class Period	1 Class Period	1 Class Period	1 Class Period	1 Class Period	1 Class Period	1 Class Period	1 Class Period	1 Class Period	1 Class Period	1 Class Period
3-6	3-7									

Interactive Questioning Tips

A question is interactive when there is "give and take" between the questioner (teacher or student) and the respondent. In Think and Discuss or when a critical thinking question is asked, it is important not to accept one-word answers. Coax more information from a student by asking follow-up questions like "How do you know?" or "Why do you think so?" Encouraging students to expand on their answers promotes active participation and stimulates higher levels of thought. These two elements are essential in developing high-level thinking skills. For example, in Lesson 3-4, students are asked to explain why a glide reflection changes orientations.

Skills Practice

Every lesson provides skill practice with Try This exercises, Exercises On Your Own, and Exercises Mixed Review. The Student Edition includes Checkpoints (pp. 143, 158) and Preparing for Standardized Tests (p. 179). In the Teacher's Edition, the Lesson Planning Options section for each lesson lists Prerequisite Skills students should know for that lesson. At the back of the Student Edition is the Skills Handbook—mini-lessons on math your students may need to review. The Chapter Support File for Chapter 3 in the Teaching Resources box includes two Practice worksheets per lesson, a worksheet for two Checkpoints, and worksheets for Cumulative Review and Standardized Test Preparation.

Diverse Learning and Teaching Styles

In your Teacher's Edition, you will find suggestions as to how you can help students complete mathematical tasks in Chapter 3 by reinforcing various learning styles. Here are some examples.

- **Visual learning** use puzzle pieces to model slides, flips, and turns (p.124), use a tracing of a tessellation to find symmetries (p.163), use diagrams to verify that multiplying the coordinates of the point of a diagram by the scale factor gives the coordinates of its image (p.168)

- **Tactile learning** use paper folding to create the reflection image of quadrilaterals (p.125), use mirrors to investigate the properties of reflections (p. 126), create pavement tiling using pattern blocks (p.159)

- **Auditory learning** describe a composition of isometries (p.147)

- **Kinesthetic learning** use a coordinate grid on the floor of the classroom and physically represent points and "act out" translations (p.133), stand at the center of a circle and describe what they see as other students slowly walk around the circle (p.140), analyze and discuss the symmetry of a car hubcap (p.155)

Alternative Activity for Lesson 3-1

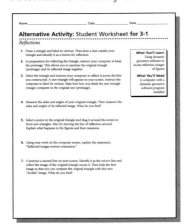

for use with Example 2, uses geometry software to draw the reflection images of figures and identify isometries through measurement.

Alternative Activity for Lesson 3-3

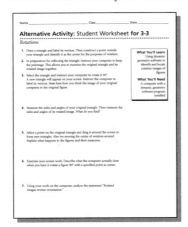

for use with Example 1, uses geometry software to draw the rotated images of figures and identify isometries through measurement.

Alternative Activity for Lesson 3-7

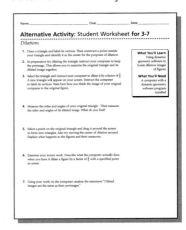

for use with the Work Together and Think and Discuss, uses geometry software to draw the dilation images of figures and informally identify similarity of figures.

Cooperative Learning Tips

When used effectively, cooperative learning can help students develop interpersonal skills, learn to perform specific roles in a group, and learn to carry out specific responsibilities. The components of Chapter 3 provide a range of cooperative learning opportunities.

- In the Student Edition, the **Work Together** parts of lessons are specifically designed for cooperative learning activities.

- In the Teacher's Edition, you will find helpful hints for addressing diverse learning styles (see page C for Chapter 3). For every lesson, you will find a **Reteaching Activity**, which may involve cooperative learning.

Materials and Manipulatives

The authors expect all students to use scientific calculators. Calculator use is integrated throughout the course.

- calculator (3-7)
- centimeter ruler (3-2, 3-7)
- clear tape (3-6)
- colored pencils (optional) (3-3)
- compass (3-3)
- graph paper (3-1, 3-2, 3-4, 3-7)
- lined paper (3-4)
- MIRA™ (optional) (3-1)
- protractor (3-1, 3-3)
- ruler (3-1, 3-6)
- scissors (3-2, 3-6)
- straightedge (3-1, 3-3, 3-4)

TECHNOLOGY OPTIONS

Technology Tools		Chapter Project	3-1	3-2	3-3	3-4	3-5	3-6	3-7
Calculator		Assumed that students have scientific calculators at any time.							
Software	Secondary Math Lab Toolkit™		✔	✔	✔	✔	✔	✔	✔
	Integrated Math Lab			✔				✔	
	Computer Item Generator		✔	✔	✔	✔	✔	✔	✔
	Student Edition						✔T		✔
Video	Video Field Trip	✔							
CD-ROM	Multimedia Geometry Lab		✔	✔	✔	✔			
Internet		See the Prentice Hall site. (http://www.phschool.com)							

✔T indicates Math Toolbox.

The Prentice Hall Geometry program offers you a rich variety of technology options. Be assured that all these options are provided as a means of enriching the program and are not essential for the successful completion of the course.

Assessment Options

The Prentice Hall Geometry Program provides you with many options. From these options, you may choose instructional materials and techniques appropriate for your students, or those necessary to meet your district's curriculum requirements. As the chart indicates, the program also supports your teaching efforts by offering you many choices for assessment.

ASSESSMENT OPTIONS

Assessment Support Materials	Chapter Project	3-1	3-2	3-3	3-4	3-5	3-6	3-7	Chapter End
Chapter Project	▲■●		▲■	▲■	▲■	▲■		▲■	▲■
Checkpoints				▲■●		▲■●			
Self-Assessment		▲■					▲■	▲■	▲■
Writing Assignment		▲■	▲	▲■	▲●	▲	▲■	▲■●	●▲
Chapter Assessment									▲■●
Alternative Assessment		■	■	■	■	■	■	■	●■
Cumulative Review									●
Standardized Test Prep		▲■		▲■				▲■	▲■●
Computer Item Generator	Can be used to create custom-made practice or assessment at any time.								

▲ = Student Edition   ■ = Teacher's Edition   ● = Teaching Resources

Checkpoints

Alternative Assessment

Chapter Assessment

Available in both Form A and Form B

Making the Right Connections

Mathematics is imbedded in nearly every walk of life. The National Council of Teachers of Mathematics (NCTM) encourages educators to recognize these connections and to emphasize them for the purpose of better educating students for success in life and in a global economy. The **Connections** chart below highlights these connections for Chapter 3.

CONNECTIONS

Lesson	Interdisciplinary Connections	Career Prep	Other Real World Connections	Math Integration	NCTM Standards
Chapter Project	Art History	Design	Space Rockets Pottery Currency		Problem Solving Connections
3-1	History Chemistry	Engineering	Emergency Vehicles Surveillance Medicine	Coordinate Geometry	Geometry and Spatial Sense Communication Problem Solving
3-2	Art Music	Photography Graphic Design Manufacturing	Navigation	Coordinate Geometry	Geometry and Spatial Sense Communication Problem Solving
3-3	Art Astronomy Language Arts	Engineering	Native American Art	Coordinate Geometry	Communication Problem Solving Connections Geometry and Spatial Sense
3-4	Art	Architecture	Kaleidoscope Wallpaper Patterns	Coordinate Geometry Probability	Geometry and Spatial Sense Communication Problem Solving
3-5	Art Literature	Design	Languages Logos Rug Designs	Geometry in 3 Dimensions Algebra Coordinate Geometry	Communication Geometry and Spatial Sense Problem Solving
3-6	Art	Architecture	Escher Prints Honeycomb Mosaics		Connections Geometry and Spatial Sense Communication Problem Solving
3-7	Art	Cartography Architecture Graphic Design	Human Development Movies Maps Photographs	Coordinate Geometry	Geometry and Spatial Sense Communication Problem Solving

CONNECTING TO PRIOR LEARNING Elicit from students examples of geometric patterns they have observed (wallpaper, stencils, floor tiles, tapestries, etc.). Explain that geometric patterns can be created using slides, flips, turns, and dilations, all of which are types of transformations.

CULTURAL CONNECTIONS Ask students if they have ever seen authentic Ukrainian-painted eggs, Native American pottery, Japanese kimonos, or African cloth. Ask knowledgeable students to present a visual display of repeating patterns found in these objects.

INTERDISCIPLINARY CONNECTIONS In ancient Greek and Roman buildings, a sculptured *frieze* often decorated the center section of an *entablature*, found above the *colonnade*. Have interested students give a verbal/visual presentation of popular frieze designs from ancient or contemporary buildings.

ABOUT THE PROJECT Students identify frieze patterns that were created using reflections, translations, rotations, and glide reflections. Students learn how to classify the patterns by their symmetries. They also design their own patterns.

Technology Options

Prentice Hall Technology

Video
• Video Field Trip 3, "Cultural Patterns," a look at African cultural designs

CHAPTER

3 **T**ransformations: Shapes in Motion

Relating to the Real World

Many geometric figures in the real world do not sit still. They move; they change shape; they change size. You can describe these changes with transformational geometry. The principles you will study here have applications in many diverse fields —from science and architecture to music and history.

Reflections	Translations	Rotations	Compositions of Reflections	Symmetry

Lessons   3-1   3-2   3-3   3-4   3-5

- Assign students to work with a partner or in small groups. Have students refer to the center row of the photograph on pages 122–123. Ask groups to describe any patterns they see.

- Have teams each draw a nonregular polygon, trace it, and cut it out. Then have them use their cutouts to create patterns similar to the one in the photograph.

TRACKING THE PROJECT You may wish to have students read Finishing the Chapter Project on page 173 to help them get an overview of the project. Set benchmark deadlines for students to show their work in progress.

CHAPTER PROJECT

FRIEZE FRAMES

Ukrainian painted eggs, dollar bills, Native American pottery, Japanese kimonos, automobile tire treads, and African cloth are products of vastly diverse cultures, but these things all have something in common. They contain strips of repeating patterns, called *frieze patterns*.

In this chapter project, you will explore the underlying relationships among frieze patterns from around the world. You will also create your own designs. You will see how distinct civilizations—separated by oceans and centuries—are linked by their use of geometry to express themselves and to beautify their world.

To help you complete the project:

- ▼ **p. 137** *Find Out by Investigating*
- ▼ **p. 143** *Find Out by Modeling*
- ▼ **p. 150** *Find Out by Investigating*
- ▼ **p. 158** *Find Out by Classifying*
- ▼ **p. 171** *Find Out by Creating*
- ▼ **p. 173** *Finishing the Project*

Tessellations	Dilations
3-6	3-7

▼ Project Resources

Teaching Resources
Chapter Support File, Ch. 3
- Chapter Project Manager and Scoring Rubric

Transparencies
39

▼ Using the Rubric

Sharing the scoring rubric for the project with your students will alert them to your expectations before they begin work on the project.

As students complete each Find Out question in the chapter, you may wish to have them evaluate their own work or a partner's work based on the scoring rubric. Students should have the opportunity to revise their work after it has been reviewed.

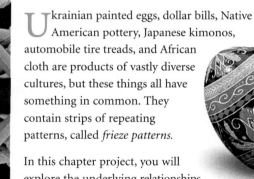

PROBLEM OF THE DAY

The diagram below shows nine points and eight lines, each line determined by three points. Rearrange the points so that ten lines can be drawn, each determined by three of the points.

Problem of the Day is also available in Transparencies.

CONNECTING TO PRIOR KNOWLEDGE Ask students: If $\triangle ABC \cong \triangle EFG$, name the corresponding sides and angles.

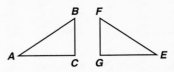

THINK AND DISCUSS p. 124

VISUAL LEARNING Have students use puzzle pieces to model slides, flips, and turns. Their irregular shapes make it easier for students to see how the transformations affect the orientation of the pieces.

Lesson Planning Options

Prerequisite Skills

• Understanding properties of congruent figures
• Graphing in the coordinate plane

Assignment Options for Exercises On Your Own

To provide flexible scheduling, this lesson can be subdivided into parts.

 Core 4–9 (a,b), 18
Extension 19

 Core 1–3, 4–9 (c), 10–17, 20, 22–28
Extension 21, 29

Use Mixed Review to maintain skills.

Resources

Student Edition

Extra Practice, p. 636
Glossary/Study Guide

Teaching Resources

Chapter Support File, Ch. 3
• Practice 3-1 (two worksheets)
• Reteaching 3-1
• Alternative Activity 3-1
• Classroom Manager 3-1
• Glossary, Spanish Resources

Transparencies

5, 40, 44, 45

124

What You'll Learn

• Identifying isometries
• Locating reflection images of figures

...And Why

To describe and explain the kinds of motions you encounter every day

What You'll Need

• straightedge
• protractor
• ruler
• graph paper
• MIRA™ (optional)

3-1 Reflections

Connections Engineering . . . and more

THINK AND DISCUSS

Part 1 An Introduction to Transformations

Have you ever put together a jigsaw puzzle? Think about opening the box and emptying all of the puzzle pieces onto a table.

1. Describe the kinds of motions you use to put the pieces together.
   Answers may vary. Sample: flips, slides, turns

You probably didn't realize it, but you use transformations when you assemble a puzzle. A **transformation** is a change in position, shape, or size of a figure. The photos below illustrate four basic transformations that you will study. Each transformed figure is the **image** of the original figure. The original figure is called the **preimage.**

The figure flips.

preimage   image

The figure slides.

preimage   image

The figure turns.

preimage   image

The figure changes size.

preimage   image

An **isometry** is a transformation in which the original figure and its image are congruent.

2. Which of the transformations shown above appear to be isometries?
   flips, slides, turns

A transformation **maps** a figure onto its image. An arrow (→) indicates a mapping. **Prime notation** is sometimes used to identify image points. In the diagram, K' (read "K prime") is the image of K. Notice that corresponding points of the original figure and its image are listed in the same order, just as corresponding points of congruent and similar figures are listed in the same order.

$\triangle JKQ \longrightarrow \triangle J'K'Q'$
$\triangle JKQ$ maps to $\triangle J'K'Q'$.

Example 1

Question 4 Students may want to draw quadrilaterals *TORN* and *SAKE* so they can see the corresponding sides and angles. Suggest that students draw irregular quadrilaterals so corresponding parts are more obvious.

WORK TOGETHER

TACTILE LEARNING Students can use either paper folding or MIRA™ to create the reflection image of their quadrilaterals. If students are using paper folding, tracing paper should be used.

Question 5 Students verify that the figures are congruent by using rulers and protractors.

EXTENSION Have students draw line *j* so that it contains a side of quadrilateral *MATH* and then draw the reflection image in line *j*. Have students next draw line *j* so that it intersects quadrilateral *MATH* in two points, then draw the reflection image in line *j*. Ask students if their responses to Questions 5 and 6 are the same for these reflections.

Example 1

In the diagram, *E'F'G'H'* is the image of *EFGH*.
a. Name the images of ∠*F* and ∠*H*.
b. List all pairs of corresponding sides.

a. ∠*F'* is the image of ∠*F*.
   ∠*H'* is the image of ∠*H*.

b. $\overline{EF}$ and $\overline{E'F'}$; $\overline{FG}$ and $\overline{F'G'}$;
   $\overline{EH}$ and $\overline{E'H'}$; $\overline{GH}$ and $\overline{G'H'}$

EFGH → *E'F'G'H'*

3. Which of the four types of transformations shown on the previous page is illustrated in Example 1? **slide**

4. **Try This** List the corresponding segments and angles for the transformation *TORN* → *SAKE*. ∠*T* and ∠*S*, ∠*O* and ∠*A*, ∠*R* and ∠*K*, ∠*N* and ∠*E*; $\overline{TO}$ and $\overline{SA}$, $\overline{OR}$ and $\overline{AK}$, $\overline{RN}$ and $\overline{KE}$, $\overline{NT}$ and $\overline{ES}$

Part 2

Reflections

A flip is also known as a *reflection*. You see reflections almost every day. This morning, for example, you probably looked in the mirror before you headed out the door. In the following activity, you will investigate some properties of reflections.

WORK TOGETHER

• Have each person in your group use a straightedge to draw a quadrilateral *MATH* on the top half of a sheet of paper. Draw a line *j* that intersects the quadrilateral at *M*.

• Fold the paper along line *j*, then use a straightedge to trace the reflection image of *MATH* onto the bottom portion of your paper. (You could also create the image by using a MIRA™.) Label the corresponding vertices of the image *M'*, *A'*, *T'*, and *H'*.

5. Measure corresponding angles and segments in *MATH* and *M'A'T'H'*. Is a reflection an isometry? Explain. **Yes; *MATH* ≅ *M'A'T'H'***

6. Make a **conjecture** about the image of a point that lies on the line of reflection. (*Hint:* Consider point *M* and its image.)
   The point is its own image.

7. a. In your original figure, did you write the labels *M*, *A*, *T*, and *H* in clockwise or counterclockwise order around the quadrilateral?
   b. In the reflection image, do the labels *M'*, *A'*, *T'*, and *H'* appear in clockwise or counterclockwise order around the quadrilateral?
   c. What property of reflections do parts (a) and (b) suggest?
   a. Answers may vary. Sample: counterclockwise
   b. Answers may vary. Sample: clockwise
   c. Reflection reverses orientation.

Additional Examples

FOR EXAMPLE 1

In the diagram, *P'Q'R'* is the image of *PQR*.

a. Name the images of ∠*Q* and ∠*R*.
   ∠*Q'*, ∠*R'*

b. List all pairs of corresponding sides. **$\overline{PQ}$ and $\overline{P'Q'}$, $\overline{QR}$ and $\overline{Q'R'}$, $\overline{RP}$ and $\overline{R'P'}$**

Discussion: *What type of transformation is illustrated?*

FOR EXAMPLE 2

Refer to the diagram in Example 2. Copy △*ABC* and draw its reflection image in *x* = 2.

Discussion: *Name the coordinates of the vertices of △ABC and △A'B'C'. What do you notice?*

125

ESL Discuss with students words that have the root *flex-* such as reflex, reflection, and flexible. Ask them how these words and the geometric meaning of reflection are related.

TACTILE LEARNING Have students use mirrors to investigate the properties of reflections. Have them hold a clock with a moving second hand up to a mirror and observe that the second hand is moving counterclockwise in the reflection. Then have them hold a 12-in. ruler perpendicular to the plane of the mirror and observe that the end of the ruler appears 12 inches away from the mirror in the reflection.

Example 2

Students now have three methods for finding a reflection image of a figure: paper folding, using MIRA™, and finding image points such that the line of reflection is the perpendicular bisector of the segment connecting a point and its image. Discuss with students why these methods produce the same results.

ERROR ALERT! In part b, the line of reflection passes through the figure. Students may be confused by this and reflect the figure about one of its vertices. **Remediation:** It sometimes helps students to reflect the part of the figure on one side of the line first, then to reflect the part of the figure on the other side of the line. Point out that parts "change sides."

Technology Options

For Exercises 10–17, students may use geometry software to draw the triangles and their reflections.

Prentice Hall Technology

 Software
• Secondary Math Lab Toolkit™
• Computer Item Generator 3-1

 CD-ROM
• Multimedia Geometry Lab 3

 Internet
• See the Prentice Hall site. (http://www.phschool.com)

• Use a straightedge to draw segments $\overline{AA'}$, $\overline{TT'}$, and $\overline{HH'}$.

8. **a.** Line *j* divides each segment you drew into two parts. Compare the lengths of the two parts of each of the segments.   **They are =.**
   b. Line *j* forms four angles with each segment you drew. Use a protractor to find the measures of each of the angles.   **90**
   c. Use your answers to parts (a) and (b) to complete the statement: Line *j* is the __?__ of the segment that connects a point and its image.   **⊥ bisector**

THINK AND DISCUSS

When you look at a word in a mirror, the image appears to be "backwards." The reflected word has the opposite **orientation** of the original word. Notice that the orientation of the word AMBULANCE in the photograph is reversed. The fronts of emergency vehicles often have mirror-image words on them so that drivers looking through rear-view mirrors can easily read them.

You discovered both of the following properties of reflections in the Work Together.

Properties of a Reflection

A reflection reverses orientation.

In the diagram, △BUG has *clockwise* orientation, so its image △B′U′G′ has *counterclockwise* orientation.

A reflection is an isometry.

In the diagram, △BUG ≅ △B′U′G′.

The other properties of reflections that you explored in the Work Together form the basis of the definition of a reflection. A **reflection** in line *r* is a transformation for which the following are true.

• If a point *A* is on line *r*, then the image of *A* is itself (that is, *A* = *A′*).

• If a point *B* is not on line *r*, then *r* is the perpendicular bisector of $\overline{BB'}$.

126

Example 3 Relating to the Real World ················

Lead students to understand that to minimize the amount of pipe needed to connect the towns, the sum of the distances between the towns and the pumping station should be as small as possible.

MAKING CONNECTIONS You may want to point out to students that in a reflection the angle of incidence equals the angle of reflection. For example, on a miniature golf hole as shown below, *P* indicates the point on the wall, ideally, where the ball should be hit from the tee to get a hole-in-one.

---

9. *Critical Thinking* Suppose you are given a point *R* and its reflection image *R'*. How could you find the line of reflection? **Construct the ⊥ bisector of $\overline{RR'}$.**

Example 2 ·······················

Coordinate Geometry Copy △*ABC* and draw its reflection image in each line.

a. the *x*-axis
b. the *y*-axis

You can find *A'*, *B'*, and *C'* by paper folding or by locating points such that the line of reflection is the perpendicular bisector of $\overline{AA'}$, $\overline{BB'}$, and $\overline{CC'}$.

a.
b.

10. **Try This** Copy △*ABC* and draw its reflection image in *x* = 3.
See margin.

Example 3 Relating to the Real World ··············

Engineering The state government wants to build a pumping station along the Alabash Canal to serve the towns of Crete and Dublin. Where along the canal should the pumping station be built to minimize the amount of pipe needed to connect the towns to the pump?

You need to find the point *P* on ℓ such that *DP* + *PC* is as small as possible. Locate *C'*, the reflection image of *C* in ℓ. Because a reflection is an isometry, *PC* = *PC'*, and *DP* + *PC* = *DP* + *PC'*. The sum *DP* + *PC'* is smallest when *D*, *P*, and *C'* are collinear. So the pump should be located at the point *P* where $\overline{DC'}$ intersects ℓ.

11. *Critical Thinking* Ursula began to solve Example 3 by reflecting point *D* in line ℓ. Will her method work? Explain. **Yes; the intersection of $\overline{D'C}$ and ℓ is the point *P* where the pump should be located.**

pages 126–127 Think and Discuss

10.

3-1 Reflections **127**

127

Exercises   ON YOUR OWN

Exercise 2 The line of reflection passes through the figure. Refer students to Example 2b for a similar problem.

Exercise 3 Students discover that the letters B, O, and X are symmetric. Students may want to investigate what other letters have this property.

Exercises 4–9 Encourage students to copy the figures and draw arrows from the vertices (as shown on page 126) to indicate orientation.

COORDINATE GEOMETRY Exercises 10–17 Have students label the coordinates of the vertices of the reflection image. Have them compare the coordinates of the figures with those of their reflection images in Exercises 10, 11, and 14. Discuss what patterns they notice. Then have them make the same comparisons in Exercises 12, 13, and 15.

WRITING Exercise 19 Some of the students' examples may be a combination of more than one transformation. For example, using a protractor to measure an angle, you must slide and turn the protractor so that it aligns with one side of the angle.

Exercise 20 Suggest students find the image of C (or D) under a reflection in the mirrored wall. They can then use the second property of reflections to deduce the following: the distance from C (or D) to the mirrored wall is the same as the distance of C' (or D') to the mirrored wall.

4a. $\overline{ID}$ and $\overline{I'D'}$, $\overline{DS}$ and $\overline{D'S'}$, $\overline{SI}$ and $\overline{S'I'}$

5a. $\overline{PQ}$ and $\overline{P'Q'}$, $\overline{QR}$ and $\overline{Q'R'}$, $\overline{RS}$ and $\overline{R'S'}$, $\overline{SP}$ and $\overline{S'P'}$

6a. $\overline{OW}$ and $\overline{O'W'}$, $\overline{WE}$ and $\overline{W'E'}$, $\overline{EZ}$ and $\overline{E'Z'}$, $\overline{ZO}$ and $\overline{Z'O'}$

7a. $\overline{AR}$ and $\overline{A'R'}$, $\overline{RT}$ and $\overline{R'T'}$, $\overline{TA}$ and $\overline{T'A'}$

8a. $\overline{AB}$ and $\overline{A'B'}$, $\overline{BC}$ and $\overline{B'C'}$, $\overline{CA}$ and $\overline{C'A'}$

9a. $\overline{RI}$ and $\overline{R'I'}$, $\overline{IT}$ and $\overline{I'T'}$, $\overline{TR}$ and $\overline{T'R'}$

10.

11.   12.

13.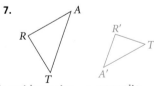

128

Exercises   ON YOUR OWN

Copy each diagram, then find the reflection image of the figure in line ℓ.

1.   2.   3.

In each diagram, the blue figure is the image of the black figure.   4a–9a. See margin.
(a) List the corresponding sides.
(b) State whether the transformation appears to be an isometry.
(c) State whether the figures have the *same* or *opposite* orientation.

4.
b. isometry   c. same

5.
b. isometry   c. opposite

6.
b. not isometry
c. same

7.
b. not isometry   c. opposite

8.
b. isometry
c. opposite

9.
b. not isometry

c. opposite

Coordinate Geometry Given points J(1, 4), A(3, 5), and R(2, 1), draw △JAR and its reflection image in the given line.   10–13. See margin.   14–17. See margin p. 129.

10. the x-axis   11. $y = 2$ 12. the y-axis   13. $x = -1$

14. $y = 5$ 15. $x = 2$ 16. $y = -x$ 17. $y = x - 3$

18. **Critical Thinking** Given that the transformation △ABC ⟶ △A'B'C' is an isometry, list everything you know about the two figures. **See below.**

19. **Writing** Describe an example from everyday life of a flip, a slide, a turn, and a size change.   See margin p. 129.

20. **Surveillance** SafeCo specializes in installing security cameras in department stores. Copy the diagram onto your paper. At what point on the mirrored wall should camera C be aimed in order to photograph door D?

18. $\angle A \cong \angle A'$, $\angle B \cong \angle B'$, $\angle C \cong \angle C'$, $\overline{AB} \cong \overline{A'B'}$, $\overline{BC} \cong \overline{B'C'}$, $\overline{CA} \cong \overline{C'A'}$

21. History An unusual characteristic of the work of 15th-century artist and scientist Leonardo da Vinci is his handwriting, which is a mirror image of normal handwriting. **a–b. See margin p. 129.**

a. Explain why the fact that da Vinci was left-handed might have made it seem normal for him to write in this manner.

b. Write the mirror image of this sentence. Use a mirror to check that your image is correct.

Copy each pair of figures, then find the line of reflection in which one figure is mapped onto the other.

22.

23.

24.

Some Drugs Aren't Ambidextrous

Your head aches. You take a pain reliever that cures this ache, but then your stomach starts to hurt. As you've no doubt noticed, many drugs have unwanted side-effects.

Most drugs are really made up of two versions of the same molecule—each a mirror image of the other. One version is known as an *R-isomer* and the other, an *S-isomer*. The isomers can have different healing properties.

Researchers have recently learned how to create pure batches of each isomer. They then run tests to determine which one produces the fewest side-effects. Drug companies can then produce drugs that contain only the "good" isomer.

For example, the R-isomer of the drug albuterol relieves asthma, while its twin has been shown to increase the chances of having future attacks.

Source: *Wall Street Journal*

25. Pharmacy Consider the two "isomers" shown. In order for this drug to cure an illness, it needs to fit into the "receptor molecule" shown.

a. Which isomer will cure the illness? **S-Isomer**

b. **Open-ended** Give three examples from everyday life of objects that come in a left-handed version and a right-handed version.

Samples: gloves, shoes, scissors

S-Isomer   R-Isomer   Receptor Molecule

26. Standardized Test Prep What is the image of (−4, 5) under a reflection in the line $y = x$? **A**

A. (5, −4)   B. (4, 5)   C. (−4, −5)   D. (4, −5)   E. (−5, 4)

14.

15.

16.

17.

19. Samples: flip: flipping a pancake; slide: opening a window that slides up; turn: turning a steering wheel; size change: enlarging a photograph

21a. Answers may vary. Sample: The writing hand would not cover what was already written.

b. Write the mirror image of this sentence.

Exercise 27 Have students describe the cartoon by writing captions for each of the four blocks.

Exercises   MIXED REVIEW

Exercises 30–32 Students classify quadrilaterals.

Exercise 33 Students review finding midpoints and slopes and writing the equation of a line.

 JOURNAL Have students include some real-world examples of reflections in their journal entries.

GETTING READY FOR LESSON 3-2 Students identify a slide and observe that each vertex is moved the same distance and in the same direction.

Wrap Up

THE BIG IDEA Ask students to describe two ways to find the reflection of a figure in a line. Ask them to describe how the preimage and image of a figure are related.

RETEACHING ACTIVITY Students use paper folding and scissors to investigate reflections of cutouts in the *x*-axis and *y*-axis. (Reteaching worksheet 3-1)

---

27. Which panels in the comic strip show the kind of reflection you studied in this lesson? Explain your answer. **See margin p. 131.**
    28a. See margin p. 131.
28. **a. Paper Folding** Plot the points $Y(-2, 5)$, $A(5, 0)$, and $K(-1, -2)$. Draw $\triangle YAK$, then use paper folding to find its image in $y = x$. Label the image $\triangle Y'A'K'$.
    b. Patterns Look for a pattern in the coordinates of $\triangle YAK$ and $\triangle Y'A'K'$. Write a general rule for finding the image of any point under a reflection in $y = x$.
    b. Switch the coordinates.
29. **Critical Thinking** Under a reflection, do all points move the same distance? If not, which points move the farthest?
    No; the points farthest from the line of reflection move the farthest.

Source: K-Hito (Ricardo Garcia López). "Macaco." © K-Hito

Exercises   MIXED REVIEW

What type of quadrilateral is $ABB'A'$?

30.

square

31.

rectangle

32.

trapezoid

33. The points $P(2, 5)$ and $Q(-4, -7)$ are reflection images of one another.
    a. Find the coordinates of the midpoint of $\overline{PQ}$. $(-1, -1)$
    b. Find the slope of $\overline{PQ}$. 2
    c. Find the slope of a line perpendicular to $\overline{PQ}$. $-\frac{1}{2}$
    d. Use your answers to parts (a) and (c) to write the equation of the line in which P is reflected to Q.
    $y = -\frac{1}{2}x - \frac{3}{2}$

Getting Ready for Lesson 3-2

34. In the diagram, an isometry maps $\triangle HUB$ to $\triangle H'U'B'$.
    a. Is the transformation a flip, slide, or turn? **slide**
    b. Compare the slopes of $\overline{HH'}$, $\overline{UU'}$, and $\overline{BB'}$.
    c. Compare the lengths of $\overline{HH'}$, $\overline{UU'}$, and $\overline{BB'}$.
    b, c. See right.

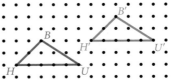

34b. The slopes are the same.
c. The lengths are the same.

Lesson Quiz

Lesson Quiz is also available in Transparencies.

1. Given points $E(-2, 2)$, $F(-3, -5)$ and $G(-1, -1)$, draw $\triangle EFG$ and its reflection image in the *y*-axis.
   $\triangle E'F'G'$ with $E'(2, 2)$, $F'(3, -5)$, and $G'(1, -1)$

2. $A'B'C'D'$ is the reflection image of $ABCD$. Name the corresponding sides. $\overline{AB}$ and $\overline{A'B'}$, $\overline{BC}$ and $\overline{B'C'}$, $\overline{CD}$ and $\overline{C'D'}$, $\overline{DA}$ and $\overline{D'A'}$

3. In the scale drawing, where along the wall should the mirror be placed so someone in the chair can see the door?

130

FOR YOUR JOURNAL

List the properties of reflections. Then draw a polygon, a line of reflection, and the reflection image of your polygon. Explain how the figures illustrate each property listed.

Students review how to add and subtract matrices. In Lesson 3-2, students will use matrices to represent coordinates of figures and translations. They will also find the coordinates of the images of translations using matrix addition.

Example ·······································

Have students notice that the dimensions of the solution are the same as the dimensions of the matrices being added.

ERROR ALERT! Exercise 2 Some students may have trouble mentally subtracting corresponding entries, especially when the entries are negative numbers. **Remediation:** These

students may want to write expressions for each entry, then simplify: $-6 - (-4) = -2, 3 - (-9) = 12, -8 - 3 = -11,$ $1 - 5 = -4.$

Exercise 9 Check that students understand what the labels on the matrices represent by asking them to identify different entries, such as the number of tenth graders involved in drama.

ADDITIONAL PROBLEM Have students create and solve a matrix problem like Exercise 9. For example, they could write matrices that represent the number of boys and girls wearing sneakers and other kinds of shoes in two of their classes, then find the sum.

Math ToolboX — Algebra Review

Matrices

Before Lesson 3-2

A **matrix** is a rectangular arrangement of numbers. A matrix is usually written inside brackets. You identify the size of a matrix by the number of rows and columns. This matrix has two rows and three columns, so it is a 2×3 matrix. Each item in a matrix is called an **entry**.

$$\begin{bmatrix} -1 & 4 & 9 \\ -5 & 3 & 7 \end{bmatrix}$$

You can add or subtract matrices if they are the same size. You do this by adding or subtracting corresponding entries.

Example

Add $\begin{bmatrix} 6 & -5 \\ 0 & 3 \end{bmatrix} + \begin{bmatrix} 1 & 8 \\ -2 & 10 \end{bmatrix}$.

$$\begin{bmatrix} 6 & -5 \\ 0 & 3 \end{bmatrix} + \begin{bmatrix} 1 & 8 \\ -2 & 10 \end{bmatrix} = \begin{bmatrix} 6+1 & -5+8 \\ 0+(-2) & 3+10 \end{bmatrix}$$ Add corresponding entries.

$$= \begin{bmatrix} 7 & 3 \\ -2 & 13 \end{bmatrix}$$

Add or subtract each pair of matrices.

1. $\begin{bmatrix} 3 & 8 \\ 1 & 5 \end{bmatrix} + \begin{bmatrix} 8 & 2 \\ 0 & 7 \end{bmatrix}$ $\begin{bmatrix} 11 & 10 \\ 1 & 12 \end{bmatrix}$

2. $\begin{bmatrix} -6 & 3 \\ -8 & 1 \end{bmatrix} - \begin{bmatrix} -4 & -9 \\ 3 & 5 \end{bmatrix}$ $\begin{bmatrix} -2 & 12 \\ -11 & -4 \end{bmatrix}$

3. $\begin{bmatrix} 1 & -6 \\ 2 & -7 \end{bmatrix} + \begin{bmatrix} \frac{1}{2} & -1 \\ \frac{2}{3} & -2 \end{bmatrix}$ $\begin{bmatrix} \frac{3}{2} & -7 \\ \frac{8}{3} & -9 \end{bmatrix}$

4. $\begin{bmatrix} \frac{1}{3} & \frac{3}{4} \\ \frac{1}{2} & \frac{2}{5} \end{bmatrix} - \begin{bmatrix} -\frac{1}{6} & \frac{1}{4} \\ -\frac{3}{5} & \frac{2}{3} \end{bmatrix}$ $\begin{bmatrix} \frac{1}{2} & \frac{1}{2} \\ \frac{11}{10} & -\frac{4}{15} \end{bmatrix}$

5. $\begin{bmatrix} 2 & 9 \\ 6 & 7 \end{bmatrix} + \begin{bmatrix} 6 & 2.3 \\ 9 & 4.1 \end{bmatrix}$ $\begin{bmatrix} 8 & 11.3 \\ 15 & 11.1 \end{bmatrix}$

6. $\begin{bmatrix} 3 & -7 & 4 \\ 0 & -4 & 9 \end{bmatrix} + \begin{bmatrix} -9 & 4 & 10 \\ 3 & -11 & 2 \end{bmatrix}$

7. $\begin{bmatrix} 5 & -3.5 \\ 10 & 14 \\ -5 & 4.7 \end{bmatrix} + \begin{bmatrix} -6.1 & 0.8 \\ 7 & -5 \\ 8.3 & 9 \end{bmatrix}$ $\begin{bmatrix} -1.1 & -2.7 \\ 17 & 9 \\ 3.3 & 13.7 \end{bmatrix}$

8. $\begin{bmatrix} 4 & 2 & 9 \\ -11 & 20 & 5 \\ -18 & 21 & -2 \end{bmatrix} - \begin{bmatrix} 8 & 17 & 4 \\ -34 & 26 & -9 \\ 3 & 0 & 17 \end{bmatrix}$

6 and 8. See margin.

9. Use the matrices to find the total number of students per grade involved in each activity. **See margin.**

Greenfield High School North

	Sports	Drama	Debate
9th	146	5	11
10th	201	15	4
11th	205	11	7
12th	176	19	13

Greenfield High School South

	Sports	Drama	Debate
9th	301	13	9
10th	345	8	6
11th	245	11	11
12th	220	11	9

---

pages 128–130 **On Your Own**

27. First and third panels; the figures in the second panel are not ≅, and the fourth panel shows a slide.

28a.

Math Toolbox   **page 131**

6. $\begin{bmatrix} -6 & -3 & 14 \\ 3 & -15 & 11 \end{bmatrix}$

8. $\begin{bmatrix} -4 & -15 & 5 \\ 23 & -6 & 14 \\ -21 & 21 & -19 \end{bmatrix}$

9. $\begin{bmatrix} 447 & 18 & 20 \\ 546 & 23 & 10 \\ 450 & 22 & 18 \\ 396 & 30 & 22 \end{bmatrix}$

PROBLEM OF THE DAY

Placing no more than one X in each small square, what is the greatest number of X's that can be put in a 3-by-3 square grid without forming a line of three X's in a row horizontally, vertically, or diagonally? **6**

Problem of the Day is also available in Transparencies.

CONNECTING TO PRIOR KNOWLEDGE Ask students to make a table of values and sketch the graphs of $y = |x|$, $y = |x| - 5$ and $y = |x| + 3$. Discuss how the graph of $y = |x|$ can be used to draw the other two graphs.

WORK TOGETHER

Have students draw their triangles on lightweight cardboard so they will be easier to trace around. Recommend that they draw triangles having sides of three different lengths. Check that students slide their cutouts without rotating them.

ALTERNATE METHOD If time does not allow for the group activity, use two transparencies with the same triangle drawn on each to illustrate a translation. Start with the two triangles on top of each other. Slide the top triangle to another location and have students discuss Questions 1–4.

Lesson Planning Options

Prerequisite Skills

- Graphing in the coordinate plane
- Adding matrices

Assignment Options for Exercises On Your Own

  Core 1–12, 16–19, 21–27
  Extension 13–15, 20, 28

Use Mixed Review to maintain skills.

Resources

 Student Edition

Skills Handbook, p. 665
Extra Practice, p. 636
Glossary/Study Guide

 Teaching Resources

Chapter Support File, Ch. 3
- Practice 3-2 (two worksheets)
- Reteaching 3-2
Classroom Manager 3-2
Glossary, Spanish Resources

 Transparencies
5, 40, 46

132

What You'll Learn

- Finding translation images of figures
- Using vectors and matrix addition to represent translations

...And Why

To use translations in the arts, computer graphics, navigation, manufacturing, music, and other fields

What You'll Need

- centimeter ruler
- scissors
- graph paper

3-2 Translations

WORK TOGETHER

- Have each member of your group draw a triangle, cut it out, and label it $\triangle PAW$.

- Place your triangle on a sheet of lined paper so that $\overline{PA}$ lies on a horizontal line. Trace the triangle, and label it $\triangle PAW$.

- Slide the cutout to another location on your paper so that $\overline{PA}$ again lies on a horizontal line. Trace the triangle, and label it $\triangle P'A'W'$.

1. Does the transformation $\triangle PAW \longrightarrow \triangle P'A'W'$ appear to be an isometry? Explain. **Yes; the triangles are $\cong$.**

2. Does the transformation $\triangle PAW \longrightarrow \triangle P'A'W'$ change the orientation of the triangle? Explain. **No; the order of vertices in the image is the same as the order of the corresponding vertices in the preimage.**

- Use a straightedge to draw $\overline{PP'}$, $\overline{AA'}$, and $\overline{WW'}$. Measure each segment with a ruler.

3. What do you notice about the lengths of the segments? **All the lengths are $=$.**

4. Notice the positions of $\overline{PP'}$, $\overline{AA'}$, and $\overline{WW'}$ in relation to one another. What appears to be true about them? Compare your answer with others in your group. **The segments are $\parallel$.**

THINK AND DISCUSS

The sliding motion that maps $\triangle PAW$ to $\triangle P'A'W'$ in the Work Together is an example of a translation. A **translation** is a transformation that moves points the same distance and in the same direction. In the Work Together, you discovered the following properties of a translation.

Properties of a Translation

A translation is an isometry.

A translation does not change orientation.

5. Elevators, escalators, and people movers all suggest translations. Name some other examples of translations from the real world.

Samples: assembly line, positions of a car on a straight road

The concept of vectors may be confusing to some students. Make sure students understand how vectors differ from rays (vectors do not go on forever in one direction) and segments $\overline{AB}$ and $\overline{BA}$ are the same but $\overrightarrow{AB}$ and $\overrightarrow{BA}$ are not). Emphasize that a vector indicates both distance and direction.

Example 1

This translation could also be accomplished by moving each vertex one unit up and three units right. However, naming the horizontal movement first is consistent with ordered pair notation.

ERROR ALERT! Question 6 Students may confuse ordered pair notation and the slope formula and write the vertical change first. **Remediation:** One way to remember the order of ordered pair notation is to remember that it is similar to an ordered pair (x, y).

Example 2

KINESTHETIC LEARNING Create a coordinate grid on the floor of your classroom using masking tape or meter sticks. (This is easily done if your floor has square tiles.) Have students physically represent the points in Example 2 and "act out" translations that take one point to another.

The distance and direction of a translation can be expressed as a *vector*. In the diagram, $\overrightarrow{TT'}$, $\overrightarrow{RR'}$, and $\overrightarrow{YY'}$ are vectors. Vectors have an *initial point* and a *terminal point*. T, R, and Y are initial points, and T', R', and Y' are terminal points. Note that although diagrams of vectors look identical to diagrams of rays, vectors do not go on forever in the indicated direction—they have a fixed length.

Example 1

Use the given vector and rectangle to create a sketch of a box.

Step 1   Step 2

Copy the rectangle, then translate each of its vertices 3 units to the right and 1 unit up. Next, connect points to form the box. Use dashed lines for parts of the figure that are hidden from view.

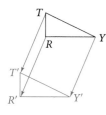

You can use *ordered pair notation*, $\langle x, y \rangle$, to represent a vector on the coordinate plane. In the notation, x represents horizontal change from the initial point to the terminal point and y represents vertical change from the initial point to the terminal point. The notation for vector $\overrightarrow{MG}$ is $\langle 5, -2 \rangle$.

6. **Try This** Describe the vector in Example 1 by using ordered pair notation.
   $\langle 3, 1 \rangle$
7. Use vector notation to describe the vector with initial point $(1, 3)$ and terminal point $(6, 1)$. $\langle 5, -2 \rangle$

Example 2

a. What is the image of P under the translation $\langle 0, -4 \rangle$?
b. What vector describes the translation $S \longrightarrow U$?

a. The vector $\langle 0, -4 \rangle$ represents a translation of 4 units down. The image of P is Q.
b. To get from S to U, you move 3 units left and 6 units down. The vector that describes this translation is $\langle -3, -6 \rangle$.

8. **Try This** Refer to the diagram in Example 2.
   a. What is the image of S under the translation $\langle -3, -1 \rangle$? R
   b. What vector describes the translation $T \longrightarrow P$? $\langle 6, 3 \rangle$

9. Describe in words the distance and direction of the translation represented by the vector $\langle 18, 0 \rangle$. **18 units to the right**

Additional Examples

FOR EXAMPLE 2 ....

Refer to the diagram in Example 2.
a. What is the image of T under the translation $\langle 3, 4 \rangle$? **(0, 3)**

b. What vector describes the translation of R to Q? $\langle 4, -4 \rangle$

Discussion: *When describing a translation, what direction do you name first?*

FOR EXAMPLE 3 ....

Refer to the diagram in Example 3. Use matrices to find the image of $\triangle SUD$ under the translation $\langle -2, 4 \rangle$.

$$\begin{bmatrix} -3 & 0 & 1 \\ 3 & -1 & 6 \end{bmatrix}$$

Discussion: *How do you represent vertices of a preimage using a matrix?*

133

	S	U	D
x-coordinate	−1	2	3
y-coordinate	−1	−5	2

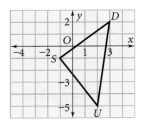

You can use matrices to help you translate figures in the coordinate plane. To do so, start by creating a matrix for the figure, as shown at the left.

Example 3 --------------------------------

Use matrices to find the image of $\triangle SUD$ under the translation $\langle 4, -5 \rangle$.

To find the image of $\triangle SUD$, you add 4 to all of the x-coordinates and −5 to all of the y-coordinates.

Vertices of Preimage   Translation Matrix   Vertices of Image

$$
\begin{matrix} S & U & D \end{matrix} \\
\begin{bmatrix} -1 & 2 & 3 \\ -1 & -5 & 2 \end{bmatrix}
+
\begin{bmatrix} 4 & 4 & 4 \\ -5 & -5 & -5 \end{bmatrix}
=
\begin{matrix} S' & U' & D' \end{matrix} \\
\begin{bmatrix} 3 & 6 & 7 \\ -6 & -10 & -3 \end{bmatrix}
$$

10. Check the answer to Example 3 by sketching $\triangle SUD$ and $\triangle S'U'D'$ on the same set of axes.   **See margin p. 135.**

Example 4 ● Relating to the Real World 🌐 ·············

Travel Yolanda Pérez is visiting San Francisco. From her hotel near Union Square, she walked 4 blocks east and 4 blocks north to the Wells Fargo History Museum to see a stagecoach and relics of the gold rush. Then she walked 5 blocks west and 3 blocks north to the Cable Car Barn Museum. How many blocks from her hotel is she now?

As shown in the diagram, she is 1 block west and 7 blocks north of her hotel.

You can also solve this problem by using vectors. The vector $\langle 4, 4 \rangle$ represents a walk of 4 blocks east and 4 blocks north. The vector $\langle -5, 3 \rangle$ represents her second walk. The solution is the sum of the x- and y-coordinates of each vector: $\langle 4, 4 \rangle + \langle -5, 3 \rangle = \langle -1, 7 \rangle$.

134

Exercise 5 Students may have difficulty recognizing corresponding points on the two figures. Suggest that they find the coordinates of the vertices.

Exercises 7–12 Students may want to copy the coordinate grid so they can trace the translations.

ERROR ALERT! Exercise 15 Because the direction vector is pictured above the figure, students may translate the figure up and to the left. **Remediation:** Remind students to find the direction vector from the initial point to the terminal point.

Example 4 shows the composition of two translations. The term **composition** describes any two transformations in which the second transformation is performed on the image of the first transformation. As the solution to Example 4 suggests, a composition of translations can be rewritten as a single translation.

pages 132–135 Think and Discuss

10.

Exercises ON YOUR OWN

In each diagram, the blue figure is the image of the red figure.
Use ordered pair notation to represent each translation.

1.

⟨1, −3⟩

2.

⟨−5, 3⟩

3. ⟨1, −1⟩

4.

⟨2, 2⟩

5.

⟨4, −2⟩

6.
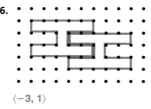

⟨−3, 1⟩

In Exercises 7–12, refer to the figure at the right.

7. What is the image of *F* under the translation ⟨−1, 4⟩? **C**

8. What vector describes the translation *G* ⟶ *H*? ⟨0, −2⟩

9. What is the image of *E* under the translation ⟨4, 1⟩? **I**

10. What vector describes the translation *B* ⟶ *E*? ⟨5, 5⟩

11. What is the image of *F* under the translation ⟨4, −1⟩? **H**

12. What vector describes the translation *I* ⟶ *C*? ⟨−6, −1⟩

Use each figure and vector to sketch a three-dimensional figure.
13–15. See margin.

13.

14.

15.
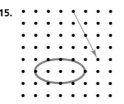

pages 135–137 On Your Own

13.

14.

15.

135

16.

22.

27b.

31a.

16. *Sailing* Emily left Galveston Bay at the east jetty and sailed 4 km north to an oil rig. She then sailed 5 km west to Redfish Island. Finally, she sailed 3 km southwest to the Spinnaker Restaurant. Draw vectors on graph paper that show her journey. **See margin.**

In Exercises 17–19, use matrix addition to find the image of each figure under the given translation.

17. Figure: △ACE with vertices A(7, 2), C(−8, 5), E(0, −6)
Translation: ⟨−9, 4⟩ **See below right.**

18. Figure: △PUN with vertices P(1, 0), U(4, 6), N(−5, 8)
Translation: ⟨11, −13⟩ **See below right.**

19. Figure: ▱NILE with vertices N(2, −5), I(2, 2),
L(−3, 4), E(−3, −3)
Translation: ⟨−3, −4⟩
$$\begin{matrix} N' & I' & L' & E' \\ \begin{bmatrix} -1 & -1 & -6 & -6 \\ -9 & -2 & 0 & -7 \end{bmatrix} \end{matrix}$$

20. *Photography* When you snap a photograph, a shutter opens to expose the film to light. The amount of time that the shutter remains open is known as the *shutter speed*. The photographer of the train used a long shutter speed to create an image that suggests a translation. Sketch a picture of your own that suggests a translation.
Check students' work.

21. *Coordinate Geometry* △MUG has coordinates M(2, −4), U(6, 6) and G(7, 2). A translation maps point M to (−3, 6). Find the coordinates of U′ and G′ under this translation. **U′(1, 16); G′(2, 12)**

22. *Visiting Colleges* Nakesha and her parents are visiting colleges. They leave their home in Enid, Oklahoma, and head for Tulsa, which is 107 mi east and 18 mi south of Enid. From Tulsa, they head to Norman, which is 83 mi west and 63 mi south of Tulsa. Where is Norman in relation to Enid? Draw a diagram to show your solution. **See margin for diagram; Norman is 24 mi east and 81 mi south of Enid.**

23. *Writing* Is the transformation △HYP ⟶ △H′Y′P′ a translation? Explain. **No. Answers may vary. Sample: a translation does not change orientation.**

Find a single translation that has the same effect as each composition of translations.

24. ⟨2, 5⟩ followed by ⟨−4, 9⟩
⟨−2, 14⟩

25. ⟨−3, 7⟩ followed by ⟨3, −7⟩
⟨0, 0⟩

26. ⟨12, 0.5⟩ followed by ⟨1, −3⟩
⟨13, −2.5⟩

27. *Coordinate Geometry* ▱ABCD has vertices A(3, 6), B(5, 5), C(4, 2), and D(2, 3). The figure is translated so that the image of point C is the origin.
a. Find the vector that describes the translation. **⟨−4, −2⟩**
b. Graph ▱ABCD and its image. **See margin.**

17.
$$\begin{matrix} A' & C' & E' \\ \begin{bmatrix} -2 & -17 & -9 \\ 6 & 9 & -2 \end{bmatrix} \end{matrix}$$

18.
$$\begin{matrix} P' & U' & N' \\ \begin{bmatrix} 12 & 15 & 6 \\ -13 & -7 & -5 \end{bmatrix} \end{matrix}$$

136 **Chapter 3** Transformations: Shapes in Motion

Chapter Project FIND OUT BY INVESTIGATING Ask students to describe wallpaper borders or stencils they have seen that have frieze patterns. Discuss how the patterns are repeated. You may want to have students look through department store catalogs or home-decorating magazines for examples. Remind students to keep their Find Out exercise work in one place, so they can complete the chapter project at the end of the chapter.

Exercises MIXED REVIEW

GETTING READY FOR LESSON 3-3 These exercises prepare students to describe rotations in Lesson 3-3. Make sure students understand how to find degrees greater than 180°.

Wrap Up

THE BIG IDEA Ask students: *Given a figure and its image under a translation, how do you find the vector that describes the translation? Given the coordinates of a point, how do you find the coordinates of its image under a translation?*

RETEACHING ACTIVITY Students draw a triangle in the first quadrant. They trace the triangle and translate it to each of the other quadrants. Then they name vectors that describe the translations. (Reteaching worksheet 3-2)

---

28. **Open-ended** You work for a company that specializes in creating unique, artistic designs for business stationery. One of your clients is Totter Toys. You have been assigned to create a design that forms a border at the top of their stationery. Create a design that involves translations to present to your client. **Check students' work.**

Totter Toys
4010 Tiptop Drive
Birchwood, TX 70988

Chapter Project *Find Out by Investigating*

A **frieze pattern,** or **strip pattern,** is a design that repeats itself along a straight line. Every frieze pattern can be mapped onto itself by a translation. Some can also be mapped onto themselves by other transformations, such as reflections.
• Decide whether each frieze pattern can be mapped onto itself by a reflection in a horizontal line, a vertical line, or both.

a. Navaho Design **b.** Design from Sandwich Islands

c. Medieval Ornament **d.** Arabian Design

a. vertical b. horizontal c. vertical d. both

Exercises MIXED REVIEW

For Exercises 29 and 30, refer to the diagram.

29. Line *t* is a __?__ of $\overline{AC}$. **bisector**

30. $AB = 3x - 8$ and $BC = 5x - 36$. Find AC. **68**

31. **a.** Algebra Graph $y = 2x - 3$, then draw its image under the translation $\langle 0, 5 \rangle$. **See margin p. 136.**
    b. Find the slope and *y*-intercept of the preimage and the image.
    c. How are the two lines related?
    b. 2, −3; 2, 2   c. The lines are ∥.

Getting Ready for Lesson 3-3

Cooking What temperature will the oven be if the knob is turned the given number of degrees in a clockwise direction?

32. 120° **200°**   33. 180° **300°**   34. 210° **350°**   35. 270° **450°**

Lesson Quiz

Lesson Quiz is also available in Transparencies.

1. Describe the image of $P(-2, 4)$ under the translation $\langle 3, -1 \rangle$. **(1, 3)**

2. Use matrix addition to find the image of $\triangle XYZ$ with vertices $X(5, 2)$, $Y(-3, 4)$, and $Z(1, -3)$ under the translation $\langle -5, 6 \rangle$. **$\triangle X'Y'Z'$ with vertices $X'(0, 8)$, $Y'(-8, 10)$, and $Z'(-4, 3)$**

3. Find a single translation that has the same effect as the translation $\langle 1, -2 \rangle$ followed by the translation $\langle 5, -3 \rangle$. **$\langle 6, -5 \rangle$**

137

CONNECTING TO PRIOR KNOWLEDGE To prepare students for drawing angles where neither side lies in a horizontal line, have students use a protractor to draw two 60° angles, each in a different position. Then have students draw two 140° angles in different positions.

WORK TOGETHER

Students may benefit from using tracing paper for this activity Have students read through Steps 1–3 before beginning Step 1. As students rotate their papers, make sure that the centers of their circles stay aligned. The results should be kaleidoscopic designs.

Lesson Planning Options

Prerequisite Skills

- Drawing angles
- Constructing congruent line segments

Assignment Options for Exercises On Your Own

Core 1–18, 20–25, 28–30
Extension 19, 26–27

Use Mixed Review to maintain skills.

Resources

 Student Edition

Skills Handbook, p. 651
Extra Practice, p. 636
Glossary/Study Guide

 Teaching Resources

Chapter Support File, Ch. 3
- Practice 3-3 (two worksheets)
- Reteaching 3-3
- Alternative Activity 3-3
Classroom Manager 3-3
Glossary, Spanish Resources

 Transparencies
5, 12, 41, 47, 48

138

What You'll Learn

- Identifying and locating rotation images of figures

...And Why

To understand real-life objects that involve rotation, such as clocks, combination locks, and laser disc players

What You'll Need

- straightedge
- colored pencils (optional)
- protractor
- compass

If you start with this in Step 4 . . .

You could end up with this . . .

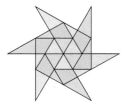

Connections Astronomy . . . *and more*

3-3 Rotations

WORK TOGETHER

Before beginning the activity, have each member of your group fold a piece of paper in half lengthwise and widthwise and then cut it into fourths.

Step 1: Place a piece of the paper over the figure below. Trace the six points on the circle, the center of the circle, and the triangle.

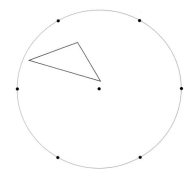

Step 2: Place the point of your pencil on the center of the circle and then rotate the paper until the six points again overlap. Trace the triangle in its new location.

Step 3: Repeat Step 2 until there are six triangles on your paper. Compare drawings within your group to be sure that your results look the same.

Step 4: Now it's your turn to be creative. Place a piece of paper over the figure above, trace the six points on the circle and the center of the circle, and then draw your own triangle on the paper.

Step 5: Place the paper from Step 4 on your desktop, and then use a blank piece of paper to repeat the process in Steps 1–3. Color your design, and then create a display of your group's designs.

THINK AND DISCUSS

In the Work Together, you used rotations to create a design. In order to describe a rotation, you need to know the center of rotation, the angle of rotation, and the direction of the rotation.

Example 1

Rotations are described in the counterclockwise direction because most students have been taught to measure angles in that direction. You may want to discuss with students rotations described with negative measures indicating clockwise direction. In this book all rotations are described with a positive degree measure.

Question 2 To show how $\overline{TE}$ was rotated about G, have students trace the six dots and the center of the circle from the Work Together. Place the center of the circle on G. Trace $\overline{TE}$. Rotate the paper through two dots (equivalent to 120°) and draw $\overline{T'E'}$.

Have students perform each step in their notebooks. In Step 1, show students how to position their protractors. For Step 2, students may need to review Construction 1 on page 40 of Lesson 1-6.

ERROR ALERT! Question 4 Some students may think that under a rotation all points move the same distance.
Remediation: Have students consider a spoke of a spinning bicycle tire. As the tire rotates 360°, the distance the outermost point on the spoke has traveled is greater than the distance the innermost point on the spoke has traveled.

The direction of a rotation can be clockwise or counterclockwise. All rotations in this book will be in a *counterclockwise* direction.

Center of rotation — Rotate counter-clockwise.

1. What was the angle of each rotation in the Work Together? (*Hint:* Each angle had the same measure.) **60°**

2. The diagram at the left shows $\overline{TE}$ rotated 120° about G.
   a. What appears to be true of EG and $E'G$? Of TG and $T'G$?
   b. What appears to be true of $m\angle TGT'$ and $m\angle EGE'$?
   2a. equal; equal   b. Both angle measures are 120.

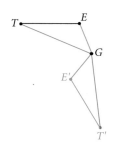

The properties of rotations that you noted in Question 2 form the basis of the definition of a rotation. A **rotation** of $x°$ about a point R is a transformation such that:
- For any point V,
  $RV' = RV$ and $m\angle VRV' = x$.
- The image of R is itself (that is, $R' = R$).

Example 1

Draw the image of $\triangle LOB$ under a 100° rotation about C.

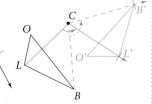

Step 1
Use a protractor to draw a 100° angle with side $\overrightarrow{OC}$.

Step 2
Use a compass to construct $\overline{O'C} \cong \overline{OC}$.

Step 3
Create B' and L' in a similar manner. Draw $\triangle L'O'B'$.

3. **Try This** Draw the image of $\triangle LOB$ under a 90° rotation about B.
   See back of book.
4. *Critical Thinking* Under a rotation, does each point move the same distance? If not, which points move the farthest? **No; the points farthest from the center of rotation move the farthest.**

A comparison of $\triangle LOB$ and $\triangle L'O'B'$ in Example 1 reveals the following properties of a rotation.

Properties of a Rotation

A rotation is an isometry.

A rotation does not change orientation.

Additional Examples

FOR EXAMPLE 1

Refer to the $\triangle LOB$ in Example 1. Copy it and draw its image under a 60° rotation about C.

Discussion: *Does the transformation change the orientation? If yes, describe how.*

FOR EXAMPLE 2

Refer to the pentagon in Example 2. Name the image of A under a 288° rotation about X. **P**

Discussion: *Name another rotation that would map A to P.*

139

Example 2 ....

Example 2

Students encountered angles with measures greater than 180 in Exercises 34–35 in Lesson 3-2. Use a circle or a coordinate grid to have students practice drawing angles with measures greater than 180.

Question 7 A 360° rotation is sometimes called a *full turn*.

Example 3 Relating to the Real World

Example 3 Relating to the Real World

KINESTHETIC LEARNING If you have block scheduling or an extended period, take students outside and use chalk to mark a large circle on the pavement. Have a student stand at the center and have another student slowly walking around the circle. Ask the students at the center to remain stationary and to describe what he or she sees. Repeat this activity but have the student at the center rotate more quickly than the students walking around the circle.

Technology Options

For Exercises 1–6, students may want to use geometry software to draw the figures and their images under the rotations.

Prentice Hall Technology

 Software
- Secondary Math Lab Toolkit™
- Computer Item Generator 3-3

 CD-ROM
- Multimedia Geometry Lab 3

 Internet
- See the Prentice Hall site. (http://www.phschool.com)

140

Example 2

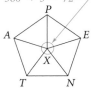

360° ÷ 5 = 72°

Regular pentagon *PENTA* is divided into five congruent triangles.
a. Name the image of *E* under a 72° rotation about *X*.
b. Name the image of *P* under a 216° rotation about *X*.

a.
72°

P is the image of *E*.

b.

216°

N is the image of *P*.

5. **Try This** Name the image of *T* under a 144° rotation about *X*. **E**

6. In Example 2, *E* ⟶ *P*, then *P* ⟶ *N*. Describe a single rotation that maps *E* to *N*. **288° rotation about *X***

7. What is the image of any point under a 360° rotation? **the same point**

What? Satellite photographs of the opposite side of the moon reveal that it is free of the large, dark regions that are visible from Earth. Early astronomers thought these regions looked like seas, so they named them *maria*, the Latin word for seas.

This portion of the moon is visible from Earth.

This portion is not.

This photo was taken in 1972 by astronauts aboard *Apollo 17*, the last flight in which humans explored the moon's surface.

Example 3 Relating to the Real World

Astronomy The motion of the moon around Earth can be modeled by the type of rotation presented in this lesson. What effect does this have on our observations of the moon?

Earth

Moon

When a figure is rotated, the point closest to the center of rotation remains closest to the center of rotation. In the case of the moon, the point on its surface closest to Earth remains closest to Earth as it moves. This means that from Earth, only one side of the moon is ever visible. Our knowledge of the moon was "one-sided" until 1966, when lunar probes transmitted pictures of the opposite side of the moon back to Earth.

Exercises   **ON YOUR OWN**

Exercises 1–6 Students draw the images of rotations when the center of rotation is outside the preimage, inside the preimage, and on the preimage.

ALTERNATIVE ASSESSMENT **Exercises 7–9** These exercises can be used to assess students' understanding of the definition of rotation. Have students discuss how they might find the solution. They can trace both figures onto a separate piece of paper and then work with them or use tracing paper on the page to copy one figure and then rotate it onto the other.

Exercises 10–17 Discuss with students the angle measures of the angles of a regular triangle, a regular quadrilateral, and a regular hexagon.

Copy each figure and point *P*. Rotate the figure the given number of degrees about *P*. Label the vertices of the image.

1. 60°

2. 90°

3. 180°

4. 140°

5. 90°

6. 45°

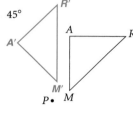

What is the measure of the rotation about *C* that maps the black figure onto the blue figure?

7.

110

8.

290

9.

180

The green segments in the figure intersect to form 30° angles. The triangle, quadrilateral, and hexagon are all regular. Find the image of each point or segment.

10. 120° rotation of *B* about *O*   H

11. 270° rotation of *L* about *O*   M

12. 60° rotation of *E* about *O*   C

13. 300° rotation of $\overline{IB}$ about *O* $\overline{BC}$

14. 120° rotation of $\overline{FE}$ about *O* $\overline{CB}$

15. 120° rotation of *F* about *H*   I

16. 180° rotation of $\overline{JK}$ about *O* $\overline{LM}$

17. 90° rotation of *L* about *M*   J

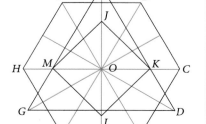

141

STANDARDIZED TEST TIP **Exercise 18** Students can trace the figure and try to rotate, translate, or reflect it to get each of the images.

MAKING CONNECTIONS **Exercise 19** If you took a time-lapse photograph of the night sky near the North Star, the arcs showing the movements of stars would be larger for stars farther from the North Star and smaller for those near the North Star. The North Star itself, near the center of rotation, would show little movement.

EXTENSION **Exercise 26** Have students find which block letters, for example, H, that also form block letters when they are rotated 180°.

Chapter Project **FIND OUT BY MODELING** Make sure students understand what "onto itself" means. Students will need to experiment to find the center of rotation for each design. Point out that the center of rotation is not always on the figure.

Exercises **MIXED REVIEW**

WRITING **Exercise 37** Have students include a graph of the triangle with their explanations.

---

pages 141–143 On Your Own

20a–c.

38.

(graph with points J, H, K)

Checkpoint page 143

7. Images and preimages under translations, reflections, and rotations are congruent to each other. Translations and rotations do not affect orientation. Reflection reverses orientation.

142

---

18. *Standardized Test Prep* Which figure is *not* the image of the figure at the left under a congruence transformation? **D**

 A. **B.** **C.** **D.** **E.**

19. *Astronomy* Refer to Example 3. Suppose Earth's motion around the sun, like the moon's motion around Earth, could be described by the type of rotation in this lesson. How would life on Earth be different?

Answers may vary. Sample: On one side of Earth it would always be day; on the other, always night.

20. **a.** *Coordinate Geometry* Graph $A(5, 2)$, then graph B, the image of A under a 90° rotation about O (the origin). (*Hint:* Consider the slope of $\overline{OA}$.) a–c. See margin.
    b. Graph C, the image of A under a 180° rotation about O.
    c. Graph D, the image of A under a 270° rotation about O.
    d. What type of quadrilateral is $ABCD$? Explain.
    Square; its sides are ≅ and its angles are ≅.

21. $\overline{M'N'}$ is the rotation image of $\overline{MN}$ about point E. Name all the congruent angles and segments in the diagram. $\overline{MN} \cong \overline{M'N'}$, $\overline{ME} \cong \overline{M'E}$, $\overline{EN} \cong \overline{EN'}$, $\angle MEN \cong \angle M'EN'$, $\angle MNE \cong \angle M'N'E$, $\angle EMN \cong \angle EM'N'$, $\angle MEM' \cong \angle NEN'$

(diagram with points M, M', N', N, E)

Copy each figure, then draw the image of $\overline{JK}$ under a 180° rotation about P.

22.

23.
(segment with J, P, J', K, K')

24. (segment J, P, K)

25. (segment K, J', J = P, K')

26. *Language Arts* The symbol ə is called a *schwa*. It is used in dictionaries to represent neutral vowel sounds such as *a* in *ago*, *i* in *sanity*, and *u* in *focus*. What transformation maps a ə to a lowercase e? 180° rotation

27. *Open-ended* Find a composition of rotations that has the same effect as a 360° rotation about a point X.
    Sample: a 288° rotation and a 72° rotation

Native American Art **Find the measure of the rotation about C that maps Q to X.** 90   108   225

28.

29.

30.

GETTING READY FOR LESSON 3-4 This exercise illustrates Theorem 3-2 (a composition of reflections in two intersecting lines is a rotation),which is presented in Lesson 3-4.

RETEACHING ACTIVITY Students locate rotation images of figures by tracing and rotating the preimage. (Reteaching worksheet 3-3)

Wrap Up

THE BIG IDEA Ask students: *Draw the preimage and image of a triangle under a rotation. Then describe the rotation by naming the center of rotation and the angle of rotation.*

Exercises   CHECKPOINT

In this Checkpoint, your students will assess their own progress in Lessons 3-1 to 3-3.

Exercise 8 Remind students that not all transformations are isometries.

Chapter Project *Find Out by Modeling*

Some frieze patterns can also be mapped onto themselves by a 180° rotation. Use tracing paper to make a copy of each pattern. Rotate your copy to help you determine whether the pattern can be mapped onto itself by a 180° rotation. Mark the centers of rotation on your copy.

a. Ancient Egyptian Ornament

b. Navaho Design

c. Oriental Design

d. Greek Vase Design

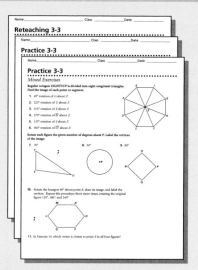

Exercises   MIXED REVIEW

Create a separate sketch for each description. 31–36. See back of book for samples.

31. skew lines

32. nonsimilar kites

33. parallel planes

34. similar trapezoids

35. perpendicular lines

36. nonsimilar rhombuses

37. Writing Determine whether a triangle with vertices (3, 2), (−1, 1), and (2, −1) is a right triangle. Explain how you know. Sample: No; the slopes of the sides are $\frac{1}{4}$, $-\frac{2}{3}$, and 3. No sides are ⊥ because the slopes are not negative reciprocals of each other.

Getting Ready for Lesson 3-4

38. Coordinate Geometry Graph H(5, 3) and J, its reflection image in the y-axis. Then graph K, the reflection image of J in the x-axis. Describe a rotation that maps H to K. See margin p. 142 for graph; 180° rotation about (0, 0)

Exercises   CHECKPOINT

Find the image of T(3, 4) under each transformation.

1. reflection in the x-axis (3, −4)

2. rotation of 90° about (0, 0) (−4, 3)

3. translation ⟨−2, 7⟩ (1, 11)

4. rotation of 270° about (0, 0) (4, −3)

5. translation ⟨1, −5⟩ (4, −1)

6. reflection in the line y = x (4, 3)

7. Writing Explain how translations, reflections, and rotations affect the congruence and orientation of figures. See margin p. 142.

8. a. List the corresponding sides for the transformation shown.
b. Is the transformation an isometry? Explain.
8a. $\overline{AD}$ and $\overline{A'D'}$, $\overline{AF}$ and $\overline{A'F'}$, $\overline{DF}$ and $\overline{D'F'}$
b. No; the image is not ≅ to the preimage.

143

PROBLEM OF THE DAY

Divide the figure into two congruent pieces. Hint: It cannot be done with a straight line.

Problem of the Day is also available in Transparencies.

CONNECTING TO PRIOR KNOWLEDGE Have students draw a triangle. Then have them find the image under a reflection in a vertical line, a horizontal line, and another line.

WORK TOGETHER

Students working in groups can experiment by drawing triangles of different sizes and parallel lines at different distances apart. Students can also draw the lines intersecting at different angles.

THINK AND DISCUSS

Students should readily accept Theorems 3-1 and 3-2 without proof after answering Questions 1–2 in the Work Together.

Lesson Planning Options

Prerequisite Skills

• Reflecting figures in lines
• Translating figures

Assignment Options for Exercises On Your Own

To provide flexible scheduling, this lesson can be subdivided into parts.

1 **Core** 1–3, 13–14
Extension 15

2 **Core** 4–12, 16–29
Extension 30–32

Use Mixed Review to maintain skills.

Resources

 Student Edition

Skills Handbook, p. 657
Extra Practice, p. 636
Glossary/Study Guide

Teaching Resources

Chapter Support File, Ch. 3
• Practice 3-4 (two worksheets)
• Reteaching 3-4
Classroom Manager 3-4
Glossary, Spanish Resources

 Transparencies
5, 41, 49

144

What You'll Learn

• Showing how reflections are related to the other isometries
• Identifying glide reflections

...And Why

To be able to describe how objects relate to one another

What You'll Need

• straightedge
• lined paper
• graph paper

3-4 Compositions of Reflections

Connections Creative Art . . . and more

WORK TOGETHER

■ Have each member of your group use a straightedge to draw figures like those at the right on a piece of lined paper. Reflect the triangle in line ℓ_1; then reflect the image in line ℓ_2.

1. Compare results within your group. What transformation that you've studied has the same effect as the composition of two reflections in parallel lines? **a translation**

■ Have each member of your group use a straightedge to draw figures like those at the left on a piece of paper. Reflect the triangle in line ℓ_3; then reflect the image in line ℓ_4.

2. Compare results within your group. What transformation that you've studied has the same effect as the composition of two reflections in intersecting lines? **a rotation**

THINK AND DISCUSS

Part 1 **Compositions of Two Reflections**

The Work Together illustrates the two properties summarized in the theorems below.

Theorem 3-1	A composition of reflections in two parallel lines is a translation.
Theorem 3-2	A composition of reflections in two intersecting lines is a rotation.

The vibrant images of a kaleidoscope are produced by repeated reflections in intersecting mirrors.

Viewing hole

Mirrors

Colored glass

Cutaway view of a kaleidoscope

Example 1 ····· Relating to the Real World 🌐 ·····

Example 2 ·····

Some students may not have seen a kaleidoscope. If possible, bring in a kaleidoscope with which students can experiment or books that show kaleidoscope images.

MAKING CONNECTIONS Sir David Brewster studied to be a minister. After a short time, he left the ministry to study optics (light). Along with making scientific contributions in that field, Brewster's interest in instruments led him to create the first kaleidoscope in 1816.

Have students trace the two P's and use paper folding to replicate each reflection.

EXTENSION Have students work in groups to find another pair of reflections that will map the left P onto the right P.

Question 3 You may want to ask students to find two reflections that map one of the P's onto the other in such a way that the first reflection does not have its image of P touching the final image.

CRITICAL THINKING Question 4 Help students see that the point about which the figure is rotated is the intersection of the two reflection lines created by the folds.

Example 1   Relating to the Real World 🌐 ·····

Creative Art Determine the angle between the mirrors in this kaleidoscope image.

This wedge is repeated 6 times in 360°.

$360° ÷ 6 = 60°$

Suppose you are given two congruent figures in random positions in a plane. Could you use reflections to map one onto the other? If so, how many reflections would be needed? Example 2 shows that if the figures have the same orientation, only two reflections are needed.

Example 2 ·····

Paper folding The two P's at the right are congruent. Use two reflections to map one figure onto the other.

Reflection 1: Pick a point on one P, then fold it onto the corresponding point on the other P.

Reflection 2: Fold the two P's that share a point onto one another.

3. **Try This** Trace the two P's in Example 2 in different locations on your paper; then use paper folding to map one figure onto the other. Check students' work.

4. *Critical Thinking* What single isometry could be used to map one of the P's onto the other? Explain. A rotation; a composition of two reflections in intersecting lines is a rotation.

Additional Examples

FOR EXAMPLE 2 ·····

In the diagram, the two L's shown are congruent. Use two reflections to map one L onto the other.

Discussion: *Did you and your classmates reflect in the same lines? in the same order?*

Answers may vary. Sample given above.

FOR EXAMPLE 3 ·····

Refer to the diagram in Example 3. Find the image of $\triangle TEX$ under the glide reflection in $\langle 6, -5 \rangle$ and $y = 0$.

Discussion: *Can you produce the same image using just reflections? If so, how many reflections would be needed?*

145

Theorem 3-3 Point out to students that reflecting a figure once in any line results in two figures with the opposite orientation. From Example 2, we know that one of those figures can be mapped onto the other with two reflections.

Have students recall from Theorem 3-2 that the composition of reflections in two intersecting lines is a translation. So it follows that the composition of three reflections in intersecting lines is a composition of a translation and a reflection, also called a glide reflection.

EXTENSION Ask students to find a transformation that is equivalent to the reflection of a figure in three parallel lines.

Example 3

TACTILE LEARNING Students may want to trace △*TEX* to illustrate the translation, then use paper folding to find the reflection.

Part 2 **Compositions of Three Reflections**

Example 2 shows that if two congruent figures have the *same* orientation, you can map one onto the other by exactly two reflections. If two congruent figures have *opposite* orientation, you may need to use three reflections.

Given: two figures with opposite orientation

Reflect one figure in any line to change its orientation.

Then reflect the image twice, as shown in Example 2.

These paper-folding techniques illustrate the following theorem.

Theorem 3-3

In a plane, two congruent figures can be mapped onto one another by a composition of at most three reflections.

Glide. Then reflect.

A composition of three reflections in lines that intersect in more than one point is called a **glide reflection.** It is called a glide reflection because any such composition of reflections can be rewritten as a translation (or glide) followed by a reflection in a line parallel to the translation vector.

5. *Critical Thinking* Explain why a glide reflection changes orientation. See below.

Example 3

Coordinate Geometry Find the image of △*TEX* under a glide reflection where the glide is given by the vector $\langle 0, -5 \rangle$ and the reflection is in $x = 0$.

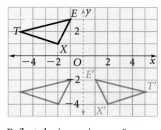

Translate △*TEX* by the vector $\langle 0, -5 \rangle$.

Reflect the image in $x = 0$.

5. Each reflection reverses the orientation once, so a glide reflection reverses the orientation 3 times. Two orientation changes cancel each other.

146

Theorem 3-4 Have students record the theorem and the diagrams in their notebooks. The diagrams provide a visual explanation of what each transformation does.

AUDITORY LEARNING Have students work with a partner. Have one student describe a composition of isometries and another students classify the result as one of the four isometries given in Theorem 3-4 .

Example 4

DIVERSITY Some students, especially those confused by the vocabulary, may need further explanation. Be sure it is clear to students that the transformation in part a is not a translation and the transformation in part b is not a reflection.

---

6. Would the result of Example 3 be the same if you reflected △*TEX* first, then translated it? **yes**

7. Try This Find the image of △*TEX* under a glide reflection given by the vector ⟨1, 0⟩ and a reflection in *y* = −2. **See margin.**

You can map any two congruent figures onto one another by a single reflection, translation, rotation, or glide reflection. These four transformations are the only isometries.

Theorem 3-4
Isometry Classification Theorem

There are only four isometries. They are the following.

reflection   translation   rotation   glide reflection

pages 144–147   Think and Discuss

7.

Example 4

Each pair of figures is congruent. What isometry maps one to the other?

a.

b.

PROBLEM SOLVING HINT
Use Logical Reasoning.

a. These figures have the same orientation, so the transformation must be either a translation or a rotation. It's obviously not a translation, so it must be a rotation.
b. These figures have opposite orientation, so the transformation must be either a reflection or a glide reflection. Since it's not a reflection, it must be a glide reflection.

Exercises   ON YOUR OWN

Creative Art What is the angle between the mirrors for each kaleidoscope image?

1.
60°

2.
$25\frac{5}{7}°$

3.
30°

147

Exercises 4–6 Students will best be able to check the orientation of the figures more easily if they rotate their books so that the bottom of each figure is close to them.

Exercises 13–16 Students should observe the number of lines of reflection and their relationship to each other to help determine the type of transformation.

ERROR ALERT! Exercises 17–20 Some students may assume that the *x*- and *y*-axes are lines of reflection.
Remediation: Point out to students that the lines are bold because they indicate the axes on the coordinate grid and not necessarily lines of reflection.

---

pages 147–150 On Your Own

7.

8.

9.

10.

148

Match each image of the figure at the left with one of the following isometries: **I.** reflection **II.** rotation **III.** translation **IV.** glide reflection

4. **a.** I **b.** IV **c.** III **d.** II

5. **a.** III **b.** IV **c.** II **d.** I

6. **a.** II **b.** III **c.** I **d.** IV

Coordinate Geometry **Find the image of △*PNB* under each glide reflection.** 7–10. See margin. 11–12. See margin p. 149.

7. ⟨2, 0⟩ and *y* = 3   **8.** ⟨0, −3⟩ and *x* = 0

9. ⟨0, 3⟩ and *x* = −2   **10.** ⟨−2, 0⟩ and *y* = −1

11. ⟨2, 2⟩ and *y* = *x*   **12.** ⟨−1, 1⟩ and *y* = −*x*

Is the isometry that maps the black figure to the blue figure a translation, reflection, rotation, or glide reflection?

glide reflection

13. translation

14. rotation

15. rotation

16. glide reflection

17. **18.** **19.** **20.**

glide reflection   reflection   glide reflection   rotation

State whether each mapping is a reflection, rotation, translation, or glide reflection.

21. $\triangle ABC \longrightarrow \triangle EDC$
    rotation
22. $\triangle EDC \longrightarrow \triangle PQM$
    glide reflection
23. $\triangle MNJ \longrightarrow \triangle EDC$
    translation
24. $\triangle HIF \longrightarrow \triangle HGF$
    reflection
25. $\triangle PQM \longrightarrow \triangle JLM$
    reflection
26. $\triangle MNP \longrightarrow \triangle EDC$
    reflection
27. $\triangle JLM \longrightarrow \triangle MNJ$
    rotation
28. $\triangle PQM \longrightarrow \triangle KJN$
    glide reflection

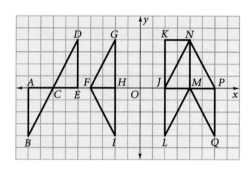

29. **Writing** Reflections and glide reflections are *odd isometries*, while translations and rotations are *even isometries*. Use what you learned in this lesson to explain why these categories make sense. **See margin.**

30. **Paper folding** Fold a rectangular piece of paper into sixths as shown. Then use scissors to cut a nonregular polygon into the folded paper. Unfold the paper and number each of the six figures represented by the holes. What isometries map Figure 1 onto Figures 2, 3, 4, 5, and 6?

reflection; reflection; rotation; translation; glide reflection

31. **Probability** Suppose you toss two cardboard cutouts of congruent figures into the air so that they land in random positions on the floor. Consider the isometry that maps one of the figures onto the other. Which of the four isometries, if any, are most likely to occur? **See below.**

32. **Architecture** These housing plans were created by the Swiss architect Le Corbusier for a development in Pessac, France. They illustrate each of the four isometries. Name the isometry illustrated by each design.

a.

translation

d.

rotation

b.

c.

reflection   glide reflection

31. Rotations and glide reflections are equally likely to occur. They are more likely to occur than translations and reflections.

11.

12.

29. Reflections and glide reflections can be expressed as compositions of odd numbers of reflections. Translations and rotations can be expressed as compositions of even numbers of reflections.

149

Wrap Up

THE BIG IDEA Ask students: *What composition of reflections has the same effect as a translation? a rotation? a glide reflection?*

RETEACHING ACTIVITY Students use paper-folding to reflect figures in lines. Then they identify transformations that map one figure onto another. (Reteaching worksheet 3-4)

Reteaching 3-4
Practice 3-4
Practice 3-4
Mixed Exercises

Lesson Quiz

Lesson Quiz is also available in Transparencies.

1. Name the type of isometry that maps △XYZ to △VYZ. **reflection**

2. Name the type of isometry that maps △XYZ to △HIJ. **translation**

3. Name the type of isometry that maps △XYZ to △QPR.
   glide reflection

150

Chapter Project ▼ *Find Out by Investigating*

Some frieze patterns can be mapped onto themselves by a glide reflection. In the diagrams, the vector shows the glide. The red line is the line of reflection.

• Which frieze patterns below can be mapped onto themselves by a glide reflection? **a, b, d**

a. Victorian Design

b. Chinese Design

c. Nigerian Design

d. Turkish Design

Exercises MIXED REVIEW

Data Analysis Refer to the circle graph.

33. Find the measure of each central angle.
    79, 130 and 151
34. What percent of people use their ATM cards fewer than six times per month?
    64%
35. Which statements are true, based on the graph?
    a. Most people use their ATM cards two or more times per month. **true**
    b. Most people have ATM cards. **false**
    c. At least 36% of people use their ATM cards one or more times per week. **true**

How often ATM cards are used per month

0–1 times **22%**
6 or more times **36%**
2–5 times **42%**

Source: *Research Partnership survey for Cirrus Systems*

Getting Ready for Lesson 3-5

Find the image of each figure under the given transformation. **36–38. Each figure maps onto itself.**

36.

Rotation of 60° about O

37.

Reflection in y-axis

38.

Rotation of 90° about O

Math ToolboX

Students use geometry software to create a symmetrical design. This activity introduces ideas of symmetry which will be presented in Lesson 3-5.

The software allows students to explore the effect of changing the shape of the figure being reflected.

ERROR ALERT! If students draw line segments instead of lines, they may not get six angles as shown in the diagram. **Remediation:** Have students read the directions carefully. Point out that each line should appear to go to the edge of the computer screen.

You may want to display students' designs. Have students observe the variety of designs that can be created using this simple technique.

ADDITIONAL PROBLEM Create a kaleidoscope with six lines of reflection. Draw a line and construct a point on the line. Rotate the figure 30° about the point and repeat until you have six lines. Add a figure to the interior of an angle and reflect it as described in the text.

Math ToolboX — Technology

Kaleidoscopes

Before Lesson 3-5

The mirrors in a kaleidoscope reflect objects to create a *symmetrical* design. Work in pairs or small groups to create your own kaleidoscope.

Construct

Check students' work.
- Use geometry software. Draw a line and construct a point on the line. Rotate the line 60° about the point. Rotate the image 60° about the point.

- Construct a polygon in the interior of an angle, as shown. Reflect the polygon in the closest line in a clockwise direction. Reflect the image in the next closest line in a clockwise direction. Continue reflecting until the kaleidoscope is filled. Then hide the lines of reflection.

Investigate

- Manipulate the original figure by dragging any of its vertices or selecting and moving it. As the figure is manipulated, what happens to the images? Does the design remain symmetrical? Continue manipulating the original figure until you are satisfied with your design. Print the design and color it. **All 6 polygons change in the same way; yes.**
- Now add other figures in addition to the original polygon. Reflect these figures to create a more interesting design, as shown at the right. (You may need to temporarily show the hidden lines of reflection.) Print your design and color it. **Check students' work.**

Extend

Create a kaleidoscope with four lines of reflection. Draw a line and construct a point on the line. Rotate the line 45° about the point and repeat until you have four lines. Add a figure to the interior of an angle and reflect it as described above.

Check students' work.

Materials and Manipulatives
- Geometry software

Transparencies
12

CONNECTING TO PRIOR KNOWLEDGE Have students sketch a rectangle, then draw a line that bisects opposite sides. Have them reflect the rectangle in the line and discuss how the preimage and image are related.

THINK AND DISCUSS

Discuss with students how the definition of symmetry of a figure relates to the symmetry property of equality and the symmetry property of congruence.

Example 1

To find lines of symmetry, students may want to copy each figure and fold the image onto itself. Another method is to place a mirror or MIRA™ on a suspected line of symmetry and check that the resulting figure is the same as the original figure.

Lesson Planning Options

Prerequisite Skills
- Rotating figures
- Reflecting figures

Assignment Options for Exercises On Your Own

To provide flexible scheduling, this lesson can be subdivided into parts.

 Core 15–18, 30–32
Extension 14, 40

 Core 1–13, 19–28, 38, 41–46
Extension 29, 33–37, 39

Use Mixed Review to maintain skills.

Resources

Student Edition
Skills Handbook, p. 664
Extra Practice, p. 636
Glossary/Study Guide

Teaching Resources
Chapter Support File, Ch. 3
- Practice 3-5 (two worksheets)
- Reteaching 3-5
Classroom Manager 3-5
Glossary, Spanish Resources

 Transparencies
5, 42

What You'll Learn
- Identifying types of symmetry in figures

...And Why
To understand a topic that influences art, dance, and poetry, and is an important tool of scientists

Connections **Advertising . . . and more**

3-5 Symmetry

THINK AND DISCUSS

Part 1 **Reflectional Symmetry**

A figure has **symmetry** if there is an isometry that maps the figure onto itself. A plane figure has **reflectional symmetry,** or **line symmetry,** if there is a reflection that maps the figure onto itself. If you fold a figure along a line of symmetry, the halves match exactly.

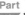

△*ABC* has line symmetry.

Line of symmetry

Example 1

Draw the lines of symmetry for each figure.

a. **b.** **c.**

a. **b.** **c.** This figure has no lines of symmetry.

Symmetry is especially important to left-handers. Because about 95% of people are right-handed, right-handed versions of objects are easier to find (and often less expensive!) than left-handed versions of the same objects.

Paul McCartney of the Beatles used converted right-handed bass guitars until he was given a left-handed Rickenbacker bass in the mid-1960s.

ERROR ALERT! Students may think that a figure that can be cut into two congruent pieces has reflectional symmetry. **Remediation:** Have students trace and cut out the parallelogram in part c. Have them manipulate it to show that it has no reflectional symmetry. Then have them cut it along its diagonal to show that it can be divided into two congruent pieces.

DIVERSITY Help students understand that "95% of people are right-handed" means that one out of twenty people is left-handed. Survey the class to find the number of left-handed people. Discuss the difficulties left-handed people sometimes experience.

ESL *Reflectional symmetry* in three-dimensional objects can also be called *plane symmetry* or, in special cases, *bilateral symmetry.*

MAKING CONNECTIONS Rock collectors, chemists, and geologists use reflectional symmetry of crystals to help identify them. Have students research types of crystals and their symmetries.

Example 2 **Relating to the Real World** ················

Students learned to draw top, front, and side views of three-dimensional objects in Lesson 2-7. In this example, only the view that most clearly suggests the plane of symmetry needs to be drawn.

CONNECTING TO STUDENTS' WORLD Have students find reflectional symmetry in three-dimensional objects around them. Have them sketch an orthographic view of the object, including a line that suggests the plane of symmetry.

Left-handed people appreciate reflectional symmetry because objects that have it can be used by both left-handers and right-handers.

Three-dimensional objects with reflectional symmetry can be divided into two congruent parts by a plane. You can sketch these symmetries in two dimensions by using orthographic views (top, front, or right side).

Example 2 **Relating to the Real World** ················

Technical Drawing Show the reflectional symmetries of each object by sketching an orthographic view.

a.

b.

a.

Top View

b.

Front View

1. *Critical Thinking* Name an object that has more than one plane of symmetry. **Samples: unlabeled cans; plain drinking glass; starfish**

153

Help students see that a figure has rotational symmetry only if the angle of rotation is 180° or less. If the only rotation that maps a figure onto itself is 360°, the figure does not have rotational symmetry.

Students can experiment by copying a figure on tracing paper, then choosing different points about which to rotate the figure.

CRITICAL THINKING Although a figure is defined to have rotational symmetry if there is a rotation of 180° or less that maps they figure onto itself, a figure may also be mapped onto itself by a rotation between 180° and 360°. Ask students to name a rotation between 180° and 360° that maps the triangle in part a onto itself.

Question 2 Suggest students look at Example 3 part c and look back at Example 1 part c. Then have students create other such examples. Students can also investigate whether a figure with line symmetry must also have rotational symmetry.

Question 3 Help students understand that a figure with point symmetry has rotational symmetry but that the converse is not always true.

WORK TOGETHER

Many examples that students find will be three-dimensional; thus the suggestion to draw orthographic views. You may want to exclude any examples that you have already mentioned in class.

Technology Options

For Exercises 38–40, students may sketch the graphs of the equations using a graphing calculator or graphing software.

Prentice Hall Technology

 Software
• Secondary Math Lab Toolkit™
• Computer Item Generator 3-5

 Internet
• See the Prentice Hall site. (http://www.phschool.com)

The spinning motion of a lathe ensures that objects created on it have rotational symmetry.

Type of Symmetry	Points
Reflectional Symmetry	1
Rotational Symmetry of 180°	2
Rotational Symmetry other than 180°	3

Part 2 Rotational Symmetry

A figure has **rotational symmetry** if there is a rotation of 180° or less that maps the figure onto itself.

Which figures have rotational symmetry? For those that do, give the angle of rotation.

a.   b.   c.

a. 120°   b. This figure does not have rotational symmetry.   c. 180°

2. If a figure has rotational symmetry, must it also have line symmetry? Explain your answer. **No; figure (c) in Example 3 has rotational symmetry but not line symmetry.**

A rotation of 180° is known as a **half-turn.** If a half-turn maps a plane figure onto itself, the figure has **point symmetry.**

3. **Try This** Which figures have point symmetry?

a.   b.   c.

yes   no   yes

So far, you've looked at figures with reflectional and rotational symmetry. As you may have guessed, figures may also have *translational* or *glide reflectional symmetry.* You will discuss these symmetries in the next lesson.

WORK TOGETHER

■ Work in groups to find examples of symmetrical objects in your classroom. For each object that you find, sketch an orthographic view and list its symmetries. You will have only ten minutes in which to search, so plan your time wisely!

■ Determine your group's score by using the chart at the left.

3-6 Teaching Notes

CONNECTING TO PRIOR KNOWLEDGE Have students who have played the game TETRIS™ explain it to others. (Seven tiles are rotated and translated to cover a rectangular playing surface without leaving any gaps.) Ask them to share any techniques or tricks they have learned.

THINK AND DISCUSS p. 159

TACTILE LEARNING If pattern blocks are available, have students create the pavement tiling shown.

Example 1   Relating to the Real World

CONNECTING TO STUDENTS' WORLD Students will most likely be familiar with Escher prints from calendars, posters, and T-shirts. Ask what they like and dislike about this type of art.

ERROR ALERT! **Question 1** Students may have some difficulty seeing a pattern of tiles that is repeated.
Remediation: Suggest they trace the pattern that they think is being repeated and see if they can cover the picture with it.

Connections **Graphic Design . . . and more**

What You'll Learn

- Identifying figures that tessellate
- Identifying symmetries of tessellations

...And Why

To recognize tessellations in nature, architecture, art, and other areas of life

What You'll Need

- scissors
- clear tape
- ruler

Who? The Dutch artist Maurits Cornelis Escher (1898–1972) used transformational geometry in intriguing ways in his work. His work is very popular with the public, scientists, and mathematicians.

3-6 Tessellations

THINK AND DISCUSS

Part 1

Identifying Figures that Tessellate

A **tessellation** is a repeating pattern of figures that completely covers a plane without gaps or overlaps. Tessellations are also called **tilings.** A set of figures that can be used to create a tessellation is said to *tessellate*. You can find tessellations in art, nature, and everyday life.

Example 1   Relating to the Real World

Art Identify the repeating figures that make up this tessellation.

Repeating figures

1. Try This Identify the repeating figures that make up the tessellation of paving tiles at the top of this page.

Lesson Planning Options

Prerequisite Skills

- Identifying symmetry
- Finding transformations of figures

Assignment Options for Exercises On Your Own

To provide flexible scheduling, this lesson can be subdivided into parts.

1   **Core** 1–3, 10–12, 17–19
    Extension 13–16

2   **Core** 4–9
    Extension 20

Use Mixed Review to maintain skills.

Resources

Student Edition
Extra Practice, p. 636
Glossary/Study Guide

Teaching Resources
Chapter Support File, Ch. 3
- Practice 3-6 (two worksheets)
- Reteaching 3-6
Classroom Manager 3-6
Glossary, Spanish Resources

Transparencies
1, 7, 42

159

Students may need some help in understanding the diagrams shown above Question 3. They illustrate that in order for a regular polygon to tessellate the plane, copies of the polygon must be able to be placed so that at a vertex shared by the polygons, the sum of the measures of the angles is 360 and the angles do not overlap. This happens when the angle measure of a regular polygon divides evenly into 360.

CRITICAL THINKING Question 3 You may need to review with students the interior angle measures of regular polygons, $\frac{(n - 2) \times 180}{n}$.

Additional Examples

FOR EXAMPLE 1 ....

Refer to page 163, Exercise 5. Identify the repeating figures in the tessellation.

FOR EXAMPLE 2 ....

Refer to the walkway of paving tiles on page 159. List the types of symmetry in the tessellation.

rotational and point symmetry in the dots shown

line symmetry in the bold-faced lines

translational symmetry

glide reflectional symmetry

Because the figures in a tessellation do not overlap or leave gaps, the sum of the measures of the angles around any vertex must be 360.

2. **a.** The tessellation shown consists of regular polygons. Find the measures of angles 1, 2, 3, and 4. **120, 90, 60, 90**

   b. Check your answer to part (a) by making sure that the sum of the measures is 360.

120 + 90 + 60 + 90 = 360 ✔

A **pure tessellation** is a tessellation that consists of congruent copies of one figure. It may surprise you that there are only three pure tessellations made up of regular polygons. To see why this is the case, consider the following diagrams.

$360° \div 60° = 6$

$360° \div 90° = 4$

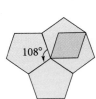

$360° \div 108° \approx 3.3$

$360° \div 120° = 3$

$360° \div 128\frac{4}{7}° \approx 2.8$

$360° \div 135° \approx 2.6$

3. *Critical Thinking* Explain why no regular polygons with more than six sides tessellate. **See below.**

Regular triangles and quadrilaterals tessellate, but what about other triangles and quadrilaterals? Work in groups to explore this problem.

WORK TOGETHER

Step 1: Have each member of your group fold four pieces of paper into sixths, as shown in the photos.
3. A regular polygon with more than 6 sides must have angles greater than 120°, and at least 3 polygons must meet at each vertex. The sum of 3 or more angles greater than 120° cannot be 360°.

160

In Step 2, suggest one member of each group draw an acute triangle, another draw an obtuse triangle, and another draw a right triangle.

Question 4a Students may observe that a triangle can tessellate a plane in more than one way. For example, a tessellation of right triangles can form a large rectangle or a large parallelogram.

In Step 3, students should see already that squares and rectangles will tessellate a plane. Have students draw other types of quadrilaterals, some concave and some convex.

Remind students that only part of the tessellation is shown in the diagram. The pattern continues in all directions of its plane.

Step 2: Draw a triangle on one of the four folded pieces of paper; then cut through all six sheets of paper to create six congruent triangles. Create six more congruent triangles by tracing one of your cutouts onto another folded piece of paper and then cutting out six triangles.

4. **a.** Try to arrange your twelve congruent triangles into a tessellation. (*Hint:* Arrange vertices so that they meet.) Compare results within your group.
   b. Use what you know about the sum of the measures of the angles of a triangle to explain your results from part (a).
   4a–b. See left.

Step 3: Set your triangles aside. Use the method in Step 2 to create twelve congruent quadrilaterals.

5. **a.** Try to arrange your twelve congruent quadrilaterals into a tessellation. Compare results within your group.
   b. Use what you know about the sum of the measures of the angles of a quadrilateral to explain your results from part (a).
   a–b. See margin p. 162.

4a. Sample:

b. The sum of the measures of the angles of a triangle is 180. Therefore, 6 triangles meeting at each vertex with 2 of each angle represented will cover the space around the vertex.

THINK AND DISCUSS

In the Work Together, you discovered the following properties of tessellations.

| **Theorem 3-5** | Every triangle tessellates. |
| **Theorem 3-6** | Every quadrilateral tessellates. |

Part 2 Tessellations and Symmetry

This pure tessellation of regular hexagons has reflectional symmetry in each of the blue lines. It has rotational symmetry centered at each of the red points. The tessellation also has two other types of symmetry—translational symmetry and glide reflectional symmetry.

Translational Symmetry

A translation maps the tessellation onto itself.

Glide Reflectional Symmetry

A glide reflection maps the tessellation onto itself.

Technology Options

For Exercise 10, students may use a drawing program or geometry software to sketch the two tessellations. Similarly, in Exercises 13–16 students can use geometry software to copy each figure onto a coordinate grid, then create a tessellation.

Prentice Hall Technology

 Software
- Secondary Math Lab Toolkit™
- Integrated Math Lab 28
- Computer Item Generator 3-6

Internet
- See the Prentice Hall site. (http://www.phschool.com)

161

Example 2

Before students determine the symmetries, they should identify the pattern being repeated. You may want to ask why there is no line symmetry or glide reflectional symmetry in part b.

Once students have created their figures, have them copy them onto lightweight cardboard and cut them out. They can then trace around the cutouts to create their tessellations.

---

page 161   Work Together

5a. Sample:

b. The sum of the measures of the angles of a quadrilateral is 360. Four quadrilaterals meeting at a vertex, each represented by a different angle, cover the space around the vertex.

Example 2

List the symmetries of each tessellation.

a.

b.

a.

b.

- Line symmetry in the blue lines
- Rotational symmetry in the red points
- Translational symmetry
- Glide reflectional symmetry

- Rotational symmetry in the red points
- Translational symmetry

WORK TOGETHER

Create your own "Escher-like" tessellation! Start by having each member of your group draw a 1.5-inch square on a blank piece of paper and cut it out.

- Sketch a curve from one vertex to a consecutive vertex.

- Cut along the curve that you sketched and slide the resulting cutout to the opposite side of the square. Tape it in place using clear tape.

- Repeat this process using the remaining two sides of the square.

- Rotate the figure you end up with. What does it look like? A penguin with a hat on? A knight on horseback? A dog with floppy ears? Sketch whatever you come up with on your figure.

- Create a tessellation using your figure.

162

Exercises **ON YOUR OWN**

Identify the repeating figure or figures that make up each tessellation. 1–3. See margin.

1.

Fabric by *Fabric Traditions*

2.

Arabian design

3.

Honeycomb

Describe the symmetries of each tessellation. Copy a portion of the tessellation and draw any centers of rotational symmetry or lines of symmetry. 4–9. Also see margin.

4.

5.

6.

7.

8.

9.

10. The figure shown at the right can be used to tile the plane in several different ways. Make copies of the figure and sketch two different tessellations. See margin.

11. *Open-ended* Find and sketch two examples of tessellations found at home or at school. Check students' work.

12. *Writing* Is it possible to tile the plane with regular decagons? Explain why or why not. No; regular decagons have more than 6 sides. No regular polygon with more than 6 sides tessellates.

pages 163–164 On Your Own

1.

2.

3.

4. rotational, reflectional, glide reflectional, and translational

5. rotational, point, reflectional, glide reflectional, and translational

6. rotational, reflectional, glide reflectional, and translational

7. point and translational

8. rotational and reflectional

9. rotational, point, and translational

10.

13.

14.

15.

16.

17.   **18.**   **19.**

Use each figure to create a tessellation on dot paper.   13–16. See margin.

13. **14.** **15.** **16.**

Identify the repeating figure or figures that make up each tessellation. 17–19. See margin.

17.   **18.**   **19.**

Mongolian design   Rice wrapped in banana leaves   Design by François Brisse

20. Follow the steps below to create an "Escher-like" tessellation based on a regular hexagon. **Check students' work.**

tape
slide
cut

- Trace and cut out the regular hexagon above.

- Sketch a curve from one vertex to an adjacent vertex.

- Cut along the curve that you sketched. Slide the resulting cutout to the opposite side of the hexagon. Tape it in place using clear tape.

- Repeat this process on the remaining two pairs of opposite sides.

- Decorate the figure that you end up with and use it to make a tessellation.

THE BIG IDEA Ask students: *Describe a tessellation of a quadrilateral that has no reflectional symmetry. What symmetries does the tessellation have?*

RETEACHING ACTIVITY Students copy a figure and create a tessellation. Then they identify the symmetries in the tessellation. (Reteaching worksheet 3-6)

A Point in Time

If you have block scheduling or an extended class period, you may wish to have students investigate these topics:

- Find two other examples of famous mosaics from other cultures. Describe their design, including any patterns or symmetries they have.
- Learn more about Juan O'Gorman, his art, Latin American architecture, and/or Mexican art.
- Research the mosaic used in the Mexico City subway system, which opened in 1968.

Exercises   MIXED REVIEW

Classify each triangle by its sides and angles.

21.

equilateral, equiangular

22.

scalene, acute

23.

scalene, right

24.

isosceles, acute

25. Given ⊙A, identify each of the following.
   a. a diameter   **b.** a major arc
   c. a minor arc   **d.** a radius
   e. a central angle
   f. a pair of adjacent arcs

25a. $\overline{BD}$ b. Sample: $\overarc{BCE}$
c. Sample: $\overarc{ED}$ d. Sample: $\overline{AE}$
e. Sample: $\angle BAE$
f. Sample: $\overarc{BE}$ and $\overarc{ED}$

26. a. Find the measure of an interior angle of a regular 3-gon, 7-gon, and 42-gon. $60, 128\frac{4}{7}, 171\frac{3}{7}$
   b. Find the sum of the measures of the three angles from part (a). **360**

Getting Ready for Lesson 3-7

27. In the diagram, $\triangle ABC \sim \triangle DEF$.
   a. Find AB and EF. **3; 10**
   b. Find the scale factor of the enlargement. **2**

not drawn to scale

FOR YOUR JOURNAL

Think about different products that you can buy at a grocery store. How is the idea of tessellation important in the design of containers for products?

Reteaching 3-6

Practice 3-6

Practice 3-6

Lesson Quiz

Lesson Quiz is also available in Transparencies.

1. Identify the repeating figures in the tessellation.
Answers may vary, but should include a parallelogram and two adjacent pentagons. Sample given above.

2. Describe the types of symmetry of the tessellation.
translational symmetry, glide reflectional symmetry, line symmetry in the bold-faced lines, rotational and point symmetry in the dots shown

---

A Point in Time

1500 — 1600 — 2000

The Grand Mosaic of Mexico

A mosaic is a picture or decorative design made by setting tiny pieces of glass, stone, or other materials in clay or plaster. A mosaic may be a tessellation. Most mosaics, however, do not have a repeating pattern of figures. The art of constructing mosaics goes back at least 6,000 years to the Sumerians, who used tiles to both decorate and reinforce walls.

The Romans gave us the word *tessellate,* from the Latin *tessellare,* "to pave with tiles." During the second century A.D., Roman architects used 2 million tiles to create the magnificent mosaic of Dionysus in Germany. Large as it was, the Dionysus was less than a third the size of the work created in **1950** by the Mexican artist

Juan O'Gorman. O'Gorman's mosaic, which depicts the cultural history of Mexico, is ten stories high and covers all four sides of the library of the National University of Mexico. Constructed of some 7.5 million stones, it is the largest mosaic in the world.

PROBLEM OF THE DAY

On a five-by-five square grid, shade squares so that the grid has rotational symmetry of 90° but no line symmetry. **Answers may vary. Sample given.**

Problem of the Day is also available in Transparencies.

CONNECTING TO PRIOR KNOWLEDGE Discuss with students the relationships between an object and its image in a magnifying glass. Ask them how the size and shape of the object are related to the size and shape of the image.

WORK TOGETHER

ESL Since students with limited English proficiency may have some trouble following the directions, you may want to arrange the groups so that they are with students having strong English skills.

Make sure students read and perform one step at a time. They might want to use a second color to draw and label R', S', T' and $\triangle R'S'T'$.

Lesson Planning Options

Prerequisite Skills

• Determining if figures are similar

Assignment Options for Exercises On Your Own

Core 1–21, 24–28, 32–40
Extension 22–23, 29–31

Use Mixed Review to maintain skills.

Resources

 Student Edition

Skills Handbook, p. 656
Extra Practice, p. 636
Glossary/Study Guide

 Teaching Resources

Chapter Support File, Ch. 3
• Practice 3-7 (two worksheets)
• Reteaching 3-7
• Alternative Activity 3-7
Classroom Manager 3-7
Glossary, Spanish Resources

 Transparencies
5, 43

What You'll Learn

• Locating dilation images of figures

...And Why

To recognize applications of dilations in maps, photographs, scale models, and architectural blueprints

What You'll Need

• centimeter ruler
• calculator
• graph paper

Connections 🌐 Human Development . . . and more

3-7 Dilations

WORK TOGETHER

■ Have each member of your group draw a triangle and a point outside the triangle. Draw your figures in roughly the same positions as shown in the diagram. Label the triangle $\triangle RST$ and the point C.

■ Draw $\overrightarrow{CR}$, $\overrightarrow{CS}$, and $\overrightarrow{CT}$.

■ Have each member of your group select a different number n from the set $\{\frac{1}{3}, \frac{1}{2}, 1\frac{1}{2}, 2, 3\}$.

■ Measure $\overline{CR}$, $\overline{CS}$, and $\overline{CT}$ to the nearest millimeter. Then calculate $n \cdot CR$, $n \cdot CS$, and $n \cdot CT$.

■ Use a ruler to locate point R' on $\overrightarrow{CR}$ so that $CR' = n \cdot CR$. Locate points S' and T' in the same manner. Draw $\triangle R'S'T'$.

1. Compare corresponding angle measures in triangles $\triangle RST$ and $\triangle R'S'T'$. What do you notice? Compare results within your group. **The corresponding angles are $\cong$.**

2. Measure the lengths of the sides of $\triangle RST$ and $\triangle R'S'T'$ to the nearest millimeter. Then use a calculator to find the values of the ratios $\frac{R'S'}{RS}$, $\frac{S'T'}{ST}$, and $\frac{T'R'}{TR}$ to the nearest hundredth. What do you notice? **Each ratio is n.**

3. Use your results from Questions 1 and 2 to complete the statement: $\triangle RST$ is ___?___ to $\triangle R'S'T'$. **similar**

THINK AND DISCUSS

The transformation that you performed in the Work Together is known as a *dilation*. Every dilation has a center and a scale factor. In the Work Together, the center of the dilation was C. The **scale factor** n described the size change from the original figure to the image. The dimensions of the image were n times that of the preimage. A **dilation** with center C and scale factor n, where $n > 0$, maps a point R to R' in such a way that R' is on $\overrightarrow{CR}$ and $CR' = n \cdot CR$. The center of dilation C is its own image (that is, $C' = C$).

Help students understand the definition of dilation by illustrating it with several examples using actual values for *n*. Point out the restriction that the values of *n* must be greater than zero.

CRITICAL THINKING Question 4 This dilation with scale factor 1 is called the identity transformation and is an isometry.

Example 1

In part a, point out that the center of the dilation, *X*, is on the figure. In part b, the center of the dilation is *O*(0, 0) and it is inside the figure.

Question 5 Students may want to review the results of the Work Together activity to help them answer the questions.

Example 2 Relating to the Real World

If students compare the height-of-head to height-of-body ratios, they will see that the ratios are not equal.

ALTERNATIVE METHOD Have students copy the diagram but instead of drawing a human figure have them draw a line segment to represent the height of the body and a dotted line segment to represent the height of the head. Then have them find the ratios of the lengths of the dotted segments to the lengths of the solid segments.

As you noticed in the Work Together, a dilation maps a figure to a similar figure. A dilation is a **similarity transformation.**

4. Critical Thinking Describe the dilation image of a figure when the scale factor is 1. When the scale factor is 1, the dilation image is the same as the preimage.

Example 1

Find the scale factor for the dilation that maps the red figure onto the blue figure.

a. $\dfrac{T'X'}{TX} = \dfrac{8+4}{4} = 3$ b. $\dfrac{K'L'}{KL} = \dfrac{2}{4} = \dfrac{1}{2}$

This is not a similarity transformation. Do you see why?
The transformation changes shape as well as size. A similarity transformation changes size only.

There are two types of dilations. If the image is larger than the original figure, the dilation is an **enlargement.** If the image is smaller than the original figure, the dilation is a **reduction.**

5. What scale factors produce enlargements? reductions?
scale factors greater than 1; scale factors less than 1

Example 2 Relating to the Real World

Newborn   2 yr   6 yr   12 yr   20 yr

Human Development
The diagram shows the growth of a human male from infancy through adulthood. Can human development be modeled by a dilation? Explain.

No. If human development could be modeled by a dilation, the red line would align with the chin in each figure. The 5 ft 9 in. adult figure shown would have a head about $1\frac{3}{4}$ ft long!

Additional Examples

FOR EXAMPLE 1

Refer to the diagram in Example 1a. If *XT* is 2 and *TT'* is 3, find the scale factor for the dilation that maps △*XRT* to △*X'R'T'*. **2.5**

Discussion: *Can you determine* $\dfrac{R'X'}{RX}$ *and* $\dfrac{R'T'}{RT}$ *?*

FOR EXAMPLE 3

Refer to the diagram in Example 3. Use matrices to find the image of △*PZG* under a dilation centered at the origin with scale factor $\frac{3}{2}$.

$$\begin{bmatrix} 3 & -1.5 & 1.5 \\ 0 & 0.75 & -3 \end{bmatrix}$$

Discussion: *Is the dilation an enlargement or a reduction? How do you know?*

VISUAL LEARNING Using the diagrams above Example 3, help students verify that multiplying the coordinates of the point by the scale factor gives the coordinates of its image. The diagrams show that the distance from the origin to the image is *n* times the distance from the origin to the preimage.

Technology Options

Exercises 13–15, students may use graphing calculators to multiply matrices by scalars. For Exercise 19, students may use construction tools in geometry software to construct the dilation image.

Prentice Hall Technology

Software
• Secondary Math Lab Toolkit™
• Computer Item Generator 3-7

Internet
• See the Prentice Hall site. (http://www.phschool.com)

168

To find the image of a point on the coordinate plane under a dilation with center $(0, 0)$, you multiply the *x*-coordinate and *y*-coordinate by the scale factor. Here are two examples.

Scale factor 4
$(x, y) \longrightarrow (4x, 4y)$

Scale factor $\frac{1}{3}$
$(x, y) \longrightarrow (\frac{1}{3}x, \frac{1}{3}y)$

You can use matrices to perform dilations that are centered at the origin.

Example 3

Use matrices to find the image of △*PZG* under a dilation centered at the origin with scale factor 3.

$\begin{array}{c} x\text{-coordinate} \\ y\text{-coordinate} \end{array} \begin{matrix} P & Z & G \\ \begin{bmatrix} 2 & -1 & 1 \\ 0 & \frac{1}{2} & -2 \end{bmatrix} \end{matrix}$

To find the dilation image of △*PZG*, you multiply all the *x*-coordinates and *y*-coordinates by 3.

Vertices of Preimage   Vertices of Image

$3 \cdot \begin{bmatrix} 2 & -1 & 1 \\ 0 & \frac{1}{2} & -2 \end{bmatrix} = \begin{bmatrix} 6 & -3 & 3 \\ 0 & \frac{3}{2} & -6 \end{bmatrix}$

6. Try This Use matrices to find the image of △*PZG* under a dilation centered at the origin with scale factor $\frac{1}{2}$. See left.

6. $\begin{bmatrix} 1 & -\frac{1}{2} & \frac{1}{2} \\ 0 & \frac{1}{4} & -1 \end{bmatrix}$

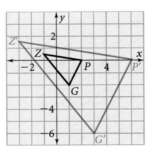

The type of multiplication shown in Example 3, in which each entry of a matrix is multiplied by the same number, is called **scalar multiplication**.

Exercises **ON YOUR OWN**

Copy △*TBA* and point *O*. Draw △*T′B′A′* under the dilation with the given center and scale factor. 1–4. See margin p. 169.

1. Center *O*, scale factor $\frac{1}{2}$

2. Center *B*, scale factor 3

3. Center *T*, scale factor $\frac{1}{3}$

4. Center *O*, scale factor 2

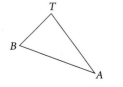

Finishing the Chapter Project

PROJECT DAY You may wish to plan a project day on which students share their completed projects. Encourage groups to explain their processes as well as their products.

PROJECT NOTEBOOK Have students review their project work and bring their notebooks up to date.

- Have students review the sketches, classifications, and designs needed for the project.
- Ask groups to share any insights they found when completing the project, such as how they identify different transformations.

Finishing the Chapter Project

CHAPTER PROJECT

FRIEZE FRAMES

Find Out questions and activities on pages 137, 143, 150, 158, and 171 will help you complete your project. Prepare a frieze pattern display. Include a brief explanation of frieze patterns as well as your original designs for each of the seven types of frieze patterns. Find more examples of frieze patterns from various cultures, as well as examples from buildings, clothing, and other places in your home, school, and community. Classify each example into one of the seven categories, and include them in your display.

Reflect and Revise

Ask a classmate to review your display with you. Together, check that your diagrams and explanations are clear and your information accurate. Have you used geometric terms correctly? Is the display attractive, organized, and complete? Have you included material that no one else has included? Revise your work as needed. Consider doing more research.

Follow Up

Use logical reasoning and what you've learned about transformations to explain why there are no more than seven different frieze patterns. List all other possible combinations of symmetries and show how each can be ruled out.

For More Information

Appleton, Le Roy H. *American Indian Design and Decoration.* New York: Dover, 1971.

Hargittai, István and Magdolna. *Symmetry: A Unifying Concept.* Berkeley, California: Ten Speed Press, 1994.

Schuman, Jo Miles. *Art from Many Hands: Multicultural Art Projects for Home and School.* Englewood Cliffs, New Jersey: Prentice Hall, 1981.

Stevens, Peter S. *Handbook of Regular Patterns: An Introduction to Symmetry in Two Dimensions.* Cambridge, Massachusetts: MIT, 1981.

page 172 Mixed Review

47.

3 Wrap Up

Key Terms

composition (p. 135)
dilation (p. 166)
enlargement (p. 167)
entry (p. 131)
frieze pattern (p. 137)
glide reflection (p. 146)
glide reflectional symmetry (p. 161)
half-turn (p. 154)
image (p. 124)
isometry (p. 124)
line symmetry (p. 152)
map (p. 124)
matrix (p. 131)
orientation (p. 126)

point symmetry (p. 154)
preimage (p. 124)
prime notation (p. 124)
pure tessellation (p. 160)
reduction (p. 167)
reflection (p. 126)
reflectional symmetry (p. 152)
rotation (p. 139)
rotational symmetry (p. 154)
scalar multiplication (p. 168)
scale factor (p. 166)
similarity transformation (p. 167)
strip pattern (p. 137)
symmetry (p. 152)

tessellation (p. 159)
tiling (p. 159)
transformation (p. 124)
translation (p. 132)
translational symmetry (p. 161)

How am I doing?

![SELF ASSESSMENT]

• Describe the different transformations and their properties.
• State the different types of symmetry and draw examples of each.

Reflections   3-1

A **transformation** is a change made to the position, shape, or size of a figure. An **isometry** is a transformation in which the original figure and its image are congruent. The diagram shows a **reflection** of B to B′ in line r. A reflection is an isometry that changes a figure's orientation.

Coordinate Geometry Given points $A(6, 4)$, $B(-2, 1)$, and $C(5, 0)$, draw $\triangle ABC$ and its reflection image in the given line. **1–4. See margin.**

1. the x-axis   **2.** $x = 4$ **3.** $x = -3$ **4.** $y = x$

Trace each figure, then find its reflection image in line j.

5.
6.
7.
8.

9. Standardized Test Prep What is the image of $(5, 4)$ under a reflection in $y = 2$? **E**
   A. $(-5, 4)$ **B.** $(5, -4)$ **C.** $(-1, 4)$ **D.** $(-5, -4)$ **E.** $(5, 0)$

174

Translations   3-2

A **translation** is a transformation that moves points the same distance and
in the same direction. A translation is an isometry that does not change
orientation. You can use vectors and matrices to describe a translation.

Under a **composition** of two transformations, the second transformation is
performed on the image of the first.

10. Open-ended Draw a figure in the fourth quadrant. Draw a translation
vector under which the figure would move to the second quadrant.
See margin for sample.

**Use matrix addition to find the image of each figure under the given
translation.**

11. △ABC with vertices A(5, 9), B(4, 3), C(1, 2)
Translation: ⟨2, 3⟩ **A′(7, 12), B′(6, 6), C′(3, 5)**

12. △RST with vertices R(0, −4), S(−2, −1), T(−6, 1)
Translation: ⟨−4, 7⟩
R′(−4, 3), S′(−6, 6), T′(−10, 8)

**Find a single translation that has the same effect as each composition of
translations.**

13. ⟨4, 8⟩ followed by ⟨−2, 0⟩
⟨2, 8⟩

14. ⟨−5, −7⟩ followed by ⟨3, 6⟩
⟨−2, −1⟩

15. ⟨10, −9⟩ followed by ⟨1, 5⟩
⟨11, −4⟩

Rotations   3-3

The diagram shows a **rotation** of point V about point R through x°.
A rotation is an isometry that does not change orientation.

**Copy each figure and point P. Rotate the figure the given number of
degrees about P. Label the vertices of the image.**

16. 180°   **17.** 135°   **18.** 60°   **19.** 90°

Find the image of each point under a 90° rotation about the origin.

20. (5, 2)   **21.** (0, 3)   **22.** (−4, 1)   **23.** (7, 0)   **24.** (−2, −8)   **25.** (0, 0)
(−2, 5)   (−3, 0)   (−1, −4)   (0, 7)   (8, −2)   (0, 0)

Compositions of Reflections   3-4

A composition of reflections in two parallel lines is a translation. A
composition of reflections in two intersecting lines is a rotation. The
diagram shows a **glide reflection.** The only four isometries are reflection,
translation, rotation, and glide reflection.

10.

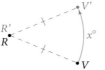

Match each image of the figure at the left with one of the following isometries. I. reflection II. rotation III. translation IV. glide reflection

26. a. II b. I c. III d. IV

27. a. III *ine* b. IV c. II d. I

28. △*TAM* has vertices *T*(0, 5), *A*(4, 1), and *M*(3, 6). Find the image of △*TAM* under a glide reflection in ⟨−4, 0⟩ and *y* = −2.
   T′(−4, −9), *A*′(0, −5), *M*′(−1, −10)

Symmetry   3-5

A figure has **symmetry** if there is an isometry that maps the figure onto itself. A plane figure has **reflectional symmetry,** or **line symmetry,** if there is a line in which the figure is reflected onto itself. A figure has **rotational symmetry** if there is a rotation of 180° or less that maps the figure onto itself. If a plane figure can be mapped onto itself by a rotation of 180° (a **half-turn**), it has **point symmetry.**

Point Symmetry

What type(s) of symmetry does each figure have? If it has rotational symmetry, state the angle of rotation.

29.

30.

31.

reflectional   72° rotational   90° rotational, point

Tessellations   3-6

A **tessellation,** or **tiling,** is a repeating pattern of figures that completely covers a plane without gaps or overlaps. Every triangle and quadrilateral tessellates. Tessellations can have many kinds of symmetries, including **translational symmetry** and **glide reflectional symmetry.**

Translational Symmetry
A translation maps the tessellation onto itself.

Glide Reflectional Symmetry
A glide reflection maps the tessellation onto itself.

176

Students may work these exercises independently or in small groups. The skills previewed will help prepare students for studying properties of triangles.

In Exercises 32–34, (a) identify the repeating figure(s) that make up each tessellation, and (b) describe the symmetries of each tessellation. 32–34. See margin.

32.   **33.**   **34.**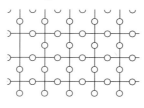

Dilations   3-7

The diagram shows a **dilation** with center C and **scale factor** n. A dilation is a **similarity transformation** because it maps figures to similar figures. When the scale factor is greater than 1, the dilation is an **enlargement.** When the scale factor is less than 1, the dilation is a **reduction.** In the coordinate plane, you can use **scalar multiplication** to find the image of a figure under a dilation centered at the origin.

Use matrices to find the image of each set of points under a dilation centered at the origin with the given scale factor.   35–38. See margin.

35. $M(-3, 4)$, $A(-6, -1)$, $T(0, 0)$, $H(3, 2)$; scale factor 5

36. $A(7, -1)$, $N(-4, -3)$, $D(0, 2)$; scale factor 2

37. $W(4, 5)$, $I(2, 6)$, $T(3, 8)$, $H(0, 7)$; scale factor 3

38. $F(-4, 0)$, $U(5, 0)$, $N(-2, -5)$; scale factor $\frac{1}{2}$

39. Writing Explain how each of the five transformations you studied in this chapter affects the orientation of a figure and its image.   **Rotations, dilations and translations preserve orientation. Reflections and glide reflections reverse orientation.**

Getting Ready for..▶ CHAPTER 4

Find the coordinates of the midpoint of the segment with the given endpoints.

40. $C(3, 5)$ and $D(1, 11)$ **41.** $E(6, 7)$ and $F(-4, 7)$ **42.** $T(5, 8)$ and $W(5, 0)$
    (2, 8)   (1, 7)   (5, 4)

Classify each triangle by its sides and angles.

43.   **44.**   **45.**   **46.**
isosceles, acute   scalene, right   isosceles, obtuse   scalene, acute

32a.

   b. rotational, point, reflectional, translational, glide reflectional

33a. ☐ and △

   b. point, reflectional, translational, glide reflectional

34a. ⬖ and ○

   b. rotational, point, reflectional, translational, glide reflectional

35.
$$\begin{array}{cccc} M' & A' & T' & H' \\ \begin{bmatrix} -15 & -30 & 0 & 15 \\ 20 & -5 & 0 & 10 \end{bmatrix} \end{array}$$

36.
$$\begin{array}{ccc} A' & N' & D' \\ \begin{bmatrix} 14 & -8 & 0 \\ -2 & -6 & 4 \end{bmatrix} \end{array}$$

37.
$$\begin{array}{cccc} W' & I' & T' & H' \\ \begin{bmatrix} 12 & 6 & 9 & 0 \\ 15 & 18 & 24 & 21 \end{bmatrix} \end{array}$$

38.
$$\begin{array}{ccc} F' & U' & N' \\ \begin{bmatrix} -2 & 2\frac{1}{2} & -1 \\ 0 & 0 & -2\frac{1}{2} \end{bmatrix} \end{array}$$

177

Resources

Teaching Resources

Chapter Support File, Ch. 3
• Chapter assessment, Forms A and B
• Alternative Assessment
Chapter Assessment, Spanish Resources

Teacher's Edition

See also p. 122E for assessment options

Software

Computer Item Generator

Assessment   page 178

1. $A'(-11, 0)$, $B'(-9, -2)$, $C'(-11, -5)$, $D'(-15, -1)$

2. $A'(-3, 8)$, $B'(-5, 6)$, $C'(-3, 3)$, $D'(1, 7)$

3. $A'(0, 3)$, $B'(2, 1)$, $C'(5, 3)$, $D'(1, 7)$

4. $A'(2, 0)$, $B'\left(\frac{2}{3}, -1\frac{1}{3}\right)$, $C'\left(2, -3\frac{1}{3}\right)$, $D'\left(4\frac{2}{3}, -\frac{2}{3}\right)$

5. $A'(-3, 3)$, $B'(-1, 1)$, $C'(-3, -2)$, $D'(-7, 2)$

6. $A'(0, 3)$, $B'(-2, 1)$, $C'(-5, 3)$, $D'(-1, 7)$

7. $A'(0, -3)$, $B'(-2, -1)$, $C'(-5, -3)$, $D'(-1, -7)$

8. $A'(15, 0)$, $B'(5, -10)$, $C'(15, -25)$, $D'(35, -5)$

9. $A'(1, 10)$, $B'(-1, 12)$, $C'(1, 15)$, $D'(5, 11)$

18. rotational, point, reflectional, translational, glide reflectional

178

---

3 Assessment

Coordinate Geometry **Find the coordinates of the vertices of the image of *ABCD* under each transformation.**

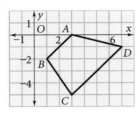

1. reflection in $x = -4$ 1–9. See margin.

2. translation $\langle -6, 8 \rangle$

3. rotation of 90° about the point $(0, 0)$

4. dilation with scale factor $\frac{2}{3}$ centered at the origin

5. glide reflection in $\langle 0, 3 \rangle$ and $x = 0$

6. reflection in $y = x$

7. rotation of 270° about the point $(0, 0)$

8. dilation with scale factor 5 centered at $(0, 0)$

9. glide reflection in $\langle -2, 0 \rangle$ and $y = 5$

What type of transformation has the same effect as each composition of transformations?

10. translation $\langle 4, 0 \rangle$ followed by reflection in $y = -4$ glide reflection

11. translation $\langle 4, 8 \rangle$ followed by $\langle -2, 9 \rangle$ translation

12. reflection in $y = 7$, then in $y = 3$ translation

13. reflection in $y = x$, then in $y = 2x + 5$ rotation

14. *Writing* Line m intersects $\overline{UH}$ at N, and $UN = NH$. Must H be the reflection image of U in line m? Explain why or why not. See back of book.

Open-ended **Sketch a figure that has each type of symmetry.** 15–17. See back of book for samples.

15. reflectional   16. rotational   17. point

18. Describe the symmetries of this tessellation. Copy a portion of the tessellation and draw any centers of rotational symmetry or lines of symmetry.

Also see margin.

What type(s) of symmetry does each figure have?

20. rotational, point, reflectional

19.   20.

rotational, reflectional

21. *Standardized Test Prep* Which of the following letters does *not* tessellate? C

A. B. H K C.

D. L E. E

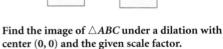

Find the image of $\triangle ABC$ under a dilation with center $(0, 0)$ and the given scale factor.
22–24. See back of book.

22. $A(2, 4)$, $B(3, 7)$, $C(5, 1)$; scale factor 4

23. $A(0, 0)$, $B(-3, 2)$, $C(1, 7)$; scale factor $\frac{1}{2}$

24. $A(-2, 2)$, $B(2, -2)$, $C(3, 4)$; scale factor 3

Preparing for Standardized Tests

Standardized tests, such as those administered for state assessment, the SAT, or the ACT, include regular math questions, quantitative comparison questions, open-ended problems, and free response questions (which the SAT calls *grid-ins*).

MULTIPLE CHOICE QUESTIONS are followed by five answer choices, one of which is correct. **Exercises 1–8** are multiple choice questions.

QUANTITATIVE COMPARISON QUESTIONS ask students to compare two quantities. **Exercises 9 and 10** are quantitative comparison questions.

FREE RESPONSE QUESTIONS do not give answer choices. Students must provide one correct answer on their own. **Exercises 11 and 12** are free response questions.

OPEN-ENDED PROBLEMS allow for more than one solution. Students must construct their own responses instead of choosing a single answer. The responses students give will help you determine the depth of their understanding and what difficulties, if any, they are experiencing. This section has no open-ended problem.

STANDARDIZED TEST TIP Exercise 4 Help students see that comparing the slopes is the most effective approach, not drawing a diagram.

For Exercises 1–10, choose the correct letter.

1. What is the image of $(-3, 8)$ reflected in $y = 4$?
E **A.** $(3, 8)$ **B.** $(3, -8)$ **C.** $(-3, -8)$
D. $(11, 8)$ **E.** $(-3, 0)$

2. Which angles could an obtuse triangle have? B
  I. a right angle   **II.** two acute angles
  III. an obtuse angle   **IV.** two vertical angles

  A. I and II   **B.** II and III   **C.** III and IV
  D. I and IV   **E.** none of the above

3. What is the image of $(4, 5)$ rotated 270° about the origin? D
  A. $(-5, 4)$ **B.** $(-4, -5)$ **C.** $(-5, -4)$
  D. $(5, -4)$ **E.** none of the above

4. Which lines are perpendicular to $y = 2x - 4$? C
  I. $y = \frac{1}{2}x + 6$ **II.** $y = 0.5x + 11$
  III. $y = 2x + 7$ **IV.** $y = -0.5x - 1$

  A. I and II   **B.** III only   **C.** IV only
  D. II and IV   **E.** I, II, and IV

5. The point $(2, 7)$ is reflected in the y-axis, then translated by $\langle 0, -7 \rangle$. Where is its image? A
  A. x-axis   **B.** third quadrant
  C. fourth quadrant   **D.** origin
  E. first quadrant

6. Which figure does *not* tessellate? C
  A. 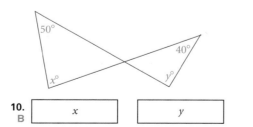   **B.**

  C.   **D.**

  E. none of the above

 7. Calculator What is the distance between the points $(3, 5)$ and $(-4, -9)$? A

  A. 15.7   **B.** 4.1   **C.** 6.1
  D. 15   **E.** 21

8. What is the midpoint of the segment with endpoints $(0, -4)$ and $(-4, 7)$? C
  A. $(-4, 3)$ **B.** $(-2, 3)$ **C.** $\left(-2, \frac{3}{2}\right)$
  D. $\left(-4, \frac{3}{2}\right)$ **E.** $(2, -3)$

Compare the boxed quantity in Column A with the boxed quantity in Column B. Choose the best answer.

  A. The quantity in Column A is greater.
  B. The quantity in Column B is greater.
  C. The two quantities are equal.
  D. The relationship cannot be determined on the basis of the information supplied.

Column A	Column B

$\triangle ABC \rightarrow \triangle A'B'C'$

9. C | the scale factor | AB |

10. B | x | y |

Find each answer.

11. Which transformations are isometries?
  reflection, rotation, translation, glide reflection

12. You are building a scale model of a building. The front of the actual building will be 60 ft wide and 100 ft tall. The front of your model is 3 ft by 5 ft. What is the scale factor of the reduction? $\frac{1}{20}$

Resources

Teaching Resources
Chapter Support File, Ch. 3
• Standardized Test Practice
• Cumulative Review

Teacher's Edition
See also p. 122E for assessment options

Triangle Relationships

To accommodate flexible scheduling, some lessons are divided into parts.
Assignment Options are given in the Lesson Planning Options for each lesson.

4-1 Using Logical Reasoning (pp. 182–187)

Part 1 Conditionals and Converses
Part 2 Biconditionals, Inverses, and Contrapositives

Key Terms: biconditional, conclusion, conditional, contrapositive, converse, hypothesis, inverse, negation, truth value

4-2 Isosceles Triangles (pp. 188–193)

Key Terms: base, base angle, legs, vertex angle

4-3 Preparing for Proof (pp. 194–199)

Key Terms: paragraph proof, two-column proof

4-4 Midsegments of Triangles (pp. 201–206)

Key Terms: midsegment

4-5 Using Indirect Reasoning (pp. 207–211)

Key Terms: indirect reasoning

4-6 Triangle Inequalities (pp. 213–218)

Part 1 Triangle Inequality Theorem
Part 2 Inequalities Relating Sides and Angles

4-7 Bisectors and Locus (pp. 219–225)

Part 1 Perpendicular Bisectors and Locus
Part 2 Angle Bisectors and Locus

Key Terms: distance from a point to a line, locus

4-8 Concurrent Lines (pp. 227–232)

Part 1 Perpendicular Bisectors and Angle Bisectors
Part 2 Medians and Altitudes

Key Terms: altitude of a triangle, concurrent, median of a triangle, point of concurrency

PACING OPTIONS

This chart suggests pacing only for the core lessons and their parts, and it is provided merely as a possible guide. It will help you determine how much time you have in your schedule to cover other features, such as the Chapter Project, Math Toolboxes, Wrap Up, and Assessment.

	1 Class Period	1 Class Period	1 Class Period	1 Class Period	1 Class Period	1 Class Period	1 Class Period	1 Class Period	1 Class Period
Traditional (40–45 min class periods)	4-1 ▼1	4-1 ▼2	4-2	4-3	4-4	4-5	4-6 ▼1	4-6 ▼2	4-7 ▼1
Block Scheduling (90 min class periods)	4-1 ▼1 ▼2	4-2	4-3	4-4	4-5	4-6 ▼1 ▼2	4-7 ▼1 ▼2	4-8 ▼1 ▼2	

What Students Will Learn and Why

In this chapter, students build on their logical reasoning skills, learned in Chapter 1, by learning how to write and interpret different types of conditional statements, to use different styles of proofs to write convincing arguments, and to write convincing arguments using indirect reasoning. To solve problems they use and apply properties of isosceles triangles, midsegments, and inequalities involving triangle side lengths and angle measures. Finally, students use properties of angle bisectors, perpendicular bisectors, altitudes, and medians to solve locus problems. Students become better problem solvers and logical thinkers, and they come to understand how geometric figures are used in architecture, design, and transportation.

Discussing the Chapter/Building on Experience

The concept map below relates chapter topics to real-world applications. You and your class may wish to add to the map or develop maps of your own. The center oval describes the topic of the chapter. The next level displays topics within the lessons. The outer ovals reflect applications of the content. As you and your class build a concept map, invite students to discuss applications with which they are familiar.

1 Class Period	1 Class Period	1 Class Period	1 Class Period	1 Class Period	1 Class Period	1 Class Period	1 Class Period	1 Class Period	1 Class Period	1 Class Period
4-7 ▽2	4-8 ▽1	4-8 ▽2								

Interactive Questioning Tips

A question is interactive when there is "give and take" between the questioner (teacher or student) and the respondent. In Think and Discuss or when a critical thinking question is asked, it is important to involve different students each time, even if it means calling on students who do not volunteer. If a particular student is known to be shy, help him or her by starting out with an easy question as a confidence builder. In Lesson 4-5, students are asked to explain their strategy for the game *What's My Number*. This is an opportunity to involve many students.

Skills Practice

Every lesson provides skill practice with Try This exercises, Exercises On Your Own, and Exercises Mixed Review. The Student Edition includes Checkpoints (pp. 206, 225) and Cumulative Review (p. 239). In the Teacher's Edition, the Lesson Planning Options section for each lesson lists Prerequisite Skills students should know for that lesson. At the back of the Student Edition is the Skills Handbook—mini-lessons on math your students may need to review. The Chapter Support File for Chapter 4 in the Teaching Resources box includes two Practice worksheets per lesson, a worksheet for two Checkpoints, and worksheets for Cumulative Review and Standardized Test Preparation.

Diverse Learning and Teaching Styles

In your Teacher's Edition, you will find suggestions as to how you can help students complete mathematical tasks in Chapter 4 by reinforcing various learning styles. Here are some examples.

- **Visual learning** students identify isosceles triangles in the classroom (p. 188), draw triangles to apply theorems (p. 216), copy the diagrams of a pool to see why the center is the point of concurrency of the angle bisectors (p. 228)

- **Tactile learning** students use straws to build a model of a swing set (p. 203), create a flexible triangle using popsicle sticks (p. 215), cut out circles and tape straws along diameters (p. 221)

- **Auditory learning** students work in groups to read through solutions (p. 202), remember the meaning of terms by their prefixes (p. 228)

- **Kinesthetic learning** students demonstrate properties of a perpendicular bisector (p. 220)

Alternative Activity for Lesson 4-2

for use with Theorems 4-1 and 4-2, uses geometry software to explore and establish properties of isosceles triangles.

Alternative Activity for Lesson 4-6

for use with the Work Together, Example 1, and Example 3, uses geometry software to build triangles and explore the inequalities relating sides and the angles opposite them.

Alternative Activity for Lesson 4-7

for use with the Work Together and Examples, uses geometry software to draw, measure, and manipulate angle bisectors and perpendicular bisectors to establish equidistance theorems.

180C

Cooperative Learning Tips

When used effectively, cooperative learning can help students develop interpersonal skills, learn to perform specific roles in a group, and learn to carry out specific responsibilities. The components of Chapter 4 provide a range of cooperative learning opportunities.

- In the Student Edition, the **Work Together** parts of lessons are specifically designed for cooperative learning activities.

- In the Teacher's Edition, you will find helpful hints for addressing diverse learning styles (see page C for Chapter 4). For every lesson, you will find a **Reteaching Activity**, which may involve cooperative learning.

Materials and Manipulatives

The authors expect all students to use scientific calculators. Calculator use is integrated throughout the course.

- compass (4-2, 4-7)
- MIRA™ (4-7)
- protractor (4-6)
- ruler (4-6, 4-7)
- scissors (4-2, 4-4, 4-6, 4-8)
- straightedge (4-2, 4-4, 4-7)
- straws (4-6)

TECHNOLOGY OPTIONS

Technology Tools		Chapter Project	4-1	4-2	4-3	4-4	4-5	4-6	4-7	4-8
Calculator		Assumed that students have scientific calculators at any time.								
Software	Secondary Math Lab Toolkit™		✔	✔	✔	✔	✔	✔	✔	✔
	Integrated Math Lab					✔				✔
	Computer Item Generator		✔	✔	✔	✔	✔	✔	✔	✔
	Student Edition					✔T		✔		✔T
Video	Video Field Trip	✔								
CD-ROM	Multimedia Geometry Lab			✔		✔		✔	✔	
Internet		See the Prentice Hall site. (http://www.phschool.com)								

✔T indicates Math Toolbox.

The Prentice Hall Geometry program offers you a rich variety of technology options. Be assured that all these options are provided as a means of enriching the program and are not essential for the successful completion of the course.

Assessment Options

The Prentice Hall Geometry Program provides you with many options. From these options, you may choose instructional materials and techniques appropriate for your students, or those necessary to meet your district's curriculum requirements. As the chart indicates, the program also supports your teaching efforts by offering you many choices for assessment.

ASSESSMENT OPTIONS

Assessment Support Materials	Chapter Project	4-1	4-2	4-3	4-4	4-5	4-6	4-7	4-8	Chapter End
Chapter Project	▲■	▲■		▲■	▲■			▲■		▲■
Checkpoints					●▲■			●▲■		
Writing Assignment		▲	▲■	▲	▲■●		▲■	●▲	▲■	●▲
Chapter Assessment										▲●
Alternative Assessment	■		■	■	■	■	■	■	■	●■
Cumulative Review										●▲■
Standardized Test Prep		▲■	▲■	▲■	▲		▲■	▲■		▲●
Computer Item Generator	Can be used to create custom-made practice or assessment at any time.									

▲ = Student Edition   ■ = Teacher's Edition   ● = Teaching Resources

Checkpoints

Alternative Assessment

Chapter Assessment

Available in both Form A and Form B

Making the Right Connections

Mathematics is imbedded in nearly every walk of life. The National Council of Teachers of Mathematics (NCTM) encourages educators to recognize these connections and to emphasize them for the purpose of better educating students for success in life and in a global economy. The **Connections** chart below highlights these connections for Chapter 4.

CONNECTIONS

Lesson	Interdisciplinary Connections	Career Prep	Other Real World Connections	Math Integration	NCTM Standards
Chapter Project	Language Arts		Puzzles Riddles		Problem Solving Connections
4-1	Literature Chemistry	Advertising	Advertisements	Algebra Coordinate Geometry Probability	Algebra Communication Problem Solving Reasoning
4-2	Art	Landscaping	Crafts Architecture Graphic Arts Communications	Algebra Coordinate Geometry	Algebra Connections Communications Problem Solving
4-3	Literature	Writing	Punch Clock Passport	Logical Reasoning Coordinate Geometry	Reasoning Communication Problem Solving
4-4	Art	Architecture Surveying	Swimming Creative Arts	Coordinate Geometry Algebra	Coordinate Geometry Connections Communication Problem Solving
4-5	Literature		Mysteries Consumer Issues Drawbridges	Coordinate Geometry Probability	Reasoning Connections Communication Problem Solving
4-6		Architecture	Landscaping Tools	Geometry in 3 Dimensions Probability	Reasoning Connections Communication Problem Solving
4-7	History	City Planning	National Landmarks Baseball Jet Vapors	Coordinate Geometry Logical Reasoning	Connections Communication Problem Solving
4-8	History	Park Design Recreation	Origami	Coordinate Geometry Geometry in 3 Dimensions	Connections Coordinate Geometry Communication Problem Solving

4 Triangle Relationships

CONNECTING TO PRIOR LEARNING To help students see how logical reasoning is related to the real world, ask: *You want to entertain nine friends three at a time, over twelve school days. How would you arrange it so that no two students are invited on the same day?* (Have students choose nine names to represent friends.)

CULTURAL CONNECTIONS While the origin of logic puzzles dates back to ancient Greece, they were made popular in England in the 19th century by Charles L. Dodgson, also known as Lewis Carroll, the author of the Alice-in-Wonderland classic, *Through the Looking Glass.* Ask students to share some of their favorite riddles and brain teasers with the class.

INTERDISCIPLINARY CONNECTIONS Help students see that the logical thinking skills they develop studying geometric proofs have implications in many diverse fields, such as law, journalism, computer programming, and engineering.

ABOUT THE PROJECT The Chapter Project gives students the opportunity to explore ways of solving logic puzzles and to create their own mind benders. In the Find Out questions found throughout the chapter, students make lists of possible solutions and analyze them, drawing diagrams to organize their reasoning.

Technology Options

Prentice Hall Technology

Video
• Video Field Trip 4, "Brain Twisters," a look at how video game developers deal with problems in logic

CHAPTER

4 Triangle Relationships

Relating to the Real World

You are sitting in a meeting around a large table. An important decision needs to be made. Your boss turns to you and asks, "So, what do you think we should do?" Your response is clear and well-reasoned, and your co-workers nod in approval. The reasoning skills that you learn now will help you to succeed in life. In this chapter you will study the tools needed to become a better problem solver and logical thinker.

Using Logical Reasoning	Isosceles Triangles	Preparing for Proof	Midsegments of Triangles	Using Indirect Reasoning
Lessons 4-1	4-2	4-3	4-4	4-5

PROJECT NOTEBOOK Encourage students to keep all project-related materials in a separate folder or notebook. **See Chapter Project and Scoring Rubric in Chapter Support File.**

- Have students work in groups to solve the following riddle. Then discuss the strategies groups used to find the answer. Find two integers that satisfy all the following conditions:
  1. Both integers are even.
  2. The sum of the integers is negative.
  3. The product of the integers is –96.
  4. Neither integer is a perfect square.
  5. Neither integer is a factor of the other.
  6. Neither integer is a cube. **6 and –16**

- Have students work in groups to solve the following puzzle. Then discuss the strategies groups used to find the answer. Invert a triangle of ten pennies (one penny in the top row, two pennies in the second row, three pennies in the third row, and four pennies in the bottom row) by moving only three pennies. **Put the outer two pennies from the bottom row in the second row, one on either side of the row. Place the penny from the top row below the two pennies left in the bottom row.**

TRACKING THE PROJECT You may wish to have students read Finishing the Chapter Project on page 233 to help them get an overview of the project. Set benchmark deadlines for students to show their work in progress.

CHAPTER PROJECT

PUZZLING PIECES

A paleontologist makes sense of the past by piecing together fossils. By using logical reasoning, she makes a few bones tell the story of an entire species. That feeling of discovery—that sense of "aha!"—has driven people throughout history to use logic to solve puzzles.

In your project for this chapter, you will explore ways of solving logic puzzles. You will also create your own puzzles. You will see how logic, though used for amusement, is the backbone of mathematics—a powerful tool for determining truth.

To help you complete the project:

▼ **p. 187** *Find Out by Listing*
▼ **p. 198** *Find Out by Organizing*
▼ **p. 205** *Find Out by Analyzing*
▼ **p. 225** *Find Out by Writing*
▼ **p. 233** *Finishing the Project*

Triangle Inequalities	Bisectors and Locus	Concurrent Lines
4-6	4-7	4-8

▼ Project Resources

 Teaching Resources
Chapter Support File, Ch. 4
- Chapter Project Manager and Scoring Rubric

Transparencies
50

▼ Using the Rubric

Sharing the scoring rubric for the project with your students will alert them to your expectations before they begin work on the project.

As students complete each Find Out question in the chapter, you may wish to have them evaluate their own work or a partner's work based on the scoring rubric. Students should have the opportunity to revise their work after it has been reviewed.

CONNECTING TO PRIOR KNOWLEDGE Give students examples of if-then statements and have them decide if they are true or false. Examples include: If an angle is a right angle, then its measure is 90°. If a polygon has seven sides, then it is a hexagon. If a figure is reflected over two lines, then the transformation is a translation.

THINK AND DISCUSS

If-then statements are often symbolized as "if p, then q" or "$p \Rightarrow q$" where p represents the hypothesis and q represents the conclusion.

Example 1

Make sure students see that the "if" and "then" are not part of the hypothesis and the conclusion.

Lesson Planning Options

Prerequisite Skills

• Understanding properties of polygons
• Understanding transformations

Assignment Options for Exercises On Your Own

To provide flexible scheduling, this lesson can be subdivided into parts.

 Core 1–10
Extension 27

 Core 11–26, 28–31
Extension 32–35

Use Mixed Review to maintain skills.

Resources

Student Edition
Skills Handbook, p. 650
Extra Practice, p. 637
Glossary/Study Guide

Teaching Resources
Chapter Support File, Ch. 4
• Practice 4-1 (two worksheets)
• Reteaching 4-1
Classroom Manager 4-1
Glossary, Spanish Resources

Transparencies
20, 51, 55

What You'll Learn
• Writing and interpreting different types of conditional statements

...And Why
To help you analyze situations and become a better problem solver

4-1 Using Logical Reasoning

Connections Literature . . . and more

THINK AND DISCUSS

Part 1 Conditionals and Converses

■ If Raúl's major is bagpipe, then he attends Carnegie-Mellon University.

■ If a second goes by, then Earth has moved another $18\frac{1}{2}$ mi along its orbit.

■ If a movie is scary, then the concession stands sell more popcorn.

■ If you are not completely satisfied, then your money will be refunded.

1. You make and hear *if-then* statements like these many times each day. What are some *if-then* statements you have heard? **Check students' work.**

Another name for an *if-then statement* is a **conditional.** Every conditional has two parts. The part following *if* is the **hypothesis,** and the part following *then* is the **conclusion.**

Example 1

Identify the hypothesis and conclusion in this statement:
If it is February, then there are only 28 days in the month.

Hypothesis: It is February.
Conclusion: There are only 28 days in the month.

2. Try This Identify the hypothesis and conclusion in the photo caption at the left. **You want double the love; buy a pair.**

When you determine whether a conditional is true or false, you determine its **truth value.** To show that a conditional is false, you need to find only one *counterexample* for which the hypothesis is true and the conclusion is false. The conditional in Example 1 is false because during a leap year February has 29 days.

3. Find a counterexample for this conditional: If the name of a state contains the word *New*, then the state borders an ocean. **New Mexico does not border an ocean.**

Many sentences can be written as conditionals. For example, the sentence

Quadrilaterals have four sides.

can be rewritten in if-then form as

If a polygon is a quadrilateral, then it has four sides.

If you want double the love, then buy a pair.

Help students see that a conditional statement cannot be called true by finding one or more examples where it is true. A conditional needs to be proven true. Proving conditionals will be investigated further in Lesson 4-3.

Question 3 You may want to display a map for students to check which states border oceans.

Have students practice writing statements as conditionals. Use the theorems and postulates from Chapters 1–3 as examples. Also give students examples of statements that cannot be rewritten as conditionals, such as questions and commands.

Remediation: Have students write "if" and "then" first, leaving space in between, then interchange and write the hypothesis and the conclusion.

Question 4 Have students investigate the truth value of conditionals and their converses. They should find that the converse of a true conditional can be false and the converse of a false conditional can be true.

Using symbol notation, the converse of "if p, then q" ("$p \Rightarrow q$") is "if q, then p" ("$q \Rightarrow p$"). A biconditional statement is represented by "p iff q" or "$p \Leftrightarrow q$."

The **converse** of a conditional interchanges the hypothesis and conclusion.

Example 2

Write the converse of this statement: If a polygon is a quadrilateral, then it has four sides.

Conditional: If a polygon is a quadrilateral, then it has four sides.

Converse: If a polygon has four sides, then it is a quadrilateral.

Literature Notice that both statements in Example 2 have the same truth value. This is *not* true of all conditionals and their converses, as Alice discovers in this passage from Lewis Carroll's *Alice's Adventures in Wonderland*.

The Hatter opened his eyes very wide on hearing this; but all he *said* was "Why is a raven like a writing-desk?"

"Come, we shall have some fun now!" thought Alice. "I'm glad they've begun asking riddles—I believe I can guess that," she added aloud.

"Do you mean that you think you can find out the answer to it?" said the March Hare.

"Exactly so," said Alice.

"Then you should say what you mean," the March Hare went on.

"I do," Alice hastily replied; "at least—at least I mean what I say—that's the same thing, you know."

"Not the same thing a bit!" said the Hatter. "Why, you might just as well say that 'I see what I eat' is the same thing as 'I eat what I see'!"

The Hatter's statement "I see what I eat" can be rewritten in if-then form as "If I eat it, then I see it." The converse, "I eat what I see," can be rewritten as "If I see it, then I eat it."

4. Are the truth values for the Hatter's statement and its converse the same? Explain. No; you see everything you eat, but you do not eat everything you see.

Part 2 Biconditionals, Inverses, and Contrapositives

When a conditional and its converse are true, you can combine them as a **biconditional.** The conditionals from Example 2 can be combined as

If a polygon is a quadrilateral, then it has four sides, *and* if a polygon has four sides, then it is a quadrilateral.

This long sentence can be shortened by using the phrase *if and only if*:

A polygon is a quadrilateral *if and only if* it has four sides.

Additional Examples

FOR EXAMPLE 1

Identify the hypothesis and conclusion of this statement: If it is 12:00, then the sun has gone down. **Hypothesis: It is 12:00. Conclusion: The sun has gone down.**

Discussion: *What is the truth value of the conditional?*

FOR EXAMPLE 2

Write the converse of this statement: If two lines are vertical, then they are parallel. **If two lines are parallel, then they are vertical.**

Discussion: *Are the truth values of the conditional and its converse the same?*

FOR EXAMPLE 3

Write the two statements that make up the definition: A number is even if and only if it is divisible by 2. **If a number is even, then it is divisible by 2. If a number is divisible by 2, then it is even.**

FOR EXAMPLE 4

Write the inverse and contrapositive of the statement: If a number is divisible by 10, then it is divisible by 5. **Inverse: If a number is not divisible by 10, then it is not divisible by 5. Contrapositive: If a number is not divisible by 5, then it is not divisible by 10.**

183

Example 3

ESL Have students notice that when a converse is written, sometimes the wording of the hypothesis and the conclusion is changed slightly. Point out that "its measure is 90" became "the measure of an angle is 90."

Question 5 Help students understand that the negation of a true statement is false and the negation of a false statement is true.

Using symbol notation, the negation of p is represented by "~p." The inverse of "if *p*, then *q*" is represented by "if ~*p*, then ~*q*" ("~*p* ⇒ ~*q*") and the contrapositive by "if ~*q*, then ~*p*" ("~*q* ⇒ ~*p*").

Example 4

ALTERNATIVE METHOD Note that the contrapositive is found by going to the original statement and negating, then interchanging the hypothesis and conclusion. This is taking the converse of the inverse. The contrapositive can also be found by taking the inverse of the converse.

CRITICAL THINKING Question 7 Have students compare answers with a partner. Then have them find the truth value of the statements. Ask students if the truth values of the statements are related.

Have students draw a Venn diagram for the conditional in Question 7 and use it to explain the truth value of the inverse and contrapositive.

Technology Options

Prentice Hall Technology

 Software
- Secondary Math Lab Toolkit™
- Computer Item Generator 4-1

Internet
- See the Prentice Hall site. (http://www.phschool.com)

You learned in Chapter 1 that any good definition is "reversible." This means that any good definition can be written as a biconditional.

Example 3

Write the two statements that make up this definition: A right angle has measure 90. Then write the definition as a biconditional.

Conditional: If an angle is a right angle, then its measure is 90.

Converse: If the measure of an angle is 90, then it is a right angle.

Biconditional: An angle is a right angle if and only if its measure is 90. ■

The **negation** of a statement has the opposite meaning. For example, the negation of "An angle is acute" is "An angle is *not* acute."

5. Write the negation of each statement.
   a. Two angles are vertical.   **b.** Two lines are not parallel.
   Two angles are not vertical.   Two lines are parallel.

The **inverse** of a conditional negates both the hypothesis and the conclusion. The **contrapositive** of a conditional interchanges and negates both the hypothesis and the conclusion.

Example 4

Write the inverse and the contrapositive of this statement: If a figure is a square, then it is a rectangle.

Conditional: If a figure is a square, then it is a rectangle.

Negate both.

Inverse: If a figure is *not* a square, then it is *not* a rectangle.

Conditional: If a figure is a square, then it is a rectangle.

Negate both.

Contrapositive: If a figure is *not* a rectangle, then it is *not* a square. ■

6. Find the truth values of the three statements in Example 4.
   Conditional: true; Inverse: false; Contrapositive: true

7. Try This Write the inverse and contrapositive of this statement: If a quadrilateral is a parallelogram, then it has two pairs of parallel sides.
   See left.

7. Inverse: If a quadrilateral is not a parallelogram, then it does not have 2 pairs of ∥ sides. **Contrapositive:** If a quadrilateral does not have 2 pairs of ∥ sides, then it is not a parallelogram.

This Venn diagram shows the conditional "If a figure is a square, then it is a rectangle." It also shows its contrapositive "If a figure is *not* a rectangle, then it is *not* a square" because any point *not* in the larger circle is *not* in the smaller circle. Since the same diagram shows both statements, a conditional and its contrapositive always have the same truth value.

184

ESL Students may have trouble differentiating the meanings of the terms *converse* and *inverse,* and the terms *conditional* and *biconditional.* You may want to display a poster with explanations and examples of each.

VISUAL LEARNING Students can see how the dark and light boxes change places in the Summary of Conditionals depending on the type of statement.

Exercises ON YOUR OWN

Exercises 2–5 Make sure students do not underline "if" and "then" as part of the hypothesis and conclusion.

Exercises 6–9 You may also want students to give an example that satisfies each statement so they can see that examples can be found to satisfy false statements.

Summary of Conditionals

Statement	Form	Example
conditional	If ■, then ■.	If an angle is a straight angle, then its measure is 180.
converse	If ■, then ■.	If the measure of an angle is 180, then it is a straight angle.
inverse	If *not* ■, then *not* ■.	If an angle is *not* a straight angle, then its measure is *not* 180.
contrapositive	If *not* ■, then *not* ■.	If the measure of an angle is *not* 180, then it is *not* a straight angle.
biconditional	■ if and only if ■.	An angle is a straight angle **if and only if** its measure is 180.

Exercises ON YOUR OWN

1. Identify the hypothesis and conclusion in the cartoon.
   You send in a proof-of-purchase label; they send you a get-well card.

FRANK AND ERNEST   By BOB THAVES

BREAKFAST CEREALS

HERE'S AN INTERESTING ONE -- IF YOU SEND IN THE PROOF-OF-PURCHASE LABEL, THEY SEND YOU A GET-WELL CARD.

9-7 THAVES

For Exercises 2–5: (a) Rewrite each statement in if-then form.
(b) Underline the hypothesis once and the conclusion twice.

2. Glass objects are fragile.
   If <u>an object is made of glass</u>, then <u>it is fragile</u>.
3. $3x - 7 = 14$ implies that $3x = 21$.
   If <u>$3x - 7 = 14$</u>, then <u>$3x = 21$</u>.
4. Numbers that have 2 as a factor are even.
   If <u>a number has 2 as a factor</u>, then <u>it is even</u>.
5. An isosceles triangle has two congruent sides.
   If <u>a triangle is isosceles</u>, then <u>it has two congruent sides</u>.

Find a counterexample for each statement.

6. If it is not a weekday, then it is Saturday.
   Sunday is not a weekday.
7. Odd integers less than 10 are prime.
   1 and 9 are not prime.
8. If you live in a country that borders the United States, then you live in Canada.
   Mexico borders the United States.
9. If you play a sport with a ball and bat, then you play baseball.
   Softball and cricket are sports played with a ball and a bat.
10. a. *Open-ended* Write a conditional with the same truth value as its converse.
    b. Write a conditional whose converse has the opposite truth value.
    a–b. See margin.

pages 185–187 On Your Own

10a. Sample: If a polygon has three sides, then it is a triangle.

   b. Sample: If a quadrilateral has four ≅ sides, then it is a square.

11a. If you grow, then you will eat all of your vegetables.

   b. If you do not eat all of your vegetables, then you will not grow.

   c. If you do not grow, then you will not eat all of your vegetables.

12a. If a figure has rotational symmetry, then it has point symmetry.

   b. If a figure does not have point symmetry, it does not have rotational symmetry.

   c. If a figure does not have rotational symmetry, then it does not have point symmetry.

13a. If a △ has a 90° angle, then it is a rt. △.

   b. If a △ is not a rt. △, then it does not have a 90° angle.

   c. If a △ does not have a 90° angle, then it is not a rt. △.

14a. If a quadrilateral is not a rhombus, then it has exactly 2 ≅ sides.

   b. If a quadrilateral does not have exactly 2 ≅ sides, then it is a rhombus.

   c. If a quadrilateral is a rhombus, then it does not have exactly two ≅ sides.

185

15a. If 2 segments have the same length, then they are ≅.

b. If 2 segments are not ≅, then they have different lengths.

c. If 2 segments have different lengths, then they are not ≅.

16a. If you will not get paid, then you do not work.

b. If you work, then you will get paid.

c. If you will get paid, you work.

17a. If the sum of the measures of the angles of a polygon is 540, then it is a pentagon.

b. If a polygon is not a pentagon, then the sum of the measures of its angles is not 540.

c. If the sum of the measures of angles of a polygon is not 540, then it is not a pentagon.

18a. If the contrapositive of a conditional statement is false, then the conditional is false.

b. If a conditional statement is true, then its contrapositive is true.

c. If the contrapositive of a conditional statement is true, then the conditional statement is true.

19a. If you have a passport, then you travel from the U.S. to Kenya.

b. true; false

186

For each statement, write **(a)** the converse, **(b)** the inverse, and **(c)** the contrapositive. 11–14. See margin p. 185. 15–18. See margin.

11. If you eat all of your vegetables, then you will grow.

12. Transformations If a figure has point symmetry, then it has rotational symmetry.

13. If a triangle is a right triangle, then it has a 90° angle.

14. If a quadrilateral has exactly two congruent sides, then it is not a rhombus.

15. If two segments are congruent, then they have the same length.

16. If you do not work, you will not get paid.

17. If a polygon is a pentagon, then the sum of the measures of its angles is 540.

18. If a conditional statement is false, then its contrapositive is false.

For Exercises 19–26: **(a)** Write the converse of each statement.
(b) Determine the truth value of the statement and its converse.
(c) If both statements are true, write a biconditional. 19. See margin. 20–26. See back of book.

19. If you travel from the United States to Kenya, then you have a passport.

20. Coordinate Geometry If a point is in the first quadrant, then its coordinates are positive.

21. Chemistry If a substance is water, then its chemical formula is H_2O.

22. Transformations If a figure has two lines of symmetry, then it has rotational symmetry.

23. Coordinate Geometry If two nonvertical lines are parallel, then their slopes are equal.

24. If two angles are complementary, then the sum of their measures is 90.

25. If you are in Indiana, then you are in Indianapolis.

26. Probability If the probability that an event will occur is 1, then the event is certain to occur.

27. a. Consumer Issues Advertisements often suggest conditional statements. For example, an ad might imply that if you don't buy a product, you won't be popular. What conditional is implied in the ad at the right?
b. Research Find magazine ads that use conditionals effectively. Make a poster to display these ads.
a–b. See back of book.

Write the two conditionals that make up each biconditional. 28–29. See back of book.

28. A swimmer wins a race if and only if she swims the fastest.

29. A number is divisible by 3 if and only if the sum of its digits is divisible by 3.

30. Two angles are congruent if and only if they have the same measure. If two angles have the same measure, then they are ≅; if two angles are ≅, then they have the same measure.

For a few extra bucks, you could've had TREADMASTERS.

JUST MARRIED

TREADMASTER TIRES

31. Writing Jynona knows that vertical angles are congruent. She thinks the converse is also true. Is she correct? Explain.
No; two ≅ adjacent angles are a counterexample.

For each Venn diagram: (a) Write a conditional statement. (b) Write the contrapositive of the conditional.

32.
right triangles
triangles with exactly two acute angles

33.
regular polygons
polygons with all sides congruent

34.
lines with the same slope
parallel lines

35.
rotations
isometries

32–35. See back of book.

Chapter Project **Find Out by Listing**

Three red hats and three blue hats are packed in three boxes, with two hats to a box. The boxes are all labeled incorrectly. To determine what each box actually contains, you may select one hat from one box, without looking at the contents of that box. Explain how this will allow you to determine the contents of each box. (*Hint:* List all possible solutions; then use logic to solve.)   See back of book.

Contents: Contents: Contents:

Exercises MIXED REVIEW

Coordinate Geometry Sketch a line with the given slope containing the given point.   36–38. See back of book.

36. $m = \frac{1}{2}, (2, -6)$ **37.** $m = 1, (0, 5)$ **38.** $m = -2, (-3, 6)$ **39.** $m = \frac{1}{3}, (0, 0)$

39.

40. An angle's measure is 10 more than its supplement. Find the measures of both angles. 95; 85

41. Transformational Geometry Locate the coordinates of the image of $\triangle ABC$ with vertices $A(0, 3)$, $B(-4, -6)$, $C(6, 1)$ under a 180° rotation about the origin. $A'(0, -3), B'(4, 6), C'(-6, -1)$

Getting Ready for Lesson 4-2
Find the value of x.

42.
105
$x°$
$75°$ $30°$

43.
35
$35°$ $x°$

44.
40
$20°$ $120°$ $x°$

Lesson Quiz

Lesson Quiz is also available in Transparencies.

Exercises 1–4, use this statement: If a triangle is scalene, then no two sides are congruent.

1. Identify the hypothesis and the conclusion. **Hypothesis: A triangle is scalene. Conclusion: No two sides are congruent.**

2. Write the converse. **If no two sides of a triangle are congruent, then it is scalene.**

3. Write the inverse. **If a triangle is not scalene, then two sides are congruent.**

4. Write the contrapositive. **If two sides of a triangle are congruent, then it is not scalene.**

187

PROBLEM OF THE DAY

Show how a teacher can arrange twelve students in six rows with three students in each row so the teacher is equidistant from each row.

Problem of the Day is also available in Transparencies.

Before students begin this activity, have them review Constructions 1 and 2 and the Example of Lesson 1-6.

Students may have trouble identifying the opposite sides and angles. Illustrate for students that the side opposite an angle is intersected by a ray from the vertex in the interior of the angle.

CONNECTING TO PRIOR KNOWLEDGE Draw the following triangles on the board and have students classify them according to their angles and sides.

THINK AND DISCUSS

(ESL) VISUAL LEARNING Begin by having students identify isosceles triangles in the classroom. Then draw isosceles triangles in different positions and have students practice naming the bases, legs, base angles, and vertex angles.

Lesson Planning Options

Prerequisite Skills

- Constructing congruent segments and angles
- Finding measures of interior and exterior angles of polygons

Assignment Options for Exercises On Your Own

Core 1–15, 20–33, 35–40
Extension 16–19, 34

Use Mixed Review to maintain skills.

Resources

 Student Edition

Extra Practice, p. 637
Glossary/Study Guide

 Teaching Resources

Chapter Support File, Ch. 4
- Practice 4-2 (two worksheets)
- Reteaching 4-2
- Alternative Activity 4-2
Classroom Manager 4-2
Glossary, Spanish Resources

 Transparencies
5, 51

What You'll Learn
- Using and applying properties of isosceles triangles

...And Why
To understand a geometric figure used in the designs of many buildings and bridges

What You'll Need
- straightedge
- compass
- scissors

 TECHNOLOGY HINT

The Work Together could be done using geometry software.

vertex angle
leg
leg
base angles
base

4-2 Connections 🌐 Landscaping . . . and more

Isosceles Triangles

WORK TOGETHER

Have each member of your group construct a different isosceles triangle and then cut it out. Be sure to include acute and obtuse triangles.

- Label the triangle △ABC, with A and B opposite the congruent sides.

- Bisect ∠C by folding the triangle so that the congruent sides overlap. Label the intersection of the fold line and $\overline{AB}$ as point D.

1. What do you notice about ∠A and ∠B? Compare results within your group. **∠A ≅ ∠B**

2. **a.** What types of angles do ∠CDA and ∠CDB appear to be? **right angles**
   b. What do you notice about $\overline{AD}$ and $\overline{DB}$? **$\overline{AD} \cong \overline{DB}$**
   c. Use your answers to parts (a) and (b) to complete the statement: $\overline{CD}$ is the ___?___ of $\overline{AB}$. **⊥ bisector**

- Construct a new triangle that has two congruent angles. Cut out the triangle and label it △EFG, where ∠E ≅ ∠F.

3. Fold the triangle so that the congruent angles overlap.
   a. What do you notice about $\overline{EG}$ and $\overline{FG}$? Compare results within your group. **$\overline{EG} \cong \overline{FG}$**
   b. What type of triangle is △EFG? **isosceles**

THINK AND DISCUSS

Isosceles triangles are common in the real world. You can find them in structures such as bridges and buildings. The congruent sides of an isosceles triangle are the **legs**. The third side is the **base**. The two congruent sides form the **vertex angle**. The other two angles are the **base angles**.

Example 1

ERROR ALERT! Some students may think $x = m\angle LMN$.
Remediation: Point out to students that the disjointed arcs between $\angle LMO$ and $\angle OMN$ are used to represent two different congruent angles and not one large angle.

Question 5 To find x, students can solve an equation as in Example 1. However, students may use the results from Example 1 to reason that since $m\angle N$ is 20 less than $m\angle N$ in Example 1, x must be 20 more.

Example 2

For part a, students may want to draw $\triangle RTS$ without points U, V, or W to see that $\angle R$ and $\angle S$ are its base angles.

Your observations from the Work Together suggest the following theorems. The proofs of these theorems involve properties of congruent triangles that you will study in Chapter 8.

Theorem 4-1
Isosceles Triangle Theorem

If two sides of a triangle are congruent, then the angles opposite those sides are also congruent.

If $\overline{AC} \cong \overline{BC}$, then $\angle A \cong \angle B$.

Theorem 4-2

The bisector of the vertex angle of an isosceles triangle is the perpendicular bisector of the base.

If $\overline{AC} \cong \overline{BC}$ and $\overline{CD}$ bisects $\angle ACB$,
then $\overline{CD} \perp \overline{AB}$ and $\overline{CD}$ bisects $\overline{AB}$.

Theorem 4-3
Converse of Isosceles Triangle Theorem

If two angles of a triangle are congruent, then the sides opposite the angles are congruent.

If $\angle A \cong \angle B$, then $\overline{AC} \cong \overline{BC}$.

4. Write the Isosceles Triangle Theorem and its converse as a biconditional.   **2 sides of a △ are ≅ if and only if the angles opp. those sides are ≅.**

Example 1

Algebra Find the values of x and y.

By Theorem 4-2, you know that $\overline{MO} \perp \overline{LN}$. So $y = 90$. Because the triangle is isosceles, $\angle L \cong \angle N$. So $m\angle N = 63$.

$m\angle N + x + y = 180$ Triangle Angle-Sum Theorem
$63 + x + 90 = 180$ Substitution
$x = 27$ Subtract 153 from each side.

So $x = 27$ and $y = 90$.

5. **Try This** Suppose $m\angle L = 43$. Find the values of x and y. **47; 90**

Example 2

Complete each statement. Explain your answers.

a. $\overline{RT} \cong \underline{\ ?\ }$ b. $\overline{RU} \cong \underline{\ ?\ }$ c. $\overline{VW} \cong \underline{\ ?\ }$

a. $\overline{RT} \cong \overline{ST}$ because $\angle R \cong \angle S$.

b. $\overline{RU} \cong \overline{VU}$ because $\angle R \cong \angle RVU$.

c. $\overline{VW} \cong \overline{SW}$ because $\angle WVS \cong \angle S$.

Additional Examples

FOR EXAMPLE 1

Refer to the diagram in Example 1. If $m\angle L = 52$, find the values of x and y. **$x = 38$, $y = 90$**

FOR EXAMPLE 2

$\overline{AB} \cong \underline{\ \ ?\ \ }\ \overline{BC}$

$\overline{FD} \cong \underline{\ \ ?\ \ }\ \overline{DA}$ or $\overline{FE}$

$\overline{CE} \cong \underline{\ \ ?\ \ }\ \overline{FE}$

FOR EXAMPLE 3

Refer to the diagram in Example 3. Imagine that a segment is drawn to connect the sides of the angle marked x. Find the measures of the other two angles of the triangle. **The measure of each angle would be 30.**

Point out that while the terms "equilateral" and "equiangular" can be used interchangeably for triangles, this is not true for other polygons. For example, squares and rectangles are both equiangular but only the square is equilateral.

Question 8 Some students may write, "A triangle is equilateral if and only if it is equiangular," while others may write, "A triangle is equiangular if and only if it is equilateral." Discuss why these are both correct.

Example 3

ERROR ALERT! Some students may assume the hexagon is regular and use the Polygon Interior Angle-Sum Theorem to find *x*. **Remediation:** Point out that, although the hexagon is equilateral, you do not know it is equiangular.

EXTENSION Have students collect other landscape designs from gardening and landscaping books and magazines. Have them sketch the designs and describe them using geometric terms.

Technology Options

For Exercise 10, students may use graphing utilities to investigate possible locations for the third vertex of the triangle. For Exercise 34, students may create their own designs using drawing or geometry software, then print and decorate them.

Prentice Hall Technology

 Software
- Secondary Math Lab Toolkit™
- Computer Item Generator 4-2

 CD-ROM
- Multimedia Geometry Lab 4

 Internet
- See the Prentice Hall site. (http://www.phschool.com)

190

QUICK REVIEW

An equilateral triangle has three congruent sides. An equiangular triangle has three congruent angles.

7a–b. The sides are ≅; if 2 ∠s of a △ are ≅ , then the sides opposite them are ≅ .

6. a. Choose two sides of △*EFG*. What must be true about the angles opposite these sides? Why?
  b. Repeat part (a) with a different pair of sides.
  c. What is true about the angles of an equilateral triangle? **The three angles are ≅.**
  6a–b. The angles are ≅; base ∠s of an isosceles △ are ≅ .
7. a. Choose two angles of △*MNO*. What must be true about the sides opposite these angles? Why?
  b. Repeat part (a) with a different pair of angles.
  c. What is true about the sides of an equiangular triangle? **3 sides are ≅.**

Your observations from Questions 6 and 7 are summarized below.

Corollary to Isosceles Triangle Theorem	If a triangle is equilateral, then it is equiangular. If $\overline{XY} \cong \overline{YZ} \cong \overline{ZX}$, then $\angle X \cong \angle Y \cong \angle Z$.
Corollary to Converse of Isosceles Triangle Theorem	If a triangle is equiangular, then it is equilateral. If $\angle X \cong \angle Y \cong \angle Z$, then $\overline{XY} \cong \overline{YZ} \cong \overline{ZX}$.

8. Use the corollaries above to write a biconditional.
A triangle is equilateral if and only if it is equiangular.

Example 3 **Relating to the Real World**

Landscaping A landscaper is building a raised bed garden to fit in the hexagonal space in the diagram. The path around the garden consists of rectangles and equilateral triangles. What is the measure of the angle marked *x*?

Each angle of a rectangle measures 90. Each angle of an equilateral triangle measures 60. (Why?)

$$x + 90 + 60 + 90 = 360$$
$$x = 120$$

The measure of the angle is 120.

maple tree
willow tree
rose bushes
terraced waterfall
pond
raised bed garden
lilac bushes
railroad tie steps
tub planter
flagstone walk
apple tree
deck

Exercises O N Y O U R O W N

Algebra **Find the values of *x* and *y*.**

1. *x* = 80; *y* = 40

2. *x* = 40; *y* = 70

3. *x* = 4.5; *y* = 60

Perimeter is 54.

4. *x* = 38; *y* = 4

5. *x* = 92; *y* = 7

6. *x* = 36; *y* = 36

ABCDE is a regular pentagon.

7. *x* = 64; *y* = 71

8. *x* = 2; *y* = 5

9. Architecture The Air Force Academy Cadet Chapel has 17 spires that point to the sky. Each spire is an isosceles triangle with a 40° vertex angle. Find the measures of the base angles.
The measure of each base angle is 70.

10. Critical Thinking What are the measures of the base angles of an isosceles right triangle? Explain.
10–11. See margin.

11. Coordinate Geometry The vertices of the base angles of an isosceles triangle are at (0, 0) and (6, 0). Describe the possible locations of the third vertex.

Logical Reasoning **Determine whether each statement is true or false. If it is false, provide a counterexample.**

12. If a quadrilateral is equilateral, then it is equiangular.
False; adjacent angles of a rhombus are not ≅.
13. If a quadrilateral is equiangular, then it is equilateral.
False; a rectangle need not have 4 ≅ sides.
14. Every isosceles triangle has at least one line of symmetry. true
15. Every equilateral triangle has exactly three lines of symmetry. true

16. Graphic Arts The logo of the National Council of Teachers of Mathematics is shown at the right.
  a. Trace the logo onto your paper. Highlight an obtuse isosceles triangle in the design and then find its angle measures. a–b. See margin.
  b. Open-ended Repeat part (a) for each of the following figures: kite, pentagon, hexagon.

The triangles in the logo have these congruent sides and angles.

191

Exercises 17–18 Have students work with partners. Remind them to check that the product of the slopes of the lines through the sides of the right angle is −1.

WRITING Exercise 20 Be sure that students explain the conditional, and not the converse. You may want to ask them if the converse is true.

ALTERNATIVE ASSESSMENT **Exercises 26–32** These exercises can help you assess students' understanding of the properties of isosceles triangles by observing their ability to apply the theorems and corollaries presented in this lesson to find missing angle measures and side lengths.

Exercise 27 Help students see that the larger triangle is equilateral because each side is made up of two congruent segments.

Exercise 28 Before students can find x, they need to find the measures of the angles of a regular hexagon.

Exercise 32 Students should see that $\triangle OED$ is an isosceles triangle because all radii of $\odot O$ are congruent.

20. Yes; if a △ has at least 2 ≅ sides, it is isosceles. An equiangular △ is equilateral and has 3 ≅ sides, so it is isosceles.

34a.

page 193   Mixed Review

46. Answers may vary. Samples: $m\angle M = m\angle O$ because $MN = NO$; $m\angle M = m\angle O = 45$ because $m\angle M + m\angle O = 180 - m\angle N = 90$.

47. $\overline{DF} \parallel \overline{EG}$ because in a plane, 2 lines ⊥ to a 3rd line are ∥.

48. Answers may vary. Samples: $m\angle LJM = m\angle JLM = m\angle LJK = m\angle JLK = 45$ because base ∠s of an isoceles △ are ≅ and the vertex angle of each △ is a rt. angle. ∠MJK and ∠KLM are rt. ∠s by the Angle Addition Post. JKLM is a square by def. of square.

192

Coordinate Geometry **For each pair of points, there are six points that could be the third vertex of an isosceles right triangle. Find the coordinates of each point.**

17. (0, 0) and (5, 5)   18. (2, 3) and (5, 6)
    17–18. See right.

19. *Algebra* A triangle has angle measures $x + 15$, $3x - 35$, and $4x$.
    a. Find the value of x.   25
    b. Find the measure of each angle.   40, 40, 100
    c. What type of triangle is it? Why?   Isosceles; the △ has 2 ≅ angles.

20. *Writing* If a triangle is equiangular, is it also isosceles? Explain.   See margin.

21. a. *Communications* In the diagram, what type of triangle is formed by the cable pairs and the ground?   21a. isosceles
    b. What are the two different base lengths of the triangles?   900 ft; 1100 ft
    c. How is the tower related to each of the triangles?   Answers may vary. Sample: The tower is the ⊥ bisector of the base.

Find each value.

22. If $m\angle L = 58$, then $m\angle LKJ = $ ■.   64
23. If $JL = 5$, then $ML = $ ■.   2.5
24. If $m\angle JKM = 48$, then $m\angle J = $ ■.   42
25. If $m\angle J = 55$, then $m\angle JKM = $ ■.   35

17. (0, 5), (5, 0), (0, 10), (10, 0), (−5, 5), (5, −5)
18. (−1, 6), (2, 6), (2, 9), (5, 0), (5, 3), (8, 3)

1000 ft
800
600 .... Cables
400
200
0
├── 450 ft ──┼── 550 ft ──┤
Tower cables extend to both widths.

Television Tower 1009 ft tall

🖩 *Choose* **Use mental math, pencil and paper, or a calculator to find the values of the variables.**

26.

6
Perimeter is 20.

27.

60

28.

30
HIJKLM is a regular hexagon.

29.

50

30.

$x = 60$; $y = 30$

31.

120

32.

110
$\overline{OD}$ and $\overline{OE}$ are radii.

33.

70

$\overline{VZ}$ and $\overline{YZ}$ are angle bisectors.

Exercise 34 Help students see that the quadrilaterals inscribed within the circle are squares.

STANDARDIZED TEST TIP Exercise 36 Suggest students draw a line through the side shared by both polygons. Then students should see that $m\angle SHA$ equals the sum of 90 and the measure of one exterior angle of the hexagon.

GETTING READY FOR LESSON 4-3 These exercises prepare students to justify statements in proofs.

Wrap Up

THE BIG IDEA Ask students: *Describe all the properties of isosceles triangles you have learned thus far.*

Exercises   MIXED REVIEW

Exercise 44 Have students graph both lines to check their answers.

RETEACHING ACTIVITY Students use and apply properties of isosceles triangles to find missing angle measures. (Reteaching worksheet 4-2)

---

34. **Crafts** This design is used in Hmong crafts and in Islamic and Mexican tiles. To create it, the artist starts by drawing a circle and four equally spaced diameters.

Step 1   Step 2   Step 3

a. How many different sizes of isosceles right triangles can you find in Step 2? Trace an example of each onto your paper. **5 different triangles; see margin p. 192 for diagram.**

b. For each size of triangle that you traced, count the number of times it appears in the diagram. **8, 8, 16, 8, and 16 times, respectively**

35. **Critical Thinking** Patrick defines the base of an isosceles triangle as "the bottom side of an isosceles triangle." Is his definition a good one? Explain why or why not. **No; the base is the side opposite the vertex angle.**

36. **Standardized Test Prep** A square and a regular hexagon are placed so that they have a common side. Find $m\angle HAS$. **C**

A. 9   B. 10   C. 15   D. 20   E. 30

Algebra Find the values of *m* and *n*.

37.

$m = 20; n = 45$

38.
$m = 60; n = 30$

39.

$m = 36; n = 27$

40.
$m = 59; n = 62$

Exercises   MIXED REVIEW

Coordinate Geometry **The endpoints of a diameter of a circle are given. Find the coordinates of the center and the length of a radius.**

41. $(3, 8), (-1, 2)$ $(1, 5); \sqrt{13}$

42. $(-2, 5), (-5, 2)$ $(-3.5, 3.5); \frac{3}{2}\sqrt{2}$

43. $(3, 7), (-2, 6)$ $(0.5, 6.5); \frac{1}{2}\sqrt{26}$

44. *Coordinate Geometry* Find the equation of the line that passes through $(0, 4)$ and is parallel to $y = -3x - 5$. $y = -3x + 4$

45. Find the number of sides of a regular polygon whose exterior angles measure 15°. **24 sides**

Getting Ready for Lesson 4-3

What can you conclude from each diagram? Justify your answers. 46–48. See margin p. 192.

46.

$\angle MNP \cong \angle ONP$

47.

48.

Lesson Quiz

Lesson Quiz is also available in Transparencies.

1. Draw a right isosceles triangle. Label its vertex angle, base angles, legs, and base. **Answers will vary. Sample:**

2. The measure of one of the base angles of an isosceles triangle is 55. Find the measures of the other two angles. **55, 70**

3. The measure of an exterior angle drawn from the vertex angle of an isosceles triangle is 112. Find the measures of the angles of the triangle. **68, 56, 56**

193

PROBLEM OF THE DAY

3 chocolates	3 creams	2 chocolates 1 cream

Somehow the labels on the candy boxes got mixed up so that no label is correct. What is the least number of pieces you can test to determine which label belongs to which box? one from the box labeled "2 chocolates and 1 cream"

Problem of the Day is also available in Transparencies.

CONNECTING TO PRIOR KNOWLEDGE Ask students to use the diagram to justify the following statements: $m\angle 1 + m\angle 4 = 180$, $m\angle 4 = m\angle 2 + m\angle 3$, and $\triangle ABC$ is a right triangle.

THINK AND DISCUSS

DIVERSITY Take this opportunity to discuss the different places of birth of students. Display a map of the world on a bulletin board and use pushpins to indicate the different locations.

Lesson Planning Options

Prerequisite Skills

• Understanding properties of equality and congruence

Assignment Options for Exercises On Your Own

▼ **Core** 1–7, 10–15, 17–18
  Extension 8–9, 16

Use Mixed Review to maintain skills.

Resources

 Student Edition

Skills Handbook, p. 650
Extra Practice, p. 537
Glossary/Study Guide

 Teaching Resources

Chapter Support File, Ch. 4
• Practice 4-3 (two worksheets)
• Reteaching 4-3
Classroom Manager 4-3
Glossary, Spanish Resources

 Transparencies
52

194

Connections 🌐 *Logic Puzzles . . . and more*

What You'll Learn

• Using different styles of proofs to write convincing arguments

...And Why

To help you think logically

4-3 Preparing for Proof

THINK AND DISCUSS

In everyday life, proof takes many forms.

A passport is proof of your citizenship when traveling in foreign countries.

A punch clock record is proof of the number of hours you have worked.

A birth certificate is proof of the date and location of your birth.

1. Give some other examples of proof from everyday life. See left.

Proofs in geometry can take several forms. Each form has these basic parts:

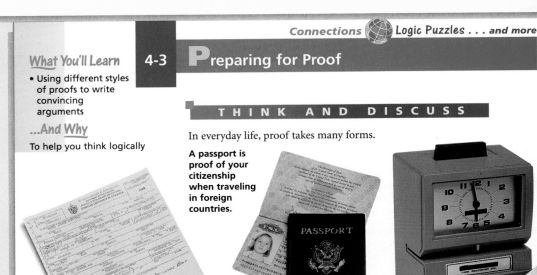

A list of the given information.

A list of what is to be proved.

A logical series of statements that lead from the given information to what is to be proved.

A diagram showing the given information.

The reasons why each statement is true. Reasons can include postulates, definitions, properties, previously stated theorems, or given facts.

1. Samples: A diploma is proof of a completed education; a cashier receipt is proof of payment or purchase; a signature is proof of delivery of a package.

The diagram shows a **two-column proof.** In this style of proof, statements appear in one column and reasons in another.

In this lesson, you will study the proofs of the four theorems at the top of the next page.

To emphasize the need for proof, have students investigate this statement: For $n = 1, 2, 3, \ldots, n^2 + n + 41$ always produces a prime number. Students will find it interesting that, although this statement is true for $n = 1, 2, 3, \ldots, 40$, it is false for $n = 41$.

ERROR ALERT! Students with poor writing and organizational skills may have difficulty setting up a two-column proof. **Remediation:** You may want to provide students with a template which leaves room for them to fill in the "Given," "Prove," "Diagram," "Statements," and "Reasons."

TACTILE LEARNING Have students draw and cut out a large right triangle. Have them tear off the non-right angles and place them over the right angle to show that together the two angles form a 90° angle.

Example

Use this proof to help students see that the steps for writing a proof are similar to the steps they use to solve word problems. Emphasize that before students begin a proof, they should understand what they need to prove, then plan what postulates, theorems, and definitions they can use to prove it. When the proof is complete, students should check that their conclusion matches what they are trying to prove.

Theorem 4-4	If a triangle is a right triangle, then the acute angles are complementary.
Theorem 4-5	If two angles of one triangle are congruent to two angles of another triangle, then the third angles are congruent.
Theorem 4-6	All right angles are congruent.
Theorem 4-7	If two angles are congruent and supplementary, then each is a right angle.

In a proof of a theorem, the *Given* information and the figure relate to the hypothesis of the theorem. You *Prove* the conclusion of the theorem.

Theorem 4-4
If a triangle is a right triangle, then the acute angles are complementary.

Hypothesis
Given: $\triangle EFG$ with right angle $\angle F$
Prove: $\angle E$ and $\angle G$ are complementary.
Conclusion

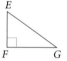

Two-Column Proof of Theorem 4-4

Statements	Reasons
1. $\angle F$ is a right angle.	1. Given
2. $m\angle F = 90$	2. Def. of right angle
3. $m\angle E + m\angle F + m\angle G = 180$	3. Triangle Angle-Sum Thm.
4. $m\angle E + 90 + m\angle G = 180$	4. Substitution
5. $m\angle E + m\angle G = 90$	5. Subtraction Prop. of Equality
6. $\angle E$ and $\angle G$ are complementary.	6. Def. of complementary angles

In a **paragraph proof,** the statements and reasons appear in sentences within a paragraph.

Example

Write a paragraph proof for Theorem 4-5.

Given: $\angle X \cong \angle Q$ and $\angle Y \cong \angle R$
Prove: $\angle Z \cong \angle S$

Paragraph Proof
By the Triangle Angle-Sum Theorem, $m\angle X + m\angle Y + m\angle Z = 180$ and $m\angle Q + m\angle R + m\angle S = 180$. By substitution, $m\angle X + m\angle Y + m\angle Z = m\angle Q + m\angle R + m\angle S$. We are given that $\angle X \cong \angle Q$ and $\angle Y \cong \angle R$ (or $m\angle X = m\angle Q$ and $m\angle Y = m\angle R$). Subtracting equal quantities from both sides of the equation leaves $m\angle Z = m\angle S$, so $\angle Z \cong \angle S$.

Additional Examples

FOR EXAMPLE

Write a two-column proof for Theorem 4-5.

Given: $\angle A \cong \angle D$; $\angle B \cong \angle E$
Prove: $\angle C \cong \angle F$

1. $\angle A \cong \angle D$; $\angle B \cong \angle E$ (given)

2. $m\angle A = m\angle D$; $m\angle B = m\angle E$ (def. of congruence)

3. $m\angle A + m\angle B + m\angle C = 180$; $m\angle D + m\angle E + m\angle F = 180$ (Triangle Angle-Sum Theorem)

4. $m\angle A + m\angle B + m\angle C = m\angle D + m\angle E + m\angle F$ (Transitive Prop. of Equality)

5. $m\angle A + m\angle B + m\angle C = m\angle A + m\angle B + m\angle F$ (substitution)

6. $m\angle C = m\angle F$ (Subtraction Prop. of Equality)

7. $\angle C \cong \angle F$ (def. of congruence)

195

WORK TOGETHER

Work in pairs.

2. Rewrite this two-column proof of Theorem 4-6 as a paragraph proof. See below.

Given: $\angle X$ and $\angle Y$ are right angles.

Prove: $\angle X \cong \angle Y$

Two-Column Proof

Statements	Reasons
1. $\angle X$ and $\angle Y$ are right angles.	1. Given
2. $m\angle X = 90$, $m\angle Y = 90$	2. Def. of right angles
3. $m\angle X = m\angle Y$, or $\angle X \cong \angle Y$	3. Substitution

3. Rewrite this paragraph proof of Theorem 4-7 as a two-column proof.

Given: $\angle W$ and $\angle V$ are congruent and supplementary. See margin p. 197.

Prove: $\angle W$ and $\angle V$ are right angles.

Paragraph Proof

$\angle W$ and $\angle V$ are congruent and supplementary, so $m\angle W = m\angle V$ and $m\angle W + m\angle V = 180$. Substituting $m\angle W$ for $m\angle V$ gives $m\angle W + m\angle W = 180$. Therefore, $m\angle W = 90$. Since $\angle W \cong \angle V$, $m\angle V = 90$, too. Thus both angles are right angles.

2. By def. of rt. angles $m\angle X = 90$ and $m\angle Y = 90$. $m\angle X = m\angle Y$ by substitution, so $\angle X \cong \angle Y$.

Exercises ON YOUR OWN

What can you conclude from each diagram? Justify your answers. 1–6. See back of book.

1.

2.

3.

4.

5.

6.

7. *Standardized Test Prep* Find the value of x in the figure. **C**
   A. 20   **B.** 30   **C.** 45   **D.** 60   **E.** none of these

8. *Open-ended* Explain the similarities and differences between paragraph and two-column proofs. Which do you prefer? Why?
See back of book.

STANDARDIZED TEST TIP **Exercise 7** Students can solve for *x* using properties of angles and triangles, or they can eliminate choices by substituting each value of *x* into the diagram, getting contradictions with incorrect angle measures.

Exercise 8 Depending on learning styles, different students may prefer different proof formats. Students should be familiar with both formats presented in this lesson, but in future lessons you may want to allow students the opportunity to use the proof format with which they feel more comfortable.

Exercise 10 Have students notice that the statement in the "Given" is not necessarily the first statement in the proof.

Exercises 13–14 You might want to agree upon conventions for abbreviating common words used in the "Reasons" column of a proof such as ∠ for angle, def. for definition, ≅ for congruent, etc.

9. Writing Russell Black Elk found this multiple-choice question in a puzzle book. Solve the puzzle and explain your solution.
E; see margin for explanation.

10. Rewrite this paragraph proof as a two-column proof.

Given: $\angle 1 \cong \angle 4$

Prove: $\angle 2 \cong \angle 3$

$\angle 1$ and $\angle 2$ are vertical angles, as are $\angle 3$ and $\angle 4$. Vertical angles are congruent, so $\angle 1 \cong \angle 2$ and $\angle 3 \cong \angle 4$. We are given that $\angle 1 \cong \angle 4$. By the Transitive Property of Congruence, $\angle 2 \cong \angle 4$ and $\angle 2 \cong \angle 3$. **See margin.**

Refer to the diagrams to complete each statement.

11. a. $\angle OKN \cong$ __?__
  b. $\angle LKO \cong$ __?__
  c. $\angle LOK \cong$ __?__

12. a. $m\angle USR =$ __?__ 58
  b. $m\angle RUS =$ __?__ 64
  c. $m\angle SUQ =$ __?__ 116
  d. $m\angle USQ =$ __?__ 32
  e. $m\angle QST =$ __?__ 90

11a. $\angle ONK$ b. $\angle MNO$ c. $\angle MON$

13. Preparing for Proof The reasons given in this proof are correct, but they are in the wrong order. List them in the correct order.

Given: $m\angle AOB = m\angle BOC$ d, f, b, a, c, e
Prove: $\overleftrightarrow{OA} \perp \overleftrightarrow{OB}$

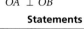

Statements	Reasons
1. $m\angle AOB = m\angle BOC$	a. Division Prop. of Equality
2. $m\angle AOB + m\angle BOC = 180$	b. Substitution
3. $m\angle AOB + m\angle AOB = 180$ or $2(m\angle AOB) = 180$	c. Def. of right angle
4. $m\angle AOB = 90$	d. Given
5. $\angle AOB$ is a right angle.	e. Def. of perpendicular lines
6. $\overleftrightarrow{OA} \perp \overleftrightarrow{OB}$	f. Angle Addition Postulate

14. Preparing for Proof Rewrite this proof as a paragraph proof.

Given: $\overline{XZ} \cong \overline{YZ}$ and $\overline{XW} \cong \overline{YW}$ See margin.
Prove: $m\angle 1 = m\angle 2$

Statements	Reasons
1. $\overline{XZ} \cong \overline{YZ}$	1. Given
2. $\angle ZXY \cong \angle ZYX$ or $m\angle ZXY = m\angle ZYX$	2. Base ∡ of an isosceles △ are ≅.
3. $\overline{XW} \cong \overline{YW}$	3. Given
4. $\angle 3 \cong \angle 4$ or $m\angle 3 = m\angle 4$	4. Base ∡ of an isosceles △ are ≅.
5. $m\angle ZXY = m\angle 1 + m\angle 3$ $m\angle ZYX = m\angle 2 + m\angle 4$	5. Angle Addition Postulate
6. $m\angle 1 + m\angle 3 = m\angle 2 + m\angle 4$	6. Substitution
7. $m\angle 1 = m\angle 2$	7. Subtraction Prop. of Equality

page 196   Work Together

3. 1. $\angle W$ and $\angle V$ are supp. (Given)
  2. $\angle W \cong \angle V$ (Given)
  3. $m\angle W + m\angle V = 180$ (Def. supp. angles)
  4. $m\angle W + m\angle W = 180$ (Substitution)
  5. $m\angle W = 90$ (Multiplication Prop. of =)
  6. $m\angle V = 90$ (Substitution)
  7. $\angle W$ and $\angle W$ are rt. angles (Def. rt. angle)

9. E; assume (A) is T. Then (B–F) are all T. But (B) is F if (C–F) are T. So the assumption that (A) is T must be F and (A) is F. Assume (B) is T. Then (C–F) are F. But (C) is T if (B) is T, so the assumption that (B) is T must be F and (B) is F. Since (A) and (B) are F, (C) is F. Since (A–C) are F, (D) is F. Since (A–D) are F, (E) is T. Since (E) is T, (F) is F.

10. 1. $\angle 1 \cong \angle 2$ (Vert. ∠s are ≅)
  2. $\angle 1 \cong \angle 4$ (Given)
  3. $\angle 2 \cong \angle 4$ (Trans. Prop. of ≅)
  4. $\angle 3 \cong \angle 4$ (Vert. ∠s are ≅.)
  5. $\angle 2 \cong \angle 3$ (Trans. Prop. of ≅)

14. You are given that $\triangle XYZ$ is an isosceles △. $\angle ZXY \cong \angle ZYX$ or $m\angle ZXY = m\angle ZYX$ because base ∠s of an isosceles △ are ≅. Similarly, $\angle 3 \cong \angle 4$ or $m\angle 3 = m\angle 4$. $m\angle ZXY = m\angle 1 + m\angle 3$ and $m\angle ZYX = m\angle 2 + m\angle 4$ by the Angle Addition Post. By Substitution, $m\angle 1 + m\angle 3 = m\angle 2 + m\angle 4$. Subtracting = quantities from each side yields $m\angle 1 = m\angle 2$.

197

ALTERNATIVE ASSESSMENT Exercise 15 This exercise can help you assess students' ability to reason logically. Students have the choice of using a paragraph proof or a two-column proof to organize their explanations.

Exercise 16 Students may not see the error in this proof if they do not remember that division by zero is undefined.

Chapter Project **FIND OUT BY ORGANIZING** You may want to start off with solving a similar type of puzzle with the class. For example, ask students to determine which person is the artist, the dancer, and the soccer player from the following clues: Kim is taller than the artist. Mike and the soccer player have practice on Monday. Ann, the tallest of the three, is in the same grade as the dancer.

Exercises 19–20 You may want to have students work with a partner. Students should check their answers by making sure that the sum of the measures of the angles is about 360.

GETTING READY FOR LESSON 4-4 This exercise prepares students to use properties of the midsegments of triangles.

---

page 199 Mixed Review

20a. False; less than half the adults want students to save or invest the money.

b. False; the diagram makes no reference to parents.

c. True; more than half the adults, 81%, said the students should not spend the money as they please.

21a.

15. *Logical Reasoning* Explain why this statement is true:
If $m\angle 1 + m\angle 2 = 180$ and $m\angle 2 + m\angle 3 = 180$, then $\angle 1 \cong \angle 3$.

By Substitution, $m\angle 1 + m\angle 2 = m\angle 2 + m\angle 3$. Subtracting = quantities from each side yields $m\angle 1 = m\angle 3$.

16. *Logical Reasoning* Explain why this proof is invalid.
Given: $a = b$
Prove: $1 = 2$ You cannot use the Division Prop. of = because $b - a = 0$.

Statements	Reasons
1. $a = b$	1. Given
2. $ab = b^2$	2. Multiplication Prop. of Equality
3. $ab - a^2 = b^2 - a^2$	3. Subtraction Prop. of Equality
4. $a(b - a) = (b + a)(b - a)$	4. Distributive Property
5. $a = b + a$	5. Division Prop. of Equality
6. $a = a + a$	6. Substitution
7. $a = 2a$	7. Distributive Property
8. $1 = 2$	8. Division Prop. of Equality

17. Supply the reasons to complete this proof of the Corollary to the Isosceles Triangle Theorem stated on page 190.
Given: $\triangle ABC$ with $\overline{AB} \cong \overline{BC} \cong \overline{CA}$
Prove: $\angle A \cong \angle B, \angle B \cong \angle C$, and $\angle A \cong \angle C$

Statements		Reasons
1. $\overline{AB} \cong \overline{BC} \cong \overline{CA}$	a. ?	
2. $\angle A \cong \angle C$	b. ?	
3. $\angle C \cong \angle B$	c. ?	
4. $\angle A \cong \angle B$	d. ?	

a. Given;
b. Isosceles Triangle Thm.;
c. Isosceles Triangle Thm.;
d. Transitive Prop. of $\cong$

18. Complete this paragraph proof.
Given: $\angle PST \cong \angle PRQ$
Prove: $\triangle PSR$ is isosceles.

$m\angle PST + m\angle PSR = 180$ and $m\angle PRQ + m\angle PRS = 180$ by the
a. ? Postulate. By the **b.** ? , $\angle PST$ and $\angle PSR$, as well as $\angle PRQ$ and $\angle PRS$, are supplementary. We are given that **c.** ? . By the Congruent Supplements Thm., **d.** ? . If two ⓛ of a △ are ≅, the sides opposite them are ≅, so **e.** ? . By **f.** ? , $\triangle PSR$ is isosceles.

a. Angle Addition
b. def. of supplementary angles
c. $\angle PST \cong \angle PRQ$
d. $\angle PSR \cong \angle PRS$ e. $\overline{PS} \cong \overline{PR}$
f. def. of isosceles △

Chapter Project **Find Out by Organizing**

A drummer, guitarist, and keyboard player named Amy, Bob, and Carla are in a band. Use the clues to determine which instrument each plays.

Carla and the drummer wear different-colored shirts.
The keyboard player is older than Bob.
Amy, the youngest band member, lives next door to the guitarist.

You can solve this type of logic puzzle by eliminating possibilities. Make a grid. Put an X in a box once you eliminate it as a possibility.

Instrument	Amy	Bob	Carla
Drums			
Guitar			
Keyboard			

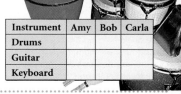

Amy is the drummer; Bob is the guitarist; Carla is the keyboard player.

THE BIG IDEA Ask students: *Describe two styles of proof and the types of reasons that can be used to justify a statement in a proof.*

RETEACHING Students practice writing two-column proofs by filling in missing statements and reasons of a partially completed proof. (Reteaching worksheet 4-3)

A Point in Time

If you have block scheduling or an extended class period, you may wish to have students investigate these topics:

• Find a mystery written by Agatha Christie, Sherlock Holmes, or another author using logical reasoning.

• Write your own detective story using logical reasoning to solve a mystery.

• Investigate what type of education and skills are required to become a mystery writer.

• Watch either of the films, *Murder on the Orient Express* or *Death on the Nile*, and present a movie review to the class.

Exercises   MIXED REVIEW

Statistics For Exercises 19 and 20, refer to the circle graph.

19. Find the measure of each central angle.
147.6, 144, 54, 14.4

20. Are the statements *true* or *false*? Explain.
  a. Most adults want students who work to save or invest money.
  b. All of those surveyed are parents of high-school students.
  c. Most adults aren't in favor of allowing students who work to spend their earnings as they please. a–c. See margin p. 198.

21. a. Transformational Geometry Graph points $A(4, -8)$ and $A'(-6, 1)$. Sketch $\overrightarrow{AA'}$.
  b. Describe the translation of A to A' in words and using ordered pair notation. **b. shift left 10 and**
  a. See margin p. 198. **up 9;** $\langle -10, 9 \rangle$

Getting Ready for Lesson 4-4

22. a. Coordinate Geometry Find the slope of the line containing $A(-2, 3)$ and $B(3, 1)$. $-\frac{2}{5}$
  b. Find the coordinates of the midpoint of $\overline{AB}$. $\left(\frac{1}{2}, 2\right)$

Where Should the Money Go?
What adults say high school students who also work should do with the money they earn:

Save or invest 41%

Spend as they please 15%

Don't know 4%

Contribute to household costs* 40%

*such as buy some of their clothes

Source: *Louis Harris & Associates survey*

Reteaching 4-3

Practice 4-3

Practice 4-3
Mixed Exercises

A Point in Time

1500   1600   1700   1800   1900   2000

The Logic of Agatha Christie

Most people are not detectives, but as a young woman, the English writer Agatha Christie (1890–1976) correctly deduced that many people would *like* to be. In 1920 she published her first book, a detective novel entitled *The Mysterious Affair at Styles* in which she introduced the eccentric and ultra-logical Belgian detective Hercule Poirot. In this and in many subsequent novels, Poirot solved mysteries not with guns or car chases but with logical reasoning. He and Agatha Christie's other principal detective character, Jane Marple, always won in the end because they were more patient, more diligent, and, above all, more *clever* than the crooks. Readers made best-sellers of many of Christie's 78 detective novels. Many of her novels, including *Murder on the Orient Express* and *Death on the Nile,* have been adapted into popular films.

To date, her books have sold some 2 billion copies in 44 languages, making Agatha Christie by far the world's top-selling writer of fiction.

Lesson Quiz

Lesson Quiz is also available in Transparencies.

1. What are the measures of $\angle B$ and $\angle C$?
45°
$m\angle B = 45$,
$m\angle C = 90$

2. What kind of figure is *ABC*? Justify your answer.
Isosceles right triangle; $AC = BC$ so the triangle is isosceles, and $m\angle C = 90$ so the triangle is right.

3. Write the proof of Theorem 4-4 on page 195 as a paragraph proof.
See back of book.

199

Math ToolboX

Students use geometry software to investigate the properties of the midsegment of a triangle. They discover that the midsegment is parallel to a side of the triangle and is half its length. These properties of a midsegment will be proved in Lesson 4-4.

Geometry software allows students to manipulate the triangle by dragging on a vertex to see certain properties of midsegments hold for all types of triangles.

Construct

ERROR ALERT! Students may try to take a short cut and approximate the placement of the midpoints *D* and *E*.

Remediation: Check that students use construction or measurement to find the midpoints.

Extend

Have students manipulate $\triangle ABC$ so it is right, acute, obtuse, and equilateral.

ADDITIONAL PROBLEM Have students measure *AD*, *DB*, *AB*, *AE*, *EC*, and *AC*. Then have them compare the ratios $\frac{AD}{DB}$ to $\frac{AE}{EC}$ and $\frac{AD}{AB}$ to $\frac{AE}{AC}$. Have students list all their conjectures about the segments.

Materials and Manipulatives

- Geometry software

Math ToolboX

Technology

Investigating Midsegments

Work in pairs or small groups.

Construct

Use geometry software to draw a triangle. Label it $\triangle ABC$. Construct the midpoints of $\overline{AB}$ and $\overline{AC}$, label them *D* and *E*, respectively, and then connect them with a *midsegment*.
Check students' work.

Investigate

- Measure the lengths of $\overline{DE}$ and $\overline{BC}$. Calculate $\frac{DE}{BC}$.

- Measure the slopes of $\overline{DE}$ and $\overline{BC}$.

- Manipulate the triangle and observe the lengths and slopes of the segments.
Check students' work.

Conjecture

List all your **conjectures** about a midsegment.
The midsegment is ∥ to a side of the △ and is half its length.

Extend

- Construct the other two midsegments in $\triangle ABC$. Measure the angles of the four triangles determined by the three midsegments. How do they compare to the angles of the original triangle? Make **conjectures.**
See below.
- Measure the sides of the four triangles. Make a **conjecture** about the four triangles determined by the midsegments of a triangle. Make a **conjecture** about the relationship between the original triangle and the four triangles. **The sides of the midsegment △ are each $\frac{1}{2}$ of the corr. side of the orig. △; the 4 △s are ≅; the 4 △s are ~ to the orig. △.**
- Measure the areas of the four triangles formed by the midsegments of a triangle. Measure the area of the original triangle. Make a **conjecture** about the areas. Do the same for perimeter. **The area of each smaller △ is $\frac{1}{4}$ the area of the orig. △; the perimeter of each smaller △ is $\frac{1}{2}$ the perimeter of the orig. △.**

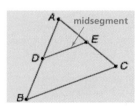

Opp. angles of the orig. △ and the midsegment △ have = measures; corr. angles in the 4 smaller △s have = measures.

off

200

CONNECTING TO PRIOR KNOWLEDGE Ask students to find the midpoint and length of a segment with endpoints $A(-5, 3)$ and $B(2, 3)$. Then have them show that the segment is parallel to a line containing $(-2, -1)$ and $(4, -1)$.

WORK TOGETHER

Have students label the vertices in the interior of the triangles so that when they cut the triangles out, the vertices will be labeled on the cut-out figures.

ERROR ALERT! Because of the orientation of $\overline{AC}$, students may not see why folding A onto C marks the midpoint of $\overline{AC}$. **Remediation:** Demonstrate with a piece of rectangular paper how folding the corners of a side onto each other folds the paper in half.

What You'll Learn
- Using properties of midsegments to solve problems

...And Why
- To help you find lengths and distances indirectly

What You'll Need
- scissors
- straightedge

Connections Architecture . . . and more

4-4 Midsegments of Triangles

WORK TOGETHER

Have each member of your group draw and cut out a large scalene triangle. Be sure to include right, acute, and obtuse triangles.

- Label the vertices of your triangle A, B, and C.

- Fold A onto C to find the midpoint of $\overline{AC}$. Do the same for $\overline{BC}$. Label the midpoints L and N, then draw $\overline{LN}$.

- Fold your triangle on $\overline{LN}$.

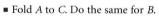

- Fold A to C. Do the same for B.

1. **a.** What type of quadrilateral does the folded triangle appear to form?
   b. What does this tell you about $\overline{LN}$ and $\overline{AB}$? **b.** $LN \parallel AB$
   a. rectangle
2. How does LN compare to AB? Explain. $LN = \frac{1}{2}AB$; when folded, A meets B, so the resulting side of the rectangle is $\frac{1}{2}AB$.
3. Make a **conjecture** about how the segment joining the midpoints of two sides of a triangle is related to the third side of the triangle.

   The segment is half as long as and $\parallel$ to the 3rd side.

THINK AND DISCUSS

The segment you constructed in the Work Together is a midsegment. A **midsegment** of a triangle is a segment connecting the midpoints of two of its sides.

Theorem 4-8
Triangle Midsegment Theorem

If a segment joins the midpoints of two sides of a triangle, then the segment is parallel to the third side and half its length.

You can prove the Triangle Midsegment Theorem by using coordinate geometry and algebra. This style of proof is called a *coordinate proof*. You begin the proof by placing a triangle in a convenient spot on the coordinate plane. You then choose variables for the coordinates of the vertices.

Theorem 4-8 is proved using a coordinate proof. Before working through the proof with students, you may want to check the validity of the theorem using numerical values for the coordinates. Students are asked to make their own numerical example in Question 4.

Discuss with students why variables are chosen instead of numbers as coordinates for the vertices in the proof. Help students see that locating the triangle at the origin does not affect the outcome of the proof but makes the computations easier.

CRITICAL THINKING Ask students to explain how you can reason from the fact that R and S have the same y-coordinates that the slope of $\overline{RS}$ equals zero.

> ### Example 1
>
> **AUDITORY LEARNING** Have students work in groups to read through the solution to Example 1. Then ask for volunteers to explain in their own words how to find AB and other volunteers to explain how to find CD.
>
> **CRITICAL THINKING Question 5** Ask students if they used theorems, postulates, or definitions to justify their answers.

Additional Examples

FOR EXAMPLE 1 ....

Refer to the diagram in Example 1. If $AB = 7$, find EG and DC.

$EG = 14$, $DG = 7$

Discussion: If $\triangle FAB$ is an equilateral triangle, what can you say about $\triangle FEG$?

FOR EXAMPLE 2 ....

Refer to the diagrams in Example 2. If the distance across the lake is 288 ft, how many strides would DeAndre have paced in Step 5?

48 strides

QUICK REVIEW

Midpoint Formula:
$$\left(\frac{x_1 + x_2}{2}, \frac{y_1 + y_2}{2}\right)$$

Distance Formula:
$$\sqrt{(x_2 - x_1)^2 + (y_2 - y_1)^2}$$

For practice with simplifying radicals, see Skills Handbook page 660.

4a. Sample: for $P(4, 8)$ and $Q(6, 0)$, $R(2, 4)$, $S(5, 4)$

b. For sample in part (a), $RS = 3$, $OQ = 6$, $RS = \frac{1}{2}OQ$ ✔

c. For sample in part (a), slope of $\overline{RS} = 0$, slope of $\overline{OQ} = 0$ ✔

5. Yes; $\overline{AB} \parallel \overline{EG}$ and $\overline{CD} \parallel \overline{EG}$; 2 lines $\parallel$ to a 3rd line are $\parallel$.

6. $BC = AD = 12.5$ cm

7. $ABCD$ is a parallelogram because its opp. sides are $\parallel$.

Coordinate Proof of Theorem 4-8

Given: R is the midpoint of $\overline{OP}$.
S is the midpoint of $\overline{QP}$.

Prove: $\overline{RS} \parallel \overline{OQ}$ and $RS = \frac{1}{2}OQ$

- Use the Midpoint Formula to find the coordinates of R and S.

$$R: \left(\frac{0 + b}{2}, \frac{0 + c}{2}\right) = \left(\frac{b}{2}, \frac{c}{2}\right) \qquad S: \left(\frac{a + b}{2}, \frac{0 + c}{2}\right) = \left(\frac{a + b}{2}, \frac{c}{2}\right)$$

- To prove that $\overline{RS}$ and $\overline{OQ}$ are parallel, show that their slopes are equal. Because the y-coordinates of R and S are the same, the slope of $\overline{RS}$ is zero. The same is true for $\overline{OQ}$. Therefore, $\overline{RS} \parallel \overline{OQ}$.

- Use the Distance Formula to find RS and OQ.

$$RS = \sqrt{\left(\frac{a + b}{2} - \frac{b}{2}\right)^2 + \left(\frac{c}{2} - \frac{c}{2}\right)^2}$$
$$= \sqrt{\left(\frac{a}{2} + \frac{b}{2} - \frac{b}{2}\right)^2 + 0^2} = \sqrt{\left(\frac{a}{2}\right)^2} = \frac{a}{2} = \frac{1}{2}a$$

$$OQ = \sqrt{(a - 0)^2 + (0 - 0)^2}$$
$$= \sqrt{a^2 + 0^2} = a$$

Therefore, $RS = \frac{1}{2}OQ$.

4. Select numerical values for the coordinates of P and Q.
   a. Use the Midpoint Formula to find the coordinates of R and S.
   b. **Verify** that $RS = \frac{1}{2}OQ$ for the values you chose.
   c. **Verify** that $\overline{RS} \parallel \overline{OQ}$ for the values you chose.

> ### Example 1
>
> In quadrilateral $EFGH$, the points A, B, C, and D are midpoints and $EG = 18$ cm. Find AB and CD.
>
> Consider $\triangle EFG$. By the Triangle Midsegment Theorem, $AB = \frac{1}{2}EG$.
>
> Using the same reasoning for $\triangle EHG$, you get $CD = \frac{1}{2}EG$. Because $EG = 18$ cm, $\frac{1}{2}EG = 9$ cm. Therefore, $AB = CD = 9$ cm.

5. **Critical Thinking** Is $\overline{AB} \parallel \overline{CD}$? **Justify** your answer.

6. **Try This** $FH = 25$ cm. Find BC and AD.

7. **Critical Thinking** What type of quadrilateral is $ABCD$? Explain.

202

Example 2 **Relating to the Real World** ·················

ESL To help students see how the Triangle Midsegment Theorem is being applied, ask leading questions, such as "Why did DeAndre not just measure the distance across the lake?" and "Why did he mark 35 paces on one side of the lake and 118 paces on the other side?"

TACTILE LEARNING If you have block scheduling or an extended class period, have students use straws or popsicle sticks to build a scale model of a swing set so that the "sides" of the swing set are isosceles triangles with a support bar at the midpoint of the sides of the triangles. Ask students to explain how they found the length of the support bar.

You can use the Triangle Midsegment Theorem to find lengths of segments that might otherwise be difficult to measure.

Example 2 **Relating to the Real World** ·················

Indirect Measurement DeAndre swims the length of a lake and wants to know the distance he swam. Here is what he does to find out.

Step 1: From the edge of the lake, he paces 35 strides and sets a stake.

Step 2: He paces 35 more strides in the same direction and sets another stake.

Step 3: He paces to the other end of the lake, counting 236 strides.

Step 4: He paces half the distance to the second stake (118 strides).

Step 5: He paces to the first stake, counting 128 strides.

If DeAndre's stride averages 3 ft, about how far did he swim?

$2(128 \text{ strides}) = 256 \text{ strides}$ Triangle Midsegment Theorem

$256 \text{ strides} \times \dfrac{3 \text{ ft}}{1 \text{ stride}} = 768 \text{ ft}$ Convert strides to feet.

DeAndre swam approximately 768 ft.

Exercises **O N   Y O U R   O W N**

Mental Math **Find the value of *x*.**

1.
9

2.
11

3.
31

Technology Options

For Exercise 5, students may use geometry software to plot the triangle and calculate the midpoints of the sides. For Exercise 7, students may draw the figure using geometry software and investigate the effects of transformations using transformation tools.

Prentice Hall Technology

Software
• Secondary Math Lab Toolkit™
• Integrated Math Lab 29
• Computer Item Generator 4-4

CD-ROM
• Multimedia Geometry Lab 4

Internet
• See the Prentice Hall site.
(http://www.phschool.com)

203

Exercise 4b Make sure that students find the perimeter of △HIJ and not △HFG.

Exercise 5b Because $\overline{HJ}$ and $\overline{EF}$ are neither horizontal nor vertical, students need to calculate their slopes to show that the two segments are parallel.

MAKING CONNECTIONS Exercise 6 The Rock and Roll Hall of Fame opened on September 1, 1995, in Cleveland, Ohio. Among its many exhibits are Buddy Holly's high school diploma, a 1968 leather stage outfit and a guitar once worn by Elvis, and John Lennon's Sergeant Pepper jacket.

ERROR ALERT! Exercise 7b Students may think only of the isometries. **Remediation:** Review the transformations studied in Chapter 3: reflections, translations, rotations, and dilations.

Exercise 8 An alternative activity is presented in the Toolbox on page 200, where students explore this problem using geometry software.

ALTERNATIVE ASSESSMENT Exercises 9–14 These exercises can help you assess students' understanding of the Triangle Midsegment Theorem by having students identify the midsegment and use it to find missing side lengths. Have students work in pairs or small groups.

---

pages 203–205   On Your Own

7a. Answers may vary. Sample:

b. Dilation with center *F* and scale factor $\frac{1}{2}$.

c. The triangles are ~.

4. $\overline{IJ}$ is a midsegment of △FGH.
   a. *IJ* = 7. Find *FG*. **14**
   b. *FH* = 13 and *GH* = 10. Find the perimeter of △HIJ. **18.5**

5. **Coordinate Geometry** The coordinates of the vertices of a triangle are E(1, 2), F(5, 6), and G(3, −2).
   a. Find the coordinates of *H*, the midpoint of $\overline{EG}$, and *J*, the midpoint of $\overline{FG}$. **H(2, 0); J(4, 2)**
   b. Verify that $\overline{HJ} \parallel \overline{EF}$. **slope of $\overline{HJ}$ = 1, slope of $\overline{EF}$ = 1 ✔**
   c. Verify that $HJ = \frac{1}{2}EF$. **$HJ = 2\sqrt{2}$, $EF = 4\sqrt{2}$, $HJ = \frac{1}{2}EF$**

6. **Architecture** The triangular face of the Rock and Roll Hall of Fame in Cleveland, Ohio, is isosceles. The length of the base is 229 ft 6 in. The face consists of smaller triangles determined by the midsegments. What is the length of the base of the highlighted triangle? **57 ft 4.5 in.**

7. a. Draw a triangle and label it △FST. Then draw the midsegment opposite $\overline{ST}$.
   b. **Transformational Geometry** Describe a transformation of △FST that produces the same diagram as in part (a).
   c. What does your answer to part (b) tell you about the triangles formed in part (a)? **See margin.**

8. **Open-ended** Draw a triangle and its three midsegments. Compare the four triangles determined by the midsegments. Repeat the experiment with a different triangle. Make a **conjecture** about your observations.
   Answers may vary. Sample: The 4 triangles are ≅.

Choose Use mental math, pencil and paper, or a calculator to find the values of the variables.

9.

60

10.

50

11.
10

12.

7.5

13.

45

14.

x = 6; y = 6.5

15. *Creative Arts* Marita is designing a kite for a competition. She plans to use a decorative ribbon to connect the midpoints of the sides of the kite. The diagonals of the kite measure 64 cm and 90 cm. Find the amount of ribbon she will need.   **154 cm**

16. *Preparing for Proof* This is a proof that the midsegments of an equilateral triangle form an equilateral triangle. The reasons given in the proof are correct, but they are in the wrong order. List them in the correct order.

    (1) e or g, (2) a or d, (3) b, (4) e or g, (5) f, (6) c, (7) a or d

    Given: Equilateral $\triangle JKL$ with midpoints T, U, and V

    Prove: $\triangle TUV$ is equilateral.

Statements	Reasons
1. $\triangle JKL$ is equilateral.	a. Def. of equilateral triangle
2. $JK = KL = JL$	b. Multiplication Prop. of Equality
3. $\frac{1}{2}JK = \frac{1}{2}KL = \frac{1}{2}JL$	c. Substitution
4. T, U, and V are midpoints.	d. Def. of equilateral triangle
5. $TU = \frac{1}{2}JK$; $UV = \frac{1}{2}JL$; $TV = \frac{1}{2}KL$	e. Given
6. $TU = UV = TV$	f. Triangle Midsegment Thm.
7. $\triangle TUV$ is equilateral.	g. Given

17. *Patterns* The vertices of the smallest square are the midpoints of the sides of the larger square. The vertices of that square are the midpoints of the largest square. Find the length of the sides of the largest square. Write a sentence or two explaining the pattern.

    1 cm

    17. **2 cm; the length of a side of the largest square = the length of the diagonal of the middle square. The length of the diagonal of that square is twice the length of the sides of the smallest square.**

Chapter Project **Find Out by Analyzing**

See margin.

Try your powers of logic on this new version of an old puzzle.

Alan, Ben, and Cal are seated as shown with their eyes closed. Three hats are placed on their heads from a box they know contains 3 red and 2 blue hats. They open their eyes and look forward.

Alan says, "I cannot deduce what color hat I'm wearing."

Hearing that, Ben says, "I cannot deduce what color I'm wearing, either."

Cal then says, "I know what color I'm wearing!"

How does Cal know what color his hat is? (*Hint*: Use one of the strategies you used to solve the previous two puzzles on pages 187 and 198.)

Alan   Ben   Cal

Find Out By Analyzing

Red; if Alan saw 2 blue hats, he would have known that he had a red hat. So at least 1 hat in front of him must be red. If Ben saw a blue hat, he would have known that he had a red hat. Cal's hat must not be blue.

Checkpoint   page 206

1a. If the measure of at least one of the angles of a triangle is 60, then the triangle is equilateral.

2a. If all the angles of a polygon are $\cong$, then the polygon is regular.

3. A converse reverses the hypothesis and the conclusion. The truth value of a converse does not depend on the truth value of the original statement. A contrapositive reverses and negates the hypothesis and the conclusion of the original statement. The truth values of a statement and its contrapositive are the same.

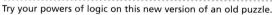

Students may want to make a table showing properties that apply to all triangles, then those that just apply to special triangles such as right triangles, isosceles triangles, and equilateral triangles.

GETTING READY FOR LESSON 4-5 These exercises prepare students to use indirect reasoning to write arguments.

Wrap Up

THE BIG IDEA Ask students: *Restate the Triangle Midsegment Theorem in your own words. Include a diagram and give an example of how it can be used to solve a problem.*

RETEACHING ACTIVITY Students draw triangles and find their midsegments. Then they use properties of midsegments to find the lengths of sides of the triangles. (Reteaching worksheet 4-4)

In this Checkpoint, your students will assess their own progress on Lessons 4-1 to 4-4.

STANDARDIZED TEST TIP Exercise 4 Students need to set different pairs of sides equal to see if there is a value of *x* that makes them the same length.

Lesson Quiz

Lesson Quiz is also available in Transparencies.

$\overline{DE}$ and $\overline{EF}$ are midsegments.
$DE = 7$ and $AB = 10$.

1. Find *AC*. 14

2. Find *EF*. 5

3. What is the perimeter of *ADEF*?
   24 units

4. What kind of quadrilateral is *ADEF*? parallelogram

206

Coordinate Geometry **Find the distance between the given points.**

18. $B(0, 9)$ and $E(4, 9)$ 4

19. $V(8, -7)$ and $W(4, -4)$ 5

20. $A(3, 2)$ and $N(-1, 0)$ $2\sqrt{5}$

21. Transformational Geometry State the coordinates of the point $(6, 2)$ after a rotation of 90° about the origin. $(-2, 6)$

22. Standardized Test Prep A circle and a square lie in a plane. What is the maximum number of points of intersection of the figures?
   A. one   **B.** two   **C.** four   **D.** six   **E.** eight
   E

Getting Ready for Lesson 4-5
Write the negation of each statement. 23–26. See right.

23. Lines *m* and *n* intersect.

24. The integer *x* is odd.

25. △*ABC* is scalene.

26. $\overline{AB} \parallel \overline{KM}$

27. A given angle is neither acute, right, nor obtuse. What is its measure? Explain how you know.
   180; it must be a straight angle.

23. Lines *m* and *n* do not intersect.
24. The integer *x* is even.
25. △*ABC* is isosceles.
26. $\overline{AB} \nparallel \overline{KM}$

Make a list of the properties of triangles you've learned so far in this chapter. Include a diagram to illustrate each property. Add to your list as you continue with the chapter.

For Exercises 1 and 2: (a) Write the converse of each conditional. 1a–2a. See margin p. 205.
(b) Determine the truth value of the conditional and its converse.
(c) If both statements are true, write a biconditional.

1. If a triangle is equilateral, then the measure of at least one of its angles is 60.
   1b. true; false

2. If a polygon is regular, then its angles are congruent.
   2b. true; false

3. Writing Explain the difference between a converse and a contrapositive. See margin p. 205.

4. Standardized Test Prep △*ABC* is isosceles, and $AC = 3x$, $AB = 2x + 30$, and $BC = 3x + 40$. Which of the following is true? C
   A. $\angle A \cong \angle B$ **B.** $\angle A \cong \angle C$ **C.** $\angle B \cong \angle C$
   D. $\angle A \cong \angle B \cong \angle C$ **E.** none of the above

5. The measures of the angles of a triangle are $6x$, $7x - 9$, and $8x$.
   a. Algebra Find the value of *x*. 9
   b. What are the measures of the angles? 54, 54, 72
   c. What type of triangle is this? Explain. Isosceles; the triangle has 2 ≅ angles.

6. Determine whether this statement is true or false: If a triangle is obtuse, then it is not isosceles. **Justify** your answer.
   See right.

6. False; a triangle with angles 30°, 30°, 120° is an obtuse isosceles triangle.

7. *M, N, O,* and *P* are midpoints of the sides of trapezoid *ABCD*. $AC = BD = 18$. Find the perimeter of *MNOP*. 36

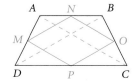

Olympic year. Olympics were not held in 1944 due to World War II. In 1896, women did not participate.)

PROBLEM OF THE DAY

A farmer has a large field with six hay stacks in one corner, half as many in another corner, twice as many in another corner, and four in a fourth corner. As the hay stacks are collected in the center of the field, one stack is scattered into the wind. How many hay stacks does the farmer have now? 24

Problem of the Day is also available in Transparencies.

CONNECTING TO PRIOR KNOWLEDGE Ask: *In which year did Elizabeth Robinson win the 100-meter dash in the Olympics?*
  a. *1935*   **b.** *1944*   **c.** *1928*   **d.** *1896*
Discuss how students can use indirect reasoning to narrow the possible answer choices down to c. (1935 was not an

THINK AND DISCUSS

VISUAL LEARNING Help students see that they used indirect reasoning to solve the Find Out by Organizing problem on page 198 by using X's to eliminate possibilities until only one possibility remained.

Example 1 | **Relating to the Real World**

ERROR ALERT! Students sometimes write the opposite of phrases such as "$25 or more" and "more than $20" as "$25 or less" and "no less than $20," respectively. **Remediation:** Help students see that, for example, "$25 or more" includes $25 as a possibility so its opposite should not.

Connections **Consumer Issues . . . and more**

What You'll Learn

• Writing convincing arguments by using indirect reasoning

...And Why

To help you in real-life situations in which proving something directly isn't possible

4-5 Using Indirect Reasoning

THINK AND DISCUSS

Suppose that your brother tells you, "Susan called a few minutes ago." You have two friends named Susan, and you know that one of them is at play rehearsal. You deduce that the other Susan must be the caller.

This type of reasoning is called indirect reasoning. In **indirect reasoning,** all possibilities are considered and then all but one are proved false. The remaining possibility must be true. Mathematical proofs involving indirect reasoning usually follow the pattern in the following example.

Example 1 | **Relating to the Real World**

Consumer Issues Use indirect reasoning to prove this statement: If Jaeleen spends more than $50 to buy two items at a bicycle shop, then at least one of the items costs more than $25.

Given: The cost of two items is more than $50.
Prove: At least one of the items costs more than $25.

bicycle helmet

bicycle safety light

■ Begin by assuming that the opposite of what you want to prove is true. That is, assume that neither item costs more than $25.

■ This means that both items cost $25 or less. This, in turn, means that the two items together cost $50 or less. This contradicts the given information that the amount spent is more than $50. So, the assumption that neither item costs more than $25 must be incorrect.

■ Therefore, at least one of the items costs more than $25.

Lesson Planning Options

Prerequisite Skills

• Writing the opposite of statements

Assignment Options for Exercises On Your Own

> **Core** 1–24
> **Extension** 25–27

Use Mixed Review to maintain skills.

Resources

📖 **Student Edition**
Skills Handbook, p. 650
Extra Practice, p. 637
Glossary/Study Guide

📦 **Teaching Resources**
Chapter Support File, Ch. 4
• Practice 4-5 (two worksheets)
• Reteaching 4-5
Classroom Manager 4-5
Glossary, Spanish Resources

🏛 **Transparencies**
53

207

Students may not feel as comfortable with the validity of indirect proofs as they do with direct proofs. Point out that the method of indirect proof is based on the fact that a statement is either true or false and that a statement cannot be true and false at the same time.

DIVERSITY Students with poor writing and organizational skills may be overwhelmed at the thought of writing an indirect proof. Have students write the explanation of each step in their own words on an index card. Then have them turn each index card over after writing that step in their proofs.

Example 2 ·······························

Some students have difficulty understanding the logic of indirect proof. Help these students understand why $m\angle N = 0$ means that $\triangle LMN$ does not exist so the assumption made is false.

Question 3 Help students set up a template on which to write their proofs. Label a paper with the key words "Given," "Prove," "Step 1," "Step 2," and "Step 3," and leave space for students to fill in the missing information.

Additional Examples

FOR EXAMPLE 1 ····························

Use indirect reasoning to prove this statement: If a movie was shown 25 times in seven days and was not shown more than four times in any one day, then it was shown at least once a day. **Given: A movie was shown 25 times in seven days and was not shown more than four times in any one day. Prove: The movie was shown at least once a day. Assume the movies was not shown at least once a day. This means that the movie was shown 25 times in six days or less. But this contradicts the given information that the movie was not shown more than four times a day (6 × 4 = 24). Therefore, the movie was shown at least once a day.**

Discussion: *Describe in your own words the steps you used to prove the statement.*

FOR EXAMPLE 2 ···························

Write an indirect proof to show that a pentagon cannot have more than four acute angles. See back of book.

Discussion: *What theorems did you use in your reasoning?*

1a. Assume that quadrilateral *TRWX* has four acute angles.
b. Assume the integer *n* is not divisible by 5.
c. Assume the shoes cost more than $20.

3. Assume that a ▭ with 3 rt. angles is not a rectangle. Then the 4th angle must be either obtuse or acute. If the angle is obtuse, then its measure is > 90 and the sum of the measures of the angles is > 360. If the angle is acute, then its measure is < 90 and the sum of the angle measures is < 360. Both cases contradict the fact that the sum of angle measures of a quadrilateral = 360. Therefore, the initial assumption is false. So a ▭ with 3 rt. angles must be a rectangle.

The three parts of the proof in Example 1 are summarized below.

Writing an Indirect Proof
··

Step 1: Assume that the opposite of what you want to prove is true.

Step 2: Use logical reasoning to reach a contradiction of an earlier statement, such as the given information or a theorem. Then state that the assumption you made was false.

Step 3: State that what you wanted to prove must be true.

1. Write the first step of an indirect proof of each statement.
   a. Quadrilateral *TRWX* does not have four acute angles.
   b. An integer *n* is divisible by 5.
   c. The shoes cost no more than $20.

2. Identify the pair of statements that form a contradiction.
   a. I. $\triangle ABC$ is acute. II and III   b. I. $m\angle 1 + m\angle 2 = 180$
       II. $\triangle ABC$ is scalene.   II. $m\angle 1 - m\angle 2 = m\angle 2$
       III. $\triangle ABC$ is equiangular.   III. $m\angle 1 \le m\angle 2$ II and III
   c. I. Both items that Val bought cost more than $10.
       II. Val spent $34 for the two items.   II and III
       III. Neither of the two items that Val bought cost more than $15.

Example 2 ·······························

Write an indirect proof.

Given: $\triangle LMN$
Prove: $\triangle LMN$ has at most one right angle.

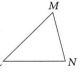

Indirect Proof

Step 1: Assume $\triangle LMN$ has more than one right angle. That is, assume that $\angle L$ and $\angle M$ are both right angles.

Step 2: If $\angle L$ and $\angle M$ are both right angles, then $m\angle L = m\angle M = 90$. According to the Triangle Angle-Sum Theorem, $m\angle L + m\angle M + m\angle N = 180$. Substitution gives $90 + 90 + m\angle N = 180$. Solving leaves $m\angle N = 0$. This means that there is no $\triangle LMN$, which contradicts the given statement. So the assumption that $\angle L$ and $\angle M$ are both right angles must be false.

Step 3: Therefore, $\triangle LMN$ has at most one right angle. ■

3. **Try This** Use indirect reasoning to show that a parallelogram with three right angles is a rectangle. See left above.

208

WORK TOGETHER

Have students keep a list of the questions asked and then discuss with the class the ones that best enable them to narrow down the answer.

Question 4 Have students describe strategies for asking questions and strategies for choosing a number that is harder to guess than others.

Exercises ON YOUR OWN

Exercises 5–6 Review with students the notation used to negate the math symbols $\cong$, $=$, $>$, $<$, and $\parallel$.

MAKING CONNECTIONS Exercise 11 The oldest drawbridge in the United States is the Missouri River Bridge in Omaha, Nebraska, built in 1893. The swing bridge is 519 ft long.

WORK TOGETHER

Play *What's My Number* in groups of three or four. Here's how to play.

- One member of the group chooses a number from 1 to 20.

- The remaining members ask yes-or-no questions about the number until they know what the number is.

- The person answering the questions records the number of questions required to guess the number.

Play the game at least three times, rotating roles with each game.

4. *Critical Thinking* Describe the best strategy for playing *What's My Number* to a friend who is just learning to play it.
   Answers may vary. Sample: At each step, divide the range of possible numbers as nearly in half as possible.

Technology Options

Prentice Hall Technology

Software
- Secondary Math Lab Toolkit™
- Computer Item Generator 4-5

Internet
- See the Prentice Hall site. (http://www.phschool.com)

Exercises ON YOUR OWN

Write the first step of an indirect proof of each statement.

1. It is raining outside.
   Assume it is not raining outside.

2. $\angle J$ is not a right angle.
   Assume $\angle J$ is a rt. angle.

3. $\triangle PEN$ is isosceles.
   Assume $\triangle PEN$ is scalene.

4. At least one angle is obtuse.
   Assume none of the angles is obtuse.

5. $\overline{XY} \cong \overline{AB}$
   Assume $\overline{XY} \not\cong \overline{AB}$.

6. $m\angle 2 > 90$
   Assume $m\angle 2 \leq 90$.

Identify the pair of statements that forms a contradiction.

7. **I.** $\triangle PQR$ is equilateral.
   II. $\triangle PQR$ is a right triangle.
   III. $\triangle PQR$ is isosceles.
   I and II

8. **I.** $ABCD$ is a parallelogram.
   II. $ABCD$ is a trapezoid.
   III. $ABCD$ has two acute angles.
   I and II

9. **I.** ℓ and m are skew.
   II. ℓ and m do not intersect.
   III. ℓ is parallel to m.
   I and III

10. **I.** $\overline{FG} \parallel \overline{KL}$
    II. $\overline{FG} \perp \overline{KL}$
    III. $\overline{FG} \cong \overline{KL}$
    I and II

What conclusion follows from each pair of statements?

11. There are three types of drawbridges: bascule, lift, and swing. This drawbridge does not swing or lift.
    This bridge is a bascule.

12. If this were the day of the party, our friends would be home. No one is home.
    The party is not today.

13. Every air traffic controller in the world speaks English on the job. Sumiko does not speak English.
    Sumiko is not an air traffic controller.

14. If two nonvertical lines are perpendicular, then the product of their slopes is -1. The product of the slopes of nonvertical lines ℓ and n is not -1.
    The lines ℓ and n are not $\perp$.

Exercise 15 You may want to allow time for students to share their proofs with partners. Then have students revise their proofs based on the comments received from their partners.

Exercises 19–22 For students having difficulty writing indirect proofs, you may want to provide an outline as in Exercise 16 and have students fill in the blanks.

ALTERNATIVE ASSESSMENT **Exercises 23–24** These exercises help you assess students' ability to write an indirect proof. Have students work with a partner and suggest that they model the proof given in Example 2.

CONNECTING TO STUDENTS' WORLD **Exercise 25** Have students work in groups to create a similar story problem. They can make themselves or their friends the characters in the problem and use familiar locations.

---

pages 209–211 On Your Own

19. Assume that the driver had not applied the brakes. Then the wheels would not have locked and there would be no skid marks. There are skid marks. Therefore, the assumption is false. The driver had applied the brakes.

20. If the temp. outside is above 32°F, water on the sidewalk cannot freeze. There is ice forming on the sidewalk. Therefore, the assumption is false. The temp. is 32°F or below.

21. Assume the polygon is a hexagon. Then the sum of measures of its interior angles is 720. But the sum of measures of the polygon's interior angles is 900, not 720. Therefore, the assumption is false. The polygon is not a hexagon.

22. Assume a quadrilateral has 4 acute angles. The measure of each acute angle is < 90. Then the sum of the measures of the angles is < 360. The sum of interior angles of a quadrilateral = 360. Therefore, the assumption is false. A quadrilateral cannot have more than 3 acute angles.

210

15. Given △*ABC* with *BC* > *AC*, use indirect reasoning to show that ∠*A* ≇ ∠*B*. **Assume ∠*A* ≅ ∠*B*. Then △*ABC* is isosceles with *BC* = *AC*. This contradicts the assumption. Therefore, ∠*A* ≇ ∠*B*.**

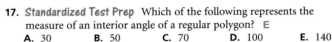

16. *Preparing for Proof* Complete this indirect proof that every quadrilateral contains at least one right or acute angle.

Assume that a quadrilateral does not contain **a.** ? . That is, assume that the measure of each of the angles is greater than **b.** ? . The sum of the measures of the four angles, then, is greater than **c.** ? . By the **d.** ? Theorem, however, the sum of the measures of the interior angles of a quadrilateral is **e.** ? . This contradicts **f.** ? , so the assumption that **g.** ? is false. Therefore, **h.** ? .

a. a rt. or acute angle b. 90
c. 360 d. Polygon Interior Angle-Sum e. 360
f. preceding statement
g. a quadrilateral does not contain an acute or a rt. angle
h. a quadrilateral contains at least one rt. or acute angle

17. *Standardized Test Prep* Which of the following represents the measure of an interior angle of a regular polygon? **E**
  A. 30   **B.** 50   **C.** 70   **D.** 100   **E.** 140

18. Earlene lives near a noisy construction site at which work ends promptly at 5:00 each weekday. Earlene thinks, "Today is Tuesday. If it were before 5:00, I would hear construction noise, but I don't hear any. So it must be later than 5:00."
  a. What does Earlene prove? **It is later than 5:00.**
  b. What assumption does she make? **It is before 5:00.**
  c. What fact contradicts the assumption? **She does not hear any noise from the construction site.**

> *PROBLEM SOLVING HINT*
> Use indirect reasoning. Eliminate all incorrect answer choices. The remaining choice must be correct.

For Exercises 19–25, write a convincing argument that uses indirect reasoning. 19–22. See margin.   23–24. See back of book.

19. Fresh skid marks appear behind a green car at the scene of an accident. Show that the driver of the green car applied the brakes.

20. Ice is forming on the sidewalk in front of Toni's house. Show that the temperature outside must be 32°F or less.

21. The sum of the measures of the interior angles of a polygon is 900. Show that the polygon is not a hexagon.

22. Show that a quadrilateral can have at most three acute angles.

23. An obtuse triangle cannot contain a right angle.

Given: △*PQR* with obtuse ∠*Q*
Prove: *m*∠*P* ≠ 90

24. If a triangle is isosceles, then a base angle is not a right angle.

Given: $\overline{BC} \cong \overline{AC}$
Prove: ∠*B* is not a right angle.

25. Mr. Pitt is a suspect in a robbery. Here are the facts:
  ■ A robbery occurred in Charlotte, North Carolina, at 1:00 A.M. on April 9.
  ■ A hotel clerk in Maine saw Mr. Pitt at 12:05 A.M. on April 9.
  ■ Mr. Pitt has an identical twin brother who was in Chicago during the time the robbery took place.
  ■ Mr. Pitt has receipts for purchases made in Maine on April 8.

  Show that Mr. Pitt was not the robber.

Mr. Pitt was in Maine on April 8 and stayed there at least until 12:05 A.M. Assume Mr. Pitt is the robber. Then he took < 55 min to travel from Maine to Charlotte. It is not possible to travel from Maine to Charlotte in 55 min or less. Therefore, Mr. Pitt is not the robber.

Exercise 32a When students use the terms to write six conditionals, they will not all be true.

Exercise 33 Students may want to draw a diagram of the transformation. They can use any isometry, but suggest that a translation is the easiest.

GETTING READY FOR LESSON 4-6 These exercises prepare students to solve problems using inequalities involving triangle side lengths.

THE BIG IDEA Ask students: *Explain in your own words the three steps of writing an indirect proof.*

RETEACHING ACTIVITY Students use indirect reasoning to arrange the statements of an indirect proof in the correct order. Then they write an indirect proof. (Reteaching worksheet 4-5)

---

26. Open-ended Describe a real-life situation in which you used an indirect argument to convince someone of your point of view. Outline your argument. Check students' work.

27. Mysteries In Arthur Conan Doyle's story "The Sign of the Four," Sherlock Holmes talks to his sidekick Watson about how a culprit enters a room that has only four entrances: a door, a window, a chimney, and a hole in the roof.

"You will not apply my precept," he said, shaking his head. "How often have I said to you that when you have eliminated the impossible, whatever remains, *however improbable,* must be the truth? We know that he did not come through the door, the window, or the chimney. We also know that he could not have been concealed in the room, as there is no concealment possible. Whence, then, did he come?"

How did the culprit enter the room? Explain.
The hole in the roof; of 5 possibilities, 4 have been eliminated.

28–31. Answers may vary. Samples are given.
Geometry in 3 Dimensions **Refer to the diagram for Exercises 28–31.**

28. Name two parallel planes.
ABCD and *EFGH*
29. Name two intersecting planes.
ABCD and *BCFG*
30. Name two skew lines.
$\overleftrightarrow{AB}$ and $\overleftrightarrow{DE}$
31. Name four coplanar points.
A, B, C, and *D*

32. a. Use the words *square, rhombus,* and *parallelogram* to write six conditionals in the form "If a figure is a __?__, then it is a __?__."
  b. Probability What is the probability that a conditional chosen at random from among the six is true? $\frac{1}{2}$
  c. Probability What is the probability that the converse of a randomly chosen statement from part (a) is true? $\frac{1}{2}$
  d. Probability What is the probability that the contrapositive of a randomly chosen statement from part (a) is true? $\frac{1}{2}$

a. See back of book.

33. Transformational Geometry An isometry maps *LEFT* ⟶ *BURN*. Which statement is *not* necessarily true? B
  A. *EF = UR*   **B.** ∠*TLE* ≅ ∠*BUR*   **C.** ∠*F* ≅ ∠*R*
  D. *LF = BR*   **E.** *FT = RN*

Getting Ready for Lesson 4-6

Coordinate Geometry **Graph the triangles whose vertices are given. List the sides in order from shortest to longest.**

34. *A*(5, 0), *B*(0, 8), *C*(0, 0)
AC, BC, AB
35. *P*(2, 4), *Q*(−5, 1), *R*(0, 0)
PR, QR, PQ
36. *G*(3, 0), *H*(4, 3), *J*(8, 0)
GH, HJ ≅ GJ

Lesson Quiz

Lesson Quiz is also available in Transparencies.

1. Identify the pair of statements that forms a contradiction.
  I. $m\angle A + m\angle B = 90$
  II. ∠*A* and ∠*B* are acute
  III. △*ABC* is an acute triangle.
  I and III

2. What conclusion can you draw from the following pair of statements? If the sum of the measures of two angles is 90, the angles are complementary. The measure of one of two angles is 100. The angles are not complementary.

3. Write a convincing argument that uses indirect reasoning to show $\sqrt{10} \neq 5$. Assume $\sqrt{10} = 5$. Then $\sqrt{10}^2 = 5^2$ and 10 = 25. But 10 ≠ 25, so $\sqrt{10} \neq 5$.

211

Students review how to use the Properties of Inequality to solve inequalities containing variables. Students will use these skills to solve problems about triangle side lengths and angle measures in Lesson 4-6.

Review the Properties of Inequality with students. Give several examples using numerical values for *a*, *b*, *c*, and *d*. Remind students that the Addition Property shows subtraction $(a - b = a + (-b))$ and the Multiplication Property shows division $\left(\frac{a}{b} = a\left(\frac{1}{b}\right)\right)$.

ERROR ALERT! Students sometimes change the direction of the inequality sign when they add or subtract a negative number from both sides. **Remediation:** Use a number line to illustrate that subtracting positive and negative numbers from both sides of an inequality does not change the direction of the inequality sign.

Example

Have students check the solution by picking values less than 3 and substituting them into the original inequality.

ADDITIONAL PROBLEM Have students make up an inequality similar to those in the exercises for each of the following solutions: $x < -3$, $x < \frac{1}{2}$, $x \le 20$, and $x \ge -14$.

Math ToolboX — Algebra Review

Solving Inequalities

Before Lesson 4-6

The solutions of an inequality are all the numbers that make the inequality true. Below is a review of the Properties of Inequality. To solve inequalities you will use the Addition and Multiplication Properties of Inequality.

Properties of Inequality

For all real numbers *a*, *b*, *c*, and *d*:

Addition	If $a > b$ and $c \ge d$, then $a + c > b + d$.
Multiplication	If $a > b$ and $c > 0$, then $ac > bc$. If $a > b$ and $c < 0$, then $ac < bc$.
Transitive	If $a > b$ and $b > c$, then $a > c$.
Comparison	If $a = b + c$ and $c > 0$, then $a > b$.

Example

Solve $-6x + 7 > 25$.

$-6x + 7 - 7 > 25 - 7$ ← Add −7 to each side (or subtract 7 from each side).

$\frac{-6x}{-6} < \frac{18}{-6}$ ← Multiply each side by $-\frac{1}{6}$ (or divide each side by −6). Remember to reverse the order of the inequality.

$x < -3$ ← Simplify.

Solve each inequality.

1. $7x - 13 \le -20$ $x \le -1$
2. $3z + 8 > 16$ $z > 2\frac{2}{3}$
3. $-2x + 5 < 16$ $x > -5\frac{1}{2}$
4. $8y + 2 \ge -14$ $y \ge -2$
5. $5a + 1 \le 91$ $a \le 18$
6. $-x - 2 > 17$ $x < -19$
7. $-4z - 10 < -12$ $z > \frac{1}{2}$
8. $9x - 8 \ge 82$ $x \ge 10$
9. $6n + 3 \le -18$ $n \le -3\frac{1}{2}$
10. $c + 13 > 34$ $c > 21$
11. $3x - 5x + 2 < 12$ $x > -5$
12. $x - 19 < -78$ $x < -59$
13. $-n - 27 \le 92$ $n \ge -119$
14. $-9t + 47 < 101$ $t > -6$
15. $8x - 4 + x > -76$ $x > -8$
16. $2(y - 5) > -24$ $y > -7$
17. $8b + 3 \ge 67$ $b \ge 8$
18. $-3(4x - 1) \ge 15$ $x \le -1$
19. $r - 9 \le -67$ $r \le -58$
20. $\frac{1}{2}(4x - 7) \ge 19$ $x \ge 11\frac{1}{4}$
21. $5x - 3x + 2x < -20$ $x < -5$
22. $9x - 10x + 4 < 12$ $x > -8$
23. $-3x - 7x \le 97$ $x \ge -9.7$
24. $8y - 33 > -1$ $y > 4$
25. $4a + 17 \ge 13$ $a \ge -1$
26. $-4(5z + 2) > 20$ $z < -1\frac{2}{5}$
27. $x + 78 \ge -284$ $x \ge -362$

CONNECTING TO PRIOR KNOWLEDGE Have students solve each of the following inequalities for *x*. Then have volunteers present their solutions to the class.

$$3x - 7 < 5 \qquad -2x + 4 < 6 \qquad \frac{x}{4} + 5 > 1$$

As students try to form triangles, emphasize that the ends of the straws must meet. Provide the following illustration to point out what is not considered a triangle.

ALTERNATIVE METHOD Have students use a compass or drawing software to try to construct triangles with different combinations of the lengths, keeping track of their results in a table.

What You'll Learn

- Using inequalities involving triangle side lengths and angle measures to solve problems

...And Why

To use triangle inequalities in solving real-world problems when only some measures of a triangle are known

What You'll Need

scissors, straws, ruler, protractor

Connections 🌐 Architecture . . . and more

4-6 Triangle Inequalities

W O R K   T O G E T H E R

Work in groups of three. Have each member of your group cut straws into 2-, 3-, 4-, 5-, and 6-in. segments.

■ Have each member pick three segments at random and test whether they form a triangle. Continue picking segments until you find three sets of segments that form a triangle and three that do not form a triangle. Record your results in a table like the one shown.

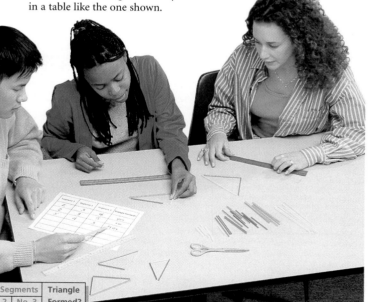

Lengths of Segments			Triangle Formed?
No. 1	No. 2	No. 3	
2	3	4	Yes
2	3	5	No
5	4	3	Yes

1. Pick a row of data that yields a triangle. Compare each quantity.
   a. Segment 1 + Segment 2 _?_ Segment 3
   b. Segment 1 + Segment 3 _?_ Segment 2   >
   c. Segment 2 + Segment 3 _?_ Segment 1   >

2. Pick a row of data that does *not* yield a triangle. Use it to complete parts (a)–(c) of Question 1.
   >, >, and =, or >, >, and < (in any order)

3. **Patterns** Compare the results of Questions 1 and 2 within your group. Look for a pattern. Write a **conjecture** about the sum of the lengths of two sides of a triangle compared to the length of the third side.

3. The sum of the lengths of any two sides of △ is > the length of the 3rd side.

213

Question 4 Ask students for other real-world examples where they applied the Triangle Inequality Theorem without knowing it. For example, ask them if they have ever crossed a street diagonally.

Question 6 Point out that the letters *a, b, c, A, B,* and *C* are positioned on the triangle so that *a* is opposite ∠*A, b* is opposite ∠*B,* and *c* is opposite ∠*C.*

Question 7 Challenge students to test their conjectures by trying to draw counterexamples.

Example 1

Help students understand that they do not have to check all combinations of sides. Checking that the sum of the lengths of the shorter two sides is greater than the length of the third side is sufficient.

Additional Examples

FOR EXAMPLE 1

Is it possible for a triangle to have sides with the given lengths? Explain.
a. 2 in., 5 in., 8 in. No; 2 + 5 ≯ 8.
b. 4 m, 6 m, 9 m Yes; 4 + 6 > 9, 6 + 9 > 4, and 4 + 9 > 6.

Discussion: *Describe how you could change the lengths in part a so a triangle could be formed.*

FOR EXAMPLE 2

A landscape architect is designing a triangular deck with sides 15 ft, 12 ft, and 18 ft. She wants to place flowering plants in the corner with the smallest angle. In which corner should she place the plants? **The corner opposite the 12-ft side**

Discussion: *Describe possible lengths of a triangle where the shortest side is 15 ft.*

THINK AND DISCUSS

Part 1 Triangle Inequality Theorem

Your observations from the Work Together suggest the following theorem.

Theorem 4-9	The sum of the lengths of any two sides of a triangle is greater than the length of the third side.
Triangle Inequality Theorem	$XY + YZ > XZ$ $YZ + XZ > XY$ $XZ + XY > YZ$

4. Use the Triangle Inequality Theorem to explain which route is the shortest distance from House A to House B.
   See margin p. 216.

Example 1

Is it possible for a triangle to have sides with the given lengths? Explain.

a. 3 cm, 7 cm, and 8 cm
$3 + 7 > 8$
$8 + 7 > 3$
$3 + 8 > 7$ **Yes**

b. 3 ft, 6 ft, and 10 ft
$3 + 6 \not> 10$ **No**

The sum of any two numbers in (a) is greater than the third number. In part (b), the sum of 3 and 6 is less than 10.

5. **Try This** Is it possible to form a triangle with side lengths 4 cm, 6 cm, and 10 cm? Explain.
   no; 4 + 6 ≯ 10

Part 2 WORK TOGETHER

Work in groups of three. Have each member of your group draw a large scalene triangle. Label each triangle as shown. Include right, obtuse, and acute triangles.

■ Measure the sides and angles of each triangle.
   Answers may vary. Sample:

6. **a.** Use the letters *A, B,* and *C* to complete:
   $m\angle\blacksquare < m\angle\blacksquare < m\angle\blacksquare$. *C, A, B*
   b. Use the letters *a, b,* and *c* to complete:
   $\blacksquare < \blacksquare < \blacksquare$. *c, a, b*

7. Compare your answer to Question 6 with others in your group. Make a **conjecture** about the longest side and the largest angle in a triangle.
   In a triangle, the angle with the least measure is opp. the shortest side. The angle with the greatest measure is opp. the longest side.

Example 2   Relating to the Real World

ERROR ALERT! **Theorem 4-10** Students may confuse the side opposite an angle with a side adjacent to the angle. **Remediation:** Have students copy △XYZ as shown in the text and use colored pencils to color-code each angle and its opposite side.

TACTILE LEARNING Have students create a flexible triangle using two popsicle sticks held together at one end by a brad and at the other end by an elastic band to make the third side. Students can manipulate the length of the side made by the elastic band and observe how the measure of the angle opposite it changes.

Question 8 Have students construct a triangle with the given side length and measure the angles to check their answers.

Theorem 4-11 Point out to students that the negation of $BC > AC$ is $BC = AC$ or $BC < AC$. Both cases need to be proven false in the indirect proof.

T H I N K   A N D   D I S C U S S

Inequalities Relating Sides and Angles

Your observations in the Work Together lead to Theorems 4-10 and 4-11.

Theorem 4-10

If two sides of a triangle are not congruent, then the larger angle lies opposite the longer side.

If $XZ > XY$, then $m\angle Y > m\angle Z$.

You will justify Theorem 4-10 in Exercise 35.

Example 2 Relating to the Real World

Architecture A landscape architect is designing a triangular deck. She wants to place benches in the two largest corners. In which corners should she place the benches?

The two largest corners are opposite the two longest sides, 27 ft and 21 ft.

8. Try This The sides of a triangle are 14 in., 7 in., and 8 in. long. The smallest angle is opposite which side? **7 in.**

Theorem 4-11

If two angles of a triangle are not congruent, then the longer side lies opposite the larger angle.

Indirect Proof of Theorem 4-11

Given: $m\angle A > m\angle B$
Prove: $BC > AC$

Step 1: Assume $BC \not> AC$. That is, assume $BC < AC$ or $BC = AC$.

Step 2: If $BC < AC$, then $m\angle A < m\angle B$ (Theorem 4-10). That contradicts the given fact that $m\angle A > m\angle B$. Therefore, the assumption that $BC < AC$ must be false.

If $BC = AC$, then $m\angle A = m\angle B$ (Isosceles Triangle Theorem). This also contradicts the given fact that $m\angle A > m\angle B$. Therefore the assumption that $BC = AC$ must be false.

Step 3: Therefore, $BC > AC$ must be true.

Technology Options

For Exercises 1–8, students may use geometry software to try to construct each triangle. For Exercise 25, students may perform the activity described using geometry software.

Prentice Hall Technology

Software
• Secondary Math Lab Toolkit™
• Computer Item Generator 4-6

CD-ROM
• Multimedia Geometry Lab 4

Internet
• See the Prentice Hall site.
(http://www.phschool.com)

215

Example 3 ....

VISUAL LEARNING To help students see that Theorem 4-10 and 4-11 only apply to one triangle, draw $\triangle XYZ$ similar to $\triangle TUV$. Show that $\angle U < \angle Z$ does not imply that $\overline{TV} < \overline{XY}$.

ALTERNATIVE ASSESSMENT Exercises 1–8 These exercises can be used to assess students' understanding of the Triangle Inequality Theorem. Have students work with partners to suggest a change to one of the side lengths where a triangle cannot be formed so that a triangle can be formed.

Exercises 13–14 Students may need to sketch and label each triangle in order to recognize which segment is opposite each angle.

GEOMETRY IN 3 DIMENSIONS Exercise 22 If possible, provide students with a three-dimensional model of a pyramid to manipulate.

---

page 214   Think and Discuss

4. Willow Lane; the length of Willow Lane is less than the sum of lengths of First St. and Second Ave. Also, the length of Willow Lane between Third St. and K St. is less than the sum of the lengths of Third St. and K St.

pages 216–218   On Your Own

22. Answers may vary. Sample: For $\triangle PTB$. $\angle T$ is a rt. angle, so the other 2 angles are acute. Then the side opp. $\angle T$ is the longest side in the $\triangle$. Therefore, $PT < PB$. Similarly, PT is $<$ the length of each of the other 3 sides.

Example 3

In $\triangle TUV$, which side is shortest?

By the Triangle Angle-Sum Theorem, $m\angle T = 60$. The smallest angle in $\triangle TUV$ is $\angle U$. Therefore, by Theorem 4-11, the shortest side is $\overline{TV}$.

Is it possible for a triangle to have sides with the given lengths? Explain.

1. 2 in., 3 in., 6 in.   2. 11 cm, 12 cm, 15 cm   3. 6 ft, 10 ft, 13 ft   4. 8 m, 10 m, 19 m
   no; 2 + 3 ≯ 6   no; 8 + 10 ≯ 19
5. 2 yd, 9 yd, 10 yd   6. 4 m, 7 m, 9 m   7. 5 in., 5 in., 5 in.   8. 1 cm, 15 cm, 15 cm

2–3, 5–8. Yes; the length of each segment is $<$ the sum of the lengths of the other 2.

List the sides of each triangle in order from shortest to longest.

9.

10.

11.

12.

$\overline{MN}, \overline{ON}, \overline{OM}$ $\overline{FH}, \overline{FG}, \overline{GH}$ $\overline{TU}, \overline{UV}, \overline{TV}$ $\overline{YZ}, \overline{XY}, \overline{XZ}$

13. $\triangle ARK$, where $m\angle A = 90$, $m\angle R = 40$, and $m\angle K = 50$
    $\overline{AK}, \overline{AR}, \overline{KR}$

14. $\triangle INK$, where $m\angle I = 20$, $m\angle N = 120$, and $m\angle K = 40$
    $\overline{KN}, \overline{IN}, \overline{IK}$

List the angles of each triangle in order from smallest to largest.

15.

16.

17.

18.

$\angle Q, \angle R, \angle S$ $\angle M, \angle L, \angle K$ $\angle G, \angle H, \angle I$ $\angle D, \angle C, \angle E$

19. $\triangle ABC$, where $AB = 8$, $BC = 5$, and $AC = 7$
    $\angle A, \angle B, \angle C$

20. $\triangle DEF$, where $DE = 15$, $EF = 18$, and $DF = 5$
    $\angle E, \angle F, \angle D$

21. $\triangle XYZ$, where $XY = 2$, $YZ = 4$, and $XZ = 3$
    $\angle Z, \angle Y, \angle X$

22. Geometry in 3 Dimensions Refer to the pyramid shown. Explain why the altitude, $\overline{PT}$, must be shorter than edges $\overline{PA}$, $\overline{PB}$, $\overline{PC}$, and $\overline{PD}$. See margin.

23. Probability A student picks two straws, one 6 cm long and the other 9 cm long. She picks another straw at random from a group of four straws whose lengths are 3 cm, 5 cm, 11 cm, and 15 cm. What is the probability that the straw she picks will allow her to form a triangle? $\frac{1}{2}$

24. Standardized Test Prep Compare the quantities in Columns A and B. Select the best answer. **A**

Column A	Column B
a	b

A. The quantity in Column A is greater.
B. The quantity in Column B is greater.
C. The quantities are equal.
D. The relationship cannot be determined from the information given.

25. Technology Darren used geometry software to draw $\triangle ACF$ and $\triangle DEH$ so that $\overline{AC} \cong \overline{DE}$ and $\overline{AF} \cong \overline{DH}$. He then manipulated point H to collect the data in the spreadsheet. $<,<; <,<; <,<; >,>; >,>$
a. Compare these values for each row of the spreadsheet.
  $m\angle FAC$ __?__ $m\angle HDE$ FC __?__ HE
b. Patterns What pattern do you notice in part (a)?
c. The pattern that you noticed is stated as the Hinge Theorem. Complete the theorem:
  Hinge Theorem *If two sides of one triangle are congruent to two sides of another triangle, and the included angle of the first triangle is greater than the included angle of the second triangle, then __?__ .*
  b–c. See margin.

	∠FAC	∠HDE	FC	HE
1	58.3	104.3	3.21	4.98
2	58.3	94.2	3.21	4.64
3	58.3	65.2	3.21	3.50
4	58.3	50.7	3.21	2.88
5	58.3	34.7	3.21	2.18

26. Critical Thinking Pliers, scissors, and many other tools are hinged. When the angle between the blades of a pair of scissors increases, what happens to the distance between the tips of the blades? Explain how this relates to the Hinge Theorem in Exercise 25. **See margin.**

27. Critical Thinking The Shau family is crossing Kansas on Highway 70. A sign reads "Topeka 110 miles, Wichita 90 miles." Avi says, "I didn't know that it was only 20 miles from Topeka to Wichita." Explain to Avi why the distance between the two cities doesn't have to be 20 miles. **The 2 cities may not be both straight ahead. For instance, Topeka might be 110 mi east, and Wichita might be 90 mi south.**

Critical Thinking Which segment is the shortest?

28.
$\overline{RS}$

29.
$\overline{CD}$

30.
$\overline{XY}$

The lengths of two sides of a triangle are given. Write an inequality to represent the range of values for z, the length of the third side.

31. 8 ft, 12 ft
  $4 < z < 20$

32. 5 in., 16 in.
  $11 < z < 21$

33. 6 cm, 6 cm
  $0 < z < 12$

34. x, y, where $x \geq y$
  $x - y < z < x + y$

217

Exercise 36 Students may have already been using this corollary unconsciously when measuring the distance between a point and a line.

Exercises   MIXED REVIEW

Exercise 37 Students can use a graph to find the coordinates of S' and Y' or find the direction vector and add its coordinates to the coordinates of S and Y.

JOURNAL Encourage students to do more than just restate the theorems. Ask them to explain in their own words the key points in the lesson, and to organize them in a way that makes most sense to them.

GETTING READY FOR LESSON 4-7 These exercises prepare students for solving locus problems.

Wrap Up

THE BIG IDEA Ask students: *Suppose you are asked to make a triangle with side lengths 5 cm, 12 cm, and 13 cm. Is it possible? If yes, explain which angle would be the largest.*

RETEACHING ACTIVITY Each student draws an obtuse, an acute, and an equilateral triangle. Then each student exchanges triangles with a partner and describes the relationship between the sides and angles of the partner's triangles. (Reteaching worksheet 4-6)

Lesson Quiz

Lesson Quiz is also available in Transparencies.

1. Is it possible for a triangle to have sides with lengths 5 ft, 8 ft, and 2 ft? Explain. **No, by the Triangle Inequality Theorem, the sum of the lengths of any two sides of a triangle is greater than the length of the third side. $5 + 2 < 8$ so a triangle cannot be formed.**

2. $m\angle B = 60$, $m\angle K = 20$, and $m\angle R = 100$. List the sides of $\triangle BKR$ in order from the shortest to the longest. $\overline{BR}, \overline{KR}, \overline{BK}$

3. $GT = 5$, $TE = 8$, and $GE = 12$. List the angles of $\triangle GTE$ in order from smallest to largest. $\angle E, \angle G, \angle T$

218

35. **Preparing for Proof** Theorem 4-10 states: If two sides of a triangle are not congruent, then the larger angle lies opposite the longer side. To prove this theorem, begin with $\triangle TOY$, with $OY > TY$. Find P on $\overline{OY}$ so that $\overline{TY} \cong \overline{PY}$. Draw $\overline{TP}$. Supply a reason for each statement.

Given: $OY > TY$ and $\overline{TY} \cong \overline{PY}$

Prove: $m\angle OTY > m\angle 3$

Statements	Reasons
1. $\overline{YP} \cong \overline{YT}$	a. __?__ Given
2. $m\angle 1 = m\angle 2$	b. __?__ Isosceles Triangle Thm.
3. $m\angle OTY = m\angle 4 + m\angle 2$	c. __?__ Angle Addition Post.
4. $m\angle OTY > m\angle 2$	4. Comparison Prop. of Ineq. (p. 212)
5. $m\angle OTY > m\angle 1$	d. __?__ Substitution
6. $m\angle 1 = m\angle 3 + m\angle 4$	e. __?__ Exterior Angle Thm.
7. $m\angle 1 > m\angle 3$	7. Comparison Prop. of Ineq.
8. $m\angle OTY > m\angle 3$	f. __?__ Transitive Prop. of Inequality

36. **Logical Reasoning** A corollary to Theorem 4-11 states: The perpendicular segment from a point to a line is the shortest segment from the point to the line. Show that $PA > PT$, given that $\overline{PT} \perp \overline{TA}$. See margin p. 217.

Exercises   MIXED REVIEW

37. **Transformational Geometry** $\triangle SKY$ has vertices $S(-1, 0)$, $K(3, 8)$, and $Y(5, 4)$. A translation maps K to $K'(2, 1)$. Find the coordinates of the images of S and Y under this translation. $S'(-2, -7)$, $Y'(4, -3)$

38. **Open-ended** Use a rhombus to create a tessellation. See below right.

39. Find the measure of an interior angle and an exterior angle of a regular 15-gon. **156; 24**

Getting Ready for Lesson 4-7

Describe the set of red points in terms of their distance from the set of blue points.

40.

41.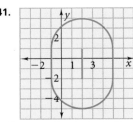

The set of red pts. is 3 units from the set of blue pts.

The set of red pts. is 3 units from the set of blue pts.

FOR YOUR JOURNAL

Write a summary of the key points of this lesson. Include diagrams with your summary where appropriate.

38.

CONNECTING TO PRIOR KNOWLEDGE Have students describe all the objects that are one foot away and six feet away from them. Make sure they describe objects in all directions including above and below them.

Have students work with a partner. One students can do the drawing and measuring and the other can record the answers to the questions.

EXTENSION Have students review the triangles they drew in the Work Together. Ask them to explain the relationship between the location of the vertex on the perpendicular bisector and the angles of the triangle.

ESL **Question 6** As students write the biconditional, check that they understand the meaning of the term "equidistant." They may want to rewrite this word as "equally distant."

What You'll Learn

• Using properties of angle bisectors and perpendicular bisectors
• Solving locus problems

...And Why

To learn methods used by circuit designers and many other professionals who solve problems in which stated conditions must be met

What You'll Need

straightedge, compass, ruler, MIRA™

TECHNOLOGY HINT

The Work Together could be done using geometry software.

4b. To construct the ⊥ bisector of a segment, you find 2 pts. that are equidistant from the endpts. The line through these pts. is the ⊥ bisector.

6. A pt. is on the ⊥ bisector of a segment if and only if it is equidistant from the endpts. of the segment.

Theorem 4-12
Perpendicular Bisector Theorem

Theorem 4-13
Converse of Perpendicular Bisector Theorem

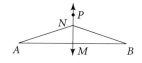

Connections   Landmarks . . . and more

4-7 Bisectors and Locus

WORK TOGETHER

■ Draw a segment and construct its perpendicular bisector by using a straightedge and a compass or a MIRA™.

■ Draw a point on the perpendicular bisector and then draw segments connecting this point to the endpoints of the segment.

1. Compare the lengths of the segments. What do you notice?
   The lengths are =.
2. Repeat this process with some other points. Does what you noticed still hold true? *yes*

3. Use what you discovered to complete this statement: If a point is on the perpendicular bisector of a segment, then   ? .
   it is equidistant from the endpts. of the segment
4. **a.** Write the converse of the statement you completed in Question 3.
   b. Explain how the converse is related to the method you use to construct a perpendicular bisector.   *See left.*
   4a. If a point is equidistant from the endpts. of a segment, then it is on the ⊥ bisector of the segment.

THINK AND DISCUSS

Part 1   Perpendicular Bisectors and Locus

The properties you discovered in the Work Together are summarized in the following theorems.

If a point is on the perpendicular bisector of a segment, then it is equidistant from the endpoints of the segment.

If a point is equidistant from the endpoints of a segment, then it is on the perpendicular bisector of the segment.

N is a pt. on the ⊥ bisector of $\overline{AB}$.

5. **a.** Given that $AN = BN$, what can you conclude about point N?
   b. Given that $\overline{MP}$ is the perpendicular bisector of $\overline{AB}$, what can you conclude about AN and BN? about $\triangle ABN$?
   $AN = BN$; $\triangle ABN$ is an isosceles $\triangle$.
6. Rewrite the two theorems as a single biconditional statement.
   See left above.

Lesson Planning Options

Prerequisite Skills

• Constructing perpendicular bisectors
• Drawing angle bisectors

Assignment Options for Exercises On Your Own

To provide flexible scheduling, this lesson can be subdivided into parts.

1 **Core** 1–9, 23–27, 33–34
Extension 17–20, 22

2 **Core** 10–16, 21, 28–32
Extension 35–37

Use Mixed Review to maintain skills.

Resources

Student Edition

Skills Handbook, p. 646
Extra Practice, p. 637
Glossary/Study Guide

Teaching Resources

Chapter Support File, Ch. 4
• Practice 4-7(two worksheets)
• Reteaching 4-7
• Alternative Activity 4-7
Classroom Manager 4-7
Glossary, Spanish Resources

Transparencies
20, 54

219

KINESTHETIC LEARNING The following activity will help demonstrate the properties of a perpendicular bisector. Have two students stand in opposite corners of the classroom. Stand on the perpendicular bisector of the segment joining the two students. Ask the class to describe your distance from the students. Move along and off the perpendicular bisector and have students discuss how your distance from the students changes.

Point out to students that the term "locus" comes from the Latin word for location and that its plural is "loci" (pronounced low-sigh).

Example 2

ERROR ALERT! Some students may think that point *C* is part of the locus. **Remediation:** Point out that *C* does not meet the condition "set of all points 1 cm from *C*."

Example 1 Relating to the Real World

Help students see that the intersection of the red segment and line *m* is the point that is the shortest equal distance from the landmarks. As you move away from the point of intersection along line *m*, the distance between the landmarks remains equal but gets longer.

Additional Examples

FOR EXAMPLE 2

Draw a point. Label it *B*. Sketch the locus of points in a plane that are 2 cm from point *B*. **Students' sketches should be a circle with center *B* and radius 2 cm.**

Discussion: *How would your sketch change if the locus contained all the points 2 cm or less from point B?*

FOR EXAMPLE 3

What is the common name for the part of a baseball field between the foul lines and beyond the infield? **outfield**

Discussion: *Describe the locations of other common places on a baseball field.*

9.

7. Given isosceles triangle △*URI* with vertex angle ∠*R*, what does Theorem 4-13 tell you about point *R*?
_R_ is on the ⊥ bisector of _UI_.

Example 1 Relating to the Real World

National Landmarks Find the set of points in Washington, D.C., that are equidistant from the Jefferson Memorial and the White House.

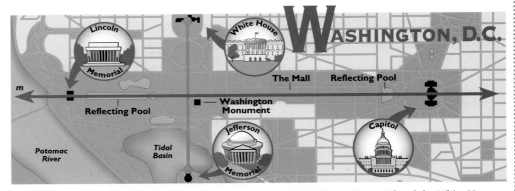

The red segment connects the Jefferson Memorial and the White House. All points on the perpendicular bisector *m* of this segment are equidistant from its endpoints. The perpendicular bisector passes through some of Washington's most famous landmarks.

8. For which landmarks does line *m* appear to be a line of symmetry?
the Lincoln Memorial, the U.S. Capitol, the Reflecting Pool
Example 1 involves the concept of locus. A **locus** is a set of points that meets a stated condition. In Example 1, the condition is "equidistant from the Jefferson Memorial and the White House." The locus is the perpendicular bisector of the segment connecting the two landmarks.

Example 2

Sketch the locus of points in a plane that are 1 cm from point *C*.

Locate several points 1 cm from *C*. Keep doing so until you see a pattern. The locus is a circle with center *C* and radius 1 cm.

Who? Benjamin Banneker (1731–1806) was an American astronomer, farmer, mathematician, and surveyor. In 1791, Banneker assisted in laying out the boundaries of Washington, D.C.

9. **Try This** Sketch the locus of points in a plane that are 1 cm from a segment *VC*. **See left above.**

220

TACTILE LEARNING Question 10 Have students cut out large circles and tape straws along their diameters. By rotating the straw around, students will see that the circle traces out a sphere.

Help students see that a locus in a plane can be a two-dimensional figure and a locus in space can be a three-dimensional figure.

Question 11 You may want to suggest that students use the triangle inequalities from Lesson 4-6.

WORK TOGETHER **p. 221**

Have students work with a partner. Make sure students refer to the diagrams to help them see how to create the angle bisector and perpendicular segments.

10. What would the locus be in Example 2 if the words "in a plane" were replaced with "in space"?
The locus in space is a sphere of radius 1 cm with center C.
As the answer to Question 10 implies, a locus of points in a plane and a locus of points in space can be quite different. For example, consider this condition: all points 3 cm from line ℓ.

11.
By Triangle Angle-Sum Thm.,
$m\angle A + m\angle ABC + m\angle ACB = 180$.
$m\angle ABC = 90$,
so $m\angle ACB + m\angle A = 90$. **Then**
$m\angle ACB < 90$ **and** $m\angle A < 90$.
Therefore, $m\angle ACB < m\angle ABC$.
Since the longer side lies opp. the larger angle, $AB < AC$.

The locus in a plane looks like this . . .

3 cm
3 cm ℓ

The locus is two parallel lines, each 3 cm from line ℓ.

The locus in space looks like this . . .

3 cm
3 cm ℓ

The locus is an endless cylinder with radius 3 cm and center-line ℓ.

QUICK REVIEW

To bisect an angle using paper folding, fold the paper so that the sides of the angle overlap.

Sides overlap.

vertex

Part 2 **Angle Bisectors and Locus**

The Work Together below involves the distance from a point to a line. The **distance from a point to a line** is the length of the perpendicular segment from the point to the line.

• A
The distance from A to n is the length of this segment.

B n

11. Let C be any point on line n other than B. Show that $AB < AC$.
See left.

WORK TOGETHER

▪ Draw an angle and use paper folding to create its bisector.

▪ Draw a point on the bisector. Use the corner of a piece of paper to create perpendicular segments from both sides of the angle to the point.

12. Measure the lengths of the two segments you drew. What do you notice? **The lengths are =.**

13. Repeat with two other points. Does what you noticed still hold true? **yes**

14. Use what you discovered to complete the statement: If a point is on the bisector of an angle, then ___?___ .
the point is equidistant from the sides of the angle

221

pages 223–225 **On Your Own**

1.

2.

3.

4.

5.

6.

7.

8.

9.

222

THINK AND DISCUSS

The property that you discovered in the Work Together is stated below. Its converse, which also is true, follows it.

Theorem 4-14
Angle Bisector Theorem

If a point is on the bisector of an angle, then it is equidistant from the sides of the angle.

Theorem 4-15
Converse of Angle Bisector Theorem

If a point in the interior of an angle is equidistant from the sides of the angle, then it is on the angle bisector.

15. **a.** Given that $m\angle ABL = m\angle CBL$, what can you conclude about AL and CL? **AL = CL**

b. Given that $AL = CL$, what can you conclude about $m\angle ABL$ and $m\angle CBL$? **$m\angle ABL = m\angle CBL$**

16. What is the locus of all points in the interior of an angle that are equidistant from the sides of the angle? **the angle bisector**

Sometimes the condition in a locus problem has more than one part.

Example 3 **Relating to the Real World**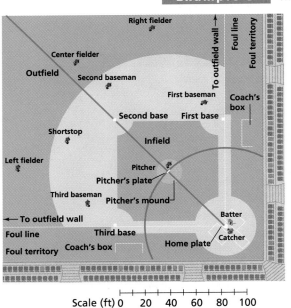

Sports What is a common name for the part of a baseball field that is equidistant from the foul lines and 60 ft 6 in. from home plate?

There are two parts to the condition stated in the problem.

Part 1: Equidistant from the foul lines

The red angle bisector contains all points equidistant from the foul lines.

Part 2: 60 ft 6 in. from home plate

The blue arc contains all points 60 ft 6 in. from home plate.

The pitcher's plate is both equidistant from the foul lines and 60 ft 6 in. from home plate.

Scale (ft) 0   20   40   60   80   100

Exercises ON YOUR OWN

Sketch and label each locus. 1–9. See margin p. 222.   10–12. See margin.

1. all points in a plane 4 cm from a point X

2. all points in a plane 1 in. from a line $\overleftrightarrow{UV}$

3. all points in a plane 1 in. from a segment $\overline{UV}$

4. all points in space 3 cm from a point F

5. all points in space a distance a from a line $\overleftrightarrow{DE}$

6. all points in a plane 1 in. from a circle with radius 0.5 in.

7. all points in a plane equidistant from two parallel lines

8. all points in a plane equidistant from the endpoints of $\overline{PQ}$

9. all points in space equidistant from two parallel lines

10. all points in a plane equidistant from $\overleftrightarrow{MN}$ and $\overleftrightarrow{OP}$ where $\overleftrightarrow{MN} \perp \overleftrightarrow{OP}$

11. all points in a plane 3 cm from $\overline{GH}$ and 5 cm from G, where $GH = 4.5$ cm

12. all points equidistant from two parallel planes

13. The locus is the two points at which the bisector of $\angle JKL$ intersects $\odot C$.
13. Find the locus of points equidistant from the sides of $\angle JKL$ and on $\odot C$.

14. *Coordinate Geometry* Write an equation for the locus of points equidistant from $(2, -3)$ and $(6, 1)$. $y = -x + 3$

15. *Sports* What is the common name for the part of a baseball field that is equidistant from first and third bases and 127 ft from home plate?   second base

16. *Standardized Test Prep* The highlighted points are the locus of points on the coordinate plane that are   C
A. 2 units from the origin and 1 unit from the y-axis.
B. 1 unit from the origin and 2 units from the y-axis.
C. 2 units from the origin and 1 unit from the x-axis.
D. 1 unit from the origin and 2 units from the x-axis.
E. none of the above

17. a. What is the locus of the tip of the minute hand on a clock?
b. What is the locus of the tip of the hour hand on a clock?
a. a circle   b. a (smaller) circle
18. *Open-ended* The smoke trails of the jets show the paths that they travel. Find a picture from a book or magazine or draw a sketch that shows an object and its path.
Check students' work.
19. *Open-ended* Give two examples of locus from everyday life, one in a plane and one in space.
See margin.
20. *Logical Reasoning* Rosie says that it is impossible to find a point equidistant from three collinear points. Is she correct? Explain your thinking.

See margin.

10.

11.

12.

19. Sample: The 50-yd line is the locus of all the pts. on a football field equidistant from the endlines; a soap bubble is the locus of all pts. at a given distance from its center.

20. Yes; the locus of pts. equidistant from the 1st and 2nd pts. is the ⊥ bisector of the segment connecting these pts. The locus of pts. equidistant from the 2nd and 3rd pts. is the ⊥ bisector of the segment connecting them. The 2 segments are collinear. So the 2 bisectors are ⊥ to a line. Therefore, the bisectors are ∥ and do not intersect. This means that there are no pts. in the locus.

223

CONNECTING TO STUDENTS' WORLD **Exercise 21** Have students bring in local maps. Have them write locus problems with two parts to describe different locations on the map. Then have them exchange problems and maps and have other students find the locations.

OPEN-ENDED **Exercise 22** While there are many correct answers, make sure that students' examples are accurate in terms of size and not just in terms of shape.

COORDINATE GEOMETRY **Exercises 23–28** Suggest that students plot a few points satisfying each condition before describing all the points in the locus.

Exercises 35–37 A locus can be used to describe a path. Before students begin these exercises, discuss an example with students such as the locus of points in the path of a ball thrown into the air which is a parabola.

Chapter Project **FIND OUT BY WRITING** Have students work in groups to generate ideas for puzzles. After students complete their puzzles, have the group evaluate them for clarity, organization, and accuracy.

23.

24.

25.

26.

27.

28.

224

21. Paul and Priscilla Wilson take new jobs in Shrevetown and need to find a place to live. Paul says "Let's try to move somewhere equidistant from both of our offices." Priscilla says, "Let's try to stay within three miles of downtown." Trace the map and suggest some locations for the Wilsons. **Anywhere on the highlighted segment.**

22. *Open-ended* Name a food with the shape described by each locus.
   a. all points in space no more than $1\frac{1}{2}$ in. from a point   **Sample: an orange**
   b. all points in space no more than $\frac{1}{2}$ in. from a circle with radius 2 in.   **Sample: a bagel**

Coordinate Geometry **Sketch each locus on the coordinate plane.** 23–28. See margin.

23. all points 3 units from the origin

24. all points 5 units from $x = 2$

25. all points equidistant from $A(0, 2)$ and $B(2, 0)$

26. all points equidistant from $P(1, 3)$ and $Q(5, 1)$

27. all points 4 units from the y-axis

28. all points equidistant from $y = 3$ and $y = -1$

Describe the locus that each blue figure represents.
30. pts. that are 2 units from the origin in the coordinate plane
31. pts. equidistant from two parallel planes

29.

pts. equidistant from the sides of $\angle A$

30.

31.

32.

pts. in space distance c from D

30–31. See above.

33. Think about the path of a child on a swing.   **a–c. See back of book.**
   a. Draw a side view of this path.
   b. Draw a top view of this path.
   c. Draw a front view of this path.

34. Alejandro draws a segment to use as the base of an isosceles triangle.
   a. Draw a segment to represent Alejandro's base. Locate three points that could be the vertex of the isosceles triangle.   **See back of book.**
   b. Describe the locus of points for the vertex of Alejandro's isosceles triangle.   **the ⊥ bisector of the base**
   c. *Writing* Explain why the locus you described is the only possibility for the vertex of the triangle.
   If the vertex is not on a ⊥ bisector of the base, then it is not equidistant from the endpts., and △ is not isosceles.

Exercises MIXED REVIEW

Exercises 38–40 Students review how to name arcs of a circle.

GETTING READY FOR LESSON 4-8 These exercises help students review how to construct midpoints and bisectors.

Wrap Up

THE BIG IDEA Ask students: *Define perpendicular bisector and angle bisector using loci.*

RETEACHING ACTIVITY Students work with partners to identify points in the classroom that are described by loci. (Reteaching worksheet 4-7)

Exercises CHECKPOINT

In this Checkpoint, your students will assess their own progress on Lessons 4-5 to 4-7.

Exercises 1–3 Students may want to begin by listing angles from smallest to largest.

OPEN-ENDED Exercise 4 Make sure students write the opposite of the conclusion, and not of the hypothesis.

Sketch each path.

35. the swimmer's left foot

36. a doorknob as the door opens

37. a knot in the middle of a jump rope as the rope is being used

35–37. See back of book.

Chapter Project ⋯⋯ **Find Out by Writing**

Make up a logic puzzle in which the solver must use clues to match the people, places, or things you describe. Have a classmate solve your puzzle. If necessary, refine your puzzle based on input from your classmate.

Check students' work.

Exercises MIXED REVIEW

Identify the following in ⊙O. ∠COB and $\overset{\frown}{BC}$ or ∠COA and $\overset{\frown}{AC}$

38. a central angle and its intercepted arc

39. two major arcs   **40.** a pair of adjacent arcs
$\overset{\frown}{CBA}$, $\overset{\frown}{CAB}$ $\overset{\frown}{AC}$, $\overset{\frown}{CB}$

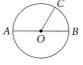

Getting Ready for Lesson 4-8

Constructions Draw a large triangle. Construct each figure. 41–42. See back of book.

41. an angle bisector   **42.** a midpoint of a side   **43.** a perpendicular bisector of a side

Same construction as in Exercise 42.

Exercises CHECKPOINT

List the sides from shortest to longest.

1.

$\overline{AB}$, $\overline{BC}$, $\overline{AC}$

2.
N, 60°, M, O
$\overline{MN}$, $\overline{MO}$, $\overline{NO}$

3.
Q, 25°, 130°, R, S
$\overline{QR} \cong \overline{RS}$, $\overline{QS}$

4. *Open-ended* Write a conditional that is true. Then write the first step of an indirect proof for your conditional. Sample: If $x = |x|$, then $x \geq 0$; assume $x < 0$.

Write the first step of an indirect proof of each statement.

5. February has fewer than 30 days.
Assume February has at least 30 days.

6. A pentagon has at most three right angles.
Assume pentagon has at least 4 rt. angles.

Sketch and label the locus of points. 7–8. See back of book.

7. all points in a plane a distance d from a line $\overleftrightarrow{PR}$

8. all points in space 1 in. from a plane

Lesson Quiz

Lesson Quiz is also available in Transparencies.

1. Sketch and label the locus of all points in a plane 1 in. from a segment $\overline{AB}$.

1 in. | 1 in.
A   B

2. Sketch and label the locus of all points in space 3 cm from a line $\overleftrightarrow{XY}$. **Locus should be an endless cylinder with radius 3 cm and center line $\overleftrightarrow{XY}$.**

3. Sketch the locus of all points equidistant from $(-2, 3)$ and $(-6, 5)$ on the coordinate plane. **Locus should be the a line through $(-4, 4)$ with slope 2.** **225**

Materials and Manipulatives

- Geometry software

Math ToolboX   Technology

Exploring Special Segments in Triangles   Before Lesson 4-8

Work in pairs or small groups.

Construct

Use geometry software.   1–4. Check students' work.

1. Construct a triangle and the three perpendicular bisectors of its sides.

2. Construct a triangle and its three angle bisectors.

3. Construct a triangle. Construct a line through a vertex of the triangle that is perpendicular to the line containing the side opposite that vertex. Similarly, draw the perpendiculars from the other two vertices. Since an *altitude* of a triangle is the segment from a vertex to the line containing the opposite side, the three lines you have drawn contain the three altitudes of the triangle.

4. Construct a triangle. Construct the midpoint of a side of the triangle and draw the segment from the midpoint to the opposite vertex. This segment is called a *median* of the triangle. Construct the other two medians.

Investigate   Check students' work.

- What do you notice about the lines, rays, or segments that you constructed in each triangle?

- Manipulate the triangles. Does the property still hold in the manipulated triangles?

Conjecture   Each set of lines intersects at a single pt.

List your **conjectures** about the angle bisectors, the perpendicular bisectors, the lines containing the altitudes, and the medians of a triangle.

Extend

- In what types of triangles do the perpendicular bisectors of the sides intersect inside the triangle? on the triangle? outside the triangle?
  acute △; right △; obtuse △
- Describe the triangles for which the lines containing the altitudes, the angle bisectors, or the medians intersect inside, on, or outside the triangles. The medians and angle bisectors always intersect inside the △. Altitudes intersect inside the △ for acute △s, at a vertex for right △s, and outside the △ for obtuse △s.

226

PROBLEM OF THE DAY

Jose, Daniel, Gina, and Carlita are all friends. Their ages are 26, 29, 32, and 35. Gina is married to the oldest person. Jose who is younger than Gina, is not the youngest. Who is married to whom and what are their ages? Jose (29) and Carlita (26), Daniel (35) and Gina (32)

Problem of the Day is also available in Transparencies.

CONNECTING TO PRIOR KNOWLEDGE Review with students the definitions of angle bisector and perpendicular bisector. Have students describe the three ways they can find each (paper folding, construction, and measurement).

WORK TOGETHER

ERROR ALERT! Step 6 Students may not see the relationship between the perpendicular bisectors of the obtuse triangle if they only look at the parts of the bisectors that lie in the interior of the triangles. **Remediation:** Have students trace the *lines* created by the folds.

THINK AND DISCUSS

ESL Help students understand the difference between collinear and concurrent. Students should be familiar with the term "point of intersection" as the point where two lines meet. Point out that the term "point of concurrency" is used for the point where *three or more* lines meet.

What You'll Learn

- Identifying properties of perpendicular bisectors, angle bisectors, altitudes, and medians of a triangle

...And Why

To understand the points of concurrency that are used in architecture, construction, and transportation

What You'll Need

- scissors

Connections • Recreation . . . and more

4-8 Concurrent Lines

WORK TOGETHER

Step 1: Each member of your group should draw and cut out five triangles: two acute, two right, and one obtuse. Make them big enough so that they are easy to fold.

Step 2: Use paper folding to create the angle bisectors of each angle of an acute triangle. What do you notice about the angle bisectors?

Step 3: Repeat Step 2 with a right and an obtuse triangle. Does what you discovered still hold true?

Folding an Angle Bisector

1. Make a **conjecture** about the bisectors of the angles of a triangle.
   The angle bisectors intersect at a point.

Folding a Perpendicular Bisector

Step 4: Use paper folding to create the perpendicular bisectors of each of the sides of an acute triangle. What do you notice?

Step 5: Repeat Step 4 with a right triangle. What do you notice?

Step 6: Draw an obtuse triangle in the middle of a piece of paper (do not cut it out!), then repeat Step 4 with this triangle. What do you notice?

2. Make a **conjecture** about the perpendicular bisectors of the sides of a triangle.
   The ⊥ bisectors of the sides intersect at a pt.

THINK AND DISCUSS

Part
1

Perpendicular Bisectors and Angle Bisectors

When three or more lines intersect in one point, they are **concurrent.** The point at which they are concurrent is the **point of concurrency.** Your explorations in the Work Together lead to the following theorems.

Theorem 4-16	The perpendicular bisectors of the sides of a triangle are concurrent at a point equidistant from the vertices.
Theorem 4-17	The bisectors of the angles of a triangle are concurrent at a point equidistant from the sides.

Lesson Planning Options

Prerequisite Skills

- Understanding the definitions of perpendicular and bisector
- Finding equations of lines

Assignment Options for Exercises On Your Own

To provide flexible scheduling, this lesson can be subdivided into parts.

 Core 6–9 (a), 13–14, 16
Extension 18

 Core 1–5, 6–9 (b), 10–12, 15
Extension 17

Use Mixed Review to maintain skills.

Resources

Student Edition
Skills Handbook, pp. 646, 664
Extra Practice, p. 637
Glossary/Study Guide

Teaching Resources
Chapter Support File, Ch. 4
- Practice 4-8 (two worksheets)
- Reteaching 4-8
Classroom Manager 4-8
Glossary, Spanish Resources

Transparencies
54, 58

227

The point of concurrency of the perpendicular bisectors is called the *circumcenter*. The point of concurrency of angle bisectors is called the *incenter*.

Theorem 4-16 In groups, have students read through the paragraph proof given on page 228. Then ask them to rewrite it in their own words. Students may want to elaborate on some of the statements and reasons to clarify the proof. For example, they may want to state explicitly the Converse of the Perpendicular Bisector Theorem.

DIVERSITY Be aware that some students have never lived in or even seen houses with yards, especially yards big enough for a swimming pool.

VISUAL LEARNING To help students see why the center of the pool is chosen to be the point of concurrency of the angle bisectors, have them copy the diagram and choose other points as the center. Using a compass, have them draw circles as large as possible within the triangle. They should see that they cannot find a larger circle.

ESL AUDITORY LEARNING Students can remember the meanings of the terms "circumscribe" and "inscribe" by their prefixes "circum-" meaning "around" and "in-" meaning "within." Review other words with these prefixes and their meanings, such as circumference, circumvent, inside, and interior.

Additional Examples

FOR EXAMPLE 1 ···························

Draw an acute triangle. Then find a point on the interior of the triangle that is equidistant from each side.
Sketches will vary. Point should be the intersection of the angle bisectors.

Discussion: *What theorem did you use to find the point?*

FOR EXAMPLE 2 ···························

Find the center of the circle that circumscribes △*CDE* with vertices *C*(0, −6), *D*(0, 0), and *E*(−8, 0).
(−4, −3)

Discussion: *How can you find the radius of the circle?*

FOR EXAMPLE 3 ···························

a. Use paper folding to create the altitudes from each of the three vertices of an obtuse triangle.
Check students' work.

b. Use paper folding to create the three medians of an obtuse triangle. **Check students' work.**

Discussion: *Describe the difference between the altitude of an acute triangle and the altitude of an obtuse triangle.*

Paragraph Proof of Theorem 4-16

Given: Lines *ℓ*, *m*, and *n* are perpendicular bisectors of the sides of △*ABC*. *X* is the intersection of lines *ℓ* and *m*.
Prove: Line *n* contains point *X*, and *X* is equidistant from *A*, *B*, and *C*.

Since *m* is the perpendicular bisector of $\overline{BC}$, $BX = CX$. Similarly, since *ℓ* is the perpendicular bisector of $\overline{AB}$, $AX = BX$. By substitution, $AX = CX$. So by the Converse of the Perpendicular Bisector Theorem, *X* is on line *n*. Since $AX = BX = CX$, *X* is equidistant from *A*, *B*, and *C*.

Example 1 Relating to the Real World ·············

Recreation The Jacksons want to install a circular pool in their backyard. They want the pool to be as large as possible. Where would the largest possible pool be located?

The point of concurrency of the angle bisectors is equidistant from the sides of the triangular yard (Theorem 4-17). If any other point were chosen as the center of the pool, it would be closer to at least one of the sides of the yard, and the pool would have to be smaller. ■

As Example 1 suggests, the points of concurrency in Theorems 4-16 and 4-17 have some interesting properties related to circles.

$QC = SC = RC$

$XI = YI = ZI$

Point *C*, called the *circumcenter*, is equidistant from the vertices of △*QRS*. The circle is *circumscribed* around the triangle.

Point *I*, called the *incenter*, is equidistant from the sides of △*TUV*. The circle is *inscribed* in the triangle.

228

Example 2

ERROR ALERT! Students may not understand why the point of concurrency of the perpendicular bisectors of the sides is used rather than the point of concurrency of the angle bisectors to find the center of the circle. **Remediation:** Reinforce that when a circle is circumscribed around a triangle, the vertices of the triangle lie on the circle. The point of concurrency of the perpendicular bisectors of the sides of the triangle is equidistant from the vertices and therefore equidistant from the circle.

TACTILE LEARNING Have students cut out four triangles, fold and label each of the four segments (angle bisectors, perpendicular bisectors, altitudes, and medians), then make a poster to display them.

Example 2

Coordinate Geometry Find the center of the circle that circumscribes △*OPS*.

Two of the perpendicular bisectors of the sides of the triangle are $x = 2$ and $y = 3$. These lines intersect at $(2, 3)$. This point is the center of the circle.

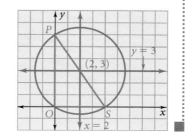

3. The 3rd ⊥ bisector passes through the pt. of intersection of the 1st two.

3. *Critical Thinking* Explain why it was not necessary to find the third perpendicular bisector in Example 2.

4. **Try This** Find the center of the circle that circumscribes the triangle with vertices $(0, 0)$, $(-8, 0)$, and $(0, 6)$. $(-4, 3)$

Part 2 Medians and Altitudes

Two other special segments of a triangle are medians and altitudes. The **median of a triangle** is a segment whose endpoints are a vertex and the midpoint of the side opposite the vertex. The **altitude of a triangle** is a perpendicular segment from a vertex to the line containing the side opposite the vertex.

Unlike angle bisectors and medians, an altitude of a triangle may lie outside the triangle. Consider the following diagrams.

Acute Triangle: Altitude is inside.   Right Triangle: Altitude is a side.   Obtuse Triangle: Altitude is outside.

You can use paper folding to find altitudes and medians.

To find an altitude . . .

Fold so that a side overlaps itself and the fold contains a vertex.

To find a median . . .

Fold one vertex to another to find the midpoint of a side,

then fold from the midpoint to the opposite vertex.

Technology Options

For Exercise 14, students may use geometry software to construct the triangle and circumscribe it with a circle. Then students can manipulate the triangle and see how the circle changes.

Prentice Hall Technology

Software
- Secondary Math Lab Toolkit™
- Integrated Math Lab 30
- Computer Item Generator 4-8

Internet
- See the Prentice Hall site. (http://www.phschool.com)

229

Example 3 ······

a. *Paper Folding* Use paper folding to create the altitudes from each of the three vertices of an acute triangle.

b. Use paper folding to create the three medians of an acute triangle.

The orange triangle shows the paper-folded medians.

The blue triangle shows the paper-folded altitudes.

Notice in Example 3 that the three altitudes and three medians are concurrent. This property holds true for any triangle.

Theorem 4-18	The lines that contain the altitudes of a triangle are concurrent.
Theorem 4-19	The medians of a triangle are concurrent.

5. *Critical Thinking* For what type of triangle is the point of concurrency of the altitudes outside the triangle? obtuse triangle

Exercises ON YOUR OWN

Is $\overline{AB}$ a perpendicular bisector, an angle bisector, an altitude, a median, or none of these?

1.

median

2.

angle bisector

3.

none of these

4.

perpendicular bisector

5.

altitude

230

Exercises 6–9 Students should understand from Question 3 that they need only to find the point of intersection of two of the perpendicular bisectors and the altitudes.

EXTENSION Exercise 12 Have students investigate the points of concurrency for the special segments and lines using isosceles and equilateral triangles.

ALTERNATIVE ASSESSMENT Exercise 13 This exercise can help you assess students' understanding of Theorems 4-16 and 4-17. Have students work with a partner. Ask them to explain how they found the location for the drinking fountain.

ERROR ALERT! Exercise 16 Students may shade the center of the circle and part of the perpendicular bisectors of the sides. **Remediation:** Remind students how to shade all the points less than a given number on a number line or all the points on the interior of a circle with a given radius.

For each triangle, give the coordinates of the point of concurrency of (a) the perpendicular bisectors of the sides and (b) the altitudes.

6.
a. (−2, −3) b. (0, 0)

7.
a. (−2, 0) b. (1, −3)

8.
a. (−1, 4) b. (4, −4)

9.
a. (0, 0) b. (−4, 0)

The points of concurrency for the lines and segments listed in I–IV have been drawn on the triangles. Match the points with the lines and segments.

I. perpendicular bisectors of sides

II. angle bisectors

III. medians

IV. altitudes

ID, IIB, IIIC, IVA
10.

IA, IIC, IIIB, IVD
11.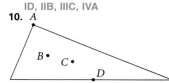

12. History of Mathematics Leonard Euler proved in 1765 that for any triangle, three of the four points of concurrency are collinear. The line that contains these three points is known as *Euler's Line*. Refer to Exercises 10 and 11 to determine which point of concurrency does *not* lie on Euler's Line. the pt. of concurrency of the angle bisectors

13. Park Design Where should park officials place a drinking fountain in Altgeld Park so that it is equidistant from the tennis court, the playground, and the volleyball court? See below.

14. Open-ended Draw a triangle and construct the perpendicular bisectors of two of its sides. Then construct the circle that circumscribes the triangle. See margin.

15. Coordinate Geometry △DEF has vertices D(0, 0), E(12, 0), and F(0, 12). x = 0, y = 0, y = x
   a. Find the equations of the lines that contain the three altitudes.
   b. Find the equations of the three perpendicular bisectors of the sides.
   c. Writing Are any of the lines in parts (a) and (b) the same? Explain.
   b. x = 6, y = 6, y = x   c. See margin.

16. Locus Three students are seated at uniform distances around a circular table. Copy the diagram and shade the points on the table that are closer to Moesha than to Jan or Chandra.

13. the pt. of concurrency of the ⊥ bisectors of segments connecting the 3 areas

---

pages 230–232 On Your Own

14. Sample:

15c. The line y = x; since the altitude from *D* bisects the base of isosceles △*DEF*, the altitude is also the ⊥ bisector of the base.

Exercise 18 Have students compare this proof with the proof of Theorem 4-16 on page 228. Ask students to point out the differences in the "Given" and "Prove" statements as well as in the arguments.

ESTIMATION Exercises 19–21 Students can use a corner of a piece of paper to estimate if an angle is greater than or less than 90°.

PORTFOLIO Share with students the criteria you will use to assess their work in portfolios, as well as how you plan to use the results. Students should understand how the rubrics assess their work, how each piece in the portfolio counts, and how the scores they get in their portfolios will affect their overall evaluation.

Wrap Up

THE BIG IDEA Ask students: *Summarize what you have learned about the special segments related to a triangle. Use diagrams and include all the properties of the segments.*

RETEACHING ACTIVITY Students draw obtuse, acute, and right triangles. Then they use protractors and straightedges to find the points of concurrency of the lines containing the altitudes. (Reteaching worksheet 4-8)

Lesson Quiz

Lesson Quiz is also available in Transparencies.

$\triangle PQR$ has vertices $P(2, 0)$, $Q(10, 0)$ and $R(2, 8)$.

1a. Draw and label the bisector of angle R. **See back of book.**

b. Draw and label the median with endpoint at Q. **See back of book.**

2. Find the point of concurrency of the altitudes. **(2, 0)**

3. Find the center of the circle that circumscribes $\triangle PQR$. **(6, 4)**

232

---

17. Manipulatives Medians of triangles have special physical properties related to balance. Draw a triangle on heavy cardboard, construct its medians and then cut it out.
  a. Put a pencil on a table and place the triangle on the pencil so that a median lies along the length of the pencil. What do you notice?
  b. Hold a pencil straight up and place the point of concurrency of the medians on the tip of the pencil. What do you notice?
  a–b. The triangle balances.

18. Preparing for Proof Complete the proof of Theorem 4-17.

  Given: Rays ℓ, m, and n are bisectors of the angles of $\triangle ABC$. X is the intersection of rays ℓ and m.
  Prove: Ray n contains point X;
  $DX = EX = FX$

Statements	Reasons
1. Rays ℓ, m, and n are bisectors of the angles of $\triangle ABC$. X is the intersection of rays ℓ and m.	a. __?__ Given
2. $FX = EX$ and $DX = FX$	b. __?__ Angle Bisector Thm.
3. $DX = EX$	c. __?__ Substitution
4. Ray n contains X.	d. __?__
5. $DX = EX = FX$	5. Transitive Prop. of Equality

d. Converse of the Angle Bisector Thm.

Exercises   MIXED REVIEW

Coordinate Geometry Classify each triangle as acute, obtuse, or right.

19. $M(-3, -4)$, $N(2, 5)$, $L(2, -4)$ **right**

20. $Q(-6, 1)$, $T(0, 0)$, $V(4, 3)$ **obtuse**

21. $B(3, -4)$, $P(3, 5)$, $J(6, 5)$ **right**

Geometry in 3 Dimensions In the diagram, *ABCD* is a square. Give an example of each figure or pair of figures.
  22–25. Samples are given.
22. a plane and a point not on the plane
  ABE and D
23. skew lines $\overleftrightarrow{AB}$ and $\overleftrightarrow{DE}$
24. intersecting planes
  ABE and BCE
25. concurrent lines   **26.** parallel lines
  $\overleftrightarrow{AB}$, $\overleftrightarrow{BC}$, $\overleftrightarrow{BE}$ $\overleftrightarrow{AB}$, $\overleftrightarrow{CD}$

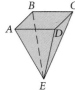

The point on which a figure balances is called the *center of gravity*.

PORTFOLIO

For your portfolio, select one or two items from your work for this chapter. Here are some possibilities.
 • corrected work
 • work that you think best shows the things you learned or did in this chapter
Explain why you have included each selection.

Finishing the Chapter Project

PROJECT DAY You may wish to plan a project day on which students share their completed projects. Encourage groups to explain their process as well as their product.

PROJECT NOTEBOOK Have students review their project work and bring their notebooks up to date.

- Have students review their puzzles and solutions in their displays.
- Ask groups to share any insights they found when completing the project, such as shortcuts or strategies they used in solving and creating logic problems.

SCORING RUBRIC

3 Student's solutions are correct. Diagrams and explanations are clear. Logic terms are used correctly. Display is attractive, organized, and comprehensive. Research is evident.

2 Student's solutions contain minor flaws. Diagrams and explanations are clear. Logic terms are used correctly with a few exceptions. Display is attractive, complete, and has some organizational structure.

1 Student's solutions have errors. Diagrams are complete but some explanations are confusing. Logic terms are not always used appropriately. Display is complete but lacks organization.

0 Major elements are incomplete or missing.

Finishing the Chapter Project

PUZZLING PIECES

Find Out questions on pages 187, 198, 205, and 225 will help you complete your project. Prepare a display of logic puzzles. Include your own puzzles and solutions, those from the Find Out questions, or those found through research. Look at *Alice's Adventures in Wonderland* as well as the books listed below. Use puzzles and solutions to illustrate terms of logic, such as *conditional* and *conclusion*. Decide how best to organize your display.

Reflect and Revise

Review your display with a classmate. Together, check that your solutions are correct and that your diagrams and explanations are clear. Have you used logic terms correctly? Is the display attractive, organized, and comprehensive? Revise your work as needed. Consider doing more research.

Follow Up

A paradox is self-contradictory. Study these three paradoxes:
1. In a town, there is a librarian who reads to every person who does not read to himself or herself.
2. **A.** Statement (B) is false.   **B.** Statement (A) is true.
3. This sentence contains two errors.

What can you conclude from each? Does the librarian read to himself? Is statement (A) true? How many errors does the sentence have? Study other paradoxes and create your own. Explain why each is a paradox.

For More Information

Gardner, Martin. *Aha! Gotcha: Paradoxes to Puzzle and Delight.* New York: W.H. Freeman and Company, 1982.

Shannon, George. *Stories to Solve: Folktales from Around the World.* New York: Greenwillow Books, 1985.

Smullyan, Raymond M. *Alice in Puzzle-Land: A Carrollian Tale for Children Under Eighty.* New York: William Morrow, 1982.

233

Resources

Student Edition
Extra Practice, p. 637
Glossary/Study Guide

Teaching Resources
Students Study Survival Handbook
Glossary, Spanish Resources

4 Wrap Up

Key Terms

altitude of a triangle (p. 229)
base (p. 188)
base angle (p. 188)
biconditional (p. 183)
conclusion (p. 182)
concurrent (p. 227)
conditional (p. 182)
contrapositive (p. 184)
converse (p. 183)
distance from a point to a
  line (p. 221)

hypothesis (p. 182)
indirect reasoning (p. 207)
inverse (p. 184)
legs (p. 188)
locus (p. 220)
median of a triangle
  (p. 229)
midsegment (p. 201)
negation (p.184)
point of concurrency
  (p. 227)

paragraph proof (p. 195)
truth value (p. 182)
two-column proof (p. 194)
vertex angle (p. 188)

How am I doing?

* State three ideas from this chapter that you think are important. Explain your choices.
* Describe the different styles of proof.

Using Logical Reasoning   4-1

An *if-then statement* is a **conditional.** The part following *if* is the **hypothesis,** and the part following *then* is the **conclusion.** You find its **truth value** when you determine if a conditional is true or false.

Statement	Form	Example
conditional	If ■, then ■.	If a polygon is a triangle, **then** it has three sides.
converse	If ■, then ■.	If a polygon has three sides, **then** it is a triangle.
inverse	If *not* ■, then *not* ■.	If a polygon is *not* a triangle, **then** it does *not* have three sides.
contrapositive	If *not* ■, then *not* ■.	If a polygon does *not* have three sides, **then** it is *not* a triangle.
biconditional	■ if and only if ■.	A polygon is a triangle **if and only if** it has three sides.

For Exercises 1–4: (a) Write the converse. (b) Determine the truth value of the conditional and its converse. (c) If both statements are true, write a biconditional.

1. If you are in Australia, then you are south of the equator.
   a. If you are south of the equator, then you are in Australia.   **b. true; false**
2. If an angle is obtuse, then its measure is greater than 90 and less than 180.   **a. If the measure of an angle is > 90 and < 180, then the angle is obtuse.**
   b. true; true   **c. An angle is obtuse if and only if its measure is > 90 and < 180.**
3. If it is snowing, then it is cold outside.
   a. If it is cold outside, then it is snowing.   **b. true; false**
4. If a figure is a square, then its sides are congruent.
   a. If the sides of a figure are ≅, then it is a square.   **b. true; false**
5. *Open-ended* Write a conditional and then write its contrapositive.
   Sample: If Boris plays the piano, then he plays chess; if Boris does not play chess, then he does not play the piano.

234

Exercises 6–9 Make sure students differentiate between when *x* is a side length and when it is an angle measure.

ERROR ALERT! Exercise 11 Students may rewrite the proof using Exercise 10 with the reasons in the wrong order. **Remediation:** Be sure they write the proof using the *solution* to Exercise 10.

Isosceles Triangles 4-2

If two sides of a triangle are congruent, then the angles opposite those sides are also congruent. The bisector of the vertex angle of an isosceles triangle is the perpendicular bisector of the base. If two angles of a triangle are congruent, then the sides opposite the angles are congruent.

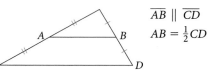

Find the values of x and y.

6.

x = 4; *y* = 65

7.

x = 60; *y* = 60

8.

x = 55; *y* = 62.5

9.

x = 65; *y* = 90

Wrap Up   pages 234–237

12. Answers may vary. Sample: ∠*ABC* is a rt. angle by def. of complementary angles and the Angle Addition Post. ∠*A* and ∠*C* are complementary because acute angles of a rt. △ are complementary.

13. ∠*E* ≅ ∠*F* because base ∠s of an isosceles △ are ≅.

14. Answers may vary. Samples: ∠*HIG* ≅ ∠*JIK* because they are vert. angles. ∠*HIG* ≅ ∠*G* and ∠*JIK* ≅ ∠*J* because base ∠s of an isosceles △ are ≅.

Midsegments of Triangles 4-3, 4-4

There are different types of proofs, including the **paragraph proof** and the **two-column proof**.

A **midsegment** of a triangle is a segment that connects the midpoints of its sides. The midsegment connecting two sides of a triangle is parallel to the third side and half its length.

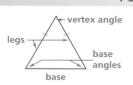

$\overline{AB} \parallel \overline{CD}$

$AB = \frac{1}{2}CD$

10. *Preparing for Proof* The reasons given in this proof are correct, but they are in the wrong order. List them in the correct order.

Given: △*BCA* ≅ △*CDE*   d, c, a, b
        △*CDE* ≅ △*EGF*

Prove: $\overline{AF} \parallel \overline{BG}$

Statements	Reasons
1. △*BCA* ≅ △*CDE* △*CDE* ≅ △*EGF*	**a.** Def. of midpoint
2. $\overline{BC} \cong \overline{CD}, \overline{DE} \cong \overline{EG}$	**b.** Triangle Midsegment Thm.
3. *C* is the midpoint of $\overline{BD}$. *E* is the midpoint of $\overline{DG}$.	**c.** Def. of congruent polygons
4. $\overline{AF} \parallel \overline{BG}$	**d.** Given

11. *Writing* Rewrite the proof above as a paragraph proof. See right.

11. By def., if the triangles are ≅, then their corres. sides are ≅. So $\overline{BC} \cong \overline{CD}$ and $\overline{DE} \cong \overline{EG}$. By def., *C* is the midpt. of $\overline{BD}$ and *E* is the midpt. of $\overline{DG}$. By the Triangle Midsegment Thm., $\overline{AF} \parallel \overline{BG}$.

What can you conclude from each diagram? Justify your answers. 12–14. See margin.

12.

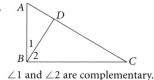

∠1 and ∠2 are complementary.

13.

14.

Exercises 18–21 Have students work with a partner. Have partners take turns writing out their indirect reasoning.

ALTERNATIVE ASSESSMENT **Exercises 26–29** To assess students' understanding of loci, give them sketches of loci and ask them to describe them in words.

Remind students that the new mathematical terms in this chapter are defined in the Glossary/Study Guide in the back of the book.

19. Assume that both numbers are odd. The product of 2 odd numbers is always odd, which contradicts the fact that their product is even. So the assumption that both numbers are odd is false, and at least 1 must be even.

20. Assume that a triangle has 2 or more obtuse angles. By def., the measure of each of these angles is > 90. Then the sum of angle measures of the △ is > 180. By the Triangle Angle-Sum Thm., the sum of angle measures of a △ is 180. Therefore the assumption was false, and a △ has no more than 1 obtuse angle.

21. Assume 1 angle of an equilateral △ is obtuse. Then its measure is > 90 and < 180. By the Isosceles Triangle Thm., the remaining angles are each ≅ to the 1st angle. By def. of ≅ angles and the Transitive Prop. of =, the measures of the 3 angles are =, and all the angles are obtuse. Then the sum of the measures of the angles is > 270. But the sum of the measures of angles of a △ is 180. Therefore, the assumption is false. An equilateral △ cannot have an obtuse angle.

Algebra **Find the value of x.**

15.

16.

17.

Using Indirect Reasoning   4-5

To use **indirect reasoning**, consider all possibilities and then prove all but one false. The remaining possibility must be true.

There are three steps in an indirect proof.

Step 1: Assume the opposite of what you want to prove is true.
Step 2: Use logical reasoning to reach a contradiction of an earlier statement, such as the given information or a theorem. Then state that the assumption you made was false.
Step 3: State that what you wanted to prove must be true.

Write a convincing argument that uses indirect reasoning.   19–21. See margin.

18. Mary walks into a newly-painted room and finds 2 paint brushes rinsing in water. Show that the room was not painted with oil-based paint.
    See above right.

20. Show that a triangle can have at most one obtuse angle.

18. Assume that the room had been painted with oil-based paint. Then the brushes would be rinsing in paint thinner, but they are not. So the assumption is false. The room must not have been painted with oil-based paint.

19. The product of two numbers is even. Show that at least one of the two numbers must be even.

21. Show that an equilateral triangle cannot have an obtuse angle.

Triangle Inequalities   4-6

The sum of the lengths of any two sides of a triangle is greater than the length of the third side. If two sides of a triangle are not congruent, the larger angle lies opposite the larger side.

List the angles and sides in order from smallest to largest.

22.

∠T, ∠R, ∠S; $\overline{SR}$, $\overline{TS}$, $\overline{TR}$

23.

∠C, ∠A, ∠B; $\overline{AB}$, $\overline{BC}$, $\overline{AC}$

24.

∠G, ∠O, ∠F; $\overline{OF}$, $\overline{FG}$, $\overline{OG}$

25. Standardized Test Prep Two sides of a triangle have lengths 4 and 7. Which could *not* be the length of the third side?   B
    A. 5   **B.** 2   **C.** 7   **D.** 10   **E.** 8

236

Getting Ready for Chapter 5

Students may work these exercises independently or in small groups. The skills previewed will help prepare students for measuring figures in a plane.

Bisectors and Locus   4-7

A point is on the perpendicular bisector of a segment if and only if it is equidistant from the endpoints of the segment. A point is on the bisector of an angle if and only if it is equidistant from the sides of the angle. A set of points that meet a stated condition is a **locus**.

Sketch and label the locus of points.

26. all points in a plane 2 cm from a circle with radius 1 cm

27. all points in a plane equidistant from two points

28. all points in space a distance a from $\overline{DS}$

29. all points in space a distance b from a point P
    See below right.

26.

27.

28.

Concurrent Lines   4-8

When three or more lines intersect in one point, they are **concurrent**.

The **median of a triangle** is a segment joining a vertex and the midpoint of the side opposite the vertex. The **altitude of a triangle** is a perpendicular segment from a vertex to the line containing the side opposite the vertex.

For any given triangle, each of the following are concurrent:

■ The perpendicular bisectors of the sides

■ The bisectors of the angles

■ The medians

■ The lines containing the altitudes

Median   Altitude

29.

Coordinate Geometry **Graph** $\triangle ABC$ **with vertices** $A(2, 3)$, $B(-4, -3)$, **and** $C(2, -3)$. **Find the coordinates of each point of concurrency.**
30–32. See margin for graphs.

30. perpendicular bisectors
    $(-1, 0)$

31. medians
    $(0, -1)$

32. altitudes
    $(2, -3)$

Getting Ready for... ➤ CHAPTER 5

Find the perimeter and area of a rectangle with the given dimensions.

33. $\ell = 5$ cm, $w = 3$ cm
    16 cm; 15 cm²

34. $\ell = 6.2$ ft, $w = 9.0$ ft
    30.4 ft; 55.8 ft²

35. $\ell = 0.5$ m, $w = 1.5$ m
    4 m; 0.75 m²

Find the value of $\sqrt{a^2 + b^2}$ **for the given values of** a **and** b.

36. $a = 4, b = 3$
    5

37. $a = 5, b = 12$
    13

38. $a = 9, b = 12$
    15

30.

31.

32.

ENHANCED MULTIPLE CHOICE QUESTIONS are more complex than traditional multiple choice questions, which assess only one skill. Enhanced multiple choice questions assess the processes that students use, as well as the end results. The questions are written so that students use more than one strategy to solve the problem. Using multiple strategies is encouraged by the National Council of Teachers of Mathematics (NCTM). **Exercise 25** is an enhanced multiple choice question.

FREE RESPONSE QUESTIONS do not give answer choices. Some exercises have more than one possible answer. Students need to give only one correct response. **Exercises 1–11, 13–16, and 18–24** are free response questions.

WRITING EXERCISES allow students to describe how they think about and understand the concepts they have learned. **Exercise 17** is a writing exercise.

OPEN-ENDED PROBLEMS allow for more than one solution. Students must construct their own responses instead of choosing from possible answers. The students' responses will help you determine the depth of their understanding and any possible areas of difficulty. **Exercises 12** is an open-ended problem.

Resources

 Teaching Resources
Chapter Support File, Ch. 4
- Chapter Assessment, Forms A and B
- Alternative Assessment Chapter Assessment, Spanish Resources

 Teacher's Edition
See also p. 180E for assessment options

 Software
- Computer Item Generator

Assessment   page 238

1a. If a polygon is an octagon, then it has 8 sides.

b. If a polygon does not have 8 sides, then it is not an octagon.

c. If a polygon is not an octagon, then it does not have 8 sides.

2a. If it is an even-numbered year, then it is a leap year.

b. If it is not a leap year, then it is not an even-numbered year.

c. If it is not an even-numbered year, then it is not a leap year.

3a. If it is not summer, then it is snowing.

b. If it is not snowing, then it is summer.

c. If it is summer, then it is not snowing.

6. Answers may vary. Sample: $\overline{DE} \parallel \overline{BC}$, $DE = \frac{1}{2}BC$; Triangle Midsegment Thm.

238

For each statement, write (a) the converse, (b) the inverse, and (c) the contrapositive.
1–3. See margin.
1. If a polygon has eight sides, then it is an octagon.

2. If it is a leap year, then it is an even-numbered year.

3. If it is snowing, then it is not summer.

Algebra **Find the values of x and y.**

4.   **5.**

$x = 40;\ y = 70$ $x = 50;\ y = 70$

6. What can you conclude from the diagram? Justify your answer.

See margin.

Identify the pair of statements that forms a contradiction.

7. **I.** $\triangle PQR$ is a right triangle.   I and II
II. $\triangle PQR$ is an obtuse triangle.
III. $\triangle PQR$ is scalene.

8. **I.** $\angle DAS \cong \angle CAT$ II and III
II. $\angle DAS$ and $\angle CAT$ are vertical.
III. $\angle DAS$ and $\angle CAT$ are adjacent.

List the angles of $\triangle ABC$ from smallest to largest.

9. $AB = 9, BC = 4, AC = 12$ $\angle A, \angle C, \angle B$

10. $AB = 10, BC = 11, AC = 9$ $\angle B, \angle C, \angle A$

11. $AB = 3, BC = 9, AC = 7$ $\angle C, \angle B, \angle A$

12. **Open-ended** Write three lengths that cannot be the lengths of sides of a triangle. Explain your answer.   Sample: 4 cm, 5 cm, and 10 cm; $4 + 5 > 10$

List the sides of each triangle in order from smallest to largest.

13.   **14.** $\overline{KV}, \overline{MV}, \overline{KM}$

$\overline{ST}, \overline{SR}, \overline{RT}$

Find the value of x.

15.   **16.**

17. **Writing** Use indirect reasoning to explain why the following statement is true: If an isosceles triangle is obtuse, then the obtuse angle is the vertex angle.
See back of book.

Coordinate Geometry **Sketch each locus on a coordinate plane.**   18–21. See back of book.

18. all points 6 units from the origin

19. all points 3 units from the line $y = -2$

20. all points equidistant from points $(2, 4)$ and $(0, 0)$

21. all points equidistant from the axes

Sketch each figure. Determine whether the point of concurrency is in the interior, exterior, or on the triangle.

22. acute triangle, perpendicular bisectors   interior

23. obtuse triangle, medians   interior

24. right triangle, altitudes   on the triangle

25. **Standardized Test Prep** $\triangle ABC$ has vertices $A(2, 5)$, $B(2, -3)$, and $C(10, -3)$. Which point of concurrency is at $(6, 1)$? **C**
A. angle bisectors   **B.** altitudes
C. perpendicular bisectors   **D.** medians
E. none of the above

Cumulative Review

Item	Review Topic	Chapter
1	Triangles	2
2, 6, 8	Transformations	3
3	Patterns and Inductive Reasoning	1
4, 12	Using Logical Reasoning	4
5	Classifying Quadrilaterals	2
7	Midsegments of Triangles	4

Item	Review Topic	Chapter
9	Polygons	2
10	Angles	1
11	Perpendicular Lines in the Coordinate Plane	2
13	Basic Constructions	1
14	Locus	4

---

4 Cumulative Review

For Exercises 1–11, choose the correct letter.

1. Which could be the measures of the angles of a triangle? **E**
 I. 37, 89, 54   II. 125, 45, 10
 III. 100, 75, 15   IV. 60, 60, 60

 A. I only   **B.** IV only   **C.** I and II
 D. II and IV   **E.** I, II, and IV

2. $\triangle DEB$ has vertices $D(3, 7)$, $E(1, 4)$, and $B(-1, 5)$. In which quadrants is the image of $\triangle DEB$ under a 90° rotation about the origin? **B**
 A. I and II   **B.** II and III   **C.** III and IV
 D. I and IV   **E.** none of the above

3. What is the next term in the sequence 1000, 200, 40, 8, . . . ? **A**
 A. 1.6   **B.** 3   **C.** 4   **D.** 0.16
 E. none of the above

4. What is the converse of the statement "If a strawberry is red, then it is ripe"? **B**
 A. If a strawberry is not red, then it is not ripe.
 B. If a strawberry is ripe, then it is red.
 C. A strawberry is ripe if and only if it is red.
 D. If a strawberry is not ripe, then it is not red.
 E. A strawberry is not ripe if and only if it is not red.

5. Which quadrilateral cannot contain four right angles? **B**
 A. square   **B.** trapezoid   **C.** rectangle
 D. rhombus   **E.** parallelogram

6. A dilation centered at the origin maps $(-3, 6)$ to $(-9, 18)$. Which of the following does *not* represent the same dilation? **C**
 A. $(0, 5) \longrightarrow (0, 15)$ **B.** $(1, -4) \longrightarrow (3, -12)$
 C. $(4, 3) \longrightarrow (9, 12)$ **D.** $(6, 2) \longrightarrow (18, 6)$
 E. $(-2, -7) \longrightarrow (-6, -21)$

7. What is the length of a midsegment parallel to the side of a triangle 6 cm long? **A**
 A. 3 cm   **B.** 9 cm   **C.** 12 cm
 D. 15 cm   **E.** none of the above

8. What is the image of $(6, -9)$ under the translation $\langle 5, -2 \rangle$? **A**
 A. $(11, -11)$ **B.** $(11, -7)$ **C.** $(1, 11)$
 D. $(-1, -11)$ **E.** none of the above

9. What type of polygon is shown? **C**

 A. triangle   **B.** quadrilateral   **C.** hexagon
 D. octagon   **E.** none of the above

Compare the boxed quantity in Column A with the boxed quantity in Column B. Choose the best answer.

 A. The quantity in Column A is greater.
 B. The quantity in Column B is greater.
 C. The two quantities are equal.
 D. The relationship cannot be determined from the information given.

Column A	Column B

$\angle CDB$ and $\angle RDM$ are vertical angles.

10. $m\angle CDB$ \qquad $m\angle BDR$ **D**

Lines ℓ and t are perpendicular.

11. the slope of ℓ \qquad the slope of t **D**

Find each answer.

12. *Open-ended* Write a conditional that has the same truth value as its converse. **Sample: If a polygon has fewer than 4 sides, then it is a** $\triangle$.

13. Construct a right triangle. Then construct the bisectors of two of its angles. **See back of book.**

14. *Coordinate Geometry* Find the locus of points in a plane equidistant from the lines $y = x$ and $y = -x$. **the coordinate axes**

Resources

Teaching Resources
Chapter Support File, Ch. 4
• Cumulative Review
• Standardized Test Practice

Teacher's Edition
See also p. 180E for assessment options

Measuring in the Plane

To accommodate flexible scheduling, some lessons are divided into parts.
Assignment Options are given in the Lesson Planning Options for each lesson.

5-1   Understanding Perimeter and Area (pp. 242–248)

Part **1** Finding Perimeter

Part **2** Finding Area

Key Terms: area of a polygon, area of a rectangle, perimeter of a polygon

5-2   Areas of Parallelograms and Triangles (pp. 249–254)

Part **1** Areas of Parallelograms

Part **2** Areas of Triangles

Key Terms: altitude, area of a parallelogram, area of a triangle, base, height

5-3   The Pythagorean Theorem and Its Converse (pp. 256–262)

Part **1** The Pythagorean Theorem

Part **2** The Converse of the Pythagorean Theorem

Key Terms: Converse of the Pythagorean Theorem, hypotenuse, legs of a right triangle, Pythagorean Theorem, Pythagorean triple

5-4   Special Right Triangles (pp. 263–268)

Part **1** 45°-45°-90° Triangles

Part **2** 30°-60°-90° Triangles

Key Terms: 45°-45°-90° triangle, 30°-60°-90° triangle

5-5   Areas of Trapezoids (pp. 269–273)

Key Terms: area of a trapezoid, base, height, legs of a trapezoid

5-6   Areas of Regular Polygons (pp. 274–278)

Key Terms: apothem, center, radius

5-7   Circles: Circumference and Arc Length (pp. 279–284)

Part **1** Circumference

Part **2** Arc Length

Key Term: arc length, circumference of a circle, concentric circles, congruent arcs, pi

5-8   Areas of Circles, Sectors, and Segments of Circles (pp. 285–290)

Part **1** Areas of Circles

Part **2** Sectors and Segments

Key Terms: area of a circle, sector of a circle, segment of a circle

PACING OPTIONS

This chart suggests pacing only for the core lessons and their parts, and it is provided merely as a possible guide. It will help you determine how much time you have in your schedule to cover other features, such as the Chapter Project, Math Toolboxes, Wrap Up, and Assessment.

	1 Class Period	1 Class Period	1 Class Period	1 Class Period	1 Class Period	1 Class Period	1 Class Period	1 Class Period	1 Class Period
Traditional (40–45 min class periods)	5-1 **1**	5-1 **2**	5-2 **1**	5-2 **2**	5-3 **1**	5-3 **2**	5-4 **1**	5-4 **2**	5-5
Block Scheduling (90 min class periods)	5-1 **1 2**	5-2 **1 2**	5-3 **1 2**	5-4 **1 2**	5-5	5-6	5-7 **1 2**	5-8 **1 2**	

What Students Will Learn and Why

In this chapter, students build on their knowledge of triangles and quadrilaterals, learned in Chapter 2, by learning to find the area and perimeter of parallelograms, triangles, trapezoids, and regular polygons. Students study the Pythagorean Theorem, its converse, and the properties of 30°-60°-90° triangles. Finally, students learn to find circumference, arc length, and area of circles, sectors, and segments of circles. The concepts in this chapter are used by architects, race car designers, and in many other careers.

Discussing the Chapter/Building on Experience

The concept map below relates chapter topics to real-world applications. You and your class may wish to add to the map or develop maps of your own. The center oval describes the topic of the chapter. The next level displays topics within the lessons. The outer ovals reflect applications of the content. As you and your class build a concept map, invite students to discuss applications with which they are familiar.

1 Class Period	1 Class Period	1 Class Period	1 Class Period	1 Class Period	1 Class Period	1 Class Period	1 Class Period	1 Class Period	1 Class Period	1 Class Period
5-6	5-7 ▼1	5-7 ▼2	5-8 ▼1	5-8 ▼2						

Interactive Questioning Tips

A question is interactive when there is "give and take" between the questioner (teacher or student) and the respondent. In Think and Discuss or when a critical thinking question is asked, it is important to allow for varying conceptual tempos among students. In Lesson 5-7, Example 3, students are asked to explain if it is possible for two arcs of different circles to have the same measure but different lengths. While some students may have an immediate response, others may need more time to consider all the elements involved, and that should certainly be encouraged. Don't rush students.

Skills Practice

Every lesson provides skill practice with Try This exercises, Exercises On Your Own, and Exercises Mixed Review. The Student Edition includes Checkpoints (pp. 268, 284) and Preparing for Standardized Tests (p. 299). In the Teacher's Edition, the Lesson Planning Options section for each lesson lists Prerequisite Skills students should know for that lesson. At the back of the Student Edition is the Skills Handbook—mini-lessons on math your students may need to review. The Chapter Support File for Chapter 5 in the Teaching Resources box includes two Practice worksheets per lesson, a worksheet for two Checkpoints, and worksheets for Cumulative Review and Standardized Test Preparation.

Diverse Learning and Teaching Styles

In your Teacher's Edition, you will find suggestions as to how you can help students complete mathematical tasks in Chapter 5 by reinforcing various learning styles. Here are some examples.

- **Visual learning** use geometry software to draw triangles and label their angle measures and side lengths (p. 258), use a map to approximate the area of trapezoid-shaped states (p. 270), find real-world examples of sectors (p. 286)

- **Tactile learning** investigate the formula for arc length using the circular objects from the Work Together (p. 281), work in groups to approximate the measurement of two large rectangles made by taping together pieces of graph paper (p. 286)

- **Auditory learning** practice repeating aloud formulas for the area of rectangles, parallelograms, and triangles (p. 251)

- **Kinesthetic learning** use measuring tape to find the dimensions and calculate the area of the school parking lot (p. 252)

Alternative Activity for Lesson 5-2

for use with theorem 5-2, Example 1, and Example 2, uses geometry software to explore the formula for area of a parallelogram.

240C

Alternative Activity for Lesson 5-3

for use with Think and Discuss, Example 1, and Example 2, uses geometry software to explore the Pythagorean Theorem by drawing and manipulating right and non-right triangles.

Alternative Activity for Lesson 5-7

for use with Work Together and Think and Discuss, uses geometry software to explore the relationship between radius and circumference and develop a formula for circumference.

Cooperative Learning Tips

When used effectively, cooperative learning can help students develop interpersonal skills, learn to perform specific roles in a group, and learn to carry out specific responsibilities. The components of Chapter 5 provide a range of cooperative learning opportunities.

- In the Student Edition, the **Work Together** parts of lessons are specifically designed for cooperative learning activities.

- In the Teacher's Edition, you will find helpful hints for addressing diverse learning styles (see page C for Chapter 5). For every lesson, you will find a **Reteaching Activity**, which may involve cooperative learning.

Materials and Manipulatives

The authors expect all students to use scientific calculators. Calculator use is integrated throughout the course.

- calculator (5-4, 5-7)
- centimeter grid paper (5-1, 5-2, 5-4)
- circular objects (5-7)
- colored paper (5-3)
- compass (5-8)
- graph paper (5-3)
- lined paper (5-5)
- metric ruler (5-4, 5-7)
- protractor (5-4)
- scissors (5-2, 5-3, 5-5, 5-8)
- straightedge (5-2, 5-3)
- string (5-7)
- tape (5-2, 5-8)

TECHNOLOGY OPTIONS

Technology Tools		Chapter Project	5-1	5-2	5-3	5-4	5-5	5-6	5-7	5-8
Calculator		Assumed that students have scientific calculators at any time.								
Software	Secondary Math Lab Toolkit™		✔	✔	✔	✔	✔	✔	✔	✔
	Integrated Math Lab			✔					✔	
	Computer Item Generator		✔	✔	✔	✔	✔	✔	✔	✔
	Student Edition		✔	✔						✔ᵀ
Video	Video Field Trip	✔								
CD-ROM	Multimedia Geometry Lab		✔		✔			✔		✔
Internet		See the Prentice Hall site. (http://www.phschool.com)								

✔ᵀ indicates Math Toolbox.

The Prentice Hall Geometry program offers you a rich variety of technology options. Be assured that all these options are provided as a means of enriching the program and are not essential for the successful completion of the course.

Assessment Options

The Prentice Hall Geometry Program provides you with many options. From these options, you may choose instructional materials and techniques appropriate for your students, or those necessary to meet your district's curriculum requirements. As the chart indicates, the program also supports your teaching efforts by offering you many choices for assessment.

ASSESSMENT OPTIONS

Assessment Support Materials	Chapter Project	5-1	5-2	5-3	5-4	5-5	5-6	5-7	5-8	Chapter End
Chapter Project	▲■●	▲■	▲■			▲■			▲■	▲■
Checkpoints					●▲■			●▲■		
Self-Assessment	▲■				▲■				▲■	
Writing Assignment	▲■		▲		●▲■		▲■	▲●■	▲■	▲●
Chapter Assessment										▲●
Alternative Assessment		■	■	■	■	■	■	■	■	■●
Cumulative Review										●
Standardized Test Prep	▲■			▲	▲■		▲	▲■		▲■●
Computer Item Generator	Can be used to create custom-made practice or assessment at any time.									

▲ = Student Edition　　■ = Teacher's Edition　　● = Teaching Resources

Checkpoints

Alternative Assessment

Chapter Assessment

Available in both Form A and Form B

Making the Right Connections

Mathematics is imbedded in nearly every walk of life. The National Council of Teachers of Mathematics (NCTM) encourages educators to recognize these connections and to emphasize them for the purpose of better educating students for success in life and in a global economy. The **Connections** chart below highlights these connections for Chapter 5.

CONNECTIONS

Lesson	Interdisciplinary Connections	Career Prep	Other Real World Connections	Math Integration	NCTM Standards
Chapter Project	History	Textile Manufacturing	Quilting Fabric Making		Connections Problem Solving
5-1	Science	Animal Science Design Tiling	Animal Care Safe Stairs Carpeting Tiling Gardening	Coordinate Geometry	Communication Problem Solving
5-2		Architecture	Landscaping	Coordinate Geometry Probability	Connections Algebra Communication Problem Solving
5-3	History		Boundaries Packaging Satellites Sewing	Algebra Coordinate Geometry Geometry in 3 Dimensions	Connections Algebra Communication Problem Solving
5-4		Design Farming	Baseball Diamonds Helicopter Blades	Algebra Geometry in 3 Dimensions	Algebra Connections Communication Problem Solving
5-5	Geography		Crafts Skateboard Ramp	Algebra Geometry in 3 Dimensions	Algebra Connections Communication Problem Solving
5-6		Engineering	Racing Cars and Boats Gazebo Satellites	Coordinate Geometry	Connections Algebra Reasoning Communication Problem Solving
5-7		Metal Working Automobile Manufacturing	Amusement Park Rides Space Travel	Coordinate Geometry	Algebra Connections Communication Problem Solving
5-8	Archaeology Biology	Food Preparation	Dart Board Animal Habitat Cake Making		Connections Communication Problem Solving

CONNECTING TO PRIOR LEARNING Discuss with students how perimeter and area are used by the following people: home decorators (in carpeting, tiling, and arranging furniture), carpenters (in estimating the amount of materials to buy), and farmers (in determining the sizes and shapes of fields to minimize erosion and maximize the amount of crops planted).

CULTURAL CONNECTIONS Until the twentieth century only natural materials, such as animal hair, plant fibers, or the products of silkworms, were used to make fabrics. Many of these materials can be found only in warmer climates in places like India, Egypt, and parts of the Americas. Ask

students what impact the development of synthetic fibers, such as rayon and polyester, has had on the U.S. economy.

INTERDISCIPLINARY CONNECTIONS Until the late 1800s, fabric making was done by skilled artisans. During the 19th century, powered textile mills were developed in England and the United States, and Eli Whitney invented the cotton gin. In the twentieth century, textile manufacturing has become fully automated in the United States. Have students research the effects technology has had on the evolution of the textile industry.

Technology Options

Prentice Hall Technology

Video
Video Field Trip 5, "Designing Patterns," a look at designing in the fashion industry with Jhane Barnes in New York

CHAPTER

5 **M**easuring in the Plane

Relating to the Real World

From architects to race car designers, many careers make use of the concepts you will learn in this chapter. You will find the perimeters and areas of polygons and circles. You will also study one of the most famous theorems in geometry: the Pythagorean Theorem.

| *Understanding Perimeter and Area* | *Areas of Parallelograms and Triangles* | *The Pythagorean Theorem and Its Converse* | *Special Right Triangles* | *Areas of Trapezoids* |

Lessons   5-1   5-2   5-3   5-4   5-5

Launching The Project

PROJECT NOTEBOOK Encourage students to keep all project-related materials in a separate folder or notebook. See Chapter Project Manager and Scoring Rubric in Chapter Support File.

- Have students who are familiar with patchwork quilts describe how patterns are designed and how quilts are made.

- Some students may own quilts that they are willing to bring to school to show classmates.

TRACKING THE PROJECT You may wish to have students read Finishing the Chapter Project on page 292 to help them get an overview of the project. Set benchmark deadlines for students to show their work in progress.

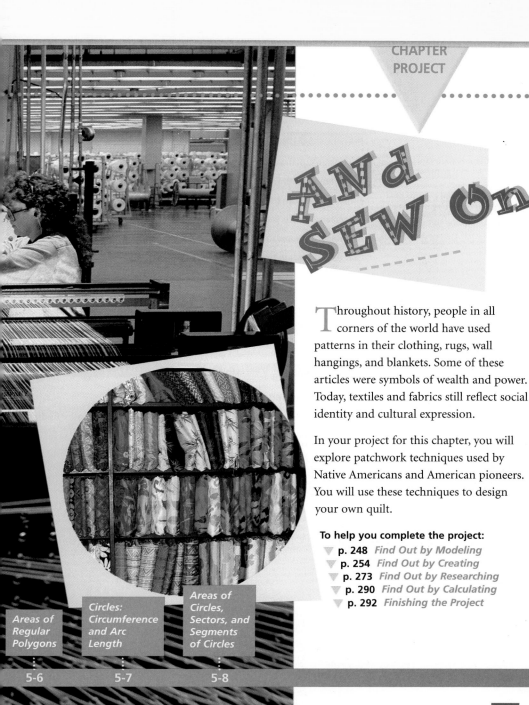

CHAPTER PROJECT

ANd SEW On

Throughout history, people in all corners of the world have used patterns in their clothing, rugs, wall hangings, and blankets. Some of these articles were symbols of wealth and power. Today, textiles and fabrics still reflect social identity and cultural expression.

In your project for this chapter, you will explore patchwork techniques used by Native Americans and American pioneers. You will use these techniques to design your own quilt.

To help you complete the project:
- ▼ **p. 248** *Find Out by Modeling*
- ▼ **p. 254** *Find Out by Creating*
- ▼ **p. 273** *Find Out by Researching*
- ▼ **p. 290** *Find Out by Calculating*
- ▼ **p. 292** *Finishing the Project*

Areas of Regular Polygons	Circles: Circumference and Arc Length	Areas of Circles, Sectors, and Segments of Circles
5-6	5-7	5-8

▼ Project Resources

Teaching Resources
Chapter Support File, Ch. 5
- Chapter Project Manager and Scoring Rubric

Transparencies
59

▼ Using the Rubric

Sharing the scoring rubric for the project with your students will alert them to your expectations before they begin work on the project.

As students complete each Find Out question in the chapter, you may wish to have them evaluate their own work or a partner's work based on the scoring rubric. Students should have the opportunity to revise their work after it has been reviewed.

PROBLEM OF THE DAY

In how many different ways can half the triangular regions in the square be shaded? (Rotations and reflections of patterns are not considered different.) **13**

Problem of the Day is also available in Transparencies.

CONNECTING TO PRIOR KNOWLEDGE Review with students the properties of squares, rectangles, and parallelograms. Have students use calculators to find the perimeter of rectangles with dimensions $\sqrt{7}$ cm by $\sqrt{13}$ cm, $\sqrt{21}$ in. by $\sqrt{21}$ in., and $\sqrt{37}$ m by $\sqrt{5}$ m.

WORK TOGETHER

As students complete Questions 1–5, they may be surprised to find no relationship between the area and the perimeter of a rectangle. They might possibly conclude for the three examples given that the perimeter of a rectangle in units is always greater than or equal to its area in square units. Ask students to find a counterexample for this hypothesis.

THINK AND DISCUSS

Discuss the meaning of the formulas for the perimeter of a square and rectangle. Emphasize that memorization without understanding will lead to confusion later in the chapter when students learn other formulas.

Lesson Planning Options

Prerequisite Skills

- Finding perimeter of polygons
- Finding distance between points in the coordinate plane

Assignment Options for Exercises On Your Own

To provide flexible scheduling, this lesson can be subdivided into parts.

 Core 1–11
Extension 39–42

 Core 12–26, 28–32, 43–44
Extension 27, 33–38

Use Mixed Review to maintain skills.

Resources

 Student Edition
Skills Handbook, pp. 646, 659
Extra Practice, p. 638
Glossary/Study Guide

 Teaching Resources
Chapter Support File, Ch. 5
- Practice 5-1 (two worksheets)
- Reteaching 5-1
Classroom Manager 5-1
Glossary, Spanish Resources

 Transparencies
1, 18, 60

242

What You'll Learn

- Finding area and perimeter of squares and rectangles

...And Why

To find the perimeters of banners, animal pens, and gardens

To find the surface area to be covered by carpet or by tiles

What You'll Need

- centimeter grid paper

Connections 🌐 *Animal Science . . . and more*

5-1 Understanding Perimeter and Area

WORK TOGETHER

In your group, draw each figure on centimeter grid paper.

- a rectangle with length 5 cm and width 3 cm
- a rectangle with base 8 cm and height 2 cm
- a rectangle with each side 4 cm

1. Record the perimeter of each rectangle. **16 cm; 20 cm; 16 cm**
2. Are the rectangles with equal perimeters congruent, similar, or neither? **neither**
3. To find the area of each rectangle, count the number of square centimeters in its interior. Record the area of each rectangle. **15 cm²; 16 cm²; 16 cm²**
4. Are the rectangles with the same area congruent, similar, or neither? **neither**
5. Do the rectangles with equal perimeters have the same area? **no**

THINK AND DISCUSS

Part 1

Finding Perimeter

In the Work Together, you found the **perimeter of a polygon** by finding the sum of the lengths of the sides. In special cases such as squares and rectangles, you may use formulas for perimeter.

$$p = 4s$$

$$p = 2b + 2h \text{ or } p = 2(b + h)$$

Question 6 You may also want to ask students the following: *Can you use the formula for the perimeter of a rectangle to find the perimeter of a square? Explain.*

Example 1

ESTIMATION Encourage students to begin by estimating *AC* using the grid. You may want to tell them that the diagonal of a unit square is about 1.4 units. Then discuss how they can use estimation to check if their solutions are reasonable.

Help students understand that the size of a square unit depends on the unit used. Have students compare the sizes of a square centimeter, a square inch, a square foot, and a square meter.

CRITICAL THINKING Postulate 5-2 Remind students that they discovered in the Work Together that the converse of this postulate is not true for rectangles. Ask students for what type of quadrilateral the converse is true and why.

Postulate 5-3 Check that students apply this postulate when finding area, not perimeter. Use the figure given in Question 9 to show that the sum of the perimeters of the region *is not* the sum of the perimeters of the nonoverlapping regions.

Question 8c Have students use the results to find the number of square inches in a rectangle with dimensions three feet by two feet. Check that students multiply 6 ft² by $\frac{144 \text{ in.}^2}{1 \text{ ft}^2}$, not $\frac{12 \text{ in.}}{1 \text{ ft}}$.

6. Can you use the formula for the perimeter of a square to find the perimeter of any rectangle? Explain.
   No; a square is a special kind of rectangle.

You can use the Distance Formula to find perimeter in the coordinate plane.

Example 1

Coordinate Geometry Find the perimeter of △ABC.

Find the length of each side. Add the lengths to find the perimeter.

$AB = 5 - (-1) = 6$

$BC = 6 - (-2) = 8$

$AC = \sqrt{(5 - (-1))^2 + (6 - (-2))^2}$ Use the Distance Formula.

$= \sqrt{6^2 + 8^2} = \sqrt{100} = 10$

$AB + BC + AC = 6 + 8 + 10 = 24$

The perimeter of △ABC is 24 units.

7. **Try This** Graph the quadrilateral with vertices $K(-3, -3)$, $L(1, -3)$, $M(1, 4)$, and $N(-3, 1)$. Find the perimeter of *KLMN*.
   Part See margin p. 245.

Part 2 Finding Area

The **area of a polygon** is the number of square units enclosed by the polygon. The blue square at the left encloses nine smaller red squares. Each red square has sides 1 cm long and is called a square centimeter. By counting square centimeters, you see that the blue square has area 9 cm².

Postulate 5-1

The area of a square is the square of the length of a side.

$A = s^2$

Postulate 5-2

If two figures are congruent, their areas are equal.

Postulate 5-3

The area of a region is the sum of the areas of its nonoverlapping parts.

8. **a. Try This** What is the area of a square whose sides are 12 in. long? **144 in.²**
   b. What is the area of a square whose sides are 1 ft long? **1 ft²**
   c. How many square inches are in a square foot? **144**
   9b–c. See margin p. 245.   **30 in.²**
9. **a.** By counting squares, find the area of the polygon outlined in blue.
   b. Use Postulate 5-1 to find the area of each square outlined in red.
   c. How does the sum of your answers to part (b) compare to your answer to part (a)? Which postulate does this **verify**?

243

Additional Examples

FOR EXAMPLE 1

Find the perimeter of △*XYZ* with coordinates $X(-3, 3)$, $Y(0, -1)$, and $Z(-3, -1)$. **12 units**

Discussion: *What is the perimeter of the image of △XYZ under a reflection in the y-axis?*

FOR EXAMPLE 2

A rectangular store sign is 4 yards long and 4 feet wide. What is its area in square feet? **48 ft²**

Discussion: *How many square yards is the area of the store sign? Explain.*

FOR EXAMPLE 3

You have 48 feet of fencing. You want to fence a rectangular section. What are the dimensions of the rectangle with the maximum area? **12 ft by 12 ft**

Theorem 5-1 Students may not be familiar with labeling the sides of a rectangle as *height* and *base*. Point out that a rectangle is a special type of parallelogram with four right angles, and the height of a rectangle is always equal to a side of the rectangle.

Technology Options

For Exercise 34, students may use computers or graphing calculators to sketch the different rectangles.

Prentice Hall Technology

 Software
- Secondary Math Lab Toolkit™
- Computer Item Generator 5-1

 CD-ROM
- Multimedia Geometry Lab 5

 Internet
- See the Prentice Hall site. (http://www.phschool.com)

You can select any side of a rectangle to be the base. Because adjacent sides are perpendicular, the length of a side adjacent to the base is the height.

Theorem 5-1 Area of a Rectangle	The area of a rectangle is the product of its base and height. $A = bh$	

To find area, you must use the same units for all dimensions.

Tennis

Champions

4 ft

2 yd

PROBLEM SOLVING

Look Back Find the area of the banner in Example 2 by first changing all units to yards. $2\frac{2}{3}$ yd²

Example 2 Relating to the Real World ·················

Design You are designing a rectangular banner. The banner will be 2 yd long and 4 ft wide. How much material will you need?

2 yd = 6 ft	Change units using 1 yd = 3 ft.
$A = bh$	Use the formula for the area of a rectangle.
$= 6(4) = 24$	Substitute 6 for *b* and 4 for *h*.

The area of the banner is 24 ft². You will need at least 24 ft² of material. ■

10. Try This Find the area of a rectangle with length 75 cm and width 2 m. **15,000 cm² or 1.5 m²**

You can use a graphing calculator or spreadsheet technology to find maximum and minimum values for area and perimeter problems.

Example 3 Relating to the Real World ·················

 Animal Science You have 32 yd of fencing. You want to make a rectangular pen for a calf you are raising for a 4-H project. What are the dimensions of the rectangle that will result in the maximum area? What is the maximum area?

Draw some possible rectangular pens and find their areas.

12 yd	11 yd	10 yd
4 yd	5 yd	6 yd
$A = 48$ yd²	$A = 55$ yd²	$A = 60$ yd²

Question 12 The generalization of the answer from Example 3 can be made on the assumption that the base and height are not restricted to integral values. Have students try the same problem with 30 feet of fencing. You can get the maximum area by enclosing a square with side length 7.5 ft.

 Exercises   O N   Y O U R   O W N

Exercises 1–3 These examples provide an opportunity to discuss choosing appropriate units of measure. For example, the perimeter of the cover of a book is best measured using centimeters or inches, while the perimeter of a house or building is best measured using feet, yards, or meters.

Exercises 6–7 Although finding the perimeter of nonrectangular figures was not reviewed in the lesson, students should not have difficulty applying the definition of perimeter given on page 242 to these figures.

VISUAL LEARNING Exercises 8–11 Some students may want to draw the rectangles in these exercises and other rectangles described in the exercise set on grid paper before calculating perimeters and areas. Encourage students to label the sides of their drawings with the appropriate units.

	A	B	C
1	b	h = 16 − b	A = bh
2	1	15	15
3	2	14	28
4	3	13	39
5	...	...	...

Create a spreadsheet to find area. Choose values for b from 0 to 15.

Make a graph of the spreadsheet values. Graph values of b on the horizontal axis and values of A on the vertical axis. Connect the points with a smooth curve.

The maximum value occurs at $b = 8$. When $b = 8$, $h = 8$ and $A = 64$.

To have the maximum area for your calf, you should fence a square with sides 8 yd long. The maximum area is 64 yd^2.

11. Subtract $2b$ from each side; then divide each side by 2.

11. *Critical Thinking* Show how the equation $h = 16 − b$ was derived from the formula $2b + 2h = 32$.

12. Use the answer to Example 3. Make a **conjecture** by completing this statement: If you have a fixed amount of fencing to enclose a rectangle, you can get the maximum area by enclosing a ___?___.
square

pages 242–245 **Think and Discuss**

7. $P = 20$

9b. 16 in.^{2} + 9 in.^{2} + 4 in.^{2} + 1 in.^{2} = 30 in.^{2}

c. They are =; Postulate 5-3: the area of a region is the sum of the areas of its non-overlapping parts.

 Exercises   O N   Y O U R   O W N

Estimation **Estimate the perimeter of each item.**   1–3. Answers may vary. Samples are given.

1. the cover of this book
about 40 in.

2. the cover of your notebook
about 42 in.

3. a classroom bulletin board
about 20 ft

Mental Math **Find the perimeter of each figure.**

4.
4 in.
7 in.
22 in.

5.
9 cm
36 cm

6.
55 ft
11 ft

7.
24 cm
6 cm
2 cm

Find the perimeter of each rectangle with the given base and height.

8. 21 in., 7 in.   56 in.
9. 16 cm, 23 cm   78 cm
10. 24 m, 36 m   120 m
11. 14 ft, 23 ft   74 ft

The figures below are drawn on centimeter graph paper. Find the area of the shaded portion of each figure.

12.
13 cm^2

13.
15 cm^2

14.
14 cm^2

15.
14 cm^2

245

COORDINATE GEOMETRY Exercises 16–19 Students can find the area by finding the base and height of the rectangle and multiplying or by counting the number of unit squares on the grid. Encourage students to use both methods as a way to check their work.

COORDINATE GEOMETRY Exercise 21 Make sure students connect the vertices in the order they are listed and then complete the polygon by connecting the last point to the first. In part c, there are many ways to divide the polygon into rectangles. Students may want to add a line between D and G and find the area of $ABCH$ minus the area of $DEFG$.

Exercise 27 Make sure students understand how much carpet is needed to cover "from the bottom of the first riser to the top of the sixth riser." Students will need this length to answer part a and part b.

MAKING CONNECTIONS Exercise 27 The spiral staircase in the Mapco-White County Coal Mine in Carni, Illinois is 1103 feet deep and has 1520 steps. Ask students to find the height of a riser if they are all the same height. **about 8.7 in.**

---

pages 245–248 **On Your Own**

21a, c.

34b.

Coordinate Geometry **Graph each rectangle *ABCD* and find its area.**

16. $A(0, 0)$, $B(0, 4)$, $C(5, 4)$, $D(5, 0)$ **20 units²**
17. $A(1, 4)$, $B(1, 7)$, $C(5, 7)$, $D(5, 4)$ **12 units²**

18. $A(-3, 2)$, $B(-2, 2)$, $C(-2, -2)$, $D(-3, -2)$ **4 units²**
19. $A(-2, -6)$, $B(-2, -3)$, $C(3, -3)$, $D(3, -6)$ **15 units²**

20. A rectangle is 11 cm wide. Its area is 176 cm². What is the length of the rectangle? **16 cm**

21. *Coordinate Geometry* Points $A(1, 1)$, $B(10, 1)$, $C(10, 8)$, $D(7, 8)$, $E(7, 5)$, $F(4, 5)$, $G(4, 8)$, and $H(1, 8)$ are the coordinates of the vertices of polygon *ABCDEFGH*. **a, c. See margin.**
   a. Draw the polygon on graph paper.
   b. Find the perimeter of the polygon. **38 units**
   c. Divide the polygon into rectangles.
   d. Find the area of the polygon. **54 units²**

22. The perimeter of a rectangle is 40 cm and the base is 12 cm. What is the area? **96 cm²**

23. A square and a rectangle have equal areas. The rectangle is 64 cm by 81 cm. What is the perimeter of the square? **288 cm**

Find the area of each rectangle with the given base and height.

24. 4 ft 6 in., 4 in.
   216 in.²
25. 1 yd 18 in., 4 yd
   6 yd²
26. 2 ft 3 in., 6 in.
   162 in.²

Building Safe Stairs

Since falls are a major cause of injury, it makes sense to be concerned about the safety of stairs. According to John Templer, the world's foremost authority on stairs, steps with a 7-in. riser and an 11-in. tread form the safest possible stairs.

Prior to his investigations, Francois Blondel's formula, dated 1675, had recommended that stair measurements conform to the formula 2(riser) + tread = 25.5 in.

Source: Smithsonian

27. *Carpeting* You use John Templer's dimensions to build a stairway with six steps. You want to carpet the stairs with a 3-ft wide runner from the bottom of the first riser to the top of the sixth riser.
   a. Find the area of the runner. **3492 in.² or $24\frac{1}{4}$ ft²**
   b. Since a roll of carpet is 12 ft across, a rectangle of carpet that measures 3 ft by 12 ft is cut from the roll to make the runner. How many square feet of the material will be wasted? **$11\frac{3}{4}$ ft²**
   c. The carpet costs $17.95/yd². You must pay for the entire piece that is cut. Find the cost of the carpet. **$71.80**
   d. Binding for the edge of the runner costs $1.75/yd. How much will the binding cost if the two long edges of the runner are bound?
   $9.43

tread

riser

Writing **Tell whether you need to know area or perimeter in order to determine how much of each item to buy. Explain your choice.**

28. edging for a garden   perimeter 29. paint for a basement floor   area

30. wallpaper for a bedroom   area 31. weatherstripping for a door   perimeter

32. Tiling The Art Club is tiling an 8 ft-by-16 ft wall at the entrance to the school. They are creating a design by using different colors of 4 in.-by-4 in. tiles. How many tiles do the students need? **1152 tiles**

33. Gardening You want to make a 900-ft² rectangular garden to grow corn. In order to keep raccoons out of your corn, you must fence the garden. You want to use the minimum amount of fencing so that your costs will be as low as possible.
    a. List some possible dimensions for the rectangular garden. Find the perimeter of each rectangle.   **Samples: 10 ft by 90 ft, 200 ft; 15 ft by 60 ft, 150 ft**
    b. Technology Create a spreadsheet listing integer values of *b* and the corresponding values of *h* and *P*. What dimensions will give you a garden with the minimum perimeter? **Check students' work; 30 ft by 30 ft**

34. You want to build a rectangular corral by using one side of a barn and fencing the other three sides. You have enough material to build 100 ft of fence. **b. See margin p. 246 for sample.**
    a. Technology Create a spreadsheet listing integer values of *b* and the corresponding values of *h* and *A*.   **Check students' work.**
    b. Coordinate Geometry Make a graph using your spreadsheet values. Graph *b* on the horizontal axis and *A* on the vertical axis.
    c. Describe the dimensions of the corral with the greatest area. **b = 50 ft, h = 25 ft**

Find the area of the shaded portion of each figure. All angles in the figures are right angles.

35.

20 m, 18 m, 5 m, 10 m, 5 m
310 m²

36.

2 yd, 4 yd, 1 yd, 4 yd, 3 yd, 3 yd
19 yd²

37.
6 cm, 6 cm
24 cm²

38.
4 in., 8 in., 4 in., 12 in.
80 in.²

Coordinate Geometry **Graph each quadrilateral *ABCD*. Find its perimeter.**

39. $A(-2, 2)$, $B(0, 2)$, $C(4, -1)$, $D(-2, -1)$ 16

40. $A(-4, -1)$, $B(4, 5)$, $C(4, -2)$, $D(-4, -2)$ 26

41. $A(0, 1)$, $B(3, 5)$, $C(5, 5)$, $D(5, 1)$ 16

42. $A(-5, 3)$, $B(7, -2)$, $C(7, -6)$, $D(-5, -6)$ 38

43. Open-ended The area of a 5 in.-by-5 in. square is the same as the sum of the areas of a 3 in.-by-3 in. square and a 4 in.-by-4 in. square. Find two or more squares that have the same total area as an 11 in.-by-11 in. square.   Samples: 2 in.-by-2 in., 6 in.-by-6 in., 9 in.-by-9 in.; 6 in.-by-6 in., 6 in.-by-6 in., 7 in.-by-7 in.

PROBLEM SOLVING HINT
Make a list of perfect squares.

247

FIND OUT BY MODELING Have students work in small groups to complete this activity. One student may want to hold the small squares together while another staples them. Watch that students staple the second pair of squares so that they form a 2 by 2 square.

GETTING READY FOR LESSON 5-2 These exercises prepare students to find the areas of triangles.

Wrap Up

THE BIG IDEA Ask students: *Describe in your own words why the formulas for the area and perimeter of a rectangle "work."*

RETEACHING ACTIVITY Students sketch all the possible rectangles with integral dimensions and an area of 60 square units. (Reteaching worksheet 5-1)

Exercises   MIXED REVIEW

Exercises 45–47 Students can graph the segment and the midpoint as a way to check their answers.

JOURNAL Ask students to include the units of measurement for area and perimeter and a diagram illustrating each. Make sure their examples are different from those found in the lesson.

Lesson Quiz

Lesson Quiz is also available in Transparencies.

1. Find the perimeter of a rectangle with base 15 in. and height 13 in.
   56 in.

2. Find the area of a rectangle with vertices $(-2, 4)$, $(-2, -2)$, $(3, 4)$, and $(3, -2)$. **30 square units**

3. You have 96 feet of fencing. You want to fence a rectangular region in such a way that it has the maximum area. What are the dimensions of the region?
   24 ft by 24 ft

---

44. **Standardized Test Prep** The length of a rectangle is increased by 50% and the width is decreased by 50%. How is the area affected? **B**
    A. increased by 25%   **B.** decreased by 25%   **C.** increased by 50%
    D. decreased by 50%   **E.** unchanged

Find Out by Modeling

You can create a quilt by sewing together congruent squares to form blocks. To model a quilt block, cut four 3 in.-by-3 in. squares out of $\frac{1}{4}$-in. graph paper. Place one square on top of another and make a seam by stapling the two squares together $\frac{1}{4}$ in. from one of the edges. Unfold the squares and press the seam flat in the back.

Repeat this with the two other squares. Then place the two sections on top of each other. Staple a $\frac{1}{4}$-in. seam from one end to the other. Unfold and press the seams back.

• What is the total area of the four paper squares that you started with? **36 in.²**

• What is the area of your finished quilt block? **30.25 in.²**

Exercises   MIXED REVIEW

Coordinate Geometry Find the coordinates of the midpoint of a segment with the given endpoints.

45. $A(4, 1)$, $B(7, 9)$
46. $G(0, 3)$, $H(3, 8)$
47. $R(-2, 7)$, $S(-6, -1)$

45. (5.5, 5)   46. (1.5, 5.5)
47. (−4, 3)

Write the converse of each conditional.

48. If you make a touchdown, then you score six points.
    If you score 6 pts., then you make a touchdown.
49. If it is Thanksgiving, then it is November.
    If it is November, then it is Thanksgiving.
50. If a figure is a square, then it is a rectangle.
    If a figure is a rectangle, then it is a square.
51. A triangle has two sides with lengths 3 m and 5 m. What is the range of possible lengths for the third side?
    between 2 m and 8 m

FOR YOUR JOURNAL

Explain the difference between area and perimeter. Use examples to show how and when each type of measurement might be used.

Getting Ready for Lesson 5-2

Each rectangle is divided into two congruent triangles. Find the area of each triangle.

52. **6 units²**
53. **2 units²**
54. **3 units²**
55. **8 units²**

CONNECTING TO PRIOR KNOWLEDGE Draw a parallelogram, a rectangle, a square, and a rhombus. Have students name each figure in as many ways as they can.

Suggest that students cut their rectangles along grid lines. This will facilitate measuring the bases, heights, and lengths. Help students see that the slope of the cut they make to form the triangle does not affect the type of figure that results, nor does cutting from one of the shorter sides to the other.

Make sure that students include in their lists of similarities that their rectangles and parallelograms have equal base lengths, heights, and areas. This will help them see why Theorem 5-2 is true.

What You'll Learn
- Finding areas of parallelograms and triangles

...And Why
To solve design problems in architecture and landscaping

What You'll Need
- centimeter grid paper
- straightedge
- scissors
- tape

Connections Architecture . . . and more

5-2 Areas of Parallelograms and Triangles

WORK TOGETHER

Have each member of your group cut out a different rectangle from centimeter grid paper.

- Record the base, height, and area of each rectangle.

- Cut out a triangle from one side of the rectangle as shown below. Tape it to the opposite side to form a parallelogram.

1. Compare each original rectangle with the parallelogram formed. With your group, list all the ways the rectangle and the parallelogram are the same and all the ways they are different. See below.

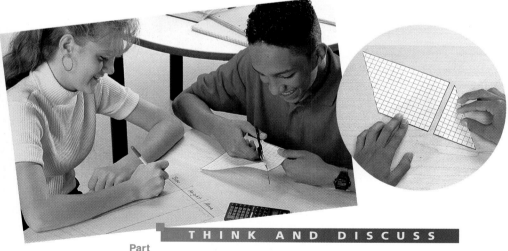

THINK AND DISCUSS

Part 1 Areas of Parallelograms

In the Work Together, you cut a rectangle into two pieces and used the pieces to form another parallelogram. The area of the parallelogram was the same as the area of the rectangle. This suggests the following theorem.

Theorem 5-2
Area of a Parallelogram

The area of a parallelogram is the product of any base and the corresponding height.

$$A = bh$$

1. Answers may vary. Sample: One pair of opp. sides of the rectangle is ≅ to one pair of opp. sides of the ▱. Their heights and areas are =. The angles of the rectangle are ≠ to the angles of the ▱.

Lesson Planning Options

Prerequisite Skills

- Understanding parallelograms and triangles

Assignment Options for Exercises On Your Own

To provide flexible scheduling, this lesson can be subdivided into parts.

▼ 1 **Core** 4, 5, 7, 16–18
Extension 33, 34

▼ 2 **Core** 1–3, 6, 8–15, 19–28
Extension 29–32, 35, 36

Use Mixed Review to maintain skills.

Resources

📖 **Student Edition**
Skills Handbook, p. 659
Extra Practice, p. 638
Glossary/Study Guide

📦 **Teaching Resources**
Chapter Support File, Ch. 5
- Practice 5-2 (two worksheets)
- Reteaching 5-2
- Alternative Activity 5-2
Classroom Manager 5-2
Glossary, Spanish Resources

🖥 **Transparencies**
1, 8, 60

Example 1

ESL Students may be confused by the use of the terms *base* and *height* in this lesson. Review their definitions and confirm that students understand that *base* and *height* can be used interchangeably with *length* and *width* when referring to rectangles. Also clarify any false understanding that the horizontal side is always the *base* or *length*.

Question 2 It may help students to turn their papers so the base to which they are going to draw an altitude is horizontal. Remind students that the altitude may not always be in the interior of the figure. Suggest that students review Part 2 of Lesson 4-8 on page 229.

ERROR ALERT! Some students may multiply the height by the noncorresponding base. **Remediation:** Point out that although any side can be the base, the height that corresponds to that base must be perpendicular to that base.

Example 2

ERROR ALERT! Some students may think that the base corresponding to height $\overline{CF}$ is $\overline{AF}$ rather than $\overline{AD}$. **Remediation:** Help students see that the base of a parallelogram is a side of the parallelogram and that it is extended to draw the height. You may want to have students use a dotted line rather than a solid line to extend the base.

Additional Examples

FOR EXAMPLE 1

What is the area of parallelogram *GHIJ* with vertices $G(-4, -2)$, $H(3, -2)$, $I(5, 3)$, and $J(-2, 3)$.
35 square units

Discussion: *Give the coordinates of a rectangle with the same area.*

FOR EXAMPLE 2

Refer to the diagram in Example 2. If $AD = 5$ in., $DE = 4$ in., and $AB = 6$ in., find CF. **4.8 in.**

FOR EXAMPLE 3

Refer to the formula in Example 3. How much force is exerted by a 65 mi/h wind blowing directly against the end of the building shown below? **about 8551 pounds**

You can choose any side to be a **base** of a parallelogram. An **altitude** is any segment perpendicular to the line containing the base drawn from the side opposite the base. The **height** is the length of the altitude.

2. Draw any parallelogram and draw altitudes to two adjacent sides. See margin p. 252.

Example 1

Coordinate Geometry What is the area of $\square PQRS$ with vertices $P(1, 2)$, $Q(6, 2)$, $R(8, 5)$, and $S(3, 5)$?

Graph $\square PQRS$. If you choose $\overline{PQ}$ as the base, then the height is 3.

$b = PQ = 5$
$h = 3$
$A = bh = 5(3)$
$ = 15$

$\square PQRS$ has area 15 square units.

3. **Try This** What is the area of $\square EFGH$ with vertices $E(-4, 3)$, $F(0, 3)$, $G(1, -2)$, and $H(-3, -2)$? **20 units^2**

You can use the area formula to find missing dimensions in a parallelogram.

Example 2

In $\square ABCD$, $\overline{DE}$ and $\overline{CF}$ are altitudes. Find CF to the nearest tenth.

Find the area of $\square ABCD$. Then use the area formula to find CF.

$A = bh$
$ = 10(12)$ Use base *AB* and height *DE*.
$ = 120$

The area of $\square ABCD$ is 120 in.^{2}.

$A = bh$
$120 = 13(CF)$ Use base *AD* and height *CF*.
$CF = \dfrac{120}{13}$ Divide each side by 13.
$ \approx 9.2$

$\overline{CF}$ is about 9.2 in. long.

4. **Try This** A parallelogram has sides 15 cm and 18 cm. The altitude perpendicular to the line containing the 15 cm side is 9 cm long. Sketch the parallelogram. Then find the length of the altitude perpendicular to the line containing the 18-cm side. **7.5 cm**

250

Some students may choose to solve the problem in Example 2 more directly by solving the equation 10(12) =13(CF). Point out how this is essentially the same as shown in the example.

WORK TOGETHER   p. 251

ALTERNATIVE METHOD Draw any △PQR. Connect the midpoints of $\overline{PQ}$ and $\overline{PR}$. Then drop a perpendicular from P to the new segment. Cut out the two triangles and rearrange the three pieces to form a rectangle. The area of the rectangle, which equals the area of the triangle, is $b(\frac{h}{2})$ or $\frac{1}{2}bh$.

AUDITORY LEARNING Have students practice repeating aloud the formulas for the area of a rectangle, parallelogram, and triangle. Remind students who say "area equals one-half base times height" that the base and height must refer to perpendicular segments.

Example 3   Relating to the Real World

DIVERSITY Depending on your geographical area, hurricanes may or may not be a threat. Students may want to share experiences they may have had with hurricanes, tornadoes, and earthquakes. Discuss the precautions one takes when living in areas with a high incidence of these potentially catastrophic events.

Part 2

WORK TOGETHER

Work in groups. Have each member of your group cut out a different parallelogram from centimeter grid paper.

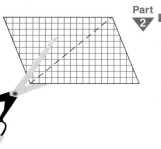

- Record the base, height, and area of each parallelogram.
- Cut each parallelogram along a diagonal as shown, forming two triangles.

5. How does the area of each triangle compare to the area of the parallelogram?   **The area of each △ is half the area of the ▱.**

THINK AND DISCUSS

Areas of Triangles

In the Work Together, you cut a parallelogram into two congruent triangles of equal area. This suggests the following theorem.

Theorem 5-3 Area of a Triangle	The area of a triangle is half the product of any base and the corresponding height. $A = \frac{1}{2}bh$	

You can choose any side to be a **base** of a triangle. The corresponding **height** is the length of an altitude drawn to the line containing that base.

Example 3   Relating to the Real World

Architecture When designing a building, an architect must be sure that the building can stand up to hurricane force winds, which have a velocity of 73 mi/h or more. The formula $F = 0.004Av^2$ gives the force F in pounds exerted by a wind blowing against a flat surface. A is the area of the surface in square feet, and v is the wind velocity in miles per hour. How much force is exerted by a 73 mi/h wind blowing directly against the side of this building?

Find the area of the side of the building.

triangle area $= \frac{1}{2}bh = \frac{1}{2}(20)6 = 60$ ft²

rectangle area $= bh = 20(12) = 240$ ft²

area of end of building $= 60 + 240 = 300$ ft²

$F = 0.004Av^2$ Use the formula for force.

$= 0.004(300)(73)^2$ Substitute 300 for A and 73 for v.

$= 6394.8$

The force is about 6400 lb.

6 ft

12 ft

20 ft

Technology Options

Students may use geometry software to draw the triangles in Exercise 28. Suggest they draw one triangle with area 12 square units, then drag its vertices to create other triangles with the same area. Students may also replicate the activity described in Exercise 29.

Prentice Hall Technology

Software
- Secondary Math Lab Toolkit™
- Integrated Math Lab 31
- Computer Item Generator 5-2

Internet
- See the Prentice Hall site. (http://www.phschool.com)

251

Exercises 4–6 The areas of these figures can be found by using the results of Exercises 1–3. Suggest that students calculate the areas in more than one way in order to verify their answers.

ALTERNATIVE ASSESSMENT **Exercises 16–18** These exercises can help you assess students' understanding of the area of a parallelogram. Check that students correctly identify a base and its corresponding height in each parallelogram.

KINESTHETIC LEARNING **Exercise 19** If you have block scheduling or an extended class period, get permission to close off a certain area of the school parking lot. Have students use measuring tape to find the dimensions and calculate the area of the section. Have them draw a diagram and write an explanation of how they found the measurements and calculated the area.

---

pages 249–250 Think and Discuss

2.

pages 252–254 On Your Own

19a. Answers may vary. Sample:
(1) Find the area of 31 ft-by-50 ft rectangle and subtract the area of 2 △s.

(2) Find the area of each small ▱. Multiply by 4 and add the area of the 15 ft-by-50 ft rectangle.

Find the area of each figure.

1. ▱ABJF
15 units²

2. △BDJ
6 units²

3. △DKJ
6 units²

4. ▱BDKJ
12 units²

5. ▱ADKF
27 units²

6. △BCJ
3 units²

7. The area of a parallelogram is 24 in.² and the height is 6 in. Find the length of the base. **4 in.**

8. An isosceles right triangle has area of 98 cm². Find the length of each leg. **14 cm**

Find the area of each shaded region.

9.

15 cm   12 cm
— 20 cm —
240 cm²

10.

3 ft
2 ft   2 ft
3 ft²

11.

3.5 cm
5.8 cm
4 cm
20.3 cm²

12.

6.9 m
4 m   4 m
27.6 m²

Coordinate Geometry (a) Graph the lines. (b) Find the area of the triangle enclosed by the lines.

13. $y = x$, $x = 0$, and $y = 7$
24.5 units²

14. $y = x + 2$, $y = 2$, $x = 6$
18 units²

15. $y = -\frac{1}{2}x + 3$, $y = 0$, $x = -2$
16 units²

Find the value of *h* in each parallelogram.

16.

h
14
8   10
11.2

17.

0.3   0.5
h
0.4
0.24

18.

13   h 12
18
about 16.6

19. *Landscaping* Taisha's Bakery has a plan for a 50 ft-by-31 ft parking lot. The four parking spaces are congruent parallelograms, the driving area is a rectangle, and the two unpaved areas for flowers are congruent triangles.
  a. *Writing* Explain two different ways to find the area of the region that must be paved. **See margin.**
  b. *Verify* your answer to part (a) by using each method to find the area. **1390 ft²**

50 ft
15 ft
10 ft
31 ft

20. *Algebra* In a triangle, a base and the corresponding height are in the ratio 3 : 2. The area is 108 in.². Find the base and the corresponding height. **18 in.; 12 in.**

252

Find the area of each figure.

21.

8 units^2

22.

9 units^2

23.

8 units^2

24a. Blank grid; the area not shaded is > the area shaded.

b. No; the figures have = area.

24. Probability Ann drew these three figures on a grid. A fly landed at random at a point on the grid.
 a. Is the fly more likely to have landed on one of the figures or on the blank grid? Explain.
 b. Suppose you know the fly landed on one of the figures. Is the fly more likely to have landed on one figure than on another? Explain.
 a–b. See margin.

28.

Find the area of each figure.

25.

25 ft

25 ft

25 ft

312.5 ft^2

26.

15 cm

21 cm

20 cm

525 cm^2

27.

200 m

120 m

40 m

60 m

12,800 m^2

28. Open-ended Using graph paper, draw an acute triangle, an obtuse triangle, and a right triangle, each with area 12 units^2.
See margin for sample.

29. Technology Juanita used geometry software to create the figure at the right. She drew segment $\overline{AB}$, chose point C, and constructed line k parallel to $\overline{AB}$ through point C. Then Juanita chose point D on line k. Next she dragged point D along line k to form different triangles. How do the areas of the triangles compare? Explain. **The areas of the △s are =; they have the same bases and = heights.**

The ancient Greek mathematician Heron is most famous for his formula for the area of a triangle in terms of its sides a, b, and c.

$$A = \sqrt{s(s - a)(s - b)(s - c)}, \text{ where } s = \frac{1}{2}(a + b + c)$$

Use Heron's formula and a calculator to find the area of each triangle. Round your answer to the nearest whole number.

30. $a = 8$ in., $b = 9$ in., $c = 10$ in.   **31.** $a = 15$ m, $b = 17$ m, $c = 21$ m
   34 in.^{2} 126 m^2

32. a. Use Heron's formula to find the area of the triangle at the right.
   b. Verify your answer to part (a) by using the formula $A = \frac{1}{2}bh$.

   a. 54 in.^{2} b. Check students' work.

15 in. 9 in. 12 in.

253

FIND OUT BY CREATING Depending on the size of the groups, students may want to make additional blocks so they can create a larger quilt. Encourage students to create their own designs. Depending on materials available, students can use crayons, markers, water colors, or colored construction paper to make their designs.

Wrap Up

THE BIG IDEA Ask students: *Explain how the formula for the area of a rectangle can be used to find the formulas for the area of a parallelogram and the area of a triangle.*

RETEACHING ACTIVITY Students draw obtuse, acute, and right triangles on grid paper with an area of 12 square units. Then they find the area of other triangles. (Reteaching worksheet 5-2)

Exercises MIXED REVIEW

TRANSFORMATIONS Exercises 37–40 Have students copy the grid and the figure. Then have them draw each image in addition to giving its coordinates.

GETTING READY FOR LESSON 5-3 These exercises prepare students for solving problems using the Pythagorean Theorem.

Reteaching 5-2
Practice 5-2
Practice 5-2
Mixed Exercises

Lesson Quiz

Lesson Quiz is also available in Transparencies.

1. Find the area of parallelogram *ABCD* with vertices $A(1, 0)$, $B(5, 0)$, $C(4, 4)$ and $D(-1, 4)$.
   16 square units

2. Find the area of a triangle enclosed by the lines $y = 0$, $y = 2x$, and $x = 4$.
   16 square units

3. Find the area of the figure.
   120 cm²

12 cm

8 cm

6 cm

254

Coordinate Geometry The vertices of a polygon are given. Graph each polygon and find its area.

33. $A(3, 9), B(8, 9), C(2, -3), D(-3, -3)$ **60 units²**

34. $E(1, 1), F(4, 5), G(11, 5), H(8, 1)$ **28 units²**

35. $M(-2, -5), L(1, -5), N(2, -2)$ **4.5 units²**

36. $R(1, 2), S(1, 6), T(4, 1)$ **6 units²**

Find Out by Creating

Your class can model a quilt by using the quilt blocks your classmates created in the *Find Out* activity on page 248. Here is one suggestion for a design.

Staple four blocks together in a row, keeping the orientation shown at the left throughout the row. Do this until you have four rows.

On each block, mark off a $\frac{1}{4}$-in. border for seams. Draw the four diagonals pictured.

Staple the rows together, turning the second and fourth row upside down. Color the blocks to create a three-dimensional illusion.

Exercises MIXED REVIEW

Transformations Find the coordinates of the images of *A*, *B*, *C*, and *D* after each transformation.

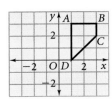

37. reflection in the line $x = 1$
    $A'(1, 3), B'(-1, 3), C'(-1, 2), D'(1, 0)$
38. translation $\langle -4, -7 \rangle$
    $A'(-3, -4), B'(-1, -4), C'(-1, -5), D'(-3, -7)$
39. rotation 180° about the point $(0, 0)$
    $A'(-1, -3), B'(-3, -3), C'(-3, -2), D'(-1, 0)$
40. Find the coordinates of the midpoint of the segment joining $P(-2, -3)$ and $Q(9, 12)$. (3.5, 4.5)

Getting Ready for Lesson 5-3

Square the lengths of the sides of each triangle. What do you notice?

41. A
     3 m   5 m
     C 4 m B
     9 + 16 = 25

42. A
     5 in.   13 in.
     C 12 in. B
     25 + 144 = 169

43. A
     6 yd   10 yd
     C 8 yd B
     36 + 64 = 100

Students review how to simplify radical expressions. Students will use this skill in Lesson 5-3 when they apply the Pythagorean Theorem.

Example 1

Some students may want to simplify radicals such as $\sqrt{8}$ and $\sqrt{294}$ before multiplying or dividing by another radical. While this is acceptable, point out that it is not necessary and is sometimes less efficient because the resulting product or quotient may still need to be simplified.

Example 2

ERROR ALERT! Some students may rewrite $\sqrt{\frac{4}{3}}$ as $\frac{\sqrt{4}}{3}$.

Remediation: Have students use a calculator to approximate the two expressions to show that they are not equivalent. Then have them approximate $\frac{\sqrt{4}}{\sqrt{3}}$ to verify that it is equivalent to $\sqrt{\frac{4}{3}}$.

ADDITIONAL PROBLEM Have students simplify the expressions $\sqrt{15} \cdot \sqrt{30}$ and $\sqrt{42} \div \sqrt{12}$. $3\sqrt{50}$; $\frac{\sqrt{14}}{2}$

Math ToolboX — Algebra Review

Simplifying Radicals

You can multiply and divide numbers that are under radical signs.

> Before Lesson 5-3

Example 1

Simplify the expressions $\sqrt{2} \cdot \sqrt{8}$ and $\sqrt{294} \div \sqrt{3}$.

$$\sqrt{2} \cdot \sqrt{8} = \sqrt{2 \cdot 8}$$ Write both numbers under one radical.
$$= \sqrt{16}$$ Simplify the expression under the radical.
$$= 4$$ Factor out perfect squares and simplify.

$$\sqrt{294} \div \sqrt{3} = \sqrt{\frac{294}{3}}$$
$$= \sqrt{98}$$
$$= \sqrt{49 \cdot 2}$$
$$= 7\sqrt{2}$$

A radical expression is in simplest radical form when all the following are true.

- The number under the radical sign has no perfect square factors other than 1.
- The number under the radical sign does not contain a fraction.
- The denominator does not contain a radical expression.

Example 2

Write $\sqrt{\frac{4}{3}}$ in simplest form.

$$\sqrt{\frac{4}{3}} = \frac{\sqrt{4}}{\sqrt{3}}$$ Rewrite the single radical as the quotient of two radicals.
$$= \frac{2}{\sqrt{3}}$$ Simplify.
$$= \frac{2}{\sqrt{3}} \cdot \frac{\sqrt{3}}{\sqrt{3}}$$ Multiply by a form of 1 to rationalize the denominator.
$$= \frac{2\sqrt{3}}{3}$$

Simplify each expression.

1. $\sqrt{5} \cdot \sqrt{10}$ $5\sqrt{2}$
2. $\sqrt{243}$ $9\sqrt{3}$
3. $\sqrt{128} \div \sqrt{2}$ 8
4. $\sqrt{\frac{125}{4}}$ $\frac{5\sqrt{5}}{2}$

5. $\sqrt{6} \cdot \sqrt{8}$ $4\sqrt{3}$
6. $\frac{\sqrt{36}}{\sqrt{3}}$ $2\sqrt{3}$
7. $\frac{\sqrt{144}}{\sqrt{2}}$ $6\sqrt{2}$
8. $\sqrt{3} \cdot \sqrt{12}$ 6

9. $\sqrt{72} \div \sqrt{2}$ 6
10. $\sqrt{169}$ 13
11. $24 \div \sqrt{8}$ $6\sqrt{2}$
12. $\sqrt{300} \div \sqrt{5}$ $2\sqrt{15}$

CONNECTING TO PRIOR KNOWLEDGE Ask students if the following can be the lengths of sides of a triangle. If yes, ask them to identify the lengths of the sides opposite the greatest and smallest angles.

a. 3, 4, 5   **b.** 4, 7, 12   **c.** 5, 6, 10   **d.** 7, 7, 14

WORK TOGETHER

Emphasize that students should draw and cut the rectangles, triangles, and squares with precision. Students may want to tape together the pieces they form so they can place the squares on top of each other and compare areas.

Question 3 Ask students to explain their reasoning. Help them see how their conclusions are related to the lengths of the sides of the right triangles cut from the rectangle.

Lesson Planning Options

Prerequisite Skills

• Simplifying radicals

Assignment Options for Exercises On Your Own

To provide flexible scheduling, this lesson can be subdivided into parts.

 Core 1–10, 23–32
Extension 37, 46–50

 Core 11–22, 33–36, 38–45, 56–58
Extension 51–55

Use Mixed Review to maintain skills.

Resources

Student Edition

Skills Handbook, p. 660
Extra Practice, p. 639
Glossary/Study Guide

Teaching Resources

Chapter Support File, Ch. 5
• Practice 5-3 (two worksheets)
• Reteaching 5-3
• Alternative Activity 5-3
Classroom Manager 5-3
Glossary, Spanish Resources

Transparencies

5, 61, 64

What You'll Learn

• Using the Pythagorean Theorem and its converse

...And Why

To solve problems involving boundaries, packaging, and satellites

What You'll Need

scissors, graph paper, colored paper, straightedge

Connections **Recreation ... and more**

5-3 The Pythagorean Theorem and Its Converse

WORK TOGETHER

Work in groups. Using graph paper, draw any rectangle. Label the sides *a* and *b*. Cut four rectangles with length *a* and width *b* from the graph paper. Then cut each rectangle on its diagonal, *c*, forming eight congruent triangles.

Cut three squares from the colored paper, one with sides of length *a*, one with sides of length *b*, and one with sides of length *c*.

Separate the pieces into groups.

Group 1: four triangles and the two smaller squares

Group 2: four triangles and the largest square

Arrange the pieces of each group to form a square.

1. Write an algebraic expression for the area of each of the squares you formed. $a^2 + b^2 + 2ab$; $c^2 + 2ab$

2. How do the areas of the two squares you formed compare?
   The areas are =.

3. What can you conclude about the areas of the squares you cut from colored paper? The area of the largest square is = to the sum of the areas of the smaller squares.

4. Express your conclusion as an algebraic equation.
   $c^2 = a^2 + b^2$

THINK AND DISCUSS

Part 1 The Pythagorean Theorem

In a right triangle, the side opposite the right angle is the longest side. It is the **hypotenuse**. The other two sides are the **legs of a right triangle**.

MAKING CONNECTIONS The Work Together presented one justification of the Pythagorean Theorem. Students will prove this theorem in a different way in Exercise 46. Students may be surprised to learn that there are at least 360 proofs of the Pythagorean Theorem. One such proof dates from 1876 and is credited to President James A. Garfield. It is shown on page 273.

Students may already be familiar with the Pythagorean Theorem and may be able to recite "$a^2 + b^2 = c^2$." Have students practice stating the theorem using words.

Sometimes the rounding directions given in a lesson may be in conflict with what students have learned about significant digits in science. Students should follow the rounding directions given for an exercise and should not be concerned about significant digits.

Example 1 Relating to the Real World ·············

Discuss the fact that, while an equation of the form $x^2 = a$ has two solutions, one positive and one negative, the negative solution is discarded, since all distances in geometry are positive.

Point out to students that when using most scientific calculators to approximate a square root, they should first enter the number, then press the square root key.

The Work Together presents a justification of the well-known right triangle relationship called the Pythagorean Theorem.

Theorem 5-4
Pythagorean Theorem

In a right triangle, the sum of the squares of the lengths of the legs is equal to the square of the length of the hypotenuse.

$$a^2 + b^2 = c^2$$

5. **a.** A right triangle has sides of lengths 20, 29, and 21. What is the length of the hypotenuse? **29**
   b. **Verify** that the Pythagorean Theorem is true for the right triangle in part (a). **$20^2 + 21^2 = 841 = 29^2$**

Example 1 Relating to the Real World

Recreation A city park department rents paddle boats at docks near each entrance to the park. About how far is it to paddle from one dock to the other?

You can find the distance between the two docks by finding the hypotenuse of the right triangle.

$a^2 + b^2 = c^2$	Use the Pythagorean Theorem.
$250^2 + 350^2 = c^2$	Substitute 250 for a and 350 for b.
$62{,}500 + 122{,}500 = c^2$	Simplify.
$185{,}000 = c^2$	
$c = \sqrt{185{,}000}$	Find the square root.

185,000 430.11626

It is about 430 m from one dock to the other.

6. **Try This** Find the length of the hypotenuse of a right triangle with legs of lengths 7 and 24. **25**

350 m

250 m

Additional Examples

FOR EXAMPLE 1 ··························

Refer to the diagram in Example 1. If the lengths of the streets connecting the docks are 175 m and 200 m, about how far is it to paddle from one dock to the other? Round your answer to the nearest ten meters.
270 m

FOR EXAMPLE 2 ··························

The hypotenuse of a right triangle has length 16 cm and one of its legs has length 10 cm. Find the length of the other leg. Leave your answer in simplest radical form. **$2\sqrt{39}$ cm**

FOR EXAMPLE 3 ··························

The numbers represent the lengths of the sides of a triangle. Classify each as acute, obtuse, or right.

a. 18, 22, 45 **b.** 24, 45, 51
a. obtuse **b. right**

257

258

QUICK REVIEW

A radical expression is in simplest radical form when all the following are true.
• The number under the radical sign has no perfect square factors other than 1.
• The number under the radical sign does not contain a fraction.
• The denominator does not contain a radical expression.

For practice with radical expressions, see Skills Handbook page 660.

Sometimes you will leave your answer in simplest radical form.

Example 2

Find the value of x. Leave your answer in simplest radical form.

Use the Pythagorean Theorem.

$a^2 + b^2 = c^2$	
$8^2 + x^2 = 20^2$	Substitute.
$64 + x^2 = 400$	Simplify.
$x^2 = 336$	Subtract 64 from each side.
$x = \sqrt{336}$	Find the square root.
$x = \sqrt{16(21)}$	Simplify.
$x = 4\sqrt{21}$	

7. Try This The hypotenuse of a right triangle has length 12. One leg has length 6. Find the length of the other leg in simplest radical form.
$6\sqrt{3}$

When the lengths of the sides of a right triangle are integers, the integers form a **Pythagorean triple.** Here are some common Pythagorean triples.

3, 4, 5   5, 12, 13   8, 15, 17   7, 24, 25

8. Open-ended Choose an integer. Multiply each number of a Pythagorean triple by that integer. **Verify** that the result is a Pythagorean triple. **Sample: 5, 12, 13; 10, 24, 26;**
$10^2 + 24^2 = 676 = 26^2$ ✔

Part 2

The Converse of the Pythagorean Theorem

You can use the Converse of the Pythagorean Theorem to determine whether a triangle is a right triangle.

Theorem 5-5
Converse of the Pythagorean Theorem

If the square of the length of one side of a triangle is equal to the sum of the squares of the lengths of the other two sides, then the triangle is a right triangle.

Who? Czech-American mathematician Olga Taussky-Todd (1906–1995) studied Pythagorean triangles. In 1970, she won the Ford Prize for her research.

The Converse of the Pythagorean Theorem leads to the inequalities below. You can use them to determine whether a triangle is obtuse or acute.

In $\triangle ABC$ with longest side c,
if $c^2 > a^2 + b^2$, then the triangle is obtuse, and
if $c^2 < a^2 + b^2$, then the triangle is acute.

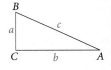

Example 3 ....

Make sure students understand that the Converse of the Pythagorean Theorem can help them classify triangles, provided the three lengths form a triangle. However, it does not indicate if three lengths actually do form a triangle. For example, 5, 4, and 10 may appear to the be lengths of sides of an obtuse triangle ($10^2 > 5^2 + 4^2$), but a triangle cannot be formed with sides measuring 5, 4, and 10 ($5 + 4 < 10$).

CRITICAL THINKING Exercises 4 and 7 Most students will recognize that the altitude bisects the base of each triangle. Ask students to justify their reasoning. (Since the vertex from which the altitude is drawn is equidistant from the endpoints, it must lie on the perpendicular bisector.)

CONNECTING TO STUDENTS' WORLD Exercise 10 Have students measure the diagonal length of a baseball diamond on a local baseball field and use the length to calculate the distance between the bases.

When? The Pythagorean Theorem is named for Pythagoras, a Greek mathematician who lived in the sixth century B.C. We now know that the Babylonians, Egyptians, and Chinese were aware of this relationship before Pythagoras.

The diagram below illustrates an ancient Greek proof of the Pythagorean Theorem for an isosceles right triangle.

Example 3 ....

The numbers represent the lengths of the sides of a triangle. Classify each triangle as acute, obtuse, or right.

a. 13, 84, 85

$$85^2 \stackrel{?}{=} 13^2 + 84^2$$
$$7225 \stackrel{?}{=} 169 + 7056$$
$$7225 = 7225$$

Compare c^2 to $a^2 + b^2$. Substitute the length of the longest side for c.
$c^2 = a^2 + b^2$

The triangle is a right triangle.

b. 6, 11, 14

$$14^2 \stackrel{?}{=} 6^2 + 11^2$$
$$196 \stackrel{?}{=} 36 + 121$$
$$196 > 157$$

Compare c^2 to $a^2 + b^2$. Substitute the length of the longest side for c.
$c^2 > a^2 + b^2$

The triangle is an obtuse triangle.

9. Try This A triangle has sides of lengths 7, 8, and 9. Classify the triangle as acute, obtuse, or right.   **acute**

Exercises   ON YOUR OWN

Algebra **Find the value of *x*. Leave your answer in simplest radical form.**

1.

2.

3.

4.

5.

6.

7.

8.

9. A 15-ft ladder is leaning against a building. The base of the ladder is 5 ft from the building. To the nearest foot, how high up the building does the ladder reach?   **14 ft**

PROBLEM SOLVING HINT
Draw a diagram.

10. A brick walkway forms the diagonal of a square playground. The walkway is 24 m long. To the nearest tenth of a meter, how long is a side of the playground?   **17.0 m**

259

pages 259–262   On Your Own

23a. The surveyor could stretch the rope to form a △ with the sides containing 3, 4, and 5 intervals.

  b. Construction of the Aswan High Dam permits flood control.

24.

Choose **Use mental math, paper and pencil, or a calculator. The lengths of the sides of a triangle are given. Classify each triangle as acute, right, or obtuse.**

11. 15, 8, 21 obtuse   **12.** 12, 16, 20 right   **13.** $2, 2\frac{1}{2}, 3$ acute   **14.** 30, 34, 16 right

15. 0.3, 0.4, 0.6 obtuse   **16.** 11, 12, 15 acute   **17.** $\sqrt{3}, 2, 3$ obtuse   **18.** 1.8, 8, 8.2 right

19. 20, 21, 28 acute   **20.** 31, 23, 12 obtuse   **21.** 30, 40, 50 right   **22.** $\sqrt{11}, \sqrt{7}, 4$ acute

23. *Ancient Egypt* Each year the Nile River overflowed its banks and deposited fertile silt on the valley farmlands. Although the flood was helpful to farmers, it often destroyed boundary markers. Egyptian surveyors used a rope with knots at 12 equal intervals to help reconstruct boundaries.
  a. *Writing* Explain how a surveyor could use this rope to form a right angle.
  b. *Research* Find out why the Nile no longer floods as it did in ancient Egypt.
     a–b. See margin.

24. *Open-ended* Draw a right triangle with three sides that are integers. Draw the altitude to the hypotenuse. Label the lengths of the three sides and the altitude. See margin for sample.

Calculator **Use the triangle at the right. Find the missing length to the nearest tenth.**

25. $a = 3, b = 7, c = \blacksquare$ 7.6   **26.** $a = 1.2, b = \blacksquare, c = 3.5$ 3.3

27. $a = \blacksquare, b = 23, c = 30$ 19.3   **28.** $a = 0.7, b = \blacksquare, c = 0.8$ 0.4

29. $a = 8, b = 8, c = \blacksquare$ 11.3   **30.** $a = \blacksquare, b = 9, c = 18$ 15.6

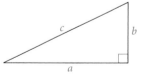

31. *Sewing* You want to embroider a square design. You have an embroidery hoop with a 6-in. diameter. Find the largest value of x such that the entire square will fit in the hoop. Round to the nearest tenth.
   4.2 in.

32. A rectangle has 10-in. diagonals and the lengths of its sides are whole numbers. Use the problem-solving strategy *Guess and Test* to find the perimeter of the rectangle.   28 in.

Find the area of each figure. Leave your answer in simplest radical form.

33.   **34.**   **35.**   **36.**

$\frac{9\sqrt{3}}{2}$ m² $12\sqrt{7}$ cm²   10.5 in.²   168 ft²

260

ALTERNATIVE ASSESSMENT **Exercises 33–36** These exercises can help you assess students' ability to use the Pythagorean Theorem to find the altitudes of triangles and parallelograms in order to apply the area formulas. Students can work in pairs alternating roles as solver and checker.

LOGICAL REASONING **Exercise 46** You may want to review with students how to expand the binomial $(b - a)^2$.

37. Coordinate Geometry You can use the Pythagorean Theorem to prove the Distance Formula. Let points $P(x_1, y_1)$ and $Q(x_2, y_2)$ be the endpoints of the hypotenuse of a right triangle.
   a. Write an algebraic expression to complete each of the following: $PR = $ ■ and $QR = $ ■. $|x_2 - x_1|; |y_2 - y_1|$
   b. By the Pythagorean Theorem, $PQ^2 = PR^2 + QR^2$. Rewrite this statement, substituting the algebraic expressions you found for PR and QR in part (a). $PQ^2 = (x_2 - x_1)^2 + (y_2 - y_1)^2$
   c. Complete the proof by finding the square root of each side of the equation that you wrote in part (b). $PQ = \sqrt{(x_2 - x_1)^2 + (y_2 - y_1)^2}$

Find a third number so that the three numbers form a Pythagorean triple.

38. 9, 41 40   **39.** 14, 48 50   **40.** 60, 61 11   **41.** 8, 17 15

42. 20, 21 29   **43.** 13, 85 84   **44.** 12, 37 35   **45.** 63, 65 16

46. Logical Reasoning You can use the diagram at the right to prove the Pythagorean Theorem.
   a. Find the area of the large square in terms of c. c^2
   b. Find the area of the large square in terms of a and b by finding the area of the four triangles and the small square.
   c. Write an equation setting your answers to part (a) and part (b) equal to each other. Complete the proof by simplifying the equation. $c^2 = 2ab + (b - a)^2; c^2 = a^2 + b^2$
   b. $2ab + (b - a)^2$

 Calculator The figures below are drawn on centimeter graph paper. Find the perimeter of each shaded figure to the nearest tenth.

47.

48.

49.

50.

12 cm   12.5 cm   17.9 cm   10.2 cm

51. Geometry in 3 Dimensions The box at the right is a rectangular solid.
   a. Use $\triangle ABC$ to find the length of the diagonal of the base, d_1.   5 in.
   b. Use $\triangle ABD$ to find the length of the diagonal of the box, d_2.   See below.
   c. You can **generalize** steps in parts (a) and (b). Use the fact that $AC^2 + BC^2 = d_1{}^2$ and $d_1{}^2 + BD^2 = d_2{}^2$ to write a one-step formula to find d_2. $d_2 = \sqrt{AC^2 + BC^2 + BD^2}$
    d. Calculator Use the formula you wrote to find the length of the longest fishing pole you can pack in a box with dimensions 18 in., 24 in., and 16 in.   34 in.
   b. $\sqrt{29}$ in. or about 5.4 in.

261

GEOMETRY IN 3 DIMENSIONS Exercises 52–55 Some students will have difficulty visualizing these segments. If possible, create a 3-dimensional coordinate system using straws. Use toothpicks to show the line segments.

EXTENSION Exercise 57 Have students review the Fibonacci Sequence from Exercise 16 of Lesson 1-1. Let x, y, z, and w represent four consecutive Fibonacci numbers. If $a = xw$, $b = 2yz$, and $c = zw - xy$, then a, b, and c form a Pythagorean triple. Have students check this for three sets of four consecutive Fibonacci numbers.

Exercises 59–61 Remind students to copy the figures and not to write in the textbook.

GETTING READY FOR LESSON 5-4 These exercises prepare students to use the properties of 45°-45°-90° triangles and 30°-60°-90° triangles.

Wrap Up

THE BIG IDEA Ask students: *Rephrase the Pythagorean Theorem in your own words. Then give two examples of how it can be used to solve real-world problems.*

RETEACHING ACTIVITY Students prove the Pythagorean Theorem by building squares on each side of a right triangle and comparing the areas of the squares. (Reteaching worksheet 5-3)

Lesson Quiz

Lesson Quiz is also available in Transparencies.

For Exercises 1–2, leave your answers in simplest radical form.

1. A right triangle has legs of length 8 cm and 14 cm. Find the length of the hypotenuse. $2\sqrt{65}$ cm

2. A right triangle has a hypotenuse of length 18 in. and a leg of length 12 in. Find the length of the other leg. $6\sqrt{5}$ in.

3. The lengths of the sides of a triangle are given. Classify each triangle as acute, right, or obtuse.
   a. 21, 72, 75 **b.** 45, 56, 40
   a. right   b. acute

262

Geometry in 3 Dimensions Points $P(x_1, y_1, z_1)$ and $Q(x_2, y_2, z_2)$ are points in a three-dimensional coordinate system. Use the following formula to find PQ. Leave your answer in simplest radical form.

$$d = \sqrt{(x_2 - x_1)^2 + (y_2 - y_1)^2 + (z_2 - z_1)^2}$$

52. $P(0, 0, 0), Q(1, 2, 3)$ $\sqrt{14}$ **53.** $P(0, 0, 0), Q(-3, 4, -6)$ $\sqrt{61}$

54. $P(-1, 3, 5), Q(2, 1, 7)$ $\sqrt{17}$ **55.** $P(3, -4, 8), Q(-1, 6, 2)$ $2\sqrt{38}$

56. **Space** The Hubble Space Telescope is orbiting Earth 600 km above Earth's surface. Earth's radius is about 6370 km. Use the Pythagorean Theorem to find the distance, x, from the telescope to Earth's horizon. Round your answer to the nearest ten kilometers. **2830 km**

600 km → / x / 6370 km

not drawn to scale

57. **a.** The ancient Greek philosopher Plato used the expressions $2n$, $n^2 - 1$, and $n^2 + 1$ to produce Pythagorean triples. Choose any integer greater than 1. Substitute for n and evaluate the three expressions. **Sample:** $n = 4$; **8, 15, 17**
   b. **Verify** that your answers to part (a) form a Pythagorean triple.
   b. $8^2 + 15^2 = 289 = 17^2$

58. **Standardized Test Prep** $\triangle ABC$ has perimeter 20 in. What is its area? **D**
   A. 12 in.^{2} **B.** 16 in.^{2} **C.** 24 in.^{2}
   D. $8\sqrt{5}$ in.^{2} **E.** $16\sqrt{5}$ in.^{2}

Exercises   MIXED REVIEW

Sketch each figure after a counterclockwise rotation of 90° about C.

59.   **60.**   **61.**

62. An angle is 87°. What is the measure of its complement? **3**

Getting Ready for Lesson 5-4

Use a protractor to find the measures of the angles of each triangle.

63. 45, 45, 90   **64.** 30, 60, 90   **65.** 45, 45, 90
   3 / $3\sqrt{2}$ / 3   2 / 4 / $2\sqrt{3}$ $\sqrt{2}$ / $\sqrt{2}$ / 2

PROBLEM OF THE DAY

One Pythagorean triple is 8, 15, 17. Find at least two other Pythagorean triples that have 15 as one of the numbers. **15, 20, 25; 15, 36, 39; 15, 112, 113**

Problem of the Day is also available in Transparencies.

CONNECTING TO PRIOR KNOWLEDGE Ask students to use the Pythagorean Theorem to find the missing lengths of the following right triangles if a, b, and c represent the lengths of the sides.

a. $a = 1$, $b = \underline{\ ?\ }$, $c = \sqrt{2}$ **b.** $a = 1$, $b = \sqrt{3}$, $c = \underline{\ ?\ }$
c. $a = 3$, $b = \underline{\ ?\ }$, $c = 6$ **d.** $a = 4$, $b = 4$, $c = \underline{\ ?\ }$

Have students work in groups of at least four students. Groups may want to exchange results and check that their conjectures hold true for other groups' results. Have students double-check any answer that does not seem to fit the pattern.

Question 4 The figures in parts a–c show isosceles right triangles in different orientations. Have students identify the legs and hypotenuse of each. Part c may be especially tricky since students observed a pattern in the Work Together where the length of the hypotenuse contains $\sqrt{2}$.

What You'll Learn

- Using the properties of 45°-45°-90° and 30°-60°-90° triangles

...And Why

To study figures in real life, including baseball diamonds and helicopter blades, which use special right triangles

What You'll Need

- centimeter grid paper
- metric ruler
- calculator
- protractor

Connections 🌐 **Sports . . . and more**

5-4 Special Right Triangles

WORK TOGETHER

Work in a group. Have each person draw a different isosceles right triangle on centimeter grid paper. Choose integer values for the lengths of the legs.

- Record the length of each leg. Then use the Pythagorean Theorem to find the length of the hypotenuse. Leave your answers in simplest radical form.

- Organize your group's data in a table like the one below. Look for a pattern relating the side lengths of each triangle.

Triangle	Leg Length	Hypotenuse Length
Triangle 1	■	■
Triangle 2	■	■

- Make a **conjecture** about the relationship between the lengths of the legs and the length of the hypotenuse of an isosceles right triangle.

THINK AND DISCUSS

Part 1 45°-45°-90° Triangles

1. What do you know about the measures of the acute angles of an isosceles right triangle? **Each angle's measure is 45.**

2. If the measures of the angles of a triangle are 45, 45, and 90, why are the legs of the triangle congruent? **Use the Converse of the Isosceles Triangle Theorem.**

Another name for an isosceles right triangle is a 45°-45°-90° triangle.

3. **a.** Use the Pythagorean Theorem to solve for y in terms of x. Leave your answer in simplest radical form. $y = x\sqrt{2}$
   b. Do the results of part (a) agree with the pattern you found in the Work Together? **yes**

4. Find the value of each variable *without* using the Pythagorean Theorem.

   a.
      b.
      c.

Lesson Planning Options

Prerequisite Skills

- Applying the Pythagorean Theorem
- Rationalizing the denominator

Assignment Options for Exercises On Your Own

To provide flexible scheduling, this lesson can be subdivided into parts.

1️⃣ **Core** 1–2, 5–6, 24
   Extension 27

2️⃣ **Core** 3–4, 7–23
   Extension 25–26

Use Mixed Review to maintain skills.

Resources

📖 **Student Edition**
Skills Handbook, p. 660
Extra Practice, p. 638
Glossary/Study Guide

📋 **Teaching Resources**
Chapter Support File, Ch. 5
- Practice 5-4 (two worksheets)
- Reteaching 5-4
Classroom Manager 5-4
Glossary, Spanish Resources

🏛 **Transparencies**
5, 61, 65

263

45°-45°-90° TRIANGLE THEOREM Another way this theorem can be stated is that in a 45°-45°-90° triangle, the lengths of the sides are in the ratio $1 : 1 : \sqrt{2}$.

| **Example 1** | Relating to the Real World .... |

TACTILE LEARNING Have students check the answer by cutting out a 90-mm by 90-mm square, folding it along its diagonal, and measuring the length of the diagonal to the nearest millimeter.

MAKING CONNECTIONS Some students may be surprised to discover that Abner Doubleday did not invent baseball in 1839. Baseball evolved from the British games cricket and rounders. Two earlier games similar to baseball were "town ball" and the "New York game" played in the 1820's.

WORK TOGETHER p. 264

After students make their lists describing △*ABC*, △*ABD*, and △*CBD*, you may want to put on the board a master list compiled from individual groups' lists. Have students add to their lists characteristics or properties that other groups noticed which they did not.

Additional Examples

FOR EXAMPLE 1 ....

A softball diamond is a square where the distance from base to base is 60 ft. To the nearest foot, how far does a person at second base throw to home plate? **85 ft**

Discussion: *If the pitcher's plate is located 40 feet from home plate, is it closer to second base or to home plate?*

FOR EXAMPLE 2 ....

Find the value of each variable.

a.

b.

a. $x = 6$, $y = 6\sqrt{3}$, **b.** $a = 2$, $b = 2\sqrt{3}$

FOR EXAMPLE 3 ....

Refer to the diagram in Example 3. If the sides of the rhombus are 8 cm long, how many square centimeters of colored glass will be needed for the panel? Round your answer to the nearest square centimeter.
55 cm²

The pattern you observed in the Work Together (and generalized in Question 3) is the basis of the following theorem.

| **Theorem 5-6** 45°-45°-90° Triangle Theorem | In a 45°-45°-90° triangle, both legs are congruent and the length of the hypotenuse is $\sqrt{2}$ times the length of a leg. $$\text{hypotenuse} = \sqrt{2} \cdot \text{leg}$$ | |

| **Example 1** | Relating to the Real World .... |

Sports A baseball diamond is a square. The distance from base to base is 90 ft. To the nearest foot, how far does the second baseman throw a ball to home plate?

The distance *d* from second base to home plate is the length of the hypotenuse of a 45°-45°-90° triangle.

$$d = 90\sqrt{2} \qquad \text{hypotenuse} = \sqrt{2} \cdot \text{leg}$$

90 ☒ 2 √ ▤ *127.27922*

The distance from second base to home plate is about 127 ft. ◼

5. a. Calculator Find $\sqrt{2}$ to the nearest thousandth. **1.414**
  b. Mental Math Use the answer to part (a) to estimate the length of a diagonal of a square with sides 100 ft long.
  141.4 ft

Part 2

WORK TOGETHER

Work with a group.

- Draw an equilateral triangle with sides 6 cm long and cut it out. Label the vertices *A*, *B*, and *C*. Fold vertex *A* onto vertex *C* as shown at the left. Unfold the triangle and label the fold-line $\overline{BD}$.

- With your group, make a list of everything you know about △*ABC*, △*ABD*, and △*CBD*, their angles and their sides.

6. Name a pair of congruent triangles. △*ABD*, △*CBD*

7. a. Find $m\angle A$, $m\angle ADB$, and $m\angle ABD$. **60; 90; 30**
  b. Name △*ABD* using its angle measures. △*ABD* is a 30°-60°-90° △.

8. a. Complete: $\overline{DB}$ is the __?__ of $\overline{AC}$. ⊥ **bisector**
  b. If $AB = 6$, what is AD? **3**
  c. Use the Pythagorean Theorem to find *BD* in simplest radical form.
  d. Find the ratios $\frac{AB}{AD}$ and $\frac{BD}{AD}$. **2; $\sqrt{3}$**   **c. $3\sqrt{3}$**

264

Students may need to be reminded that the shortest side of a triangle is always opposite the smallest angle. Point out that in a 30°-60°-90° triangle, the shortest side is always opposite the 30° angle.

30°-60°-90° Triangle Theorem Another way this theorem can be stated is that in a 30°-60°-90° triangle, the lengths of the sides are in a ratio of $1 : \sqrt{3} : 2$.

You may want to have students refer to Example 2 of the Math Toolbox on page 255 to review how to rationalize a denominator before beginning Example 2b.

Example 2

ERROR ALERT! **Part b** When students are not told which is the shortest leg, they will often apply the ratios of the sides incorrectly. **Remediation:** It may help students to remember that when going from a shorter side to a longer side, you multiply and that when going from a longer side to a shorter side, you divide.

THINK AND DISCUSS

30°-60°-90° Triangles

The ratios you found in Question 8 part (d) suggest the following theorem about 30°-60°-90° triangles.

Theorem 5-7
30°-60°-90° Triangle Theorem

In a 30°-60°-90° triangle, the length of the hypotenuse is twice the length of the shorter leg. The length of the longer leg is $\sqrt{3}$ times the length of the shorter leg.

hypotenuse $= 2 \cdot$ shorter leg

longer leg $= \sqrt{3} \cdot$ shorter leg

Justification:

Refer to $\triangle WXZ$ at the left. Since $\overline{WY}$ is the perpendicular bisector of $\overline{XZ}$, $XY = \frac{1}{2}XZ$. That means that if $XW = 2s$, then $XY = s$.

$XY^2 + YW^2 = XW^2$ — Use the Pythagorean Theorem.

$s^2 + YW^2 = (2s)^2$ — Substitute s for XY and 2s for XW.

$YW^2 = 4s^2 - s^2$ — Subtract s^2 from each side.

$YW^2 = 3s^2$

$YW = s\sqrt{3}$ — Find the square root of each side.

Example 2

Algebra Find the value of each variable.

a.

b.

a. $8 = 2x$ — hypotenuse $= 2 \cdot$ shorter leg
$x = 4$

$y = x\sqrt{3}$ — longer leg $= \sqrt{3} \cdot$ shorter leg
$y = 4\sqrt{3}$ — Substitute 4 for x.

b. $5 = d\sqrt{3}$ — longer leg $= \sqrt{3} \cdot$ shorter leg

$d = \frac{5}{\sqrt{3}} \cdot \frac{\sqrt{3}}{\sqrt{3}} = \frac{5\sqrt{3}}{3}$ — Simplify.

$f = 2d$ — hypotenuse $= 2 \cdot$ shorter leg

$f = 2 \cdot \frac{5\sqrt{3}}{3} = \frac{10\sqrt{3}}{3}$ — Substitute $\frac{5\sqrt{3}}{3}$ for d.

9. Try This The shorter leg of a 30°-60°-90° triangle has length $\sqrt{6}$. What are the lengths of the other two sides? Leave your answers in simplest radical form. $3\sqrt{2}, 2\sqrt{6}$

Technology Options

Prentice Hall Technology

Software
- Secondary Math Lab Toolkit™
- Computer Item Generator 5-4

Internet
- See the Prentice Hall site. (http://www.phschool.com)

You can use the properties of 30°-60°-90° triangles to find the dimensions you need to calculate area.

Example 3 **Relating to the Real World** ·················

Design The rhombus at the left is a glass panel for a door. How many square inches of colored glass will you need for the panel?

Draw an altitude of the rhombus. Label *x* and *h* as shown.

$$6 = 2x \qquad \text{hypotenuse} = 2 \cdot \text{shorter leg}$$
$$x = 3$$
$$h = 3\sqrt{3} \qquad \text{longer leg} = \sqrt{3} \cdot \text{shorter leg}$$

Use the value of *h* to find the area.

$$A = bh \qquad \text{Use the formula for area of a parallelogram.}$$
$$= 6(3\sqrt{3}) \qquad \text{Substitute 6 for } b \text{ and } 3\sqrt{3} \text{ for } h.$$

6 ⊠ 3 ⊠ 3 √‾ ▤ 31.176915

You will need about 31.2 in.² of colored glass.

Exercises **ON YOUR OWN**

Find the value of each variable. Leave your answer in simplest radical form.

1.

$x = 8; y = 8\sqrt{2}$

2.

15

3.

$x = 24; y = 12\sqrt{3}$

4.

$x = 5; y = 5\sqrt{3}$

5.

$x = \sqrt{2}; y = 2$

6.

$4\sqrt{2}$

7.

$x = 4; y = 2$

8.

$x = 4\sqrt{3}; y = 6$

9. a. **Farming** A conveyor belt carries bales of hay from the ground to the loft of a barn 27.5 ft above ground. The belt makes a 30° angle with the ground. How far does a bale of hay travel on the conveyor belt? **55 ft**

   b. The conveyor belt moves at 100 ft/min. How long does it take for a bale of hay to go from the ground to the barn loft? **0.55 min or 33 sec**

266

Find the value of each variable. Leave your answer in simplest radical form.

10. $60\sqrt{2}$

11. 9

12. $x = 20;\ y = 20\sqrt{3}$

13. $x = 9;\ y = 18$

14.

15.

16.

17.

14. $a = 7;\ b = 14;$ $c = 7;\ d = 7\sqrt{3}$ 15. $a = 6;\ b = 6\sqrt{2};\ c = 2\sqrt{3};\ d = 6$ 16. $a = 10\sqrt{3};\ b = 5\sqrt{3};\ c = 15;\ d = 5$

17. $a = 4;\ b = 4b$

18. **Writing** Sandra drew this triangle. Rika said that the lengths couldn't be correct. With which student do you agree? Explain.   **See margin.**

19. **Standardized Test Prep** Which of the following *cannot* be the lengths of sides of a 30°-60°-90° triangle?   **C**

A. $\frac{1}{2}, 1, \frac{\sqrt{3}}{2}$ B. $\sqrt{3}, 2\sqrt{3}, 3$ C. $1, \frac{1}{2}, \sqrt{3}$

D. $2\sqrt{2}, \sqrt{2}, \sqrt{6}$ E. $2, 4, 2\sqrt{3}$

 Calculator Find the area of each figure. When an answer is not a whole number, round to the nearest tenth.

20. 98 m²

21. 110.9 cm²

22. 288 ft²

23. 11.3 yd²

24. **Helicopters** The blades of a helicopter meet at right angles and are all the same length. The distance between the tips of two consecutive blades is 36 ft. How long is each blade? Round your answer to the nearest tenth.   **25.5 ft**

25. **Open-ended** The hypotenuse of a 30°-60°-90° triangle is 12 ft long. Write a real-life problem that you can solve using this triangle. Show your solution.   **See margin.**

26. A rhombus has a 60° angle and sides 5 cm long. What is its area? Round your answer to the nearest tenth.   **21.7 cm²**

pages 266–268 On Your Own

18. Rika; Sandra marked the shorter leg as opposite the acute angle with greater measure.

25. Sample: A garden is shaped like an equilateral △ with 12-ft sides. The entrance is the midpoint of one side and there is a bench at the opposite vertex. You need to build a straight cobblestone path from the entrance to the bench. How long is the path?

length of path = $6\sqrt{3}$ = 10.4 ft

Checkpoint page 268

8.

Lesson Quiz

1. One leg of a 45°-45°-90° triangle has length 3 cm. Find the length of the hypotenuse. **$3\sqrt{2}$ cm**

2. The shorter leg of a 30°-60°-90° triangle has length 5 in. Find the lengths of the other leg and the hypotenuse. **leg: $5\sqrt{3}$ in.; hypotenuse: 10 in.**

3. The hypotenuse of a 30°-60°-90° triangle has a length 22 m. Find the lengths of the legs of the triangle. **shorter leg: 11 m; longer leg: $11\sqrt{3}$ m**

---

27. **a. Geometry in 3 Dimensions** Find the length d, in simplest radical form, of the diagonal of a cube with sides 1 unit long. **$\sqrt{3}$ units**
    b. Find the length d of the diagonal of a cube with sides 2 units long. **$2\sqrt{3}$ units**
    c. **Generalize** Find the length d of the diagonal of a cube with sides s units long. **$s\sqrt{3}$ units**

Exercises   MIXED REVIEW

Find the slope of $\overline{AB}$.

28. $A(1, 0)$, $B(-2, 3)$ **−1**   29. $A(-5, 4)$, $B(-1, 8)$ **1**

30. Find the equation of the line with slope $\frac{1}{2}$ containing the point $(-2, 5)$.   **$y = \frac{1}{2}x + 6$**

SELF ASSESSMENT

FOR YOUR JOURNAL

Summarize what you know about special right triangles. Give two real-life examples of special right triangles.

Getting Ready For Lesson 5-5

Find the area and perimeter of each trapezoid to the nearest tenth.

31.

7 units²; 12.1 units

32.

13.5 units²; 16.8 units

Exercises   CHECKPOINT

Find the area and perimeter of each figure.

1.

84 in.²; 48 in.

2. **112 cm²; 48 cm**

3.

72 m²; 40 m

Algebra Find the value of each variable. Leave your answer in simplest radical form.

4.

5. **$x = 10$; $y = 10\sqrt{2}$**

6.

$x = 12\sqrt{3}$; $y = 24$

7. **Standardized Test Prep** Which numbers could represent the lengths of the sides of an acute triangle?   **B**
   A. 3, 4, 5   B. 6, 8, 9   C. 14, 45, 50   D. 5, 12, 13   E. 5, 9, 13

8. **Open-ended** Sketch a rectangle and a triangle with the same perimeter. Label the lengths of the sides of the figures. See margin p. 267 for sample.

PROBLEM OF THE DAY

Each triangle is a 45°-45°-90° triangle. $AB = 1$. Find BC. **16**

Problem of the Day is also available in Transparencies.

Have group members draw different trapezoids. Students who draw trapezoids with two right angles may be surprised that their two trapezoids form a rectangle. (They can also be arranged to form a non-rectangular parallelogram.) Make sure students see that a parallelogram is always formed no matter what the size or shape of the trapezoid.

CONNECTING TO PRIOR KNOWLEDGE Draw an isosceles trapezoid, a trapezoid with two right angles, and two other trapezoids in different orientations on the board. Ask students to name the figures and describe their similarities and differences.

Theorem 5-8 The area of a trapezoid can also be expressed as "the average of the lengths of the bases times the height."

Connections 🌐 Geography . . . and more

What You'll Learn

5-5 Areas of Trapezoids

Lesson Planning Options

• Finding the areas of trapezoids

...And Why

To approximate the areas of irregular figures

What You'll Need

• lined paper
• scissors

Work in groups. Fold a piece of lined paper in half along one of the lines. On two lines of the paper, draw parallel segments of different lengths. Connect the endpoints of the segments to form a trapezoid. Cut through both layers of the folded paper, so that you will have two congruent trapezoids. Label b_1, b_2, and h for each trapezoid.

■ Arrange the congruent trapezoids to form a parallelogram as shown at the left below.

1. a. Write an expression for the length of the base of the parallelogram. $b_1 + b_2$

b. Write an expression for the area of the parallelogram using b_1, b_2, and h. $(b_1 + b_2)h$

2. How does the area of each trapezoid compare to the area of the parallelogram? **The area of each trapezoid is half the area of the ▱.**

3. Use your answers to Questions 1 and 2 to write a formula for the area of each trapezoid. $\frac{1}{2}h(b_1 + b_2)$

Prerequisite Skills

• Applying the Pythagorean Theorem
• Finding the area of parallelograms

Assignment Options for Exercises On Your Own

    Core 1–5, 7–21
    Extension 6, 22–23

Use Mixed Review to maintain skills.

Resources

📖 **Student Edition**

Skills Handbook, p. 659
Extra Practice, p. 638
Glossary/Study Guide

▬ **Teaching Resources**

Chapter Support File, Ch. 5
• Practice 5-5 (two worksheets)
• Reteaching 5-5
• Alternative Activity 5-5
Classroom Manager 5-5
Glossary, Spanish Resources

In a trapezoid, the parallel sides are the **bases.** The nonparallel sides are the **legs.** The **height** h is the distance between the two parallel bases.

Your observations in the Work Together suggest the following theorem.

Theorem 5-8
Area of a Trapezoid

The area of a trapezoid is half the product of the height and the sum of the lengths of the bases.

$$A = \frac{1}{2}h(b_1 + b_2)$$

🖥 **Transparencies**
1, 18, 62

4. *Critical Thinking* When finding the area of a trapezoid, does it make a difference which base is labeled b_1 and which base is labeled b_2? Explain. **no;** $b_1 + b_2 = b_2 + b_1$

269

ERROR ALERT! Some students may assume that the bases are always the horizontal sides and that the altitude is always vertical. **Remediation:** Draw trapezoids in different orientations and have students identify the bases and height.

EXTENSION The median of a trapezoid is a segment joining the legs at their midpoints. Its length is one-half the sum of the lengths of the bases. Have students rewrite the formula for the area of a trapezoid in terms of its median m and height h.
$A = mh$

Example 1 Relating to the Real World

VISUAL LEARNING If you have block scheduling or an extended class period, have students use a map to approximate the areas of other trapezoid-shaped states such as North Dakota and Connecticut. Then have them research the actual areas.

Example 2

Have students check the answer by finding the areas of the triangle and the rectangle formed when the altitude is drawn.

You may want to make a poster displaying the area formulas presented in this chapter. Have students copy the contents of the poster onto index cards which they can use when working on the exercises at home.

Additional Examples

FOR EXAMPLE 1

Find the area of a trapezoid with height 42 in. and bases with lengths 121 in. and 145 in. **5586 in.²**

Discussion: *One student found the area by multiplying 266 by 21. Another found the area by multiplying 42 by 133. Another student multiplied 42 by 266, then divided by two. Which student is correct?*

FOR EXAMPLE 2

Refer to the diagram for Example 2. If $SR = 21$ cm and $PQ = 25$ cm, find the area of trapezoid *PQRS*. **92√3 cm²**

Discussion: *Do the lengths of $\overline{SR}$ and $\overline{PQ}$ affect the relationship between the sides of △PSE?*

Example 1 Relating to the Real World

Geography Approximate the area of Arkansas by finding the area of the trapezoid shown.

$A = \frac{1}{2}h(b_1 + b_2)$ Use the area formula for a trapezoid.

$= \frac{1}{2}(242)(190 + 250)$ Substitute.

$= 53,240$

The area of Arkansas is about 53,240 mi².

5. Try This Find the area of a trapezoid with height 7 cm and bases 12 cm and 15 cm. **94.5 cm²**

Sometimes properties of special right triangles can help you find the area of a trapezoid.

Example 2

Find the area of trapezoid *PQRS*. Leave your answer in simplest radical form.

You can draw an altitude that divides the trapezoid into a rectangle and a 30°-60°-90° triangle. Find h.

$h = 2\sqrt{3}$ longer leg = shorter leg · √3

$A = \frac{1}{2}h(b_1 + b_2)$ Use the area formula for a trapezoid.

$= \frac{1}{2}(2\sqrt{3})(5 + 7)$ Substitute.

$= 12\sqrt{3}$ Simplify.

The area of trapezoid *PQRS* is $12\sqrt{3}$ m².

6. Suppose $m\angle P = 45$. Find the area of trapezoid *PQRS*. **12 m²**

270

Exercises 3 and 5 Students may want to turn the book so that the bases of the trapezoid are horizontal.

DIVERSITY Exercise 6 Assign each group a different country. Have them approximate its area using a map. Ask students to explain which shape(s) they used: triangle, rectangle, parallelogram, trapezoid, or a combination of shapes. Then have them research cultural and historical information about the country. Choose countries where students, their parents, or their grandparents have lived.

ERROR ALERT! Exercise 7 Some students will correctly divide 80 by 40 but forget to multiply the result by 2.

Remediation: Have students substitute the value of $(b_1 + b_2)$ in the trapezoid area formula and solve for h. Then suggest they check their value of h by calculating the area using the values of b_1, b_2, and h and seeing if it equals 80 ft².

ESL Exercise 12 Some students may be unfamiliar with the term "rain gutter." If there are houses with rain gutters close to the school, take students to see them. If not, see if a hardware store will let you borrow a piece of one to bring to class. (You could assign this as an extra credit project.)

ALTERNATIVE METHOD Exercise 13 Have students draw any trapezoid and an altitude that cuts it into a triangle and a parallelogram. Then ask them to justify the trapezoid area formula using the area formulas of a parallelogram and triangle.

Find the area of each trapezoid.

1.

21 in.
16 in.
38 in.
472 in.²

2.

24.3 cm
8.5 cm
9.7 cm
144.5 cm²

3.

5 ft   3 ft
6 ft
30 ft²

4.

72 m²   6 m
10 m   8 m
36 m²

5. Geography Approximate the area of Nevada by finding the area of the trapezoid shown.   108,990 mi²

Humboldt R.
212 mi
315 mi
•Reno
★Carson City
480 mi
Las Vegas •

6. Research On a state map, select a town or county that is shaped like a trapezoid. Use the scale of the map to find values for b_1, b_2, and h. Then approximate the area.   Check students' work.

7. The area of a trapezoid is 80 ft². Its bases have lengths 26 ft and 14 ft. Find its height.   4 ft

8. a. A trapezoid has two right angles, bases of lengths 12 m and 18 m, and a height of 8 m. Sketch the trapezoid.   See margin p. 272.
b. What is the perimeter?   48 m
c. What is the area?   120 m²

Find the area of each trapezoid. Leave your answer in simplest radical form.

9.

8 ft
60°
15 ft
52√3 ft²

10.

13 in.
15 in.
9 in.   45°
375 in.²

11.

8 m
8√2 m
45°   45°
128 m²

12. Geometry in 3 Dimensions A rain gutter has a trapezoidal cross section. The bottom is 4 in. wide, the top is 6 in. wide, and the gutter is 4 in. deep. What is the area of an end-piece?   20 in.²

6 in.
4 in.
4 in.

13. Draw a trapezoid. Label its bases and height b_1, b_2, and h. Then draw a diagonal of the trapezoid.
a. Write an expression for the area of each triangle determined by the diagonal. $\frac{1}{2}hb_1$; $\frac{1}{2}hb_2$
b. Writing Explain how you can justify the trapezoid area formula using the areas of the two triangles.   The area of a figure is = to the sum of the areas of its non-overlapping parts.

14. Open-ended Draw a trapezoid. Measure its height and the lengths of its bases. Find its area.   Check students' work.

15. Crafts You plan to lace together four isosceles trapezoids and a square to make the trash basket shown. How much material will you need?   669 in.²

12 in.
14 in.
9 in.

Technology Options

For Exercise 22, students may want to graph the lines using geometry software.

Prentice Hall Technology

Software
• Secondary Math Lab Toolkit™
• Computer Item Generator 5-5

Internet
• See the Prentice Hall site. (http://www.phschool.com)

8a.

22a.

16. The area of an isosceles trapezoid is 160 cm². Its height is 8 cm and the length of its shorter base is 14 cm. Find the length of the longer base.   **26 cm**

17. *Algebra* One base of a trapezoid is twice as long as the other. The height is the average of the two bases. The area is 324 cm². Find the height and the lengths of the bases. (*Hint:* Let the lengths of the bases be 2*x* and 4*x*.)   **18 cm; 12 cm, 24 cm**

▦ Calculator **Find the area of each trapezoid to the nearest tenth.**

18.

52.6 m²

19.   **49.9 ft²**

20.   **1.8 m²**

21.   **11.3 cm²**

22. **a.** *Coordinate Geometry* Graph the lines
   x = 0, *x* = 6, *y* = 0, and *y* = *x* + 4.
   b. What quadrilateral do the lines form?   **trapezoid**
   c. Find the area of the quadrilateral.   **42 units²**
   a. See margin.

23. *Recreation* A town youth center is building a skateboarding ramp. The ramp is 4 m wide, and the surface of the ramp is modeled by the equation *y* = 0.25*x*². You want to paint the front face of the ramp. Use the triangles and trapezoids shown to approximate the area of the face.   **1.5 m²**

Exercises   MIXED REVIEW

Open-ended **Find a possible length for the third side of a triangle that has two sides with the given lengths.**

                                                                    between 5 ft and 13 ft
24. 7 cm, 10 cm   25. 2 in., 8 in.   26. 13 mm, 6 mm   **27.** 4 ft, 9 ft
between 3 cm and 17 cm   between 6 in. and 10 in.   between 7 mm and 19 mm
28. *Locus* Describe the locus of points in a plane equidistant from the sides of an angle. What is another name for this locus?   a line passing through the vertex and forming ≅ angles with the sides of the orig. angle; angle bisector

272

Getting Ready for Lesson 5-6

Find the area of each regular polygon. If your answer is not an integer, leave it in simplest radical form.

29.

$25\sqrt{3}$ cm²

30.

50 ft²

31.

$\dfrac{100\sqrt{3}}{3}$ m²

Chapter Project   Find Out by Researching

In the early 1900s, Seminoles of southern Florida developed a method of arranging strips of fabric to create geometric designs. These patchwork patterns sometimes serve to advertise the clan to which the wearer belongs. **Check students' work.**

- Research the patchwork techniques used by the Seminoles.

- Create your own Seminole patchwork design with colored paper, graphics software, or fabric.

- In the photo, notice the angled strips with trapezoids at each end. Explain, with diagrams or models, how this effect was created.

A Point in Time

1500   1600   1700   1800   1900   2000

Presidential Proof

Presidents are known more often for their foreign policy than for their mathematical creativity. James Garfield, the 20th President of the United States, was an exception. After serving as a general in the Civil War, in **1876** Garfield demonstrated this proof of the Pythagorean Theorem.

In the diagram, $\triangle NRM$ and $\triangle RPQ$ are congruent right triangles with sides of length a, b, and c. The legs of isosceles right triangle NRP have length c. The three triangles form trapezoid MNPQ. The sum of the areas of the three right triangles equals the area of trapezoid MNPQ.

Areas of Triangles $=$ Area of Trapezoid

$$\tfrac{1}{2}ab + \tfrac{1}{2}ab + \tfrac{1}{2}c^2 = \tfrac{1}{2}(a+b)(a+b)$$

$$ab + \tfrac{1}{2}c^2 = \tfrac{1}{2}a^2 + ab + \tfrac{1}{2}b^2$$

$$\tfrac{1}{2}c^2 = \tfrac{1}{2}a^2 + \tfrac{1}{2}b^2$$

$$c^2 = a^2 + b^2$$

Reteaching 5-5

Practice 5-5

Practice 5-5

Lesson Quiz

Lesson Quiz is also available in Transparencies.

1. Find the area of a trapezoid with base lengths 12 cm and 21 cm and height 8 cm. **132 cm²**

2. Find the area of the trapezoid shown.

90 ft²

3. Find the area, to the nearest tenth, of the trapezoid shown.

20.8 cm²

273

PROBLEM OF THE DAY

Six squares are made with 17 toothpicks. Remove 6 toothpicks to leave two squares. Answers will vary. Sample given.

Problem of the Day is also available in Transparencies.

CONNECTING TO PRIOR KNOWLEDGE Present students with the following diagram. Ask them what they can say about $\overline{AD}$, $\overline{DB}$, $\angle ACD$, and $\angle DCB$ and why.

THINK AND DISCUSS

ESL Students may be unfamiliar with the word *circumscribe.* Help them break it into its prefix *circum* which means "around" and its root *scribe* which means "to write."

Lesson Planning Options

Prerequisite Skills
- Recognizing characteristics of regular polygons
- Applying special right triangle theorems

Assignment Options for Exercises On Your Own

Core 1–18, 20, 22–26
Extension 19, 21

Use Mixed Review to maintain skills.

Resources

 Student Edition

Skills Handbook, pp. 659, 660
Extra Practice, p. 638
Glossary/Study Guide

 Teaching Resources

Chapter Support File, Ch. 5
- Practice 5-6 (two worksheets)
- Reteaching 5-6
Classroom Manager 5-6
Glossary, Spanish Resources

 Transparencies
13, 18, 62, 66

274

What You'll Learn
- Finding areas of regular polygons

...And Why
To find amounts of materials used in manufacturing and in architecture

QUICK REVIEW

A regular polygon is any polygon that is both equilateral and equiangular.

Connections **Racing Cars and Boats . . . and more**

5-6 Areas of Regular Polygons

THINK AND DISCUSS

You can circumscribe a circle about any regular polygon. The **center** of a regular polygon is the center of the circumscribed circle. The **radius** of a regular polygon is the distance from the center to a vertex. The **apothem** of a regular polygon is the perpendicular distance from the center to a side.

1. Suppose you have a regular *n*-gon with side *s*. The radii divide the figure into *n* congruent isosceles triangles.
   a. Write an expression for the area of each isosceles triangle in terms of the apothem *a* and the length of each side *s*. $\frac{1}{2}as$
   b. There are *n* congruent triangles. Use your answer to part (a) to write an expression for the area of the *n*-gon. $n \cdot \frac{1}{2}as$
   c. The perimeter *p* of the *n*-gon is *ns*. Substitute *p* for *ns* in your answer to part (b) to find a formula for area in terms of *a* and *p*. $\frac{1}{2}ap$

Your answers to Question 1 suggest the following theorem.

Theorem 5-9 Area of a Regular Polygon	The area of a regular polygon is half the product of the apothem and the perimeter. $A = \frac{1}{2}ap$	

Example 1

Find the area of a regular decagon with a 12.3-in. apothem and 8-in. sides.

$p = ns$ Find the perimeter.
$= 10(8) = 80$ A decagon has 10 sides; *n* = 10.
$A = \frac{1}{2}ap$ Use the formula for the area of a regular
$= \frac{1}{2}(12.3)(80) = 492$ polygon.

The regular decagon has area 492 in.²

2. **Try This** Find the area of a regular pentagon with sides of length 11.6 cm and apothem 8 cm. **232 cm²**

Question 1c Depending on the order of the variables in students' answers to parts a and b, they may have difficulty with the substitution. Help them see that, by the Commutative Property of Multiplication, they can rewrite their expressions as $\frac{1}{2}ans$, and then substitute p for ns.

CRITICAL THINKING Ask students to explain why the apothem is a perpendicular bisector and why a radius bisects an angle of the polygon. These concepts will be used throughout the lesson to find the lengths of radii, apothems, and sides.

Example 1 ·······································

VISUAL LEARNING Also have students compute the area using the method described in Questions 1 a and b: copy the diagram, triangulate the decagon, find the area of one triangle,

then multiply the area by the number of triangles. Discuss with students which method requires less work.

EXTENSION It should be obvious that a tessellation of a square can be used to fill a larger square. Students may want to investigate whether a tessellation of a hexagon can be used to fill a larger hexagon.

Example 2 Relating to the Real World ·····················

Students may be confused seeing the term radius used without seeing a circle. You may want to copy the hexagon and circumscribe it.

Help students see that the apothem, radius, and half of a side of a regular hexagon form a 30°-60°-90° triangle.

Engineers use regular polygons that tessellate because they fill the plane without wasting space. You can use special right triangles to find their areas.

Example 2 Relating to the Real World ·················

Racing Cars and boats used for racing need to be strong and durable, yet lightweight. One material that designers use to build body shells is a honeycomb of regular hexagonal prisms sandwiched between two layers of outer material. The honeycomb is plastic and provides strength and resilience without adding a lot of weight. The figure at the left is a cross section of one hexagonal cell.

The radii of a regular hexagon form six 60° angles at the center. So, you can use a 30°-60°-90° triangle to find the apothem a.

$a = 5\sqrt{3}$ longer leg = $\sqrt{3}$ · shorter leg
$p = ns$ Find the perimeter of the hexagon.
   $= 6(10) = 60$ Substitute 6 for n and 10 for s.
$A = \frac{1}{2}ap$ Find the area.
   $= \frac{1}{2}(5\sqrt{3})(60)$ Substitute.

0.5 ☒ 5 ☒ 3 √ ☒ 60 ▤ *259.80762*

The area is about 260 mm².

3. Estimation About how many hexagonal cells are in a 10 cm by 10 cm square panel? **about 40 cells**

4. Try This The apothem of a regular hexagon is 15 ft. Find the area of the hexagon. **about 779 ft²**

Example 3

Help students see why that the apothem, radius, and half of a side of an equilateral triangle form a 30°-60°-90° triangle.

PROBLEM SOLVING The altitude of an equilateral triangle is the longer leg of a 30°-60°-90° triangle. Help students sketch and label the equilateral triangle shown below.

ERROR ALERT! Question 5 Some students may think that the apothem and the radius form a 30°-60°-90° triangle with half of the side as is true of a hexagon and an equilateral triangle. **Remediation:** Point out that each angle of the square is 90°, so the radius bisects it into two 45° angles.

Exercises 1–3 Students may want to copy the figures into their notebooks and replace the numbers with the correct angle measures.

Exercises 7–10 Students can refer to Exercises 1–3 (or their notebooks) to see how to use a 30°-60°-90° triangle or a 45°-45°-90° triangle to find the missing lengths of regular polygons.

Technology Options

For Exercise 14, students may create their design using drawing or geometry software.

Prentice Hall Technology

 Software
- Secondary Math Lab Toolkit™
- Computer Item Generator 5-6

 CD-ROM
- Multimedia Geometry Lab 5

 Internet
- See the Prentice Hall site. (http://www.phschool.com)

Example 3

Find the area of an equilateral triangle with radius 14 in. Leave your answer in simplest radical form.

You can use a 30°-60°-90° triangle to find the apothem a and the length of a side s.

Use 30°-60°-90° △ to find the base and the height, $s = 14\sqrt{3}$ and $h = 21$. So the area is $\frac{1}{2}bh = 147\sqrt{3}$.

PROBLEM SOLVING

Look Back Check the solution to Example 3 by finding the area of the triangle using a different formula.

$a = 7$	hypotenuse = 2 · shorter leg
$\frac{s}{2} = 7\sqrt{3}$	longer leg = $\sqrt{3}$ · shorter leg
$s = 14\sqrt{3}$	
$p = ns$	Find the perimeter.
$p = 3(14\sqrt{3})$	Substitute 3 for n and $14\sqrt{3}$ for s.
$= 42\sqrt{3}$	
$A = \frac{1}{2}ap$	Use the formula for area of a regular polygon.
$= \frac{1}{2}(7)(42\sqrt{3})$	Substitute 7 for a and $42\sqrt{3}$ for p.
$= 147\sqrt{3}$	

The area of the triangle is $147\sqrt{3}$ in.^{2}.

5. Try This Find the area of a square with radius 4 in. **32 in.^{2}**

Each regular polygon has radii and an apothem as shown. Find the measure of each numbered angle.

1.

120; 60; 30

2.

90; 45; 45

3.

60; 30; 60

4. A regular pentagon has apothem 24.3 cm and side 35.4 cm. Find its area to the nearest tenth. **2150.6 cm^2**

5. A regular octagon has apothem 60.5 in. and side 50 in. Find its area. **12,100 in.^{2}**

6. The apothem of a regular decagon is 19 m. Each side is 12.4 m. Find its area. **1178 m^2**

 Calculator Find the area of each regular polygon to the nearest tenth.

7. **128 cm^2** **8.** **20.8 in.^{2}** **9.** **841.8 ft^2** **10.** **129.9 m^2**

276

Exercise 12 Have students work in groups to formulate a plan for finding the lengths. You may want to suggest that they let *s* represent the length of a side. One plan might be to use the special right triangles to write expressions for the areas of each figure, set each area equal to 36, and solve for *s*.

WRITING Exercise 13 Ask students to name the theorem which they use in their explanation. Also have them draw several polygons labeling the measures of the radii and apothems .

OPEN-ENDED Exercises 14 Students may want to color and/or decorate their designs, which you may then display on a bulletin board in the classroom.

ALTERNATIVE ASSESSMENT **Exercises 15–18** You can use these exercises to help you assess students' ability to use special right triangles in finding the lengths necessary to calculate the area of a regular polygon. Encourage students to use estimation to check that their answers are reasonable.

---

11. **Architecture** The floor of this gazebo is a regular octagon. Each side is 8 ft long, and its apothem is 9.7 ft. To the nearest tenth, find the area of the floor. **310.4 ft²**

12. **Calculator** The area of a regular polygon is 36 in.². Find the length of a side if the polygon has the given number of sides. Round your answer to the nearest tenth.
    a. 3 9.1 in. **b.** 4 6 in. **c.** 6 3.7 in.
    d. **Estimation** Suppose the polygon is a pentagon. What would you expect the length of its side to be? Explain. **See margin.**

13. **Writing** Explain why the radius of a regular polygon cannot be less than the apothem. **The radius is the hypotenuse of a rt. △ with the apothem as one of its legs.**

14. **Open-ended** Create a design using equilateral triangles and regular hexagons that have sides of the same length. Find the area of the completed design. **See margin for sample.**

Find the area of each regular polygon with the given radius or apothem. Leave your answer in simplest radical form.

15.

6 cm
72 cm²

16.

8√3 in.
384√3 in.²

17.

10 ft
75√3 ft²

18.

6√3 m
162√3 m²

19. **Critical Thinking** To find the area of an equilateral triangle, you can use the formula $A = \frac{1}{2}bh$ or $A = \frac{1}{2}ap$. A third way to find the area of an equilateral triangle is to use the formula $A = \frac{1}{4}s^2\sqrt{3}$.
    a. **Verify** the formula $A = \frac{1}{4}s^2\sqrt{3}$ by finding the area of Figure 1 using the formula $A = \frac{1}{2}bh$.
    b. **Verify** the formula $A = \frac{1}{4}s^2\sqrt{3}$ by finding the area of Figure 2 using the formula $A = \frac{1}{2}ap$. **a–b. See margin.**

Figure 1   Figure 2

20. **Standardized Test Prep** A square and an equilateral triangle share a common side. What is the ratio of the area of the triangle to the area of the square? **C**
    A. $1 : \sqrt{2}$ **B.** $\sqrt{2} : \sqrt{3}$ **C.** $\sqrt{3} : 4$ **D.** $\sqrt{2} : 1$ **E.** $\sqrt{3} : 1$

---

pages 276–278 On Your Own

12d. Answers may vary. Sample: about 4 in.; the length of a side of a pentagon should be between 3.7 in. and 6 in.

14.

1

$\frac{35}{2}\sqrt{3}$ unit²

19a. $h = \frac{\sqrt{3}}{2}s$

$A = \frac{1}{2}hs = \left(\frac{1}{2} \cdot \frac{\sqrt{3}}{2}\right)s^2$

$A = \frac{\sqrt{3}}{4}s^2$

b. $a = \frac{\sqrt{3}}{6}s$

$A = \frac{1}{2}ap = \frac{1}{2}\left(\frac{\sqrt{3}}{6}s\right) \cdot 3s$

$A = \frac{\sqrt{3}}{4}s^2$

page 278 Mixed Review

27.   28.   29.

277

Exercises 27–29 Students will need isometric dot paper.

Exercise 30 Ask students to explain how they found the angle measures.

GETTING READY FOR LESSON 5-7 These exercises prepare students to find circumference and arc length.

Wrap Up

THE BIG IDEA Ask students: *Describe how to find the area of a regular polygon. Define any new terms used in your description.*

RETEACHING ACTIVITY Students verify the 45°-45°-90° Triangle Theorem by drawing a square and comparing the lengths of its side, apothem, and radius. (Reteaching worksheet 5-6)

Lesson Quiz

Lesson Quiz is also available in Transparencies.

For Exercises 1–4, leave answers in simplest radical form, if necessary.

1. Find the area of a regular octagon with apothem 11.3 in. and side length 9.4 in. **424.88 in.²**

2. Find the area of an equilateral triangle with apothem 6 cm.
108$\sqrt{3}$ cm²

3. Find the area of a square with radius 10 in. **200 in.²**

4. Find the area of regular hexagon with side length 12 ft. **216$\sqrt{3}$ ft²**

21. *Coordinate Geometry* A regular octagon with center at the origin and radius 4 is graphed in the coordinate plane.
  a. (2.8, 2.8)
  a. Since V_2 lies on the line $y = x$, its x- and y-coordinates are equal. Use the Distance Formula to find the coordinates of V_2 to the nearest tenth.
  b. Use the coordinates of V_2 and the formula $A = \frac{1}{2}bh$ to find the area of $\triangle V_1 O V_2$ to the nearest tenth.
  c. Use your answer to part (b) to find the area of the octagon to the nearest tenth.
    b. 5.6 units²   **c. 44.8 units²**

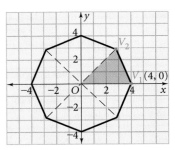

22. *Satellites* One of the smallest satellites ever developed is in the shape of a pyramid. Each of the four faces of the pyramid is an equilateral triangle with sides about 13 cm long. What is the area of one equilateral triangular face of the satellite? Round your answer to the nearest tenth. **73.2 cm²**

Find the area of each regular polygon. If your answer is not an integer, you may leave it in simplest radical form.

23.

4 cm
24√3 cm²

24.
5√2 ft
100 ft²

25.

4√3 in.
36√3 in.²

26.

3√3 m
$\frac{81\sqrt{3}}{2}$ m²

Create an isometric drawing for each foundation drawing. 27–29. See margin p. 277.

27.
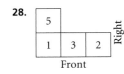

3	2
1	1

Right
Front

28.

	5	
1	3	2

Right
Front

29.

2	2
1	

Right
Front

30. The measure of an angle is three more than twice the measure of its supplement. Find the measure of the angle. **121**

Getting Ready for Lesson 5-7

⊞ Calculator **Evaluate each expression. Round your answer to the nearest hundredth.**

31. $2\pi r$ for $r = 4$ **25.13**

32. πd for $d = 7.3$ **22.93**

33. $2\pi r$ for $r = 5$ **31.42**

34. πd for $d = 11.8$ **37.07**

278

PROBLEM OF THE DAY

How can a doughnut be cut into equal pieces with three cuts of a knife? **Cut the doughnut lengthwise through its center, then cut it vertically, then horizontally.**

Problem of the Day is also available in Transparencies.

CONNECTING TO PRIOR KNOWLEDGE Draw the following circle on the board. Have student give an example of each arc and its measure.

a. minor arc
b. major arc
c. semicircle

Have students measure objects that vary in size. If time allows, have students measure more than one object and/or collect data from other groups before making conjectures.

THINK AND DISCUSS

Example 1

ERROR ALERT! Some students may not differentiate between radius and diameter and use the incorrect formula.
Remediation: Review the definitions of diameter and radius. Also draw a circle showing a diameter labeled as two radii.

Connections **Automobiles . . . and more**

5-7 Circles: Circumference and Arc Length

What You'll Learn

• Finding the circumference of a circle and the length of an arc

...And Why

To solve problems involving auto safety, metalworking, and amusement park rides

What You'll Need

• circular objects
• string
• metric ruler
• calculator

WORK TOGETHER

Work in groups. Each member of your group should have one circular object such as a juice can or a jar lid.

▪ Measure the diameter of each circle to the nearest millimeter.

▪ Find the circumference of each circle by wrapping a string around each object. Straighten the string and measure its length to the nearest tenth of a centimeter.

▪ Organize your group's data in a table like the one below. Calculate the ratio $\frac{\text{circumference}}{\text{diameter}}$ to the nearest hundredth.

Name of Object	Circumference (C)	Diameter (d)	$\frac{C}{d}$
jelly-jar lid	19.6 cm	6.2 cm	3.16

1. Make a **conjecture** about the relationship between the circumference and the diameter of a circle. **The circumference is about 3 times the diameter.**

THINK AND DISCUSS

Part 1 Circumference

The ratios you found in the Work Together are estimates of the number **pi** (π), the ratio of the circumference of a circle to its diameter.

Theorem 5-10
Circumference of a Circle

The circumference of a circle is π times the diameter.

$$C = \pi d \quad \text{or} \quad C = 2\pi r$$

Example 1

Find the circumference of $\odot A$ and $\odot B$. Leave your answer in terms of π.

a.

$C = \pi d$
$C = 12\pi$ in.

b.

$C = 2\pi r$
$C = 2 \cdot \pi \cdot 5.3$
$C = 10.6\pi$ cm

2. Try This What is the radius of a circle with circumference 18π m?
9 m

Lesson Planning Options

Prerequisite Skills

• Finding arc measures

Assignment Options for Exercises On Your Own

To provide flexible scheduling, this lesson can be subdivided into parts.

1 **Core** 1–8
   Extension 26–27

2 **Core** 9–22, 24–25
   Extension 23

Use Mixed Review to maintain skills.

Resources

Student Edition

Skills Handbook, pp. 646, 659
Extra Practice, p. 638
Glossary/Study Guide

Teaching Resources

Chapter Support File, Ch. 5
• Practice 5-7 (two worksheets)
• Reteaching 5-7
• Alternative Activity 5-7
Classroom Manager 5-7
Glossary, Spanish Resources

Transparencies
12, 63

279

Additional Examples

FOR EXAMPLE 1

Find the circumference of the following circles. Leave your answers in terms of π.

a. a circle with diameter 16 cm

b. a circle with radius 4 in.

a. 16π cm   b. 8π in.

Discussion: *If the ratio of the diameters of two circles is 2:1, what is the ratio of their circumferences?*

FOR EXAMPLE 2

The radii of two concentric circles are 4.5 cm and 5.2 cm. How much greater is the circumference of the larger circle than that of the smaller circle? 1.4π

Discussion: *If the radius of a circle is increased by 1, how much does its circumference increase?*

FOR EXAMPLE 3

The diameter of a circle is 12 cm.

a. $\overset{\frown}{AB}$ has measure 60. Find its length. 2π

b. $\overset{\frown}{ACD}$ has measure 210. Find its length. 7π

Since the number π is irrational, you cannot write it as a decimal. You can use 3.14, $\frac{22}{7}$, or the $\boxed{\pi}$ key on your calculator as approximations for π.

Two circles that lie in the same plane and have the same center are **concentric circles**.

Example 2 Relating to the Real World

⊞ Automobiles A manufacturer advertises that a new car has a turning radius of only 16.1 ft. The distance between the two front tires is 4.7 ft. How much farther do the outside tires have to travel in making a complete circle than the tires on the inside?

The outside and inside tires travel on concentric circles. The radius of the outer circle is 16.1 ft. To find the radius of the inner circle, you must subtract 4.7 ft.

circumference of outer circle $= 2\pi(16.1) = 32.2\pi$

radius of the inner circle $= 16.1 - 4.7 = 11.4$ ft

circumference of inner circle $= 2\pi(11.4) = 22.8\pi$

The difference in the two distances is $32.2\pi - 22.8\pi = 9.4\pi$.

9.4 ☒ $\boxed{\pi}$ ▤ 29.530971

The outside tires travel about 29.5 ft farther than the inside tires.

⊞ **3. Try This** The diameter of a bicycle wheel is 26 in. To the nearest whole number, how many revolutions does the wheel make when the bicycle travels 100 yd? **44 revolutions**

16.1 ft

4.7 ft

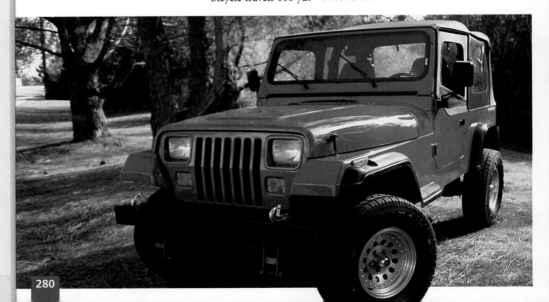

Question 3 Help students understand that as a bicycle makes one revolution, the distance the bicycle has traveled is the circumference of the wheel. Also check that students correctly convert yards to inches.

CONNECTING TO STUDENTS' WORLD Question 3 Have students measure the diameter of their bicycle tire or of a friend's bicycle tire. Have them calculate the number of revolutions the tire will make over a given distance.

Emphasize the difference between arc length and arc measure. Students may want to think of arc length as "distance" and arc measure as "amount of turn." Discuss real-world examples to illustrate the need for both measures.

E x a m p l e 3

CRITICAL THINKING Ask students to explain why "$\pi(16)$" is used in part a and "$2\pi(15)$" is used in part b.

TACTILE LEARNING If you have block scheduling or an extended class period, have students investigate the formula for arc length using the circular objects from the Work Together as follows. Mark the endpoints of an arc. Roll the object along a ruler to measure the arc to the nearest millimeter. Then calculate the arc length by measuring the central angle and then using the formula. Compare the results.

Part
2 **Arc Length**

In Chapter 2 you found the measure of an arc in degrees. You can also find the **arc length,** which is a fraction of a circle's circumference.

An arc of 60° represents $\frac{60}{360}$ or $\frac{1}{6}$ of the circle. Its arc length is $\frac{1}{6}$ the circumference of the circle.

This observation suggests the following generalization.

Theorem 5-11
Arc Length

The length of an arc of a circle is the product of the ratio $\frac{\text{measure of the arc}}{360}$ and the circumference of the circle.

length of $\widehat{AB} = \frac{m\widehat{AB}}{360} \cdot 2\pi r$

Technology Options

E x a m p l e 3

Find the length of the arc shown in red on each circle. Leave your answer in terms of π.

a.

b.

length of $\widehat{XY} = \frac{m\widehat{XY}}{360} \cdot \pi d$

length of $\widehat{XY} = \frac{90}{360} \cdot \pi(16)$

$\qquad = 4\pi$ in.

length of $\widehat{XPY} = \frac{m\widehat{XPY}}{360} \cdot 2\pi r$

length of $\widehat{XPY} = \frac{240}{360} \cdot 2\pi(15)$

$\qquad = 20\pi$ cm

4. Try This Find the length of a semicircle with radius 1.3 m. Leave your answer in terms of π. **1.3π m**

5. Critical Thinking Is it possible for two arcs of different circles to have the same measure, but different lengths? Support your answer with an example. **Yes; see margin p. 282 for diagram.**

6. Critical Thinking Is it possible for two arcs of different circles to have the same length but have different measures? Support your answer with an example. **Yes; see margin p. 282 for diagram.**

Your answers to Questions 5 and 6 illustrate that for arcs to be congruent two things must be true. **Congruent arcs** are arcs that have the same measure and are in the same circle or in congruent circles.

281

Exercises 5–8 You may want to have all students use the π key so that all students' answers should be the same.

Mental Math **Exercises 10–12** Suggest students use mental math to answer these exercises.

ALTERNATIVE ASSESSMENT **Exercise 13** This exercise can be used to help you assess students' understanding of circumference by noting their ability to find the diameter and radius of a circle given its circumference.

OPEN-ENDED **Exercise 18** You may want to suggest to students having difficulty with this problem that they consider drawing concentric circles.

---

pages 279–281 **Think and Discuss**

5. Sample:

length of

$\overset{\frown}{AB} = \frac{70}{360} \cdot 2\pi(15) \approx 18.3$ mm

length of

$\overset{\frown}{CD} = \frac{70}{360} \cdot 2\pi(11) \approx 13.4$ mm

6. Sample:

length of

$\overset{\frown}{AB} = \frac{60}{360} \cdot 2\pi(12) \approx 4\pi$ mm

length of

$\overset{\frown}{CD} = \frac{90}{360} \cdot 2\pi(8) \approx 4\pi$ mm

282

Exercises **O N   Y O U R   O W N**

Find the circumference of $\odot O$. Leave your answer in terms of π.

1. 15π cm

2. 10π ft

3. 3.7π in.

4. ½π m

▦ **Calculator** Find the circumference of each circle with the given radius or diameter. Round your answer to the nearest hundredth.

5. $r = 9$ in.   56.55 in.

6. $d = 7.3$ m   22.93 m

7. $d = \frac{1}{2}$ yd   1.57 yd

8. $r = 0.13$ cm
   0.82 cm

Find the circumference of each circle. Then find the length of the arc shown in red on each circle. Leave your answer in terms of π.

9.

10.

11.

12.

28π cm; 3.5π cm   24π ft; 8π ft   36π m; 27π m   36π in.; 33π in.

13. The circumference of a circle is 100π in. Find each of the following.
    a. the diameter   100 in.
    b. the radius   50 in.
    c. the length of an arc of 120°
       $\frac{100}{3}\pi$ in.

14. **Coordinate Geometry** The endpoints of a diameter of a circle are $A(1, 3)$ and $B(4, 7)$. Find each of the following.
    a. the coordinates of the center   b. the diameter   c. the circumference
       (2.5, 5)   5   5π

▦ 15. **Metalworking** Miya constructed a wrought-iron arch to top the entrance to a mall. The 11 bars between the two concentric semicircles are each 3 ft long. Find the length of the wrought iron used to make this structure. Round your answer to the nearest foot.   **105 ft**

16. A 60° arc of $\odot A$ has the same length as a 45° arc of $\odot B$. Find the ratio of the radius of $\odot A$ to the radius of $\odot B$.   **3 : 4**

17. **Space Travel** The orbit of the space station *Mir* is 245 mi above Earth. How much greater is the circumference of *Mir's* orbit than the circumference of Earth? Earth's radius is about 3960 mi. Leave your answer in terms of π.   **490π mi**

18. **Open-ended** Use a compass and protractor to draw two noncongruent arcs with the same measure.   **See margin p. 283 for sample.**

Calculator **Find the length of the arc shown in red on each circle. Round your answer to the nearest hundredth.**

19.

23 m

36.13 m

20.

4.1 ft

45°

16.10 ft

21.

9 m   25°

O

3.93 m

22.

50°

7.2 in.

8.17 in.

23. Find the perimeter of the shaded portion of the figure at the right. Leave your answer in terms of π. **2π in.**

4 in.

4 in.

24. Standardized Test Prep The length of $\widehat{AB}$ is 6π cm and $m\widehat{AB}$ = 120. What is the diameter of the circle? **D**
A. 2 cm   B. 6 cm   C. 9 cm
D. 18 cm   E. 24 cm

25. Coordinate Geometry Find the length of a semicircle with endpoints (3, 7) and (3, −1). Round your answer to the nearest tenth. **12.6**

CALVIN AND HOBBES by Bill Watterson

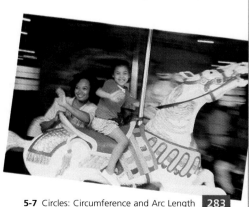

Cartoon **Use what you learned from Calvin's father to answer the following questions.**

26. In one revolution, how much farther does a point 10 cm from the center of the record travel than a point 3 cm from the center? Round your answer to the nearest hundredth. **43.98 cm**

27. Writing Kendra and her mother plan to ride the merry-go-round. Two horses on the merry-go-round are side by side. For a more exciting ride, should Kendra sit on the inside or the outside? Explain your reasoning. **See margin.**

pages 282–283 On Your Own

18. Sample:

70°

70°

27. Outside; the outside horse is further away from the center than the inside horse. It moves faster because, in a given amount of time, it covers a greater distance.

page 284 Mixed Review

28.

A   B

29.

m

n

TRANSFORMATIONS Exercise 30 You may want students to include a graph with their answer.

GETTING READY FOR LESSON 5-8 These exercises prepare students to find the area of a circle.

Wrap Up

THE BIG IDEA Ask students: *Explain how you find the length of an arc. Define any new vocabulary you use in your explanation.*

RETEACHING ACTIVITY Students draw a circle and an arc. Then they calculate the length of the arc and measure its length using string. (Reteaching worksheet 5-7)

In this Checkpoint, your students will assess their own progress in Lessons 5-5 to 5-7.

Exercises 2–3 Students who have trouble with these exercises should review their answers to Exercises 1 and 3 on page 276 and also review special right triangles.

WRITING Exercise 10 Check that students use geometry vocabulary correctly in their explanations.

Lesson Quiz

Lesson Quiz is also available in Transparencies.

For Exercises 1–4, leave your answers in terms of π.

1. Find the circumference of a circle with radius 2.7 in. **5.4 π in.**

2. Find the radius of a circle with circumference 10.2π cm. **5.1 cm**

3. A circle has a diameter of length 9 cm. Find the length of $\overset{\frown}{AC}$ on the circle if $\overset{\frown}{AC}$ measures 45°. **$\frac{9\pi}{8}$ cm**

4. A circle has a radius of length 18 cm. Find the length of $\overset{\frown}{QRS}$ on the circle if $\overset{\frown}{QRS}$ measures 270°. **27π cm**

284

Locus Sketch and label each locus. **28–29. See margin p. 283.**

28. all points in a plane equidistant from points A and B

29. all points in space equidistant from parallel lines m and n

30. Transformations A triangle has vertices $A(3, 2)$, $B(4, 1)$, and $C(4, 3)$. Find the coordinates of the image of the triangle under a glide reflection in $\langle 0, 1 \rangle$ and $x = 0$. **$A'(-3, 3)$, $B'(-4, 2)$, $C'(-4, 4)$**

Getting Ready for Lesson 5-8

Estimation A circle is drawn on three different grids. Use the scale of each grid to estimate the area of each circle in square inches. **31–33. Estimates may vary slightly.**

31.

$\frac{1}{2}$ in.

about 1 in.²

32.

$\frac{1}{4}$ in.

about 1 in.²

33.

$\frac{1}{8}$ in.

about 1 in.²

Find the area of each trapezoid or regular polygon. Leave your answer in simplest radical form.

1. 7 cm **110 cm²**
10 cm
15 cm

2. **72$\sqrt{3}$ in.²**
6 in.

3. **27$\sqrt{3}$ ft²**
3 ft

Calculator Find the circumference of a circle with the given radius. Round your answer to the nearest hundredth.

4. 8 in. **50.27 in.** **5.** 2 m **12.57 m** **6.** 5 ft **31.42 ft** **7.** 1.4 km **8.80 km** **8.** 9 mm **56.55 mm**

9. In a circle of radius 18 mm, $m\overset{\frown}{AB} = 45$. Find the length of $\overset{\frown}{AB}$. Leave your answer in terms of π. **4.5π mm**

10. Writing Explain at least two ways to find the area of an equilateral triangle. Use an example to illustrate your explanation. **Answers may vary. See back of book for sample.**

WORK TOGETHER

PROBLEM OF THE DAY

If the points shown are equally spaced, and if each arc measures 180, find the length of the path along the arcs from A to B. **6.5π**

Problem of the Day is also available in Transparencies.

CONNECTING TO PRIOR KNOWLEDGE Draw a circle and a diameter. Label it 12 cm. Ask students to identify the following:

a. d **b.** r **c.** $2r$ **d.** r^2

WORK TOGETHER

DIVERSITY It is important that students cut the circle and its wedges carefully so that the resulting figure will look like a parallelogram. Students who have physical or visual difficulties may have trouble and should be paired with students who can help them fold and cut accurately.

THINK AND DISCUSS

ERROR ALERT! Theorem 5-12 Some students will confuse doubling the radius with squaring the radius. **Remediation:** Point out that squaring a number means multiplying the number by itself. Then have students practice several examples.

Connections **Food . . . and more**

What You'll Learn
- Computing the areas of circles, sectors, and segments of circles

...And Why
To solve real-world problems in food preparation, archaeology, and biology

What You'll Need
- compass
- scissors
- tape

5-8 Areas of Circles, Sectors, and Segments of Circles

WORK TOGETHER

Work in groups. Have each member of your group use a compass to draw a large circle. Fold the circle in half horizontally and vertically. Cut the circle into four wedges on the fold lines. Then fold each wedge into quarters. Cut each wedge on the fold lines. You will have 16 wedges. Tape the wedges to a piece of paper to form the figure below.

1. How does the area of the figure compare with the area of the circle?
   They are =.
2. The base of the figure is formed by arcs of the circle. Write an equation relating the length of the base b to the circumference C of the circle. $b = \frac{1}{2}C$
3. Write an equation for the length of the base b in terms of the radius r of the circle. $b = \pi r$
4. If you increase the number of wedges, the figure you create becomes more and more like a rectangle with base b and height r. Write an expression for the area of the rectangle in terms of r. πr^2

THINK AND DISCUSS

Part 1 Areas of Circles

Your observations in the Work Together suggest the following theorem.

Theorem 5-12
Area of a Circle

The area of a circle is the product of π and the square of the radius.

$$A = \pi r^2$$

5. **Try This** What is the area of a circle with radius 15 cm? Leave your answer in terms of π. **225π cm²**

Lesson Planning Options

Prerequisite Skills
- Finding areas of parallelograms
- Finding the measures of arcs

Assignment Options for Exercises On Your Own

To provide flexible scheduling, this lesson can be subdivided into parts.

1 **Core** 1–10
   Extension 11

2 **Core** 12–23, 28–29
   Extension 24–27

Use Mixed Review to maintain skills.

Resources

📖 **Student Edition**
Skills Handbook, pp. 656, 659
Extra Practice, p. 638
Glossary/Study Guide

📦 **Teaching Resources**
Chapter Support File, Ch. 5
- Practice 5-8 (two worksheets)
- Reteaching 5-8
Classroom Manager 5-8
Glossary, Spanish Resources

📽 **Transparencies**
12, 63, 67

285

Example 1 Relating to the Real World ················

TACTILE LEARNING Have students work in groups to make two large rectangles by taping together four pieces of one-inch graph paper, being careful to align the grid lines. Then have them draw a 10-in. circle and a 12-in. circle on each. Ask students to approximate the number of square inches in each circle. Have them compare their approximations with $25\pi \approx 78.5$ and $36\pi \approx 113.1$

EXTENSION An interesting extension to this problem is: *If a small slice is one-eighth of a small pizza, how many small slices would equal the amount of pizza in a medium pizza?* about $11\frac{1}{2}$

CONNECTING TO STUDENTS' WORLD Question 6 Have students contact a local pizza restaurant to find out the diameters and prices of a small and a large pizza. Have them determine which pizza is a better buy. Discuss how the pizza problem assumes consistent thickness, which may or may not be the case in real life.

VISUAL LEARNING Use physical models if possible. Trivial Pursuit™ pieces are good models of sectors. Have students brainstorm other real-world examples of sectors such as a piece of pie, a piece of watermelon, or the section between two hands on a clock.

Theorem 5-13 Have students compare the similarities and differences between finding the length of an arc and finding the area of a sector.

Additional Examples

FOR EXAMPLE 1 ·····························

A goat is tied with a rope 8 m long. How much more area does the goat have access to if the 8-m rope is replaced with a 9-m rope? Round your answer to the nearest meter.

area of 8-m grazing circle
$= 8^2\pi = 64\pi$

area of 9-m grazing circle
$= 9^2\pi = 81\pi$

difference in area $= 17\pi \approx 53$
The goat has an additional 53 m².

FOR EXAMPLE 2 ·····························

A circle has diameter 14 in. What is the area of a sector bounded by an 80° arc? Round your answer to the nearest tenth. 34.2 in.²

FOR EXAMPLE 3 ·····························

A circle has radius 8 cm. Find the area of a segment of the circle bounded by a 120° arc. Round your answer to the nearest tenth.

area of sector $= \frac{120}{360}(64\pi) = \frac{64\pi}{3}$

area of triangle $= \frac{1}{2}(8\sqrt{3} \times 4) = 16\sqrt{3}$

area of segment $= \frac{64\pi}{3} - 16\sqrt{3} \approx 39.3$

39.3 cm²

Example 1 Relating to the Real World ···········

🍴 **Food** The diameter of a small pizza is 10 in. How much more pizza do you get if you order a medium pizza with diameter 12 in.?

radius of small pizza $= \frac{10}{2} = 5$ $r = \frac{d}{2}$

radius of medium pizza $= \frac{12}{2} = 6$ $r = \frac{d}{2}$

Use the formula for the area of a circle.

area of small pizza $= \pi(5)^2 = 25\pi$ $A = \pi r^2$

area of medium pizza $= \pi(6)^2 = 36\pi$ $A = \pi r^2$

difference in area $= 36\pi - 25\pi = 11\pi$

11 ☒ 🔲 ▤ *34.557519*

The medium pizza has about 35 in.² more pizza than the small pizza.

6. Suppose the small pizza in Example 1 costs $5.00 and the medium pizza costs $6.00. Which pizza is a better buy? Explain your answer.
See margin p. 288.

Sectors and Segments   Part ▼ 2

A **sector of a circle** is the region bounded by two radii and their intercepted arc. A slice of pizza is an example of a sector of a circle. You name a sector using one endpoint of the arc, the center of the circle, and the other endpoint of the arc. Sector *XOY* is at the left.

The area of a sector is a fractional part of the area of a circle. The ratio of a sector's area to a circle's area is $\frac{\text{measure of the arc}}{360}$.

Theorem 5-13 Area of a Sector of a Circle	The area of a sector of a circle is the product of the ratio $\frac{\text{measure of the arc}}{360}$ and the area of the circle. Area of sector $AOB = \frac{m\widehat{AB}}{360} \cdot \pi r^2$

Example 2

Find the area of sector *ZOM*. Leave your answer in terms of π.

area of sector $ZOM = \frac{m\widehat{ZM}}{360} \cdot \pi r^2$

$= \frac{72}{360} \cdot \pi(20)^2$

$= 80\pi$

The area of sector *ZOM* is 80π cm².

7. Calculator A circle has diameter 8.2 m. What is the area of a sector with a 125° arc? Round your answer to the nearest tenth. **18.3 m²**

segment of a circle

The part of a circle bounded by an arc and the segment joining its endpoints is a **segment of the circle.** To find the area of a segment, draw radii to form a sector. The area of the segment equals the area of the sector minus the area of the triangle formed.

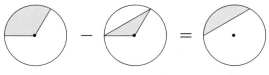

Area of sector   Area of triangle   Area of segment

Example 3

 Find the area of the shaded segment.

area of sector $AOB = \frac{m\widehat{AB}}{360} \cdot \pi r^2$ Formula for area of a sector

$= \frac{90}{360} \cdot \pi(10)^2$ Substitute.

$= \frac{1}{4} \cdot 100\pi$

$= 25\pi$

area of $\triangle AOB = \frac{1}{2}bh$ Formula for area of a triangle

$= \frac{1}{2}(10)(10)$ Substitute.

$= 50$

area of segment $= 25\pi - 50$

25 ☒ π ⊟ 50 ⊟ 28.539816

The area of the segment is about 28.5 in.²

8. Try This A circle has radius 12 cm. Find the area of a segment of the circle bounded by a 60° arc and the segment joining its endpoints. Round your answer to the nearest tenth. **13.0 cm²**

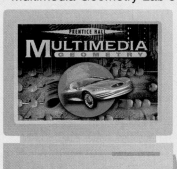

Exercises 1–4 Use these exercises to check that students substitute *r, not d,* into πr^2 and correctly evaluate r^2. In Exercise 3, some students may have trouble finding one-half of $\frac{3}{4}$.

Exercise 5 Have students explain how they found the diameter. Make sure that they take the square root of 225 before doubling it.

Exercise 11 Help students see that the radius of the circle that the diver can cover is the shorter leg of the right triangle formed by the diver's line and a line perpendicular to the floor of the ocean.

ESTIMATION Exercises 12–15 Encourage students to use estimation to check the reasonableness of their answers.

ESL **Exercise 16** Some students will not know what a dartboard is. Draw a sketch on the board of a dartboard with concentric circles and one with sectors. Ask students what they are called in their native languages.

---

pages 285–287 **Think and Discuss**

6. Medium; the cost per in.² is about 6 cents for the small pizza and about 5 cents for the medium pizza.

Find the area of each circle. Leave your answers in terms of π.

1. 400π m²

20 m

2. 64π ft²

16 ft

3. $\frac{9}{64}\pi$ in.²

$\frac{3}{4}$ in.

4.

0.5 m
0.25π m²

5. A circle has area 225π m². What is its diameter? 30 m

6. How many circles with radius 4 in. will have the same total area as a circle with radius 12 in.? 9

7. **Coordinate Geometry** The endpoints of a diameter of $\odot A$ are (2, 1) and (5, 5). Find the area of $\odot A$. Leave your answer in terms of π. 6.25π units²

Calculator **Find the area of each circle. Round your answer to the nearest hundredth.**

8. $r = 7$ ft
153.94 ft²

9. $d = 8.3$ m
54.11 m²

10. $d = 0.24$ cm
0.05 cm²

11. **Archaeology** Off the coast of Sweden, divers are working to bring up artifacts from a ship that sank several hundred years ago. The line to a diver is 100 ft long, and the diver is working at a depth of 80 ft. What is the area of the circle that the diver can cover? Round your answer to the nearest square foot. 11,310 ft²

100 ft
80 ft

Find the area of each shaded sector of a circle. Leave your answer in terms of π.

12.

45°
18 yd
40.5π yd²

13.
16 cm
64π cm²

14.
12 in.
30°
12π in.²

15.
26 m
120°
$\frac{169}{6}\pi$ m²

16. **Games** A dartboard has a diameter of 20 in. and is divided into 20 congruent sectors. Find the area of one sector. Round your answer to the nearest tenth. 15.7 in.²

17. **Animal Habitats** In the Pacific Northwest, a red fox has a circular home range with a radius of about 718 m. To the nearest thousand, about how many square meters are in a red fox's home range?
1,620,000 m²

ALTERNATIVE ASSESSMENT **Exercises 18–21** These exercises can be used to help you assess students' understanding of the objectives of this lesson: computing areas of circles, sectors, and segments. Have students write the formula(s) they use for each problem.

Exercises 24–27 This set of exercises can be a nice group activity. Have students work together on a plan for solving each exercise.

 Calculator **Find the area of each shaded segment of a circle. Round your answer to the nearest hundredth.**

18.
120°
6 cm

19.
8 ft

20.
6 m
60°

21.
18 ft

22.11 cm²   18.27 ft²   3.26 m²   925.41 ft²

22. Writing The American Institute of Baking suggests a technique for cutting and serving a tiered cake. The tiers of a cake have the same height and have diameters 8 in. and 13 in. The top layer and the circle directly under it are cut into 8 pieces and the exterior ring of the 13-inch layer is cut into 12 pieces. Which piece would be biggest, a top, bottom-inside, or bottom-outside piece? Explain your answer.
See margin.

23. A sector of a circle with a 90° arc has area 36π in.². What is the radius of the circle?   12 in.

Find the area of the shaded figure. Leave your answer in terms of π.

24.
8 ft   8 ft

25.
14 in.

26.
10 m

27.
4 m

(64 − 16π) ft²   (784 − 196π) in.²   (200 − 50π) m²   4π m²

28. Open-ended Draw a diagram for a sector of a circle such that the sector has area 16π cm². Label the radius of the circle and the measure of the arc of the sector.   See margin for sample.

29. An 8 ft-by-10 ft floating dock is anchored in the middle of a pond. The bow of a canoe is tied to one corner of the dock with a 10-ft rope.
 a. Sketch a diagram of the area in which the bow of the canoe can travel.
 b. Write a plan for finding the area.   a–b. See margin.
 c. Find the area. Round your answer to the nearest square foot.   about 239 ft²

10 ft
8 ft
10 ft

pages 288–290 On Your Own

22. Bottom-outside; since the heights of all the pieces are the same, the piece with the greater base area has the greater volume. The area of a top and a bottom-inside piece is ≈ 6.3 in.²; the area of a bottom-outside piece is ≈ 6.9 in.².

28.

120°
4√3 cm

29a.
10 ft
10 ft
8 ft   dock
2 ft

b. the area of $\frac{3}{4}$ circle with radius 10 ft and $\frac{1}{4}$ circle with radius 2 ft

FIND OUT BY CALCULATING Have students work in groups to discuss a plan for finding the percents. One plan might be to let the side of each square be 8, then find the ratio of the area of the square minus the area of circle to the area of square for each.

DATA ANALYSIS Exercises 30–32 Review with students why the vertical scale is drawn with a "zig zag" at the bottom.

PORTFOLIO Share with students the criteria you will use to assess their work in portfolios, as well as how you plan to use the results. Students should understand how the rubrics assess their work, how each piece in the portfolio

counts, and how the scores they get in their portfolios will affect their overall evaluation.

Wrap Up

THE BIG IDEA Ask students to define in their own words *sector* and *segment of a circle*. Then have them explain how to find the area of each.

RETEACHING ACTIVITY Students draw a circle on grid paper and estimate its area. Then they calculate its area using the formula for the area of a circle. (Reteaching worksheet 5-8)

Lesson Quiz

Lesson Quiz is also available in Transparencies.

For Exercises 1–2, leave your answers in terms of π.

1. Find the area of a circle with diameter 22 m. **$121\pi\,\text{m}^2$**

2. A circle has radius 4 in. Find the area of a sector bounded by a 75° arc. **$\frac{10\pi}{3}$ in.²**

3. A circle has diameter 10 m. Find the area of a segment bounded by a 90° arc. Round your answer to the nearest tenth. **7.1 m²**

4. Find the diameter of a circle with area $169\pi\,\text{cm}^2$. **26 cm**

290

Find Out by Calculating

The circles on this quilt were sewn onto the background cloth. Cutting circles from rectangles leaves some waste. Explore whether you can reduce waste by using smaller circles.

- Compare the percent of material wasted when the shaded circles are cut from squares A, B, and C below. **Each method wastes the same amount of material.**

A. B. C.

- Estimate how many times longer it would take to cut out the 16 circles from square C than the 1 circle from square A. Support your estimate with calculations.

4 times as long; a circle in C has $\frac{1}{4}$ of the circumference of a circle in A, but there are 16 circles in C.

Data Analysis Use the line graph for Exercises 30–32. 30–32. Answers may vary slightly.

30. In 1990, how much did the average person spend on media such as printed material, videos, and recordings? **$380**

31. How much has spending increased from 1990 to 1994? **$90**

32. **Predict** how much the average person will spend on media in the year 2000. **Sample: $625**

33. What is the area of a 30°-60°-90° triangle with hypotenuse 12 cm? Leave your answer in simplest radical form. **$18\sqrt{3}$ cm²**

Annual Dollars Spent per Person on Media

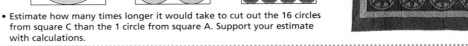

The measures of two angles of a triangle are given. Find the measure of the third angle. Then classify the triangle by its sides and angles.

34. 54°, 108°
35. 72°, 36°
36. 36°, 54°
37. 78°, 34°
38. 60°, 60°
39. 90°, 45°

34. 18; scalene, obtuse
35. 72; isosceles, acute
36. 90; scalene, right
37. 68; scalene, acute
38. 60; equilateral, acute
39. 45; isosceles, right

PORTFOLIO

For your portfolio, select one or two items from your work for this chapter. Here are some possibilities.
- corrected work
- a journal entry
Explain why you have included each selection.

Students investigate the ratio of the perimeters and areas of inscribed regular polygons to the circumferences and areas of the circles in which they are inscribed.

The software allows students to increase the number of sides of the inscribed regular polygon easily, to find the measurements and ratios accurately, and to manipulate the size of the circle.

Investigate

ERROR ALERT! Some students may change the size of the circle without changing the size of the triangle. **Remediation:** Make sure that the vertices of the triangle remain on the circle.

Students may want to compare their results with other pairs or groups before making their conjectures.

Extend

Introduce the idea of limits by discussing the ratios $\frac{perimeter}{circumference}$ and $\frac{polygon\ area}{circle\ area}$ as the number of sides become infinitely large.

ADDITIONAL PROBLEM Ask students to use geometry software to find the triangle with the largest area that can be inscribed in a circle. Many will be surprised to find it is an equilateral triangle and not an obtuse triangle.

Math ToolboX — Technology

Materials and Manipulatives
- Geometry software

Exploring Area and Circumference

After Lesson 5-8

A polygon that is *inscribed* in a circle has all its vertices on the circle. Work in pairs or small groups. Investigate the ratios of the perimeters and areas of inscribed regular polygons to the circumference and area of the circle in which they are inscribed. Begin by making a table like this.

Regular Polygon			Circle		Ratios	
Sides	Perimeter	Area	Circumference	Area	Perimeter / Circumference	Polygon Area / Circle Area
3						

Construct

Use geometry software to construct a circle. Find its circumference and area and record them in your table. Inscribe an equilateral triangle in the circle. Your software may be able to do this for you automatically, or you can construct three points on the circle and move them so they are approximately evenly spaced on the circle. Then draw the triangle. **Check students' work.**

Investigate

Use your geometry software to measure the perimeter and area of the triangle and to calculate the ratios $\frac{triangle\ perimeter}{circle\ circumference}$ and $\frac{triangle\ area}{circle\ area}$. Record the results.

Manipulate the circle to change its size. Do the ratios you calculated stay the same or change? **The ratios do not change with size.**

Now inscribe a square in a circle and fill in your table for a polygon of four sides. Do the same for a regular pentagon.

Conjecture

What will happen to the ratios $\frac{perimeter}{circumference}$ and $\frac{polygon\ area}{circle\ area}$ as you increase the number of sides of the polygon? **As the number of sides increases, each ratio comes closer to 1.**

Extend

- Extend your table to include polygons of 12 sides. Does your conjecture still hold? Compare the two columns of ratios in your table. How do they differ? **Yes; the ratio of perimeter to circumference gets closer to 1 faster than the ratio of the areas.**

- Estimate the perimeter and area of a polygon of 100 sides that is inscribed in a circle with a radius of 10 cm. **about 63 cm; about 314 cm²**

Finishing the Chapter Project

PROJECT DAY You may wish to plan a project day during which students share their completed projects. Encourage groups to explain their processes as well as their products.

PROJECT NOTEBOOK Have students review their project work and bring their notebooks up to date.

- Have students show the models of quilts and the patchwork designs they made and explain the techniques they used to create them.
- Ask groups to share any insights they found when completing the project, such as how they used geometric shapes to design their quilt patterns.

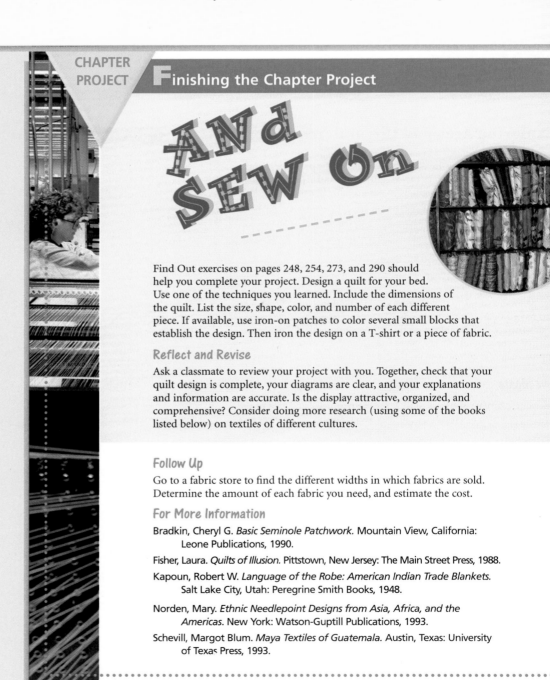

CHAPTER PROJECT

Finishing the Chapter Project

AND SEW On

Find Out exercises on pages 248, 254, 273, and 290 should help you complete your project. Design a quilt for your bed. Use one of the techniques you learned. Include the dimensions of the quilt. List the size, shape, color, and number of each different piece. If available, use iron-on patches to color several small blocks that establish the design. Then iron the design on a T-shirt or a piece of fabric.

Reflect and Revise

Ask a classmate to review your project with you. Together, check that your quilt design is complete, your diagrams are clear, and your explanations and information are accurate. Is the display attractive, organized, and comprehensive? Consider doing more research (using some of the books listed below) on textiles of different cultures.

Follow Up

Go to a fabric store to find the different widths in which fabrics are sold. Determine the amount of each fabric you need, and estimate the cost.

For More Information

Bradkin, Cheryl G. *Basic Seminole Patchwork.* Mountain View, California: Leone Publications, 1990.

Fisher, Laura. *Quilts of Illusion.* Pittstown, New Jersey: The Main Street Press, 1988.

Kapoun, Robert W. *Language of the Robe: American Indian Trade Blankets.* Salt Lake City, Utah: Peregrine Smith Books, 1948.

Norden, Mary. *Ethnic Needlepoint Designs from Asia, Africa, and the Americas.* New York: Watson-Guptill Publications, 1993.

Schevill, Margot Blum. *Maya Textiles of Guatemala.* Austin, Texas: University of Texas Press, 1993.

5 Wrap Up

Key Terms

altitude (p. 250)
apothem (p. 274)
arc length (p. 281)
area of a circle (p. 285)
area of a parallelogram (p. 249)
area of a polygon (p. 243)
area of a rectangle (p. 244)
area of a square (p. 243)
area of a trapezoid (p. 269)
area of a triangle (p. 251)
base (pp. 250, 251, 269)
center (p. 274)
circumference of a circle (p. 279)

concentric circles (p. 280)
congruent arcs (p. 281)
Converse of the Pythagorean Theorem (p. 258)
45°-45°-90° triangle (p. 264)
height (pp. 250, 251, 269)
hypotenuse (p. 256)
legs of a right triangle (p. 256)
legs of a trapezoid (p. 269)
perimeter of a polygon (p. 242)
pi (p. 279)
Pythagorean Theorem (p. 257)
Pythagorean triple (p. 258)

radius (p. 274)
sector of a circle (p. 286)
segment of a circle (p. 287)
30°-60°-90° triangle (p. 265)

How am I doing?

- State three ideas from this chapter that you think are important. Explain your choices.
- Explain how to find the area of different polygons.

Understanding Perimeter and Area   5-1

The **perimeter of a polygon** is the sum of the lengths of its sides.

The formula for the perimeter of a square is $P = 4s$. The formula for the perimeter of a rectangle is $P = 2b + 2h$.

The **area of a polygon** is the number of square units it encloses. The area of a region is the sum of the area of its nonoverlapping parts. If two figures are congruent, their areas are equal.

The formula for the **area of a square** is $A = s^2$. The formula for the **area of a rectangle** is $A = bh$.

Find the perimeter and area of each figure.

1.

8 cm

32 cm; 64 cm²

2.

6 ft
13 ft

38 ft; 78 ft²

3.

3 in.
5 in.

32 in.; 40 in.²

4. *Open-ended* Draw a polygon with perimeter 33 cm. **Sample:**

5.5 cm

Chapter 5 Wrap Up   **293**

293

Exercises 5–7 Make sure students understand which figures have a factor of one-half in the area formula.

ERROR ALERT! **Exercises 8–10** Some students may want to use special right triangles. **Remediation:** Point out that the measures of the acute angles cannot be determined.

Areas of Parallelograms and Triangles 5-2

You can find the area of a parallelogram or a triangle if you know the **base** and **height**. The **area of a parallelogram** is $A = bh$. The **area of a triangle** is $A = \frac{1}{2}bh$.

Find the area of each figure.

5.

10 m²

5 m

4 m

6.

90 in.²

10 in.

9 in.

7.

33 ft²

6 ft

11 ft

The Pythagorean Theorem and Its Converse 5-3

The **Pythagorean Theorem** states that in a right triangle the sum of the squares of the lengths of the legs equals the square of the length of the hypotenuse, or $a^2 + b^2 = c^2$.

Positive integers a, b, and c form a **Pythagorean triple** if $a^2 + b^2 = c^2$.

The **Converse of the Pythagorean Theorem** states that if the square of the length of one side of a triangle is equal to the sum of the squares of the lengths of the other two sides, then the triangle is a right triangle.

In a triangle with longest side c, if $c^2 > a^2 + b^2$, the triangle is obtuse, and if $c^2 < a^2 + b^2$, the triangle is acute.

Find each value of x. If your answer is not an integer, you may leave it in simplest radical form.

8.

x

20

12

16

9.

14

x

16

$2\sqrt{113}$

10.

8

x

15

17

Special Right Triangles 5-4

In a **45°-45°-90° triangle,** both legs are congruent and the length of the hypotenuse is $\sqrt{2}$ times the length of a leg.

In a **30°-60°-90° triangle,** the length of the hypotenuse is twice the length of the shorter leg. The length of the longer leg is $\sqrt{3}$ times the length of the shorter leg.

Find the value of each variable. If your answer is not an integer, you may leave it in simplest radical form.

11.

$x = 9\sqrt{3}; y = 18$

12.

$x = 12\sqrt{2}$

13.

$x = \dfrac{20\sqrt{3}}{3}; y = \dfrac{40\sqrt{3}}{3}$

14. Standardized Test Prep A triangle has sides with lengths 4, 4, and $4\sqrt{2}$. What kind of triangle is it?   **E**

  A. acute isosceles   **B.** scalene right   **C.** equilateral
  D. obtuse right   **E.** isosceles right

Areas of Trapezoids   5-5

The two parallel sides of a trapezoid are **bases.** The nonparallel sides are **legs.** The **height** is the perpendicular distance between the two bases. The **area of a trapezoid** is $A = \frac{1}{2}h(b_1 + b_2)$.

Find the area of each trapezoid. If your answer is not an integer, you may leave it in simplest radical form.

15.

18 m²

16.

16 ft²

17.

96√3 mm²

18. Writing Explain how the formula for the area of a trapezoid is related to the formula for the area of a triangle.   Every trapezoid can be divided into 2 △s with height *h* and bases b_1 and b_2.

Areas of Regular Polygons   5-6

The **center** of a regular polygon is the center of its circumscribed circle. The **radius** is the distance from the center to a vertex. The **apothem** is the perpendicular distance from the center to a side. The area of a regular polygon with apothem *a* and perimeter *p* is $A = \frac{1}{2}ap$.

⊞ **Calculator** Sketch each regular polygon with the given radius. Then find its area. Round your answer to the nearest tenth.

19. triangle; radius 4 in.   **20.** square; radius 8 mm   **21.** hexagon; radius 7 cm
    20.8 in.²   128 mm²   127.3 cm²

295

Exercises 25–27 Have students work in groups to discuss how to find the area of each shaded region. In Exercise 25, ask students if there's a "shortcut" to finding the area of the shaded region.

Remind students that the new mathematical terms in this chapter are defined in the Glossary/Study Guide in the back of the book.

Getting Ready For Chapter 6

Students may work these exercises independently or in small groups. The skills previewed will help prepare students for studying solids.

Circles: Circumference and Arc Length   5-7

The **circumference of a circle** is $C = \pi d$ or $C = 2\pi r$. The **length of an arc** is a fraction of a circle's circumference.

The length of $\overset{\frown}{AB} = \frac{m\overset{\frown}{AB}}{360} \cdot 2\pi r$.

Find the circumference of each circle and the length of each arc shown in red. Leave your answer in terms of π.

22.

4 in.
110°

8π in.; $\frac{22}{9}\pi$ in.

23.

320°
7 m

14π m; $\frac{14}{9}\pi$ m

24.

3 mm
120°

6π mm; π mm

Areas of Circles, Sectors, and Segments of Circles   5-8

The **area of a circle** is $A = \pi r^2$. The part of a circle bounded by two radii and their intercepted arc is a **sector of a circle.**

The area of sector $APB = \frac{m\overset{\frown}{AB}}{360} \cdot \pi r^2$.

The part of a circle bounded by an arc and the segment joining its endpoints is a **segment of a circle.** The area of a segment of a circle is the difference between the areas of the related sector and triangle.

A · sector of a circle
B
P
segment of a circle
C

Calculator Find the area of each shaded region. Round your answer to the nearest hundredth.

25.

3 ft
8 ft

76.97 ft²

26.

8 m

18.27 m²

27.

120° 6 cm

40.96 cm²

Getting Ready for...► CHAPTER

6

Find the area of each figure. If your answer is not an integer, round to the nearest tenth.

28.

2 in.

24 in.²

29.

6 cm

98.4 cm²

30.

11 ft 6 ft
18 ft

684 ft²

296

5 Assessment

Find the perimeter of each figure.

1.

3 cm
7 cm
20 cm

2.
2 in.
8 in. 4 in.
13 in.
58 in. 16 in.

3. You have 64 ft of fencing. What are the dimensions of the rectangle of greatest area you could enclose? **16 ft by 16 ft**

Find the area of each figure. If your answer is not an integer, round to the nearest tenth.

4.

3 in.
9 in.²

5.

12 in.
11 in.
176 in.² 16 in.

6.

12 ft
13 ft
78 ft²

7.

6 mm
72 mm²

8.

8 m
9 m
60°
62.4 m²

9.

3 in.
3 in.
6 in.
13.5 in.²

10. *Coordinate Geometry* A quadrilateral has vertices at $A(0, 7)$, $B(-2, 7)$, $C(-2, 0)$, and $D(0, 0)$. Find the area and perimeter of $ABCD$.
14 units²; 18 units

11. *Open-ended* An equilateral triangle, a square, and a regular pentagon all have the same perimeter. What can this perimeter be if all figures have sides that are integers?

any multiple of 60

Find the area of each regular polygon. Round to the nearest tenth.

12.

4 ft
41.6 ft²

13.
6 cm
7.2 cm
172.8 cm²

The lengths of two sides of a right triangle are given. Find the length of the third side. Leave your answers in simplest radical form.

14. one leg 9, other leg 6 $3\sqrt{13}$

15. one leg 12, hypotenuse 17 $\sqrt{145}$

16. hypotenuse 20, leg 10 $10\sqrt{3}$

17. *Standardized Test Prep* Which integers form Pythagorean triples? **E**
  I. 15, 36, 39
  II. 6, 8, 10
  III. 16, 30, 34
  IV. 10, 12, 14
  A. I only   **B.** IV only   **C.** II and III
  D. III and IV   **E.** I, II, and III

Find the values of the variables. Leave your answers in simplest radical form.

18.
7
x
11
$x = \sqrt{170}$

19.
15
x
13
$x = 2\sqrt{14}$

20.

y
11
x
$x = \dfrac{11\sqrt{2}}{2}; y = \dfrac{11\sqrt{2}}{2}$

21.
x
y
30°
12
$x = 4\sqrt{3}; y = 8\sqrt{3}$

Resources

Teaching Resources
Chapter Support File, Ch. 5
• Chapter Assessment, Forms A and B
• Alternative Assessment Chapter Assessment, Spanish Resources

Teacher's Edition
See also p. 240E for assessment options

Software
Computer Item Generator

297

The lengths of three sides of a triangle are given. Describe each triangle as acute, right, or obtuse.

22. 9 cm, 10 cm, 12 cm acute

23. 8 m, 15 m, 17 m right

24. 5 in., 6 in., 10 in. obtuse

25. **Writing** Explain how you can use the length of the shorter side of a 30°-60°-90° triangle to find the lengths of the other two sides.
   See margin.

Find the length of each arc shown in red. Leave your answers in terms of π.

26.

27.

$\frac{10}{3}\pi$ in. 1.5π cm

28.

29.

$\frac{10}{3}\pi$ m $\frac{21\pi}{4}$ ft

30. **Standardized Test Prep** Which length is greatest? C
   A. the diagonal of a 4-in. square
   B. the diameter of a circle with 3-in. radius
   C. the circumference of a circle with 2-in. radius
   D. the length of a semicircle of a circle with diameter 6 in.
   E. the perimeter of a 2 in.-by-3 in. rectangle

Find the area and circumference of a circle with the given radius or diameter. Leave your answers in terms of π.

31. $r = 4$ cm   32. $d = 10$ in.

33. $d = 7$ ft   34. $r = 12$ m

31. 16π cm²; 8π cm   32. 25π in.²; 10π in.
33. 12.25π ft²; 7π ft   34. 144π m²; 24π m

Calculator Find the area of each shaded region. Round your answer to the nearest hundredth.

35.
31.42 m²

36.
8.38 in.²

37.
30.10 ft²

38.
41.10 cm²

39. **Open-ended** Use a compass to draw a circle. Shade a sector of the circle and find its area.
   See margin for sample.

Find the area of each figure. Leave your answer in terms of π.

40.

41.

$(196 + 24.5\pi)$ ft² $(72 + 18\pi)$ cm²

42. **Sports** Netball players in different positions are restricted to different parts of the court. A wing defense can play in the center third and in her own goal third, except in the semicircle around the net. How much area does she have to play in? Round your answer to the nearest tenth. 2931.2 ft²

Standardized tests, such as those administered for state assessment, the SAT, or the ACT, include regular math questions, quantitative comparison questions, open-ended problems, and free response questions (which the SAT calls *grid-ins*).

MULTIPLE CHOICE QUESTIONS are followed by five answer choices, one of which is correct. **Exercises 1–8** are multiple choice questions.

QUANTITATIVE COMPARISON QUESTIONS ask students to compare two quantities. **Exercises 9 and 10** are quantitative comparison questions.

FREE RESPONSE QUESTIONS do not give answer choices. Students must provide one correct answer on their own. **Exercises 11 and 12** are free response questions.

OPEN-ENDED PROBLEMS allow for more than one solution. Students must construct their own responses instead of choosing a single answer. The responses students give will help you determine the depth of their understanding and what difficulties, if any, they are experiencing. **Exercise 14** is an open-ended problem.

STANDARDIZED TEST TIP **Exercise 3** A common error is for students to compare the sum of the given sides to the third side and forget to compare other combinations of sides. In this example, these students may choose a. They notice that $6 + 3 \not> 12$ and $6 + 3 \not> 9$ but they fail to see that $3 + 1 \not> 6$.

---

5 Preparing for Standardized Tests

For Exercises 1–10, choose the correct letter.

1. What is the area of a rectangle with vertices at $(-2, 5), (3, 5), (3, -1),$ and $(-2, -1)$? **A**
   A. 30 **B.** 25 **C.** 4 **D.** 24 **E.** 56

2. An isosceles triangle has two angles measuring 49 and 82. What is the measure of the third angle? **B**
   A. 82 **B.** 49 **C.** 51
   D. 8 **E.** none of the above

3. The lengths of two sides of a triangle are 6 cm and 3 cm. What *cannot* be the length of the third side? **E**
   I. 12 cm **II.** 9 cm **III.** 5 cm **IV.** 1 cm
   A. I and II **B.** II and III **C.** III and IV
   D. I and IV **E.** I, II, and IV

4. What is the circumference of a circle with radius 5 ft? **C**
   A. 5π ft **B.** 25π ft **C.** 10π ft
   D. 125π ft **E.** 15π ft

5. The length of the hypotenuse of an isosceles right triangle is 8 in. What is the length of one leg? **B**
   A. 4 in. **B.** $4\sqrt{2}$ in. **C.** $8\sqrt{2}$ in.
   D. 2 in. **E.** none of the above

6. Which figure has area 30 ft²? **D**

   E. none of the above

7. Which *cannot* be the perimeter of an equilateral triangle with integer side lengths? **C**
   A. 36 m **B.** 48 m **C.** 16 m **D.** 24 m **E.** 9 m

8. $\overline{DE}$ is a midsegment of $\triangle ABC$. Find DE. **A**

   A. 11.5 mm **B.** 11 mm **C.** 10.5 mm
   D. 10 mm **E.** 5 mm

Compare the boxed quantity in Column A with the boxed quantity in Column B. Choose the best answer.
   A. The quantity in Column A is greater.
   B. The quantity in Column B is greater.
   C. The two quantities are equal.
   D. The relationship cannot be determined on the basis of the information supplied.

Column A	Column B
perimeter of square $RSTV = 12x$	

9. side of $RSTV$ | $3x$ **C**

10. RT | RV **A**

11. *Critical Thinking* Is it possible to sketch a triangle in which exactly one of the altitudes is outside the triangle? Explain. See margin p. 298.

12. The area of a circle is 144π cm². What is the area of a sector with a 90° arc? **36π cm²**

13. *Writing* Explain how to use the Converse of the Pythagorean Theorem to determine if three numbers can represent the lengths of the sides of a right triangle. Include an example. See margin p. 298.

14. *Open-ended* Draw a circle. Then draw a second circle with a sector with a 90° arc so that the area of the sector equals the area of the first circle. See margin p. 298 for sample.

Resources

Teaching Resources
Chapter Support File, Ch. 5
• Standardized Test Practice
• Cumulative Review

Teacher's Edition
See also p. 240E for assessment options

To accommodate flexible scheduling, some lessons are divided into parts.
Assignment Options are given in the Lesson Planning Options for each lesson.

PACING OPTIONS

This chart suggests pacing only for the core lessons and their parts, and it is
provided merely as a possible guide. It will help you determine how much
time you have in your schedule to cover other features, such as the Chapter
Project, Math Toolboxes, Wrap Up, and Assessment.

	1 Class Period	1 Class Period	1 Class Period	1 Class Period	1 Class Period	1 Class Period	1 Class Period	1 Class Period	1 Class Period
Traditional (40–45 min class periods)	6-1	6-2 **1**	6-2 **2**	6-3 **1**	6-3 **2**	6-4 **1**	6-4 **2**	6-5 **1**	6-5 **2**
Block Scheduling (90 min class periods)	6-1	6-2 **1 2**	6-3 **1 2**	6-4 **1 2**	6-5 **1 2**	6-6 **1 2**	6-7	6-8 **1 2**	

What Students Will Learn and Why

In this chapter, students build on their knowledge of figures in the plane, learned in Chapters 1–5, by learning to measure figures in space. They learn to recognize nets of various space figures and how to find the surface area and volume of prisms, cylinders, pyramids, cones, and spheres. Then students learn how to recognize composite space figures and find their surface areas and volumes. Finally, they learn how to use geometric models to find the probability of events. Concepts learned in this chapter will help students describe everyday objects they see, such as office buildings, water towers, and video cassette cases.

Discussing the Chapter/Building on Experience

The concept map below relates chapter topics to real-world applications. You and your class may wish to add to the map

or develop maps of your own. The center oval describes the topic of the chapter. The next level displays topics within the lessons. The outer ovals reflect applications of the content. As you and your class build a concept map, invite students to discuss applications with which they are familiar.

1 Class Period	1 Class Period	1 Class Period	1 Class Period	1 Class Period	1 Class Period	1 Class Period	1 Class Period	1 Class Period	1 Class Period	1 Class Period
6-6 ①	6-6 ②	6-7	6-8 ①	6-8 ②						

Interactive Questioning Tips

A question is interactive when there is "give and take" between the questioner (teacher or student) and the respondent. In Think and Discuss or when a critical thinking question is asked, it is important to encourage a student to respond in a manner consistent with his or her learning style. A student who is primarily a visual learner might be encouraged to go to the chalkboard and illustrate with a diagram a point that he or she is trying to make. For example, in Lesson 6-2, students are asked to explain the reasoning for the design of CD packaging.

Skills Practice

Every lesson provides skill practice with Try This exercises, Exercises On Your Own, and Exercises Mixed Review. The Student Edition includes Checkpoints (pp. 322, 343) and Cumulative Review (p. 359). In the Teacher's Edition, the Lesson Planning Options section for each lesson lists Prerequisite Skills students should know for that lesson. At the back of the Student Edition is the Skills Handbook—mini-lessons on math your students may need to review. The Chapter Support File for Chapter 6 in the Teaching Resources box includes two Practice worksheets per lesson, a worksheet for two Checkpoints, and worksheets for Cumulative Review and Standardized Test Preparation.

Diverse Learning and Teaching Styles

In your Teacher's Edition, you will find suggestions as to how you can help students complete mathematical tasks in Chapter 6 by reinforcing various learning styles. Here are some examples.

- **Visual learning** create pyramids and discuss their features (p. 316), use stacks of papers, index cards, and /or coins to explain the term *cross section* and Cavalieri's Principle (p. 324), study the relationship between the base of a pyramid and the surface area of a sphere (p. 338)

- **Tactile learning** measure the height and radius of cones of different sizes (p. 318), investigate how many cones of rice it takes to fill a cylinder (p. 332)

- **Auditory learning** write and verbalize formulas to help with retention (p. 318), remember that the area of a triangle is $\frac{1}{2}$ the area of a rectangle in 2 dimensions and the volume of a pyramid is $\frac{1}{3}$ the volume of a prism in 3 dimensions (p. 331)

- **Kinesthetic learning** make a game board and toss coins to experiment with probability (p. 350)

Alternative Activity for Lesson 6-2

for use with theorem 6-1 and Example 1, uses geometry software to explore surface area and lateral area of right rectangular prisms.

Alternative Activity for Lesson 6-4

for use with theorems 6-6 and 6-7, Example 1, and Example 2, uses geometry software to explore volume of rectangular prisms and cylinders.

Alternative Activity for Lesson 6-5

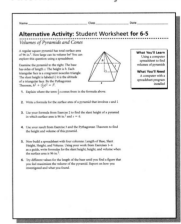

for use with theorem 6-8, Example 1, and Example 2, uses geometry software to explore volume of pyramids and creates a formula for the surface area of the pyramid

Cooperative Learning Tips

When used effectively, cooperative learning can help students develop interpersonal skills, learn to perform specific roles in a group, and learn to carry out specific responsibilities. The components of Chapter 6 provide a range of cooperative learning opportunities.

- In the Student Edition, the **Work Together** parts of lessons are specifically designed for cooperative learning activities.

- In the Teacher's Edition, you will find helpful hints for addressing diverse learning styles (see page C for Chapter 6). For every lesson, you will find a **Reteaching Activity**, which may involve cooperative learning.

Materials and Manipulatives

The authors expect all students to use scientific calculators. Calculator use is integrated throughout the course.
- calculator (6-3, 6-4, 6-5, 6-6)
- cardboard (6-5)
- centimeter grid paper (6-1)
- compass (6-3)
- foam balls (6-6)
- metric ruler (6-3)
- $\frac{1}{4}$-in. graph paper (6-2)
- protractor (6-3)
- rice (6-5)
- ruler (6-5, 6-6)
- scissors (6-1, 6-3, 6-5, 6-6)
- straightedge (6-1, 6-2)
- string (6-6)
- tacks (6-6)
- tape (6-1, 6-3, 6-5)
- unit cubes (6-4, 6-7)

TECHNOLOGY OPTIONS

Technology Tools		Chapter Project	6-1	6-2	6-3	6-4	6-5	6-6	6-7	6-8
Calculator		Assumed that students have scientific calculators at any time.								
Software	Secondary Math Lab Toolkit™		✔	✔	✔	✔	✔	✔	✔	✔
	Integrated Math Lab					✔				✔
	Computer Item Generator		✔	✔	✔	✔	✔	✔	✔	✔
	Student Edition			✔T						
Video	Video Field Trip	✔								
CD-ROM	Multimedia Geometry Lab		✔		✔		✔	✔		
Internet		See the Prentice Hall site. (http://www.phschool.com)								

✔T indicates Math Toolbox.

The Prentice Hall Geometry program offers you a rich variety of technology options. Be assured that all these options are provided as a means of enriching the program and are not essential for the successful completion of the course.

Assessment Options

The Prentice Hall Geometry Program provides you with many options. From these options, you may choose instructional materials and techniques appropriate for your students, or those necessary to meet your district's curriculum requirements. As the chart indicates, the program also supports your teaching efforts by offering you many choices for assessment.

ASSESSMENT OPTIONS

Assessment Support Materials	Chapter Project	6-1	6-2	6-3	6-4	6-5	6-6	6-7	6-8	Chapter End
Chapter Project	▲■●	▲■	▲■		▲■	▲■				▲■
Checkpoints				▲■●			▲■●			
Self-Assessment			▲■		▲■	▲■		▲■	▲■	▲■
Writing Assignment		▲	▲■	▲●	▲■	▲■	▲■●	▲■	▲■	▲●
Chapter Assessment										▲●
Alternative Assessment	■	■	■	■	■	■	■	■	■	■●
Cumulative Review										▲■●
Standardized Test Prep		▲■	▲	▲■			▲■		▲■	●
Chapters 1–6 Assessment										●
Computer Item Generator	Can be used to create custom-made practice or assessment at any time.									

▲ = Student Edition   ■ = Teacher's Edition   ● = Teaching Resources

Checkpoints

Alternative Assessment

Chapter Assessment

Available in both Form A and Form B

Making the Right Connections

Mathematics is imbedded in nearly every walk of life. The National Council of Teachers of Mathematics (NCTM) encourages educators to recognize these connections and to emphasize them for the purpose of better educating students for success in life and in a global economy. The *Connections* chart below highlights these connections for Chapter 6.

CONNECTIONS

Lesson	Interdisciplinary Connections	Career Prep	Other Real World Connections	Math Integration	NCTM Standards
Chapter Project	Economics	Design Manufacturing			Connection Problem Solving
6-1	History Biology	Manufacturing	Textiles Cracker Box		Connections Communication Problem Solving
6-2	History	Design Machinery	CD Cases Video Cassette Boxes Frieze Patterns	Algebra Geometry in 3 Dimensions Coordinate Geometry	Connections Communication Problem Solving
6-3	Social Studies	Manufacturing Architecture	Great Pyramid of Giza Tower Roofs Hourglass	Algebra Coordinate Geometry	Connections Communication Problem Solving
6-4	Geography	Environmental Engineer Plumbing	Aquarium Tanks Water-Supply Tunnel Landscaping	Geometry in 3 Dimensions	Connections Communication Problem Solving
6-5		Architecture	Teepee Transamerica Building	Algebra Coordinate Geometry	Connections Communication Problem Solving
6-6	Science	Manufacturing	Soccer Balls Ball of String Meteorology	Algebra Coordinate Geometry Geometry in 3 Dimensions	Connections Communication Problem Solving
6-7		Manufacturing Engineering	Silo Backpack Carpentry	Algebra Coordinate Geometry	Connections Communication Problem Solving
6-8	Astronomy		Commuting Dart Game Archery Sonar Sub		Probability Communication Problem Solving

CONNECTING TO PRIOR LEARNING Ask students to use vocabulary from geometry to describe the shapes of the sides or faces of three-dimensional objects such as a desk, a filing cabinet, or a flag pole.

CULTURAL CONNECTIONS Many countries throughout the world do not have supermarket chains. In such countries, there may be different markets for meats, fish, produce, and dry goods. Ask students what the advantages and disadvantages are of being able to buy all their groceries at one large supermarket. Have students who have lived in or visited countries outside the United States share with the class their knowledge of bazaars and markets.

INTERDISCIPLINARY CONNECTIONS There are approximately 23,000 supermarkets in the United States. Supermarkets represent only 10% of U.S. food stores, but supermarkets sell 70% of the food. Students might be interested in researching the history of supermarkets and superstores in the United States.

Technology Options

Prentice Hall Technology

Video
Video Field Trip 6, "The Perfect Cut," an introduction to the work of diamond cutters

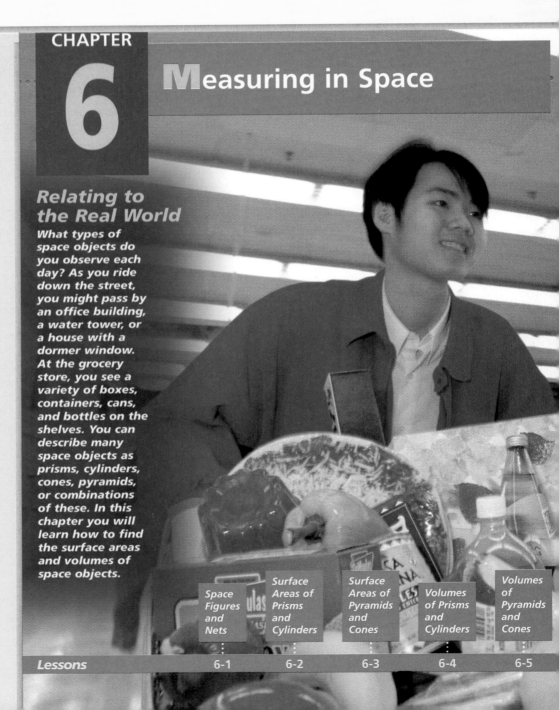

CHAPTER

6

Measuring in Space

Relating to the Real World

What types of space objects do you observe each day? As you ride down the street, you might pass by an office building, a water tower, or a house with a dormer window. At the grocery store, you see a variety of boxes, containers, cans, and bottles on the shelves. You can describe many space objects as prisms, cylinders, cones, pyramids, or combinations of these. In this chapter you will learn how to find the surface areas and volumes of space objects.

| *Space Figures and Nets* | *Surface Areas of Prisms and Cylinders* | *Surface Areas of Pyramids and Cones* | *Volumes of Prisms and Cylinders* | *Volumes of Pyramids and Cones* |

Lessons   6-1   6-2   6-3   6-4   6-5

ABOUT THE PROJECT Students explore designs of packages and what a manufacturer might consider when designing the packaging of a product. Then they design and construct their own package.

Launching the Project

PROJECT NOTEBOOK Encourage students to keep all project-related materials in a separate folder or notebook. **See Chapter Project Manager and Scoring Rubric** in Chapter Support File.

- Ask students: *Why are the drinks you buy at a fast food restaurant sold in cups that are wider at the top than at the bottom? Why are books rectangular and not round or trapezoid-shaped? Why are many toys in packages unassembled?*

- Ask students if the package design of any products they use has changed (toothpaste containers, soft drink containers, juice boxes). Why do they think the packaging has been changed?

TRACKING THE PROJECT You may wish to have students read Finishing the Chapter Project on page 353 to help them get an overview of the project. Set benchmark deadlines for students to show their work in progress.

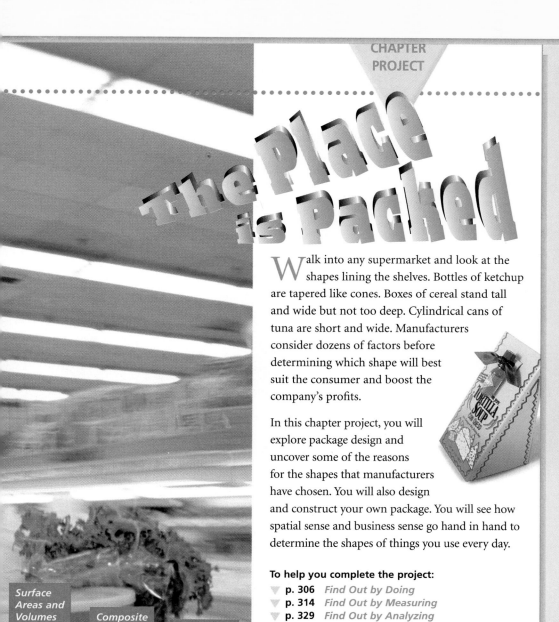

CHAPTER PROJECT

The Place is Packed

Walk into any supermarket and look at the shapes lining the shelves. Bottles of ketchup are tapered like cones. Boxes of cereal stand tall and wide but not too deep. Cylindrical cans of tuna are short and wide. Manufacturers consider dozens of factors before determining which shape will best suit the consumer and boost the company's profits.

In this chapter project, you will explore package design and uncover some of the reasons for the shapes that manufacturers have chosen. You will also design and construct your own package. You will see how spatial sense and business sense go hand in hand to determine the shapes of things you use every day.

To help you complete the project:

▼ p. 306 *Find Out by Doing*
▼ p. 314 *Find Out by Measuring*
▼ p. 329 *Find Out by Analyzing*
▼ p. 335 *Find Out by Investigating*
▼ p. 353 *Finishing the Project*

Surface Areas and Volumes of Spheres

Composite Space Figures

Geometric Probability

6-6   6-7   6-8

▼Project Resources

Teaching Resources
Chapter Support File, Ch. 6
- Chapter Project Manager and Scoring Rubric

Transparencies
68

▼Using the Rubric

Sharing the scoring rubric for the project with your students will alert them to your expectations before they begin work on the project.

As students complete each Find Out question in the chapter, you may wish to have them evaluate their own work or a partner's work based on the scoring rubric. Students should have the opportunity to revise their work after it has been reviewed.

PROBLEM OF THE DAY

A rectangle encloses a triangle and a quarter circle. Find the area of the shaded region to the nearest tenth. **91.5 in.²**

6 in.
10 in.
10 in.   10 in.

Problem of the Day is also available in Transparencies.

CONNECTING TO PRIOR KNOWLEDGE Ask students to give examples of three-dimensional objects in the classroom. Have them describe the objects using geometric terms. Then have them create a classification system for the objects using "objects with a square side," "objects with a circular side," "objects that have points," etc.

·THINK AND DISCUSS p. 302

ESL VISUAL LEARNING Make sure students understand the difference between "polyhedron" and "polygon." Have available models of different polyhedrons and cutouts of different polygons for students to manipulate.

ERROR ALERT! Some students may think that spheres and cylinders are polyhedrons. **Remediation:** Emphasize that the surfaces of polyhedrons are polygons.

WORK TOGETHER p. 302

Provide students with centimeter grid paper to use for the nets. Have students keep their models to use in the next Work Together on page 303.

Lesson Planning Options

Prerequisite Skills

- Recognizing polygons

Assignment Options for Exercises On Your Own

Core 1–16
Extension 17

Use Mixed Review to maintain skills.

Resources

 Student Edition

Skills Handbook, pp. 646, 648, 659
Extra Practice, p. 639
Glossary/Study Guide

 Teaching Resources

Chapter Support File, Ch. 6
- Practice 6-1 (two worksheets)
- Reteaching 6-1
Classroom Manager 6-1
Glossary, Spanish Resources

 Transparencies
2, 7, 69

302

Connections 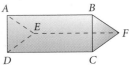 **Packaging . . . and more**

What You'll Learn

- Recognizing nets of various space figures

...And Why

To help you visualize the faces of space figures that you encounter in everyday life

What You'll Need

straightedge, centimeter grid paper, scissors, tape

Who? Grace Chisholm Young (1868–1944) was the first woman to officially receive a doctorate in Germany. In her *First Book of Geometry,* she provides nets to cut out and fold to help students visualize theorems in solid geometry.

6-1 Space Figures and Nets

THINK AND DISCUSS

As you can see in the photo below, most buildings are polyhedrons. A **polyhedron** is a three-dimensional figure whose surfaces are polygons. The polygons are the **faces** of the polyhedron. An **edge** is a segment that is the intersection of two faces. A **vertex** is a point where edges intersect.

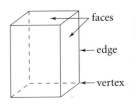

faces
edge
vertex

1. a. Try This How many faces does the polyhedron below have? **5**
   b. How many edges does it have? **9**
   c. How many vertices does it have? **6**

A **net** is a two-dimensional pattern that you can fold to form a three-dimensional figure. Packagers use nets to design boxes.

WORK TOGETHER

- Working in a group, draw a larger copy of this net on grid paper. Cut it out and fold it to make a cube.
  They are ≅ squares.
2. a. Describe the faces of the cube.
   b. Write a definition of cube.
   See back of book.
- Draw a larger copy of this net on grid paper. Cut it out and fold it to make a pyramid.

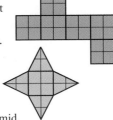

3. a. Describe the faces of the pyramid.
   b. Describe the faces of other pyramids you have seen.
   c. Complete this definition: A pyramid is a polyhedron whose base is a polygon and whose other faces are ___?___. **triangles**

3a. 1 face is a square. The other 4 are △s.
  b. Sample: 1 base is a hexagon, 6 faces are △s.

DIVERSITY Students with fine motor difficulties may have trouble cutting and folding nets. It may be easier for students to cut and tape the nets if they make their copies very large.

Question 3b Provide students with models of pyramids that have triangular, square, and hexagonal bases.

THINK AND DISCUSS p. 303

Example Relating to the Real World

Question 4 Help students see that there are many nets for the same polyhedron. The net depends on how the polyhedron is "unfolded."

CONNECTING TO STUDENTS' WORLD Have each student bring in an empty cereal, pasta, tissue, or other type of box to cut into a net. Remember to have them cut off any overlapping sections.

WORK TOGETHER p. 303

Give students centimeter grid paper to use for their nets. Students will also need the cube and pyramid models they made in the Work Together on page 302.

Question 6 The objective is for students to derive the formula $E = F + V - 2$. Note that this is equivalent to $F + V = E + 2$.

THINK AND DISCUSS

Example Relating to the Real World

Packaging Draw a net for the graham cracker box. Label the net with the appropriate dimensions.

4. Draw a different net for this box. Include the dimensions.
See back of book.

WORK TOGETHER

Work in a group to draw larger copies of the nets below. Use the nets to make three-dimensional models.

| Figure 1 | Figure 2 | Figure 3 |

5. Complete the table below, using these three models and the cube and pyramid you made for the Work Together on page 302.

Polyhedron	Number of Faces (F)	Number of Vertices (V)	Number of Edges (E)
Cube	6	8	12
Pyramid	5	5	8
Figure 1	6	8	12
Figure 2	4	4	6
Figure 3	5	6	9

6. Look for a pattern in your table. Write a formula for *E* in terms of *F* and *V.* Then, compare your results with those of other groups. Euler discovered that this relationship is true for any polyhedron. This formula is known as Euler's Formula. $E = F + V - 2$

Additional Examples

FOR EXAMPLE

Draw a net for the cereal box. Label the net with the appropriate dimensions.

Answers will vary. Sample:

Draw a net for the tissue box. Label the net with the appropriate dimensions.

Answers will vary. Sample:

303

Exercises **O N   Y O U R   O W N**

Exercises 1–7 Students may want to make larger copies of the nets, cut them out, and fold them to make the polyhedrons.

ALTERNATIVE ASSESSMENT Exercises 3–7 You may want to assess students' understanding of nets by drawing five figures similar to those shown in Exercises 3–7 and have students make a net for each figure.

DIVERSITY Exercise 8 Have students research geometric figures in the textiles of native cultures and have them present their findings to the class.

Technology Options

Prentice Hall Technology

Software
- Secondary Math Lab Toolkit™
- Computer Item Generator 6-1

 CD-ROM
- Multimedia Geometry Lab 6

 Internet
- See the Prentice Hall site. (http://www.phschool.com)

304

1. Which nets will fold to make a cube? A, B, D

A.   B.   C.   D.

2. Which nets will fold to make a pyramid with a square base? A, B, D

A.   B.   C.   D.

Match each three-dimensional figure with its net.

3. B   **4.** D   **5.** E   **6.** C   **7.** A

A.   B.   C.   D.   E.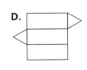

See below.

8. The fourth-century Andean textile at the right is now on display at the Museum of Fine Arts, Boston, Massachusetts.
   a. Which of the three outlined figures could be nets for the same polyhedron?
   b. Describe this polyhedron.
   a. Fig. 2 and Fig. 3
   b. a cube

Spatial Visualization **Think about how each net can be folded to form a cube. What is the color of the face that will be opposite the red face?**

9. blue   10. green   11. brown   12. purple

13. **a.** There are eleven different nets for a cube. Four of them are shown above. Draw as many of the other seven as you can. **See margin.**
    b. *Writing* If you were going to make 100 cubes for a mobile, which of the eleven nets would you use? Explain why. **See right.**

14. There are seven different nets for a pyramid with a square base. Draw as many of them as you can. **See margin.**

15. The total area of a net for a cube is 216 in.². What is the length of an edge of the cube? **6 in.**

16. **a.** *Open-ended* Draw a polyhedron whose faces are all rectangles. Label the lengths of its edges.
    b. Use graph paper to draw two different nets for the polyhedron. **See margin.**

17. There are five regular polyhedrons. They are called *regular* because all their faces are congruent regular polygons, and the same number of faces meet at each vertex. They are also called Platonic Solids after the Greek philosopher Plato (427–347 B.C.)

| Tetrahedron | Hexahedron | Octahedron | Dodecahedron | Icosahedron |

a. Match each of the nets below with a Platonic Solid.

A.   B.   C.   D.   E.

icosahedron   octahedron   hexahedron   tetrahedron   dodecahedron

b. Which two Platonic Solids have common names? What are those names?   **tetrahedron, hexahedron; triangular pyramid, cube**
c. *Verify* that Euler's Formula, which you discovered in the Work Together on page 303, is true for an octahedron. **12 = 8 + 6 − 2**

PROBLEM SOLVING HINT
Two nets are the same if one is a rotation or reflection of the other.

13b. **Answers may vary. Sample: Use the net from Ex. 12; it can be copied many times with the least waste.**

16a. **Sample:**

16b. **Answers may vary. For sample in part (a):**

13a.

14.

Lesson Quiz

Lesson Quiz is also available in Transparencies.

In Exercises 1–2, draw a net for the figure. Label the net with the appropriate dimensions.

1. See back of book.

20 cm | Pasta
5 cm
15 cm

2. See back of book.

5 cm / 5 cm
8 cm
5 cm

3. Describe the three-dimensional figure with the following net.

a pyramid with a hexagonal base

306

Chapter Project *Find Out by Doing*

With one or two sheets of cardboard and a rubber band, you can make a pop-up version of one of the Platonic Solids.

• Draw and cut out two larger copies of this net. All of the faces are congruent regular pentagons.

• Fold along the dotted lines and then flatten again.

• Place one net on top of the other as shown. (The flaps of the top pattern should fold downward and the flaps of the bottom upward.) Hold the patterns flat and stretch a rubber band (shown in red) over and under the protruding vertices. Watch the flat patterns pop into a dodecahedron. **Check students' work.**

1 in.
1 in.

Exercises | **MIXED REVIEW**

18. a. Biology The size of a jaguar's territory depends on how much food is available. Where there is a lot of food, such as in a forest, jaguars have circular territories about 3 mi in diameter. Use $\pi \approx 3$ to **estimate** the area of such a region. **about 6.75 mi²**

   b. Where food is less available, a jaguar may need up to 200 mi². **Estimate** the radius of this circular territory. **about 8 mi**

19. Open-ended Draw a triangle that has no lines of symmetry. **sample: a scalene triangle**

20. Constructions Copy $\overline{TR}$. Construct its perpendicular bisector. **See margin p. 307**

T ———————— R

21. In $\triangle ABC$, $AC = 20$, $AB = 18$, and $BC = 13$. Which angle of the triangle has the greatest measure? **$\angle B$**

Getting Ready for Lesson 6-2
Find the area of each net.

22. 96 cm²

4 cm
4 cm

23. 40π cm²

4 cm
8 cm
← 4π cm →

24. 36√3 m²

6 m

Math ToolboX — Algebra Review

Before Lesson 6-2

Dimensional Analysis

You can use conversion factors to change from one unit of measure to another. The process of analyzing units to decide which conversion factors to use is called **dimensional analysis.**

Since 60 min = 1 h, $\frac{60 \text{ min}}{1 \text{ h}}$ equals 1. You can use $\frac{60 \text{ min}}{1 \text{ h}}$ to convert hours to minutes.

$$7 \text{ h} \cdot \frac{60 \text{ min}}{1 \text{ h}} = 420 \text{ min}$$

The hour units cancel, and the result is minutes.

Sometimes you need to use a conversion factor more than once.

Example

The area of the top of a desk is 8 ft^2. Convert the area to square inches.

You need to convert feet to inches.

feet to inches   feet to inches

$$8 \text{ ft} \cdot \text{ft} \cdot \frac{12 \text{ in.}}{1 \text{ ft}} \cdot \frac{12 \text{ in.}}{1 \text{ ft}} = 8 \text{ ft} \cdot \text{ft} \cdot \frac{12 \text{ in.}}{1 \text{ ft}} \cdot \frac{12 \text{ in.}}{1 \text{ ft}}$$

The feet units cancel. The result is square inches.

$$= 8 \cdot 12 \cdot 12 \text{ in.}^2 \quad \longleftarrow \text{Simplify.}$$
$$= 1152 \text{ in.}^2$$

The area of the desktop is 1152 in.^{2}.

Choose the correct conversion factor for changing the units.

1. centimeters to meters B
  A. $\frac{100 \text{ cm}}{1 \text{ m}}$ **B.** $\frac{1 \text{ m}}{100 \text{ cm}}$

2. yards to feet A
  A. $\frac{3 \text{ ft}}{1 \text{ yd}}$ **B.** $\frac{1 \text{ yd}}{3 \text{ ft}}$

3. inches to yards B
  A. $\frac{36 \text{ in.}}{1 \text{ yd}}$ **B.** $\frac{1 \text{ yd}}{36 \text{ in.}}$

Write each quantity in the given unit.

4. 4 m = ■ cm 400
5. 360 in. = ■ yd 10
6. 9 mm = ■ cm 0.9
7. 17 yd = ■ ft 51

8. 2.5 ft = ■ in. 30
9. 35 m = ■ km 0.035
10. 2 yd = ■ in. 72
11. 23 cm = ■ mm 230

12. 2 ft^2 = ■ in.^{2} 288
13. 500 mm^2 = ■ cm^2 5
14. 840 in.^{2} = ■ ft^2 $5\frac{5}{6}$
15. 3 km^2 = ■ cm^2

16. 7 m^2 = ■ km^2 0.000 007
17. 360 in.^{2} = ■ yd^2 $\frac{5}{18}$
18. 900 cm^3 = ■ m^3 0.0009
19. 4 yd^3 = ■ ft^3 108

15. 30,000,000,000

page 306 Mixed Review

20.

6-2 Teaching Notes

PROBLEM OF THE DAY

A cube with side length 3 units is painted on the outside, then cut into 27 unit cubes. Describe how many faces are painted on each of the unit cubes. **8 with three faces painted, 12 with two faces painted, 6 with one face painted, 1 with no faces painted**

Problem of the Day is also available in Transparencies.

CONNECTING TO PRIOR KNOWLEDGE Ask students to find the area of each of the following nets.

4 in.
4 in.
2 cm
6 cm

Lesson Planning Options

Prerequisite Skills

- Finding perimeter and area of polygons
- Finding circumference and area of circles

Assignment Options for Exercises On Your Own

To provide flexible scheduling, this lesson can be subdivided into parts.

1 **Core** 1–5, 7 14–16, 22–23
Extension 17

2 **Core** 6, 8–13, 18–21, 24–26
Extension 27

Use Mixed Review to maintain skills.

Resources

Student Edition

Skills Handbook, pp. 646, 653, 659
Extra Practice, p. 639
Glossary/Study Guide

Teaching Resources

Chapter Support File, Ch. 6
- Practice 6-2 (two worksheets)
- Reteaching 6-2
- Alternative Activity 6-2
Classroom Manager 6-2
Glossary, Spanish Resources

Transparencies

15, 16, 18, 69, 73

308

WORK TOGETHER

You may want to bring in old and new CD cases for students to look at before beginning this activity.

Have students begin by carefully taping together four pieces of $\frac{1}{4}$-in. grid paper to form a 23-in. by 16-in. rectangle.

DIVERSITY This activity provides a good opportunity for students to share what music they listen to. Students may want to bring in and play music from their native countries. Encourage students to be tolerant and respectful of other people's preferences in music.

Connections **Machinery . . . and more**

What You'll Learn

- Investigating the surface areas and lateral areas of prisms and cylinders

...And Why

To use surface areas of objects in daily life, from CD cases and videocassette boxes to buildings and storage tanks

What You'll Need

- straightedge
- $\frac{1}{4}$-in. graph paper

3. Answers may vary. Sample: 2 orig. packages were exactly the same size as 1 vinyl record, so they could fit in the record bins easily.

6-2 Surface Areas of Prisms and Cylinders

WORK TOGETHER

In 1993 the music recording industry changed the size of compact disc packaging. The change to smaller packaging was made in response to the concerns of major recording artists who were worried about the effects of wasted packaging on the environment. Nets for the two packages are shown.

Work with a group. Draw nets on graph paper for each of the two packages.

1. a. What is the area of the net for the pre-1993 CD packaging? **152$\frac{1}{2}$ in.²**
  b. What is the area of the net for the new, smaller CD packaging? **65$\frac{1}{2}$ in.²**
  c. How many square inches of packaging are saved by using the smaller packaging? **87 in.²**

2. How many pairs of congruent rectangles are in each net? **3 pairs; 3 pairs**

3. *Critical Thinking* Why do you think the earlier packaging was so large? **See above left.**

 308 Chapter 6 Measuring in Space

(ESL) The new vocabulary in this lesson may be overwhelming to some students. You may want to make and display a poster of a prism and a cylinder labeling their parts. Emphasize that the *base of a prism* is a face but the *base of a polygon* is a side.

Question 4 Ask students to explain how a prism is named. Help them see that a prism is classified according to its base.

Have students use the three figures above Question 5 to practice identifying bases, lateral faces, and altitudes. Point out that in the first figure, any pair of opposite faces could be considered the bases.

ERROR ALERT! Some students may think that a right triangular prism is a prism with a base that is a right triangle. **Remediation:** Point out that when "right" describes a prism, the lateral faces are rectangles. Provide physical models and/or draw sketches of right triangular prisms with bases that are not right triangles.

Have students use the diagram at the bottom of the page to give the area of each lateral face. Help students see that $ah + bh + ch + dh = (a + b + c + d)h = ph$.

Part 1 Lateral Areas and Surface Areas of Prisms

Bases / Lateral edge / Lateral face

pentagonal prism

The CD packages in the Work Together are examples of rectangular prisms. A **prism** is a polyhedron with two congruent, parallel **bases.** The other faces are **lateral faces.** A prism is named for the shape of its bases.

4. Match each prism with one of the following names: triangular prism, rectangular prism, hexagonal prism, octagonal prism.

a.   **b.**   **c.**

rectangular prism   triangular prism   octagonal prism

An **altitude** of a prism is a perpendicular segment that joins the planes of the bases. The **height** *h* of the prism is the length of an altitude. A prism may be either *right* or *oblique*. In a **right prism** the lateral faces are rectangles and a lateral edge is an altitude. In this book you may assume that a prism is a right prism unless you are told otherwise.

right prisms   **oblique prism**

5. *Open-ended* Draw a right triangular prism and an oblique triangular prism. Draw and label an altitude in each figure.   See margin p. 311.

The **lateral area** of a prism is the sum of the areas of the lateral faces. The **surface area** is the sum of areas of the lateral faces and the two bases. You can also find these areas by using formulas.

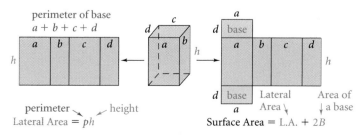

perimeter of base
$a + b + c + d$

perimeter ⟶ ⟵ height
Lateral Area = *ph*

Surface Area = L.A. + 2*B*

Additional Examples

FOR EXAMPLE 1 ....

A right triangular prism has a height of 5 cm. Its base is an equilateral triangle with side length 2 cm and height $\sqrt{3}$ cm. Find (a) the lateral area and (b) the surface area of the prism. Round your answers to the nearest tenth.   **a. 30 cm² b. 33.5 cm²**

FOR EXAMPLE 2 ....

A cylindrical cement pipe has length 500 ft and diameter 3 ft. If you are to paint the exterior of the pipe, how many square feet will you paint? Round your answer to the nearest square foot.   **4712 ft²**

Discussion: *If the pipe is 6 in. thick, explain how to find the surface area of the interior of the pipe.*

309

Theorem 6-1 Make sure that students distinguish between lowercase *b* and uppercase *B*. Uppercase *B*, used in the formula for surface area, refers to the area of a base of the prism, while lowercase *b* refers to the length of a side of a polygon.

CRITICAL THINKING Question 6 Ask students to use the formula for the surface area of a right prism to write a special formula for the surface area of a cube.

S.A. $= 4s(s) + 2(s^2) = 6s^2$

Point out that the third cylinder shown on the bottom of the page is called an oblique cylinder. Because the bases of all cylinders are circles, cylinders are not classified as prisms are.

Technology Options

Prentice Hall Technology

 Software
- Secondary Math Lab Toolkit™
- Computer Item Generator 6-2

 Internet
- See the Prentice Hall site. (http://www.phschool.com)

Theorem 6-1
Lateral and Surface Areas of a Right Prism

The lateral area of a right prism is the product of the perimeter of the base and the height.

L.A. $= ph$

The surface area of a right prism is the sum of the lateral area and the areas of the two bases.

S.A. $=$ L.A. $+ 2B$

p is the perimeter of a base.

B is the area of a base.

Example 1

Find (a) the lateral area and (b) the surface area of the prism.

The hypotenuse of the triangular base is 5 cm, because the sides form a Pythagorean triple.

a. L.A. $= ph$ Use the formula for Lateral Area.
       $= 12 \cdot 6$ $p = 3 + 4 + 5 = 12$ cm
       $= 72$

The lateral area of the prism is 72 cm^2.

b. S.A. $=$ L.A. $+ 2B$ Use the formula for Surface Area.
       $= 72 + 2(6)$ $B = \frac{1}{2}(3 \cdot 4) = 6$ cm^2
       $= 84$

The surface area of the prism is 84 cm^2.

6. **Try This** A **cube** is a prism with square faces. Suppose a cube has edges 5 in. long. What is its lateral area? its surface area?
100 in.^{2}; 150 in.^{2}

Part 2 Lateral Areas and Surface Areas of Cylinders

Like a prism, a **cylinder** has two congruent parallel bases. However, the bases of a cylinder are circles. An **altitude** of a cylinder is a perpendicular segment that joins the planes of the bases. The **height** *h* of a cylinder is the length of an altitude.

right cylinders   **oblique cylinder**

In this book you may assume that a cylinder is a *right* cylinder, like the first two cylinders above, unless you are told otherwise.

310

To find the lateral area of a cylinder, visualize "unrolling" it. The area of the resulting rectangle is the **lateral area** of the cylinder. The **surface area** of a cylinder is the sum of the lateral area and the areas of the two circular bases. You can find formulas for these areas by looking at a net for a cylinder.

Theorem 6-2
Lateral and Surface Areas of a Right Cylinder

The lateral area of a right cylinder is the product of the circumference of the base and the height of the cylinder.

$$\text{L.A.} = 2\pi rh, \text{ or } \text{L.A.} = \pi dh$$

The surface area of a right cylinder is the sum of the lateral area and the areas of the two bases.

$$\text{S.A.} = \text{L.A.} + 2B$$

B is the area of a base.

7. Try This The radius of the base of a cylinder is 4 in. and its height is 6 in.
 a. Find the lateral area of the cylinder in terms of π. 48π in.^{2}
 b. Find the surface area of the cylinder in terms of π. 80π in.^{2}

Example 2 Relating to the Real World

▦ Machinery The wheel of the steamroller at the left is a cylinder. How many square feet does a single revolution of the wheel cover? Round your answer to the nearest square foot.

The area covered is the lateral area of a cylinder that has a diameter of 5 ft and a height of 7.2 ft.

L.A. = πdh Use the formula for Lateral Area of a cylinder.
  = $\pi(5)(7.2)$ Substitute.
  = 36π Simplify.

36 ☒ π ▤ 113.09734

A single revolution of this steamroller wheel covers about 113 ft^2. ■

8. Estimation Use $\pi \approx 3$ to estimate the lateral area and surface area of a cylinder with height 10 cm and radius 10 cm.
  about 600 cm^2; about 1200 cm^2

5 ft

7.2 ft

311

Exercises ON YOUR OWN

Exercises 1–4 If possible, provide students with cubes with which they can replicate the figures and count the number of squares on the surface of each.

ALTERNATIVE ASSESSMENT **Exercise 9** This exercise can help you assess students' understanding of prisms and surface area. Have students work in small groups. Each student can perform every calculation, then they can compare answers. Students will need to use the 30°-60°-90° Triangle Theorem to find the area of the hexagonal base.

ERROR ALERT! Exercise 13 Students may calculate the surface area of the straw, adding the area of the bases to the lateral area. **Remediation:** Bring in straws and have students describe the surface of a straw.

Exercise 14 You may want to bring in a video cassette tape box so students can see which end is open.

---

pages 312–314 On Your Own

16.

10 cm
5 cm
4 cm

Exercises ON YOUR OWN

Each structure is made of 12 unit cubes. What is the surface area of each figure?

1. 38 units²

2. 32 units²

3. 38 units²

4. 38 units²

Choose Use mental math, paper and pencil, or a calculator to find the lateral and surface areas of each figure.

5. 6 ft, 6 ft, 6 ft — 144 ft²; 216 ft²

6. 2 cm, 8 cm — 32π cm²; 40π cm²

7. 6 in., 12 in., 8 in. — 288 in.²; 336 in.²

8. 6 m, 9 m — 54π m²; 72π m²

9. a. Classify the prism. **right hexagonal prism**
   b. The bases are regular hexagons. Find the sum of their areas.
   c. Find the lateral area of the prism. **240 cm²**
   d. Find the surface area of the prism. **(240 + 48√3) cm²**
   b. **48√3 cm²**

10 cm, 4 cm

Calculator Find the lateral area of each object. When an answer is not a whole number, round to the nearest tenth.

10. 4 in. **81.7 in.²**, Orange Juice, 6½ in.

11. **880 cm²**, 22 cm, 5 cm

12. **96 in.²**, 4 in., 8 in., 5 in.

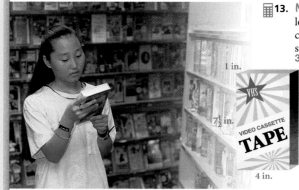

13. Manufacturing A standard drinking straw is 195 mm long and has a diameter of 6 mm. How many square centimeters of plastic are needed to make 1000 straws? Round your answer to the nearest hundred. **36,800 cm²**

14. Packaging A typical video cassette tape box is open on one side. How many square inches of cardboard are in a typical video-cassette tape box? **75.5 in.²**

15. Algebra A triangular prism has base edges 4 cm, 5 cm, and 6 cm long. Its lateral area is 300 cm². What is the height of the prism? **20 cm**

16. Open-ended Draw a net for a rectangular prism with a surface area of 220 cm². **See margin.**

1 in.
VHS
7½ in.
VIDEO CASSETTE
TAPE
4 in.

17. a. *Geometry in 3 Dimensions* List the three coordinates (*x*, *y*, *z*) for vertices *A, B, C,* and *D* of the rectangular prism. **See below.**
   b. What is *AB*? **5** **c.** What is *BC*? **3** **d.** What is *CD*? **4**
   e. What is the surface area of the prism? **94 units²**
   17a. *A* (3, 0, 0), *B* (3, 5, 0), *C* (0, 5, 0), *D* (0, 5, 4)

18. *Estimation* Estimate the surface area of a cube with edges 4.95 cm long. **about 150 cm²**

19. *Writing* Explain how a cylinder and a prism are alike and how they are different. **See margin.**

19. Answers may vary. Sample: Each is a 3-dimensional object with 2 ∥ and ≅ bases. These bases are circles in a cylinder and polygons in a prism.

 Calculator **Find the surface area of each figure. When an answer is not a whole number, round to the nearest tenth.**

20.
3 cm
6 cm
70.7 cm²

21.
12 m
6 m
619.1 m²

22.
4 in.
8 in.
4 in.
125.3 in.²

23.
Cereal
29 cm
6.5 cm
19 cm
1726 cm²

24. a. *Coordinate Geometry* Suppose the rectangle shown at the right is rotated 360° about the *y*-axis. What space figure will the rotating rectangle generate? **right cylinder**
   b. Find the surface area of this figure in terms of *π*. **48π**
   c. What will be the surface area in terms of *π* if the rectangle is rotated 360° about the *x*-axis? **24π**

25. *Standardized Test Prep* If the radius and height of a cylinder are both doubled, then the surface area is ▆. **D**
   A. the same   **B.** doubled   **C.** tripled   **D.** quadrupled
   E. not enough information given to determine the amount of change in the surface area
   6 m; 3 m

26. *Algebra* The sum of the height and radius of a cylinder is 9 m. The surface area of the cylinder is 54π m². Find the height and radius.

27. *Frieze Patterns* From about 3500 B.C. to 2500 B.C., Sumerians etched cylindrical stones to form seals. They used the imprint from rotating the seal to make an official signature. These seals make interesting frieze patterns.
   a. Two and one-quarter revolutions of a cylinder created the frieze pattern at the right. What are the dimensions of the cylinder? Round to the nearest tenth.
   b. What type of transformation appears in the frieze pattern?
   a. *r* = 0.7 cm, *h* = 4 cm
   b. a translation

4.5 cm
4 cm
4.5 cm

Chapter Project **FIND OUT BY MEASURING** Check that the containers students collect can be cut open. As they cut them open, make sure that they are careful not to cut off any of the overlapping pieces. Remind students to omit the overlapping sections in calculating the surface area of the container, but to include them in their calculations of the total area of the packaging.

SELF ASSESSMENT **JOURNAL** Students may want to make two lists, one for products packaged in cylindrical containers, and another for products packaged in boxes shaped like prisms.

GETTING READY FOR LESSON 6-3 These exercises prepare students to find the slant height of a pyramid.

Wrap Up

THE BIG IDEA Ask students: *Explain how to find the surface area of both a prism and a cylinder.*

RETEACHING ACTIVITY Students copy and cut out a net and fold it to make a prism. Then they calculate its lateral area and surface area. (Reteaching worksheet 6-2)

Exercises   MIXED REVIEW

Exercises 31–33 Have students include a graph with their answer.

Exercise 34 Students can review biconditionals in Lesson 4-1.

Lesson Quiz

Lesson Quiz is also available in Transparencies.

1. The length of a side of a cube is 8 cm. Find the surface area of the cube. **384 cm²**

2. A length of each side of the base of a right hexagonal prism is 5 in. The height of the prism is 12 in. Find the lateral area. **360 in.²**

3. The radius of a cylinder is 9 in. The height of the cylinder is 25 in. Find the surface area of the cylinder to the nearest tenth. **1922.7 in.²**

4. The base of a right rectangular prism has length 15 ft and width 8 ft. The height of the prism is 20 ft. Find the surface area. **1160 ft²**

314

Chapter Project **Find Out by Measuring**

Collect some empty cardboard containers shaped like prisms and cylinders.

• Measure each container and calculate its surface area.

• Flatten each container by carefully separating the places where it has been glued together. Find the total area of the packaging material used.

• For each container, find the percent by which the area of the packaging material exceeds the surface area of the container.

1. How does an unfolded and flattened prism-shaped package differ from a net for a prism?

2. Compare the percents you calculated. What did you find out about the amount of extra material needed for prism-shaped containers? for cylindrical containers?

3. Why would a manufacturer be concerned about the surface area of a package? about the amount of material used to make the package? Check students' work.

Exercises   MIXED REVIEW

Find the area of each figure. You may leave answers in simplest radical form.

28.

7 in.

10 in.

70 in.²

29.

13 cm

6 cm

7 cm

60 cm²

30.

12 ft

30°

24√3 ft²

Transformations Find the coordinates of the images of points
$B(-4, 2)$, $I(0, -3)$, and $G(1, 0)$ under each reflection.

31. in the y-axis
  $B'(4, 2), I'(0, -3), G'(-1, 0)$

32. in the x-axis
  $B'(-4, -2), I'(0, 3), G'(1, 0)$

33. in the line $x = 4$
  $B'(12, 2), I'(8, -3), G'(7, 0)$

34. Write a definition for a trapezoid. Write your definition as a biconditional. **A quadrilateral is a trapezoid if and only if exactly 1 pair of its sides is ‖.**

Getting Ready for Lesson 6-3

Calculator Use a calculator to find the length of each hypotenuse to the nearest tenth.

35.

8 in.

15.3 in.

13 in.

36.

11.4 m

9 m

7 m

37.

17.7 cm

13 cm

12 cm

SELF ASSESSMENT **FOR YOUR JOURNAL**

Give examples of products that are usually packaged in cylindrical containers. Then give examples of products that are usually packaged in boxes that are prisms. Explain why you think manufacturers choose particular container shapes.

Students investigate the surface area of rectangular prisms with the same volume but different base lengths. Students apply the formulas for surface area and volume that they learned in Lesson 6-2.

By using a spreadsheet, students can quickly calculate the surface areas of prism with different side lengths. The results are organized in a table for easy comparison, and computational errors are avoided.

Investigate

ERROR ALERT! Some students may incorrectly input the formulas into the spreadsheet. **Remediation:** Have students check that their spreadsheet is set up correctly by calculating by hand the height and surface area for the first value they enter in Column A.

Help students see that the values for the side of the base can be larger than 100 or less than 1.

ADDITIONAL PROBLEM If a cylinder has a volume of 100 cm³, what integral dimensions would give the smallest surface area? $r = 1$, $h = \frac{100}{\pi}$

Math ToolboX — Technology

Exploring Surface Area

After Lesson 6-2

Materials and Manipulatives
- Spreadsheet software

Transparencies
15, 16

Work in pairs or small groups.

Input

Use your spreadsheet program to investigate the surface areas of rectangular prisms with square bases. Consider square prisms with a volume of 100 cm³ and see how the surface area (S.A.) changes as the length of the side (s) of a base changes.

height (h) of prism
side (s) of base

The volume of a prism equals the area of a base times its height ($V = Bh$). Therefore, the height of the prism equals the volume divided by the area of the base ($h = \frac{V}{B} = \frac{V}{s^2}$). The surface area of a square prism equals two times the area of the base plus four times the area of a face (S.A. $= 2B + 4sh = 2s^2 + 4sh$). Set up your spreadsheet as follows.

	A	B	C
1	Square Prisms with a Volume of 100 cm³		
2			
3	sides (s) of base	height (h) of prism	Surface Area (S.A.)
4		= 100/A4^2	= 2*A4^2+4*A4*B4

Investigate

Copy the formulas down several rows and enter different values for the length of the side of the base in Column A. How small can the surface area be? How large can it be? **about 130 cm²; arbitrarily large**

Conjecture

Which dimensions give a very large surface area? Which dimensions give the smallest surface area? How do the side of the base and the height compare in the prism of smallest surface area? What is the shape of the square prism that has the smallest surface area? **either a large side length or a large height; $s = h \approx 4.6$ cm; length of side of base = height; cube**

Extend

- If a square prism has a volume of 1000 cm³, what dimensions would give the smallest surface area? **10 cm-by-10 cm-by-10 cm**

PROBLEM OF THE DAY

What is the smallest diameter of a log from which you can cut a 10-cm square post. $10\sqrt{2}$ cm

Problem of the Day is also available in Transparencies.

CONNECTING TO PRIOR KNOWLEDGE Give students the following net for a square pyramid. Ask them to identify the solid and find the area of the net.

$4\sqrt{3}$ cm

8 cm

THINK AND DISCUSS

VISUAL LEARNING As you discuss the features of a pyramid, have physical models available for students. You can create pyramids from nets or make them with straws or pipe cleaners. For each pyramid, have students measure the slant height and the length of an edge of the base.

ERROR ALERT! Some students will have trouble differentiating between the height and slant height of a pyramid.
Remediation: Reinforce that the height of a pyramid is perpendicular to the base of the pyramid. Also, it may help them to think of the slant height as the distance they would travel walking up the center of a pyramid wall.

Lesson Planning Options

Prerequisite Skills

• Finding perimeter and area of polygons
• Finding circumference and area of circles

Assignment Options for Exercises On Your Own

To provide flexible scheduling, this lesson can be subdivided into parts.

1 **Core** 2, 4, 5, 7, 13, 15, 27–28
Extension 25, 30

2 **Core** 1, 3, 6, 8–10, 12, 14, 16–24, 26
Extension 11, 29

Use Mixed Review to maintain skills.

Resources

Student Edition

Skills Handbook, pp. 646, 659
Extra Practice, p. 639
Glossary/Study Guide

Teaching Resources

Chapter Support File, Ch. 6
• Practice 6-3 (two worksheets)
• Reteaching 6-3
Classroom Manager 6-3
Glossary, Spanish Resources

Transparencies

15, 16, 18, 70, 74

What You'll Learn

• Finding the lateral areas and surface areas of pyramids and cones

...And Why

To find the lateral areas of pyramids, such as the Great Pyramid at Giza, and of conical tower roofs

What You'll Need

calculator, metric ruler, compass, protractor, scissors, tape

height
h
ℓ — slant height

$A = \frac{1}{2}s\ell$
ℓ
s
ℓ — s base s — ℓ
s
ℓ

Connections **Social Studies ... and more**

6-3 **Surface Areas of Pyramids and Cones**

THINK AND DISCUSS

Part 1 *Lateral Areas and Surface Areas of Pyramids*

Many Egyptian pharaohs built pyramids as burial tombs. The Fourth Dynasty, 2615–2494 B.C., was the age of the great pyramids. The builders knew and understood the mathematical properties of a pyramid.

the vertex
lateral edge
lateral face
altitude
base
base edge

A **pyramid** is a polyhedron in which one face (the **base**) can be any polygon and the other faces (the **lateral faces**) are triangles that meet at a common vertex (called the **vertex** of the pyramid). You can name a pyramid by the shape of its base. The **altitude** of a pyramid is the perpendicular segment from the vertex to the plane of the base. The length of the altitude is the **height** h of the pyramid.

A **regular pyramid** is a pyramid whose base is a regular polygon. The lateral faces are congruent isosceles triangles. The **slant height** ℓ is the length of the altitude of a lateral face of the pyramid. In this book, you can assume a pyramid is regular unless you are told otherwise.

You can find a formula for the lateral area of a pyramid by looking at its net. The **lateral area** is the sum of the areas of the congruent lateral faces.

L.A. $= 4(\frac{1}{2}s\ell)$ The area of each lateral face is $\frac{1}{2}s\ell$.

     $= \frac{1}{2}(4s)\ell$ Commutative Property of Multiplication

     $= \frac{1}{2}p\ell$ The perimeter p of the base is $4s$.

To find the **surface area** of a pyramid, add the area of its base to its lateral area.

Students may be curious why *l* is used to represent slant height rather than *s*. Remind them that *s* is used to represent the length of a side of a polygon.

Theorem 6-3 Point out that this theorem is only true for regular pyramids. If the pyramid is not regular, the slant height could be different on each lateral face.

CRITICAL THINKING Ask students how the formula for the surface area of a prism and the formula for the surface area of a regular pyramid are alike and how they are different.

Theorem 6-3
Lateral and Surface
Areas of a Regular
Pyramid

The lateral area of a regular pyramid is half the product of the perimeter of the base and the slant height.

$$\text{L.A.} = \tfrac{1}{2}p\ell$$

The surface area of a regular pyramid is the sum of the lateral area and the area of the base.

$$\text{S.A.} = \text{L.A.} + B$$

1. Try This A regular hexagonal pyramid has base edges 60 m long and slant height 35 m. Find the perimeter of its base and its lateral area.
360 m; 6300 m²

Sometimes the slant height of a pyramid is not given. You must calculate it before you can find the lateral or surface area.

E x a m p l e   1   **Relating to the Real World** 🌐   ··················

🔲 *Social Studies* The Great Pyramid at Giza, Egypt, was built about 2580 B.C. as a final resting place for Pharaoh Khufu. At the time it was built, its height was about 481 ft. Each edge of the square base was about 756 ft long. What was the lateral area of the pyramid?

- The legs of right △*ABC* are the height of the pyramid and the apothem of the base. The height of the pyramid is 481 ft. The apothem of the base is $\frac{756}{2}$, or 378 ft. You can use the Pythagorean Theorem to find the slant height ℓ.

$$\ell^2 = AC^2 + BC^2$$
$$\ell^2 = 481^2 + 378^2$$
$$\ell = \sqrt{481^2 + 378^2} \quad \text{Find the square root of each side.}$$

481 $\boxed{x^2}$ $\boxed{+}$ 378 $\boxed{x^2}$ $\boxed{=}$ $\boxed{\sqrt{\ }}$ *611.75567*

- Now use the formula for the lateral area of a pyramid. The perimeter of the base is approximately 4 · 756, or 3024 ft.

$$\text{L.A.} = \tfrac{1}{2}p\ell$$
$$= \tfrac{1}{2}(3024)(611.75567) \quad \text{Substitute.}$$

0.5 $\boxed{\times}$ 3024 $\boxed{\times}$ 611.75567 $\boxed{=}$ *924974.57*

The lateral area of the Great Pyramid at Giza was about 925,000 ft².

2. Try This Find the surface area of the Great Pyramid at Giza.
about 1,500,000 ft²

Additional Examples

FOR EXAMPLE 1 ···························

The Transamerica Building in San Francisco is a pyramid. The length of each edge of the square base is 149 ft and the slant height of the pyramid is 800 ft. What is the lateral area of the pyramid? **238,400 ft²**

FOR EXAMPLE 2 ···························

The radius of the base of a cone is 12 in. The slant height is 30 in. Find the lateral area in terms of π.
360π in.²

Discussion: *Is the lateral area of a cone with radius 30 in. and slant height 12 in. greater or less than the lateral area of the cone in Additional Example 2? Explain.*

317

Technology Options

Prentice Hall Technology

Software
- Secondary Math Lab Toolkit™
- Computer Item Generator 6-3

CD-ROM
- Multimedia Geometry Lab 6

Internet
- See the Prentice Hall site. (http://www.phschool.com)

318

Part 2 Lateral Areas and Surface Areas of Cones

 Who? The Greek mathematician Apollonius (about 225 B.C.) wrote a work about the cone and its cross sections. His *Conic Sections* earned him the title "The Great Geometer."

A **cone** is like a pyramid, but its base is a circle. In a **right cone** the **altitude** is a perpendicular segment from the vertex to the center of the base. The **height** *h* is the length of the altitude. The **slant height** ℓ is the distance from the vertex to a point on the edge of the base. In this book, all the cones discussed will be right cones.

The formulas for the lateral area and surface area of a cone are similar to those for a pyramid.

Theorem 6-4 Lateral and Surface Areas of a Right Cone	The lateral area of a right cone is half the product of the circumference of the base and the slant height. $$L.A. = \frac{1}{2} \cdot 2\pi r \cdot \ell, \text{ or } L.A. = \pi r \ell$$ The surface area of a right cone is the sum of the lateral area and the area of a base. $$S.A. = L.A. + B$$

Example 2

The radius of the base of a cone is 15 cm. Its height is 20 cm. Find its lateral area in terms of π.

- To determine the lateral area, you first must find the slant height ℓ.

  $\ell^2 = 20^2 + 15^2$ Use the Pythagorean Theorem.

  $ = 400 + 225$ Simplify.

  $ = 625$

  $\ell = 25$ Find the square root of each side.

  The slant height of the cone is 25 cm.

- Now you can use the formula for the lateral area of a cone.

  $L.A. = \pi r \ell$

  $ = \pi(15)25$ Substitute.

  $ = 375\pi$ Simplify.

The lateral area of the cone is 375π cm^2.

3. a. *Calculator* Find the lateral area of the cone in Example 2 to the nearest square centimeter.   1178 cm^2

    b. Find the surface area of the cone to the nearest square centimeter. 1885 cm^2

Check that students understand that the slant height of each cone is 8 cm and that the circumference of the base of the cone equals the length of the arc of the shaded region.

DIVERSITY Students who are physically challenged may not be able to do the cutting, folding, and taping in this activity. Make sure that they participate as much as possible so they feel included in the activity.

CONNECTING TO STUDENTS' WORLD Exercises 5–8 Have students collect pyramid-shaped and cone-shaped objects. Then have them find the appropriate measures and calculate the surface area of each.

---

9. Answers may vary. Sample: A cone and a pyramid are 3-dimensional figures with only 1 base. The base of a cone is a circle. The base of a pyramid is a polygon, and the lateral faces are △s.

W O R K   T O G E T H E R

■ Work in a group. Use a compass to draw three congruent circles with radii 8 cm. Use a protractor to draw the shaded sectors shown below.

180°   135°   90°

Figure 1   **Figure 2**   **Figure 3**

	C	r	L.A.
1	8π	4	32π
2	10π	5	40π
3	12π	6	48π

Cone	C	r	L.A.
1	■	■	■
2	■	■	■
3	■	■	■

■ Cut out the sectors. Tape the radii of each sector together, without overlapping, to form a cone without a base.

4. Find the slant height of each cone.   8 cm; 8 cm; 8 cm

5. Find the circumference *C* and radius *r* of each cone. Then find the lateral area of each cone. Record your results in a table like the one shown at the left.   See above left.

Exercises   O N   Y O U R   O W N

▦ *Choose* Use mental math, pencil and paper, or a calculator to find the slant height of each figure.

1. 17 cm

15 cm, ℓ, 8 cm

2. 50 m

40 m, ℓ, 60 m, 60 m

3. 12.8 m

ℓ, 10 m, 8 m

4. 5 cm, ℓ

10 cm, 10 cm, 10 cm

Find the lateral area of each figure. You may leave answers in terms of π.

5.
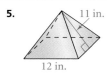
11 in., 12 in.

264 in.²

6.

8 ft, 6 ft

24π ft²

7.

8 in., 4 in.

80 in.²

8.

18 m, 16 m

about 165π m²

9. *Writing* How are a cone and a pyramid alike? How are they different?   See margin.

10. *Architecture* The roof of the tower in a castle is shaped like a cone. The height of the roof is 30 ft and the radius of the base is 15 ft. What is the area of the roof? Round your answer to the nearest tenth.   1580.6 ft²

319

11. $(\ell + r)r\pi = \ell r\pi + \pi r^2 = \text{L.A.} + B$; Anita's formula needs fewer keystrokes than the L.A. + B formula.

12. Cylinder; the lateral area of the cylinder is 48π in.² and the lateral area of the 2 cones is 30π in.²

15. S.A. = 64 cm²

6 cm
4 cm
4 cm

---

11. *Critical Thinking* Anita says that when she uses her calculator to find the surface area of a cone she uses the formula S.A. $= (\ell + r)r\pi$. Explain why this formula works. Why do you think Anita uses this formula? **See margin.**

12. *Manufacturing* The hourglass shown at the right is made by connecting two glass cones inside a glass cylinder. Which has more glass, the two cones or the cylinder? Explain. **See margin.**

13. A regular square pyramid has base edges 10 in. long and height 4 in. Sketch the pyramid and find its surface area. Round your answer to the nearest tenth. **228.1 in.²**

14. *Algebra* The lateral area of a cone is 48π in.². The radius is 12 in. Find the slant height. **4 in.**

15. *Open-ended* Draw a pyramid with a lateral area of 48 cm². Label its dimensions. Then find its surface area. **See margin for samples.**

16. **a.** *Coordinate Geometry* Describe the figure that is formed when the right triangle at the right is rotated 360° about the *x*-axis. Find its lateral area. Leave your answer in terms of π. **right cone; 15π**
b. What is the lateral area of the figure formed when the triangle is rotated 360° about the *y*-axis? Leave your answer in terms of π. **20π**

6 in.
8 in.

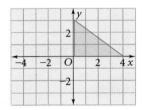

🖩 *Calculator* **Find the lateral area of each figure to the nearest tenth.**

17. 8.5 m / 6 m
80.1 m²

18. 6 m / 12 m
203.6 m²

19. 2.2 cm / 5.9 cm
43.5 cm²

20. 6 m / 2 m
37.5 m²

🖩 *Calculator* **Find the surface area of each figure to the nearest tenth.**

21. 6 in. / 8 in.
179.4 in.²

22. 18 cm / 12 cm
452.4 cm²

23. 6 cm / 6 cm
62.4 cm²

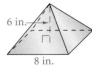

24. 13 cm / 8 cm
478.3 cm²

320

25. Paper Folding Follow the directions below to fold a dollar bill into a regular triangular pyramid, called a *tetrahedron*. Then find the surface area of your tetrahedron. How does this compare with the area of the dollar bill? They are =.

Step 1. Fold in half.

Step 2. Unfold and fold corners to foldline.

Step 3. Fold bottom left corner up.   **Step 4. Fold top left corner down.**   **Step 5. Open and form this tetrahedon.**

26. Standardized Test Prep The cylinder and cone have the same height 1 and the same radius $\sqrt{3}$. How does the lateral area x of the cylinder compare with the lateral area y of the cone? **A**
    A. $x = y$ **B.** $x = 2y$ **C.** $x > 2y$
    D. $x < 2y$ **E.** cannot be determined

27. Writing Suppose you could climb to the top of the Great Pyramid in Egypt. Which route would be shorter, a route along a lateral edge or along the altitude of a side? Which of these routes is steeper? Explain your answers. **See margin.**

28. Algebra The lateral area of a pyramid with a square base is 240 ft². Its base edges are 12 ft long. Find the height of the pyramid. **8 ft**

29. Algebra The surface area of a cone is 24π cm² and the lateral area is 15π cm². Find the slant height and the height of the cone. **5 cm; 4 cm**

30. Research Find out about ancient Mexican and Egyptian pyramids. How are they alike? How are they different? **Summarize** your findings in a short report. **Check students' work.**

Pyramid of the Sun, Teotihuacán, Mexico

27. Altitude of a side; altitude of a side; the altitude is shorter because it is one leg of a rt. △ whose hypotenuse is a lateral edge, and it is steeper because it is shorter.

page 322   Mixed Review

38. Sample:

Checkpoint   page 322

7. Each formula is the product of the perimeter of a base and the height. The formulas are different because the perimeter is computed differently for each figure.

Lesson Quiz

Lesson Quiz is also available in Transparencies.

1. The length of a base edge of a square pyramid is 10 cm. The slant height of the pyramid is 15 cm. Find the surface area. **400 cm²**

2. The diameter of a cone is 24 m and the slant height is 20 m. Find the surface area of the cone to the nearest tenth. **1206.4 m²**

3. The length of an edge of the base of a square pyramid is 8 ft. The height of the pyramid is 3 ft. Find the surface area. **144 ft²**

4. The diameter of a cone is 10 cm and the height is 12 cm. Find the surface area of the cone to the nearest tenth. **282.7 cm²**

322

Exercises MIXED REVIEW

Coordinate Geometry Find the lengths of the sides of triangles with the given vertices. Then classify each triangle by its sides. **33.** $WX = \sqrt{82}$, $XY = 3\sqrt{5}$, $YW = \sqrt{13}$; scalene

31. $A(0, 4)$, $B(-3, 0)$, $C(3, 0)$ **32.** $K(5, 0)$, $L(1, 4)$, $M(1, -1)$ **33.** $W(-2, 7)$, $X(-3, -2)$, $Y(0, 4)$
$AB = 5$, $BC = 6$, $AC = 5$; isosceles $KL = 4\sqrt{2}$, $LM = 5$, $KM = \sqrt{17}$; scalene

Write the converse of each statement. Determine whether the converse is true or false. If false, give a counterexample.

34. If two lines are skew, then they do not intersect. If 2 lines do not intersect, then they are skew; false; 2 ∥ lines.

35. If two angles are complementary, then the sum of their measures is 90. If the sum of measures of 2 angles is 90, then they are complementary; true.

36. **Transformations** Which letters of the alphabet can be rotated less than 360° and still look like the preimage? State each letter and the angle(s) of rotation. H, I, N, O, S, X, Z; all can be rotated 180°.

Getting Ready for Lesson 6-4

37. There are no hidden holes in the structure at the right. How many cubes make up this structure? **60 cubes**

38. **Open-ended** Sketch a prism made with 24 unit cubes. Label its dimensions. **See margin p. 321.**

39. A cube is made of 27 unit cubes. What are its dimensions? **3 by 3 by 3**

Exercises CHECKPOINT

Calculator Find the surface area of each figure. When an answer is not a whole number, round to the nearest tenth.

1.
12 in.
4 in. 6.3 in.
297.6 in.²

2.
11 cm
4 cm
377.0 cm²

3.
←10 m
4 m
185.6 m²

4.
8 ft
10 ft
288.7 ft²

5. **Space Shuttle** The space shuttle *Atlantis* brought a docking module to the space station *Mir*. The module is a cylinder with an 8-ft diameter and a height of 15 ft. What is the surface area of the docking module? Round your answer to the nearest tenth. **477.5 ft²**

6. **Open-ended** Draw a net for a regular triangular pyramid. Sample:

7. **Writing** Explain how the formulas for the lateral area of a prism and a cylinder are alike and how they are different. **See margin p. 321.**

CONNECTING TO PRIOR KNOWLEDGE Present students with the following bases of prisms and ask them to calculate the area of each.

WORK TOGETHER

Students should discover that volume can be found by multiplying the area of the base of the prism by its height. If unit cubes are not available, sugar cubes may be used.

Question 7 Students may have made a similar observation in the Math Toolbox on page 315, where they found the dimensions of prisms with the same volume.

What You'll Learn

• Finding the volumes of prisms and cylinders

...And Why

To find the space needed to store packages and the amount of water needed to fill an aquarium

What You'll Need

• unit cubes
• calculator

Connections 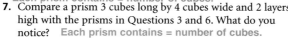 Landscaping . . . and more

6-4 Volumes of Prisms and Cylinders

WORK TOGETHER

Work with a group. Explore the volume of a prism with unit cubes.

1. Make a single-layer rectangular prism that is 4 cubes long and 2 cubes wide. The prism will be 4 units by 2 units by 1 unit. How many cubes are in the prism? **8**

2. Add a second layer to your prism to make a prism 4 units by 2 units by 2 units. How many cubes are in this prism? **16**

3. Add a third layer to your prism to make a prism 4 units by 2 units by 3 units. How many cubes are in this prism? **24**

4. How many cubes would be in the prism if you added two additional layers of cubes for a total of 5 layers? **40**

5. How many cubes would be in the prism if there were 10 layers? **80**

6. Compare a prism 2 cubes long by 3 cubes wide and 4 layers high with the prism in Question 3. What do you notice?
Each prism contains = number of cubes.

7. Compare a prism 3 cubes long by 4 cubes wide and 2 layers high with the prisms in Questions 3 and 6. What do you notice? *Each prism contains = number of cubes.*

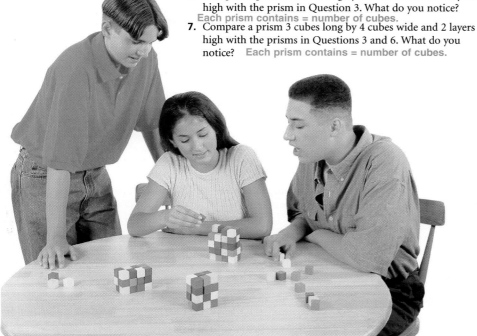

Lesson Planning Options

Prerequisite Skills

• Finding the area of polygons and circles
• Applying the special right triangle theorems

Assignment Options for Exercises On Your Own

To provide flexible scheduling, this lesson can be subdivided into parts.

▼ **Core** 2, 3, 6–12
Extension 19–20, 25

▼ **Core** 1, 4, 5, 13–18, 21, 24
Extension 22–23

Use Mixed Review to maintain skills.

Resources

Student Edition
Skills Handbook, pp. 646, 659
Extra Practice, p. 639
Glossary/Study Guide

Teaching Resources
Chapter Support File, Ch. 6
• Practice 6-4 (two worksheets)
• Reteaching 6-4
• Alternative Activity 6-4
Classroom Manager 6-4
Glossary, Spanish Resources

Transparencies
15, 16, 18, 70, 75

323

ERROR ALERT! Question 8 Some students may multiply by 3 (since there are 3 feet in a yard) and conclude that $1 \text{ yd}^3 = 3 \text{ ft}^3$. **Remediation:** Refer students to the Math Toolbox on page 307 to review how to convert units. Help students see that to convert from cubic yards to cubic feet, they can multiply as follows:

$$1 \text{ yd}^3 \cdot \frac{3 \text{ ft}}{1 \text{ yd}} \cdot \frac{3 \text{ ft}}{1 \text{ yd}} \cdot \frac{3 \text{ ft}}{1 \text{ yd}} = 27 \text{ ft}^3.$$

ESL VISUAL LEARNING Theorem 6-5 Use a stack of paper, index cards, and/or coins to explain the term *cross section* and to illustrate Cavalieri's Principle. Although oblique cylinders are not used in this book, the coin model will help students see that this principle applies to cylinders as well as to prisms.

Students are already familiar with the relationship between the area of a parallelogram and the area of a rectangle. Discuss with students how this is like the relationship between the volume of an oblique prism and the volume of a right prism.

Theorem 6-6 Make sure students understand that the formula for the volume of a prism applies to all prisms but that the formula for surface area of a prism applies to right prisms only.

Students may already be familiar with the formula for the volume of a "box" ($V = lwh$). Help students see how this formula is consistent with $V = Bh$.

Additional Examples

FOR EXAMPLE 1

Find the volume of each prism. Round your answer to the nearest tenth, if necessary.

a. a rectangular prism with height 10 cm and a base with length 15 cm and width 12 cm 1800 cm^3

b. a triangular prism with height 12 in. and a base that is an equilateral triangle with side length 5 in. 129.9 in.^3

Discussion: *Give the dimensions of a triangular prism with the same volume as the rectangular prism in part a.*

FOR EXAMPLE 2

A cylindrical oil tank has a diameter of 120 ft and a height of 50 ft. About how many gallons of oil can the tank hold? Round your answer to the nearest thousand gallons.
4,230, 000 gallons

Discussion: *Can two tanks, each with diameter 60 ft and height 50 ft hold more, less, or the same amount of oil as the tank in Additional Example 2? Explain.*

324

Part 1 Volumes of Prisms

1 yd / 1 ft

Volume is the space that a figure occupies. It is measured in cubic units such as cubic inches (in.^3), cubic feet (ft^3), or cubic centimeters (cm^3). The volume of a cube is the cube of the length of its edge, or $V = e^3$.

8. How many cubic feet are in a cubic yard? 27 ft^3

9. How many cubic inches are in a cubic foot? in a cubic yard?
1728 in.^3; $46,656 \text{ in.}^3$
Each of the two stacks of paper at the left contains the same number of sheets. The first stack forms a right prism; the second forms an oblique prism. The stacks have the same height. The area of every cross section parallel to a base is the area of one sheet of paper. The stacks have the same volume. These stacks illustrate the following principle.

Theorem 6-5
Cavalieri's Principle

If two space figures have the same height and the same cross-sectional area at every level, then they have the same volume.

10. a. Try This What are the areas of the shaded cross sections of the space figures below? 6 cm^2
b. Each of these figures has a height of 7 cm. What do you know about the volumes of these figures? The volumes are =.

You can use what you discovered in the Work Together, along with Cavalieri's Principle, to find the volume of any prism.

Theorem 6-6
Volume of a Prism

The volume of a prism is the product of the area of a base and the height of the prism.

$$V = Bh$$

11. Try This Find the volume of each of the space figures in Question 10.
The volume of each prism is 42 cm^3.

Question 11 Point out to students that the volume of all space figures, not just rectangular prisms, is measured in cubic units.

ERROR ALERT! In Part b, students may have trouble identifying the height of a prism when the height is not vertical.
Remediation: Remind students that the height of a prism is the perpendicular distance between the bases. Then have them practice identifying bases and altitudes of prisms that are in different orientations.

You may need to review with students how to find the height of an equilateral triangle.

Theorem 6-7 Have students compare Theorems 6-6 and 6-7. Have them observe that they need to remember just one formula for the volume of prisms and cylinders, $V = Bh$. When the figure is a prism, B will be the area of a polygon. When the figure is a cylinder, B will be the area of a circle.

EXTENSION Have students form two cylinders using $8\frac{1}{2}$-in. by 11-in. paper, one with the height $8\frac{1}{2}$ in. and the other with the height 11 in. Ask students to guess which has the greater volume, then calculate the volumes to test their guesses. Most students will guess incorrectly that the volumes are equal. $8\frac{1}{2}$ in. height: $V = 81.8$ in.³; 11 in. height: $V = 63.2$ in.³

Example 1

Find the volume of each prism.

a.   **b.**

a. $V = Bh$ Use the formula for volume.
  $= 480 \cdot 10$ $B = 24 \cdot 20 = 480$ cm²
  $= 4800$ Simplify.

The volume of the rectangular prism is 4800 cm³.

b. The base of the triangular prism is an equilateral triangle. An altitude of the triangle divides it into two 30°-60°-90° triangles.

  $V = Bh$ Use the formula for volume.
  $= 16\sqrt{3} \cdot 10$ $B = \frac{1}{2} \cdot 8 \cdot 4\sqrt{3} = 16\sqrt{3}$ in.²
  $= 160\sqrt{3}$ Simplify.

The volume of the triangular prism is $160\sqrt{3}$ in.³.

12. Try This The volume of a triangular prism is 1860 cm³. Its base is a right triangle with legs 24 cm and 10 cm long. **See left.**
  a. Draw and label a diagram.
  b. Find the area of the base of the prism.
  c. Find the height of the prism.

13. Try This Find the volume of this oblique prism with rectangular bases. **550 in.³**

12a.

b. 120 cm²

c. 15.5 cm

Students may construct the table in the Find Out by Analyzing activity using a spreadsheet.

Prentice Hall Technology

Software
 • Secondary Math Lab Toolkit™
 • Integrated Math Lab 33
 • Computer Item Generator 6-4

Internet
 • See the Prentice Hall site. (http://www.phschool.com)

Part 2 Volumes of Cylinders

The formula for the volume of a cylinder is similar to the formula for the volume of a prism.

Theorem 6-7
Volume of a Cylinder

The volume of a cylinder is the product of the area of a base and the height of the cylinder.

$$V = Bh, \text{ or } V = \pi r^2 h$$

325

Sometimes you need to convert units of measure to solve a problem.

Example 2 Relating to the Real World

Aquarium Tanks The main tank at the Living Seas Aquarium at EPCOT Center in Florida is the largest enclosed tank in the world. It is a cylinder with diameter 203 ft and height 25 ft. About how many million gallons of water does this tank hold? (1 gal $\approx$ 231 in.³)

■ Find the volume of the tank in cubic feet.

$r = \frac{203}{2} = 101.5$ The radius equals half the diameter.

$V = \pi r^2 h$ Use the formula for the volume of a cylinder.

$V = \pi (101.5)^2(25)$ Substitute.

[π] [×] 101.5 [x²] [×] 25 [=] 809136.8229

■ To convert cubic feet to cubic inches, multiply by 12^3.

809,136.8229 [×] 12 [yˣ] 3 [=] 1398188430

■ To find the number of gallons the tank can hold, divide by 231.

1,398,188,430 [÷] 231 [=] 6052763.766

The main tank can hold about 6 million gallons of water.

For practice with converting measurements, see Skills Handbook, page 653.

14. The main tank at the New England Aquarium in Boston, Massachusetts, has a diameter of 40 ft and is 23 ft deep. **a. 216,000 gal**

   a. What is the capacity of this tank? Round your answer to the nearest thousand gallons.

   b. How does the size of this tank compare with the size of the one at the Living Seas Aquarium?

   The New England Aquarium tank is about $\frac{1}{30}$ the size of the Living Seas Aquarium tank.

326

Exercises   **O N   Y O U R   O W N**

Exercises 1–8 Students practice using the formulas for volumes of prisms and cylinders. Remind students to write and say the appropriate formula before finding the volume. Check that students express their answers in the appropriate units.

OPEN-ENDED Exercise 11 Students may want to review the Math Toolbox on page 315 (Exploring Surface Area) before completing this exercise.

Exercise 13 Have students consult the Student Handbook for the conversion of feet to miles.

STANDARDIZED TEST TIP **Exercise 14** Students may find it easier to substitute into $V = s^3$ and solve for s.

Exercises   **O N   Y O U R   O W N**

Choose Use mental math, paper and pencil, or a calculator to find the volume of each figure. When an answer is not an integer, round to the nearest tenth.

1.

8 in.

6 in.

904.8 in.³

2.

6 ft

6 ft

6 ft

216 ft³

3.

5 in.

8 in.

2 in.

80 in.³

4.

16 m

8 m

804.2 m³

Calculator Find the volume of each figure. When an answer is not a whole number, round to the nearest tenth.

5. 4 cm

10 cm

125.7 cm³

6.

6 ft

4 ft
square base
96 ft³

7.

18 cm

6 cm

280.6 cm³

8.

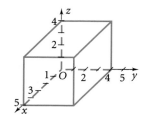

9 m

6 m

841.8 m³

9. a. What is the volume of a 7 ft-by-4 ft-by-1 ft waterbed mattress? **28 ft³**
   b. To the nearest pound, what is the weight of the water in a full mattress? (Water weighs 62.4 lb/ft³.) **1747 lb**

10. *Geometry in 3 Dimensions* Find the volume of the rectangular prism at the right. **80 units³**

11. *Open-ended* Give the dimensions of two rectangular prisms that each have a volume of 80 cm³ but have different surface areas.
   Sample: 2 cm-by-2 cm-by-20 cm, 4 cm-by-4 cm-by-5 cm

12. *Landscaping* Zia is planning to landscape her backyard. The yard is a 70 ft-by-60 ft rectangle. She plans to put down a 4-in. layer of topsoil. She can buy bags of topsoil at $2.50 per 3-ft³ bag, with free delivery. Or, she can buy bulk topsoil for $25.00 per yd³, plus a $20 delivery fee. Which option is less expensive? Explain. **Bags; the cost of 1 yd³ of bagged topsoil is $22.50 and there is no delivery charge.**

13. *Water Resources* One of the West Delaware water-supply tunnels is a 105-mi long cylinder with a diameter of 13.5 ft. To the nearest million cubic feet, how much earth was removed when the tunnel was built? **79 million ft³**

14. *Standardized Test Prep* The volume of a cube is 1000 cm³. What is its surface area? **B**
   A. 60 cm²
   B. 600 cm²
   C. 100 cm²
   D. about 4630 cm²
   E. cannot be determined

327

ALTERNATIVE ASSESSMENT **Exercises 15–18** These exercises can help you assess students' understanding of the formulas for volume by their ability to manipulate them to find the height of a cylinder or a prism with a given volume. Have students work in small groups or pairs to complete these exercises.

MAKING CONNECTIONS Exercise 20 John Priestly first discovered that green plants affect air in 1772. He observed that placing a candle under a jar extinguished its flame. However, when he placed a sprig of mint under a jar for a few days and then added a candle, the candle burned for a short time.

GEOMETRY IN 3 DIMENSIONS Exercise 25 Students can use the methods suggested on pages 313 and 320 to visualize the figure.

pages 327–329 On Your Own

19c. **Answers may vary. Sample:** No; the volume of the "improved" cube is $\frac{1}{8}$ the volume of the "ordinary" cube.

Find Out by Analyzing

Answers may vary. Sample:

l	w	h	V	S.A	V : S.A.
6	6	6	216	216	1 : 1
2	3	36	216	372	18 : 31
3	3	24	216	306	36 : 51
4	6	9	216	228	18 : 19

Find the height of each prism or cylinder with the given volume.

15. 5 in. / h / 5 in. / 5 in.
V = 125 in.³

16. h 3 cm / 9 cm
V = 243π cm³

17. 6 ft 3 ft / h
V = 27 ft³

18. 3 m 4 m / h
V = 12π m³

19. **a.** What is the volume of the "ordinary" cube in the cartoon if each edge is 18 in. long? **5832 in.³**
   b. What is the volume of the "improved" cube if each edge is half as long as an edge of the "ordinary" cube? **729 in.³**
   c. Writing Do you agree with the cartoon statement that the "improved" cube is half the size of the "ordinary" cube? Explain. **See margin.**

20. Environmental Engineering A scientist has suggested that one way to keep indoor air relatively pollution free is to provide two or three pots of flowers such as daisies for every 100 ft² of floor space with an 8-ft ceiling. How many pots of daisies would a 35 ft-by-45 ft-by-8 ft classroom need? **32 to 47**

21. **a.** The volume of a cylinder is 600π cm³. The radius of a base of the cylinder is 5 cm. What is the height of the cylinder? **24 cm**
   b. The volume of a cylinder is 135π cm³. The height of the cylinder is 15 cm. What is the radius of a base of the cylinder? **3 cm**

GUINDON © News America Syndicate, 1985

An improved cube (right), half the size of ordinary cubes. It has a convenient carrying handle.

A cylinder has been cut out of each figure. Find the volume of the remaining figure. Round your answer to the nearest tenth.

22. ⊢—— 6 cm ——⊣ / 2 cm / 5 cm
125.7 cm³

23. 4 in. / 6 in. / 6 in. / 6 in.
140.6 in.³

24. Plumbing The outside diameter of a pipe is 5 cm. The inside diameter is 4 cm. If the pipe is 4 m long, what is the volume of the metal used for this length of pipe? Round your answer to the nearest whole number. **2827 cm³**

FIND OUT BY ANALYZING This activity reinforces the fact that different prisms can have the same volume.

Exercises MIXED REVIEW

Exercises 26–29 Encourage students to use the Triangle Inequality Theorem. Then have them confirm their answers by measuring the lengths of the sides of the triangle.

JOURNAL Students may want to survey friends and relatives to see how they use volume on a daily basis at home and at work.

GETTING READY FOR LESSON 6-5 These exercises prepare students to find the volumes of pyramids and cones.

Wrap Up

THE BIG IDEA Ask students: *Describe how to find the volume of a prism and cylinder. Explain how the methods are the same and how they are different.*

RETEACHING ACTIVITY Students find the volume of part of a pint container and a measuring cup. (Reteaching worksheet 6-4)

---

25. **a.** *Geometry in 3 Dimensions* What is the volume, in terms of π, of the cylinder formed if the rectangle at the right is rotated 360° about the *x*-axis? **16π units^3**

   b. What is the volume, in terms of π, if the rectangle is rotated 360° about the *y*-axis? **32π units^3**

Reteaching 6-4

Practice 6-4

Practice 6-4

Mixed Exercises

Find the volume of each cylinder to the nearest tenth.

Find the volume of each prism to the nearest whole number.

Find Out by Analyzing

Copy and complete the table below for four *different* rectangular prisms that each have a volume of 216 cm^3. See margin p. 328.

Length (cm)	Width (cm)	Depth (cm)	Volume (V) (cm^3)	Surface Area (S.A.) (cm^2)	Ratio V : S.A.
6	6	■	216	■	■
■	■	■	216	■	■

1. Which of the prisms uses the container material most efficiently? least efficiently? Explain. **6 by 6 by 6; 2 by 3 by 36; see right.**

2. Why would a manufacturer be concerned with the ratio of volume to surface area? **to minimize the cost of packaging**

3. Why do you think cereal boxes are not shaped to give the greatest ratio of volume to surface area?

> The lower the ratio, the more material is being used to enclose the same volume.

3. Answers may vary. Sample: A cereal box is used for promoting the product, so it needs a large surface area on its front.

Exercises MIXED REVIEW

Draw and label △*ABC*. List the sides from shortest to longest.

26. $m\angle A = 67$, $m\angle B = 34$, $m\angle C = 79$

28. $m\angle A = 98$, $m\angle B = 73$, $m\angle C = 9$
$\overline{AB}, \overline{AC}, \overline{BC}$

26. $\overline{AC}, \overline{BC}, \overline{AB}$
27. $\overline{AC}, \overline{AB}, \overline{BC}$

27. $m\angle A = 101$, $m\angle B = 13$, $m\angle C = 66$

29. $m\angle A = 28$, $m\angle B = 81$, $m\angle C = 71$
$\overline{BC}, \overline{AB}, \overline{AC}$

30. *Critical Thinking* The area of a triangle is 24 cm^2. The longest side of the triangle is 13 cm long. The second longest side is 12 cm long. Is the triangle a right triangle? Explain. **No; the rt. △ would have sides 5, 12, 13 and area 30 cm^2.**

Getting Ready for Lesson 6-5

Use the Pythagorean Theorem to find the height *h* of each space figure.

31.

32.

FOR YOUR JOURNAL

Describe some everyday situations in which you would want to know the volumes of prisms.

Lesson Quiz

Lesson Quiz is also available in Transparencies.

1. A rectangular prism has height 3 cm, base length 6 cm, and base width 5 cm. Find the volume of the prism. **90 cm^3**

2. A triangular prism has height 24 in. Its base is a right triangle with legs 9 in. and 12 in. Find the volume of the prism. **1296 in.^{3}**

3. A cylinder has height 18 m and diameter 24 m. Find the volume of the cylinder to the nearest cubic meter. **8143 m^3**

329

CONNECTING TO PRIOR KNOWLEDGE Have students find the volume of a prism with a square base of length 5 cm and height 8 cm and the volume of a cylinder with a diameter of 5 cm and height 8 cm.

WORK TOGETHER

Students investigate the volume of a pyramid. Have students begin by making a conjecture about the volume of a pyramid relative to the volume of a prism with the same base and height. (Some may make the conjecture that the volume of the pyramid is one-half the volume of the prism.)

Questions 1–2 It is important that students realize that the relationship between the volumes of a prism and a pyramid depends on their having the same base and height.

Lesson Planning Options

Prerequisite Skills

• Finding the area of polygons and circles
• Applying the Pythagorean Theorem

Assignment Options for Exercises On Your Own

To provide flexible scheduling, this lesson can be subdivided into parts.

▼ **Core** 3, 7, 10, 15, 16
Extension 17

▼ **Core** 1, 2, 4–6, 8, 9, 11, 13, 14, 19–24
Extension 12, 18

Use Mixed Review to maintain skills.

Resources

Student Edition

Skills Handbook, pp. 646, 659
Extra Practice, p. 639
Glossary/Study Guide

Teaching Resources

Chapter Support File, Ch. 6
• Practice 6-5 (two worksheets)
• Reteaching 6-5
• Alternative Activity 6-5
Classroom Manager 6-5
Glossary, Spanish Resources

 Transparencies
15, 16, 18, 71, 76

330

What You'll Learn
• Finding volumes of pyramids and cones

...And Why
To solve problems concerning the amount of space in things such as a convention center or a popcorn box

What You'll Need
• cardboard
• ruler
• scissors
• tape
• rice
• calculator

Connections Architecture . . . and more

6-5 Volumes of Pyramids and Cones

WORK TOGETHER

You know how to find the volume of a prism. Work in a group to explore the volume of a pyramid.

■ Draw the nets shown below on cardboard.

■ Cut out the nets and tape them together to make a cube and a regular square pyramid. Each model will have one open face.

1. Compare the areas of the bases of the cube and the pyramid.
   The areas are =.
2. Compare the heights of the cube and the pyramid.
   The heights are =.
3. Fill the pyramid with rice. Then pour the rice from the pyramid into the cube. How many pyramids full of rice does the cube hold?
   about 3 pyramids
4. The volume of the pyramid is what fractional part of the volume of the cube? $\frac{1}{3}$

THINK AND DISCUSS

Part 1 Volumes of Pyramids

The Work Together demonstrates the following theorem.

Theorem 6-8
Volume of a Pyramid

The volume of a pyramid is one third the product of the area of the base and the height of the pyramid.

$$V = \frac{1}{3}Bh$$

Oblique Pyramid

Because of Cavalieri's Principle, the volume formula is true for all pyramids, including *oblique* pyramids. The **height** h of an oblique pyramid is the length of the perpendicular segment from the vertex to the plane of the base.

Example 1 Relating to the Real World

Architecture The Pyramid is an arena in Memphis, Tennessee. The area of the base of the Pyramid is about 300,000 ft². Its height is 321 ft. What is the volume of the Pyramid?

$V = \frac{1}{3}Bh$ Use the formula for the volume of a pyramid.

$\quad = \frac{1}{3}(300,000)(321)$ Substitute.

$\quad = 32,100,000$ Simplify.

The volume is about 32,100,000 ft³.

    5. Try This Find the volume of a regular square pyramid with base edges 12 in. long and height 8 in. **384 in.³**

331

Example 2

Students are accustomed to solving for the slant height (the hypotenuse of the right triangle) in order to find the surface area. Point out that in this example, they are solving for the height which is a leg of the right triangle.

TACTILE LEARNING If you have block scheduling or an extended class period, have students repeat the Work Together activity using cones and cylinders. Provide nets of a cone and a cylinder with the same height and base. Then have students make the figures and investigate how many cones of rice it takes to fill the cylinder.

Example 3

Review the calculator keystrokes with students, especially how to input $\frac{1}{3}$ and $(15)^2$.

EXTENSION Have students investigate frustums made from sections of cones, such as popcorn buckets, megaphones, paper drinking cups, and dog dishes. Have groups research the formulas for the area of frustums made from cones and pyramids and present their results to the class.

Technology Options

For Exercise 11, students may use a spreadsheet to display the possible dimensions.

Prentice Hall Technology

 Software
- Secondary Math Lab Toolkit™
- Computer Item Generator 6-5

 CD-ROM
- Multimedia Geometry Lab 6

 Internet
- See the Prentice Hall site. (http://www.phschool.com)

332

To find the volume of a pyramid you need to know its height.

Example 2

Find the volume of a regular square pyramid with base edges 40 ft long and slant height 25 ft.

- Find the height of the pyramid.

$$25^2 = h^2 + 20^2 \qquad \text{Use the Pythagorean Theorem.}$$
$$625 = h^2 + 400 \qquad \text{Simplify.}$$
$$h^2 = 225 \qquad \text{Subtract 400 from each side.}$$
$$h = 15 \qquad \text{Find the square root of each side.}$$

- Find the volume of the pyramid.

$$V = \frac{1}{3}Bh \qquad \text{Use the formula for volume of a pyramid.}$$
$$= \frac{1}{3}(40 \cdot 40)15 \qquad \text{Substitute.}$$
$$= 8000 \qquad \text{Simplify.}$$

The volume of the pyramid is 8000 ft³.

6. Try This Find the volume of a regular square pyramid with base edges 24 m long and slant height 13 m. **960 m³**

Part 2

Volumes of Cones

In the Work Together, you discovered that the volume of a pyramid is one third the volume of a prism with the same base and height. You can also find that the volume of a cone is one third the volume of a cylinder with the same base and height.

Theorem 6-9 Volume of a Cone	The volume of a cone is one third the product of the area of the base and the height. $$V = \frac{1}{3}Bh, \text{ or } V = \frac{1}{3}\pi r^2 h$$

This volume formula applies to all cones, including *oblique* cones.

Example 3

Find the volume of the oblique cone with diameter 30 ft and height 25 ft. Round to the nearest whole number.

$r = \frac{30}{2} = 15$ The radius is half the diameter.

$V = \frac{1}{3}\pi r^2 h$ Use the formula for the volume of a cone.

$= \frac{1}{3}\pi(15)^2 25$ Substitute.

`1 ÷ 3 × π × 15 x² × 25 =` **5890.4862**

The volume of the cone is about 5890 ft³.

7. Try This Find the volume of a cone with radius 3 in. and height 8 in. Round to the nearest tenth. **75.4 in.³**

Exercises   ON YOUR OWN

 Calculator Find the volume of each figure. When an answer is not a whole number, round to the nearest tenth.

1.

9 in.
7 in.
115.5 in.³

2.
23.0 in.³

$5\frac{1}{2}$ in.
4 in.

3.
122.5 in.³

7.5 in.
7 in.
square base

4.
10 cm
12 cm
301.6 cm³

5. a. Mental Math A cone with radius 3 ft and height 10 ft has a volume of 30π ft³. What is its volume when the radius is doubled? **120π ft³**
   b. What is the volume when the height of the original cone is doubled? **60π ft³**
   c. What is the volume when both the radius and the height of the original cone are doubled? **240π ft³**

6. a. The largest tepee in the United States belongs to a member of the Crow (Native Americans of the Great Plains). It is 43 ft high and 42 ft in diameter. Find its volume to the nearest cubic foot. **19,858 ft³**
   b. How does this compare with the volume of your classroom?
   Check students' work.

COORDINATE GEOMETRY Exercise 12 Students should now be familiar with this type of problem. If they made a visual model for Exercise 24 in Lesson 6-2, it can also be used for this problem.

CRITICAL THINKING Exercise 13 Ask students how the volume of a cone with radius r and height h compares to the volume of two cones with radii $\frac{r}{2}$ and height h.

Exercise 16 Students will need to use the 30°-60°-90° Triangle Theorem to find the area of the base.

Exercise 17 The Transamerica Building has "wings" for stability. Do not have students include the "wings" when they find the volume.

ESL **Exercises 17–18** You may want to pair students with strong English skills with those who are less proficient in English for these word problems.

Find the volume of each figure. You may leave answers in terms of π or in simplest radical form.

7. 300 in.^{3}

8. $\frac{80}{3}\pi$ cm^3

9. $\frac{16}{3}\pi$ ft^3

10.
180$\sqrt{3}$ cm^3
Samples: height: 50 in., radius: 6 in.; height: 18 in., radius: 10 in.

11. Open-ended A cone has a volume of 600π in.^{3}. Find two possible sets of dimensions for the height and radius of the cone.

12. a. Coordinate Geometry Suppose you rotate the right triangle shown 360° about the x-axis. What is the volume of the resulting cone in terms of π? 12π units^3
 b. Suppose you rotate the triangle 360° about the y-axis. What is the volume in terms of π? 16π units^3

13. The two cylinders pictured at the right are congruent. How does the volume of the larger cone compare to the total volume of the two smaller cones? Explain. They are =.

14. The volume of a cone is 36π cm^3. If the radius is 6 cm, what is the height of the cone? 3 cm

15. The volume of a regular square pyramid is 600 in.^{3}. The height is 8 in. What is the length of each base edge? 15 in.

16. To the nearest tenth, find the volume of a regular hexagonal pyramid with base edges 12 cm long and height 15 cm.
1870.6 cm^3

17. a. Architecture The Transamerica Building in San Francisco is a pyramid 800 ft tall with a square base 149 ft on each side. What is its volume to the nearest thousand cubic feet? 5,920,000 ft^3
 b. If the Transamerica Building had been built as a *prism* with the same square base, how tall to the nearest foot would it have to be to have the same volume as the existing building? 267 ft

18. *Critical Thinking* A movie theater sells popcorn in cylindrical containers that are 4 in. in diameter and 10 in. high. As a special promotion, the theater plans to sell popcorn in a cone-shaped container for the same price. The diameter of the container will remain the same. The promotional cone will use the same amount of cardboard as the cylindrical container. Do you think this promotional cone is a good value? Why or why not?

Answers may vary. Sample: No; the volume of the cone is smaller than the volume of the cylinder.

19. Which container has the greatest volume? **pyramid**

Figure 1

Figure 2

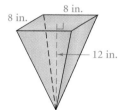
Figure 3

Algebra **Find the value of the variable in each figure. You may leave answers in simplest radical form.**

20. **6**

Volume = $18\sqrt{3}$

21.

Volume = 21π

22. $3\sqrt{2}$

Volume = 24π

23.
9

Volume = 150

24. *Writing* The figures at the right can be covered by an equal number of straws that are the same length. Describe how Cavalieri's Principle could be adapted to compare the areas of these figures. See below.

24. If 2 figures have the same height, and if, at every level, the line ∥ to the base intersects the figures in ≅ segments, then their areas are =.

335

Exercise 25 Students may want to review the distance formula in Lesson 1-8 and slope in Lesson 2-3.

JOURNAL Check that students use *base*, *area of base*, *height*, *slant height*, and their abbreviations accurately.

GETTING READY FOR LESSON 6-6 These exercises prepare students to measure spheres.

Wrap Up

THE BIG IDEA Ask students: *Explain how the volume formulas for a pyramid and a cone are similar and different.*

RETEACHING ACTIVITY Students calculate the volume of cones and pyramids. (Reteaching worksheet 6-5)

Geometry at Work

For further information about the training necessary to be a packaging engineer, have students contact a local engineering school. You may want to invite a local engineer to class to discuss what they do.

Encourage students to investigate these topics:

- the training necessary to become an engineer
- the math and computer skills used by an engineer
- the different types of engineers and the companies that employ them

Lesson Quiz

Lesson Quiz is also available in Transparencies.

Find the volume of each figure. Round to the nearest tenth, if necessary.

1. a cone with diameter 9 in. and height 16 in. **339.3 in.**^{3}

2. a square pyramid with base length 6 cm and height 9.5 cm **114 cm**^{3}

3. a cone with radius 12 mm and slant height 20 mm **2412.7 mm**^{3}

4. a square pyramid with base length 10 ft and slant height 13 ft **400 ft**^{3}

25. The vertices of quadrilateral *ABCD* are $A(-4, -1)$, $B(-1, 3)$, $C(7, -3)$, and $D(4, -7)$.
  a. Use the Distance Formula to find the length of each side. $AB = 5$, $BC = 10$, $CD = 5$, $AD = 10$
  b. Find the slope of each side. See below.
  c. Determine the most accurate name for quadrilateral *ABCD*. rectangle

26. Movies The largest permanent movie screen in the world is in Jakarta, Indonesia. It is 96 ft by 70.5 ft. What is its area? **6768 ft**^{2}

Getting Ready for Lesson 6-6

▥ Calculator **Find the area and circumference of a circle with the given radius. Round answers to the nearest tenth.**

27. 6 in. 113.1 in.^{2}; 37.7 in.

28. 5 cm 78.5 cm^2; 31.4 cm

29. 2.5 ft 19.6 ft^2; 15.7 ft

30. 1.2 m 4.5 m^2; 7.5 m

FOR YOUR JOURNAL

Explain why finding the volume of a cylinder is like finding the volume of a prism. Then explain why finding the volume of a cone is like finding the volume of a pyramid.

Geometry at Work

Packaging Engineer

E ach year, more than one trillion dollars in manufactured goods are packaged in some kind of a container. To create each new box, bag, or carton, packaging engineers must balance such factors as safety, environmental impact, and attractiveness against cost of production.

Consider the three boxes of dishwasher detergent. All three boxes have volumes of 108 in.^{3}, the volume of a standard box of automatic dishwasher detergent. The boxes have different shapes, however, and different surface areas. The box on the left has the greatest surface area and therefore costs the most to produce. Nevertheless, despite the higher cost, the box on the left has become standard. There are many reasons

why a company might choose more expensive packaging. In this case, the least expensive package on the right is too difficult for a consumer to pick up and pour. To offset the extra cost, packaging engineers try to choose a package design that will attract enough additional buyers to outweigh the higher cost of production.

Mini Project: Choose a product that you enjoy using. Design and make a new package for the product. Calculate the surface area and volume of your package and describe advantages it has over the current package.

25b. $AB = \frac{4}{3}$, $BC = -\frac{3}{4}$, $CD = \frac{4}{3}$, $AD = -\frac{3}{4}$

PROBLEM OF THE DAY

Margo has a cube, each face painted a different color. In how many ways can she place the numbers 1, 2, 3, 4, 5, and 6 on the cube so that the pairs 1 and 6, 2 and 5, and 3 and 4 are on opposite faces? **48**

Problem of the Day is also available in Transparencies.

CONNECTING TO PRIOR KNOWLEDGE Have students calculate the volume of the following:

a. a cylinder with diameter 4 cm and height 16 cm

b. a regular square pyramid with base length 8 in. and height 14 in.

In this activity, students should discover that it takes twice as much string to cover the curved surface of half a foam ball than to cover the circular region.

ALTERNATIVE METHOD Bring in a beach ball. Have students draw and cut out at least four circles with the same diameter as the ball. Then have them cover the ball with the circles, cutting the circles into pieces and arranging them over the surface of the ball. Students will discover that, after covering the ball with two such circles, it is only about half covered.

What You'll Learn
- Calculating the surface areas and volumes of spheres

...And Why
To solve real-world problems such as finding the surface area of a soccer ball and the volume of a scoop of ice cream

What You'll Need
- ruler
- scissors
- tacks
- foam balls (cut in half)
- string
- calculator

Connections 🌐 **Manufacturing . . . and more**

6-6 Surface Areas and Volumes of Spheres

WORK TOGETHER

How do you compute the surface area of Earth or the amount of leather covering a baseball? Work in a group to explore the surface area of a sphere.

- The surface of half a foam ball consists of two parts—a plane circular region and a curved surface. Place a tack in the center of the circular region. Wind string around the tack covering the entire circular region.

- Once the circular region is covered, cut off any excess string. Measure the length x of string that covered the circular region.

- Place a tack in the center of the curved surface. Wind another string around the tack covering the entire curved surface.

- Once the curved surface is covered, cut off any excess string. Measure the length y of the string that covered the curved surface.

1. a. How do x and y compare? **$y > x$**
   b. Express y as a multiple of x. **$y = 2x$**

2. a. How much string would you need to cover the entire surface of an uncut foam ball? Express your answer as a multiple of y. **2y**
   b. Express your answer to part (a) as a multiple of x. **4x**

3. A string of length x covers an area of πr^2 where r is the radius of the foam ball. Substitute πr^2 for x in the expression you wrote for Question 2(b) to find a formula for the surface area of a sphere. **$A = 4\pi r^2$**

4. A radius is a segment that has one endpt. at the center and the other endpt. on the sphere.

THINK AND DISCUSS

Part 1 Finding the Surface Area of a Sphere

A **sphere** is the set of all points in space equidistant from a given point called the **center**.

4. How would you define a *radius* of a sphere? **See above.**

5. How would you define a *diameter* of a sphere?
   a segment passing through the center with endpts. on the sphere

---

Lesson Planning Options

Prerequisite Skills
- Finding the area of circles
- Understanding cubes and cube roots

Assignment Options for Exercises On Your Own

To provide flexible scheduling, this lesson can be subdivided into parts.

1 Core 1–4, 16
Extension 14, 26

2 Core 5–13, 15, 17–18, 22–25, 27
Extension 19–21

Use Mixed Review to maintain skills.

Resources

📖 **Student Edition**
Skills Handbook, pp. 646, 659
Extra Practice, p. 639
Glossary/Study Guide

📋 **Teaching Resources**
Chapter Support File, Ch. 6
- Practice 6-6 (two worksheets)
- Reteaching 6-6
Classroom Manager 6-6
Glossary, Spanish Resources

📽 **Transparencies**
18, 71

337

Example 1 Relating to the Real World ······················

Question 6 If possible, bring in a soccer ball so students can see that the sides of the "hexagons" and "pentagons" are curves. This example is a preview of spherical geometry, which will be discussed in Lesson 7-5.

CONNECTING TO STUDENTS' WORLD Have students calculate the surface areas and volumes of other spheres such as a globe, a beach ball, or an orange. They can approximate the radius ($r = \frac{C}{2\pi}$) of each sphere by measuring the circumference of a great circle with a piece of string.

Some students will have trouble following the derivation of the formula for the volume of a sphere. You may want to show in more detail how to get from $\frac{1}{3} \cdot nBr$ to $\frac{1}{3}(4\pi r^2) \cdot r$ to $\frac{1}{3} \cdot 4\pi r^3$.

VISUAL LEARNING The justification of the formula for the volume of a sphere uses the concept of limits. Help students see that as the number of pyramids increases, the size of the base of the pyramid decreases. As this happens, the combined area of the bases becomes closer and closer to the actual surface area of the sphere.

Additional Examples

FOR EXAMPLE 1 ···························

Find the surface area of a sphere with diameter 18 in. Round your answer to the nearest tenth.
1017.9 in.²

Discussion: *Describe the dimensions of a cylinder having a smaller surface area than the sphere.*

Find the surface area of a sphere inscribed in a cube with side length 24 cm. Round your answer to the nearest tenth. **1809.6 cm²**

FOR EXAMPLE 2 ···························

The volume of a sphere is 904.78 cm³. What is the surface area of the sphere? Round your answer to the nearest tenth. **452.4 cm²**

Discussion: *How does the surface area of a cube with the same volume compare to the surface area of the sphere?*

The surface area of a sphere is 5026.55 in.². What is the volume of the sphere? Round your answer to the nearest tenth. **33,510.3 in.³**

Your discovery in the Work Together leads to the following theorem.

Theorem 6-10
Surface Area of a Sphere

The surface area of a sphere is four times the product of π and the square of the radius of the sphere.

$$\text{S.A.} = 4\pi r^2$$

Example 1 Relating to the Real World ······················

Manufacturing Manufacturers make soccer balls with a radius of 11 cm by sewing together 20 regular hexagons and 12 regular pentagons. Templates for guiding the stitching are shown at the left. Approximate the surface area of a soccer ball to the nearest square centimeter using the following two methods.

Method 1:
Find the sum of the areas of the pentagons and hexagons.

regular pentagon	regular hexagon
$A = \frac{1}{2}ap$	$A = \frac{1}{2}ap$
$= \frac{1}{2}(3.1)(5 \cdot 4.5)$	$= \frac{1}{2}(3.9)(6 \cdot 4.5)$
$= 34.875$	$= 52.65$

Area of the 12 regular pentagons $= (12)(34.875) = 418.5$

Area of the 20 regular hexagons $= (20)(52.65) = 1053$

The sum of the areas of the pentagons and the hexagons is about 1472 cm².

Method 2:
Use the formula for the surface area of a sphere.

$\text{S.A.} = 4\pi r^2$ Use the formula for surface area.
$= 4 \cdot \pi \cdot 11^2$ Substitute.

4 ⊠ π ⊠ 11 x² ▤ *1520.5308*

The surface area of the soccer ball is about 1521 cm².

6. Compare the answers for the two methods. Explain why they differ. **Answers may vary. Sample: Method 2 yields a greater number; the pentagons and hexagons on the ball stretch and curve when the ball is pumped up.**

Pentagon diagram: 4.5 cm, 3.1 cm, 4.5 cm

Hexagon diagram: 4.5 cm, 3.9 cm, 4.5 cm

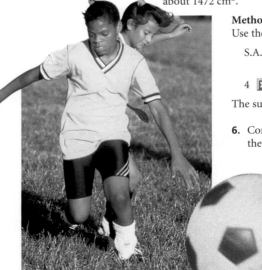

Part 2 Finding the Volume of a Sphere

You can fill a sphere with a large number n of small pyramids. The vertex of each pyramid is the center of the sphere. The height of each pyramid is approximately the radius r of the sphere. The sum of the areas of all the bases approximates the surface area of the sphere. You can use this model to derive a formula for the volume of a sphere.

Volume of each pyramid $= \frac{1}{3}Bh$

$$
\begin{aligned}
\text{Sum of the volumes} \\
\text{of } n \text{ pyramids}
\end{aligned}
\quad
\begin{aligned}
&= n \cdot \frac{1}{3}Br && \text{Substitute } r \text{ for } h. \\
&= \frac{1}{3} \cdot (nB) \cdot r \\
&= \frac{1}{3} \cdot (4\pi r^2) \cdot r && \text{Replace } nB \text{ with the surface area of a sphere.} \\
&= \frac{4}{3}\pi r^3
\end{aligned}
$$

The volume of a sphere is $\frac{4}{3}\pi r^3$.

| **Theorem 6-11** **Volume of a Sphere** | The volume of a sphere is four thirds the product of π and the cube of the radius of the sphere. $$V = \frac{4}{3}\pi r^3$$ | |

Example 2

 The volume of a sphere is 4849.05 m³. What is the surface area of the sphere? Round your answer to the nearest tenth.

- Find the radius r.

$$V = \frac{4}{3}\pi r^3 \quad \text{Use the formula for the volume of a sphere.}$$

$$4849.05 = \frac{4}{3}\pi r^3 \quad \text{Substitute.}$$

$$4849.05\left(\frac{3}{4\pi}\right) = r^3 \quad \text{Multiply both sides by } \frac{3}{4\pi}.$$

$$\sqrt[3]{4849.05\left(\frac{3}{4\pi}\right)} = r \quad \text{Find the cube root of each side.}$$

4849.05 ☒ 3 ÷ 4 ÷ π ▤ ˣ√ȳ 3 ▤ *10.500001*

The radius of the sphere is about 10.5 m.

- Find the surface area of the sphere.

$$S.A. = 4\pi r^2 \quad \text{Use the formula for the surface area of a sphere.}$$

$$= 4\pi(10.5)^2 \quad \text{Substitute.}$$

4 ☒ π ☒ 10.5 x² ▤ *1385.4424*

The surface area of the sphere is about 1385.4 m².

QUICK REVIEW

The *cube root* of x is the number that when *cubed* is x.

339

---

7. Try This The volume of a sphere is 20,579 in.³. What is the radius of the sphere to the nearest whole number?   about 17 in.

8. Try This The radius of a sphere is 15 m. What is the volume to the nearest hundred?   14,100 m³

When a plane and a sphere intersect in more than one point, the intersection is a circle. If the center of the circle is also the center of the sphere, the circle is called a **great circle** of the sphere. The circumference of a great circle is the **circumference of the sphere.** A great circle divides a sphere into two **hemispheres.**

9. Geography What is the name of the best-known great circle on Earth?
the equator

10. Geography Describe the Northern Hemisphere of Earth.
the region on the surface of Earth north of the equator

Exercises   ON YOUR OWN

Calculator **Find the surface area of each ball to the nearest tenth.**

1.
$d = 23.9$ cm
1794.5 cm²

2.
$d = 68$ mm
14,526.7 mm² or 145.3 cm²

3.
23.8 in.²
$d = 2\frac{3}{4}$ in.

4.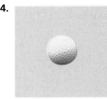
$d = 1.68$ in.
8.9 in.²

5. Coordinate Geometry Find the surface area and volume of the sphere formed by rotating the semicircle at the right 360° about the *x*-axis. Leave your answers in terms of π. 64π units²; $\frac{256}{3}\pi$ units³

6. A balloon has a 14-in. diameter when it is fully inflated. Half the air is let out of the balloon. Assuming the balloon is a sphere, what is the new diameter? Round your answer to the nearest inch.   11 in.

7. Meteorology On July 16, 1882, a massive thunderstorm over Dubuque, Iowa, produced huge hailstones. The diameter of some of the hailstones was 17 in. Ice weighs about 0.033 lb/in.³. What was the approximate weight of these hailstones to the nearest pound?   85 lb

Find the volume of each sphere. Leave your answers in terms of π.

8.

5 ft

$\frac{500}{3}\pi$ ft^3

9.

12 cm

$288\,\pi$ cm^3

10.

15 in.

$\frac{1125}{2}\pi$ in.^{3}

11.

8 cm

$\frac{2048}{3}\pi$ cm^3

12. **Sports** The circumference of a bowling ball is about 27 in. Find its volume to the nearest tenth. **332.4 in.^{3}**

13. If the sphere of ice cream shown melts, is the cone large enough to hold the melted ice cream? Explain. **No; the volume of the ice cream is $\frac{4}{3}$ times the volume of the cone.**

4 cm

4 cm   4 cm

12 cm

14. **Geometry in 3 Dimensions** The center of a sphere has coordinates $(0, 0, 0)$. The radius of the sphere is 5. **See below for examples.**
　　a. Name the coordinates of six points on the sphere.
　　b. Tell whether each of the following points is inside, outside, or on the sphere. (*Hint:* Use the formula from page 262.)
　　　　$A(0, -3, 4)$, $B(1, -1, -1)$, $C(4, -6, -10)$
　　　　on; inside; outside

Believe It Or Not

J.C. Payne, a Texas farmer, is the world champion string collector. The ball of string he wound over a three-year period has a circumference of 41.5 ft. It weighed 13,000 lb.

Listed in the Guinness Book of Records, the ball of string is now on display in a museum devoted to oddities. It took almost a dozen men with forklift trucks to load the ball onto a truck to move it to the museum.

15. **a.** What is the volume of the ball of string to the nearest cubic foot? **1207 ft^3**
　　b. What is the weight of the string per cubic foot? **10.8 $\frac{lb}{ft^3}$**
　　c. If the diameter of the string is 0.1 in., what is the approximate length of the string to the nearest mile? (*Hint:* Think of the unwound string as a long cylinder.) **4191 mi**

CALCULATOR HINT

When answers will be used in later calculations, keep or store them in unrounded form so that rounding errors will not be introduced into the final answer.

16. The radius of Earth is approximately 3960 mi. The area of Australia is about 2,940,000 mi^2.
　　a. Find the surface area of the Southern Hemisphere. **about 98,530,400 mi^2**
　　b. **Probability** If a meteorite falls randomly in the Southern Hemisphere, what is the probability that it will fall in Australia? **about 3%**

14a. Samples: (5, 0, 0), (−5, 0, 0), (0, 5, 0), (0, −5, 0), (0, 0, 5), (0, 0, −5), (0, 3, 4), (−4, 0, 3)

pages 340–343 On Your Own

27a. Cube; the edge of the cube is about 1.61 times as long as the radius *r* of the sphere. The surface area of the cube, about $15.59r^2$, is > surface area of the sphere, about $12.57r^2$.

page 343 Mixed Review

28.

29.

30.

31.

32. 1001, 110110; 1st number has horizontal and vertical lines of symmetry and point symmetry, the 2nd only has the horizontal line of symmetry.

342

17. The sphere just fits in a cube with edges 6 in. long.
   a. What is the radius of the sphere? 3 in.
   b. What is the volume of the space between the sphere and cube to the nearest tenth? 102.9 in.³

18. *Open-ended* Give the dimensions of a cylinder and a sphere that have the same volume. Sample: sphere radius 3 in.; cylinder radius 3 in., height 4 in.

19. The sphere just fits in the cylinder. Archimedes (about 287–212 B.C.) asked to have this figure engraved on his tombstone because he was the first to find the ratio of the volume of the sphere to the volume of the cylinder. What is the ratio that Archimedes discovered? 2 : 3

20. Which is greater, the total volume of three balls that each have diameter of 3 in. or the volume of one ball that has a diameter of 8 in.? Explain your answer. See below.

21. A cube with edges 6 in. long just fits in the sphere. The diagonal of the cube is the diameter of the sphere. $6\sqrt{3}$ in.; $3\sqrt{3}$ in.
   a. Find the length of the diagonal of the cube and the radius of the sphere. Leave your answers in simplest radical form.
   b. What is the volume of the space between the sphere and the cube to the nearest tenth? 371.7 in.³

22. *Estimation* Use $\pi \approx 3$ to estimate the surface area and volume of a sphere with radius 30 cm. 10,800 cm²; 108,000 cm³

23. *Standardized Test Prep* The cone and sphere just fit in cubes that are the same size. What is the ratio of the volume of the cone to the volume of the sphere? A
   A. 1 : 2   **B.** 1 : 3   **C.** 1 : 4
   D. 2 : 3   **E.** cannot be determined

24. a. The number of square meters of surface area of a sphere equals the number of cubic meters of volume. What is the radius of the sphere? 3 m
   b. *Algebra* The ratio of the surface area of a sphere in square meters to its volume in cubic meters is 1 : 5. What is the radius of the sphere? 15 m

25. *Science* The density of steel is about 0.28 lb/in.³. Could you lift a steel ball with radius 4 in.? with radius 6 in.? Explain. See below.

26. A plane that intersects a sphere is 8 cm from the center of the sphere. The radius of the sphere is 17 cm. What is the area of the cross section to the nearest whole number? 707 cm²

27. a. *Algebra* If a cube and a sphere have the same volume, which has the greater surface area? Explain. See margin.
   b. *Writing* Explain why spheres are rarely used for packaging.
   Answers may vary. Sample: Spheres are very difficult to stack.
   20. 8 in. ball; $\frac{256\pi}{3} > \frac{27\pi}{2}$
   25. Answers may vary. Sample: No; no; the balls weigh 75 lb and 253 lb, respectively.

6 in.

OPEN-ENDED Exercise 32 Discuss the symmetries of the two examples given before students begin this exercise.

GETTING READY FOR LESSON 6-7 These exercises prepare students to find the areas of composite space figures.

Wrap Up

THE BIG IDEA Ask students: *Explain how to find the surface area and volume of a sphere.*

RETEACHING ACTIVITY Students discover another way to find the formula for the surface area of a sphere. (Reteaching worksheet 6-6)

In this Checkpoint, your students will assess their own progress in Lessons 6-2 to 6-6.

STANDARDIZED TEST TIP Exercise 5 Make sure that students check the answer choices first to see that the answer can be left in terms of π.

CRITICAL THINKING Exercise 6 Help students realize that the length of a can is six times the radius of one ball (which is also the radius of the can).

Make a sketch for each description. 28–31. See margin p. 342 for samples.

28. a pair of supplementary angles

29. an obtuse triangle and one midsegment

30. a polygon with three lines of symmetry

31. a line segment and its perpendicular bisector

32. Open-ended Binary numbers are written with only the digits 0 and 1. These digits can be written so they have both vertical and horizontal lines of symmetry. Using such digits, write two binary numbers that do not have the same symmetries and describe the differences. See margin p. 342 for sample.

Reteaching 6-6

Practice 6-6

Practice 6-6
Mixed Exercises

Getting Ready for Lesson 6-7

Calculator **Find the total volume of each pair of figures to the nearest tenth.**

33.

8 m
3 m
6 m
261.3 m³

7 m
4 m

34.

5 ft
3 ft
4 ft
9 ft
456.1 ft³

8 ft
4 ft

Calculator **Find the surface area and the volume of each figure to the nearest tenth.**

1.
60.2 ft²; 22.5 ft³

3 ft
5 ft

2.

5 cm
16 cm
659.7 cm²; 1256.6 cm³

3.
10 in.
6 in.
332.9 in.²; 377.0 in.³

4.

3 m
113.1 m²; 113.1 m³

5. Standardized Test Prep What is the surface area of a sphere with radius 5 in.? **C**
  A. 5π in.²   **B.** 20π in.²   **C.** 100π in.²   **D.** 125π in.²   **E.** $166\frac{2}{3}\pi$ in.²

6. Critical Thinking Tennis balls are packaged as shown at the right. Which is greater, the volume of a tennis ball or the space around the three balls? Explain.

The remaining volume is $2\pi r^3$, which is $> \frac{4}{3}\pi r^3$ (volume of one ball).

Lesson Quiz

Lesson Quiz is also available in Transparencies.

For Exercises 1–4, round each answer to the nearest tenth, if necessary.

1. Find the surface area of a sphere with radius 3.5 cm. **153.9 cm²**

2. Find the volume of a sphere with diameter 13 in. **1150.3 in.³**

3. A sphere has volume 1436.8 ft³. Find its radius. **7.0 ft**

4. A sphere has volume 7238.2 m³. Find its surface area. **1809.6 m²**

CONNECTING TO PRIOR KNOWLEDGE Have students identify three-dimensional objects in the classroom that are not prisms, cylinders, pyramids, or cones. Ask what space figure or figures they resemble.

WORK TOGETHER

TACTILE LEARNING Students will discover that you can find the volume of a composite space figure by adding the volume of its parts, but this is not true for the surface area of a composite space figure.

Question 1 You may want to have students find the surface area and volume in two ways: counting faces of unit cubes and using formulas.

ERROR ALERT! Question 3 Some students will add the surface areas. **Remediation:** Have students find the surface area by counting the number of faces (unit squares) and comparing that total to the sum of the surface areas. Discuss why they are not the same.

Lesson Planning Options

Prerequisite Skills

- Finding volume of three-dimensional figures
- Finding surface area of three-dimensional figures

Assignment Options for Exercises On Your Own

Core 1–13, 15–17
Extension 14

Use Mixed Review to maintain skills.

Resources

 Student Edition

Skills Handbook, pp. 646, 659
Extra Practice, p. 639
Glossary/Study Guide

 Teaching Resources

Chapter Support File, Ch. 6
- Practice 6-7 (two worksheets)
- Reteaching 6-7
Classroom Manager 6-7
Glossary, Spanish Resources

 Transparencies
15, 16, 72

Connections 🌐 **Agriculture . . . and more**

What You'll Learn

- Recognizing composite space figures, which combine two or more simple figures

...And Why

To find the volumes and surface areas of composite space figures such as silos and backpacks

What You'll Need

- unit cubes

6-7 Composite Space Figures

WORK TOGETHER

1. Work in a group to build the prisms shown in Figures 1 and 2 using unit cubes. Find the surface area and volume of each prism. **52 units², 24 units³; 22 units², 6 units³**

2. What is the sum of the surface areas of the two prisms? What is the sum of their volumes? **74 units²; 30 units³**

3. Place one prism on top of the other as in Figure 3. Find the surface area and volume of the resulting space figure. **62 units²; 30 units³**

4. Compare your answers to Questions 2 and 3. How does the relationship of the volumes differ from that of the surface areas? **The volume of the combined figures = the sum of the volumes of the prisms; the surface area of the combined figures does not = the sum of the surface areas of the prisms.**

Figure 1

Figure 2

Figure 3

THINK AND DISCUSS

You can use what you know about the volumes of three-dimensional figures such as prisms, pyramids, cones, cylinders, and spheres to find the volume of a composite space figure. A **composite space figure** combines two or more of these figures. The volume of a composite space figure is the sum of the volumes of the figures that are combined.

> **Example 1** **Relating to the Real World** 🌐

📊 **Agriculture** Find the volume of the grain silo at the left.

The silo combines a cylinder and a hemisphere.

- Volume of the cylinder $= \pi r^2 h = \pi (10)^2 (40) = 4000\pi$
- Volume of the hemisphere $= \frac{1}{2}(\frac{4}{3}\pi r^3) = \frac{2}{3}\pi (10)^3 = \frac{2000\pi}{3}$
- Volume of the composite figure $= 4000\pi + \frac{2000\pi}{3}$

4000 ⊠ π ⊞ 2000 ⊠ π ⊟ 3 ⊟ *14660.766*

The volume of the silo is about 14,700 ft³.

10 ft
20 ft
40 ft

This is a good opportunity to review the three-dimensional figures presented in the chapter and the formulas for finding their volumes and surface areas.

Example 1 Relating to the Real World ················

Point out to students the steps used in this problem: identify which figures combine to make the composite space figure, find the volume of each, then find the sum of the volumes.

Question 5b Students can divide the figure into two rectangular prisms by "slicing" the figure horizontally or vertically. In this case, either method produces the same two prisms.

Example 2 Relating to the Real World ················

Give students further explanation as to why the height of the prism is 11 in. and the radius of the hemisphere is 6 in.

Question 6 Have students begin by identifying which surfaces this includes, their shapes, and their dimensions.

---

5. Try This Find the volume of each composite space figure to the nearest whole number.

a.

4 cm
8 cm
5 cm

385 cm³

b.

2 in.
4 in.
2 in.
4 in.
1 in.

12 in.³

You can use geometric figures to approximate the shape of a real-world object. Then you can estimate the volume and surface area of the object.

Example 2 Relating to the Real World ················

Estimation What space figures can you use to approximate the shape of the backpack? Use these space figures to estimate the volume of the backpack.

- You can use a prism and half of a cylinder to approximate the shape of the backpack.

11 in.
12 in.
4 in.
6 in.
4 in.

- Volume of the prism $= Bh = (12 \cdot 4)11 = 528$
- Volume of the half cylinder $= \frac{1}{2}(\pi r^2 h) = \frac{1}{2}\pi(6)^2(4)$
  $= \frac{1}{2}\pi(36)(4) \approx 226$
- Sum of the two volumes $= 528 + 226 = 754$

The approximate volume of the backpack is 754 in.³.

6. What is the approximate surface area of this backpack? **588 in.²**

7. Try This Describe the space figures that you can use to approximate the shape of each object. **See left.**

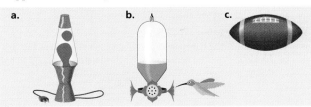

a. **b.** **c.**

7a. parts of 3 cones
 b. hemisphere, cylinder, cone
 c. Answers may vary.
    Sample: cylinder, 2 cones

FOR EXAMPLE 1 ··························

Find the volume of the wastebasket. Round to the nearest tenth.
2.6 ft³

3 ft
1 ft

Discussion: *How could you change the dimensions of the wastebasket so that it could hold at least 4 cubic feet of trash?*

FOR EXAMPLE 2 ··························

What space figures can you use to approximate the shape of the mailbox? Use these space figures to estimate the volume of the mailbox.

10 in.
6 in.
18 in.

The mailbox combines the volume of half a cylinder and a prism.

Volume of half the cylinder: **254.469**

Volume of prism: **756**

Sum of the two volumes: **1010.469**

The volume of the mailbox is about **1010 in.³**.

Discussion: *What is the approximate surface area of the mailbox?*

345

Exercise 2 This figure can be divided into two rectangular prisms either horizontally or vertically. The two methods result in different prisms but the sum of their volumes is the same.

OPEN-ENDED Exercise 4 Have students exchange their figures with a partner and make the missing calculation.

WRITING Exercise 6 Point out that some space figures are composites of more than two shapes.

ALTERNATIVE ASSESSMENT Exercise 7 You can use these exercises to help you assess students' ability to recognize three-dimensional figures generated by rotating two-dimensional figures about an axis. Have students work with a partner to decide how to divide the figure and to find the dimensions of each piece.

WRITING Exercise 11 Refer students to Exercise 17 in Lesson 6-1 on page 305 for illustrations of the Platonic Solids.

Technology Options

Prentice Hall Technology

 Software
- Secondary Math Lab Toolkit™
- Computer Item Generator 6-7

 Internet
- See the Prentice Hall site. (http://www.phschool.com)

Find the volume of each composite space figure. You may leave answers in terms of π.

1. 6 in. **864π in.³** 20 in. 12 in.

2. 2 cm **144 cm³** 3 cm 4 cm 2 cm 6 cm 8 cm

3. **10,368 ft³** 9 ft 15 ft 24 ft 24 ft

4. **Open-ended** Draw a composite three-dimensional figure, label its dimensions, and find either its surface area or its volume. **See back of book for sample.**

5. **Manufacturing** Find the volume of the lunch box shown at the right to the nearest cubic inch. **501 in.³**

3 in. 6 in. 6 in. 10 in.

6. **Writing** Describe your home, school, or some other building that is a composite space figure. Explain why it is a composite space figure. **Check students' work.**

7. **a. Coordinate Geometry** Draw a sketch of the composite space figure formed by rotating this triangle 360° about the *x*-axis. **See back of book.**
   b. Find the volume of the figure in terms of π. **32π units³**

Describe space figures that you can use to approximate the shape of each object. 8–10. **Answers may vary. Samples are given.**

8. sphere, cone

9. cone, hemisphere

10. parts of 2 pyramids

11. **Writing** Describe how you would find the volume of an octahedron if you know the length of an edge. (See the picture on page 305.) **See back of book.**

12. In the diagram at the right, what is the volume of the space between the cylinder and the cone to the nearest cubic inch? **335 in.³**

13. **a.** A cylinder is topped with a hemisphere with radius 15 ft. The total volume of the composite figure is 6525π ft³. Sketch the figure.
    b. Algebra Find the height of the cylinder and the height of the composite figure to the nearest whole number. **19 ft; 34 ft**

8 in. 10 in.

13a. 15 ft

346

14. **Coordinate Geometry** Find the surface area of the figure formed by rotating the figure at the right 360° about the *y*-axis. Leave your answer in terms of π. **20π units^2**

15. **Carpentry** Builders use a plumb bob to establish a vertical line. To the nearest cubic centimeter, find the volume of the plumb bob shown at the right. It combines a hexagonal prism with a pyramid. **73 cm^3**

Engineering Steelworkers use I-beams like the one shown to build bridges and overpasses.

16. To the nearest cubic foot, find the volume of steel needed to make the beam. **36 ft^3**

17. **a.** To the nearest square foot, what is the surface area of the beam? **237 ft^2**

   b. One gallon of paint covers about 450 square feet. How many 1-gallon cans of paint do you need to paint the beam? **1 can**

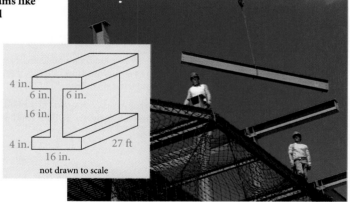

not drawn to scale

Exercises MIXED REVIEW

Write an indirect proof for each statement.

18. If a triangle is isosceles, then a base angle is not a right angle. **See back of book.**

19. In $\triangle MNP$, if $MP < MN$, then $\angle P \not\cong \angle N$. **See below.**

20. **Coordinate Geometry** Find the circumference of a circle if the endpoints of a diameter are $(3, 7)$ and $(3, -1)$. Leave your answer in terms of π. **8π units^2**

FOR YOUR JOURNAL

Describe an object in your classroom that is a composite space figure. Explain how you can approximate its volume.

Getting Ready for Lesson 6-8

You roll a number cube. Find each probability.

21. $P(4)$ $\frac{1}{6}$

22. $P(\text{odd number})$ $\frac{1}{2}$

23. $P(\text{prime number})$ $\frac{1}{2}$

24. $P(2 \text{ or } 5)$ $\frac{1}{3}$

19. **Assume $\angle P \cong \angle N$. By the Converse of the Isos. Triangle Thm., $\overline{MN} \cong \overline{MP}$, which contradicts the hypothesis. Therefore, $\angle P \not\cong \angle N$.**

CONNECTING TO PRIOR KNOWLEDGE Ask students to explain how they would solve the following problem: *A coin is tossed four times. Are you more likely to get two heads and two tails or three heads and one tail?* Review the terms *sample space*, *possible outcomes*, and *favorable outcomes*.

THINK AND DISCUSS

Two models for geometric probability are presented in this lesson: the segment model and the area model. Make sure students understand the use of each.

Example 1 — Relating to the Real World

Have students copy $\overline{AB}$ onto a number line. Then have them use the number line to count the number of minutes between 0 and 15. Point out that their result is the same as the length of $\overline{AR}$: $AR = |15 - 0| = 15$.

Lesson Planning Options

Prerequisite Skills

- Understanding probability
- Finding areas of circles and polygons

Assignment Options for Exercises On Your Own

To provide flexible scheduling, this lesson can be subdivided into parts.

1. **Core** 5, 7, 8, 10
   Extension 11

2. **Core** 1–4, 6, 9, 13
   Extension 12

Use Mixed Review to maintain skills.

Resources

Student Edition
Skills Handbook, p. 661
Extra Practice, p. 639
Glossary/Study Guide

Teaching Resources
Chapter Support File, Ch. 6
- Practice 6-8 (two worksheets)
- Reteaching 6-8
- Alternative Activity 6-8
Classroom Manager 6-8
Glossary, Spanish Resources

Transparencies
1, 5, 7, 72

What You'll Learn

- Using geometric models to find the probability of events

...And Why

To solve probability problems about games, waiting times, and other random events

QUICK REVIEW

The probability of an event is the ratio of the number of favorable outcomes to the number of possible outcomes.

$$P(\text{event}) = \frac{\text{favorable outcomes}}{\text{possible outcomes}}$$

6-8 Geometric Probability

THINK AND DISCUSS

Part 1 — Using a Segment Model

Mathematicians use models to represent the real world. **Geometric probability** uses geometric figures to represent occurrences of events. Then the occurrences can be compared by comparing measurements of the figures.

Example 1 — Relating to the Real World

Commuting Mr. Hedrick's bus runs every 25 minutes. If he arrives at his bus stop at a random time, what is the probability that he will have to wait 10 minutes or more?

Assuming the bus is stopped for a negligible length of time, the 25 minutes between bus arrivals can be represented by $\overline{AB}$.

$$
\begin{array}{ccccccc}
A & & & & & & B \\
\hline
0 & 5 & 10 & 15 & 20 & 25 &
\end{array}
$$

If Mr. Hedrick arrives 5 minutes after a bus has left (represented by point C on the segment below), he has to wait 20 minutes for a bus to arrive at time B. If he arrives 20 minutes after a bus has left (represented by point D), he has to wait only 5 minutes. If he arrives at any time represented by a point on $\overline{AR}$, he has to wait 10 minutes or more.

$$
\begin{array}{ccccccc}
A & C & & R & D & B \\
\hline
0 & 5 & 10 & 15 & 20 & 25
\end{array}
$$

$$P(\text{waiting 10 min or more}) = \frac{\text{length of } \overline{AR}}{\text{length of } \overline{AB}}$$
$$= \frac{15}{25} = \frac{3}{5}$$

The probability that Mr. Hedrick waits 10 minutes or more is $\frac{3}{5}$, or 60%.

1. **Try This** What is the probability that Mr. Hedrick has to wait 20 minutes or more? $\frac{1}{5}$ or 20%

2. **Critical Thinking** Suppose a bus arrives at Mr. Hedrick's bus stop every 25 minutes and waits 5 minutes before leaving. Draw a diagram and find the probability that Mr. Hedrick has to wait 10 minutes or more to get on the bus.

$$
\begin{array}{ccccccc}
A & & & B & C \\
\hline
0 & 5 & 10 & 15 & 20 & 25
\end{array}
$$

A : 1st bus leaves; B : 2nd bus arrives; C : 2nd bus leaves; $\frac{2}{5}$ or 40%

Part 2 ▼ **Using an Area Model**

For some probability situations, you can use an area model.

Example 2 Relating to the Real World ··············

12 in.

12 in.

📊 **Dart Game** At a carnival, you can win prizes if you throw a dart into the blue, yellow, or red regions of a 12 in.-by-12 in. dartboard. The radii of the concentric circles are 1, 2, and 3 inches. Assume that your dart lands on the board and that it is equally likely to land on any point. Find the probability of hitting each colored region.

$$P(\text{blue}) = \frac{\text{blue area}}{\text{area of square}} = \frac{\pi(1)^2}{12^2} = \frac{\pi}{144} \approx 2.2\%$$ Use a calculator.

$$P(\text{yellow}) = \frac{\text{yellow area}}{\text{area of square}} = \frac{\pi(2^2) - \pi(1^2)}{12^2} = \frac{3\pi}{144} \approx 6.5\%$$

$$P(\text{red}) = \frac{\text{red area}}{\text{area of square}} = \frac{\pi(3^2) - \pi(2^2)}{144} = \frac{5\pi}{144} \approx 10.9\%$$

The probability of hitting the blue region is about 2.2%, of hitting the yellow region is about 6.5%, and of hitting the red region is about 10.9%.

3. Try This What is the probability of winning some prize? about 19.6 %

5. No; the probability would be quadrupled.

4. Try This What is the probability of winning no prize? about 80.4%

5. Critical Thinking If the radius of the blue circle were doubled, would the probability of hitting blue be doubled? Explain. See left.

FOR EXAMPLE 1 ···························

Between 6 A.M. and 8 A.M., a commuter train runs every 15 minutes. If you arrive at the train station at a random time, what is the probability that you will have to wait more than 5 minutes? $66\frac{2}{3}\%$

Discussion: *Which is more likely, you will wait more than ten minutes or less than ten minutes?*

FOR EXAMPLE 2 ···························

Refer to the diagram in Example 2.

a. What is the probability you will land in the blue or yellow region? $\approx 8.7\%$

b. What is the probability that you will land in the blue or red region? $\approx 13.1\%$

FOR EXAMPLE 3 ···························

Refer to the diagram in Example 3. What is the probability that the quarter lands within the green circle if it lands on a square with a 10-in. side and the circle had a radius of 2 in.? $\approx 7.4\%$

349

Some carnival games are more difficult than they appear. Consider the following coin toss game.

8 in.

8 in.

1 in.

$\frac{17}{32}$ in.

1 in.

$\frac{15}{32}$ in.

Example 3 **Relating to the Real World**

Coin Toss To win a prize, you must toss a quarter so that it lands entirely within a green circle of radius 1 in. The radius of a quarter is $\frac{15}{32}$ in. Suppose that the center of a tossed quarter is equally likely to land at any point within the 8-in. square shown at the left. What is the probability that a quarter will land completely within the green circle?

When a quarter is within the green circle, its center must be more than $\frac{15}{32}$ in. from the edge of the circle. So, the center of the quarter must be less than $\frac{17}{32}$ in. from the center of the green circle. This means that the center of the quarter must be within the dashed circle of radius $\frac{17}{32}$ in. as shown in the diagram.

$$P(\text{quarter within green circle}) = \frac{\text{area of dashed circle}}{\text{area of square}}$$

$$= \frac{\pi\left(\frac{17}{32}\right)^2}{(8)^2} \approx 1.4\%$$

The probability of the quarter landing in the green circle is only about 1.4%.

6. **Try This** Suppose you toss 100 quarters. Would you expect to win a prize? **yes**

7. **a.** *Critical Thinking* For every 1000 quarters tossed, about how many prizes would be won? **about 14 prizes**
   b. Suppose the prize is $10. About how much profit would the game operator expect for every 1000 quarters tossed? **about $110**

Exercises **ON YOUR OWN**

Darts are thrown at random at each of the boards shown. If a dart hits the board, find the probability that it will land in the shaded area.

1.

$\frac{2}{5}$ or 40%

2.

120°

about 67%

3.

about 61%

4.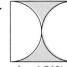

about 21%

5. *Transportation* A rapid transit line runs trains every ten minutes. Draw a geometric model and find the probability that randomly arriving passengers will not have to wait more than four minutes.

 40%

0 2 4 6 8 10

350

Exercises 6–11 Make sure students read the directions and remember to sketch a geometric model for each exercise. You may want to have students work in groups to solve these problems.

ERROR ALERT! **Exercise 8** Some students may use the Pythagorean Theorem instead of the Triangle Inequality Theorem. **Remediation:** Reinforce that the Triangle Inequality Theorem gives criteria for the lengths of sides of triangles in general, while the Pythagorean Theorem gives criteria for the lengths of sides of right triangles only.

ESL **Exercise 9–11** Students may be unfamiliar with the terms "archery," "drawbridge," and "meteorites." Encourage students to look these terms up in a dictionary. If possible, provide illustrations of each.

ALTERNATIVE ASSESSMENT **Exercise 11** The following activity can be used to help you assess students' understanding of geometric probability. Have students research the area of five other countries and calculate the probability that a meteorite landing on Earth will land in one of those countries.

Sketch a geometric model for each exercise and solve.

6. *Ducking Stool* At a fund raiser, volunteers sit above a tank of water hoping that they won't get wet. You can trip the ducking mechanism by throwing a baseball at a metal disk mounted in front of a 1-m square backboard. The volunteer gets wet even if only the edge of the baseball hits the disk. The radius of a baseball is 3.6 cm and the radius of the disk is 8 cm. What is the probability that a baseball that hits the backboard at a random point will hit the disk? **about 4.2%**

7. Amy made a tape recording of a choir rehearsal. The recording began 21 minutes into the 60-minute tape and lasted 8 minutes. Later she inadvertently erased a 15-minute segment somewhere on the tape.
   a. Make a drawing showing the possible starting times of the erasure. Explain how Amy knows that the erasure did not start after the 45-minute mark.
   b. Make a drawing showing the starting times of the erasure that would erase the entire choir rehearsal. Find the probability that the entire rehearsal was erased.

7a. The erasure must start at least 15 min before the end of the tape.

```
0                45
●────────────────●────
0  10 20 30 40 50 60
```

b.
```
   14 21                   7
├──●━━▶───┼──┼──┼──┼──   ──
0  10 20 30 40 50 60     45
```

8. Kimi has a 4-in. straw and a 6-in. straw. She wants to cut the 6-in. straw into two pieces so that the three pieces form a triangle.
   a. If she cuts the straw to get two 3-in. pieces, can she form a triangle? **yes**
   b. If the two pieces are 1 in. and 5 in., can she form a triangle? **no**
   c. If Kimi cuts the straw at a random point, what is the probability that she can form a triangle? $\frac{2}{3}$

9. *Archery* An archery target with a radius of 61 cm has five scoring zones of equal widths. The colors of the zones are gold, red, blue, black, and white. The width of each colored zone is 12.2 cm and the radius of the gold circle is also 12.2 cm. If an arrow hits the target at a random point, what is the probability that it hits the gold region? **4%**

10. During the summer, the drawbridge over the Quisquam River is raised every half hour to allow boats to pass. It remains open for 5 min. What is the probability that a motorist arriving at the bridge will find it raised? $\frac{1}{6}$

11. *Astronomy* Meteorites (mostly dust-particle size) are continually bombarding Earth. The radius of Earth is about 3960 mi. The area of the United States is about 3,679,245 mi². What is the probability that a meteorite landing on Earth will land in the United States? **about 1.9%**

Exercises MIXED REVIEW

Wrap Up

Lesson Quiz

Lesson Quiz is also available in Transparencies.

For Exercises 1–2, sketch a geometric model for each exercise and solve.

1. A news radio station gives a weather update every 12 minutes. If you turned on the radio at a random time, what is the probability that you would wait more than 5 minutes to hear the weather update? $58\frac{1}{3}\%$ **Models vary. Sample:**

```
0    5    10 12
```

2. A circle is inscribed in a square with side length 12 cm. What is the probability that the point of a tack dropped onto the square will land outside the circle? ≈ **21.5%; Models vary. Sample:**

12 cm

6 cm

352

12. a. *Open-ended* Design a dartboard game to be used at a charity fair. Specify the size and shape of the regions of the board. **12a-b. Check students' work.**
  b. *Writing* Describe the rules for using your dartboard and the prizes that winners receive. Explain how much money you would expect to raise if the game were played 100 times.

13. *Sonar Sub Search* A ship is trying to locate a disabled remote-controlled research submarine. The captain has determined that the submarine is within a 2000 m-by-2000 m square region. The depth of the ocean in this region is about 6000 m. The ship moves to a position in the center of the square region. Its sonar sends out a signal that covers a conical region. What is the probability that the ship will locate the submarine with the first pulse? **about 26%**

Exercises MIXED REVIEW

Data Analysis **Use the triple bar graph for Exercises 14–16.**

14. Which type of TV show is more popular with Latin American teens than with other teens? **Olympics**

15. In which region is stand-up comedy most popular? **U.S.**

16. *Critical Thinking* How can you tell that each teen who was polled was allowed to choose more than one type of TV show? **The total for all categories for each region is > 100%.**

What Teens 15–18 Like to Watch on TV by Region of the World

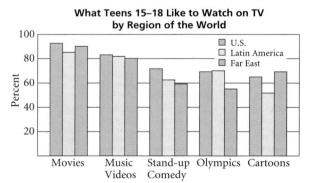

Legend: U.S., Latin America, Far East

Categories: Movies, Music Videos, Stand-up Comedy, Olympics, Cartoons

Find the perimeter of each figure.

17.
3 cm
2 cm
5 cm 16 cm

18.
15 in.
60 in.
25 in.

Finishing the Chapter Project

PROJECT DAY You may wish to plan a project day during which students share their completed projects. Encourage groups to explain their processes as well as their products.

PROJECT NOTEBOOK Have students review their project work and bring their notebooks up to date.

- Have students review their package designs along with their measurements and calculations.

- Ask groups to share any insights they found when completing the project, such as how they decided what package design to use.

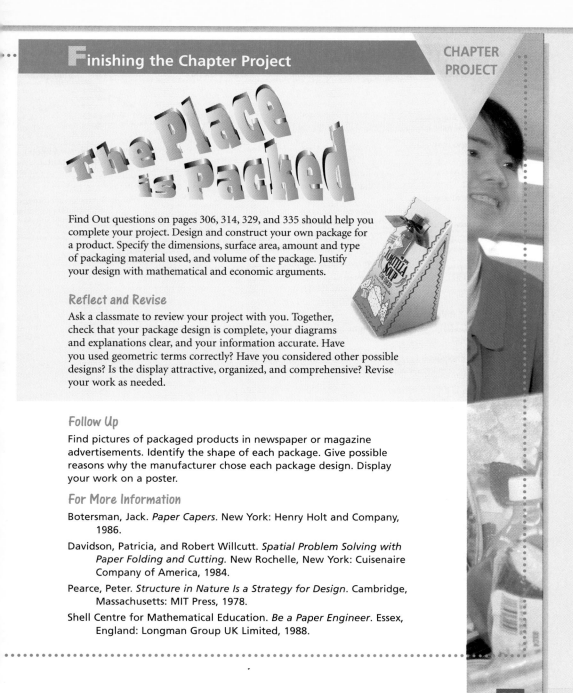

Finishing the Chapter Project

CHAPTER PROJECT

The Place is Packed

Find Out questions on pages 306, 314, 329, and 335 should help you complete your project. Design and construct your own package for a product. Specify the dimensions, surface area, amount and type of packaging material used, and volume of the package. Justify your design with mathematical and economic arguments.

Reflect and Revise

Ask a classmate to review your project with you. Together, check that your package design is complete, your diagrams and explanations clear, and your information accurate. Have you used geometric terms correctly? Have you considered other possible designs? Is the display attractive, organized, and comprehensive? Revise your work as needed.

Follow Up

Find pictures of packaged products in newspaper or magazine advertisements. Identify the shape of each package. Give possible reasons why the manufacturer chose each package design. Display your work on a poster.

For More Information

Botersman, Jack. *Paper Capers.* New York: Henry Holt and Company, 1986.

Davidson, Patricia, and Robert Willcutt. *Spatial Problem Solving with Paper Folding and Cutting.* New Rochelle, New York: Cuisenaire Company of America, 1984.

Pearce, Peter. *Structure in Nature Is a Strategy for Design.* Cambridge, Massachusetts: MIT Press, 1978.

Shell Centre for Mathematical Education. *Be a Paper Engineer.* Essex, England: Longman Group UK Limited, 1988.

Wrap Up

SELF ASSESSMENT

HOW AM I DOING? Have students work in small groups. Ask each group to make a short presentation explaining how to find the surface area of the different space figures presented in this chapter. Each presentation must include a visual aid and a sample problem.

KEY TERMS The numbers in parentheses direct students to the pages where the terms are used or defined. Students should be able to (1) write a simple explanation of each term, (2) illustrate the term with a diagram, or (3) give an example that uses the term.

STANDARDIZED TEST TIP   Exercise 2 Students can use Euler's formula or just count the edges.

Resources

 Student Edition
Extra Practice, p. 639
Glossary/Study Guide

 Teaching Resources
Study Skills Handbook
Glossary, Spanish Resources

Wrap Up   pages 354–357

1.

354

---

6 Wrap Up

Key Terms

altitude (pp. 309, 310, 316, 318)
bases (pp. 309, 316)
center (p. 337)
circumference of a sphere (p. 340)
composite space figure (p. 344)
cone (p. 318)
cube (p. 310)
cylinder (p. 310)
edge (p. 302)
faces (p. 302)
geometric probability (p. 348)
great circle (p. 340)

height (pp. 309, 310, 316, 318, 331)
hemisphere (p. 340)
lateral area (pp. 309, 311, 316)
lateral face (pp. 309, 316)
net (p. 302)
oblique cylinder (p. 310)
oblique prism (p. 309)
polyhedron (p. 302)
prism (p. 309)
pyramid (p. 316)
regular pyramid (p. 316)
right cone (p. 318)
right cylinder (p. 310)

right prism (p. 309)
slant height (pp. 316, 318)
sphere (p. 337)
surface area (pp. 309, 311, 316)
vertex (pp. 302, 316)
volume (p. 324)

How am I doing?

SELF ASSESSMENT

- State three ideas from this chapter that you think are important. Explain your choices.
  - Describe how to find the volumes and surface areas of different space figures.

Space Figures and Nets

6-1

A **polyhedron** is a three-dimensional figure whose surfaces are polygons. The polygons are **faces** of the polyhedron. An **edge** is a segment that is the intersection of two faces. A **vertex** is a point where edges intersect. A **net** is a two-dimensional pattern that folds to form a three-dimensional figure.

1. *Open-ended* Draw a net for the space figure at the right.
   See margin for sample.
2. *Standardized Test Prep* Which figure has the most edges? D
   A. rectangular prism   **B.** hexagonal prism
   C. pentagonal prism   **D.** octagonal prism
   E. cannot be determined from the information given

Match each three-dimensional figure with its net.

3. C

4. A

5. B

A.

B.

C.

Surface Areas of Prisms and Cylinders   6-2

The **lateral area** of a **right prism** is the product of the perimeter of the base and the height. The **surface area** of a prism is the sum of the lateral area and the areas of the two bases.

The **lateral area** of a **right cylinder** is the product of the circumference of the base and the height of the cylinder. The **surface area** is the sum of the lateral area and the areas of the two bases.

p is the perimeter of a base.

L.A. $= ph$
S.A. $=$ L.A. $+ 2B$

B is the area of a base.

L.A. $= 2\pi rh$
or πdh
S.A. $=$ L.A. $+ 2B$

B is the area of a base.

Find the surface area of each figure. You may leave answers in terms of π.

6.

3 cm
2 cm
4 cm
36 cm²

7.

3 m
8 m
66π m²

8.

8 in.
6 in.
4 in.
208 in.²

9.
5 ft
12 ft
170π ft²

Surface Areas of Pyramids and Cones   6-3

The **lateral area** of a **regular pyramid** is half the product of the perimeter of the base and the slant height. The **surface area** is the sum of the lateral area and the area of the base.

The **lateral area** of a **right cone** is half the product of the circumference of the base and the slant height. The **surface area** is the sum of the lateral area and the area of the base.

L.A. $= \frac{1}{2}p\ell$
S.A. $=$ L.A. $+ B$

B is the area of a base.

L.A. $= \pi r\ell$
S.A. $=$ L.A. $+ B$

B is the area of a base.

📟 Calculator **Find the lateral area and surface area of each figure. When an answer is not a whole number, round to the nearest tenth.**

10.

11 ft
5 ft
172.8 ft²; 251.3 ft²

11.

10 cm
8 cm
160 cm²; 224 cm²

12.

4 in.
6 in.
37.7 in.²; 50.3 in.²

13.

10 m
16 m
320 m²; 576 m²

355

Exercises 14–17 Remind students that they can learn just one formula for the volume of prisms and cylinders: $V = Bh$.

Exercises 19–22 Check that students use $V = \frac{1}{3}Bh$ and not $V = \frac{1}{2}Bh$.

Volumes of Prisms and Cylinders 6-4

The **volume** of a space figure is the space that the figure occupies. Volume is measured in cubic units.

The **volume** of a **prism** is the product of the area of a base and the height of the prism.

The **volume** of a **cylinder** is the product of the area of a base and the height of the cylinder.

$V = Bh$

B is the area of a base.

$V = Bh$
or $\pi r^2 h$

$B = \pi r^2$

Find the volume of each figure. You may leave answers in terms of π.

14.

5 ft
5 ft
10 ft
250 ft³

15.
6 cm
3 cm
54π cm³

16.
18 in.
14 in.
7 in.
1764 in.³

17.

4 m
8 m
32π m³

18. Writing Compare finding the volume and the surface area of a prism. What are the similarities and differences?
To find the surface area of a prism, you must find the sum of the areas of the bases and the lateral area. To find the volume, you must find the product of the area of a base and the height.

Volumes of Pyramids and Cones 6-5

The **volume** of a **pyramid** is one third the product of the area of the base and the height of the pyramid.

The **volume** of a **cone** is one third the product of the area of the base and the height of the cone.

$V = \frac{1}{3}Bh$

B is the area of the base.

$V = \frac{1}{3}Bh$
or $\frac{1}{3}\pi r^2 h$

B is the area of the base.

Calculator **Find the volume of each figure. Round to the nearest tenth.**

19. 235.6 mm³
9 mm
5 mm

20. 149.3 ft³
7 ft
8 ft

21. 2 m
3 m
6 m³

22. 301.6 cm³
8 cm
12 cm

Surface Areas and Volumes of Spheres 6-6

A **sphere** is the set of points in space equidistant from a given point called the **center**.

The **surface area of a sphere** is four times the product of π and the square of the radius of the sphere. The **volume of a sphere** is $\frac{4}{3}$ the product of π and the cube of the radius of the sphere.

S.A. $= 4\pi r^2$
$V = \frac{4}{3}\pi r^3$

356

Getting Ready for Chapter 7

Students may work these exercises independently or in small groups. The skills previewed will help prepare students to study parallel lines.

Calculator **Find the surface area and volume of a sphere with the given radius or diameter. Round answers to the nearest tenth.**

23. 314.2 in.^{2}; 523.6 in.^{3}
24. 153.9 cm^2; 179.6 cm^3

23. $r = 5$ in. **24.** $d = 7$ cm **25.** $d = 4$ ft **26.** $r = 0.8$ ft

25. 50.3 ft^2; 33.5 ft^3
26. 8.0 ft^2; 2.1 ft^3

27. *Sports* The circumference of a lacrosse ball is 8 in. Find its volume to the nearest tenth of a cubic inch. 8.6 in.^{3}

Composite Space Figures   6-7

A **composite space figure** combines two or more space figures. The volume of a composite figure is the sum of the volumes of the combined figures.

Calculator **Find the volume of each figure. When an answer is not a whole number, round to the nearest tenth.**

28.

29.

30.

263.9 m^3 162 cm^3 280 in.^{3}

Geometric Probability   6-8

Geometric probability uses geometric figures to represent occurrences of events. You can use a segment model or an area model. Compare the part that represents favorable outcomes to the whole, which represents all outcomes.

Darts are thrown at random at each of the boards shown. If a dart hits the board, find the probability that it will land in the shaded area.

$\frac{1}{6}$ or about 16.7%

31. $\frac{1}{2}$ or 50% **32.** $\frac{3}{8}$ or 37.5% **33.**

34. *Critical Thinking* If you are modeling probability with a segment, does the length of the segment matter? Explain. No; you model probability by ratio of lengths of segments.

Getting Ready for.. ▶ CHAPTER

Use the rectangular prism at the right.

35. List three pairs of parallel segments.

36. List three pairs of perpendicular segments.

Samples are given.
35. $\overline{AB}$, $\overline{EF}$, $\overline{CD}$
36. $\overline{AB}$, $\overline{BC}$, $\overline{BF}$

7

357

Resources

 Teaching Resources

Chapter Support File, Ch. 6
- Chapter Assessment, Forms A and B
- Alternative Assessment

Chapter Assessment, Spanish Resources

 Teacher's Edition

See also p. 300E for assessment options

 Software
Computer Item Generator

Assessment   page 358

1.

5 in.
6 in.

2.

10 cm

4 cm

358

---

6 Assessment

Draw a net for each figure. Label the net with appropriate dimensions.

1.
4 in.
6 in.

2.
4 cm
10 cm

1–2. See margin for samples.

3. **a.** *Aviation* The "black box" information recorder on an airplane is a rectangular prism. The base is 15 in. by 8 in., and it is 15 in. to 22 in. tall. What are the largest and smallest possible volumes for the box?
   b. Newer flight data recorders are smaller and record more data. A new recorder is 8 in. by 8 in. by 13 in. What is its volume?

3a. 2640 in.³; 1800 in.³   b. 832 in.³

Calculator Find the volume and surface area of each figure. When an answer is not a whole number, round to the nearest tenth.

4.

4 cm
11 cm
5 cm
220 cm³; 238 cm²

5.

4 ft
268.1 ft³; 201.1 ft²

6.
6 m   5 m
157.1 m³; 201.2 m²

7.
9 in.
8 in.
172.0 in.³; 208 in.²

8.
8 cm
3 cm
226.2 cm³; 207.3 cm²

9.

1 in.   12 in.
6 in.
81.4 in.³; 195.3 in.²

10. *Open-ended* Draw two different space figures that have a volume of 100 in.³. Label the dimensions of each figure. **See back of book for sample.**

11. **a.** Describe the figure that is formed when the triangle is rotated 360° about the *y*-axis.
    b. What is its volume and lateral area in terms of π?   **16π units³; 20π units²**
    11a. cone

12. How many gallons of paint do you need to paint the walls of a bedroom? The floor is 12 ft by 15 ft and the walls are 7 ft high. One gallon of paint covers about 450 square feet.   **1 gal**

13. *Standardized Test Prep* Which of these space figures has the greatest volume?   **B**
    A. cube with an edge of 5 cm
    B. cylinder with radius 4 cm and height 4 cm
    C. pyramid with a square base with sides of 6 cm and height 6 cm
    D. cone with radius 4 cm and height 9 cm
    E. rectangular prism with a 5 cm-by-5 cm base and height 6 cm

14. *Writing* Describe a real-world situation in which you would use the volume of an object. Then describe another situation in which you would use the lateral area of an object. **See back of book.**

15. **a.** *Estimation* What space figures can you use to approximate the shape of the spring water bottle?
    b. Estimate the volume of the bottle.
    a. a cylinder and a cone
    b. approx. 20 in.³

1 in.
6 in.
2 in.

16. *Probability* Every 20 minutes from 4:00 P.M. to 7:00 P.M., a commuter train crosses Main Street. For three minutes a gate stops cars from passing as the train goes by. What is the probability that a motorist driving by during this time will have to stop at the train crossing?   **15%**

17. *Probability* What is the probability that a dart tossed randomly at this board will hit the shaded area?   **½ or 50%**

Cumulative Review

Item	Review Topic	Chapter
1	Rotations	3
2	Volume	6
3	Circumference	5
4	Polygons	2
5, 7	Pythagorean Theorem	5
6	Area of a Trapezoid	5
8	Midpoints	1
9	Symmetry	3
10	Angles	1

6 Cumulative Review

For Exercises 1–8, choose the correct letter.

1. Which are rotations of the figure at the right? **E**

I.   **II.**

III.   **IV.**

   A. I only   **B.** IV only   **C.** II and IV
   D. I, III and IV   **E.** I, II, III, and IV

2. What is the volume of the prism? **B**

4 cm 6 cm 9 cm

   A. 228 cm³   **B.** 216 cm³   **C.** 76 cm³
   D. 19 cm³   **E.** none of the above

3. What is the circumference of a circle with radius 9? **C**
   A. 4.5π **B.** 9π **C.** 18π
   D. 81π **E.** none of the above

4. Which figure is *not* a convex polygon? **A**

   A.   **B.**

   C.   **D.**

   E. none of the above

5. The lengths of the hypotenuse and one leg of a right triangle are 10 and 15. Find the length of the other leg to the nearest whole number. **D**
   A. 8   **B.** 9   **C.** 10   **D.** 11   **E.** 12

6. What is the area of the trapezoid? **C**

8 in. 10 in. 6 in. 6.5 in. 18.5 in.

   A. 75 in.²   **B.** 43 in.²   **C.** 79.5 in.²
   D. 159 in.²   **E.** none of the above

Compare the boxed quantity in Column A with the boxed quantity in Column B. Choose the best answer.

   A. The quantity in Column A is greater.
   B. The quantity in Column B is greater.
   C. The two quantities are equal.
   D. The relationship cannot be determined on the basis of the information supplied.

Column A	Column B

7. $AB^2 + AD^2$ | BD^2 **C**

8. the x-coordinate of the point halfway between $(3, 6)$ and $(-5, 2)$ | the y-coordinate of the point halfway between $(9, 1)$ and $(7, -3)$ **C**

Find each answer.

9. **Open-ended** Sketch a figure with line and point symmetry. See back of book for sample.

10. What is the measure of the angle formed by the minute hand and the hour hand? **120**

Reasoning and Parallel Lines

To accommodate flexible scheduling, some lessons are divided into parts.
Assignment Options are given in the Lesson Planning Options for each lesson.

7-1   Parallel Lines and Related Angles (pp. 363–369)

Part **1** Angles Formed by Intersecting Lines

Part **2** Angles Formed by Parallel Lines

Key Terms: alternate interior angles, corresponding angles, same-side interior angles, transversal

7-2   Proving Lines Parallel (pp. 371–376)

Key Term: flow proof

7-3   Constructing Parallel and Perpendicular Lines (pp. 377–383)

Part **1** Constructing Parallel Lines

Part **2** Constructing Perpendicular Lines

7-4   Parallel Lines and Perspective Drawing (pp. 385–391)

Key Terms: one-point perspective, perspective drawing, two-point perspective, vanishing point

7-5   Exploring Spherical Geometry (pp. 392–397)

Key Terms: Euclidean geometry, spherical geometry

PACING OPTIONS

This chart suggests pacing only for the core lessons and their parts, and it is provided merely as a possible guide. It will help you determine how much time you have in your schedule to cover other features, such as the Chapter Project, Math Toolboxes, Wrap Up, and Assessment.

	1 Class Period	1 Class Period	1 Class Period	1 Class Period	1 Class Period	1 Class Period	1 Class Period	1 Class Period	1 Class Period
Traditional (40–45 min class periods)	7-1 **1** **2**	7-2	7-3 **1** **2**	7-4	7-5				
Block Scheduling (90 min class periods)	7-1 **1** **2**	7-2	7-3 **1** **2**	7-4 7-5					

What Students Will Learn and Why

In this chapter, students build on their understanding of parallel and perpendicular lines, learned in Chapter 1. They learn to relate the measures of angles formed by parallel lines and a transversal so that they can recognize conditions that result in parallel lines. They then construct parallel and perpendicular lines. Students also learn to write flow proofs and draw objects in one- and two-point perspective. Finally, students study some of the basic ideas of spherical geometry. The concepts presented in this chapter are applied by architects, builders, and graphic artists.

Discussing the Chapter/Building on Experience

The concept map below relates chapter topics to real-world applications. You and your class may wish to add to the map or develop maps of your own. The center oval describes the topic of the chapter. The next level displays topics within the lessons. The outer ovals reflect applications of the content. As you and your class build a concept map, invite students to discuss applications with which they are familiar.

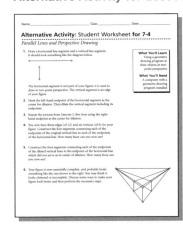

Interactive Questioning Tips

A question is interactive when there is "give and take" between the questioner (teacher or student) and the respondent. In Think and Discuss or when a critical thinking question is asked, it is important to encourage students to explain their answers in detail. One effective strategy to consider is to have students work in groups. They can discuss the question among themselves, then appoint a spokesperson to give the answer. This promotes active participation and develops high-level thinking skills. For example, in Lesson 7-4, Question 4, students are asked to describe the type of perspective an artist might paint, based on the position of an easel.

Skills Practice

Every lesson provides skill practice with Try This exercises, Exercises On Your Own, and Exercises Mixed Review. The Student Edition includes a Checkpoint (p. 383) and Preparing for Standardized Tests (p. 403). In the Teacher's Edition, the Lesson Planning Options section for each lesson lists Prerequisite Skills students should know for that lesson. At the back of the Student Edition is the Skills Handbook—mini-lessons on math your students may need to review. The Chapter Support File for Chapter 7 in the Teaching Resources box includes two Practice worksheets per lesson, a worksheet for the Checkpoint, and worksheets for Cumulative Review and Standardized Test Preparation.

Diverse Learning and Teaching Styles

In your Teacher's Edition, you will find suggestions as to how you can help students complete mathematical tasks in Chapter 7 by reinforcing various learning styles. Here are some examples.

- **Visual learning** use models to illustrate postulates and theorems (p. 364), observe that in a flow proof statements are written in a box and the justifications are written underneath (p. 372), diagram planes and lines to observe the difference (p. 393)

- **Tactile learning** observe physical models (p. 372), practice drawing cubes in one- and two-point perspective (p. 386)

- **Auditory learning** work in pairs to describe angles as alternate interior, same-side interior, corresponding, or neither (p. 365), work in pairs to explain why Constructions 6 and 7 work (p. 380), remember meanings of latitude and longitude by the roots of the words (p. 392)

- **Kinesthetic learning** identify and sketch diagrams of lines on their school building that appear parallel cut by a transversal (p. 367), observe perspective by viewing students of similar size at the opposite end of a field (p. 385)

Alternative Activity for Lesson 7-2

for use with Example 1, uses geometry software to explore dilations and to investigate the converse of the corresponding angle postulate.

Alternative Activity for Lesson 7-3

for use with Think and Discuss and Example 1, uses geometry software to explore parallel lines.

Alternative Activity for Lesson 7-4

for use with pages 386–387, uses geometry software to construct figures in two-point perspective.

Cooperative Learning Tips

When used effectively, cooperative learning can help students develop interpersonal skills, learn to perform specific roles in a group, and learn to carry out specific responsibilities. The components of Chapter 7 provide a range of cooperative learning opportunities.

- In the Student Edition, the **Work Together** parts of lessons are specifically designed for cooperative learning activities.

- In the Teacher's Edition, you will find helpful hints for addressing diverse learning styles (see page C for Chapter 7). For every lesson, you will find a **Reteaching Activity**, which may involve cooperative learning.

Materials and Manipulatives

The authors expect all students to use scientific calculators. Calculator use is integrated throughout the course.

- compass (7-3)
- globe, ball, or foamball (7-5)
- protractor (7-1, 7-2, 7-5)
- ruler (7-1, 7-2, 7-4)
- square dot paper (7-2)
- straightedge (7-3)
- string (7-5)

TECHNOLOGY OPTIONS

Technology Tools		Chapter Project	7-1	7-2	7-3	7-4	7-5
Calculator		Assumed that students have scientific calculators at any time.					
Software	Secondary Math Lab Toolkit™		✔	✔	✔	✔	✔
	Integrated Math Lab		✔	✔			
	Computer Item Generator		✔	✔	✔	✔	✔
	Student Edition		✔ᵀ	✔	✔	✔ᵀ	
Video	Video Field Trip	✔					
CD-ROM	Multimedia Geometry Lab		✔	✔	✔		✔
Internet		See the Prentice Hall site. (http://www.phschool.com)					

✔ᵀ indicates Math Toolbox.

The Prentice Hall Geometry program offers you a rich variety of technology options. Be assured that all these options are provided as a means of enriching the program and are not essential for the successful completion of the course.

Assessment Options

The Prentice Hall Geometry Program provides you with many options. From these options, you may choose instructional materials and techniques appropriate for your students, or those necessary to meet your district's curriculum requirements. As the chart indicates, the program also supports your teaching efforts by offering you many choices for assessment.

ASSESSMENT OPTIONS

Assessment Support Materials	Chapter Project	7-1	7-2	7-3	7-4	7-5	Chapter End
Chapter Project	▲■●	▲■		▲■	▲■	▲■	▲■
Checkpoints				▲■●			
Self-Assessment							
Writing Assignment		▲■	▲	▲●	▲■	▲■	▲●
Chapter Assessment							▲■●
Alternative Assessment		■	■	■	■	■	■●
Cumulative Review							●
Standardized Test Prep			▲■	▲			▲■●
Computer Item Generator	Can be used to create custom-made practice or assessment at any time.						

▲ = Student Edition ■ = Teacher's Edition ● = Teaching Resources

Checkpoints

Alternative Assessment

Chapter Assessment

Available in both Form A and Form B

Making the Right Connections

Mathematics is imbedded in nearly every walk of life. The National Council of Teachers of Mathematics (NCTM) encourages educators to recognize these connections and to emphasize them for the purpose of better educating students for success in life and in a global economy. The **Connections** chart below highlights these connections for Chapter 7.

CONNECTIONS

Lesson	Interdisciplinary Connections	Career Prep	Other Real World Connections	Math Integration	NCTM Standards
Chapter Project	Economics Sociology	Architecture Construction	Spider Webs Telephone Cables	Algebra	Communication Connections
7-1	History Science Physical Education	Aviation City Planner	Measuring Earth Architecture Traffic Flow Photography	Probability Algebra Transformational Geometry	Problem Solving Communication Connections Reasoning
7-2	Health	Graphic Arts Drafting	Woodworking Carpentry Furniture Olympics	Coordinate Geometry Transformational Geometry	Problem Solving Communication Connections Reasoning
7-3	Computer Science Art	Computer Graphics	Arts and Crafts Fiber Optics Technology	Coordinate Geometry	Problem Solving Communication Connections
7-4	Art Computer Science	Technical Art	Photography Painting Computer Drawing Optical Illusions	Transformational Geometry	Problem Solving Communication Connections
7-5	Geography Social Studies History	Travel Computer Engineering	Maps Navigation	Algebra	Problem Solving Reasoning Structure Communication

CONNECTING TO PRIOR LEARNING Have students look through books and magazines to find examples of buildings and houses. Have them identify lines that appear parallel or perpendicular. Ask students why it is important for architects and builders to know if lines are parallel or perpendicular. Ask if anyone has ever been in an older house where the floors and ceilings were not parallel planes.

CULTURAL CONNECTIONS The first telephone signals were transmitted over copper wires. Next radio signals were used to connect parts of the world not accessible by wire. Optical fibers are now replacing wire because a single strand of fiber can transmit 2 billion bits of information per second and can carry 30,000 telephone signals. Ask students how satellite communication is turning the world into a "global village."

INTERDISCIPLINARY CONNECTIONS Telephone networks connect not only telephones but also modems and fax machines around the world. Ask students who are experienced on the Internet to explain to the class how they use a modem to access the Internet and communicate through cyberspace.

Technology Options

Prentice Hall Technology

Video
Video Field Trip 7, "Cyber Map," an interview with one of the authors of Netscape™ software

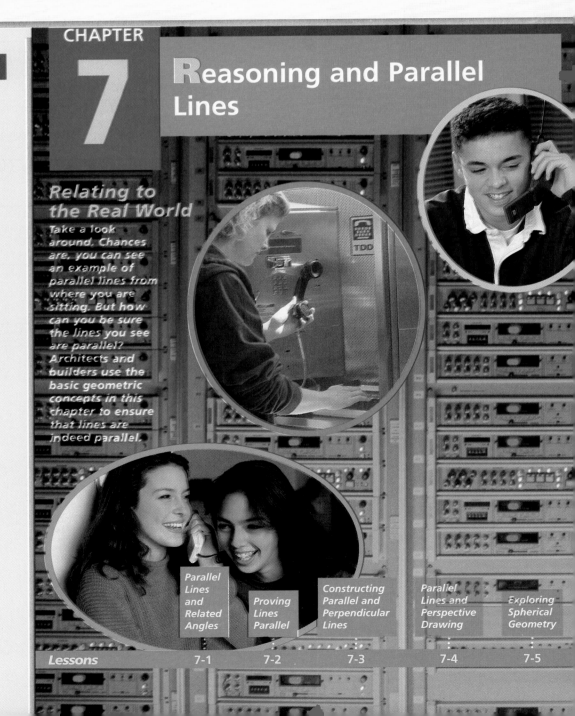

CHAPTER

7 Reasoning and Parallel Lines

Relating to the Real World

Take a look around. Chances are, you can see an example of parallel lines from where you are sitting. But how can you be sure the lines you see are parallel? Architects and builders use the basic geometric concepts in this chapter to ensure that lines are indeed parallel.

Lessons	7-1	7-2	7-3	7-4	7-5
	Parallel Lines and Related Angles	Proving Lines Parallel	Constructing Parallel and Perpendicular Lines	Parallel Lines and Perspective Drawing	Exploring Spherical Geometry

Launching the Project

PROJECT NOTEBOOK Encourage students to keep all project-related materials in a separate folder or notebook. **See Chapter Project Manager and Scoring Rubric in Chapter Support File.**

- Have students bring in local street maps. Have them identify two locations and find the paths along roads they can take from one to the other. Ask which is the shortest path.
- Have students connect their desks with string using the least amount of string possible.

TRACKING THE PROJECT You may wish to have students read Finishing the Chapter Project on page 398 to help them get an overview of the project. Set benchmark deadlines for students to show their work in progress.

CHAPTER PROJECT

NEWS NETWORK

Like the strands of an immense spider web, unseen cables join your telephone to millions of others. Similarly, your street is part of a vast system of roads enabling you to travel from your house to just about any other house in the country. We live amid telephone, television, and computer networks, networks of highways and hallways, and networks that join airports, bus stops, and people. Though varied in purpose, each of these networks can be modeled geometrically by a collection of connected points.

In your project for this chapter, you will explore some simple networks to see how economic and social issues can affect their design. You will also design your own network for your school or community. You will see that when it comes to solving complex, real-world problems, practicality and mathematics are constant partners.

To help you complete the project:

▼ **p. 369** *Find Out by Investigating*
▼ **p. 382** *Find Out by Designing*
▼ **p. 391** *Find Out by Investigating*
▼ **p. 396** *Find Out by Modeling*
▼ **p. 398** *Finishing the Project*

▼ Project Resources

Teaching Resources
Chapter Support File, Ch. 7
- Chapter Project Manager and Scoring Rubric

Transparencies
77

▼ Using the Rubric

Sharing the scoring rubric for the project with your students will alert them to your expectations before they begin work on the project.

As students complete each Find Out question in the chapter, you may wish to have them evaluate their own work or a partner's work based on the scoring rubric. Students should have the opportunity to revise their work after it has been reviewed.

Students use geometry software to investigate the relationships among the eight angles formed by a pair of parallel lines and a transversal. These angle relationships will be presented formally in Lesson 7-1.

Using the software enables students to manipulate the lines while parallel lines remaining parallel. They can observe the effect that changing the positions of the lines has on the angle measures.

ERROR ALERT! Students who take a short cut and draw two lines that appear parallel instead of constructing them may not observe any angle relationships because when they manipulate the lines, the parallel lines do not remain parallel.

Remediation: These students need to start over and construct parallel lines.

Conjecture

Students can use numbers to specify certain angles. Even better would be their describing the positions of the angles, such as "between the parallel lines," "on the same side of the transversal," or "above each parallel line."

ADDITIONAL PROBLEM Have students construct two parallel lines and draw a transversal. Then have them construct a line parallel to the transversal. Ask: *What relationships exist among the angles formed? How many different measures are there?*

Materials and Manipulatives

- Geometry software

 Transparencies
8, 10

Exploring Parallel Lines and Related Angles

Before Lesson 7-1

Work in pairs or small groups.

Construct

Use geometry software to construct two parallel lines. Make sure that the lines remain parallel when you manipulate them. Construct a point on each line. Then construct the line through these two points. This line is called a *transversal*. **Check students' work.**

Investigate

Measure each of the eight angles formed by the parallel lines and the transversal and record the measurements. Manipulate the lines and record the new measurements. What relationships do you notice?

$m\angle 1 = m\angle 3 = m\angle 5 = m\angle 7,$
$m\angle 2 = m\angle 4 = m\angle 6 = m\angle 8$

Conjecture

When two parallel lines are intersected by a transversal, what are the relationships among the angles formed? Make as many **conjectures** as possible. **Sample: 2 sets of 4 ≅ angles are formed.**

Yes; the angles formed by 3 ∥ lines have a
Extend relation similar to the one for the angles
formed by 2 ∥ lines; 2

- Use your software to construct three or more parallel lines. Construct a line that intersects one of the lines. Does it intersect the other lines also? If it does, what relationships exist among the angles formed? How many different measures are there?

- Construct two parallel lines and draw a transversal that is perpendicular to one of the parallel lines. What do you discover?

All the angles formed by these lines are rt. angles.

362

PROBLEM OF THE DAY

A regular hexagon is inscribed in a circle. To the nearest percent, what is the probability that a random point within the circle is outside the hexagon? **17%**

Problem of the Day is also available in Transparencies.

CONNECTING TO PRIOR KNOWLEDGE Draw the following diagram and ask students to identify all vertical angles, supplementary angles, and adjacent angles.

Question 1 Students may not understand what is meant by the interior and exterior of two lines. Copy the diagram and shade the interior with one color and the exterior with another.

Make sure students understand that pairs of angles can be identified when *any* two lines are cut by a transversal.

Question 3 Use this question to review the terms *adjacent* and *supplementary.*

Example 1 Relating to the Real World ················

Help students identify the lines that form ∠1 and ∠2. They may want to trace only those lines onto a piece of paper.

What You'll Learn

- Identifying pairs of angles formed by two lines and a transversal
- Relating the measures of angles formed by parallel lines and a transversal

...And Why

To understand how parallel lines are used in building, city planning, and construction

What You'll Need

- ruler
- protractor

Connections Aviation . . . *and more*

7-1 Parallel Lines and Related Angles

THINK AND DISCUSS

Part 1 Angles Formed by Intersecting Lines

A **transversal** is a line that intersects two coplanar lines at two distinct points. The diagram shows the eight angles formed by the transversal and the two lines.

1. **a.** ∠3 and ∠6 are in the *interior* of ℓ and m. Name another pair of angles in the interior of ℓ and m. **Sample: ∠4 and ∠5**
   b. Name a pair of angles in the *exterior* of ℓ and m. **Sample: ∠1 and ∠7**
2. **a.** ∠1 and ∠4 are on *alternate sides* of the transversal *t*. Name another pair of angles on alternate sides of *t*. **Sample: ∠5 and ∠8**
   b. Name a pair of angles on the *same side* of *t*. **Sample: ∠1 and ∠3**

You can use the terms in Questions 1 and 2 to describe pairs of angles.

  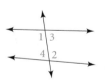

∠1 and ∠2 are **alternate interior angles**, as are ∠3 and ∠4.

∠1 and ∠4 are **same-side interior angles**, as are ∠2 and ∠3.

∠5 and ∠4 are **corresponding angles**, as are ∠6 and ∠2, ∠1 and ∠7, and ∠3 and ∠8.

3. In the diagrams above, ∠1 and ∠3 are not alternate interior angles. What term decribes their positions in relation to each other?
   adjacent angles

Example 1 Relating to the Real World ················

Aviation In the diagram of Lafayette Regional Airport, the black segments are runways and the grey areas are taxiways and terminal buildings. Classify ∠1 and ∠2 as alternate interior angles, same-side interior angles, or corresponding angles.

∠1 and ∠2 are corresponding angles.

Lafayette Regional Airport Lafayette, Louisiana

Lesson Planning Options

Prerequisite Skills

- Understanding parallel and perpendicular lines
- Understanding vertical and supplementary angles

Assignment Options for Exercises On Your Own

To provide flexible scheduling, this lesson can be subdivided into parts.

1 **Core** 1–3, 19–27
Extension 14–16

2 **Core** 4–13, 17–18, 28–38
Extension 39–41

Use Mixed Review to maintain skills.

Resources

Student Edition

Skills Handbook, p. 650
Extra Practice, p. 642
Glossary/Study Guide

Teaching Resources

Chapter Support File, Ch. 7
- Practice 7-1 (two worksheets)
- Reteaching 7-1
Classroom Manager 7-1
Glossary, Spanish Resources

Transparencies
8, 10, 78, 86

363

Directions for using geometry software to investigate the angles formed by parallel lines and a transversal are given in the Math Toolbox on page 362.

Check that students state "if two *parallel* lines are cut by a transversal" as the hypothesis of each conjecture they make.

VISUAL LEARNING Use models to illustrate the postulate and theorems, such as dividers from cardboard boxes or straws held together by brads. Emphasize that the names of the angle pairs do not depend on the lines being parallel but that the relationships between their measures do.

When writing reasons in proofs, remind students that it is better to write out the statement of the theorem or postulate rather than using its name. Due to space constraints, students may want to use abbreviations for parallel ($\parallel$), angles ($\angle$s), and congruent ($\cong$).

Additional Examples

FOR EXAMPLE 1 ....

Classify each pair of angles as alternate interior angles, same-side interior angles, or corresponding angles.

a. $\angle 4$ and $\angle 2$ **b.** $\angle 3$ and $\angle 4$

   a. **same-side interior angles**
   b. **corresponding angles**

Discussion: *Identify a pair of alternate interior angles.*

FOR EXAMPLE 2 ....

Write a plan for the following proof.

Given: *PQRS is a parallelogram.*
Prove: $\angle 1 \cong \angle 3$

Answers may vary. Sample:
Plan for Proof: To show $\angle 1 \cong \angle 3$, show that $\angle 1$ and $\angle 2$ are supplementary and that $\angle 2$ and $\angle 3$ are supplementary. Then $\angle 1 \cong \angle 3$.

Discussion: *Use the Plan for Proof to write a paragraph proof.*

364

Part 2 WORK TOGETHER

Work with a partner.

TECHNOLOGY HINT
The Work Together could be done with geometry software.

- Draw two parallel lines using lined paper or the two edges of a ruler. Then draw a transversal that intersects the two parallel lines.

- Use a protractor to measure each of the eight angles formed. Record the measures on your drawing.

   4. Make **conjectures** about the measures of corresponding angles, alternate interior angles, and same-side interior angles. Compare your results with those of your classmates.
   The measures of corresp. angles are = ; the measures of alt. interior angles are = ; the sum of the measures of same-side interior angles is 180.

THINK AND DISCUSS

Angles Formed by Parallel Lines

The results of the Work Together lead to the following postulate and theorems.

Postulate 7-1 Corresponding Angles Postulate	If two parallel lines are cut by a transversal, then corresponding angles are congruent. If $\ell \parallel m$, then $\angle 1 \cong \angle 5$, $\angle 2 \cong \angle 6$, $\angle 3 \cong \angle 7$, and $\angle 4 \cong \angle 8$.
Theorem 7-1 Alternate Interior Angles Theorem	If two parallel lines are cut by a transversal, then alternate interior angles are congruent. If $\ell \parallel m$, then $\angle 3 \cong \angle 6$ and $\angle 4 \cong \angle 5$.
Theorem 7-2 Same-Side Interior Angles Theorem	If two parallel lines are cut by a transversal, then the pairs of same-side interior angles are supplementary. If $\ell \parallel m$, then $\angle 3$ and $\angle 5$ are supplementary, and so are $\angle 4$ and $\angle 6$.

Proof of Theorem 7-1
Given: $a \parallel b$
Prove: $\angle 1 \cong \angle 3$

Statements	Reasons
1. $a \parallel b$	1. Given
2. $\angle 1 \cong \angle 2$	2. If $\parallel$ lines, then corresponding $\angle$s are $\cong$.
3. $\angle 2 \cong \angle 3$	3. Vertical angles are $\cong$.
4. $\angle 1 \cong \angle 3$	4. Transitive Prop. of Congruence

When writing a proof, it is often helpful to start by writing a plan. The plan should describe how you can reason from the given information to what you want to prove.

Example 2

Write a plan for the proof of Theorem 7-2.

Given: $a \parallel b$

Prove: $\angle 1$ and $\angle 2$ are supplementary.

Plan for Proof To show that $m\angle 1 + m\angle 2 = 180$, show that $m\angle 3 + m\angle 2 = 180$ and that $m\angle 1 = m\angle 3$. Then substitute $m\angle 1$ for $m\angle 3$.

5. Use the Plan for Proof to write a two-column proof of Theorem 7-2.
   See margin p. 366.
6. **Try This** Find the measure of each angle.

   a. $\angle 1$ 110   b. $\angle 2$ 70   c. $\angle 3$ 70
   d. $\angle 4$ 110   e. $\angle 5$ 110   f. $\angle 6$ 70

Example 3 — Relating to the Real World

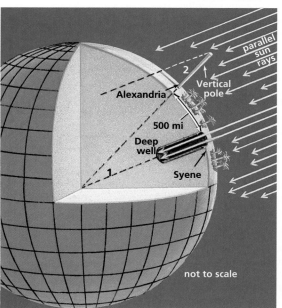

not to scale

Measuring Earth About 220 B.C., Eratosthenes estimated the circumference of Earth. He achieved this remarkable feat by assuming that Earth is a sphere and that the sun's rays are parallel. He knew that the sun was directly over the town of Syene on the longest day of the year, because sunlight shone directly down a deep well. On that day, he measured the angle of the shadow of a vertical pole in Alexandria, which was 5000 stadia (about 500 miles) north of Syene. How did Eratosthenes know that $\angle 1 \cong \angle 2$? And how could he compute the circumference of Earth knowing $m\angle 1$?

Since $\angle 1$ and $\angle 2$ are alternate interior angles formed by the sun's parallel rays, the angles are congruent. The angle Eratosthenes measured was 7.2°. This is $\frac{1}{50}$ of 360°, so 500 mi is $\frac{1}{50}$ of the circumference of Earth. His estimate of 25,000 mi is very close to the actual value.

365

---

pages 364–365   Think and Discuss

5. 1. $m\angle 3 + m\angle 2 = 180$ (Angle Add. Post.) 2. $a \parallel b$ (Given)
   3. $m\angle 1 = m\angle 3$ (If ∥ lines, then corres. ∠s are ≅.) 4. $m\angle 1 + m\angle 2 = 180$ (Substitution) 5. ∠1 and ∠2 are supplementary. (Def. of supplementary angles)

pages 366–369   On Your Own

1. ∠1 and ∠2: corresponding, ∠3 and ∠4: alt. interior, ∠5 and ∠6: corresponding

2. ∠1 and ∠2: same-side interior, ∠3 and ∠4: corresponding, ∠5 and ∠6: corresponding

3. ∠1 and ∠2: corresponding, ∠3 and ∠4: same-side interior, ∠5 and ∠6: : alt. interior

4. If ∥ lines, then corres. ∠s are ≅.; if ∥ lines, then same-side int. ∠s are supplementary.

5. If ∥ lines, then corres. ∠s are ≅.; if ∥ lines, then same-side int. ∠s are supplementary.

6. If ∥ lines, then same-side int. ∠s are supplementary.); if ∥ lines, then alt. int. ∠s are ≅.

7. If ∥ lines, then same-side int. ∠s are supplementary.; if ∥ lines, then same-side int. ∠s are supplementary.

8. If ∥ lines, then corres. ∠s are ≅.

9. If ∥ lines, then alt. int. ∠s are ≅.

10. If ∥ lines, then same-side int. ∠s are supplementary.

366

Exercises   ON YOUR OWN

Classify each pair of angles labeled with the same color as alternate interior angles, same-side interior angles, or corresponding angles.   1–3. See margin.

1.

2.

3.

Find $m\angle 1$ and then $m\angle 2$. State the theorems or postulates that justify your answers.   4–7. See margin for sample justifications.

4. 75, 105   5. 120, 60   6. 100, 70   7. 70, 110

State the theorem or postulate that justifies each statement about the figure at the right.   8–13. See margin.

8. ∠1 ≅ ∠2

9. ∠3 ≅ ∠4

10. $m\angle 5 + m\angle 6 = 180$

11. ∠5 ≅ ∠2

12. ∠5 ≅ ∠8

13. ∠3 ≅ ∠9

14. **Open-ended** The letter **Z** illustrates alternate interior angles. Find at least two other letters that illustrate the pairs of angles presented in this lesson. For each letter, show which types of angles are formed. See margin.

15. a. **Transformational Geometry** Lines ℓ and m are parallel, and line t is a transversal. Under the translation ⟨−4, −4⟩, the image of each of the angles ∠1, ∠2, ∠3, and ∠4 is its __?__ angle.   **corresponding**
    b. Under a rotation of 180° in point X, the image of each of the angles ∠3, ∠4, ∠5, and ∠6 is its __?__ angle.   **alt. interior**

16. **Writing** Look up the meaning of the prefix *trans-*. Explain how the meaning of the prefix relates to the word *transversal*.   See margin.

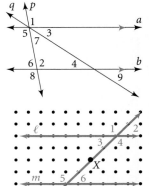

17. a. **Probability** Suppose that you pick one even-numbered angle and one odd-numbered angle from the diagram. Find the probability that the two angles are congruent. $\frac{1}{2}$
    b. **Open-ended** Write a probability problem of your own based on the diagram. Then solve it.
    Sample: Suppose you pick 2 even-numbered angles. What is the probability that they are supplementary? $\frac{2}{3}$

18. a. Architecture This photograph contains many examples of parallel lines cut by transversals. Given that *a* ‖ *b* and $m\angle 1 = 68$, find $m\angle 2$. **68**

  b. Given that *c* ‖ *d* and $m\angle 3 = 42$, find $m\angle 4$. **138**

For Exercises 19–27, refer to the diagram below right.

19. Name all pairs of corresponding angles formed by the transversal *p* and lines *ℓ* and *m*. ∠1 and ∠9, ∠2 and ∠10, ∠5 and ∠11, ∠6 and ∠12

20. Name all pairs of alternate interior angles formed by the transversal *ℓ* and lines *p* and *q*. ∠2 and ∠7, ∠3 and ∠6

Name the relationship between ∠2 and each of the given angles. In each case, state which line is the transversal. 22. corresponding, *p*

21. ∠3 **22.** ∠10 **23.** ∠7 **24.** ∠4
same-side interior angle, *ℓ*   alt. interior, *ℓ*   corresponding, *ℓ*

Find all angles that have the given relationship to ∠6.

25. alternate interior **26.** corresponding **27.** same-side interior
  ∠3, ∠9   ∠8, ∠12   ∠7, ∠10

28. Preparing for Proof Supply the reasons to complete this proof.

  Given: *B* is the midpoint of $\overline{AC}$.
  E is the midpoint of $\overline{AD}$.
  Prove: $\angle 1 \cong \angle 2$

Statements	Reasons
1. *B* is the midpoint of $\overline{AC}$. *E* is the midpoint of $\overline{AD}$.	**a.** ? Given
2. $\overline{BE} \parallel \overline{CD}$	**b.** ? △ Midsegment Thm.
3. $\angle 1 \cong \angle 2$	**c.** ? If ‖ lines, then corres. ∠s are ≅.

29. Preparing for Proof Complete this paragraph proof.

  Given: *BERT* is a parallelogram.   a. *BERT* is a ▱
  Prove: $\angle 1 \cong \angle 2$ b. def. of ▱

  We are given that **a.** ? . By **b.** ? , $\overline{ER} \parallel \overline{BT}$.
  $\angle 1 \cong \angle 2$ because **c.** ? .
  c. if ‖ lines, then alt. int. ∠s are ≅

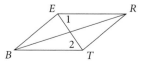

11. If ‖ lines, then alt. int. ∠s are ≅.

12. If ‖ lines, then corres. ∠s are ≅.

13. If ‖ lines, then corres. ∠s are ≅.

14. Samples: N illustrates alt. interior angles; F and E illustrate corres. angles and same-side interior angles.

16. Answers may vary. Sample: In words such as transcontinental and trans-Atlantic, *trans-* means *crossing*. A *transversal* is a line that *crosses* other lines.

39. Conjecture: If 2 lines are ‖, same-side exterior angles formed by these lines and a transversal are supplementary.

  1. *a* ‖ *b* (Given) 2. $m\angle 4 = m\angle 6$ (If ‖ lines, then corres. ∠s are ≅.) 3. $m\angle 5 + m\angle 6 = 180$ (Angle Addition Post.) 4. $m\angle 5 + m\angle 4 = 180$ (Substitution) 5. ∠4 and ∠5 are supplementary. (Def. of supplementary angles)

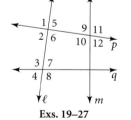

Exs. 19–27

367

40. Because $a \parallel b$ and $\angle 1$ and $\angle 2$ are corres. $\angle$s, $m\angle 1 = m\angle 2$, $m \perp a$, so $m\angle 1 = 90$. By substitution, $m\angle 2 = 90$. Therefore, $m \perp b$ by def. of $\perp$ lines.

41. Answers may vary. Sample: $\perp$ parking does not waste any space but makes it harder to park a car. Slanted parking makes it easier to park a car and makes the direction of traffic clear, but there are fewer parking spaces because some space in each corner is wasted.

Find Out by Investigating

If there is only 1 access road to a school, you must leave via the same road you came on.

200 mi

Add $\overline{AB}$, $\overline{CG}$, $\overline{KL}$, $\overline{FJ}$; 120 miles.

Algebra **Find the values of the variables.**

30.

31.

32.

33.

34.

35.

36.

37.

$v = 42$, $w = 25$, $x = 76$, $y = 37$

38. $\angle 1$ and $\angle 3$ are *alternate exterior angles*. Write a two-column proof of this statement: If two parallel lines are cut by a transversal, then alternate exterior angles are congruent.
Given: $a \parallel b$
Prove: $\angle 1 \cong \angle 3$
Plan for Proof: Show that $\angle 1 \cong \angle 3$ by showing that both angles are congruent to $\angle 2$.

1. $a \parallel b$ (Given) 2. $\angle 2 \cong \angle 3$ (If $\parallel$ lines, then corres. $\angle$s are $\cong$.) 3. $\angle 1 \cong \angle 2$ (Vert. angles are $\cong$.) 4. $\angle 1 \cong \angle 3$ (Trans. Prop. of $\cong$)

39. *Critical Thinking* $\angle 4$ and $\angle 5$ are *same-side exterior angles*. Make a **conjecture** about the same-side exterior angles formed by two parallel lines and a transversal. Prove your conjecture. See margin p. 367.

40. Use the diagram to write a paragraph proof of this statement: If a transversal is perpendicular to one of two parallel lines, then it is perpendicular to the other line.
Given: $a \parallel b$, $m \perp a$
Prove: $m \perp b$ See margin.

41. *Traffic Flow* You are designing the parking lot for a local shopping area, and are considering the two arrangements shown. Give the advantages and disadvantages of each. See margin.

CONNECTING TO STUDENTS' WORLD Exercises 46–48 Have students design a similar survey. Get permission for them to distribute it at lunch to male and female students who play musical instruments. Have them collect the data and display it in a double bar graph like the one shown.

Exercise 49 Remind students that the circumference of a sphere is the length of a great circle.

Exercise 50b Have students draw a sketch to show how the pictures would fit on the poster.

GETTING READY FOR LESSON 7-2 These exercises prepare students to write flow proofs.

Wrap Up

THE BIG IDEA Ask students to define the special angle pairs they learned in this lesson and draw an illustration of each.

RETEACHING ACTIVITY Students draw a pair of parallel lines and a transversal. They measure one of the eight angles formed and then find the other seven. (Reteaching worksheet 7-1)

Chapter Project *Find Out by Investigating*

Once a month a math coordinator starts at school *A*, drives to the 11 other schools labeled *B* through *L* on the map, and returns to *A*.

- Why must the coordinator backtrack on some of the roads?
- Sketch the shortest route that can be taken. How long is it?
- What additional roads could be built so that the trip could be made without backtracking? Minimize the total length of the new roads. Sketch the shortest route and find its length.

See margin p. 368.

The distance from any school to an adjacent school is 10 mi.

Exercises MIXED REVIEW

Coordinate Geometry Find the coordinates of the midpoint of $\overline{AB}$.

42. $A(0, 9)$, $B(1, 5)$
(0.5, 7)

43. $A(-3, 8)$, $B(2, -1)$
(−0.5, 3.5)

44. $A(10, -1)$, $B(-4, 7)$
(3, 3)

45. $A(-5, -11)$, $B(2, 6)$
(−1.5, −2.5)

Data Analysis Use the double bar graph for Exercises 46–48.

46. What percent of female players selected the piano as their favorite instrument? **50%**

47. Given 50 randomly selected male players, about how many are drummers? **5**

48. Do males or females prefer guitar more?
males

49. **Sports** The circumference of a regulation basketball is between 75 cm and 78 cm. What are the smallest and largest surface areas a basketball can have? Give your answers to the nearest whole unit. **1790 cm²; 1937 cm²**

50. a. **Photography** A regular-sized photo is 3 in. by 5 in. A larger-sized photo is 4 in. by 6 in. What percent more paper is used for a larger-sized photo than for a regular photo? **60%**
b. You are making a poster of photos from a class trip. What is the greatest number of regular-sized photos you can fit on a 2 ft-by-3 ft poster? What is the greatest number of larger-sized photos you can fit?
56 photos; 36 photos

Favorite Musical Instruments

The top four choices of instruments from a 1994 survey of current and former players

Piano 17% 50%

Guitar 8% 36%

Drums 11% 1%

Flute 2% 8%

Key
♪ Male
♪ Female

Source: *National Association of Music Merchants*

Getting Ready for Lesson 7-2

Write the converse of each conditional statement.

51. If the sky is blue, then there are no clouds in the sky.
If there are no clouds in the sky, then the sky is blue.

52. If ℓ and *m* are parallel, then corresponding angles $\angle 1$ and $\angle 2$ are congruent.
52. If corres. angles $\angle 1$ and $\angle 2$ are $\cong$, then ℓ and *m* are $\parallel$.

Lesson Quiz

Lesson Quiz is also available in Transparencies.

1. Classify each pair of angles as corresponding, alternate interior, or same-side interior.
a. $\angle 7$ and $\angle 8$ **corresponding**
b. $\angle 6$ and $\angle 8$ **same-side interior**

2. State the postulate or theorem that justifies each statement.
a. $\angle 1 \cong \angle 2$
b. $m\angle 5 + m\angle 6 = 180$
See back of book.

369

Students solve systems of equations in two variables using substitution. They will use this skill in the exercises given in the following lessons.

Example 1

Help students see that the solution of a linear system gives the coordinates of the point where the graphs of the equations intersect. It follows that two equations whose graphs are parallel have no point of intersection and no solution and that two equations whose graphs are the same line have infinitely many solutions.

Example 2

Point out that students need to solve one of the equations for x or y before they can substitute into the second equation.

ERROR ALERT! Students may not understand when a system has infinitely many solutions or no solution. **Remediation:** Make sure students understand that there are infinitely many solutions when a system simplifies to a true statement and there are no solutions when a system simplifies to a false statement.

ADDITIONAL PROBLEM Have students solve the following system of equations which has infinitely many solutions.

$$\begin{cases} 2x + 6y = 10 \\ x = 5 - 3y \end{cases}$$

Transparencies
5, 8, 9, 10

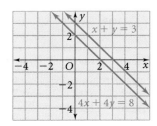

Math ToolboX — Algebra Review

Systems of Linear Equations

After Lesson 7-1

You can solve a system of equations in two variables by using substitution to create a one-variable equation.

Example 1

Solve the system: $y = 3x + 5$
$ y = x + 1$

$y = x + 1$ ← Start with one equation.
$3x + 5 = x + 1$ ← Substitute $3x + 5$ for y.
$2x = -4$ ← Solve for x.
$x = -2$

Substitute -2 for x in either equation and solve for y.

$y = x + 1$
$ = (-2) + 1 = -1$

Since $x = -2$ and $y = -1$, the solution is $(-2, -1)$.

The graph of a linear system with *no solution* is two parallel lines, and the graph of a linear system with *infinitely many solutions* is one line.

Example 2

Solve the system: $x + y = 3$
$ 4x + 4y = 8$

$x + y = 3$
$ x = 3 - y$ ← Solve the first equation for x.
$4(3 - y) + 4y = 8$ ← Substitute $3 - y$ for x in the second equation.
$12 - 4y + 4y = 8$ ← Simplify.
$12 = 8$ ← False!

Since $12 = 8$ is a false statement, the system has no solution.

Solve each system of equations.

1. $y = x - 4$ $(-3, -7)$
$ y = 3x + 2$

2. $2x - y = 8$ $(5, 2)$
$ x + 2y = 9$

3. $3x + y = 4$ no solution
$ -6x - 2y = 12$

4. $y = -x + 2$ inf. many solutions
$ 2y = 4 - 2x$

5. $y = 2x + 1$ $(8, 17)$
$ y = 3x - 7$

6. $x - y = 4$ no solution
$ 3x - 3y = 6$

370

CONNECTING TO PRIOR KNOWLEDGE Discuss examples of parallel lines (the lines on a football field or the sides of a street), and why knowing that they are parallel is important.

WORK TOGETHER

Have students work with a partner on this activity.

ALTERNATIVE METHOD Attach three straws to each other with paper clips or brads so that one straw crosses the other two straws. Identify a pair of corresponding angles formed by the straws. Turn the straws until the angles appear congruent. Ask what appears to be true of the straws.

THINK AND DISCUSS

Review the fact that the converse of a statement is written by interchanging the hypothesis with the conclusion.

Example 1

For a quick review of dilations and the properties of similarity transformations, refer students to Lesson 3-7.

Connections Woodworking . . . and more

What You'll Learn

7-2 Proving Lines Parallel

* Recognizing conditions that result in parallel lines
* Writing proofs that involve parallel lines

...And Why

To ensure parallel lines in construction and graphic arts

What You'll Need

* protractor
* ruler
* dot paper

2. $\overleftrightarrow{AB} \parallel \overleftrightarrow{A'C}$

TECHNOLOGY HINT

The Work Together could also be done using geometry software.

WORK TOGETHER

* Draw a segment on dot paper and label it $\overleftrightarrow{AB}$. Draw and label a point C not on $\overleftrightarrow{AB}$. Draw $\overline{BC}$.

* Translate $\angle ABC$ so that the image of B is C. Label the image $\angle A'CC'$.

1. What is true of $\angle ABC$ and $\angle A'CC'$? Explain. $\angle ABC \cong \angle A'CC'$; translation is an isometry.

2. What appears to be true of $\overleftrightarrow{AB}$ and $\overleftrightarrow{A'C}$? See left.

3. Use your answers to Questions 1 and 2 to complete this statement:
If two lines are cut by a transversal so that a pair of corresponding angles are congruent, then __?__.
the lines are $\parallel$

THINK AND DISCUSS

In the Work Together, you discovered that the converse of the Corresponding Angles Postulate is true.

Postulate 7-2
Converse of Corresponding Angles Postulate

If two lines are cut by a transversal so that a pair of corresponding angles are congruent, then the lines are parallel.

If $\angle 1 \cong \angle 2$, then $\ell \parallel m$.

Example 1

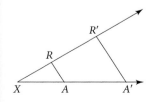

Transformational Geometry $\overleftrightarrow{R'A'}$ is the image of $\overleftrightarrow{RA}$ under a dilation centered at X. Show that $\overleftrightarrow{RA} \parallel \overleftrightarrow{R'A'}$.

Because a dilation is a similarity transformation, $\triangle XRA \sim \triangle XR'A'$. Corresponding angles of similar polygons are congruent, so $\angle RAX \cong \angle R'A'X$. Since $\overrightarrow{XA'}$ is a transversal of $\overline{RA}$ and $\overline{R'A'}$, by the Converse of the Corresponding Angles Postulate, $\overleftrightarrow{RA} \parallel \overleftrightarrow{R'A'}$.

Lesson Planning Options

Prerequisite Skills

* Understanding the definition of a dilation
* Understanding the characteristics of prisms

Assignment Options for Exercises On Your Own

Core 1–3, 5–28, 30–35
Extension 4, 29, 36–37

Use Mixed Review to maintain skills.

Resources

Student Edition

Skills Handbook, pp. 646, 650
Extra Practice, p. 642
Glossary/Study Guide

Teaching Resources

Chapter Support File, Ch. 7
* Practice 7-2 (two worksheets)
* Reteaching 7-2
* Alternative Activity 7-2
Classroom Manager 7-2
Glossary, Spanish Resources

Transparencies
5, 8, 10, 78

371

Theorems 7-3 and 7-4 Make sure that students understand the difference between these theorems and the theorems presented in Lesson 7-1.

Discuss with students that the steps of a flow proof can be started at any step. They can even start with the conclusion and work backwards. Once all the steps are written down, arrows are used to show the flow of the statements and reasons.

VISUAL LEARNING Point out that in a flow proof, the statements are written in a box and the justifications are written underneath.

After students know that the Alternate Interior Angles Theorem and its converse are true, have them write the two statements as a biconditional.

TACTILE LEARNING If possible, provide a physical model for students. A lightweight cardboard box such as a cereal box or a tissue box can be made to slant. Or, construct the frame of a prism using pipe cleaners or straws and tape.

Additional Examples

FOR EXAMPLE 1

$\overline{H'I'}$ is the image of $\overline{HI}$ under a dilation centered at G. Show that $\overline{H'I'} \parallel \overline{HI}$.
See back of book.

FOR EXAMPLE 2

Write a paragraph proof.

Given: ∠1 and ∠2 are supplementary; $m\angle 3 = m\angle 4$

Prove: $\ell \parallel q$ **See back of book.**

Discussion: *Write a two-column proof. Which proof do you prefer? Why?*

FOR EXAMPLE 3

What type of quadrilateral can have angles of 72°, 108°, 45°, and 135°?
a trapezoid

Discussion: *With the given angles, is the quadrilateral necessarily a trapezoid?*

In Lesson 7-1, you proved the Alternate Interior Angles Theorem and the Same-Side Interior Angles Theorem by using the Corresponding Angles Postulate. You can prove the converses of these theorems by using the converse of the postulate.

Theorem 7-3
Converse of Alternate Interior Angles Theorem

If two lines are cut by a transversal so that a pair of alternate interior angles are congruent, then the lines are parallel.

If ∠1 ≅ ∠2, then $\ell \parallel m$.

Theorem 7-4
Converse of Same-Side Interior Angles Theorem

If two lines are cut by a transversal so that a pair of same-side interior angles are supplementary, then the lines are parallel.

If ∠2 and ∠4 are supplementary, then $\ell \parallel m$.

This is a **flow proof** of Theorem 7-3. Arrows show the logical connections between the statements. Reasons are written below the statements.

Flow Proof of Theorem 7-3
Given: ∠1 ≅ ∠2
Prove: $\ell \parallel m$

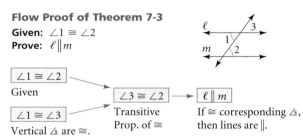

```
┌─────────┐
│ ∠1 ≅ ∠2 │ ─────────┐
└─────────┘          ↓
Given            ┌─────────┐      ┌───────┐
                 │ ∠3 ≅ ∠2 │ ───→ │ ℓ ‖ m │
┌─────────┐      └─────────┘      └───────┘
│ ∠1 ≅ ∠3 │ ───→  Transitive      If ≅ corresponding ∠s,
└─────────┘        Prop. of ≅      then lines are ‖.
Vertical ∠s are ≅.
```

Write a paragraph proof.
Given: ∠*BAC* and ∠*ACD* are supplementary.
∠*CDF* and ∠*DFE* are supplementary.
Prove: $\overline{AB} \parallel \overline{EF}$

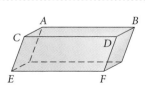

∠*BAC* and ∠*ACD* are supplementary same-side interior angles formed by transversal $\overline{AC}$ with $\overline{AB}$ and $\overline{CD}$. So, $\overline{AB} \parallel \overline{CD}$. Similarly, ∠*CDF* and ∠*DFE* are supplementary same-side interior angles formed by transversal $\overline{DF}$ with $\overline{CD}$ and $\overline{EF}$. So, $\overline{CD} \parallel \overline{EF}$. Since $\overline{AB}$ and $\overline{EF}$ are parallel to the same segment, they are parallel to each other (Theorem 2-5).

4. Try This Write a flow proof for Example 2. **See margin p. 374.**

372

Example 3

Point out that the trapezoid formed is actually an isosceles trapezoid because the base angles are congruent.

CRITICAL THINKING Ask students to make conjectures about the angles of a parallelogram and the angles of an isosceles trapezoid. Then have them draw an example of each type of figure and measure the angles to test their conjectures.

Example 4 Relating to the Real World

ESL Students may be unfamiliar with the terms "miter box" and "backsaw." The picture should help to illustrate these terms. All students need to understand is that these tools can be used to cut 45° angles.

EXTENSION Have students prove that if two lines are cut by a transversal so that a pair of alternate exterior angles (or same-side exterior angles) are congruent, then the lines are parallel.

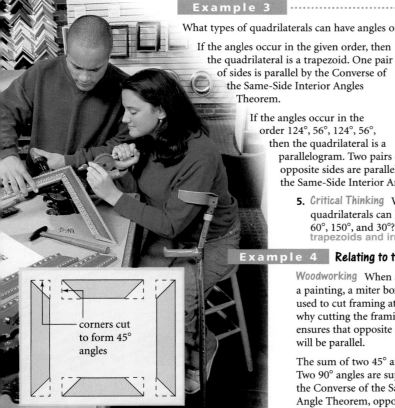

Example 3

What types of quadrilaterals can have angles of 56°, 56°, 124°, and 124°?

If the angles occur in the given order, then the quadrilateral is a trapezoid. One pair of sides is parallel by the Converse of the Same-Side Interior Angles Theorem.

If the angles occur in the order 124°, 56°, 124°, 56°, then the quadrilateral is a parallelogram. Two pairs of opposite sides are parallel by the Converse of the Same-Side Interior Angles Theorem.

5. *Critical Thinking* What types of quadrilaterals can have angles of 120°, 60°, 150°, and 30°?
   trapezoids and irregular quadrilaterals

Example 4 — Relating to the Real World

Woodworking When a frame is made for a painting, a miter box and a backsaw are used to cut framing at 45° angles. Explain why cutting the framing at this angle ensures that opposite sides of the frame will be parallel.

The sum of two 45° angles is a 90° angle. Two 90° angles are supplementary, so by the Converse of the Same-Side Interior Angle Theorem, opposite sides of the frame are parallel.

corners cut to form 45° angles

Exercises ON YOUR OWN

Which lines or segments are parallel? Justify your answer with a theorem or postulate.   2. *CA∥HR;* If ≅ corres. ∠s, then lines are ∥.

1.

2.

3.

BE∥CG; If ≅ corres. ∠s, then lines are ∥.

m∠J + m∠L = 180

3. *JO∥LM;* If supplementary same-side int. ∠s, then lines are ∥.

Technology Options

Exercise 4 can be done using geometry software. Students can manipulate the original triangle to see that the parallelogram does not depend on the type of triangle.

Prentice Hall Technology

Software
- Secondary Math Lab Toolkit™
- Integrated Math Lab 36
- Computer Item Generator 7-2

CD-ROM
- Multimedia Geometry Lab 7

Internet
- See the Prentice Hall site. (http://www.phschool.com)

373

ALTERNATIVE ASSESSMENT **Exercise 4** You can use this exercise to help you assess students' understanding of Theorem 7-3. Check that they recognize that the diagonal is a transversal passing through both pairs of opposite sides and that two pairs of congruent corresponding angles of the triangles form congruent pairs of alternate interior angles.

Exercises 5–14 Make sure that students state the entire theorem or postulate they use to justify their answers.

ERROR ALERT! **Exercise 15** Some students may not realize that they are using a theorem when they conclude that ∠1 ≅ ∠6 or ∠9 ≅ ∠12. **Remediation:** Have students review vertical angles in Lesson 1-7.

Exercise 16 Have students use the flow proof on page 372 as a model.

Exercises 17–18 Encourage students to start by writing a plan for each proof. You may want to have students complete these exercises in groups.

---

pages 371–373 **Think and Discuss**

4.

∠BAC and ∠ACD are supp.	∠CDF and ∠DFE are supp.
Given	Given

↓ ↓

AB ∥ CD	EF ∥ CD

Converse of Same-Side Interior ∠s Thm. | Converse of Same-Side Interior ∠s Thm.

↘ ↙

AB ∥ EF

2 lines ∥ to a 3rd line are ∥.

pages 373–376 **On Your Own**

4.

The 2 △s are ≅, so ∠1 ≅ ∠4 and ∠2 ≅ ∠3. These 2 pairs of alt. interior angles are ≅; therefore, opp. sides of the quadrilateral are ∥.

5. If ≅ corres. ∠s, then lines are ∥.

7. If supplementary same-side int. ∠s, then lines are ∥.

9. If ≅ alt. int. ∠s, then lines are ∥.

11. If supplementary same-side int. ∠s, then lines are ∥.

12. If ≅ corres. ∠s, then lines are ∥.

14. If ≅ corres. ∠s, then lines are ∥.

20a. Each of the 2 lines forms a right angle with the same line. All right ∠s are ≅. Then the corres. angles are ≅, so the lines are ∥.

374

4. Paper cutting Use the method shown in the diagram to cut out two congruent triangles. Join the two triangles so that they form a parallelogram. Use what you learned in this lesson to **justify** that the figure is indeed a parallelogram. **See margin.**

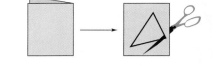

Refer to the diagram. Use the given information to determine which lines, if any, must be parallel. If any lines are parallel, use a theorem or postulate to tell why. 5–14. See margin for reasoning.

5. ∠1 ≅ ∠3 a ∥ b

6. ∠1 ≅ ∠6 no ∥ lines

7. ∠6 is supplementary to ∠7. a ∥ b

8. ∠11 ≅ ∠7 no ∥ lines

9. ∠5 ≅ ∠10 ℓ ∥ m

10. m∠7 = 70, m∠9 = 110 no ∥ lines

11. ∠2 is supplementary to ∠3. a ∥ b

12. ∠8 ≅ ∠6 a ∥ b

13. ∠9 ≅ ∠3 no ∥ lines

14. ∠2 ≅ ∠10 ℓ ∥ m

15. If ∠1 ≅ ∠12, what theorems or postulates can you use to show that ℓ ∥ m?
Vertical ∠s are ≅, and if ≅ corres. ∠s, then lines are ∥.

16. Preparing for Proof Use this Plan for Proof to write a flow proof. Refer to the diagram at the right. See back of book.

Given: ℓ ∥ m, ∠4 ≅ ∠10
Prove: a ∥ b

Plan for Proof: Show that a ∥ b by showing that the corresponding angles ∠2 and ∠4 are congruent. Show that they are congruent by showing that they are both congruent to ∠10.

Refer to the diagram for Exercises 5–18 to write a flow proof.
17–18. Answers may vary. See back of book.

17. **Given:** a ∥ b, ∠7 ≅ ∠10
Prove: ℓ ∥ m

18. **Given:** ℓ ∥ m, ∠7 and ∠12 are supplementary.
Prove: a ∥ b

19. Carpentry A *T-bevel* is a tool used by carpenters to draw congruent angles. By loosening the locking lever, the carpenter can adjust the angle. Explain how the carpenter knows that the two lines that he has drawn using the T-bevel are parallel.
If corres. angles are ≅, then the lines are ∥.

Angle can be adjusted by loosening the locking lever.

Diagram (Exs. 5–18): lines *a* and *b* cut by transversals ℓ and *m*, with angles labeled 1/5, 9/11 on line *a*; 2/6, 10/12; 3/7, 4/8 on line *b*.

Exs. 5–18

20. a. Writing Explain why this statement is true: In a plane, two lines perpendicular to the same line are parallel. **See margin p. 374.**

b. Geometry in 3 Dimensions Use this rectangular prism to explain why the words "in a plane" are needed in part (a). **See right.**

c. Geometry in 3 Dimensions Use the rectangular prism to find three lines that are parallel to each other, but that are not all in the same plane. Are any two of these lines in the same plane? $\overleftrightarrow{AC}$, $\overleftrightarrow{BD}$, $\overleftrightarrow{HF}$; yes

Sample: $\overleftrightarrow{AC}$, $\overleftrightarrow{BD}$, $\overleftrightarrow{HF}$; yes

21. Standardized Test Prep The measures of the angles of a quadrilateral are $x + 10$, $2x + 20$, $x + 70$, and $2x - 40$. What type or types of quadrilateral could this be? **D**

I. parallelogram **II.** trapezoid **III.** square

A. I only **B.** II only **C.** III only **D.** I and II only **E.** I and III only

▦ *Choose* **Use paper and pencil, mental math, or a calculator to determine the value of *x* for which $\ell \parallel m$.**

22. 30

23. 50

24. 59

25. 31

26. 5

27. 20

28. Rewrite this paragraph proof of Theorem 7-4 as a flow proof. **See back of book.**

Given: $\angle 1$ and $\angle 2$ are supplementary.
Prove: $\ell \parallel m$

By the Angle Addition Postulate, $m\angle 1 + m\angle 3 = 180$. Therefore, $\angle 1$ and $\angle 3$ are supplementary. It is given that $\angle 1$ and $\angle 2$ are supplementary, so by the Congruent Supplements Theorem, $\angle 2 \cong \angle 3$. $\angle 2$ and $\angle 3$ are corresponding angles, so by the Converse of the Corresponding Angles Postulate, $\ell \parallel m$.

29. a. Furniture The legs of the chairs shown form similar isosceles triangles. Explain how you know that the seat of the chair is parallel to the ground. **a–b. See margin.**

b. Open-ended Give an example of another type of furniture that shows parallel lines. Include a sketch showing the lines.

29a. The △s are ~ and isosceles, so the 4 base angles are ≅. Then the alt. interior angles are ≅, so the lines are ∥.

b. Sample: In a bookcase, the edges of shelves are ∥ to each other.

31. Each line and the flat surface form a corres. angle that is congruent to the 60° angle of the drawing △. Since the corres. angles are ≅, the lines are ∥.

32. Opp. sides are ∥ because if same-side int. ∠s are supplementary, then lines are ∥.

33. 2 distinct pairs of same-side interior angles are supplementary, so one pair of sides is ∥.

34. No 2 angles are supplementary or ≅.

35. All the angles are rt. angles and 2 pairs of opp. sides are ∥.

36. The given line and its image are ∥ if the orig. line is ∥ to the line of reflection.

37. 1. $\overline{A'B'}$ is the reflection of $\overline{AB}$ in line *m*. (Given) 2. $\overline{AA'} \perp m$ and $\overline{BB'} \perp m$ (Def. of reflection) 3. $\overline{AA'} \parallel \overline{BB'}$ (In a plane, 2 lines ⊥ to 3rd are ∥.)

b. Answers may vary. Sample: $\overleftrightarrow{CE}$ and $\overleftrightarrow{BD}$ are each ⊥ to $\overleftrightarrow{CD}$, but they are not ∥.

30. *Coordinate Geometry* Given the equations of two lines in the coordinate plane, explain how you can prove that they are parallel. Show that the slopes are =.

31. *Drafting* Explain why the lines shown in the diagram are parallel. See margin p. 375.

What type of quadrilateral is *PLAN?* **Explain your answers.** 32–35. See margin p. 375 for explanations.

32. $m\angle P = 72$, $m\angle L = 108$, $m\angle A = 72$, $m\angle N = 108$ parallelogram

33. $m\angle P = 59$, $m\angle L = 37$, $m\angle A = 143$, $m\angle N = 121$ trapezoid

34. $m\angle P = 67$, $m\angle L = 120$, $m\angle A = 73$, $m\angle N = 100$ irregular quadrilateral

35. $m\angle P = 90$, $m\angle L = 90$, $m\angle A = 90$, $m\angle N = 90$ rectangle

36. *Transformations* Under what circumstances will a line be parallel to its image under a reflection? Draw a diagram to support your explanation. See margin p. 375.

37. *Transformations* Write a two-column proof. (*Hint:* Refer to the definition of a reflection in Lesson 3-1.)

Given: $\overline{A'B'}$ is the reflection image of $\overline{AB}$ in line m.
Prove: $\overline{AA'} \parallel \overline{BB'}$ See margin p. 375.

The artist draws a line, slides the triangle along the flat surface, and draws another line.

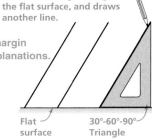

Flat surface — 30°-60°-90° Triangle

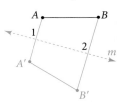

Exercises **MIXED REVIEW**

Find the area of a semicircular region with the given radius. Round your answer to the nearest tenth.

38. 8 in. — 100.5 in.^{2}

39. 10 cm — 157.1 cm^2

40. 4 ft — 25.1 ft^2

41. 1.2 m — 2.3 m^2

42. **a.** *Olympics* The torch used for the 1996 Olympic Games in Atlanta is approximately cylindrical. Its length is 32 in., and its diameter is 2.25 in. What is its volume? Round your answer to the nearest whole unit. 127 in.^{3}

b. The torch has 22 equally-spaced prongs around the top representing the number of cities that have hosted Olympic Games. How many degrees apart are the prongs? Round your answer to the nearest tenth. 16.4°

Getting Ready for Lesson 7-3

Constructions Draw each figure and then use a compass and straightedge to construct a figure congruent to the one you drew.

43. an obtuse angle   44. a segment   45. a triangle
43–45. Check students' work.

Coretta Scott King carried the Olympic torch in 1996.

086

PROBLEM OF THE DAY

The circumference of the base of a cylinder is 8 in. and the height is 6 in. A spiral stripe is drawn around the cylinder exactly once. It reaches the top directly above the spot where it left the bottom. What is the length of the stripe? **10 in.**

Problem of the Day is also available in Transparencies.

CONNECTING TO PRIOR KNOWLEDGE Have students draw an angle, then use a compass and a straightedge to draw an angle congruent to it. Discuss the steps they used.

THINK AND DISCUSS

ESL **VISUAL LEARNING** Demonstrate Construction 5 and the other constructions in this lesson on the board. Have students model each construction at their desks. As you perform each step, verbalize your actions using precise terminology.

Question 1 Point out that constructions must be justified before they can be used in other constructions.

Example 1

Make sure that students draw the segments representing rays longer than the larger segment. In this example, $\overrightarrow{AZ}$ and $\overrightarrow{AB}$ should be drawn with "lengths" greater than a.

Connections **Technology . . . and more**

7-3 Constructing Parallel and Perpendicular Lines

What You'll Learn
• Constructing parallel and perpendicular lines

...And Why
To be able to use parallels and perpendiculars in arts and crafts

What You'll Need
straightedge, compass

Construction 5
Parallel through a Point Not on a Line

QUICK REVIEW
Instructions for constructing congruent angles are on page 40.

Part 1 **Constructing Parallel Lines**

THINK AND DISCUSS

You can use what you know about corresponding angles and parallel lines to construct parallel lines.

Construct a line parallel to a given line and through a given point not on the line.
Given: Line ℓ and point N not on ℓ

Step 1
Label two points H and J on ℓ.
Draw $\overleftrightarrow{HN}$.

Step 2
Construct $\angle 1$ with vertex at N so that $\angle 1 \cong \angle JHN$ and the two angles are corresponding angles. Label the line you just constructed m.

$\ell \parallel m$

1. Explain why lines ℓ and m are parallel.
If $\cong$ corres. $\angle$s, then lines are $\parallel$.

Example 1

Use the segments shown at the left to construct a trapezoid with bases of lengths a and b.

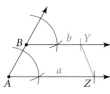

Step 1: Construct $\overline{AZ}$ with length a.

Step 2: Draw a point B not on $\overline{AZ}$. Then draw $\overrightarrow{AB}$.

Step 3: Construct a line parallel to $\overrightarrow{AZ}$ through B.

Step 4: Construct Y so that $BY = b$. Then draw $\overline{YZ}$. $ZABY$ is a trapezoid.

Lesson Planning Options

Prerequisite Skills
• Constructing congruent angles
• Constructing perpendicular bisectors

Assignment Options for Exercises On Your Own

To provide flexible scheduling, this lesson can be subdivided into parts.

1 **Core** 1, 8–10
Extension 3

2 **Core** 2, 4–7, 11–17
Extension 18–20

Use Mixed Review to maintain skills.

Resources

Student Edition
Extra Practice, p. 642
Glossary/Study Guide

Teaching Resources
Chapter Support File, Ch. 7
• Practice 7-3 (two worksheets)
• Reteaching 7-3
• Alternative Activity 7-3
Classroom Manager 7-3
Glossary, Spanish Resources

Transparencies
79

377

Additional Examples

FOR EXAMPLE 1 ....

Use the segments shown in Example 1 to construct a parallelogram with sides of lengths *a* and *b.*

FOR EXAMPLE 2 ....

Use geometry software to construct an isosceles triangle in which the base and the height have the same length.

Part 2 Constructing Perpendicular Lines

The two constructions that follow are based on Theorem 4-13: If a point is equidistant from the endpoints of a segment, then it is on the perpendicular bisector of the segment.   **2. *A* and *B* are equidistant from the endpts. of $\overline{CD}$.**

2. Explain why $\overleftrightarrow{AB}$ must be the perpendicular bisector of $\overline{CD}$.

3. *Critical Thinking* Turn to page 42 and study the method for constructing a perpendicular bisector of a segment. Explain why that construction works.   **Intersections of the 2 arcs are equidistant from the endpts. of the segment.**

Construction 6
Perpendicular through a Point on a Line

Construct the perpendicular to a given line at a given point on the line.
Given: Point *P* on line ℓ

Step 1
Place the compass tip on *P.* Draw arcs intersecting ℓ in two points. Label the points *A* and *B.*

Step 2
Open the compass wider. With the compass tip on *A,* draw an arc above point *P.*

Step 3
Without changing the compass setting, place the compass tip on *B.* Draw an arc that intersects the arc from Step 2. Label the point of intersection *C.*

Step 4
Draw $\overleftrightarrow{CP}$.

$\overleftrightarrow{CP} \perp \ell$

Justification of Construction 6

You constructed *A* and *B* so that *AP* = *BP.* You constructed *C* so that *AC* = *BC.* Because *P* and *C* are both equidistant from the endpoints of $\overline{AB}$, $\overleftrightarrow{CP}$ is the perpendicular bisector of $\overline{AB}$. So $\overleftrightarrow{CP} \perp \ell$.

4. **Try This** Draw a line $\overleftrightarrow{EF}$. Construct a line $\overleftrightarrow{FG}$ so that $\overleftrightarrow{EF} \perp \overleftrightarrow{FG}$.
   See back of book.

MAKING CONNECTIONS There are some figures that cannot be constructed. This puzzled Greek mathematicians, and it was not until the nineteenth century that mathematicians proved that you cannot construct a square with the same area as a given circle, a cube with twice the area of a given cube, or an angle one-third the measure of a given angle.

Construction 7 Have students compare Constructions 6 and 7 to see that the only difference is where the compass tip is placed at the start of each construction. The rest of the steps are the same.

American artist Sol LeWitt creates wall-sized drawings that contain geometric figures such as arcs and perpendicular lines. To create arcs, he uses simple, large-scale compasses like the one shown below. He often employs local students to assist in creating his artwork. The two works shown here were on display at the Addison Gallery in Andover, Massachusetts.

Construction 7
Perpendicular through a Point Not on a Line

Construct the perpendicular to a given line from a given point not on the line.
Given: line ℓ and point R not on ℓ

Step 1
Open your compass to a distance greater than the distance from R to ℓ. With the compass tip on R, draw an arc that intersects ℓ at two points. Label the points E and F.

Step 2
Keep the same compass setting. Place the compass point on E and make an arc.

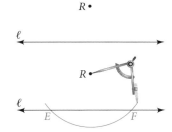

Step 3
Keep the same compass setting. With the compass tip on F, draw an arc that intersects the arc from Step 2. Label the point of intersection G.

Step 4
Draw $\overleftrightarrow{GR}$.

$\overleftrightarrow{GR} \perp \ell$

AUDITORY LEARNING Question 6 Have students work with a partner. Have one student explain why Construction 6 works. Then have the other student explain why Construction 7 works.

Example 2 ··

The diagram shows the construction of a right triangle starting with a leg that is vertical. The same steps can be used to construct a right triangle when the segment in Step 1 is in any position.

Exercises   ON YOUR OWN

Exercise 1 Make sure that students have use of a compass and straightedge for this and other exercises in this lesson. You may want to have students work on these exercises in class so they will not need to bring a compass home.

TRANSFORMATIONS Exercise 2 Help students see that they can find the image of $\overline{PQ}$ by first using Construction 7 to draw a line perpendicular to ℓ through P and a line perpendicular to ℓ through Q.

---

pages 380–383 On Your Own

1. Sample:

2.

3a. Answers may vary. Sample:

b. Draw any line through the pt. so that it intersects the original line. Construct an alt. interior angle ≅ to the angle formed by the 2 lines. The constructed angle should have the given pt. as its vertex and the drawn line as 1 of its sides.

4a. *R* and *S* are equidistant from the endpts. of the segment formed by the intersection of 2 ⊙s, so $\ell \perp m$.

380

5.

5. Try This Draw a line $\overleftrightarrow{CX}$ and a point Z not on the line. Construct $\overleftrightarrow{ZB}$ so that $\overleftrightarrow{ZB} \perp \overleftrightarrow{CX}$. **See left.**

6. Critical Thinking Explain why Construction 7 works. $\overleftrightarrow{RG}$ is the ⊥ bisector of $\overline{EF}$.

Example 2 ························

▣ **Technology** Use geometry software to construct a right triangle in which one leg is twice as long as the other.

Step 1: Draw a segment of any length.

Step 2: Construct a line perpendicular to the segment through one of its endpoints.

Step 3: On the line, construct two segments congruent to the original segment.

Step 4: Draw the hypotenuse of the triangle. Hide the construction points and lines.

Exercises   ON YOUR OWN

1. Draw a line ℓ and a point S not on ℓ. Construct a line m through S so that $m \parallel \ell$. **See margin.**

2. Transformations Draw a line ℓ and a segment $\overline{PQ}$ as shown at the right. Construct the reflection image of $\overline{PQ}$ in line ℓ. (*Hint:* Construct a line perpendicular to ℓ through P. Construct P' on the perpendicular so that ℓ bisects $\overline{PP'}$.) **See margin.**

3. a. Draw an acute angle on your paper. Construct an angle congruent to the angle you drew so that the two angles are alternate interior angles. (*Hint:* The figure you end up with should look like a **Z**.) **a–b. See margin.**

b. Writing Explain how to construct a line parallel to a given line through a point not on the line by using the Converse of the Alternate Interior Angles Theorem.

4. Line m was constructed perpendicular to ℓ through P by this method.
- Draw two points on ℓ and label them R and S.
- Construct a circle with center R and radius PR.
- Construct a circle with center S and radius PS.
- Draw line m through the intersections of the circles.

a. Critical Thinking Why is line m perpendicular to line ℓ? **See margin.**

b. Draw a line b and a point C not on b. Construct the perpendicular through C using this two-circle method. **Check students' work.** Their diagrams should look similar to the construction at the right.

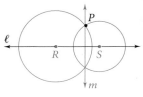

Exercise 5b Students may need a review of symmetry. Refer students to Lesson 3-5.

Exercise 6 Students show by construction that if two lines in a plane are perpendicular to the same line, they are parallel.

Exercises 7–15 Students use the constructions in this lesson to construct quadrilaterals and triangles. You may want to have students work in pairs on these exercises. Check that students do not skip steps in the constructions or try to draw instead of construct.

5. a. Technology In this computer drawing, R and Q are the intersections of $\odot P$ and line n, all three circles are congruent, and line m is determined by the intersection of $\odot Q$ and $\odot R$. Explain why line m must be perpendicular to line n.

b. Symmetry Describe the symmetries of this drawing.
a–b. See below right.

6. a. Draw a line t and a point P on t. Construct a line s through P so that $s \perp t$.

b. Draw a point R that is neither on t nor s. Construct a line q through R so that $q \perp s$.

c. Critical Thinking How are q and t related? Explain.
a–c. See margin.

For Exercises 7–16, use the segments at the right.
7–9. See margin.

7. Draw a line m. Construct a point C so that the distance from C to m is b. (*Hint:* Construct a perpendicular from a point on the line.)

8. Construct a trapezoid with bases of lengths a and b.

9. Construct an isosceles trapezoid with legs of length a.
10a. See margin.

10. a. Construct a quadrilateral with a pair of parallel sides of length c.

b. What type of quadrilateral does the figure appear to be?
parallelogram

11. a. Construct a triangle with side lengths a, b, and c. Label the triangle $\triangle ABC$, where A is opposite the side of length a, and so on.

b. Construct the altitude from C.   a–b. See back of book.

12. Construct a right triangle in which the length of a leg is a and the length of the hypotenuse is c.   12–13. Answers may vary. See back of book for samples.

13. Construct a right triangle with legs of lengths b and $\frac{1}{2}b$.
See back of book.

14. a. Construct an isosceles right triangle with legs of length b.

b. What is the length of the hypotenuse of this triangle? $b\sqrt{2}$

15. Construct a rectangle with base b and height c.   See back of book.

16. Locus Draw a segment of any length. Construct the locus of points in a plane a distance a from the segment.   See back of book for sample.

a

b

c

6a–b.

c. They are ∥; in a plane, 2 lines ⊥ to a 3rd are ∥.

7.

8.

9.

10a.

5a. Answers may vary. Sample: The points of intersection of $\odot Q$ and $\odot R$ are equidistant from the endpts. of $\overline{QR}$.

b. The drawing has m as its line of symmetry.

381

EXTENSION Exercise 17 Also ask students what is true of *m* and *k*. Have them justify their answer.

CRITICAL THINKING Exercise 18 Have students explain how to construct a 45° angle.

ALTERNATIVE ASSESSMENT Exercise 19 This exercise can help you assess students' understanding of constructions by having students perform each construction before they explain how it works.

Chapter Project **FIND OUT BY DESIGNING** Help students see that this problem differs from the Find Out By Investigating problem in Lesson 7-1 because in this activity, the cable does not have to follow the roads.

19a. ①-④: construct 2 ⊥ lines.
⑤: construct a rt. △ with a hypotenuse that is twice the length of a leg.

b. ①-③: construct an equilateral △.
④-⑥: construct the angle bisector.

c. ①-③: construct an equilateral △.
④-⑤: construct the ⊥ bisector of a side.

20a.

b.

Find Out by Designing

Answers may vary. Sample:

The most efficient design requires 110 mi of cable to link all 12 schools.

---

17. Paper Folding You can use paper folding to create a perpendicular to a given line through a given point. Fold the paper so the line overlaps itself and so the fold line contains the point.
  a. Draw a line *m* and a point *W* not on the line. Use paper folding to create the perpendicular through *W*. Label the fold line *k*.
  b. Use paper folding to create a line perpendicular to *k* through *W*. Label this fold line *p*.   **a–b. Check students' work.**
  c. What is true of *p* and *m*? **Justify** your answer.   17c. *p*‖*m*; in a plane, 2 lines ⊥ to 3rd are ‖.

18. Critical Thinking Jane was trying to construct a 45°-45°-90° triangle, but couldn't figure out how to construct a 45° angle. Lenesha told her that she didn't need to know how to construct a 45° angle in order to construct the triangle. What construction procedure do you think Lenesha had in mind? **Construct an isosceles rt. △.**

19. Three methods for constructing a 30°-60°-90° triangle are shown. The numbers indicate the order in which the arcs should be drawn. Explain why each method works. **a–c. See margin.**

a.   **b.**   **c.**

20a–b. See margin.
20. a. Open-ended Construct a rectangle whose length is twice its width.
  b. Construct a rectangle whose length is four times its width.
  c. Critical Thinking How could you construct a rectangle whose length is 1.5 times its width? (*Hint:* Use a ratio equivalent to 1.5 : 1.)
  Construct a rectangle with length 3 units and width 2 units.

Chapter Project **Find Out by Designing**

Design a network of fiber-optic cables to link the 12 schools labeled A–L in the diagram. Assume that a computer at each school can be programmed to route a signal from that school to any other school, even if the signal has to pass through other schools on the way. Assume also that a single cable can handle both incoming and outgoing signals—just as a two-lane road handles traffic in both directions. In your design, try to use the fewest miles of cable possible. The cables do not have to coincide with roads. When you've completed your design, compare it with those of your classmates. Describe the design that you recommend and explain your recommendation. **See margin.**

The distance from any school to an adjacent school is 10 mi.

382

COORDINATE GEOMETRY Exercise 24 Students will need to find the slope and then substitute into $y = mx + b$ to solve for b.

GETTING READY FOR LESSON 7-4 These exercises prepare students to draw objects in one- and two-point perspective.

Wrap Up

THE BIG IDEA Ask students: *Explain in your own words how to construct a line perpendicular to a given line through a point not on the line.*

RETEACHING ACTIVITY Students construct right triangles with given side lengths. (Reteaching worksheet 7-3)

In this Checkpoint, your students will assess their own progress in Lessons 7-1 through 7-3.

Exercises 1–9 Make sure that students state both the hypothesis and conclusion of each theorem and postulate. Check that they use the theorems, postulates, and their converses appropriately.

If a triangle can be drawn with sides of the given lengths, will the triangle be acute, right, or obtuse? Explain.

23. acute; $5^2 < 4^2 + 4^2$

21. 2, 3, 5   **22.** 3, 4, 6   **23.** 4, 5, 4

Cannot form a △; 2 + 3 = 5   22. obtuse; $6^2 > 3^2 + 4^2$

24. *Coordinate Geometry* Write the equation of a line through (5, −2) and (4, 3). $y = -5x + 23$

25. You may leave your answers to parts (a–c) in terms of π.
  a. A circle has radius 8 cm. Two radii of the circle form a 120° angle. What is the arc length of the intercepted arc? $\frac{16}{3}\pi$ cm
  b. What is the area of the entire circle? 64π cm²
  c. What is the area of the 120° sector? $\frac{64}{3}\pi$ cm²

Getting Ready for Lesson 7-4

Draw a prism with the given figure as a base.   26–28. See back of book for samples.

26.   **27.**   **28.**

State the theorem or postulate that justifies each statement.
1–8. See back of book.

1. $\angle 1 \cong \angle 3$ **2.** If $\angle 5 \cong \angle 9$, then $d \parallel e$.

3. $m\angle 1 + m\angle 2 = 180$ **4.** If $\angle 4 \cong \angle 7$, then $d \parallel e$.

5. $\angle 1 \cong \angle 4$ **6.** $\angle 7 \cong \angle 9$

7. If $\angle 3 \cong \angle 8$, then $d \parallel e$.   **8.** $\angle 4 \cong \angle 5$

9. If $m\angle 8 + m\angle 6 = 180$, then $d \parallel e$.
  If supplementary same-side int. $\angle$s, then lines are $\parallel$.

10. Draw a line m and a point D on m. Then construct a line n through D so that $n \perp m$.   See back of book for sample.

11. *Open-ended* Construct a trapezoid with a right angle and with one base twice the length of the other.   See back of book for sample.

12. *Standardized Test Prep* Which of the following statements is *not* always true if two parallel lines m and n are cut by transversal t?   C
  A. Corresponding angles are congruent.   **B.** Alternate interior angles are congruent.
  C. Exterior angles are congruent.   **D.** Four of the eight angles formed are congruent.
  E. Pairs of same-side interior angles are supplementary.

Reteaching 7-3

Practice 7-3

Practice 7-3
Mixed Exercises

Lesson Quiz

Lesson Quiz is also available in Transparencies.

For Exercises 1–3, refer to the diagram.

1. Construct a line parallel to n through Q.

2. Construct the perpendicular to n at T.   See back of book.

3. Construct the perpendicular to n from Q.   See back of book.

383

Math ToolboX

Students use geometry software to construct a regular prism with one- point perspective. Students draw objects in one- and two-point perspective in Lesson 7-4.

Using geometry software, students are able to view the prism from different positions by manipulating the point outside the prism. Students can also change the shape of the prism.

Construct

ERROR ALERT! Some students lacking proficiency in using the software may have trouble performing the constructions.
Remediation: Pair students with a strong understanding of the software with students less proficient in its use.

As students construct their prisms, suggest that they do not construct cubes. The results will not be as interesting.

Investigate

You may want to allow students to check the computer images of other students and compare them to their own.

ALTERNATIVE ASSESSMENT Allow students to construct their own prism, print several different views of it, and explain how they constructed the prism and created each view.

Materials and Manipulatives

• Geometry software

Math ToolboX — Technology

Perspective Drawing

Before Lesson 7-4

Work in pairs or small groups using geometry software to construct a rectangular prism in one-point perspective.

Construct

Construct a rectangle *ABCD* for the front of your prism. Start with $\overline{AB}$ and construct perpendiculars at *A* and *B*. Locate point *C* on the perpendicular through *B*. *D* is the intersection of the perpendicular through *C* with the perpendicular through *A*. Hide the lines and construct the segments for the rectangle.

Draw a point *E* outside the rectangle. Construct $\overleftrightarrow{EA}$, $\overleftrightarrow{EB}$, $\overleftrightarrow{EC}$, and $\overleftrightarrow{ED}$.

Now construct the rectangular back of the prism. Locate a point *G* on $\overline{EA}$ and construct a line through *G* parallel to $\overline{AB}$. Construct the intersection *H* of this line with $\overleftrightarrow{EB}$. Construct the line through *H* parallel to $\overline{BC}$. Continue with similar constructions to locate *J* and *K*. Hide all the lines and draw the sides of rectangle *GHJK*.

Complete the prism by drawing the remaining edges, $\overline{AG}$, $\overline{BH}$, $\overline{CJ}$, and $\overline{DK}$.
Check students' work.

Investigate

Manipulate point *E*. Explore how the position of *E* affects the appearance of the prism. Where is *E* when it seems that you are looking down on the prism and can see its left side? looking directly into the prism? looking up at the prism and can see its right side? **Above and to the left; inside *ABCD*; below and to the right.**

Manipulate points *G*, *C*, *B*, and *A* to change the shape of the prism.

Extend

Draw a house in one-point perspective. Pretend that you are in a helicopter in front of this house and you rise straight up into the sky. Use the software to print several "snapshots" of the house as you would see it from the helicopter. **Check students' work.**

384

lines that appear to meet or will meet if extended. Discuss why they appear that way.

THINK AND DISCUSS

(ESL) **KINESTHETIC LEARNING** Make sure students understand the term *perspective*. A visual example might help. Take students to one end of a football field. Choose two students of similar height. Have one student stand ten yards away and the other stand at the opposite end of the field. Students should observe that the student standing closer to them appears taller. Discuss why a perspective drawing would show the nearer student taller than the student farther away.

CONNECTING TO PRIOR KNOWLEDGE Have students look through magazines or catalogs to find examples of parallel

---

Connections 🌐 Technical Art . . . and more

7-4 Parallel Lines and Perspective Drawing

What You'll Learn
- Drawing objects in one- and two-point perspective

...And Why
To create realistic pictures of real-world objects such as buildings

What You'll Need
- ruler

THINK AND DISCUSS

Perspective drawing is a way of drawing objects on a flat surface so that they look the same as they appear to the eye.

Art Techniques for drawing objects in perspective were developed by the ancient Greeks and Romans, but were lost to the Western world until the beginning of the Renaissance in the early 1400s. Renaissance artists used the geometry of perspective to produce works that were far more lifelike and realistic than earlier works.

Before the Renaissance . . .

Artist unknown; English manuscript illumination (c. 1400) depicting Marco Polo setting out from Venice in 1271

The size of objects in pre-Renaissance art had more to do with their importance to the artist than to their positions in space.

After the Renaissance . . .

Jacopo Bellini, *The Palace of Herod*, 15th Century

Bellini's sketchbook contains some of the earliest examples of the application of the principles of perspective drawing.

1. Discussion Notice in the painting of Marco Polo's departure from Venice that the ships in the foreground are about the same size as the rowboat behind them. Find other examples of objects that are out of perspective in the painting.

   Sample: People in the rowboat are smaller than people right behind them.

Lesson Planning Options

Prerequisite Skills
- Drawing polygons

Assignment Options for Exercises On Your Own

Core 1–10, 12–16, 18–19
Extension 11, 17

Use Mixed Review to maintain skills.

Resources

📖 **Student Edition**
Extra Practice, p. 642
Glossary/Study Guide

🗄 **Teaching Resources**
Chapter Support File, Ch. 7
- Practice 7-4 (two worksheets)
- Reteaching 7-4
- Alternative Activity 7-4
Classroom Manager 7-4
Glossary, Spanish Resources

📽 **Transparencies**
79, 82, 83

385

Discuss the value of perspective drawings because it is impossible to draw a three-dimensional object in two dimensions and preserve all lengths, angle measures, and parallel lines.

MAKING CONNECTIONS Fernand Léger (1881–1955), a major figure in the development of cubism, also took an interest in many arts besides painting. He designed sets for ballets and motion pictures. He also worked with ceramics and designed stained glass windows and mosaics.

TACTILE LEARNING Demonstrate the steps for drawing a cube in one- and two-point perspective and have students model them at their desks. Some students may find drawing in perspective confusing but after practice, most will find it fun.

RESEARCH Students who show an interest in perspective drawing may want to do further research on vanishing points and the branch of mathematics called projective geometry.

EXTENSION Have students cut a square out of a piece of poster board. Have them shine a flashlight onto the square so the shadow falls on a flat surface. Ask students to describe the shape of the shadow as they change the position of the flashlight.

The work of some modern artists broke from a strict rendering of objects in perspective. The French artist Fernand Léger broke the rules of perspective in this painting in order to call attention to specific colors and shapes.

Léger's paintings during the 1930s made strong visual connections to mechanical objects. Even the people in his paintings tended to have a smooth, mechanical look.

Fernand Léger, *Mother and Child*, 1936

The key to perspective drawing is the use of vanishing points. A **vanishing point** is a point on the "horizon" of a picture where parallel lines "meet." Here is how to draw a cube in **one-point perspective.**

Step 1: Draw a square. Then draw a horizon line and a vanishing point on the line.

Step 2: Lightly draw segments from the vertices of the square to the vanishing point.

Step 3: Draw a square for the back of the cube. Each vertex should lie on a segment you drew in Step 2.

Step 4: Complete the figure by using dashes for hidden sides of the cube. Erase unneeded lines.

2. Try This Draw a shoe box in one-point perspective. See margin p. 388.

Two-point perspective involves the use of two vanishing points.

Step 1: Draw a vertical segment. Then draw a horizon line and two vanishing points on the line.

Step 2: Lightly draw segments from the endpoints of the segment to each vanishing point.

386

Make sure that students do not make any false assumptions when drawing in one- and two-point perspective. For example, they may assume that the vanishing point needs to be above the center of the square in one-point perspective or that the vertical segment must be on the perpendicular bisector of the segment between the two vanishing points in two-point perspective.

In order to draw a cube and not another prism, make sure that the two vertical lines students draw in Step 3 are equidistant from the original vertical segments.

ERROR ALERT! In Step 4 of drawing a cube in two-point perspective, students may not see that they are drawing segments from the endpoints of the segment to the "opposite" vanishing point. **Remediation:** When demonstrating these steps, perform each step in a different color and make sure to verbalize what you are doing.

Example Relating to the Real World ························

Make sure students understand that in part a, the lines converge to one vanishing point and in part b, the lines converge to two vanishing points.

Step 3: Draw two vertical segments between the segments of Step 2.

Step 4: Draw segments from the endpoints of the segments you drew in Step 3 to the vanishing points.

Step 5: Complete the figure by using dashes for hidden sides of the figure. Erase unneeded lines.

3. Try This Draw a shoe box in two-point perspective. See margin p. 388.

Example Relating to the Real World ·········

Technical Art Is the object drawn in one- or two-point perspective?

a.

b.

a.

One-point perspective

b.

Two-point perspective

Note: placed Who block below.

To decide whether to use two-point perspective or one-point perspective, you need to know the relationship between the objects you are drawing and you.

Who? Julie Dorsey, an Associate Professor of Architecture at the Massachusetts Institute of Technology, used principles of perspective to develop a computer program for the Metropolitan Opera in New York. The program enables designers to design stage sets and to simulate lighting effects on them.

One-Point Perspective

The faces of the buildings are parallel to you, so use one-point perspective.

Two-Point Perspective

None of the faces of the buildings are parallel to you, so use two-point perspective.

Technology Options

Prentice Hall Technology

Software
- Secondary Math Lab Toolkit™
- Computer Item Generator 7-4

Internet
- See the Prentice Hall site. (http://www.phschool.com)

387

MAKING CONNECTIONS Students interested in photography may enjoy the following project: Have students take pictures of parallel lines from different vantage points, bring in the developed prints, and describe the vanishing points on each.

Make sure that students in each group start with the same rectangle so that they draw the same "box."

CONNECTING TO STUDENTS' WORLD If you have block scheduling or an extended class period, have students make perspective drawings of a school hallway or the school's football field.

ALTERNATIVE ASSESSMENT Exercises 1–4 You can use these exercises to help you assess students' understanding of one- and two-point perspective by having them copy each figure and identify the vanishing points.

Exercises 5–6 Students may find it fun to enact these scenarios in their homes using similar objects.

pages 385–388 Think and Discuss

2.

3.

page 388 Work Together

5.

3	2	3
2	1	2
3	2	3

If the square shown is the front of the box, the number in each region is the number of sides of the box the "viewer" can see when the vanishing pt. is in that region.

pages 388–391 On Your Own

7.

8.

C

A
B

4. *Critical Thinking* Three artists set up easels around a historical building in Paris. Each artist plans to paint a realistic view of the building. Based on the positions of their easels, which type of perspective will each artist's painting show?
Artists A and C's paintings will show 1-pt. perspective; artist B's painting will show 2-pt. perspective.

Work in groups to explore how the placement of the vanishing point affects a drawing. Have each member of your group draw a box in one-point perspective. Vary the positions of the horizon lines and vanishing points within your group.

5. Where is the vanishing point when the "viewer" can see three sides of the box? two sides? one side?
See margin.

Is the object drawn in one- or two-point perspective?

1.

2-pt. perspective

2.

1-pt. perspective

3.

2-pt. perspective

4.

1-pt. perspective

Study each diagram at the left. Match each position in the diagram to what the viewer would see from that point.

5.

I. B

II. C

III. A

6.

I. B

II. C

III. A

Exercise 10 Students may want to review isometric and orthographic drawings in Lesson 2-7. Ask students which drawing the computer artist starts with.

CRITICAL THINKING Exercise 10 Discuss what happens to the objects' shadows when the lights coincide with the camera. *They disappear.*

CONNECTING TO STUDENTS' WORLD Exercise 11a Students may enjoy drawing the figures in Exercises 1–4 *not* in proper perspective.

RESEARCH Exercise 11b Students should be able to find information on cubism in any encyclopedia. Suggest that students also research the founders of cubism, Pablo Picasso and Georges Braque.

Copy each prism and locate the vanishing point(s). 7–8. See margin p. 388.

7.

8.

9.

See margin.

9.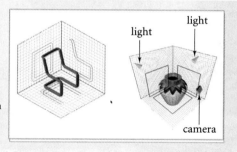

A Computer's Perspective

Ray Dream Designer™ is a software program that allows artists to create 3D objects and scenes. The artist starts by drawing top, front, and side views of an object. The program uses this information to assemble a 3D image of the object.

Each object the artist creates is then placed in a scene such as a room or a street. Finally, the artist positions a "camera" and "lights" within the scene. The computer automatically draws all the objects from the viewpoint of the camera.

light

light

camera

10. Describe the position of the camera for each of these views.

a. side   b. front   c. top

11. **a.** Refer to the cartoon to explain why an artist might purposefully paint a scene not in proper perspective.
   b. Research Find out about the Cubist movement in painting. What techniques did these artists use? What were they trying to communicate?
   a. See margin.
   b. Check students' work.

11a. **Answers may vary. Sample:** The artist is trying to show more than one view of an object, just as we might think of an object in more than one way.

12. Parts of the painting are in perspective, but the painting as a whole is not in perspective.

13. The painting is in perspective. The edges of the road converge to a vanishing point.

14. The students closer to the vanishing pt. appear to be taller.

15. The 4 non-horizontal lines appear to converge at the vanishing pt. So the upper horizontal line appears to be longer.

16. The middle 2 horizontal lines appear to bulge near the vanishing pt.

17. **Answers may vary. Sample:** ‖ lines converge to vanishing pts., but instead of converging along straight lines, they converge along curved paths. So the images look like they are projected onto the surface of a sphere.

Exercises 14–15 Challenge students to copy the figures and add lines to show that the segments are the same length and the students are the same height.

Exercise 16 Have students copy the diagram and connect the diagonal lines. Ask them how they can use the postulate and theorems in Lesson 7-2 to show the lines are parallel.

DIVERSITY Exercise 17 This exercise provides a good opportunity for the photographers in your class to share what they know about cameras. Discuss careers in photography.

Chapter Project **FIND OUT BY INVESTIGATING** Students should discover that a network is traceable if all the vertices are even or if exactly two are odd. Make sure students understand even and odd vertices and create enough networks to see this pattern.

18a. Sample: **b. Sample:**

c. In an isometric view, the lines that are ∥ in reality are ∥ in the drawing. In 1-pt. perspective view, only the lines that are ⊥ to the horizon remain ∥. All other lines meet at the vanishing pts.

page 391   Mixed Review

20a. If the acute angles of a △ are complementary, then the △ is a rt. △.

21a. If it is July 4, then it is a national holiday in the United States.

22a. If a figure is a ▱, then it is a rectangle.

Fine Art **Explain how each artist used or did not use perspective.** 12–13. See margin p. 389.

12. Stuart Davis, *New York/Paris No. 2*, 1931

Stuart Davis once wrote "I never ask the question 'Does this picture have depth or is it flat?' I consider such a question irrelevant."

13. Richard Estes, *Holland Hotel*, 1984

Richard Estes' paintings are so realistic that they are easily mistaken for photographs.

Optical Illusions **Explain how the concepts you learned in this lesson relate to each of these optical illusions.** 14–16. Answers may vary. See margin p. 389 for samples.

14.

The students appear to be different heights.

15.

The horizontal segments appear to be different lengths.

16.

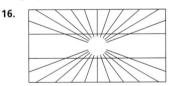

The horizontal lines appear to be curved.

17. *Photography* This photograph was taken with a type of lens called a *fish-eye lens.* Describe how this type of lens affects parallel lines and vanishing points. See margin p. 389.

18. a. Create an isometric drawing of a box.   a–c. See margin.
    b. Draw the same box in two-point perspective.
    c. *Writing* Compare how parallel lines appear in each drawing.

Exercises · MIXED REVIEW

Exercises 20–22 Have students give a counterexample for each false statement.

JOURNAL Have students share their responses with the class. Create a master list on the board of the disadvantages students describe.

GETTING READY FOR LESSON 7-5 These exercises prepare students to study some of the basic ideas of spherical geometry.

Wrap Up

THE BIG IDEA Ask students: *Describe how to draw a three-dimensional object with one- and two-point perspective.*

RETEACHING ACTIVITY Students draw prisms in one- and two-point perspective and identify vanishing points in their partner's drawings. (Reteaching worksheet 7-4)

19. *Open-ended* You can draw block letters in either one-point perspective or two-point perspective. Write your initials in block letters using one-point perspective and two-point perspective. **Check students' work.**

Chapter Project · Find Out by Investigating

Each of the points in the two networks at the right is a *vertex* of the network. An *odd vertex* is on an odd number of paths. *O* is an odd vertex. An *even vertex* is on an even number of paths. *E* is an even vertex.   **odd: 2, even: 2; odd: 4, even: 1**

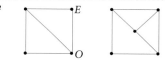

- How many odd and even vertices does each network have?
- Try to trace each network without lifting your pencil from your paper or retracing any path. (You may go over a vertex more than once.)   **The 1st network is traceable; the 2nd is not.**
- Make your own network, and then try to trace it. Record your results in a table like this one. Keep drawing and tracing networks until you see a pattern relating the number of odd and even vertices to whether the network is traceable.

Diagram of Network	Odd Vertices	Even Vertices	Traceable?
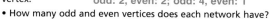	0	5	yes

A network with more than 2 odd vertices is not traceable.

Exercises · MIXED REVIEW

In Exercises 20–22: **(a)** Write the converse of each conditional. **(b)** Determine the truth value of the conditional and its converse. **20a, 21a, 22a. See margin p. 390.**

20. If a triangle is a right triangle, then its acute angles are complementary. **b. true; true**

21. If it is a national holiday in the United States, then it is July 4.
b. false; true

22. If a figure is a rectangle, then it is a parallelogram.
b. true; false

23. *Transformational Geometry* Describe the image of a circle with center $(4, -2)$ and radius 2 under a dilation with scale factor 3 centered at the origin. **a circle with center at $(12, -6)$ and radius 6**

FOR YOUR JOURNAL

Perspective drawings make drawings of three-dimensional objects look more realistic. However, perspective drawings have some disadvantages. Describe some of them.

Getting Ready for Lesson 7-5

Find the sum of the measures of the angles of each spherical triangle.

24. 212
 —32°

25. 270

26. 304
124°

Lesson Quiz

Lesson Quiz is also available in Transparencies.

1. Draw a prism in one-point perspective. **Answers may vary.**
Sample:

2. Draw a prism in two-point perspective. **Answers may vary.**
Sample:

391

PROBLEM OF THE DAY

A cube has edges of length 5 cm. If a fly lands on a vertex and then walks along the edges, what is the greatest distance the fly could walk before coming to a vertex a second time and without retracing an edge?

just under 40 cm

Problem of the Day is also available in Transparencies.

CONNECTING TO PRIOR KNOWLEDGE Using a globe, ask students to identify a radius, a diameter, and a great circle. Then have students identify the North Pole, the South Pole, the equator, lines of longitude, lines of latitude, and where they live.

WORK TOGETHER

Have students work in groups of four. Provide each with a globe, beach ball, basketball, or volleyball. If students are using a ball, have them mark points on the ball using stickers or tape. Remind them not to write on the balls or globes.

TACTILE LEARNING Students should discover that between two points that are opposite each other, there is no shortest path and between any two points not opposite each other, there is exactly one shortest path.

AUDITORY LEARNING Students can remember that latitude lines go sideways because latitude has the same root as the word lateral (e.g., a lateral pass), whereas the longitude lines run North to South because they are all "long."

Lesson Planning Options

Prerequisite Skills

- Identifying a radius, diameter, and great circle of a sphere

Assignment Options for Exercises On Your Own

Core 1–4, 6–19
Extension 5, 20

Use Mixed Review to maintain skills.

Resources

Student Edition
Extra Practice, p. 642
Glossary/Study Guide

Teaching Resources
Chapter Support File, Ch. 7
- Practice 7-5 (two worksheets)
- Reteaching 7-5
Classroom Manager 7-5
Glossary, Spanish Resources

Transparencies
80, 84

392

Connections 🌐 Navigation . . . and more

What You'll Learn
- Using some of the basic ideas of spherical geometry

...And Why
To better understand the properties of the sphere on which we live

What You'll Need
- globe, ball, or foam ball
- string
- protractor

7-5 Exploring Spherical Geometry

WORK TOGETHER

1. On a globe or ball, select two points that are opposite each other. That is, select two points that are endpoints of a diameter, such as the North and South poles on a globe. Find the shortest path between the points by holding a string taut between them. Is there one shortest path between the points? **no**

2. Now hold the string taut between two points that are not opposite one another. Is there one shortest path between the points? **yes**

3. Form a triangle on a globe or ball by taping string between three points. Use a protractor to estimate the measures of the three angles formed. Is the sum of the measures of the angles of a triangle on a sphere equal to 180? **no**

4. Now form larger triangles on the globe or ball and measure the three angles. Does the sum seem to depend on the size of the triangle? Explain. **yes; the larger the △, the greater the sum.**

THINK AND DISCUSS

On this map, it looks like the red segment parallel to the lines of latitude is the shortest path from San Francisco to Tokyo. But on the globe, the red string shows that the shortest path is actually quite different.

DIVERSITY Bernhard Riemann (1826–1866), a German mathematician, is credited with the development of spherical geometry. Have students research the contributions of other mathematicians from Germany, Russia, and Hungary in the nineteenth century. (See Exercise 20 for suggestions.)

ESL **VISUAL LEARNING** Students may have trouble understanding that *plane* and *line* can have different meanings in spherical geometry. This concept is especially difficult for ESL students who may have just learned what these terms mean in Euclidean geometry. You may want to make a poster displaying the diagram on page 393. Also have students copy the diagram into their notebooks along with the meanings of the terms.

Make sure students understand that the lines of longitude and the equator are not the only great circles. Make a model or draw a diagram to show other great circles.

As the travel routes indicate, geometry on a sphere is different from geometry on a plane. The geometry of flat planes, straight lines, and points is called **Euclidean geometry.** In **spherical geometry,** *point* has the same meaning as in Euclidean geometry, but *line* and *plane* do not. In spherical geometry, a "plane" is the surface of a sphere and a "line" is a great circle of a sphere. Recall that a great circle is the intersection of a sphere and a plane that contains the center of the sphere.

Great circle

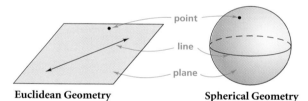

point

line

plane

Euclidean Geometry   **Spherical Geometry**

Navigation Lines of latitude and longitude are used to identify positions on Earth, much as *x*- and *y*-coordinates identify points on the coordinate plane. Which of these lines are great circles?

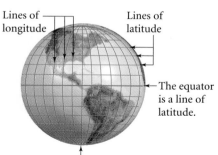

Lines of longitude

Lines of latitude

The equator is a line of latitude.

The lines of longitude all pass through the North and South Poles.

All the lines of longitude are great circles. The equator is the only line of latitude that is a great circle. All the other lines of latitude are circles smaller than a great circle.

Who? The physicist Albert Einstein (1879–1955) found that a non-Euclidean geometry was the best model for the paths of light rays over the huge distances of the universe.

You discovered in the Work Together that there are many shortest paths between any two points that are opposite each other on a sphere. You also discovered that there is only one shortest path between two points that are not opposite each other. Each of these shortest paths is an arc of a great circle.

Additional Example

FOR EXAMPLE ....

Identify the line of latitude and the line of longitude through your city or town. Which of these lines is a great circle? **the longitude line**

Discussion: *How many shortest paths are there from your city or town to Tokyo? to the North Pole?*

Approximate the point on the globe opposite your city or town. How many shortest paths are there between your city or town and this point? **many**

Discussion: *How do you find the shortest path between two points on a globe not opposite each other?*

393

Technology Options

Prentice Hall Technology

Software
- Secondary Math Lab Toolkit™
- Computer Item Generator 7-5

CD-ROM
- Multimedia Geometry Lab 7

Internet
- See the Prentice Hall site. (http://www.phschool.com)

5. **Try This** How many shortest paths are there between San Francisco and Tokyo? Explain your answer. **There is only 1 shortest path, because the pts. are not opp. each other.**

6. In Euclidean geometry, if two lines intersect, they intersect in exactly one point. Does this property hold in spherical geometry? **No; they always intersect at 2 pts.**

The study of parallel lines is an important part of Euclidean geometry. This study is based on the following postulate.

Postulate 7-3 Euclid's Parallel Postulate	Through a point not on a line, there is one and only one line parallel to the given line.

In spherical geometry, two lines (great circles) always intersect. Therefore, there are no parallel lines. The parallel postulate for spherical geometry is stated below.

Postulate 7-4 Spherical Geometry Parallel Postulate	Through a point not on a line, there is no line parallel to the given line.

 Who? Non–Euclidean geometry has been the focus of mathematician Linda G. Keen's work. She wrote her Ph.D. thesis on Riemann surfaces in 1964. She has returned to the subject in many subsequently published papers.

In the Work Together you found that the sum of the measures of the angles of a spherical triangle is greater than 180. Each of these spherical triangles has two right angles, so the sum of the measures of their angles exceeds 180 by the size of the vertex angle.

Comparison of Properties of Euclidean and Spherical Geometry

Property	Euclidean Geometry	Spherical Geometry
1. Given a line ℓ and a point P not on ℓ, there exists	one and only one line parallel to ℓ.	no line through P parallel to ℓ.
2. The sum of the measure of the angles of a triangle is	180.	greater than 180.
3. Two distinct lines intersect in	at most one point.	two points.
4. Through two given points, there is	one and only one line.	at least one line.
5. The shortest distance between two points is the length of	a segment.	an arc of a great circle.

394

The chart at the bottom of page 394 summarizes the differences between Euclidean geometry and spherical geometry presented in this lesson. Make sure students understand each property and can illustrate each with an example or counterexample.

CRITICAL THINKING Ask students to describe a pair of points through which exactly one line passes in spherical geometry.

Exercise 4 This problem illustrates that the Segment Addition Postulate in Euclidean geometry is not true in spherical geometry. The distance from Bergen to Montevideo in not the sum of the distances from Bergen to Melbourne and from Melbourne to Montevideo.

1–3. See margin for sample.

Draw a sketch to illustrate each property of spherical geometry.

1. There are pairs of points on a sphere through which more than one line can be drawn.

2. A triangle can have more than one right angle.

3. You can draw two equiangular triangles that each have different angle measures.

4. *Geography* Bergen, Norway; Melbourne, Australia; and Montevideo, Uruguay, are on the same great circle. The distance from Bergen to Melbourne is about 9990 miles and the distance from Melbourne to Montevideo is about 7370 miles. Use the fact that the circumference of Earth is about 24,900 miles to find the distance from Montevideo to Bergen. **7540 mi**

5. *Open-ended* Find three locations on a globe that are on a great circle and find the distances between them. **Check students' work.**

Draw a counterexample to show that the following properties of Euclidean geometry are not true in spherical geometry.
6–11. See margin for sample.

6. Through a point not on line ℓ, there exists one and only one line perpendicular to ℓ.

7. Two coplanar lines that are perpendicular to the same line do not intersect.

8. A triangle can have at most one obtuse angle.

9. If a triangle contains a right angle, then the other two angles in the triangle are complementary.

10. If two angles of one triangle are congruent to two angles of another triangle, then the third angles are congruent.

11. If *A, B,* and *C* are three points on a line, then exactly one of the points is between the other two.

Bergen, Norway

Montevideo, Uruguay   Melbourne, Australia

pages 395–397   On Your Own

1.   2.

3.   6.

7. See diagram for Exercise 6.

8. △*ABC* has 3 obtuse ∠s.

9. See diagram for Exercise 2.

10.   11.

∠*ADB* ≇ ∠*ADC*

395

Exercises 15–19 Students will need a globe, ball, or balloon to complete these exercises. Make sure students do not write on the globes or balls but use string and tape to make the figures.

 Chapter Project **FIND OUT BY MODELING** Students may want to make a two-dimensional network, like the one shown below, on which they can trace the path.

Exercises 21–23 Students may want to review Lesson 3-6 for properties of figures that tessellate.

PORTFOLIO Share with students the criteria you will use to assess their work in portfolios, as well as how you plan to use the results. Students should understand how the rubrics assess their work, how each piece in the portfolio counts, and how the scores they get in their portfolios will affect their overall evaluation.

14a. Euclid's Parallel Postulate

b. alt. int. ∠s are ≅

c. Angle Addition Postulate

d. $m\angle A + m\angle B + m\angle 2 = 180$

page 397 **Mixed Review**

21.

23.

12. *Writing* This figure seems to show parallel lines on a sphere. Explain why they are not parallel lines. **At least 1 of the 2 curves is not a great circle, so it is not a line.**

13. *Critical Thinking* Does the concept of a *ray* have any meaning in spherical geometry? Explain. **See right.**

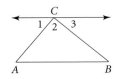

13. No; any "ray" would end up circling back on itself and would therefore be a line.

14. A well-known proof of the Triangle Angle-Sum Theorem is based on the concepts you studied in this chapter. Complete the proof. **See margin.**

> **Given:** △ABC
> **Prove:** $m\angle A + m\angle B + m\angle 2 = 180$
>
> By **a.** __?__ , there is exactly one line through C parallel to $\overleftrightarrow{AB}$. If two parallel lines are cut by a transversal, then **b.** __?__ , so $m\angle A = m\angle 1$ and $m\angle B = m\angle 3$. By **c.** __?__ , $m\angle 1 + m\angle 2 + m\angle 3 = 180$. By Substitution, **d.** __?__ = 180.

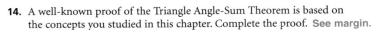

The following statements are true in Euclidean geometry. Make figures on a globe, ball, or balloon to help you decide which statements are false in spherical geometry.

15. Vertical angles are congruent. **true**

16. An equilateral triangle is equiangular. **true**

17. The base angles of an isosceles triangle are congruent. **true**

18. Through a point on a line ℓ there exists one and only one line perpendicular to ℓ. **true**

19. The measure of an exterior angle of a triangle equals the sum of the measures of its two remote interior angles. **false**

20. In the 19th century, the Russian mathematician Nickolai Lobachevsky (1793–1856) and the Hungarian mathematician Janos Bolyai (1802–1860) independently developed a geometry that kept all of Euclid's postulates except his parallel postulate. They assumed that, in a plane, more than one parallel can be drawn to a given line through a given point. This geometry can be modeled on a saddle-shaped surface. Lines a and b are two lines through X that do not intersect c. So, they are parallel to c. Consider a triangle drawn on such a surface. Is the sum of the measures of the angles of this triangle less than, equal to, or greater than 180? **< 180**

Chapter Project *Find Out by Modeling*

A snail lives in a cubical glass terrarium with edges 1 ft long. How far does the snail have to go to visit all eight vertices of the cube? How far does it have to go to travel along all twelve edges of the cube? **7 ft; 15 ft**

396

Wrap Up

THE BIG IDEA Ask students: *Explain the meanings of line and plane in spherical geometry. Then give two examples of properties in Euclidean geometry that are not true in spherical geometry.*

RETEACHING ACTIVITY Students investigate angles in spherical geometry using a globe or ball. (Reteaching worksheet 7-5)

A Point in Time

If you have block scheduling or an extended class period you may wish to have students investigate these topics:

- Create your own map. Then determine the minimum number of colors needed to color it so that no two regions sharing a boundary are the same color.

- Research how mathematicians determine if two, three, or four colors are needed to color a map. (Actually, mathematicians are still trying to determine an efficient method for determining which maps only require three colors and which maps require four colors.)

Exercises   MIXED REVIEW

Does each figure tessellate? If so, create a tessellation with it. 21, 23. See margin p. 396 for tessellation.

21.

22.

23. 150° 60° 150°

yes   no   yes

Algebra Find the *slope of a line* that is perpendicular to the line with the given equation.

24. $y = -3x - 4$ $\frac{1}{3}$

25. $y = \frac{3}{2}x + 6$ $-\frac{2}{3}$

26. $2x - y = 7$ $-\frac{1}{2}$

27. $6x + 2y = -3$ $\frac{1}{3}$

28. The altitude to the hypotenuse of an isosceles right triangle has length 5 cm. What is the area of the triangle? **25 cm²**

29. The measures of two complementary angles are in the ratio of 2 to 3. Find their measures. **36, 54**

30. *Standardized Test Prep* A point (x, y) is reflected in a line parallel to the y-axis. Which point could be its reflection image? **B**
  A. $(2x, 2y)$ **B.** $(-2x, y)$ **C.** $(x, 2y)$ **D.** $(x, -2y)$ **E.** $(2x, -y)$

SELF ASSESSMENT

PORTFOLIO

For your portfolio, select one or two items from your work for this chapter. Here are some possibilities:
- corrected work
- most-improved work
- drawings or models you have made

Explain why you have included each selection.

A Point in Time

1500   1600   1700   1800   1900   2000

Computer Proofs

Regions that border one another on a map are shaded different colors so that you can tell them apart. Suppose that you wanted to color the regions of a map and, in doing so, use the least number of colors possible. How many would you need? As it turns out, the answer is four. Mathematicians had known this for years, but were unable to *prove* that the minimum number was four.

Then in 1976, mathematicians Kenneth Appel and Wolfgang Haken found that all maps could be divided into 1936 categories. Using 1000 hours of computer time, they analyzed every category and proved that each could be shaded with four colors. Appel and Haken have shown the value of a computer for proving enormously complex theorems.

Name_____ Class_____ Date_____
Reteaching 7-5

Name_____ Class_____ Date_____
Practice 7-5

Name_____ Class_____ Date_____
Practice 7-5
Mixed Exercises

1. How many points of intersection do two great circles have? Draw an example on sphere D.

2. What is the minimum number of points of intersection of three great circles? Draw an example on sphere E.

3. What is the maximum number of points of intersection three great circles? Draw an example on sphere F.

Draw counter examples on the spheres to show that the following properties of Euclidean geometry are not true in spherical geometry.

4. A triangle can have at most one right angle.

5. A line can intersect another in at most one point.

6. An equiangular triangle has angles that measure 60°.

7. Two lines perpendicular to a third line will never intersect.

Lesson Quiz

Lesson Quiz is also available in Transparencies.

Decide whether the following statements are true or false in spherical geometry.

1. A triangle can have more than one obtuse angle. true

2. The measures of the angles of an equiangular triangle must be 60°. false

3. If two lines are perpendicular to a third line, then they are parallel. false

4. Two lines can intersect in more than one point. true

397

Finishing the Chapter Project

PROJECT DAY You may wish to plan a project day during which students share their completed projects. Encourage groups to explain their processes as well as their products.

PROJECT NOTEBOOK Have students review their project work and bring their notebooks up to date.

- Have students share their projects within groups. Ask each group to choose the network most likely to be adopted by the school.

- Have each group present for class selection the network most likely to be adopted by the school.

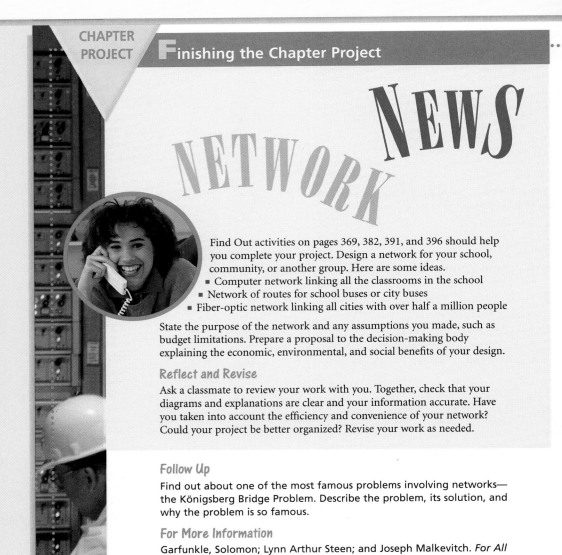

CHAPTER PROJECT

Finishing the Chapter Project

NETWORK NEWS

Find Out activities on pages 369, 382, 391, and 396 should help you complete your project. Design a network for your school, community, or another group. Here are some ideas.

- Computer network linking all the classrooms in the school
- Network of routes for school buses or city buses
- Fiber-optic network linking all cities with over half a million people

State the purpose of the network and any assumptions you made, such as budget limitations. Prepare a proposal to the decision-making body explaining the economic, environmental, and social benefits of your design.

Reflect and Revise

Ask a classmate to review your work with you. Together, check that your diagrams and explanations are clear and your information accurate. Have you taken into account the efficiency and convenience of your network? Could your project be better organized? Revise your work as needed.

Follow Up

Find out about one of the most famous problems involving networks—the Königsberg Bridge Problem. Describe the problem, its solution, and why the problem is so famous.

For More Information

Garfunkle, Solomon; Lynn Arthur Steen; and Joseph Malkevitch. *For All Practical Purposes: Introduction to Contemporary Mathematics.* New York: W. H. Freeman, 1988.

Jacobs, Harold R. *Mathematics, A Human Endeavor.* New York: W. H. Freeman, 1982.

RouteSmart Street Routing Software. Mineola, New York: Bowne Distinct, 1995.

398

HOW AM I DOING? Have students work in small groups. Ask each group to make a short presentation explaining three important ideas from this chapter. Each presentation must include a visual aid and a sample problem.

KEY TERMS The numbers in parentheses direct students to the pages where the terms are used or defined. Students should be able to (1) write a simple explanation of each term, (2) illustrate the term with a diagram, or (3) show an example that uses the term.

Exercises 1–3 Students will need to use the theorems and postulate from Lesson 7-1 along with what they know about supplementary and vertical angles.

STANDARDIZED TEST TIP Exercise 6 Make sure that students do not confuse *complementary* and *supplementary*.

---

7 Wrap Up

Key Terms

alternate interior angles (p. 363)
corresponding angles (p. 363)
Euclidean geometry (p. 393)
flow proof (p. 372)
one-point perspective (p. 386)
perspective drawing (p. 385)
same-side interior angles (p. 363)
spherical geometry (p. 393)
transversal (p. 363)
two-point perspective (p. 386)
vanishing point (p. 386)

How am I doing?

- State three ideas from this chapter that you think are important. Explain your choices.
- Describe how you can determine if lines are parallel.

Parallel Lines and Related Angles   7-1

A **transversal** is a line that intersects two coplanar lines at two distinct points. Line *t* is a transversal of lines ℓ and *m*. ∠1 and ∠4 are **corresponding angles.** ∠3 and ∠4 are **alternate interior angles.** ∠2 and ∠4 are **same-side interior angles.**

If two parallel lines are cut by a transversal, then the following are true.

- Corresponding angles are congruent.
- Alternate interior angles are congruent.
- Same-side interior angles are supplementary.

Find *m*∠1 and then *m*∠2. State the theorem or postulate that justifies your answer.   1–3. See margin for sample justifications.

1.
120, 120

2.
75, 105

3.
55, 90

4. *Writing* Which angles of a parallelogram must be supplementary? Explain your answer. See margin.

5. *Open-ended* Describe two corresponding angles formed by lines in your classroom. Check students' work.

6. *Standardized Test Prep* If two parallel lines are cut by a transversal, which angles could be complementary? C

I. alternate interior angles   II. same-side interior angles   III. corresponding angles

A. I only   B. II only   C. I and III only   D. II and III only   E. I, II, and III

Resources

Student Edition
Extra Practice, p. 642
Glossary/Study Guide

Teaching Resources
Study Skills Handbook
Glossary, Spanish Resources

Wrap Up   pages 399–401

1. If ∥ lines, then corres. ∠s are ≅; vertical ∠s are ≅.

2. If ∥ lines, then same-side int. ∠s are supplementary; if ∥ lines, then alt. int. ∠s are ≅.

3. If ∥ lines, then same-side int. ∠s are supplementary; if ∥ lines, then alt. int. ∠s are ≅.

4. Consecutive angles; opp. sides are ∥, so same-side interior angles are supplementary.

399

ALGEBRA Exercises 7–9 Students can check their solutions by substituting the value of *x* into each expression and finding the measure of each angle.

ERROR ALERT! **Exercise 10** Some students may try to construct the parallelogram so that the opposite sides have lengths *a* and *b*. **Remediation:** Remind students that the opposite sides of parallelograms are congruent so *a* and *b* must be lengths of adjacent sides.

10.

11a.

Proving Lines Parallel

7-2

Two lines cut by a transversal are parallel if any of the following are true.

- Corresponding angles are congruent.
- Alternate interior angles are congruent.
- Same-side interior angles are supplementary.

A **flow proof** uses arrows to show the logical connections between the statements. Reasons are written below the statements.

Algebra **Determine the value of *x* for which $\ell \parallel m$.**

7.

20

8.

20

9.

24

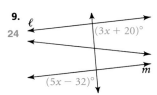

Constructing Parallel and Perpendicular Lines

7-3

You can construct a line parallel to a given line through a given point not on the line. You can also construct the perpendicular to a given line through a given point on the line or through a given point not on the line.

Use the segments at the right.

10. Construct a parallelogram with side lengths *a* and *b*. See margin.

11. a. Construct a right triangle with a leg of length *b* and a hypotenuse with length 2*b*. See margin.

   b. What is the length of the other leg? $b\sqrt{3}$

   c. *Critical Thinking* Find the measure of each angle. 30, 60, 90

Parallel Lines and Perspective Drawing

7-4

You can use **perspective drawing** to draw three-dimensional objects on a flat surface so that they look the same as they appear to the eye. Perspective drawing involves the use of vanishing points. A **vanishing point** is a point on the "horizon" of the drawing where parallel lines "meet." When there is one vanishing point, the drawing is in **one-point perspective**. When the drawing has two vanishing points, it is in **two-point perspective**.

one-point perspective

two-point perspective

400

ALTERNATIVE ASSESSMENT **Exercises 12–14** Another way you can assess students' understanding of perspective drawing is by asking them to draw an object in one- and two-point perspective.

Remind students that the new mathematical terms in this chapter are defined in the Glossary/Study Guide in the back of the book.

Getting Ready for Chapter 8

Students may work these exercises independently or in small groups. The skills previewed will help prepare students to prove triangles congruent.

Copy each figure and locate the vanishing point(s). 12–14. See margin.

12.

13.

14.

Exploring Spherical Geometry   7-5

The geometry of points, straight lines, and flat planes is **Euclidean geometry.** Geometry on a sphere is **spherical geometry.** In spherical geometry, "point" has the same meaning as in Euclidean geometry, but a "line" is a great circle of the sphere, and a "plane" is the surface of the sphere.

Great circle

Some statements that are true in Euclidean geometry are not true in spherical geometry. For example, in Euclidean geometry, there is one and only one line parallel to a given line through a given point not on the line. This is Euclid's Parallel Postulate. In spherical geometry, there is no line parallel to a given line through a point not on the line.

Draw a counterexample to show that the following properties of Euclidean geometry are not true in spherical geometry. 15–18. See margin for samples.

15. An equiangular triangle cannot have a right angle. **16.** Perpendicular lines intersect at one point.

17. A right triangle has two acute angles. **18.** Two points determine a line.

Getting Ready for... ▶ CHAPTER 8

Find the value of each variable.

19. $x = 60$; $y = 30$

20. $x = 9$; $y = 9\sqrt{2}$; $z = 45$

21. $y = 4$; $z = 2\sqrt{3}$

Given that $\triangle ABC \cong \triangle DEF$, **find the value of each variable.** $w = 88$; $x = 7$; $y = 52$; $z = 40$

22. $x = 8$; $y = 55$

23. $x = 35$; $y = 10$; $z = 10$

24.

12.

13.

14.

15.   **16.**

17. See diagram for Exercise 15.

18.

401

Assessment

ENHANCED MULTIPLE CHOICE QUESTIONS are more complex than traditional multiple choice questions, which assess only one skill. Enhanced multiple choice questions assess the processes that students use, as well as the end results. The questions are written so that students use more than one strategy to solve the problem. Using multiple strategies is encouraged by the National Council of Teachers of Mathematics (NCTM). **Exercise 5** is an enhanced multiple choice question.

FREE RESPONSE QUESTIONS do not give answer choices. Some exercises have more than one possible answer. Students need to give only one correct response. **Exercises 1–4, 6–15, and 17–18** are free response questions.

WRITING EXERCISES allow students to describe how they think about and understand the concepts they have learned. **Exercise 19** is a writing exercise.

OPEN-ENDED PROBLEMS allow for more than one solution. Students must construct their own responses instead of choosing from possible answers. The students' responses will help you determine the depth of their understanding and any possible areas of difficulty. **Exercise 16** is an open-ended problem.

Resources

Teaching Resources

Chapter Support File, Ch. 7
• Chapter Assessment, Forms A and B
• Alternative Assessment
Chapter Assessment, Spanish Resources

Teacher's Edition

See also p. 360E for assessment options

Software

Computer Item Generator

Assessment   page 402

1. If ∥ lines, then corres. ∠s are ≅; if ∥ lines, then alt. int. ∠s are ≅.

2. If ∥ lines, then alt. int. ∠s are ≅; if ∥ lines, then same-side int. ∠s are supplementary.

3. If ∥ lines, then corres. ∠s are ≅; if ∥ lines, then same-side int. ∠s are supplementary.

4. If ∥ lines, then corres. ∠s are ≅; if ∥ lines, then same-side int. ∠s are supplementary.

10.

11.

402

7 Assessment

1–4. See margin for sample justifications.
Find $m\angle 1$, and then $m\angle 2$. State the theorems or postulates that justify your answers.

1.

65, 65

2.   85°

85, 110

3.   85°

85, 95

4.   70°

70, 110

5. **Standardized Test Prep** Two lines are parallel. What could be the measures of two of their same-side interior angles? **D**

  I. 40 and 140   **II.** 90 and 90
  III. 60 and 60   **IV.** 27 and 27

  A. I only   **B.** II only   **C.** II and III
  D. I and II   **E.** I, II, and III

Algebra **Determine the value of x for which $\ell \parallel m$.**

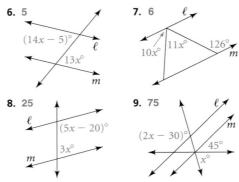

6. 5   7. 6

8. 25   9. 75

10. Draw a line m and a point T on the line. Construct a line through T perpendicular to m.
  See margin for sample.

11. Draw an angle $\angle ABC$. Then construct line m through C so that $m \parallel \overleftrightarrow{BA}$. Construct D on m so that $ABCD$ is a parallelogram.
  See margin for sample.

12. Construct a rectangle.
  See back of book for sample.

Is each object drawn in one- or two-point perspective?

13.

2-pt. perspective

14.

1-pt. perspective

15.

2-pt. perspective

16. **Open-ended** Sketch a three-dimensional object in one-point perspective.
  See back of book for sample.

Draw a counterexample to show that the following properties of Euclidean geometry are not true in spherical geometry.

17. The measures of the angles of an equiangular triangle are 60.

18. Through any two points, there is only one line.

19. **Writing** Describe how the meanings of *point*, *line*, and *plane* differ in spherical geometry and Euclidean geometry. Include a sketch.
  17–19. See back of book for samples.

Preparing for Standardized Tests

Standardized tests, such as those administered for state assessment, the SAT, or the ACT, include regular math questions, quantitative comparison questions, open-ended problems, and free response questions (which the SAT calls *grid-ins*).

MULTIPLE CHOICE QUESTIONS are followed by five answer choices, one of which is correct. **Exercises 1–6** are multiple choice questions.

QUANTITATIVE COMPARISON QUESTIONS ask students to compare two quantities. **Exercises 7–9** are quantitative comparison questions.

FREE RESPONSE QUESTIONS do not give answer choices. Students must provide one correct answer on their own. **Exercise 10** is a free response question.

OPEN-ENDED PROBLEMS allow for more than one solution. Students must construct their own responses instead of choosing a single answer. The responses students give will help you determine the depth of their understanding and what difficulties, if any, they are experiencing. **Exercise 11** is an open-ended problem.

STANDARDIZED TEST TIP Exercise 6 In order to solve this problem, students will need to remember that an altitude of an isosceles triangle cuts the triangle into two 30°-60°-90° triangles.

For Exercises 1–9, choose the correct letter.

1. What is the surface area of a sphere with radius 7 cm? **C**

  A. $\frac{196}{3}\pi$ cm^2 **B.** 49π cm^2 **C.** 196π cm^2

  D. 14π cm^2 **E.** $\frac{1372}{3}\pi$ cm^2

2. Two of the angles of a triangle on a sphere are right angles. What could be the measure of the third angle? **E**

  I. 45   **II.** 90   **III.** 135   **IV.** 180

  A. I and II   **B.** II and III   **C.** III and IV
  D. I and IV   **E.** I, II, and III

3. Which drawing is in two-point perspective? **D**

  A.   **B.**

  C.   **D.**

  E. none of the above

4. Which can you use to prove two lines parallel? **B**
  A. supplementary corresponding angles
  B. congruent alternate interior angles
  C. congruent vertical angles
  D. congruent same-side interior angles
  E. none of the above

5. What kind of symmetry does the figure have? **C**
  A. 60° rotational symmetry
  B. 90° rotational symmetry
  C. line symmetry
  D. point symmetry
  E. all of the above

6. One leg of an isosceles right triangle is 3 in. long. What is the length of the hypotenuse? **B**

  A. 3 in.   **B.** $3\sqrt{2}$ in.   **C.** $3\sqrt{3}$ in.
  D. 6 in.   **E.** none of the above

Compare the boxed quantity in Column A with the boxed quantity in Column B. Choose the best answer.
  A. The quantity in Column A is greater.
  B. The quantity in Column B is greater.
  C. The two quantities are equal.
  D. The relationship cannot be determined on the basis of the information supplied.

	Column A	Column B
7. **B**	the sum of the measures of the angles of a triangle in Euclidean geometry	the sum of the measures of the angles of a triangle in spherical geometry
8. **A**	the volume of a cone with radius 8 in. and height 9 in.	the volume of a cylinder with radius 3 in. and height 6 in.
9. **B**	the number of pairs of corresponding angles formed by two parallel lines and a transversal	the number of pairs of alternate interior angles formed by three parallel lines and a transversal

Find each answer. 10–11. See back of book.

10. A cone has the same radius and height as a cylinder. How are their volumes related?

11. *Writing* Describe two ways in which a triangle on a sphere differs from a triangle in a plane.

Resources

Teaching Resources
Chapter Support File, Ch. 7
• Standardized Test Practice
• Cumulative Review

Teacher's Edition
See also p. 360E for assessment options.

403

To accommodate flexible scheduling, some lessons are divided into parts. Assignment Options are given in the Lesson Planning Options for each lesson.

PACING OPTIONS

This chart suggests pacing only for the core lessons and their parts, and it is provided merely as a possible guide. It will help you determine how much time you have in your schedule to cover other features, such as the Chapter Project, Math Toolboxes, Wrap Up, and Assessment.

	1 Class Period	1 Class Period	1 Class Period	1 Class Period	1 Class Period	1 Class Period	1 Class Period	1 Class Period	1 Class Period
Traditional (40–45 min class periods)	8-1 **1**	8-1 **2**	8-2 **1**	8-2 **2**	8-3	8-4 **1**	8-4 **2**	8-5 **1**	8-5 **2**
Block Scheduling (90 min class periods)	8-1 **1** **2**	8-2 **1** **2**	8-3	8-4 **1** **2**	8-5 **1** **2**				

What Students Will Learn and Why

In this chapter, students build on their knowledge of triangles, learned in Chapters 2 and 4. They learn to prove two triangles congruent by the SSS Postulate, SAS Postulate, ASA Postulate, AAS Theorem, and HL Theorem. Students also learn to use triangle congruence and CPCTC to prove that parts of two triangles are congruent. Finally, students learn to identify congruent overlapping triangles and to prove two triangles congruent by first proving two other triangles congruent. Students apply these concepts to indirect measurement and learn how the concepts are applied in engineering and construction.

Discussing the Chapter/Building on Experience

The concept map below relates chapter topics to real-world applications. You and your class may wish to add to the map or develop maps of your own. The center oval describes the topic of the chapter. The next level displays topics within the lessons. The outer ovals reflect applications of the content. As you and your class build a concept map, invite students to discuss applications with which they are familiar.

Interactive Questioning Tips

A question is interactive when there is "give and take" between the questioner (teacher or student) and the respondent. In Think and Discuss or when a critical thinking question is asked, try to adjust for the varying ability levels among students by asking questions that are appropriately challenging to the individual. This practice gives all students a chance to succeed and increases the level of participation. In Lesson 8-2, Question 6, students are asked to explain how to use the ASA Postulate. Expect gradations in students' answers.

Skills Practice

Every lesson provides skill practice with Try This exercises, Exercises On Your Own, and Exercises Mixed Review. The

Student Edition includes Checkpoints (p. 425) and Cumulative Review (p. 445). In the Teacher's Edition, the Lesson Planning Options section for each lesson lists Prerequisite Skills students should know for that lesson. At the back of the Student Edition is the Skills Handbook—mini-lessons on math your students may need to review. The Chapter Support File for Chapter 7 in the Teaching Resources box includes two Practice worksheets per lesson, a worksheet for two Checkpoints, and worksheets for Cumulative Review and Standardized Test Preparation.

Diverse Learning and Teaching Styles

In your Teacher's Edition, you will find suggestions as to how you can help students complete mathematical tasks in Chapter 8 by reinforcing various learning styles. Here are some examples.

- **Visual learning** trace triangles and mark congruent sides (p. 407), copy figures and mark congruent sides and angles to help differentiate between ASA and AAS (p. 416), use tracing paper to redraw separately overlapping triangles in a complex figure to help visualize discrete triangles (p. 433)

- **Tactile learning** cut out triangles and place them on top of each other so the right angles match up (p. 420), draw the quadrilateral with sides as marked in the figure and justify their answers by measuring the angles with a protractor (p. 429)

- **Kinesthetic learning** use congruent triangles to measure indirectly across a football field, parking lot, or road, and then compare those results with the actual measurement (p. 427)

Alternative Activity for Lesson 8-1

for use with the Work Together and Think and Discuss, uses geometry software to explore the SAS Postulate.

Alternative Activity for Lesson 8-2

for use with the Work Together and Think and Discuss, uses geometry software to explore the ASA postulate.

Alternative Activity for Lesson 8-3

for use with the Work Together and Think and Discuss, uses geometry software to explore the HL Theorem.

Cooperative Learning Tips

When used effectively, cooperative learning can help students develop interpersonal skills, learn to perform specific roles in a group, and learn to carry out specific responsibilities. The components of Chapter 8 provide a range of cooperative learning opportunities.

- In the Student Edition, the **Work Together** parts of lessons are specifically designed for cooperative learning activities.

- In the Teacher's Edition, you will find helpful hints for addressing diverse learning styles (see page C for Chapter 8). For every lesson, you will find a **Reteaching Activity**, which may involve cooperative learning.

Materials and Manipulatives

The authors expect all students to use scientific calculators. Calculator use is integrated throughout the course.

- compass (8-1, 8-2, 8-3)
- colored pencils or pens (8-5)
- protractor (8-1, 8-3)
- ruler (8-1, 8-3)
- scissors (8-1, 8-2)
- straightedge (8-1, 8-2)
- straws (8-1)
- tracing paper (8-5)

TECHNOLOGY OPTIONS

Technology Tools		Chapter Project	8-1	8-2	8-3	8-4	8-5
Calculator		Assumed that students have scientific calculators at any time.					
Software	Secondary Math Lab Toolkit™		✔	✔	✔	✔	✔
	Integrated Math Lab		✔	✔			
	Computer Item Generator		✔	✔	✔	✔	✔
	Student Edition		✔ᵀ				
Video	Video Field Trip	✔					
CD-ROM	Multimedia Geometry Lab		✔	✔	✔		✔
Internet		See the Prentice Hall site. (http://www.phschool.com)					

✔ᵀ indicates Math Toolbox.

The Prentice Hall Geometry program offers you a rich variety of technology options. Be assured that all these options are provided as a means of enriching the program and are not essential for the successful completion of the course.

Assessment Options

The Prentice Hall Geometry Program provides you with many options. From these options, you may choose instructional materials and techniques appropriate for your students, or those necessary to meet your district's curriculum requirements. As the chart indicates, the program also supports your teaching efforts by offering you many choices for assessment.

ASSESSMENT OPTIONS

Assessment Support Materials	Chapter Project	8-1	8-2	8-3	8-4	8-5	Chapter End
Chapter Project	▲ ■ ●	▲ ■		▲ ■	▲ ■		▲ ■
Checkpoints				▲ ■ ●			
Self-Assessment		▲ ■	▲ ■			▲ ■	▲ ■
Writing Assignment		▲ ■	▲ ■	▲ ●		▲	●
Chapter Assessment							▲ ■ ●
Alternative Assessment		■	■	■	■	■	■ ●
Cumulative Review							▲ ■ ●
Standardized Test Prep			▲ ■	▲ ■		▲ ■	▲ ■ ●
Computer Item Generator	Can be used to create custom-made practice or assessment at any time.						

▲ = Student Edition ■ = Teacher's Edition ● = Teaching Resources

Checkpoints

Alternative Assessment

Chapter Assessment

Available in both Form A and Form B

Making the Right Connections

Mathematics is imbedded in nearly every walk of life. The National Council of Teachers of Mathematics (NCTM) encourages educators to recognize these connections and to emphasize them for the purpose of better educating students for success in life and in a global economy. The **Connections** chart below highlights these connections for Chapter 8.

CONNECTIONS

Lesson	Interdisciplinary Connections	Career Prep	Other Real World Connections	Math Integration	NCTM Standards
Chapter Project	Home Economics Engineering	Construction	Bridges Quilts		Connections Communication
8-1		Construction	Bridges Cartoons		Communication Problem Solving Reasoning
8-2	History	Die Making	Lacrosse Nets Crystals	Geometry in 3 Dimensions Probability	Communication Problem Solving Reasoning
8-3	History Science	Clock Repair Landscape Architecture	Tents	Geometry in 3 Dimensions Coordinate Geometry	Communication Problem Solving Reasoning
8-4	History		Sinkholes	Data Analysis	Communication Problem Solving Reasoning
8-5	Home Economics	Engineering	Clothing Design	Coordinate Geometry	Communication Problem Solving Reasoning

CONNECTING TO PRIOR LEARNING Have students review the quilt designs they made for the Chapter 5 project. Have them identify figures, especially triangles, that appear congruent. Ask students why they think the figures are congruent.

CULTURAL CONNECTIONS The first bridges were made from tree trunks or large stones thrown across streams, or from twisted bamboo shoots or creepers hung across streams. Today in Japan the Akashi-Kaikyo Bridge, connecting Kobe on the mainland with Awaji on Awaji Island, measures 3910 meters in length with a center span of 1990 meters.

INTERDISCIPLINARY CONNECTIONS The development of the suspension bridge allowed large bodies of water to be spanned. The brooklyn Bridge, designed by John A. Roebling in 1869 and completed in 1883, was the first steel-wired suspension bridge. Ask interested students to present a verbal/visual report on the importance of the arch in bridge constructions: concrete arch, steel arch, continuous truss, simple truss, suspension, longspan cantilever.

ABOUT THE PROJECT Students explore how engineers use triangles to construct safe, strong, stable structures. Then they

Technology Options

Prentice Hall Technology

Video
Video Field Trip 8, "Dome on the Range," a look at the work of a geometric dome designer

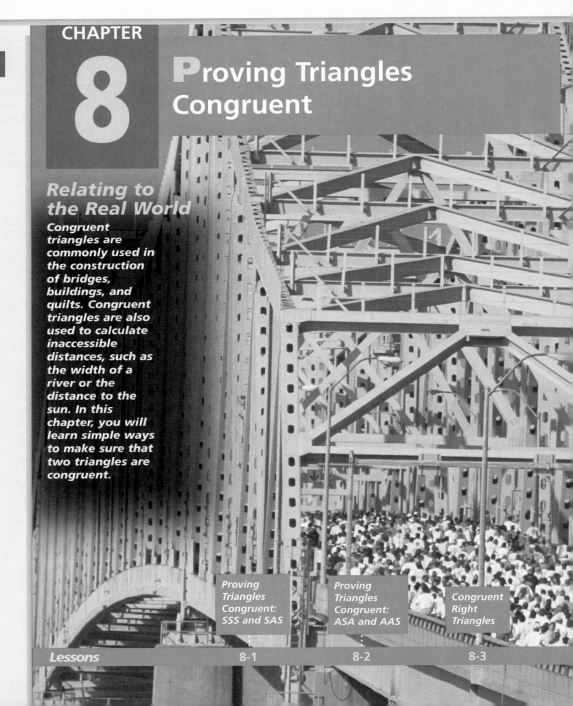

CHAPTER

8 **P**roving Triangles Congruent

Relating to the Real World

Congruent triangles are commonly used in the construction of bridges, buildings, and quilts. Congruent triangles are also used to calculate inaccessible distances, such as the width of a river or the distance to the sun. In this chapter, you will learn simple ways to make sure that two triangles are congruent.

Lessons	Proving Triangles Congruent: SSS and SAS	Proving Triangles Congruent: ASA and AAS	Congruent Right Triangles
	8-1	8-2	8-3

apply these ideas to build their own bridges using toothpicks or craft sticks.

Launching the Project

PROJECT NOTEBOOK Encourage students to keep all project-related materials in a separate folder or notebook. **See Chapter Project Manager and Scoring Rubric in Chapter Support File.**

- Ask students if they ever built a tower using playing cards. Ask them how they placed the first cards and why.

- Have students study the photographs shown on this page. Discuss why the objects were constructed as they were.

TRACKING THE PROJECT You may wish to have students read Finishing the Chapter Project on page 440 to help them get an overview of the project. Set benchmark deadlines for students to show their work in progress.

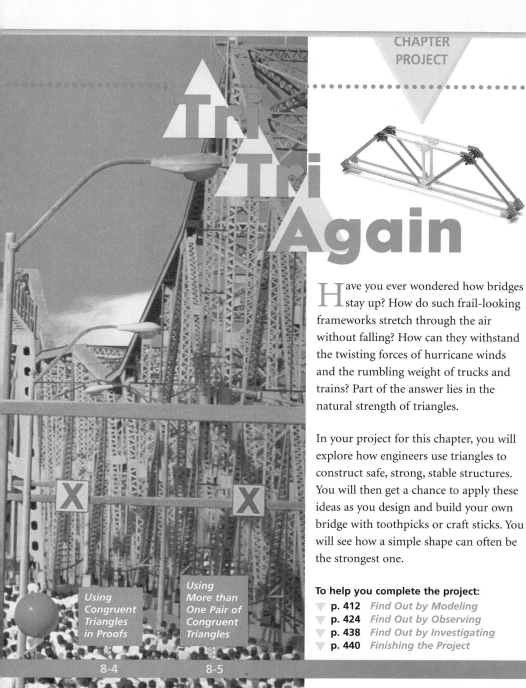

CHAPTER PROJECT

Tri Tri Again

Have you ever wondered how bridges stay up? How do such frail-looking frameworks stretch through the air without falling? How can they withstand the twisting forces of hurricane winds and the rumbling weight of trucks and trains? Part of the answer lies in the natural strength of triangles.

In your project for this chapter, you will explore how engineers use triangles to construct safe, strong, stable structures. You will then get a chance to apply these ideas as you design and build your own bridge with toothpicks or craft sticks. You will see how a simple shape can often be the strongest one.

To help you complete the project:

▼ **p. 412** *Find Out by Modeling*
▼ **p. 424** *Find Out by Observing*
▼ **p. 438** *Find Out by Investigating*
▼ **p. 440** *Finishing the Project*

Using Congruent Triangles in Proofs

Using More than One Pair of Congruent Triangles

8-4   8-5

▼ Project Resources

Teaching Resources
Chapter Support File, Ch. 8
- Chapter Project Manager and Scoring Rubric

Transparencies
85

▼ Using the Rubric

Sharing the scoring rubric for the project with your students will alert them to your expectations before they begin work on the project.

As students complete each Find Out question in the chapter, you may wish to have them evaluate their own work or a partner's work based on the scoring rubric. Students should have the opportunity to revise their work after it has been reviewed.

405

PROBLEM OF THE DAY

The lengths of the sides of a right triangle are all integers. Two of those integers are primes that differ by 50. Compute the smallest possible length for the third side. **The two sides have length 11 and 61 and the third side has length 60.**

Problem of the Day is also available in Transparencies.

CONNECTING TO PRIOR KNOWLEDGE Draw congruent triangles on the board. Have students identify the congruent parts and then write congruence statements about the triangles.

WORK TOGETHER p. 406

Have students work in groups of four. You may want to cut the straws ahead of time and give each student six pieces of different lengths (including a 2-in., 3-in., and 4-in. piece).

ALTERNATIVE METHOD Have students use geometry software to construct a triangle. Then have them construct another triangle with the same side lengths. Students can then answer Questions 1–2 of the Work Together.

THINK AND DISCUSS p. 406

Review with students the importance of naming corresponding parts in the same order when writing congruence statements for triangles.

Lesson Planning Options

Prerequisite Skills

- Understanding congruence
- Constructing angles and segments

Assignment Options for Exercises On Your Own

To provide flexible scheduling, this lesson can be subdivided into parts.

1 Core 5, 15, 21, 25
Extension 24

2 Core 1–4, 6–14, 16–18
Extension 19–20, 22–23

Use Mixed Review to maintain skills.

Resources

 Student Edition

Skills Handbook, p. 650
Extra Practice, p. 641
Glossary/Study Guide

 Teaching Resources

Chapter Support File, Ch. 8
- Practice 8-1 (two worksheets)
- Reteaching 8-1
- Alternative Activity 8-1
Classroom Manager 8-1
Glossary, Spanish Resources

 Transparencies
86, 89

What You'll Learn

- Proving two triangles congruent using the SSS and SAS postulates

...And Why

To develop an understanding of congruent triangles, which are important in the design and construction of buildings and bridges

What You'll Need

- protractor
- ruler
- straws
- scissors
- compass
- straightedge

Connections · Bridges . . . and more

8-1 Proving Triangles Congruent: SSS and SAS

WORK TOGETHER

■ Have each person in your group use straws to make a triangle with sides 2 in., 3 in., and 4 in. long. Compare your triangles.

1. Make a **conjecture** about two triangles in which three sides of one triangle are congruent to three sides of the other triangle. **They are ≅.**

2. **Verify** your conjecture by selecting other lengths for the sides of a triangle. Have each person in your group make the triangle. Compare your triangles. **Check students' work.**

THINK AND DISCUSS

Part 1 Using the SSS Postulate

In Lesson 2-6, you learned that if two triangles have three pairs of congruent corresponding angles and three pairs of congruent corresponding sides, then the triangles are congruent.

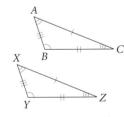

If you know this, then you know this.

$\angle A \cong \angle X$ $\triangle ABC \cong \triangle XYZ$
$\angle B \cong \angle Y$
$\angle C \cong \angle Z$
$\overline{AB} \cong \overline{XY}$
$\overline{AC} \cong \overline{XZ}$
$\overline{BC} \cong \overline{YZ}$

In the Work Together, you discovered that you don't need all six of the congruence statements to ensure that two triangles are congruent. If you know that corresponding sides are congruent, then you know that the triangles are congruent.

Postulate 8-1
Side-Side-Side Postulate
(SSS Postulate)

If three sides of one triangle are congruent to three sides of another triangle, then the two triangles are congruent.

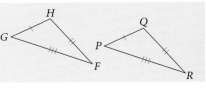

$\triangle GHF \cong \triangle PQR$

Side-Side-Side Postulate Point out to students that this postulate is abbreviated "SSS Postulate" where "S" stands for "Side."

Example 1   Relating to the Real World

VISUAL LEARNING Some students may have difficulty seeing that the three sides are congruent. It may help if they trace △ABD and △CBD separately and then mark the congruent sides.

Point out to students that the proof would be incomplete without Statement 4 in the proof. Make sure students write "SSS Postulate " and not just "SSS" because they will be learning the SSS Similarity Theorem in Lesson 10-2.

Question 4 Remind students not to assume information that is not explicitly stated or which they cannot justify. In this example, $\overline{RK}$ and $\overline{ST}$ may look congruent but cannot be assumed to be congruent.

Example 1   Relating to the Real World

Bridges Do you have enough information to prove the two triangles in the bridge congruent? If so, write a two-column proof.

Given: $\overline{AB} \cong \overline{CB}, \overline{AD} \cong \overline{CD}$
Prove: $\triangle ABD \cong \triangle CBD$

QUICK REVIEW

The Reflexive Property of Congruence tells you that a segment, such as $\overline{BD}$ in this figure, is congruent to itself. It also tells you that an angle is congruent to itself.

Plan for Proof To prove the triangles are congruent, you can use the SSS Postulate. You are given that two pairs of sides are congruent. You can use the Reflexive Property of Congruence to show that $\overline{BD}$ in △ABD is congruent to $\overline{BD}$ in △CBD.

Statements	Reasons
1. $\overline{AB} \cong \overline{CB}$	**1.** Given
2. $\overline{AD} \cong \overline{CD}$	**2.** Given
3. $\overline{BD} \cong \overline{BD}$	**3.** Reflexive Property of $\cong$
4. $\triangle ABD \cong \triangle CBD$	**4.** SSS Postulate

3. Answers may vary. Sample: By Reflexive Prop. of $\cong$, $\overline{BD} \cong \overline{BD}$. Since $\overline{AB} \cong \overline{CB}$ and $\overline{AD} \cong \overline{CD}$, 3 corres. sides of the 2 △s are $\cong$. The △s are $\cong$ by SSS.

3. A two-column proof is just one way to write this proof. Rewrite the proof as a paragraph proof or as a flow proof. See left.

4. Try This $\overline{RS} \cong \overline{TK}$. What additional information do you need to prove that △RSK ≅ △TKS by the SSS Postulate? $\overline{RK} \cong \overline{TS}$

Additional Examples

FOR EXAMPLE 1 ....

Do you have enough information to prove the two triangles are congruent? If so, write a two-column proof.

Yes; **Given:** $\overline{CA} \cong \overline{DR}, \overline{CD} \cong \overline{AR}$
Prove: △CAR ≅ △RDC
1. $\overline{CA} \cong \overline{DR}$ (Given)
2. $\overline{CD} \cong \overline{AR}$ (Given)
3. $\overline{CR} \cong \overline{CR}$ (Reflexive Property of $\cong$)
4. △CAR ≅ △RDC (SSS Postulate)

FOR EXAMPLE 2 ....

Given: $\overline{MA} \cong \overline{DE}, \overline{AN} \cong \overline{EG}$, $\angle A \cong \angle E$

From the given information, can you prove △MAN ≅ △DEG? Explain.

Yes; $\angle A$ is the included angle between $\overline{MA}$ and $\overline{AN}$ and $\angle E$ is the included angle between $\overline{DE}$ and $\overline{EG}$. These triangles are congruent by the SAS Postulate.

Part 2

WORK TOGETHER

Work in groups of three.

- Have each person use a straightedge to draw one of the following types of triangles: acute, obtuse, right. Make sure that at least one of the triangles is scalene. Label your triangle △HAM.

- Exchange triangles within your group. Use a compass and straightedge to construct a copy of ∠H. Label the angle ∠L.

- On one side of ∠L, construct $\overline{LT}$ congruent to $\overline{HM}$. On the other side of ∠L, construct $\overline{LE}$ congruent to $\overline{HA}$. Draw $\overline{ET}$, forming △LET.

- Cut out the triangles. Place one triangle over the other so that the corresponding parts match.

5. Make a **conjecture.** What seems to be true when an angle of one triangle is congruent to an angle of another triangle, and the two pairs of sides that form these angles are congruent? **The △s are ≅.**

THINK AND DISCUSS

Using the SAS Postulate

The word *included* is used frequently when referring to the angles and the sides of a triangle.

$\overline{AN}$ is included between ∠N and ∠A.

∠C is included between $\overline{NC}$ and $\overline{AC}$.

6. Which angle is included between $\overline{NC}$ and $\overline{AN}$? ∠N

7. Which side is included between ∠C and ∠N? $\overline{NC}$

The conjecture you made in the Work Together suggests another important postulate for proving triangles congruent.

Postulate 8-2
Side-Angle-Side Postulate
(SAS Postulate)

If two sides and the included angle of one triangle are congruent to two sides and the included angle of another triangle, then the two triangles are congruent.

△CBA ≅ △DFE

408

Example 2

Point out that you cannot prove △RED ≅ △CAT by the SSS Postulate or the SAS Postulate because you do not know $\overline{DE} \cong \overline{AT}$ or $\angle R \cong \angle C$. This does not mean that they are not congruent, however. To prove they are *not* congruent, you would need to show a pair of corresponding sides or a pair of corresponding angles are *not* congruent.

Question 9 Since all angles and all sides of an equilateral triangle are congruent, students may be confused as to which sides and angles are corresponding. In this example, they can use the triangle congruence statement to determine which sides must correspond.

Question 10 Ask students what kind of triangles △RED and △CAT are and what is special about their angles.

Exercises ON YOUR OWN

Exercises 3–4 Students sometimes are confused when the triangles have different orientations. You may want to ask students to write congruence statements as a way to check their ability to recognize corresponding parts.

8. Try This What additional information do you need to prove the triangles congruent by the SAS Postulate?

a.

$\overline{LG} \cong \overline{MN}$

b.

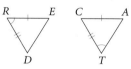

$\overline{QR} \cong \overline{SR}$

Example 2

Given: $\overline{RE} \cong \overline{CA}$, $\overline{RD} \cong \overline{CT}$, $\angle R \cong \angle T$

From the information given, can you prove △RED ≅ △CAT? Explain.

No, there is not enough information to prove △RED ≅ △CAT. ∠T is not *included* between the congruent sides. △RED may or may not be congruent to △CAT.

9. Try This In Example 2, suppose you also know that △CAT is equilateral. Can you prove △RED ≅ △CAT? Explain. **See left.**

9. Yes; an equilateral △ is also equiangular, so ∠C ≅ ∠T ≅ ∠R. The △s are ≅ by SAS.

10. Try This Suppose that in Example 2, RE = CA = RD = CT = 7 and $m\angle R = m\angle T = 58$. **See margin.**
  a. Sketch each figure, labeling angles and sides with their measures.
  b. Can you prove that △RED ≅ △CAT? Explain.
  No; since both △s are isosceles, m∠C = 64 and the included angles are ≠.

pages 408–409 Think and Discuss

10a.

Exercises ON YOUR OWN

Try to answer these questions without drawing a figure.

1. Which side is included between ∠X and ∠Z in △XYZ? $\overline{XZ}$

2. Which angle is included between $\overline{XY}$ and $\overline{XZ}$ in △XYZ? ∠X

Name the triangle congruence postulate you can use to prove each pair of triangles congruent.

3. SAS

4. SSS

5. Critical Thinking Suppose a friend insists that since you can prove triangles congruent using the SSS Congruence Postulate, there should be an AAA Congruence Postulate. Draw two triangles that will show that your friend's assumption is incorrect.

Sample:

Decide whether you can use the SSS or SAS Postulate to prove that the triangles below are congruent. If so, write the congruence and identify the postulate. If not, write *not possible*.

6. $\triangle ANG \cong \triangle RWT$; SAS

7. $\triangle JKL \cong \triangle NMO$; SSS

8. not possible

9. not possible

10. $\triangle TBR \cong \triangle SBR$; SSS

11. $\triangle PQR \cong \triangle NMO$; SAS

12. $\triangle GAE \cong \triangle CAE$; SAS

13. $\triangle XYP \cong \triangle QYZ$; SAS

14. not possible

15. Open-ended List several places where you have seen congruent triangles used. Samples: support structures of bridges; scaffolding

16. Preparing for Proof Supply the reasons in this proof.

Given: X is the midpoint of $\overline{AG}$ and of $\overline{NR}$.
Prove: $\triangle ANX \cong \triangle GRX$

Statements	Reasons
1. $\angle 1 \cong \angle 2$	a. _?_
2. X is the midpoint of $\overline{AG}$.	b. _?_
3. $\overline{AX} \cong \overline{GX}$	c. _?_
4. X is the midpoint of $\overline{NR}$.	d. _?_
5. $\overline{NX} \cong \overline{RX}$	e. _?_
6. $\triangle ANX \cong \triangle GRX$	f. _?_

Vertical $\angle$s are $\cong$.
Given
Def. of midpt.
Given
Def. of midpt.
SAS

17. Paper Folding Draw an isosceles triangle. Fold the bisector of the vertex angle. Are the two triangles formed congruent? How do you know? Check students' work; yes; SAS Post.

18. Complete the flow proof.

Given: $\overline{AE} \cong \overline{DE}$, $\overline{AB} \cong \overline{DC}$

Prove: $\triangle ABE \cong \triangle DCE$

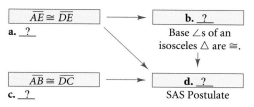

a. ___?___ $\boxed{\overline{AE} \cong \overline{DE}}$ → **b.** ___?___   Base ∠s of an isosceles △ are ≅.

c. ___?___ $\boxed{\overline{AB} \cong \overline{DC}}$ → **d.** ___?___   SAS Postulate

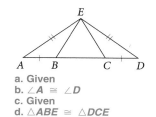

a. Given
b. $\angle A \cong \angle D$
c. Given
d. $\triangle ABE \cong \triangle DCE$

Write a two-column proof. 19–20. See margin.

19. Given: $\overline{AE}$ and $\overline{BD}$ bisect each other.
Prove: $\triangle ACB \cong \triangle ECD$

20. Given: $\overline{GK}$ bisects $\angle JGM$, $\overline{GJ} \cong \overline{GM}$
Prove: $\triangle GJK \cong \triangle GMK$

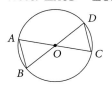

21. a. What two symbols are combined to form the congruence symbol? = (equality) and ~ (similarity)
   b. Writing Explain why the congruence symbol makes sense.
   ≅ figures have ~ shapes and corres. measures are =.

Choose Write a two-column proof, a paragraph proof, or a flow proof. 22–23. Answers may vary. See margin for samples.

22. Given: $\odot O$ with A, B, C, D on the circle
   Prove: $\triangle AOB \cong \triangle COD$

23. Given: $\overline{FG} \parallel \overline{KL}$, $\overline{FG} \cong \overline{KL}$
   Prove: $\triangle FGK \cong \triangle KLF$

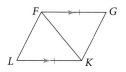

pages 409–412   On Your Own

19. 1. $\overline{AE}$ and $\overline{BD}$ bisect each other. (Given) **2.** $\overline{AC} \cong \overline{EC}$; $\overline{BC} \cong \overline{DC}$ (Def. of segment bisector) **3.** $\angle ACB \cong \angle ECD$ (Vertical ∠s are ≅.) **4.** $\triangle ACB \cong \triangle ECD$ (SAS)

20. 1. $\overline{GK}$ bisects $\angle JGM$ (Given) **2.** $\angle JGK \cong \angle MGK$ (Def. of angle bisector) **3.** $\overline{GJ} \cong \overline{GM}$ (Given) **4.** $\overline{GK} \cong \overline{GK}$ (Reflexive Prop. of ≅) **5.** $\triangle GJK \cong \triangle GMK$ (SAS)

22. 1. $\overline{AO} \cong \overline{BO} \cong \overline{CO} \cong \overline{DO}$ (All radii of a $\odot$ are ≅.) **2.** $\angle AOB \cong \angle COD$ (Vertical ∠s are ≅.) **3.** $\triangle AOB \cong \triangle COD$ (SAS)

23. 1. $\overline{FG} \parallel \overline{KL}$ (Given) **2.** $\angle GFK \cong \angle LKF$ (If ∥ lines, then alt. int. ∠s are ≅.) **3.** $\overline{FG} \cong \overline{KL}$ (Given) **4.** $\overline{FK} \cong \overline{KF}$ (Reflexive Prop. of ≅) **5.** $\triangle FGK \cong \triangle KLF$ (SAS)

JOURNAL Have students label the vertices of the triangles in their diagrams. Then ask them to write congruence statements for each pair.

GETTING READY FOR LESSON 8-2 These exercises prepare students to explore the ASA Postulate and the AAS Theorem.

Chapter Project **FIND OUT BY MODELING** Students discover that triangles are more stable or rigid than quadrilaterals. Discuss with students real-world examples such as ironing boards, scaffolding, and frames of roofs where triangles are used for stability.

Wrap Up

THE BIG IDEA Ask students to describe the differences between the SSS Postulate and the SAS Postulate.

RETEACHING ACTIVITY Students measure sides and angles to show triangles congruent by the SSS and SAS Postulates. (Reteaching worksheet 8-1)

Exercises MIXED REVIEW

Exercises 26–28 Students review how to use the formulas for volume and surface area of spheres, cones, and prisms.

Lesson Quiz

Lesson Quiz is also available in Transparencies.

Name the additional congruent corresponding part needed to prove the triangles congruent by the given postulate.

1. $\triangle TAB \cong \triangle PDG$ by the SSS Postulate: $\overline{TA} \cong \overline{PD}$, $\overline{AB} \cong \overline{DG}$
$\overline{TB} \cong \overline{PG}$

2. $\triangle WNO \cong \triangle BTZ$ by the SAS Postulate: $\overline{WN} \cong \overline{BT}$, $\overline{ON} \cong \overline{ZT}$
$\angle N \cong \angle T$

3. Write a two-column proof.

Given: $\overline{YG}$ bisects $\overline{XZ}$, $\overline{YX} \cong \overline{YZ}$
Prove: $\triangle XYG \cong \triangle ZYG$

See back of book.

412

---

24. *Critical Thinking* Suppose you construct two isosceles triangles so that the four legs are the same length. Can you prove that the triangles are congruent? **Justify** your answer, or give a counterexample.
No; an equilateral △ and an isosceles rt. △ with ≅ legs are ≠.

25. *Critical Thinking* Janet knows that the four sides of quadrilateral *ABCD* are congruent to the four sides of quadrilateral *EFGH*. Are the two quadrilaterals necessarily congruent? Explain.
No; their ∠s may not be ≅.

Chapter Project **Find Out by Modeling**

Many structures have straight beams that meet at *joints*. You can use models to explore ways to strengthen joints.

- Cut seven cardboard strips about 6 in. by $\frac{1}{2}$ in. Make a square frame and a triangular frame. Staple across the joints, as shown.

- With your fingertips, hold each model flat on a desk or table and try to change its shape. Which shape is more stable? triangle

- Cut another cardboard strip and use it to form a brace for the square frame. Is it more rigid? Why do you think the brace works?
  Yes; the brace makes 2 rigid △s.

Exercises MIXED REVIEW

Calculator Find the volume and surface area of each figure to the nearest tenth.

26.

904.8 in.³; 452.4 in.²

27.

12 mm

5 mm

314.2 mm³; 282.7 mm²

28.

6 cm

12 cm   6 cm

12 cm   6 cm

648 cm³; 504 cm²

29. One angle of an isosceles triangle is 112°. Find the measures of the other two angles. 34, 34

Getting Ready for Lesson 8-2

30. For $\triangle STP$, which sides are *not* included between $\angle S$ and $\angle T$? *SP* and *TP*

31. *Constructions* Draw an obtuse angle on your paper. Label it ∠1. Construct ∠*A* so that $\angle A \cong \angle 1$. Check students' work.

FOR YOUR JOURNAL

Summarize the two ways that you learned to prove triangles congruent in this lesson. Include diagrams.

Students discover that there is no SSA or AAA Postulate. This exploration extends Lesson 8-1 and previews Lesson 8-2 in which students learn the ASA Postulate and AAS Theorem.

The geometry software allows students to construct triangles with congruent angles and sides and then to manipulate them while maintaining the congruences.

ERROR ALERT! Students who are not experienced with the geometry software may have difficulty with the constructions and manipulations. **Remediation:** Pair students with more experience with those with less experience.

Investigate

Help students see that ∠A is a non-included angle relative to sides $\overline{AC}$ and $\overline{CE}$. ∠E is also a non-included angle.

Construct

Make sure students *construct* and not *draw* $\overline{BC}$ and $\overline{DE}$ as parallel segments so that when the positions of sides $\overline{DE}$ and $\overline{BC}$ are changed, the segments remain parallel.

ADDITIONAL PROBLEM Have students construct two triangles with two pairs of corresponding angles and the included side congruent. Then have students construct two triangles with two pairs of corresponding angles and a non-included side congruent. For each pair, ask: *What appears to be true about the triangles?*

Math ToolboX

Technology

Material and Manipulatives

- Geometry software

Exploring SSA and AAA

After Lesson 8-1

Work in pairs or small groups.

Construct

Use geometry software to construct ray $\overrightarrow{AB}$. Draw a circle with center C that intersects $\overrightarrow{AB}$ in two points. Construct $\overline{AC}$. Construct a point E on the circle and construct $\overline{CE}$. **Check students' work.**

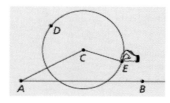

Investigate

Move point E around the circle until E is on $\overrightarrow{AB}$ and forms △ACE. Then move E to another point on the circle that is also on $\overrightarrow{AB}$ to form another △ACE. In the two triangles, compare the measures of ∠A, $\overline{AC}$, and $\overline{CE}$. Are two sides and a nonincluded angle of one triangle congruent to two sides and a nonincluded angle of the other triangle? Are the two triangles congruent? Do you get the same results if you change the size of ∠A and the size of the circle? **yes; no; yes**

Construct

Construct rays $\overrightarrow{AB}$ and $\overrightarrow{AC}$. Construct $\overline{BC}$ to create △ABC. Construct a line parallel to $\overline{BC}$ that intersects $\overrightarrow{AB}$ and $\overrightarrow{AC}$ at points D and E to form △ADE. **Check students' work.**

Investigate

Are three angles of △ABC congruent to three angles of △ADE? Manipulate the figure to change the positions of sides $\overline{DE}$ and $\overline{BC}$. Do the corresponding angles of the triangles remain congruent? Are the two triangles congruent? Can the two triangles be congruent? **yes; yes; no; only when the segments coincide**

Conjecture

Do you think there is a SSA congruency theorem? Do you think there is an AAA congruency theorem? Explain your answers. **No; no; the above constructions demonstrate SSA △s that are not ≅ and AAA △s that are not ≅.**

Extend

Manipulate the first figure you drew so that ∠A is obtuse. Now can the circle intersect $\overrightarrow{AB}$ twice? Can two triangles be formed? Could there be a SSA congruency theorem if the congruent angles are obtuse? **no; no; yes**

CONNECTING TO PRIOR KNOWLEDGE Draw a pair of triangles with two pairs of angles and the included sides congruent. Ask students to name the congruent corresponding parts.

WORK TOGETHER

Have students work in groups of four. Within each group, students should check each other's constructions to make sure that each step is performed.

ALTERNATIVE METHOD Have students perform the constructions using geometry software. Have them drag one triangle onto the other so that corresponding angles match, then answer Question 2.

Lesson Planning Options

Prerequisite Skills

- Constructing angles and segments
- Writing proofs

Assignment Options for Exercises On Your Own

To provide flexible scheduling, this lesson can be subdivided into parts.

1 Core 10, 12, 18, 20, 22
Extension 15, 23

2 Core 1–9, 11, 13–14, 19, 21
Extension 16–17

Use Mixed Review to maintain skills.

Resources

 Student Edition

Skills Handbook, p. 650
Extra Practice, p. 641
Glossary/Study Guide

Teaching Resources

Chapter Support File, Ch. 8
- Practice 8-2 (two worksheets)
- Reteaching 8-2
- Alternative Activity 8-2
Classroom Manager 8-2
Glossary, Spanish Resources

 Transparencies
86, 90

What You'll Learn

- Proving two triangles congruent by the ASA Postulate and the AAS Theorem

...And Why

To understand the use of congruent figures in constructed objects such as lacrosse nets

What You'll Need

- compass
- straightedge
- scissors

8-2 Proving Triangles Congruent: ASA and AAS

WORK TOGETHER

Have each person in your group draw a different triangle. Label each triangle △ABC.

① Construct $\overline{XZ}$ such that $\overline{XZ} \cong \overline{AC}$.

② At X, construct an angle congruent to ∠A.
③ At Z, construct an angle congruent to ∠C.
④ Label point Y as shown.

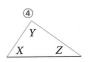

1. Cut out △ABC and △XYZ. Place △ABC over △XYZ so that corresponding angles match. Are the triangles congruent? Compare your results with those of others in your group. **yes**

2. Make a **conjecture.** What seems to be true when two angles and the included side of one triangle are congruent to two angles and the included side of another triangle? **When 2 angles and the included side of 1 △ are ≅ to 2 angles and the included side of another △, the △s are ≅.**

THINK AND DISCUSS

Part 1 **Using the ASA Postulate**

Your investigation in the Work Together involved two angles and an included side.

Postulate 8-3

Angle-Side-Angle Postulate (ASA Postulate)

If two angles and the included side of one triangle are congruent to two angles and the included side of another triangle, then the two triangles are congruent.

△GBH ≅ △KPN

3. **Try This** Write a congruence statement for the two triangles you can prove congruent by the ASA Postulate. **△CAT ≅ △GDO**

In Lesson 8-1, students learned to identify an angle included between two sides. You may want to review *included side* and give several examples before stating the Angle-Side-Angle Postulate.

Example 1 Relating to the Real World ················

When writing a plan for a proof, some students will go into more detail than others. In this example, some students may want to include what is given as part of their plan. Encourage students to write a plan that is clear enough for them to write the proof.

DIVERSITY Lacrosse originated as "baggataway," a game played by North American Indians. It was played by two teams which had up to two hundred men on each side. The senior medicine man from each tribe stood in the goal area. Lacrosse received its modern name from French Canadians who observed that the netted stick used by the Indians resembled a bishop's crosier.

Example 2 ···

Help students see how this proof "flows" from statements to conclusions. Discuss how the two arrows coming from the statement "$\angle B \cong \angle Y$" show that it is used to prove both $\angle C \cong \angle Z$ and $\triangle ABC \cong \triangle XYZ$.

Example 1 Relating to the Real World ············

Front view of net

Lacrosse Write a plan for the following proof.

Given: $\angle CAB \cong \angle DAE$, $\overline{AB} \cong \overline{AE}$, $\angle ABC$ and $\angle AED$ are right angles.
Prove: $\triangle ABC \cong \triangle AED$

> **Plan for Proof** To prove $\triangle ABC \cong \triangle AED$, you can use the ASA Postulate. First prove that $\angle ABC \cong \angle AED$.

4. Use the plan in Example 1 to write a two-column proof.
   See below left.

You can use the ASA Postulate to prove that if two angles and a nonincluded side of one triangle are congruent to two angles and the corresponding nonincluded side of another triangle, then the triangles are congruent.

Example 2 ··············

Given: $\angle A \cong \angle X$, $\angle B \cong \angle Y$, $\overline{BC} \cong \overline{YZ}$
Prove: $\triangle ABC \cong \triangle XYZ$

Flow Proof

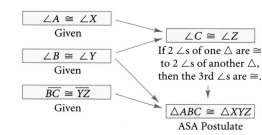

4. 1. $\angle CAB \cong \angle DAE$;
   $\overline{AB} \cong \overline{AE}$ (Given)
2. $\angle ABC$ and $\angle AED$ are rt. angles. (Given)
3. $\angle ABC \cong \angle AED$
   (All rt. $\angle$s are $\cong$.)
4. $\triangle ABC \cong \triangle AED$ (ASA)

Additional Examples

FOR EXAMPLE 1 ·······················

Write a plan for the following proof.

Given: $\angle MNP \cong \angle ONP$,
$\angle MPN \cong \angle OPN$

Prove: $\triangle MNP \cong \triangle ONP$

Answers may vary. Sample: To prove $\triangle MNP \cong \triangle ONP$, you can use the ASA Postulate. First prove that $\overline{NP} \cong \overline{NP}$.

FOR EXAMPLE 2 ···························

Write a flow proof.

Given: $\overline{PQ} \cong \overline{TS}$, $\angle P \cong \angle S$

Prove: $\triangle PQR \cong \triangle STR$

See back of book.

415

Angle-Angle-Side Theorem Point out that this is a theorem and not a postulate.

ERROR ALERT! Students may think that any three pairs of corresponding congruent parts are sufficient to prove triangles congruent. **Remediation:** Have students investigate SSA and AAA. Refer them to the Math Toolbox on page 413 for a technology investigation of SSA and AAA.

CRITICAL THINKING Question 6 Ask students what additional information is needed to prove the triangles are congruent by ASA.

VISUAL LEARNING Exercises 1–8 Students may want to copy the figures and mark the congruent sides and angles in the following way to help them differentiate between ASA and AAS.

Technology Options

For Exercise 13, students may draw the triangles using geometry software.

Prentice Hall Technology

 Software
- Secondary Math Lab Toolkit™
- Integrated Math Lab 38
- Computer Item Generator 8-2

 CD-ROM
- Multimedia Geometry Lab 8

 Internet
- See the Prentice Hall site.
(http://www.phschool.com)

416

Part 2 **Using the AAS Theorem**

In Example 2, the ASA Postulate was used in the flow proof to prove the following theorem.

Theorem 8-1
Angle-Angle-Side Theorem (AAS Theorem)

If two angles and a nonincluded side of one triangle are congruent to two angles and the corresponding nonincluded side of another triangle, then the triangles are congruent.

$$\triangle DCM \cong \triangle GXT$$

5. Try This Supply the missing reasons in the proof.

Given: $\overline{XQ} \parallel \overline{TR}$, $\overline{XR}$ bisects $\overline{QT}$.
Prove: $\triangle XMQ \cong \triangle RMT$

Statements	Reasons
1. $\overline{XQ} \parallel \overline{TR}$	a. __?__ Given
2. $\angle Q \cong \angle T$	b. __?__ b–c. If ∥ lines, then alt.
3. $\angle X \cong \angle R$	c. __?__ int. ∠s are ≅.
4. $\overline{XR}$ bisects $\overline{QT}$.	d. __?__ Given
5. $\overline{TM} \cong \overline{QM}$	e. __?__ Def. of segment bisector
6. $\triangle XMQ \cong \triangle RMT$	f. __?__ AAS

6. Critical Thinking Explain how you could prove the triangles in Question 5 congruent using the ASA Postulate.
Answers may vary. Sample: Replace Statement 3 in the proof with ∠XMQ ≅ ∠RMT (Vertical ∠s are ≅.)

Tell whether the ASA Postulate or the AAS Theorem can be applied directly to prove the triangles congruent. If the triangles *cannot* be proven congruent, write *not possible*.

1.

AAS

2.

5 m   5 m

not possible

3.

4 in.   40°   40°   4 in.

AAS

4.

not possible

5.

ASA

6.

ASA

7.

not possible

8.

3 m
30°
30°
3 m

ASA

Preparing for Proof What additional information would you need to prove the triangles congruent by the stated postulate or theorem?

9. AAS Theorem $\angle D \cong \angle B$

10. ASA Postulate $\overline{QP} \cong \overline{QT}$

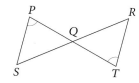

11. AAS Theorem $\angle M \cong \angle P$

12. SAS Postulate $\overline{RV} \cong \overline{VT}$

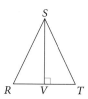

13. a. *Open-ended* Draw a triangle. Draw a second triangle that is congruent to the first one and shares a common side with it. **See margin for sample.**
   b. Think about how you drew your second triangle. What congruence postulate or theorem did you use to make the second triangle congruent to the first one? **SSS, SAS, or ASA**

14. *Preparing for Proof* Supply the missing statements and reasons.

Given: $\overline{PQ} \perp \overline{QS}$, $\overline{RS} \perp \overline{QS}$, T is the midpoint of $\overline{PR}$.
Prove: $\triangle PQT \cong \triangle RST$

Statements	Reasons
1. $\overline{PQ} \perp \overline{QS}$, $\overline{RS} \perp \overline{QS}$	**1.** Given
2. $\angle Q$ and $\angle S$ are right angles.	**a.** __?__ Def. of $\perp$ lines
3. $\angle Q \cong \angle S$	**b.** __?__ All rt. $\angle$s are $\cong$.
c. __?__ $\angle QTP \cong \angle STR$	**4.** Vertical angles are $\cong$.
5. T is the midpoint of $\overline{PR}$.	**5.** Given
6. $\overline{PT} \cong \overline{RT}$	**d.** __?__ Def. of midpoint
7. $\triangle PQT \cong \triangle RST$	**e.** __?__ AAS

15. *Geometry in 3 Dimensions* The top portion of this quartz crystal is a hexagonal pyramid. The lateral edges of the pyramid are congruent and the base edges of the pyramid are congruent. Are the triangles that form the lateral faces of the pyramid congruent? **Justify** your answer. **yes; SSS**

pages 416–418 On Your Own

13a.

18. 1. $\overline{DH}$ bisects $\angle BDF$ (Given)
2. $\angle BDH \cong \angle FDH$ (Def. of angle bisector) 3. $\overline{DH} \cong \overline{DH}$ (Reflexive Prop. of $\cong$) 4. $\angle 1 \cong \angle 2$ (Given)
5. $\triangle BDH \cong \triangle FDH$ (ASA)

19. 1. $\overline{FG} \parallel \overline{JH}$ (Given) 2. $\angle FGJ \cong \angle HJG$ (If $\parallel$ lines, then alt. int. $\angle$s are $\cong$.) 3. $\angle F \cong \angle H$ (Given)
4. $\overline{JG} \cong \overline{GJ}$ (Reflexive Prop. of $\cong$) 5. $\triangle FGJ \cong \triangle HJG$ (AAS)

20. 1. $\overline{AE} \parallel \overline{BD}$ (Given) 2. $\angle A \cong \angle DBC$ (If $\parallel$ lines, then corres. $\angle$s are $\cong$.) 3. $\angle E \cong \angle D$ (Given)
4. $\overline{AE} \cong \overline{BD}$ (Given) 5. $\triangle AEB \cong \triangle BDC$ (ASA)

21. 1. $\angle MON \cong \angle QOP$ (Vertical $\angle$s are $\cong$.) 2. $\angle N \cong \angle P$ (Given)
3. $\overline{MO} \cong \overline{QO}$ (Given) 4. $\triangle MON \cong \triangle QOP$ (AAS)

page 419 Mixed Review

26.

418

16. Probability Here are six congruence statements about the triangles at the right.

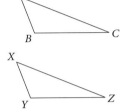

$$\angle A \cong \angle X \qquad \angle B \cong \angle Y \qquad \angle C \cong \angle Z$$
$$\overline{AB} \cong \overline{XY} \qquad \overline{AC} \cong \overline{XZ} \qquad \overline{BC} \cong \overline{YZ}$$

There are 20 ways to choose groups of three statements from these six statements. What is the probability that a set of three congruence statements chosen at random from the six listed will guarantee that the triangles are congruent? $\frac{13}{20}$

17. Writing Anita claims that it is possible to rewrite any proof that uses the AAS Theorem as a proof that uses the ASA Postulate. Do you agree with Anita? Explain why or why not. **Yes; by Thm. 4-5, if 2 $\angle$s of one $\triangle$ are $\cong$ to 2 $\angle$s of another $\triangle$, then the third $\angle$s are $\cong$.**

Choose Write a two-column proof, a paragraph proof, or a flow proof.

18. Given: $\overline{DH}$ bisects $\angle BDF$, $\angle 1 \cong \angle 2$
Prove: $\triangle BDH \cong \triangle FDH$

18–21. Answers may vary. See margin for samples.

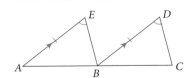

19. Given: $\angle F \cong \angle H$, $\overline{FG} \parallel \overline{JH}$
Prove: $\triangle FGJ \cong \triangle HJG$

20. Given: $\overline{AE} \parallel \overline{BD}$, $\overline{AE} \cong \overline{BD}$, $\angle E \cong \angle D$
Prove: $\triangle AEB \cong \triangle BDC$

21. Given: $\angle N \cong \angle P$, $\overline{MO} \cong \overline{QO}$
Prove: $\triangle MON \cong \triangle QOP$

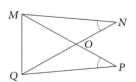

22. Standardized Test Prep Which of the following can you conclude based on the figure at the right? **A**
  I. $\triangle ADE$ is isosceles.   **II.** $\triangle ABE \cong \triangle DCE$
III. $\triangle BDE$ is isosceles.   **IV.** $\angle EBC \cong \angle ECB$

  A. I, II, and IV only   **B.** I, II, and III only   **C.** II, III, and IV only
  D. I, III, and IV only   **E.** III and IV only

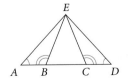

23. Critical Thinking Explain why $\triangle ABC$ cannot be congruent to $\triangle FDE$.
The hypotenuse of a rt. $\triangle$ is longer than each leg. So $FE > 5$ cm and $\overline{FE} \not\cong \overline{AC}$.

JOURNAL Encourage students to include diagrams with their explanations.

GETTING READY FOR LESSON 8-3 These exercises prepare students to investigate congruent right triangles.

Wrap Up

THE BIG IDEA Ask students to explain the differences between the ASA Postulate and the AAS Theorem.

RETEACHING ACTIVITY Students construct pairs of congruent triangles and show they are congruent using the ASA Postulate and AAS Theorem. (Reteaching worksheet 8-2)

Geometry at Work

ESL Make sure students understand that the term "die maker" does not refer to a person who makes number cubes. To clarify, discuss how die making is used in the auto industry.

Encourage students to investigate these topics:
- the education necessary to become a die maker
- the types of businesses that hire die makers
- how die making is used in the automotive industry
- the first automobile to be made using dies
- the technology used by die makers (electrical discharge machines, electrochemical milling, electrochemical grinding, and ultrasonic machining)

Exercises   MIXED REVIEW

Coordinate Geometry **Find the coordinates of the midpoint of the segment with the given endpoints.**

24. $(4, 7)$ and $(2, 9)$ **(3, 8)**

25. $(-1, 8)$ and $(5, -8)$ **(2, 0)**

26. Constructions Draw a line ℓ and a point M not on ℓ. Construct a line n through M so that $n \perp \ell$. **See margin p. 418 for sample.**

FOR YOUR JOURNAL

Explain why "included" and "noninclude" are necessary terms in the SAS Postulate, the ASA Postulate, and the AAS Theorem.

Getting Ready for Lesson 8-3

Find the value of each variable. If an answer is not a whole number, leave it in simplest radical form.

27.

60°, y, x, 7

$x = \dfrac{7\sqrt{3}}{3}; y = \dfrac{14\sqrt{3}}{3}$

28.

x, 11, 14

$x = 5\sqrt{3}$

29.

x, y, 4

$x = 4; y = 4\sqrt{2}$

Reteaching 8-2

Practice 8-2

Practice 8-2
Mixed Exercises

Geometry at Work

Die Maker

Two centuries ago, all manufactured articles were made by hand. Each article produced was slightly different from the others. In 1800, inventor Eli Whitney recognized that manufacturing could be greatly speeded up by using *congruent* parts. Whitney made a *die,* or mold, for each part of a musket he was producing for the U.S. Army. This allowed standard-sized muskets to be put together rapidly, and it ushered in the era of *mass production.*

Today, die makers are highly skilled industrial workers. To create a new product, die makers use metal, plastic, rubber, or other materials to create dies. During manufacture, a part is shaped by its die. This ensures that parts are congruent.

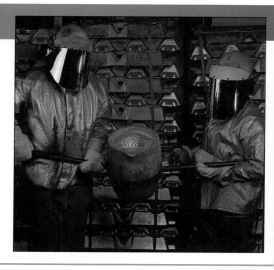

Mini Project: Research Write a paragraph on the use of molds and castings to produce congruent parts.

Lesson Quiz

Lesson Quiz is also available in Transparencies.

Tell whether the ASA Postulate or the AAS Theorem can be applied directly to prove the triangles congruent.

1. **AAS Theorem**

2. **ASA Postulate**

3. Write a flow proof to prove $\triangle FCD \cong \triangle FED$ using the AAS Theorem.

See back of book.

419

PROBLEM OF THE DAY

A circle is circumscribed about one equilateral triangle and is inscribed in another equilateral triangle. Find the ratio of the areas of the triangles. 1 to 4 (Hint: Draw a diagram and rotate the smaller triangle 180°.)

Problem of the Day is also available in Transparencies.

CONNECTING TO PRIOR KNOWLEDGE Draw the following pairs of triangles on the board and have students explain why they are congruent.

Have students work in groups of three or four. Students in each group should pick the same values for *x* and *y*.

TACTILE LEARNING Question 1 Students may want to cut the triangles out and place them on top of each other so the right angles match up.

THINK AND DISCUSS

Note that the HL Theorem applies only to right triangles and that there is no SSA Theorem that applies to all triangles.

Lesson Planning Options

Prerequisite Skills

• Writing proofs
• Understanding the SSS, ASA, and SAS Postulates and the AAS Theorem

Assignment Options for Exercises On Your Own

Core 1–9, 11–13, 18–20
Extension 10, 14–17

Use Mixed Review to maintain skills.

Resources

 Student Edition

Skills Handbook, p. 650
Extra Practice, p. 641
Glossary/Study Guide

Teaching Resources

Chapter Support File, Ch. 8
• Practice 8-3 (two worksheets)
• Reteaching 8-3
• Alternative Activity 8-3
Classroom Manager 8-3
Glossary, Spanish Resources

 Transparencies
87

420

What You'll Learn

• Proving triangles congruent using the HL Theorem

...And Why

To investigate congruence in applications such as fabric for tents

What You'll Need

• compass
• protractor
• ruler

QUICK REVIEW

The hypotenuse of a right triangle is the longest side.

Connections **Tents . . . and more**

8-3 Congruent Right Triangles

WORK TOGETHER

■ As a group, select two numbers from the set {2, 3, 4, 5, 6, 7}. Let *x* equal the smaller number and *y* the larger. Have each group member draw a right triangle at the corner of a piece of paper with a leg *x* in. long and a hypotenuse *y* in. long. (An example using 5 and 2 is shown.)

2 in. / 5 in.

1. Compare triangles within your group and make a **conjecture.** If the hypotenuse and a leg of one right triangle are congruent to the hypotenuse and a leg of another right triangle, then __?__. the △s are ≅

■ **Verify** your conjecture by selecting two more numbers from the set and creating more right triangles.

THINK AND DISCUSS

In the Work Together, you saw that all triangles formed with a given length for a leg and a given length for a hypotenuse are congruent. This observation leads to the following theorem.

Theorem 8-2
Hypotenuse-Leg Theorem (HL Theorem)

If the hypotenuse and a leg of one right triangle are congruent to the hypotenuse and leg of another right triangle, then the triangles are congruent.

Proof of Theorem 8-2

Given: $\triangle PQR$ and $\triangle XYZ$ are right triangles, $\overline{QR} \cong \overline{YZ}$, and $\overline{PQ} \cong \overline{XY}$

Prove: $\triangle PQR \cong \triangle XYZ$

Let $PQ = XY = a$ and $QR = ZY = c$.
By the Pythagorean Theorem, $a^2 + PR^2 = c^2$ and $a^2 + XZ^2 = c^2$. Using the Subtraction Property of Equality, you get $PR^2 = c^2 - a^2$ and $XZ^2 = c^2 - a^2$. So $PR^2 = XZ^2$ and $PR = XZ$. By the SSS Postulate, $\triangle PQR \cong \triangle XYZ$.

ALTERNATIVE METHOD In the proof of Theorem 8-2, the variables a and c are introduced to avoid substitution. If you do not want to introduce new variables, begin the proof as follows: By the Pythagorean Theorem, $PQ^2 + PR^2 = QR^2$ and $XY^2 + XZ^2 = ZY^2$. By substitution, $XY^2 + PR^2 = ZY^2$. Using the Subtraction Property of Equality, you get $PR^2 = ZY^2 - XY^2$ and $XZ^2 = ZY^2 - XY^2$.

Example 1 Relating to the Real World ·················

Note that in the explanation, $\triangle CPA$ and $\triangle MPA$ are established as right triangles. This is necessary when using the HL Theorem to prove two triangles congruent.

Point out that although only two letters are used to name the HL Theorem, there are three conditions, as stated on page 421.

Example 2 ·······························

CRITICAL THINKING Ask students to explain why $\angle CBD$, $\angle DBE$, and $\angle ABE$ are right angles.

ALTERNATIVE ASSESSMENT You can assess students' understanding of flow proof by having them work in groups to rewrite the flow proof in Example 2 as a paragraph or two-column proof.

Example 1 Relating to the Real World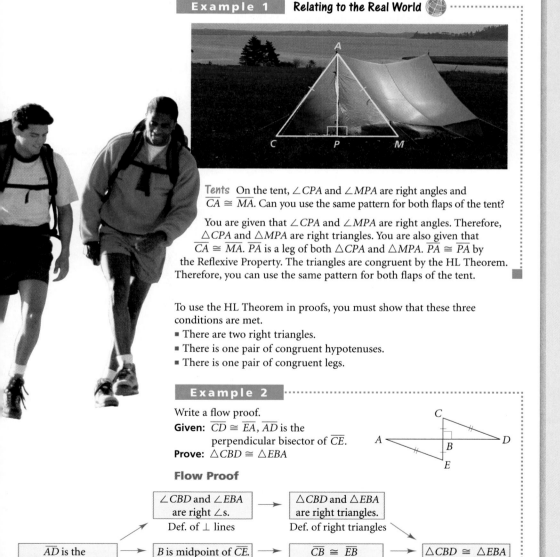

Tents On the tent, $\angle CPA$ and $\angle MPA$ are right angles and $\overline{CA} \cong \overline{MA}$. Can you use the same pattern for both flaps of the tent?

You are given that $\angle CPA$ and $\angle MPA$ are right angles. Therefore, $\triangle CPA$ and $\triangle MPA$ are right triangles. You are also given that $\overline{CA} \cong \overline{MA}$. $\overline{PA}$ is a leg of both $\triangle CPA$ and $\triangle MPA$. $\overline{PA} \cong \overline{PA}$ by the Reflexive Property. The triangles are congruent by the HL Theorem. Therefore, you can use the same pattern for both flaps of the tent. ■

To use the HL Theorem in proofs, you must show that these three conditions are met.
- There are two right triangles.
- There is one pair of congruent hypotenuses.
- There is one pair of congruent legs.

Example 2 ···············

Write a flow proof.
Given: $\overline{CD} \cong \overline{EA}$, $\overline{AD}$ is the perpendicular bisector of $\overline{CE}$.
Prove: $\triangle CBD \cong \triangle EBA$

Flow Proof

```
                    ┌──────────────────┐      ┌──────────────────┐
                    │ ∠CBD and ∠EBA    │ ───▶ │ △CBD and △EBA    │
                    │ are right ∠s.    │      │ are right triangles.│
                    └──────────────────┘      └──────────────────┘
                      Def. of ⊥ lines         Def. of right triangles
  ┌──────────────┐   ┌──────────────────┐   ┌──────────┐   ┌──────────────┐
  │ AD is the    │──▶│ B is midpoint of │──▶│ CB ≅ EB  │──▶│ △CBD ≅ △EBA │
  │ ⊥ bisector   │   │ CE.              │   └──────────┘   └──────────────┘
  │ of CE.       │   └──────────────────┘   Def. of midpoint   HL Theorem
  └──────────────┘     Def. of bisector
      Given                                ┌──────────┐
                                           │ CD ≅ EA  │
                                           └──────────┘
                                              Given
```

Additional Examples

FOR EXAMPLE 1 ·····························

From the information given in the diagram, can you prove $\triangle TIA \cong \triangle XIA$? Explain.

Yes; $\angle TIA$ and $\angle XIA$ are right angles. Therefore, $\triangle TIA$ and $\triangle XIA$ are right triangles. The hypotenuses of the triangles are congruent ($\overline{TA} \cong \overline{XA}$) and a pair of legs are congruent ($\overline{IA} \cong \overline{IA}$). Therefore the triangles are congruent by the HL Theorem.

FOR EXAMPLE 2 ·····························

Write a flow proof.

Given: $\overline{BD} \perp \overline{AC}$, $\overline{AB} \cong \overline{CB}$
Prove: $\triangle ADB \cong \triangle CDB$

See back of book.

421

Technology Options

For Exercise 11, students may use graphing software to graph the figure. For Exercise 16, students may use geometry software or a drawing program to draw the triangles.

Prentice Hall Technology

 Software
- Secondary Math Lab Toolkit™
- Computer Item Generator 8-3

 CD-ROM
- Multimedia Geometry Lab 8

 Internet
- See the Prentice Hall site. (http://www.phschool.com)

422

2. *Critical Thinking* Suppose you know that two legs of one right triangle are congruent to two legs of another right triangle. How could you prove the triangles congruent? Explain. **Since the rt. angles are ≅, the △s are ≅ by SAS.**

3. **Try This** Complete the proof.

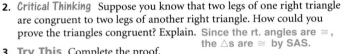

Given: $\overline{WJ} \cong \overline{KZ}$, ∠JWZ and ∠ZKJ right angles.
Prove: $\triangle WJZ \cong \triangle KZJ$

Statements	Reasons
1. ∠JWZ and ∠ZKJ are rt. ∡s.	a. __?__ Given
2. △WJZ and △KZJ are rt. ▵.	b. __?__ Def. of rt. △
c. __?__ $\overline{JZ} \cong \overline{JZ}$	3. Reflexive Property of ≅
d. __?__ $\overline{WJ} \cong \overline{KZ}$	4. Given
5. △WJZ ≅ △KZJ	e. __?__ HL Thm.

Exercises ON YOUR OWN

1. *Standardized Test Prep* Which set of conditions does *not* provide enough information to prove that △ABC ≅ △ADC? **E**
   - **A.** ∠1 ≅ ∠2, ∠5 ≅ ∠6
   - **B.** $\overline{AD} \cong \overline{AB}$, ∠3 and ∠4 are right angles.
   - **C.** $\overline{AD} \cong \overline{AB}$, $\overline{DC} \cong \overline{BC}$
   - **D.** ∠5 ≅ ∠6, ∠3 and ∠4 are right angles.
   - **E.** $\overline{AD} \cong \overline{AB}$, ∠5 ≅ ∠6

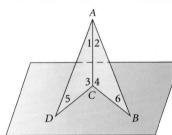

What additional information would you need to prove the triangles congruent by the HL Theorem?

2. △BLT ≅ △RKQ

∠T and ∠Q are rt. angles.

3. △XRV ≅ △TRV

$\overline{XV} \cong \overline{TV}$ or $\overline{RX} \cong \overline{RT}$

4. △TRY ≅ △EYR

$\overline{TY} \cong \overline{ER}$ or $\overline{TR} \cong \overline{EY}$

5. △ACQ ≅ △GCJ

∠AQC and ∠GJC are rt. angles.

6. △BDC ≅ △FEA

$\overline{BC} \cong \overline{FA}$

7. △STR ≅ △PQN

$\overline{RT} \cong \overline{NQ}$

DIVERSITY Exercise 9 Take this opportunity to discuss careers in landscaping and horticulture. Help students see the wide range of skills required in such fields. For example, a landscaper designs landscapes, uses plants to improve air quality in buildings, knows the climate and soil conditions required by different plants, and is an expert in plant diseases. Have students research the educational requirements to become a landscape architect.

COORDINATE GEOMETRY Exercise 11 Students use the relationship between the slopes of perpendicular lines to show that △EGD and △EGF are right triangles.

Exercises 12–13 Encourage students to begin by writing a plan for each proof.

MAKING CONNECTIONS Exercise 14 Aristarchus of Samos is also known for his belief in a heliocentric world system, the view of the universe that places Earth and other planets in motion around the Sun. His beliefs were rejected in favor of a geocentric world system, which places Earth at the center of the universe, until the sixteenth century when Copernicus demonstrated the superiority of the heliocentric system in explaining astronomic observations.

RESEARCH Exercise 14b Students will need to research the distance from the Sun to Earth (≈ 93,000,000 mi.) and from the moon to Earth (≈ 240,000 mi.). They should be able to find this information in an almanac or an encyclopedia.

8. **Critical Thinking** Quadrilateral *ABCD* is a kite with *AB* = *AD* and *BC* = *DC*. ∠*ABC* and ∠*ADC* are right angles. Name all the pairs of congruent right triangles in the diagram. For each pair, explain how you know that the triangles are congruent. **See margin.**

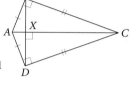

9. **Writing** While working for a landscape architect, you are told to lay out a flower bed in the shape of a right triangle with sides of 3 yd and 7 yd. Explain what else you need to know in order to make the flower bed. **You need to know which side is the hypotenuse.**

10. **Geometry in 3 Dimensions** Write a paragraph proof.
   Given: $\overline{BE} \perp \overline{EA}$, $\overline{BE} \perp \overline{EC}$, △*ABC* is equilateral.
   Prove: △*AEB* ≅ △*CEB* **See margin.**

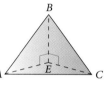

11. **a.** **Coordinate Geometry** Graph the points *E*(−1, −1), *F*(−2, −6), *G*(−4, −4), and *D*(−6, −2). Connect the points with segments.
   b. Find the slopes of $\overline{DG}$, $\overline{GF}$, and $\overline{GE}$. **−1; −1; 1**
   c. Use your answer to part (b) to describe ∠*EGD* and ∠*EGF*. **They are rt. ∠s.**
   d. Use the Distance Formula to find *DE* and *FE*. **$\sqrt{26}$; $\sqrt{26}$**
   e. Write a paragraph to prove that △*EGD* ≅ △*EGF*. **See margin.**

Write a two-column proof. **12–13. See margin.**

12. **Given:** $\overline{EB} \cong \overline{DB}$, ∠*A* and ∠*C* are right angles, *B* is the midpoint of $\overline{AC}$.
   Prove: △*BEA* ≅ △*BDC*

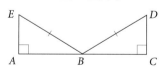

13. **Given:** ⊙*O*, ∠*M* and ∠*N* are right angles.
   Prove: △*LMO* ≅ △*LNO*

14. **History** About 300 B.C., Aristarchus of Samos devised a method for determining the relative distances to the sun and moon. He reasoned that the angle between the sun, the moon, and Earth is 90° when they are positioned as shown in the diagram.
   a. Explain why the two triangles shown must be congruent.
   b. **Research** Aristarchus also reasoned that it takes longer for the moon to go from the first quarter to the last quarter than from the last to the first. He attempted the difficult measurement of that time difference and used it to find the size of the angles of the triangles. From this he estimated that the sun is 20 times farther from us than the moon is. How accurate was his estimate?
   a–b. See margin p. 424.

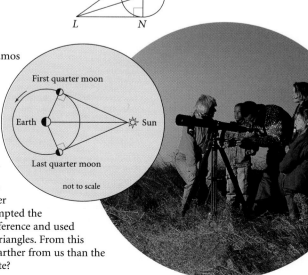

First quarter moon

Earth

Sun

Last quarter moon

not to scale

---

pages 422–424 On Your Own

8. △*ABC* ≅ △*ADC* by SSS Post. or SAS Post.; △*ABX* ≅ △*ADX* by HL Thm.; △*BXC* ≅ △*DXC* by HL Thm.

10. Since △*ABC* is equilateral, $\overline{AB} \cong \overline{CB}$. △*AEB* and △*CEB* have the leg $\overline{BE}$ in common. Since both △s are rt. △s by def., △*AEB* ≅ △*CEB* by HL Thm.

11a.

12. 1. ∠*A* and ∠*C* are rt. angles. (Given) 2. △*BEA* and △*BDC* are rt. △s. (Def. of rt. △s) 3. *B* is the midpt. of $\overline{AC}$. (Given) 4. $\overline{AB} \cong \overline{CB}$ (Def. of midpoint) 5. $\overline{EB} \cong \overline{DB}$ (Given) 6. △*BEA* ≅ △*BDC* (HL Thm.)

e. △*EGD* and △*EGF* share a common leg $\overline{EG}$. Since the hypotenuses are ≅, the right △s are ≅ by HL Thm.

13. 1. $\overline{OM}$ and $\overline{ON}$ are radii of ⊙*O*. (Given) 2. $\overline{OM} \cong \overline{ON}$ (All radii of a ⊙ are ≅.) 3. ∠*M* and ∠*N* are rt. angles. (Given) 4. △*LMO* and △*LNO* are rt. △s. (Def. of rt. △s) 5. $\overline{OL} \cong \overline{OL}$ (Reflexive Prop. of ≅) 6. △*LMO* ≅ △*LNO* (HL Thm.)

423

14a. The △s are rt. △s with a common hypotenuse and ≅ legs. By HL Thm., the △s are ≅.

b. His estimate was inaccurate. The sun is about 390 times further away from Earth than the moon.

15. Measure the distance from the corner of the room to one corner of the table. The room is a rectangle, so the table forms a rt. △ with the walls. Since the length of the table is the hypotenuse and is the same for each △, if 1 pair of legs are ≅, the △s are ≅ by the HL Thm.

16a. **18.**

19.

20.

15. *Open-ended* A table has been placed in the corner of a room. What measurements would you make with a tape measure in order to place a matching table in the other corner at exactly the same angle? Explain why your method works. **See margin for sample.**

16. a. *Open-ended* Draw a triangle that has line symmetry and one that does not have line symmetry. **See margin for sample.**

b. *Critical Thinking* Explain why any triangle with line symmetry must be isosceles. **See below.**

17. *Clock Repair* To repair an antique clock, a 12-toothed wheel has to be made by cutting right triangles out of a regular polygon that has twelve 4-cm sides. The hypotenuse of each triangle is a side of the regular polygon, and the shorter leg is 1 cm long. Explain why the twelve triangles must be congruent. **See below.**

Constructions **Copy the triangle on your paper and construct a triangle congruent to it using the method stated.** 18–20. See margin for samples.

18. by SAS

19. by HL

20. by ASA

16b. The sides that are images of each other must be ≅.
17. All sides of a regular polygon are ≅. Since the △s are rt. △s and the shorter legs of all the △s are ≅, by HL Thm., all the △s are ≅.

424

Exercises 21–26 Students review the relationship between pairs of angles formed when two parallel lines are cut by a transversal.

GETTING READY FOR LESSON 8-4 These exercises prepare students to use triangle congruence to prove parts of triangles congruent.

In this Checkpoint, your students will assess their own progress in Lessons 8-1 to 8-3.

Exercises 1–6 Students may want to begin by making a list of all the ways they can prove two triangles congruent.

OPEN-ENDED Exercise 7 Ask students if they can draw a pair of right triangles with the given conditions.

Wrap Up

THE BIG IDEA Ask students to explain why the HL Theorem only applies to right triangles.

RETEACHING ACTIVITY Students determine if triangles are congruent by the HL Theorem. (Reteaching worksheet 8-3)

Exercises   MIXED REVIEW

State the postulate or theorem that justifies each statement.

21. $m\angle 1 + m\angle 3 = 180$ **22.** $\angle 5 \cong \angle 8$

23. $m\angle 4 + m\angle 8 = 180$ **24.** $\angle 3 \cong \angle 7$

25. $\angle 1 \cong \angle 6$ **26.** $\angle 5 \cong \angle 11$
21–26. See back of book.

 27. Calculator A circle has radius 5 m. Two radii form a 35° angle. What is the area of the sector between them to the nearest hundredth? **7.64 m²**

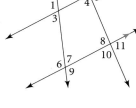

Getting Ready for Lesson 8-4

28. Given that $\triangle TRC \cong \triangle HGV$, list everything you know about the two triangles.
$\angle T \cong \angle H$; $\angle C \cong \angle V$; $\angle R \cong \angle G$;
$\overline{TR} \cong \overline{HG}$; $\overline{RC} \cong \overline{GV}$; $\overline{TC} \cong \overline{HV}$

Exercises   CHECKPOINT

State the postulate or theorem you can use to prove the triangles congruent. If the triangles cannot be proven congruent, write not possible.

1.   ASA

2.   SSS

3.   SAS

4.

5.

6.

not possible   AAS   HL

7. a. Open-ended Draw two triangles that have two pairs of congruent sides and one pair of congruent angles, but are not congruent. **See back of book for sample.**
   b. Can you draw two noncongruent triangles that have two pairs of congruent angles and one pair of congruent sides? Explain. **See back of book.**

8. Standardized Test Prep Which congruence statement cannot be used to prove two triangles congruent? **E**
   A. AAS   **B.** SAS   **C.** SSS   **D.** ASA   **E.** AAA

9. Writing Use the HL Theorem as a model to write an HA Theorem. Is the theorem true? **Justify** your answer. **See back of book.**

Lesson Quiz

Lesson Quiz is also available in Transparencies.

Give the additional information needed to prove the triangles congruent by the HL Theorem.

1. $\triangle BAT \cong \triangle GEM$
   $\angle B$ and $\angle G$ are right angles
   $\overline{BA} \cong \overline{GE}$
   $\overline{AT} \cong \overline{EM}$

2. $\triangle MNO \cong \triangle PQR$
   $\overline{MN} \cong \overline{PQ}$
   $\overline{MO} \cong \overline{PR}$
   $\angle N$ and $\angle Q$ are right angles

3. $\triangle CDE \cong \triangle CDF$
   $\overline{CD} \perp \overline{EF}$
   $\overline{CE} \cong \overline{CF}$

4. $\triangle FOR \cong \triangle MIK$
   $\angle F$ and $\angle M$ are right angles
   $\overline{OR} \cong \overline{IK}$
   $\overline{FO} \cong \overline{MI}$ or $\overline{FR} \cong \overline{MK}$

425

CONNECTING TO PRIOR KNOWLEDGE Draw the following triangles. Ask students: *If △GHI ≅ △JKL by the SSS Postulate, can you say that ∠H ≅ ∠K? ∠I ≅ ∠J?*

THINK AND DISCUSS

The abbreviation CPCTC is helpful when writing reasons in proofs. Encourage students, however, to state the entire phrase when verbalizing it.

ERROR ALERT! Question 1 Students may not recognize that $\overline{AB} \parallel \overline{DC}$. **Remediation:** Suggest that they extend $\overline{AB}, \overline{DC},$ and $\overline{DB}$. This will help them recognize that $\overleftrightarrow{DB}$ is a transversal cutting $\overleftrightarrow{AB}$ and $\overleftrightarrow{DC}$.

Lesson Planning Options

Prerequisite Skills

- Applying the SSS, SAS, and ASA Postulates and the AAS and HL Theorems
- Writing Proofs

Assignment Options for Exercises On Your Own

To provide flexible scheduling, this lesson can be subdivided into parts.

1. **Core** 1–8, 10, 12
   Extension 15

2. **Core** 9, 11, 13, 16–17
   Extension 14

Use Mixed Review to maintain skills.

Resources

Student Edition

Skills Handbook, p. 650
Extra Practice, p. 641
Glossary/Study Guide

Teaching Resources

Chapter Support File, Ch. 8
- Practice 8-4 (two worksheets)
- Reteaching 8-4
Classroom Manager 8-4
Glossary, Spanish Resources

Transparencies
87

What You'll Learn
- Using triangle congruence and CPCTC to prove that parts of two triangles are congruent

...And Why

To see how triangle congruence has been used in the past to measure distances indirectly

Connections History . . . *and more*

8-4 **U**sing Congruent Triangles in Proofs

THINK AND DISCUSS

Part 1 **Using CPCTC**

In the previous lessons you learned to use SSS, SAS, ASA, AAS, and HL to prove that two triangles are congruent. Once you know that triangles are congruent, you can make conclusions about corresponding segments and angles because **C**orresponding **P**arts of **C**ongruent **T**riangles are **C**ongruent. A shorthand way of writing this is **CPCTC.**

1. a. Suppose you know that △ABD ≅ △CDB by SAS. Which additional pairs of sides and angles are congruent by CPCTC?

   b. *Critical Thinking* What other conclusions can you make about segments in this figure?

a. $\overline{AD} \cong \overline{CB}, \angle A \cong \angle C, \angle 2 \cong \angle 3$ **b.** $\overline{AB} \parallel \overline{DC}, \overline{AD} \parallel \overline{BC}$

Example 1

Given: $\overline{AC} \cong \overline{EC}, \overline{BC} \cong \overline{DC}$
Prove: $\angle A \cong \angle E$

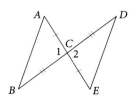

Plan for Proof You can show that $\angle A \cong \angle E$ if you can show that these angles are corresponding parts of congruent triangles. Prove that △ABC ≅ △EDC and then use CPCTC.

Statements	Reasons
1. $\overline{AC} \cong \overline{EC}$	1. Given
2. $\overline{BC} \cong \overline{DC}$	2. Given
3. $\angle 1 \cong \angle 2$	3. Vertical angles are ≅.
4. △ABC ≅ △EDC	4. SAS Postulate
5. $\angle A \cong \angle E$	5. CPCTC

2. a. *Try This* State two relationships that are true for $\overline{AB}$ and $\overline{ED}$ in Example 1. $\overline{AB} \parallel \overline{ED}, \overline{AB} \cong \overline{ED}$

   b. *Justify* your answers. **If ≅ corres. ∠s, then lines are ∥; CPCTC**

Example 1

Emphasize that the intermediate step of this proof is proving $\triangle ABC \cong \triangle EDC$. Once this is proven, you can use CPCTC to prove the angles congruent.

Question 2b Students should not have difficulty with this question if they successfully answered Question 1.

Example 2 — Relating to the Real World

ESL Some students may be unfamiliar with the expression "paced off." You may want to demonstrate what it means by pacing off the length of the classroom.

Discuss with students the logical reasoning given in the proof. Begin by discussing why $\angle 1 \cong \angle 2$ and why $\angle 3$ and $\angle 4$ are right angles. Point out that, although $\triangle DEF$ and $\triangle DEG$ are right triangles, they cannot be proven congruent by HL because you do not know $\overline{DF} \cong \overline{DG}$.

KINESTHETIC LEARNING If you have block scheduling or an extended class period, you may want to have students reenact the measurement technique. Students could use congruent triangles to measure indirectly across a football field, part of a parking lot, or a local road. Then they could find the actual measurement and compare the results.

According to legend, one of Napoleon's officers used congruent triangles to estimate the width of a river. The officer stood on the riverbank and lowered the visor of his cap until the farthest thing he could see was the edge of the opposite bank of the river. He then turned and noted the spot on his side of the river that was in line with his eye and the tip of his visor. The officer then paced off the distance to this spot and declared that distance to be the width of the river!

Example 2 — Relating to the Real World

History Write a proof to show why Napoleon's officer was correct in stating that the distance he paced off equaled the distance across the river.

Given: $\angle EDG \cong \angle EDF$, $\angle DEG$ and $\angle DEF$ are right angles.
Prove: $\overline{EF} \cong \overline{EG}$

Statements	Reasons
1. $\angle EDG \cong \angle EDF$	1. Given
2. $\overline{DE} \cong \overline{DE}$	2. Reflexive Property of $\cong$
3. $\angle DEG$ and $\angle DEF$ are right $\angle$.	3. Given
4. $\angle DEG \cong \angle DEF$	4. All right angles are $\cong$.
5. $\triangle DEF \cong \triangle DEG$	5. ASA Postulate
6. $\overline{EF} \cong \overline{EG}$	6. CPCTC

PROBLEM SOLVING

Look Back What other angles or sides can be proven congruent in Example 2?

$\angle G \cong \angle F,$
$\overline{DG} \cong \overline{DF}$

3. About how wide was the river if the officer stepped off 20 paces and each pace was about $2\frac{1}{2}$ ft? **about 50 ft**

Additional Examples

FOR EXAMPLE 1 ....

Write a plan for the proof.

Given: $\angle M \cong \angle P$, X is the midpoint of $\overline{MP}$.
Prove: $\overline{MN} \cong \overline{PO}$. **See back of book.**

FOR EXAMPLE 2 ....

The legs of an ironing board bisect each other. Write a proof to show the board is parallel to the floor by showing that the alternate interior angles are congruent. **See back of book.**

FOR EXAMPLE 3 ....

Write a paragraph proof.

Given: $\angle D \cong \angle B$, $\angle DAC \cong \angle BCA$
Prove: $\overline{AB} \cong \overline{CD}$ **See back of book.**

427

Example 3 ·······················

In Example 3, students draw the bisector of the vertex angle and show that the triangles formed are congruent by the SAS Postulate. In Question 4, students draw the altitude from the vertex angle and show that the two triangles formed are congruent by the HL Theorem. In Exercise 13 students will prove that the bisector of the vertex angle of an isosceles triangle is the perpendicular bisector of the base.

Example 4 ·······················

Help students understand how the hypothesis and conclusion of the Angle Bisector Theorem are translated into the Given and Prove statements of the proof. Make sure students understand why proving $\overline{PM} \cong \overline{PN}$ implies that P is equidistant from $\overrightarrow{LM}$ and $\overrightarrow{LN}$.

Technology Options

For Exercises 16–17, students may perform the construction using geometry software.

Prentice Hall Technology

Software
• Secondary Math Lab Toolkit™
• Computer Item Generator 8-4

Internet
• See the Prentice Hall site. (http://www.phschool.com)

QUICK REVIEW

Isosceles Triangle Theorem
If two sides of a triangle are congruent, then the angles opposite those sides are congruent.

4d. By def., $\overline{XA} \perp \overline{YZ}$ and $\triangle XYA$ and $\triangle XZA$ are rt. $\triangle$s. It is given that $\overline{XY} \cong \overline{XZ}$, and by Reflexive Prop. of $\cong$, $\overline{XA} \cong \overline{XA}$. Thus, $\triangle XYA \cong \triangle XZA$ by HL Thm., and $\angle Y \cong \angle Z$ by CPCTC.

QUICK REVIEW

Angle Bisector Theorem
If a point is on the bisector of an angle, then it is equidistant from the sides of the angle.

The **distance from a point to a line** is the length of the perpendicular segment from the point to the line.

Part 2 Proving Theorems

You can use congruent triangles to prove many of the theorems you discovered in earlier chapters.

Example 3

Write a paragraph proof of the Isosceles Triangle Theorem.

Begin with isosceles $\triangle XYZ$ with $\overline{XY} \cong \overline{XZ}$. Draw $\overline{XB}$, the bisector of the vertex angle $\angle X$.

Given: $\overline{XY} \cong \overline{XZ}$, $\overline{XB}$ bisects $\angle YXZ$.
Prove: $\angle Y \cong \angle Z$

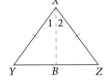

Paragraph Proof

By the definition of angle bisector, $\angle 1 \cong \angle 2$. You are given that $\overline{XY} \cong \overline{XZ}$, and by the Reflexive Property of Congruence, $\overline{XB} \cong \overline{XB}$. Thus, $\triangle XYB \cong \triangle XZB$ by the SAS Postulate, and $\angle Y \cong \angle Z$ by CPCTC. ∎

4. **Try This** There is more than one way to prove the Isosceles Triangle Theorem. Complete the following steps for a different proof.
   a. Use $\triangle XYZ$ from Example 3 and instead of drawing the bisector of $\angle X$, draw the altitude $\overline{XA}$ from X to $\overline{YZ}$. **See margin p. 429.**
   b. Write a new *Given* statement. $\overline{XY} \cong \overline{XZ}$, $\overline{XA}$ is altitude of $\triangle XYZ$.
   c. What postulate or theorem can you use to prove $\triangle XYA \cong \triangle XZA$? **HL Thm**
   d. Write your proof in paragraph form. **See left.**

Example 4 outlines a proof of the Angle Bisector Theorem.

Example 4

Write a plan for the following proof.

Given: $\overrightarrow{LP}$ bisects $\angle MLN$,
$\overline{PM} \perp \overrightarrow{LM}$,
$\overline{PN} \perp \overrightarrow{LN}$
Prove: $\overline{PM} \cong \overline{PN}$

Plan for Proof $\overline{PM}$ and $\overline{PN}$ are corresponding parts of $\triangle LMP$ and $\triangle LNP$. These triangles are congruent by the AAS Theorem because a bisector forms congruent angles, perpendiculars form congruent right angles, and $\overline{LP} \cong \overline{LP}$ by the Reflexive Property of Congruence. ∎

5. *Choose* Use the Plan for Proof in Example 4. Write a two-column proof, a paragraph proof, or a flow proof.
   Answers may vary. See margin p. 429 for sample.

428

Exercises ON YOUR OWN

Exercises 1–6 Make sure students state the triangle congruence as part of their explanation.

TACTILE LEARNING Exercise 7 Have students draw the quadrilateral with sides as marked in the figure. Have students justify their answers by measuring ∠A and ∠C with a protractor.

MAKING CONNECTIONS Exercise 8 The city of Ubar, believed to have existed in Southwestern Oman from 2800 B.C. to about 100 A.D., fell into a sinkhole created by the collapse of an underground limestone cavern. Called "Atlantis of the sands" by Lawrence of Arabia, the fabled city was located in 1992 using images from satellites and spacecraft.

CRITICAL THINKING Exercise 8 Ask students if it is possible to find the diameter of the sinkhole using the technique of Napoleon's officers described in Example 2.

Exercises ON YOUR OWN

Explain how you would use SSS, SAS, ASA, AAS, or HL with CPCTC to prove each statement.

1. $\overline{AB} \cong \overline{CB}$

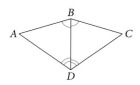

Use ASA to prove △ABD ≅ △CBD.

2. ∠M ≅ ∠R

Use SSS to prove △EMO ≅ △ORE.

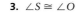

3. ∠S ≅ ∠O

Use SAS to prove △STP ≅ △OTP.

4. $\overline{KP} \cong \overline{LM}$

Use SAS to prove △KPN ≅ △LMN.

5. ∠R ≅ ∠P

Use HL to prove △OER ≅ △OEP.

6. $\overline{CT} \cong \overline{RP}$

Use AAS to prove △CYT ≅ △RYP.

7. Karen cut this pattern for stained glass so that AB = CB and AD = CD. Must ∠A be congruent to ∠C? How do you know? Explain.

Yes; the △s are ≅ by SSS, and the angles are ≅ by CPCTC.

EARTH NEWS

Sinkhole Swallows House

The large sinkhole in this photo occurred suddenly in 1981 in Winter Park, Florida, following a severe drought. Increased water consumption speeds formation of sinkholes by lowering the water table. This leads to the collapse of underground caverns that have formed in underlying limestone.

8. A geometry class indirectly measured the distance across a sinkhole in a nearby field. They measured distances as shown in the diagram. Explain how to use their measurements to find the distance across the sinkhole. **The vertical angles are ≅, so the △s are also ≅ by SAS. The distance across the sinkhole is 26.5 yd by CPCTC.**

pages 426–428 Think and Discuss

4a.

5. $\overrightarrow{LP}$ bisects ∠MLN (Given) 2. ∠1 ≅ ∠2 (Def. of angle bisector) 3. $\overline{PM} \perp \overline{LM}$ and $\overline{PN} \perp \overline{LN}$ (Given) 4. ∠LMP and ∠LNP are rt. ∠s. (Def. of ⊥ lines) 5. ∠LMP ≅ ∠LNP (All rt. ∠s are ≅.) 6. $\overline{LP} \cong \overline{LP}$ (Reflexive Prop. of ≅) 7. △LMP ≅ △LNP (AAS) 8. $\overline{PM} \cong \overline{PN}$ (CPCTC)

9. Theorem 4-3 states that if two angles of a triangle are congruent, then the sides opposite the angles are congruent.

To prove this theorem, begin with $\triangle ABC$ with $\angle A \cong \angle C$ and draw the bisector of $\angle B$. Supply a reason for each statement in the proof.

Given: $\angle A \cong \angle C$, $\overline{BD}$ bisects $\angle ABC$.
Prove: $\overline{AB} \cong \overline{CB}$

Statements	Reasons
1. $\angle A \cong \angle C$	a. __?__ Given
2. $\overline{BD}$ bisects $\angle ABC$.	b. __?__ Given
3. $\angle 1 \cong \angle 2$	c. __?__ Def. of angle bisector
4. $\overline{BD} \cong \overline{BD}$	d. __?__ Reflexive Prop. of $\cong$
5. $\triangle ABD \cong \triangle CBD$	e. __?__ AAS
6. $\overline{AB} \cong \overline{CB}$	f. __?__ CPCTC

10. The reasons given in the proof below are correct, but they are in the wrong order. List them in the correct order. d, c, e, b, a

Given: O is the center of the circle.
Prove: $\overline{AB} \cong \overline{CD}$

Statements	Reasons
1. O is the center of the circle.	a. CPCTC
2. $\overline{AO} \cong \overline{CO}$, $\overline{BO} \cong \overline{DO}$	b. SAS Postulate
3. $\angle 1 \cong \angle 2$	c. All radii of a circle are $\cong$.
4. $\triangle ABO \cong \triangle CDO$	d. Given
5. $\overline{AB} \cong \overline{CD}$	e. Vertical angles are $\cong$.

11. Theorem 4-12 states that if a point is on the perpendicular bisector of a segment, then it is equidistant from the endpoints of the segment.

Supply the reasons for the following flow proof of the theorem.

Given: $\ell \perp \overline{AB}$, ℓ bisects $\overline{AB}$ at C, P is on ℓ.
Prove: $PA = PB$

CRITICAL THINKING Exercise 13 Ask students to use the diagram from Exercise 13 and write a plan to prove the following. Then have them discuss the similarities and differences between their plan and the Plan for Proof given in Exercise 13.

Given: Isosceles △ABC with $\overline{BD} \perp \overline{AC}$, $\overline{BD}$ bisects $\overline{AC}$.
Prove: $\overline{BA} \cong \overline{BC}$, $\overline{BD}$ bisects ∠ABC.

Exercise 14 Make sure students understand that *O* is the center of the circle.

CONSTRUCTIONS Exercises 16–17 Students use congruent triangles to justify two of the constructions they learned in Lesson 1-6 and 7-3.

---

12. *Choose* Write a two-column proof, a paragraph proof, or a flow proof. **Answers may vary. See margin for sample.**

    Given: $\overline{FB} \perp \overline{AD}$, $\overline{GC} \perp \overline{AD}$,
    $\overline{FB} \cong \overline{GC}$, $\overline{AE} \cong \overline{DE}$
    Prove: $\overline{AB} \cong \overline{DC}$

13. Theorem 4-2 states that the bisector of the vertex angle of an isosceles triangle is the perpendicular bisector of the base. **Answers may vary. See margin for sample.**

    Use the following Plan for Proof to write a paragraph proof for the theorem.

    Given: Isosceles △ABC with $\overline{BA} \cong \overline{BC}$,
    $\overline{BD}$ bisects ∠ABC.
    Prove: $\overline{BD} \perp \overline{AC}$, $\overline{BD}$ bisects $\overline{AC}$.

    Plan for Proof You can show that $\overline{BD} \perp \overline{AC}$ by showing that ∠BDA ≅ ∠BDC and using the fact that congruent supplementary angles are right angles. You can show that $\overline{BD}$ bisects $\overline{AC}$ by showing that $\overline{AD} \cong \overline{CD}$. These angles and segments are corresponding parts of △ABD and △CBD. Prove that △ABD ≅ △CBD.

14. *Choose* Write a two-column proof, a paragraph proof, or a flow proof.

    Given: $\overline{ZK} \perp \overline{JQ}$ in ⊙O
    Prove: $\overline{JW} \cong \overline{QW}$

    Answers may vary.
    See margin for sample.

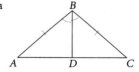

15. **a.** How can you prove △BGF ≅ △BGD? **Use SAS on 2 legs and rt. angle.**
    b. BD = 8 cm. What other segment is 8 cm long? *Justify* your answer. **$\overline{BF}$; CPCTC**
    c. How can you prove △FAB ≅ △BCD? (*Hint:* Use your results from part (b).) **The △s are rt. △s with ≅ hypotenuses and ≅ legs. By HL, △FAB ≅ △BCD.**

16. *Constructions* The construction of the bisector of ∠A is shown below.

  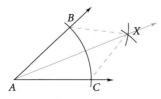

$\overline{AB} \cong \overline{AC}$ because they are radii of the same circle. $\overline{BX} \cong \overline{CX}$ because the same compass setting was used to draw both arcs. Use these facts to prove that $\overrightarrow{AX}$ bisects ∠BAC. $\overline{AX} \cong \overline{AX}$ by Reflexive Prop. of ≅. △ABX ≅ △ACX by SSS, and ∠BAX ≅ ∠CAX by CPCTC. $\overrightarrow{AX}$ bisects ∠BAC by def. of angle bisector.

---

pages 429–432 On Your Own

12. 1. $\overline{AE} \cong \overline{DE}$ (Given) 2. △AED is isosceles. (Def. of isos. △) 3. ∠A ≅ ∠D (Base ∠s of an isosceles △ are ≅.) 4. $\overline{FB} \perp \overline{AD}$, $\overline{GC} \perp \overline{AD}$ (Given) 5. ∠ABF and ∠DCG are rt. ∠s. (Def. of ⊥ lines) 6. ∠ABF ≅ ∠DCG (All rt. ∠s are ≅.) 7. $\overline{FB} \cong \overline{GC}$ (Given) 8. △ABF ≅ △DCG (AAS) 9. $\overline{AB} \cong \overline{DC}$ (CPCTC)

13. It is given that $\overline{BA} \cong \overline{BC}$ and $\overline{BD}$ bisects ∠ABC. ∠ABD ≅ ∠CBD by def. of ∠ bisector, and ∠A ≅ ∠C because base ∠s of an isosceles △ are ≅. Then △ABD ≅ △CBD by ASA. $\overline{AD} \cong \overline{CD}$ by CPCTC. Therefore, $\overline{BD}$ bisects $\overline{AC}$ by def. of segment bisector. By the Angle Addition Post., m∠ADB + m∠CDB = 180. ∠ADB ≅ ∠CDB by CPCTC. So, the measure of each angle is $\frac{1}{2}$(180) = 90, and ∠s are rt. by def. of rt. ∠s. Therefore, $\overline{BD} \perp \overline{AC}$ by def. of ⊥ lines.

14. 1. $\overline{OJ} \cong \overline{OQ}$ (All radii of a ⊙ are ≅.) 2. $\overline{OW} \cong \overline{OW}$ (Reflexive Prop. of ≅) 3. $\overline{ZK} \perp \overline{JQ}$ (Given) 4. ∠OWJ and ∠OWQ are rt. angles. (Def. of ⊥ lines) 5. △OWJ and △OWQ are rt. △s. (Def. of rt. △) 6. △OJW ≅ △OQW (HL Thm.) 7. $\overline{JW} \cong \overline{QW}$ (CPCTC)

17b. $\overline{CP} \cong \overline{CP}$ by Reflexive Prop. of ≅. Then, △APC ≅ △BPC by SSS and ∠APC ≅ ∠BPC by CPCTC. Therefore, m∠APC = m∠BPC = 90 by Angle Addition Post., and the ∠s are rt. by def. of rt. ∠s. Then, $\overline{CP} \perp \overline{AB}$ by def. of ⊥ lines.

431

Exercises MIXED REVIEW

Exercises 18–20 Students review transformations.

CONNECTING TO STUDENTS' WORLD Exercise 21 Have students survey each other to find out how many school days a year students miss due to colds. Then have them display the data in a circle graph.

GETTING READY FOR LESSON 8-5 These exercises prepare students to identify congruent overlapping triangles.

Wrap Up

THE BIG IDEA Ask students: *Explain how congruent triangles can be used to measure indirectly.*

RETEACHING ACTIVITY Students use triangle congruence and CPCTC to complete a two-column proof, then write two two-column proofs. (Reteaching worksheet 8-4)

Lesson Quiz

Lesson Quiz is also available in Transparencies.

Explain how you could use SSS, SAS, ASA, AAS, or HL with CPCTC to prove each statement.

1. $\angle PQR \cong \angle TQR$
See back of book.

2. $\overline{FG} \cong \overline{FI}$
See back of book.

3. Write a proof.
Given: $\overline{DC} \cong \overline{CE}$ and $\overline{DE}$ is a diameter in $\odot O$.
Prove: $\angle DOC$ and $\angle COE$ are right angles. See back of book.

432

---

17. Constructions The construction of a line perpendicular to line ℓ through point P on ℓ is shown here. **a.** $\overline{PA} \cong \overline{PB}$; $\overline{AC} \cong \overline{BC}$
  a. Which segments are congruent by construction?
  b. Prove that $\overleftrightarrow{CP}$ is perpendicular to ℓ. (*Hint:* Copy the diagram and draw $\overline{CA}$ and $\overline{CB}$.) See margin p. 431.

Exercises MIXED REVIEW

Copy each figure and draw its image under the given transformation.

18. reflection in line m

19. 90° counterclockwise rotation about point P

20. a translation of $\langle -2, 4 \rangle$

Data Analysis For Exercises 21–23, use the circle graph.

21. What percent of people knew the number of days they take off from work because of colds? **89%**

22. What percent of the people said they take off four or fewer days annually because of colds? **84%**

23. What is the measure of the central angle of the sector for the people who take one or two days off because of colds? **about 79°**

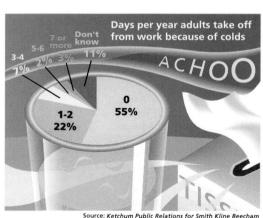

Source: Ketchum Public Relations for Smith Kline Beecham

Getting Ready For Lesson 8-5

Copy and label each triangle. Draw its image under a reflection in the red line. State which sides or angles a pair of triangles have in common.

24.

$\overline{AC}$

25.

$\angle E$

26.

$\angle G$

PROBLEM OF THE DAY

How many noncongruent triangles can you make by joining any three points on a 3-by-3 dot grid? **8**

Problem of the Day is also available in Transparencies.

CONNECTING TO PRIOR KNOWLEDGE Draw the figure on the board and have students identify all the triangles. Ask them which triangles appear congruent.

ESL Some students may not understand the term overlapping. Use an overhead projector and transparencies with overlays to illustrate its meaning.

Question 1 Some students will see the overlapping triangles △AFC and △BCF but miss △ABC and △BAF.

THINK AND DISCUSS

Example 1

VISUAL LEARNING Students can visualize discrete triangles in a complex figure by using tracing paper to redraw overlapping triangles separately.

What You'll Learn

- Identifying congruent overlapping triangles
- Proving two triangles congruent by first proving two other triangles congruent

...And Why

To be able to visualize overlapping triangles and use pairs of congruent triangles in real-world situations such as engineering

What You'll Need

- tracing paper
- colored pencils or pens

Connections ⊕ Engineering . . . and more

8-5 Using More than One Pair of Congruent Triangles

WORK TOGETHER

Work with a partner. Trace the diagram below and take turns finding pairs of congruent triangles. Use a different colored pencil to outline each pair you find. Then answer the questions below.

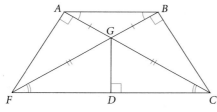

1. Write a congruence statement for each pair of triangles that you colored. State the congruence postulate or theorem you could use to prove the triangles congruent. Compare your results with those of another group. **See back of book.**

2. **a.** Name a pair of congruent triangles that overlap.
   b. Identify the common side the triangles share.
   a. Sample: △ABC, △BAF
   b. For sample in part (a): $\overline{AB}$

Part 1 **THINK AND DISCUSS**

Using Overlapping Triangles in Proofs

In the Work Together, you identified pairs of overlapping triangles that share a common side. Some overlapping triangles share a common angle. It is helpful to separate and redraw the overlapping triangles.

Example 1

Separate and redraw △DFG and △EHG. Identify the common angle.

common angle

Lesson Planning Options

Prerequisite Skills

- Applying the SSS, SAS, and ASA Postulates and the AAS and HL Theorems
- Writing Proofs

Assignment Options for Exercises On Your Own

To provide flexible scheduling, this lesson can be subdivided into parts.

1 **Core** 1–9, 16
   Extension 10

2 **Core** 11–15
   Extension 17–18

Use Mixed Review to maintain skills.

Resources

📖 **Student Edition**
Skills Handbook, p. 650
Extra Practice, p. 641
Glossary/Study Guide

📁 **Teaching Resources**
Chapter Support File, Ch. 8
- Practice 8-5 (two worksheets)
- Reteaching 8-5
Classroom Manager 8-5
Glossary, Spanish Resources

🏛 **Transparencies**
88, 91, 92

433

Additional Examples

FOR EXAMPLE 2 ·····························

Write a two-column proof.

B   C   D
A   E

Given: $\overline{BA} \cong \overline{DE}$, $\overline{BE} \cong \overline{DA}$

Prove: $\angle BEA \cong \angle DAE$ **See back of book.**

FOR EXAMPLE 3 ·····························

Write a paragraph proof.
Given:
$\angle 1 \cong \angle 2$,
$\overline{BD} \cong \overline{BE}$,
$\angle 3 \cong \angle 4$
Prove:
$\triangle DAF \cong \triangle ECF$ **See back of book.**

B
1   2
D   E
3   F   4
A   C

3. **Engineering** The diagram below shows triangles from the scaffolding workers used when they repaired and cleaned the Statue of Liberty.
   a. Identify the common side in $\triangle ADC$ and $\triangle BCD$. $\overline{CD}$
   b. Name another pair of triangles that share a common side.
   Answers may vary. Sample: $\triangle BCD$ and $\triangle BED$

A   F   C
B   D
E

You can use common angles and common sides to prove overlapping triangles congruent.

Example 2 ·····························

Given: $\angle ZWX \cong \angle YXW$,
$\angle ZXW \cong \angle YWX$
Prove: $\overline{WZ} \cong \overline{XY}$

Z   Y
W   X

Separate the overlapping triangles. Then write a two-column proof.

Z   Y
W   X   W   X

Plan for Proof To use CPCTC to show that $\overline{WZ} \cong \overline{XY}$, you must first prove that $\triangle ZWX \cong \triangle YXW$.

Proof

Statements	Reasons
1. $\angle ZWX \cong \angle YXW$, $\angle ZXW \cong \angle YWX$	1. Given
2. $\overline{WX} \cong \overline{WX}$	2. Reflexive Property of $\cong$
3. $\triangle ZWX \cong \triangle YXW$	3. ASA Postulate
4. $\overline{WZ} \cong \overline{XY}$	4. CPCTC

Example 3

Help students see that they cannot prove $\triangle GED \cong \triangle JEB$ from the information given. However, they can prove that $\triangle AED \cong \triangle CEB$. Proving $\triangle AED \cong \triangle CEB$ allows them to identify other pairs of congruent parts to then prove $\triangle GED \cong \triangle JEB$.

CRITICAL THINKING Ask students what they can say about the relationship between segments AB and DC and segments BC and AD. Also ask them what they can conclude about point E.

Question 4 Before students complete the proof, have them read through the statements and write a plan for the proof. Make sure they understand which pairs of triangles are being used and why.

Part 2 Using Two Pairs of Congruent Triangles

Sometimes you can prove that one pair of triangles is congruent and then use corresponding congruent parts of those triangles to prove that another pair of triangles is congruent.

Example 3

Given: E is the midpoint of $\overline{AC}$ and $\overline{DB}$.
Prove: $\triangle GED \cong \triangle JEB$

There is not enough information about $\triangle GED$ and $\triangle JEB$ to prove that they are congruent. But you can prove that $\triangle AED \cong \triangle CEB$. Then you can use corresponding congruent parts of these triangles to prove that $\triangle GED \cong \triangle JEB$.

Paragraph Proof

Since E is the midpoint of $\overline{AC}$ and $\overline{DB}$, $\overline{AE} \cong \overline{CE}$ and $\overline{DE} \cong \overline{BE}$. $\angle AED \cong \angle CEB$ because vertical angles are congruent. Therefore, $\triangle AED \cong \triangle CEB$ by SAS. $\angle D \cong \angle B$ by CPCTC, and $\angle GED \cong \angle JEB$ because they are vertical angles. Therefore, $\triangle GED \cong \triangle JEB$ by ASA.

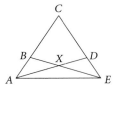

WORK TOGETHER

Work with a partner.

4. Copy and complete the two-column proof below using two pairs of congruent triangles. After you prove the first pair of triangles congruent, separate and redraw the second pair of overlapping triangles that you need to use.

Given: $\overline{CA} \cong \overline{CE}$, $\overline{BA} \cong \overline{DE}$
Prove: $\overline{BX} \cong \overline{DX}$

Statements	Reasons
1. $\overline{CA} \cong \overline{CE}$	a. __?__ Given
2. $\angle CAE \cong \angle CEA$	b. __?__ See below.
3. $\overline{AE} \cong \overline{AE}$	c. __?__ Reflexive Prop. of $\cong$
4. $\overline{BA} \cong \overline{DE}$	d. __?__ Given
5. $\triangle BAE \cong \triangle DEA$	e. __?__ SAS
6. $\angle ABE \cong \angle EDA$	f. __?__ CPCTC
7. $\angle BXA \cong \angle DXE$	g. __?__ Vertical $\angle$s are $\cong$.
8. $\triangle BXA \cong \triangle DXE$	h. __?__ AAS
9. $\overline{BX} \cong \overline{DX}$	i. __?__ CPCTC

b. Base $\angle$s of an isosceles $\triangle$ are $\cong$.

Technology Options

For Exercise 18, students may draw the parallelogram and diagonals using geometry software.

Prentice Hall Technology

Software
• Secondary Math Lab Toolkit™
• Computer Item Generator 8-5

CD-ROM
• Multimedia Geometry Lab 8

Internet
• See the Prentice Hall site. (http://www.phschool.com)

Exercises 1–3 Some students can identify the common side or angle by observation. Some will want to trace the figures separately. Make sure students do not write in the book.

Exercises 4–9 Students should begin by tracing and separating the overlapping triangles. Have them mark the angles and sides that are congruent.

Exercise 10 Students use what they know about special angles formed by parallel lines and transversals to find missing angle measures. Then they use the angle measures to prove that triangles are congruent.

pages 436–438   On Your Own

10a. $m\angle 1 = 56$, $m\angle 2 = 56$, $m\angle 3 = 34$; $m\angle 4 = 90$; $m\angle 5 = 22$; $m\angle 6 = 34$; $m\angle 7 = 34$; $m\angle 8 = 68$; $m\angle 9 = 112$

In each diagram, the red and blue triangles are congruent. Identify their common side or angle.

1. $\angle M$

2. $\overline{DF}$

3. $\overline{XY}$

Name a pair of overlapping congruent triangles in each diagram. State whether the triangles are congruent by SSS, SAS, ASA, AAS, or HL.

4. Given: $\overline{MP} \cong \overline{QL}$, $\overline{LP} \perp \overline{LM}$, $\overline{LP} \perp \overline{PQ}$

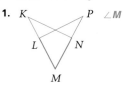
$\triangle MLP$, $\triangle QPL$; HL

5. Given: $\overline{RS} \cong \overline{UT}$, $\overline{RT} \cong \overline{US}$

$\triangle STU$, $\triangle TSR$; SSS

6. Given: $\overline{QD} \cong \overline{UA}$, $\angle QDA \cong \angle UAD$

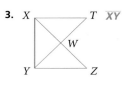
$\triangle QDA$, $\triangle UAD$; SAS

7. Given: $\overline{PQ} \parallel \overline{UR}$, $\overline{QT} \parallel \overline{RS}$, $\overline{QT} \cong \overline{RS}$

$\triangle PQT$, $\triangle URS$; AAS

8. Given: $\overline{AC} \cong \overline{BC}$, $\angle A \cong \angle B$

$\triangle CAE$, $\triangle CBD$; ASA

9. Given: $\odot O$, $\overline{WY} \perp \overline{YX}$, $\overline{ZX} \perp \overline{YX}$

$\triangle WYX$, $\triangle ZXY$; HL

10. a. Design The figure below is part of a clothing design pattern. In the figure, $\overline{AB} \parallel \overline{DE} \parallel \overline{FG}$, $\overline{AB} \perp \overline{BC}$, $\overline{GC} \perp \overline{AC}$. $\triangle DEC$ is isosceles with base $\overline{DC}$, and $m\angle A = 56$. Find the measures of all the numbered angles in the figure.

b. $\overline{AB} \cong \overline{FC}$. Name two congruent triangles and tell how you can prove them congruent.

10a. See margin.
10b. $\triangle ABC$, $\triangle FCG$; AAS or ASA

436

ALTERNATIVE ASSESSMENT **Exercises 11–12** You can use these exercises to help you assess students' ability to prove two triangles congruent by first proving two other triangles congruent. Have students work in groups and check that everyone can explain the group's plan.

EXTENSION Exercises 13–14 Have students rewrite the completed proofs as paragraph or flow proofs.

STANDARDIZED TEST TIP **Exercise 15** Some students will focus on the figure and ignore the Given statement below it. Point out to them that the Given statement should tip them off that they need to use it in combination with the figure to prove two triangles are congruent.

Preparing for Proof **Write a plan for a proof.**

11. Given: ∠1 ≅ ∠2, ∠3 ≅ ∠4
   Prove: △QET ≅ △QEU

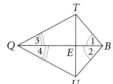

Prove △QTB ≅ △QUB by ASA. So QT ≅ QU. Then use SAS to prove △QET ≅ △QEU.

12. Given: $\overline{AD} \cong \overline{ED}$, *D* is the midpoint of $\overline{BF}$.
   Prove: △ADC ≅ △EDG   See margin.

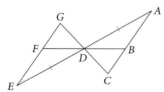

Preparing for Proof **Copy and complete each two-column proof.**

13. Given: $\overline{ER} \cong \overline{IT}$, $\overline{ET} \cong \overline{IR}$, ∠TDI and ∠ROE are right ⦣.
   Prove: $\overline{TD} \cong \overline{RO}$

Statements	Reasons
1. $\overline{ER} \cong \overline{IT}$, $\overline{ET} \cong \overline{IR}$	a. ___?___ Given
2. $\overline{EI} \cong \overline{EI}$	b. ___?___ Reflexive Prop. of ≅
c. △ERI ≅ △___?___ ITE	d. ___?___ SSS
e. ∠REO ≅ ∠___?___ TID	4. CPCTC
5. ∠TDI and ∠ROE are right ⦣.	f. ___?___ Given
6. ∠TDI ≅ ∠ROE	g. ___?___ All rt. ∠s are ≅.
7. △TDI ≅ △ROE	h. ___?___ AAS
i. ___?___ ≅ ___?___ TD; RO	j. ___?___ CPCTC

14. Given: $\overline{AB} \perp \overline{BC}$, $\overline{DC} \perp \overline{BC}$, $\overline{AC} \cong \overline{DB}$
   Prove: $\overline{AE} \cong \overline{DE}$

Statements	Reasons
1. $\overline{AB} \perp \overline{BC}$, $\overline{DC} \perp \overline{BC}$	a. ___?___ Given
2. ∠ABC and ∠DCB are rt. ⦣.	b. ___?___ Def. of ⊥ lines
3. △ABC and △DCB are rt. ⦣.	c. ___?___ Def. of rt. △s.
4. $\overline{AC} \cong \overline{DB}$	d. ___?___ Given
e. ___?___ ≅ ___?___ BC; BC	5. Reflexive Property of ≅
6. △ABC ≅ △DCB	f. ___?___ HL Thm.
7. ∠A ≅ ∠D, $\overline{AB} \cong \overline{DC}$	g. ___?___ CPCTC
h. ∠AEB ≅ ∠___?___ DEC	i. ___?___ Vertical ∠s are ≅.
9. △ABE ≅ △DCE	j. ___?___ AAS
k. ___?___ ≅ ___?___ AE; DE	l. ___?___ CPCTC

15. *Standardized Test Prep* In order to prove $\overline{JW} \cong \overline{QX}$ in the diagram at the right, what would you prove first? **B**

A. △ZJW ≅ △KQX B. △KJZ ≅ △ZQK
C. △JWK ≅ △QXZ D. $\overline{ZW} \cong \overline{KX}$
E. Not enough information is given.

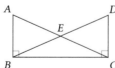

Given: $\overline{ZQ} \parallel \overline{KJ}$, $\overline{ZQ} \cong \overline{KJ}$, ∠1 ≅ ∠2

12. Answers may vary. Sample:
Prove △EFD ≅ △ABD by SAS. Then prove ∠E ≅ ∠A and ∠ADC ≅ ∠EDG. Use ASA to prove △ADC ≅ △EDG.

16. 1. $\overline{AC} \cong \overline{EC}$ and $\overline{CB} \cong \overline{CD}$ (Given)
   2. ∠C ≅ ∠C (Reflexive Prop. of ≅)
   3. △ACD ≅ △ECB (SAS)
   4. ∠A ≅ ∠E (CPCTC)

17. Since $\overline{TQ}$ bisects $\overline{PR}$, $\overline{PQ} \cong \overline{RQ}$. Since $\overline{TQ} \perp \overline{PR}$, ∠PQT and ∠RQT are ≅ rt. ∠s. Also, $\overline{QT} \cong \overline{QT}$, so △PQT ≅ △RQT by SAS. ∠PTQ ≅ ∠RTQ by CPCTC. Since $\overline{TQ}$ bisects ∠VQS, ∠VQT ≅ ∠SQT. So, △VQT ≅ △SQT by ASA, and $\overline{VQ} \cong \overline{SQ}$ by CPCTC.

18a.

$\overline{AE}$, $\overline{CE}$; $\overline{BE}$, $\overline{DE}$; $\overline{AB}$, $\overline{CD}$; $\overline{BC}$, $\overline{AD}$

b. Opp. sides of a parallelogram are ∥, so ∠BAC ≅ ∠DCA and ∠BCA ≅ ∠DAC. So △BAC ≅ △DCA by ASA, and $\overline{AB} \cong \overline{CD}$ and $\overline{BC} \cong \overline{AD}$ by CPCTC. △AEB ≅ △CED by ASA (or AAS), so $\overline{AE} \cong \overline{CE}$ and $\overline{BE} \cong \overline{DE}$ by CPCTC.

437

Lesson Quiz

Lesson Quiz is also available in Transparencies.

Separate the overlapping triangles. Then write a two-column proof, a paragraph proof, or a flow proof.

1. Given: $\angle XTZ \cong \angle WTY$,
$\overline{XT} \cong \overline{WT}$,
$\angle X \cong \angle W$

Prove: $\overline{XZ} \cong \overline{WY}$

See back of book.

2. Given: $\overline{BA} \cong \overline{BD}$, $\angle A \cong \angle D$

Prove: $\overline{AC} \cong \overline{DE}$

See back of book.

438

Choose **Write a two-column proof, a paragraph proof, or a flow proof.**

16. Given: $\overline{AC} \cong \overline{EC}$, $\overline{CB} \cong \overline{CD}$
Prove: $\angle A \cong \angle E$

16–17. Answers may vary. See margin p. 437 for samples.

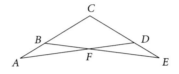

17. Given: $\overline{TQ}$ is the perpendicular bisector of $\overline{PR}$; $\overline{TQ}$ bisects $\angle VQS$.
Prove: $\overline{VQ} \cong \overline{SQ}$

18. a. *Open-ended* Draw a parallelogram and its diagonals. Label your diagram and list all the pairs of congruent segments. See margin p. 437 for sample.
b. *Writing* Explain how you can be sure that the segments you listed must be congruent. See margin p. 437.

Chapter Project ▽ ***Find Out by Investigating***

In the Find Out question on page 412, you tested the strength of two-dimensional models. Now investigate the strength of three-dimensional models.

Use toothpicks or craft sticks and glue to construct a cube and a tetrahedron (a triangular pyramid).

• Which model is stronger? tetrahedron See below.
• Describe how you could strengthen the weaker model.

Use toothpicks or craft sticks and glue to construct a structure that can support the weight of your geometry book. Check students' work.

Answers may vary. Sample: you could glue in diagonals of the cube.

Exercises **MIXED REVIEW**

Coordinate Geometry **Graph** $\triangle ABC$ **with vertices** $A(5, 5)$, $B(5, 1)$, **and** $C(1, 1)$.

19. Classify $\triangle ABC$ by its sides and angles. isosceles rt. △

20. Find the length of $\overline{AC}$. Leave your answer in simplest radical form. $4\sqrt{2}$

21. Find the area and perimeter of $\triangle ABC$. Leave your answer in simplest radical form. 8 units²; $(8 + 4\sqrt{2})$ units

22. *Calculator* The interior of a cylindrical mug has diameter 8 cm and is 9 cm deep. How much liquid can it hold? Round your answer to the nearest milliliter. (*Hint:* 1 cm³ = 1 mL)   452 mL

PORTFOLIO

For your portfolio, select one or two items from your work for this chapter. Here are some possibilities.
• most improved work
• a journal entry
• a constructed model
Explain why you have included each selection.

Getting Ready for Chapter 9

Students may work these exercises independently or in small groups. The skills previewed will help prepare students to study the properties of parallelograms.

Using Congruent Triangles in Proofs   8-4

Once you know that triangles are congruent, you can make conclusions about corresponding segments and angles because **corresponding parts of congruent triangles are congruent (CPCTC).** You can use congruent triangles in the proofs of many theorems.

Explain how you would use SSS, SAS, ASA, AAS, or HL with CPCTC to prove each statement.   13–15. Answers will vary. See margin for samples.

13. $\overline{TV} \cong \overline{YW}$ **14.** $\overline{BE} \cong \overline{DE}$ **15.** $\overline{KN} \cong \overline{ML}$

Using More than One Pair of Congruent Triangles   8-5

You can prove overlapping triangles congruent. You can also use the common or shared sides and angles of triangles in congruence proofs.

Name a pair of overlapping congruent triangles in each diagram. State whether the triangles are congruent by SSS, SAS, ASA, AAS, or HL.

16.   **17.**   **18.**

△ADB, △ACE; SAS   △FIH, △GHI; SAS   △PST, △RAT; ASA

Getting Ready for .... ▶ CHAPTER

9

Coordinate Geometry **Graph and label each quadrilateral with the given vertices. Use slope and/or the Distance Formula to determine the most precise name for each figure.**

19. $A(-2, 3)$, $B(1, 3)$, $C(1, -7)$, $D(-2, -7)$ **20.** $W(-1, 0)$, $X(2, -2)$, $Y(4, 1)$, $Z(1, 3)$
rectangle   square

21. $Q(-1, -2)$, $R(1, 4)$, $S(5, 4)$, $T(3, -2)$ **22.** $K(-6, 1)$, $L(-3, 5)$, $M(5, 1)$, $N(-3, -3)$
parallelogram   kite

23. The four sides of parallelogram *ABCD* are congruent. Therefore *ABCD* is a rhombus. List as many properties of the diagonals of a rhombus as you can find.   See margin.

13. Use AAS to show △*TVY* ≅ △*YWX*. $\overline{TV} \cong \overline{YW}$ by CPCTC.

14. Use ASA to show △*BCE* ≅ △*DCE*. $\overline{BE} \cong \overline{DE}$ by CPCTC.

15. Use HL to show △*KLM* ≅ △*MNK*. $\overline{KN} \cong \overline{ML}$ by CPCTC.

23. The diagonals are ⊥ bisectors of each other. Each diagonal is an angle bisector of 2 of the angles of the rhombus. The area of the rhombus is half the product of the lengths of the diagonals.

443

Assessment

ENHANCED MULTIPLE CHOICE QUESTIONS are more complex than traditional multiple choice questions, which assess only one skill. Enhanced multiple choice questions assess the processes that students use, as well as the end results. The questions are written so that students use more than one strategy to solve the problem. Using multiple strategies is encouraged by the National Council of Teachers of Mathematics (NCTM). **Exercise 8** is an enhanced multiple choice question.

FREE RESPONSE QUESTIONS do not give answer choices. Some exercises have more than one possible answer. Students need to give only one correct response. **Exercises 1–6, and 9–12** are free response questions.

WRITING EXERCISES allow students to describe how they think about and understand the concepts they have learned. **Exercise 7** is a writing exercise.

OPEN-ENDED PROBLEMS allow for more than one solution. Students must construct their own responses instead of choosing from possible answers. The students' responses will help you determine the depth of their understanding and any possible areas of difficulty. **Exercise 13** is an open-ended problem.

Resources

📦 Teaching Resources
Chapter Support File, Ch. 8
• Chapter Assessment,
Forms A and B
• Alternative Assessment
Chapter Assessment, Spanish
Resources

📖 Teacher's Edition
See also p. 404E for assessment options

💾 Software
Computer Item Generator

Assessment   page 444

7. **Answers may vary. Sample: 2 equilateral △s with diff. lengths of sides are a counterexample.**

9. 1. $\overline{SA} \cong \overline{GA}$ (Radii of the same ⊙ are ≅.) 2. $\overline{ST} \cong \overline{GT}$ (Radii of the same ⊙ are ≅.) 3. $\overline{AT} \cong \overline{AT}$ (Reflexive Prop. of ≅)
4. △GAT ≅ △SAT (SSS)

10. $\overline{LN}$ bisects ∠OLM. (Given)
2. ∠OLN ≅ ∠MLN (Def. of angle bisector) 3. $\overline{LN}$ bisects ∠ONM. (Given) 4. ∠ONL ≅ ∠MNL (Def. of angle bisector) 5. $\overline{LN} \cong \overline{LN}$ (Reflexive Prop. of ≅)
6. △OLN ≅ △MLN (ASA)

444

---

8 Assessment

State the postulate or theorem you would use to prove each pair of triangles congruent. If the triangles *cannot* be proven congruent, write *not possible*.

1. **SAS**

2. **HL**

3. **not possible**

4. **SSS**

5. **ASA**

6. **AAS**

7. **Writing** Explain why you cannot use AAA to prove two triangles congruent. **See margin.**

8. *Standardized Test Prep* △ABC ≅ △DEF. Which of the following are true? **C**
   I. ∠A ≅ ∠D   II. $\overline{BC} \cong \overline{DF}$
   III. ∠C ≅ ∠E   IV. $\overline{DE} \cong \overline{AB}$
   A. I and II   **B.** II and III   **C.** I and IV
   D. III and IV **E.** I, II, and IV

Write a two-column proof, a paragraph proof, or a flow proof. **9–10. Answers may vary. See margin for samples.**

9. **Given:** ⊙A and ⊙T
   Prove: △GAT ≅ △SAT
   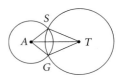

10. **Given:** $\overline{LN}$ bisects ∠OLM and ∠ONM.
    Prove: △OLN ≅ △MLN

Name a pair of overlapping congruent triangles in each diagram. State whether the triangles are congruent by SSS, SAS, ASA, AAS, or HL.

11. **Given:** $\overline{CE} \cong \overline{DF}$,
    $\overline{CF} \cong \overline{DE}$
    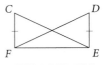
    △CEF, △DFE; SSS

12. **Given:** $\overline{RT} \cong \overline{QT}$,
    $\overline{AT} \cong \overline{ST}$
    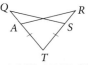
    △QST, △RAT; SAS

13. **Open-ended** Draw a kite and its diagonals. Which diagonal divides the kite into two congruent triangles? Explain how you know they are congruent. **See below.**

13. the diagonal that connects the vertices of the ∠s that are not ≅; SSS

Cumulative Review

Item	Review Topic	Chapter
1	Congruent Figures	2
2, 8	Parallel Lines and Related Angles	7
3	Congruent Triangles	8
4	Volume	6
5	Spherical Geometry	7

Item	Review Topic	Chapter
6	Quadrilaterals	2
7	Triangle Inequalities	4
9	Perspective Drawing	7
10	Logical Reasoning	4
11	Constructing Perpendicular Lines	7

8 Cumulative Review

For Exercises 1–8, choose the correct letter.

1. Quadrilateral $ABCD \cong QRST$. Which segment is congruent to $\overline{TS}$? **E**

A. $\overline{AB}$ **B.** $\overline{BC}$ **C.** $\overline{BA}$ **D.** $\overline{CB}$ **E.** $\overline{DC}$

2. Which condition(s) will allow you to prove that $\ell \parallel m$? **E**

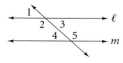

   I. $\angle 1 \cong \angle 4$ **II.** $\angle 2 \cong \angle 5$
  III. $m\angle 2 + m\angle 4 = 180$ **IV.** $\angle 3 \cong \angle 4$

A. I only   **B.** II only
C. I and II only   **D.** III and IV only
E. I, II, III, and IV

3. By which postulate or theorem are the triangles congruent? **A**

A. SAS   **B.** SSS   **C.** ASA
D. AAS   **E.** HL

4. Which solid has the least volume? **C**

E. It cannot be determined from the information given.

5. In spherical geometry, how many lines are perpendicular to a line at a given point on the line? **B**

A. 0   **B.** 1   **C.** 2
D. 3   **E.** infinitely many

6. $WXYZ$ is a rectangle. Which segment is longest? **C**

A. $\overline{WX}$ **B.** $\overline{YZ}$ **C.** $\overline{WY}$ **D.** $\overline{ZW}$
E. It cannot be determined from the information given.

Compare the boxed quantity in Column A with the boxed quantity in Column B. Choose the best answer.

A. The quantity in Column A is greater.
B. The quantity in Column B is greater.
C. The two quantities are equal.
D. The relationship cannot be determined on the basis of the information supplied.

Column A	Column B

7. $m\angle A$ $m\angle B$ **A**

8. $m\angle 1$ $m\angle 2$ **C**

9, 11. See back of book for samples.
Find each answer.

9. Open-ended Sketch an object in two-point perspective.

10. Write the contrapositive of the conditional "If the trees have leaves, it is not winter." **See below.**

11. Constructions Draw a line. Construct a line perpendicular to the first line.

10. If it is winter, then the trees do not have leaves.

Quadrilaterals

To accommodate flexible scheduling, some lessons are divided into parts.
Assignment Options are given in the Lesson Planning Options for each lesson.

9-1 Properties of Parallelograms (pp. 448–453)

Key Term: consecutive angles

9-2 Proving That a Quadrilateral Is a Parallelogram (pp. 454–460)

9-3 Properties of Special Parallelograms (pp. 462–468)

Part **1** Properties of Rhombuses
Part **2** Properties of Rectangles and Parallelograms

9-4 Trapezoids and Kites (pp. 470–476)

Key Term: base angles

9-5 Organizing Coordinate Proofs (pp. 478–482)

9-6 Using Coordinate Geometry in Proofs (pp. 483–487)

Key Term: midsegment of a trapezoid

PACING OPTIONS

This chart suggests pacing only for the core lessons and their parts, and it is
provided merely as a possible guide. It will help you determine how much
time you have in your schedule to cover other features, such as the Chapter
Project, Math Toolboxes, Wrap Up, and Assessment.

	1 Class Period	1 Class Period	1 Class Period	1 Class Period	1 Class Period	1 Class Period	1 Class Period	1 Class Period	1 Class Period
Traditional (40–45 min class periods)	9-1	9-2	9-3 **1**	9-3 **2**	9-4	9-5	9-6		
Block Scheduling (90 min class periods)	9-1	9-2	9-3 **1** **2**	9-4	9-5 9-6				

What Students Will Learn and Why

In this chapter, students will build on their knowledge of parallelograms, learned in Chapter 2, by learning properties of parallelograms and finding characteristics of quadrilaterals that indicate they are parallelograms. Then students find properties of rectangles, rhombuses, squares, trapezoids, and kites. Finally, students learn to choose convenient placement of coordinate axes on figures and prove theorems using figures in the coordinate plane. Throughout the chapter, students see how these concepts are used in designing playgrounds, kites, and flags, and solving problems in navigation, construction, and design.

or develop maps of your own. The center oval describes the topic of the chapter. The next level displays topics within the lessons. The outer ovals reflect applications of the content. As you and your class build a concept map, invite students to discuss applications with which they are familiar.

Discussing the Chapter/Building on Experience

The concept map below relates chapter topics to real-world applications. You and your class may wish to add to the map

A question is interactive when there is "give and take" between the questioner (teacher or student) and the respondent. In Think and Discuss or when a critical thinking question is asked, it is important to encourage students to explain their answers in detail. Encouraging students to explain their answers promotes active participation and stimulates higher levels of thought. These two elements are essential in developing high-level thinking skills. For example, in Lesson 9-6 students are asked to explain why it is enough to prove just two consecutive sides congruent in order to prove that parallelogram *TWVU* is a rhombus.

Skills Practice

Every lesson provides skill practice with Try This exercises, Exercises On Your Own, and Exercises Mixed Review. The

Student Edition includes Checkpoints (pp. 460, 482) and Preparing for Standardized Tests (p. 493). In the Teacher's Edition, the Lesson Planning Options section for each lesson lists Prerequisite Skills students should know for that lesson. At the back of the Student Edition is the Skills Handbook—mini-lessons on math your students may need to review. The Chapter Support File for Chapter 9 in the Teaching Resources box includes two Practice worksheets per lesson, a worksheet for two Checkpoints, and worksheets for Cumulative Review and Standardized Test Preparation.

Diverse Learning and Teaching Styles

In your Teacher's Edition, you will find suggestions as to how you can help students complete mathematical tasks in Chapter 9 by reinforcing various learning styles. Here are some examples.

- **Visual learning** draw parallel lines and transversals of varying slopes on lined paper and measure the segment of each transversal cut by the parallel lines (p. 450), copy triangles and mark corresponding angles on the diagram as they are read in the proof (p. 463), draw several trapezoids and identify the legs and base angles (p. 470)

- **Tactile learning** make a parallel ruler using straws and brads (p. 457), prove theorem 9-11 by drawing a rhombus, cutting it along its diagonals and rearranging the resulting triangles to form a rectangle (p. 463), make a cutout of a 10-unit square and trace it in different positions on the coordinate grid (p. 478)

- **Auditory learning** present completed proofs to other students (p. 467)

- **Kinesthetic learning** sketch and discuss geometric patterns on buildings and houses (p. 471)

Alternative Activity for Lesson 9-1

for use with Theorems 9-1, 9-2, and 9-3, uses geometry software to manipulate parallelograms.

Alternative Activity for Lesson 9-2

for use with Theorems 9-5 and 9-6, uses geometry software to manipulate quadrilaterals.

Alternative Activity for Lesson 9-4

for use with Theorems 9-16 and 9-17, uses geometry software to construct and manipulate isosceles trapezoids.

Cooperative Learning Tips

When used effectively, cooperative learning can help students develop interpersonal skills, learn to perform specific roles in a group, and learn to carry out specific responsibilities. The components of Chapter 9 provide a range of cooperative learning opportunities.

- In the Student Edition, the **Work Together** parts of lessons are specifically designed for cooperative learning activities.

- In the Teacher's Edition, you will find helpful hints for addressing diverse learning styles (see page C for Chapter 9). For every lesson, you will find a **Reteaching Activity**, which may involve cooperative learning.

Materials and Manipulatives

The authors expect all students to use scientific calculators. Calculator use is integrated throughout the course.

- centimeter grid paper (9-3)
- compass (9-1)
- 11-by-11 peg geoboard (9-2)
- graph paper (9-5, 9-6)
- lined paper (9-4)
- protractor (9-1, 9-3)
- ruler (9-1, 9-3)
- scissors (9-1, 9-3, 9-4)
- straightedge (9-2, 9-4, 9-5, 9-6)

TECHNOLOGY OPTIONS								
Technology Tools		**Chapter Project**	**9-1**	**9-2**	**9-3**	**9-4**	**9-5**	**9-6**
Calculator		Assumed that students have scientific calculators at any time.						
Software	Secondary Math Lab Toolkit™		✔	✔	✔	✔	✔	✔
	Integrated Math Lab			✔				✔
	Computer Item Generator		✔	✔	✔	✔	✔	✔
	Student Edition				✔T	✔T	✔	
Video	Video Field Trip	✔						
CD-ROM	Multimedia Geometry Lab		✔		✔	✔		✔
Internet		See the Prentice Hall site. (http://www.phschool.com)						

✔T indicates Math Toolbox.

The Prentice Hall Geometry program offers you a rich variety of technology options. Be assured that all these options are provided as a means of enriching the program and are not essential for the successful completion of the course.

Assessment Options

The Prentice Hall Geometry Program provides you with many options. From these options, you may choose instructional materials and techniques appropriate for your students, or those necessary to meet your district's curriculum requirements. As the chart indicates, the program also supports your teaching efforts by offering you many choices for assessment.

ASSESSMENT OPTIONS

Assessment Support Materials	Chapter Project	9-1	9-2	9-3	9-4	9-5	9-6	Chapter End
Chapter Project	▲ ■ ●	▲ ■		▲ ■	▲ ■			▲ ■
Checkpoints			▲ ■ ●			▲ ■ ●		
Self-Assessment			▲		▲ ■		▲ ■	▲ ■
Writing Assignment		▲	▲	▲ ■	▲	▲ ■	▲ ■	●
Chapter Assessment								▲ ■ ●
Alternative Assessment		■	■	■	■	■	■	●
Cumulative Review								●
Standardized Test Prep			▲ ■	▲ ■	▲			▲ ■ ●
Computer Item Generator	Can be used to create custom-made practice or assessment at any time.							

▲ = Student Edition   ■ = Teacher's Edition   ● = Teaching Resources

Checkpoints

Alternative Assessment

Chapter Assessment

Available in both Form A and Form B

Making the Right Connections

Mathematics is imbedded in nearly every walk of life. The National Council of Teachers of Mathematics (NCTM) encourages educators to recognize these connections and to emphasize them for the purpose of better educating students for success in life and in a global economy. The *Connections* chart below highlights these connections for Chapter 9.

CONNECTIONS

Lesson	Interdisciplinary Connections	Career Prep	Other Real World Connections	Math Integration	NCTM Standards
Chapter Project	Art	Design	Kites		Connections
9-1	Home Economics		Measuring Sewing Building a Kite	Algebra Probability Logical Reasoning	Algebra Communication Problem Solving Reasoning
9-2	Geography Home Economics		Navigation Weaving	Algebra Probability Logical Reasoning Coordinate Geometry	Algebra Communication Problem Solving Reasoning
9-3	Science Social Studies	Carpentry Auto Mechanics	Community Service	Algebra Logical Reasoning	Algebra Communication Problem Solving Reasoning
9-4	Art	Architecture Design	Picture Framing	Algebra Geometry in 3 Dimensions	Algebra Communication Problem Solving
9-5	Science History	Design	Archaeology Egyptian Relief Sculpture	Geometry in 3 Dimensions Coordinate Geometry	Coordinate Geometry Communication Problem Solving Connections
9-6	Art History Science		Flag Mobiles	Coordinate Geometry Logical Reasoning	Coordinate Geometry Communication Reasoning Problem Solving

CONNECTING TO PRIOR LEARNING In this chapter, students will extend their understanding of quadrilaterals by studying properties of parallelograms. Review with students the tree diagram of quadrilaterals in Chapter 2. Discuss the similarities and differences among parallelograms, rhombuses, rectangles, and squares. Have students give real-world examples of each. Then discuss the definitions of kite and trapezoid. Also give real-world examples.

CULTURAL CONNECTIONS Kites have been in use by Asian peoples from time immemorial. Kite-flying as a sport has long been a national pastime of the Koreans, Chinese, Japanese, and Malayans. Kites flying at night over a house were believed to keep evil spirits away.

INTERDISCIPLINARY CONNECTIONS In 1752 Ben Franklin demonstrated the electrical nature of lightning by flying a kite with a metal key hanging from it. Kites have long been used for weather observations. Ask students to research other ways kites have been used in meteorological research and in space exploration.

Technology Options

Prentice Hall Technology

Video
Video Field Trip 9, "Hanging in the Wind," a view from the hang glider's perspective

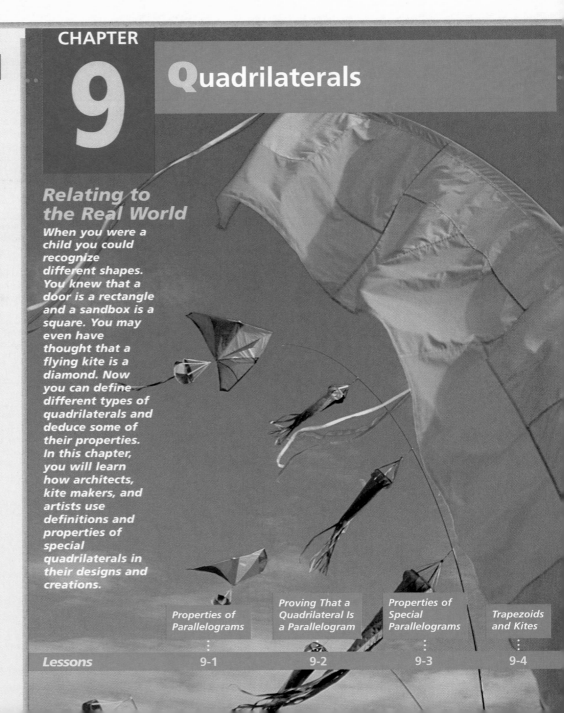

CHAPTER

9 **Q**uadrilaterals

Relating to the Real World

When you were a child you could recognize different shapes. You knew that a door is a rectangle and a sandbox is a square. You may even have thought that a flying kite is a diamond. Now you can define different types of quadrilaterals and deduce some of their properties. In this chapter, you will learn how architects, kite makers, and artists use definitions and properties of special quadrilaterals in their designs and creations.

Properties of Parallelograms	*Proving That a Quadrilateral Is a Parallelogram*	*Properties of Special Parallelograms*	*Trapezoids and Kites*
Lessons 9-1	9-2	9-3	9-4

ABOUT THE PROJECT Students will make a fully functioning kite using a sheet of paper and two staples. Then they explore how the weight and form of a kite affect its ability to fly. Finally, students will design, build, and fly their own kites.

TRACKING THE PROJECT You may wish to have students read Finishing the Chapter Project on page 488 to help them get an overview of the project. Set benchmark deadlines for students to show their work in progress.

Launching the Project

PROJECT NOTEBOOK Encourage students to keep all project-related materials in a separate folder or notebook. See Chapter Project Manager and Scoring Rubric in Chapter Support File.

• Ask students to share their own experiences with kites. Ask them to describe the shapes and features of kites they have flown. Have them share techniques they used in flying them.

CHAPTER
PROJECT

GO FLY A KITE

I f you think kites are mere child's play, think again. From ancient China to modern times, geometric arrangements of fabric and rods have helped people rescue sailors, vanquish enemies, predict the weather, invent the airplane, study wind power, and, of course, entertain with displays of aerodynamic artistry.

In your project for this chapter, you will turn a sheet of paper and couple of staples into a fully functioning kite. You will explore how weight and form determine whether a kite sinks or soars. Finally you will design, build, and fly your own kite. You will see how geometry can make a kite light and strong—spelling the difference between flight and failure.

To help you complete the project:

▼ **p. 453** *Find Out by Doing*
▼ **p. 468** *Find Out by Analyzing*
▼ **p. 476** *Find Out by Researching*
▼ **p. 488** *Finishing the Project*

Organizing Coordinate Proofs

Using Coordinate Geometry in Proofs

9-5   9-6

▼ Project Resources

 Teaching Resources
Chapter Support File, Ch. 9
• Chapter Project Manager and Scoring Rubric

Transparencies
93

▼ Using the Rubric

Sharing the scoring rubric for the project with your students will alert them to your expectations before they begin work on the project.

As students complete each Find Out question in the chapter, you may wish to have them evaluate their own work or a partner's work based on the scoring rubric. Students should have the opportunity to revise their work after it has been reviewed.

447

PROBLEM OF THE DAY

Give the dimensions of at least 5 different, nonsimilar rectangles in which the length, the width, and the length of the diagonals are all integers. **Answers may vary.**
Sample: 3 by 4, 5 by 12, 7 by 24, 16 by 30 , 39 by 80

Problem of the Day is also available in Transparencies.

CONNECTING TO PRIOR KNOWLEDGE Draw the following quadrilaterals. Ask students which appear to be parallelograms and have them find the missing angle measures.

WORK TOGETHER

Begin by reviewing the definition of parallelogram. Make sure that students label the points in order as shown on the diagram so the directions will make sense. Have students label the vertices on the inside of the parallelogram so when they cut it out, the labels remain on the figure.

ALTERNATIVE METHOD To avoid the use of a ruler and a protractor, have students cut out two copies of their parallelograms. Then they can compare sides and angles by rotating the figures and placing them on top of each other.

Lesson Planning Options

Prerequisite Skills

- Understanding definition of a parallelogram
- Using congruent triangles and CPCTC

> ### Assignment Options for Exercises On Your Own
>
> **Core** 1–30
> **Extension** 31–33
>
> Use Mixed Review to maintain skills.

Resources

 Student Edition

Skills Handbook, pp. 650, 667
Extra Practice, p. 642
Glossary/Study Guide

 Teaching Resources

Chapter Support File, Ch. 9
- Practice 9-1 (two worksheets)
- Reteaching 9-1
- Alternative Activity 9-1
Classroom Manager 9-1
Glossary, Spanish Resources

 Transparencies
94, 97, 98

Connections 🌐 *Art . . . and more*

What You'll Learn

- Finding relationships among angles, sides, and diagonals of parallelograms

...And Why

To make designs using parallelograms

What You'll Need

- ruler
- protractor
- compass
- scissors

9-1 Properties of Parallelograms

WORK TOGETHER

Work with a partner.

- Draw three noncollinear points to make three vertices of a large parallelogram. Label them A, B, and C. Draw $\overline{AB}$ and $\overline{BC}$.
- Construct a line parallel to $\overline{BC}$ through A and a line parallel to $\overline{AB}$ through C. Label their point of intersection D.
- Cut out ▱ABCD. Use a protractor and ruler to compare the opposite sides and opposite angles of ABCD.

  1. Make **conjectures** about the relationship between opposite sides and the relationship between opposite angles of a parallelogram. *See below.*
- Draw $\overline{AC}$ and $\overline{BD}$. Label the point of intersection E. Use paper folding or a ruler to compare AE to CE and BE to DE.

  2. Make a conjecture about the relationship between the diagonals of a parallelogram. **The diagonals of a ▱ bisect each other.**

     1. Opp. sides are ≅ ; opp. angles are ≅ .

THINK AND DISCUSS

The results of the Work Together are the basis of this lesson's theorems.

Theorem 9-1

Opposite sides of a parallelogram are congruent.

If *ABCD* is a parallelogram, then $\overline{AB} \cong \overline{CD}$ and $\overline{BC} \cong \overline{DA}$.

In planning this tessellation, Escher used the fact that opposite sides of a parallelogram are congruent.

Example 1

Use a flow proof to prove Theorem 9-1: Opposite sides of a parallelogram are congruent.

Given: $\square\,ABCD$
Prove: $\overline{AB} \cong \overline{CD}, \overline{BC} \cong \overline{DA}$

Flow Proof

3. a. What is true about the two triangles formed by one diagonal of a parallelogram? **The $\triangle$s are $\cong$.**
  b. **Preparing for Proof** How would you prove your conclusion in part (a)? **Use the proof in Example 1 without the last step.**

Theorem 9-2

Opposite angles of a parallelogram are congruent.
If *ABCD* is a parallelogram, then $\angle A \cong \angle C$ and $\angle B \cong \angle D$.

Answers may vary. See back of book for sample.
4. Preparing for Proof Give a plan for proof for Theorem 9-2.

5. a. **Try This** In $\square ABCD$, $m\angle 1 = 48$ and $m\angle BCD = 70$. Find the measures of $\angle BAD$, $\angle 2$, $\angle 3$, and $\angle 4$. **70; 22; 22; 48**
  b. Find the measures of $\angle B$ and $\angle D$. **110; 110**

Angles of a polygon that share a common side are **consecutive angles.** In the figure at the left, $\angle S$ and $\angle T$ are consecutive angles. So are $\angle T$ and $\angle W$.

6. a. Suppose the measures of two consecutive angles of a parallelogram are *x* and *y*. By Theorem 9-2, the other two angles also have measures of *x* and *y*. Use algebra and the fact that the sum of the measures of the angles of a quadrilateral is 360 to show that the consecutive angles are supplementary. **See back of book.**
  b. **Try This** In $\square RSTW$, $m\angle R = 112$. Find the measure of each angle of the parallelogram.
  $m\angle S = 68$; $m\angle T = 112$; $m\angle W = 68$

449

9-1 Properties of Parallelograms **449**

Example 2

TACTILE LEARNING Have students draw a parallelogram and its diagonals. Have them trace each diagonal with a different color, then cut out the four triangles formed. By manipulating the triangles, students can observe that the two pieces of each diagonal are congruent.

ERROR ALERT! Some students may misinterpret Theorem 9-3 to mean that the diagonals are congruent. **Remediation:** Draw a parallelogram with consecutive angles measuring 30° and 150°. Draw the diagonals. It should be clear to students that the diagonals are not congruent.

ALGEBRA Question 7 Students may need to review how to solve a system of linear equations. Refer them to the Math Toolbox on page 370.

VISUAL LEARNING Have students draw three parallel lines on three consecutive lines of a lined sheet of paper. Then have them draw three transversals with different slopes. Using a ruler, have them measure the segments of each transversal cut by the parallel lines. Then have them repeat the activity beginning by drawing parallel lines on the first, second, and fourth lines of the paper. Ask students to summarize their results.

Technology Options

For Exercise 13, students may draw the parallelograms using geometry software. For Exercises 31–33, students may graph the preimage and image of the figure using graphing software.

Prentice Hall Technology

 Software
- Secondary Math Lab Toolkit™
- Computer Item Generator 9-1

 CD-ROM
- Multimedia Geometry Lab 9

 Internet
- See the Prentice Hall site. (http://www.phschool.com)

Theorem 9-3   The diagonals of a parallelogram bisect each other.

Example 2

Use a two-column proof to prove Theorem 9-3.

Given: ▱ ABCD
Prove: $\overline{AC}$ and $\overline{BD}$ bisect each other at E.

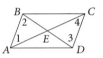

Statements	Reasons
1. ABCD is a parallelogram.	1. Given
2. $\overline{AB} \parallel \overline{DC}$	2. Definition of parallelogram
3. $\angle 1 \cong \angle 4$; $\angle 2 \cong \angle 3$	3. If ∥ lines, then alt. int. ∠ are ≅.
4. $\overline{AB} \cong \overline{CD}$	4. Opposite sides of a parallelogram are ≅.
5. $\triangle ABE \cong \triangle CDE$	5. ASA
6. $\overline{AE} \cong \overline{CE}$; $\overline{BE} \cong \overline{DE}$	6. CPCTC
7. $\overline{AC}$ and $\overline{BD}$ bisect each other at E.	7. Definition of bisect

7. Algebra In the figure for Example 2, suppose that $AE = 4x$, $EC = 3y$, $BE = x + 1$, and $ED = y$. Solve the system of linear equations to find the values of x and y. **$x = 3$; $y = 4$**

In Exercise 28, you will use Theorem 9-1 to prove the following theorem.

Theorem 9-4   If three (or more) parallel lines cut off congruent segments on one transversal, then they cut off congruent segments on every transversal.

If $\overleftrightarrow{AB} \parallel \overleftrightarrow{CD} \parallel \overleftrightarrow{EF}$ and $\overline{AC} \cong \overline{CE}$, then $\overline{BD} \cong \overline{DF}$.

Example 3   Relating to the Real World

Measuring You want to divide a blank card into three equal rows and you do not have a ruler. Apply Theorem 9-4 to do this using a piece of lined paper and a straightedge.

The lines of the paper are parallel and equally spaced. Place a corner of the top edge of the card on the first line of the paper. Place the corner of the bottom edge on the fourth line. Mark the points where the second and third lines intersect the card. The marks will be equally spaced because the edge of the card is a transversal for the equally spaced parallel lines of the paper. Repeat for the other side of the card. Connect the marks.

450

Example 3 Relating to the Real World ·················

EXTENSION Have students perform the activity described in the example. Give students different sizes of index cards or cut different-sized rectangles from heavy paper.

CRITICAL THINKING Ask students to explain how the activity described in the example is an application of Theorem 9-4.

Exercises ON YOUR OWN

MAKING CONNECTIONS Exercise 11 Isaac Merrit Singer made the first practical sewing machine with a foot treadle instead of a hand crank in 1851. His first machines sold for $75 each, expensive in those days, leading him to devise installment buying plans. He is credited with creating the first consumer-appliance industry, devising multi-million dollar advertising campaigns, and initiating a system of providing service with sales.

PROBABILITY Exercise 12 Suggest that students draw a parallelogram, label the angles, list all possible combinations of two angles, then check if each angle pair is supplementary.

OPEN-ENDED Exercise 13a Students may want to make two such parallelograms using straws, uncooked spaghetti, toothpicks, or craft sticks.

ALTERNATIVE ASSESSMENT Exercises 14–16 You can use these exercises to help you assess students' understanding of the theorems in this lesson by their ability to apply them in these proofs. Have students work with a partner and allow them to choose the form of proof.

Exercises ON YOUR OWN

Find the measures of the numbered angles for each parallelogram. 4. $m\angle 1 = 95$; $m\angle 2 = 37$; $m\angle 3 = 37$

1.

2.

3.

4.

$m\angle 1 = 118$; $m\angle 2 = 62$; $m\angle 3 = 118$ $m\angle 1 = 81$; $m\angle 2 = 28$; $m\angle 3 = 71$

Find the length of $\overline{AP}$ in each parallelogram. 2. $m\angle 1 = 38$; $m\angle 2 = 32$; $m\angle 3 = 110$

5. 32

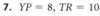

6. $YP = 8$, $TR = 10$

4

7. $YP = 8$, $TR = 10$

16

8. $MD = \frac{1}{2} AD$

21

9. The perimeter of parallelogram *RSTW* is 48 cm. If *RS* = 17 cm, find the lengths of the other sides of the parallelogram.   *ST* = 7 cm; *TW* = 17 cm; *WR* = 7 cm

10. The perimeter of parallelogram *EFGH* is 48 in. If *EF* is 5 in. less than *EH*, find the lengths of all four sides.   *EF* = 9.5 in.; *FG* = 14.5 in.; *GH* = 9.5 in.; *HE* = 14.5 in.

11. **Sewing** Suppose you don't have a ruler. Explain how to space 6 buttons equally on a baby's sweater if you know where the first and last buttons must be placed and you have a large piece of lined paper.   See margin.

12. **a. Probability** If two angles of a parallelogram that is not a rectangle are randomly selected, what is the probability that they will be supplementary? $\frac{2}{3}$

   b. Probability If two angles of a rectangle are randomly selected, what is the probability that they will be supplementary? 1

13. **a. Open-ended** Sketch two parallelograms whose corresponding sides are congruent but whose corresponding angles are not congruent.

   b. Critical Thinking Is there an SSSS congruence theorem for parallelograms? Explain.
   a–b. See margin.

14. **Given:** ▱ *LENS* and ▱ *NGTH*
   Prove: $\angle L \cong \angle T$
   14–15. Answers may vary. See margin for samples.

15. **Given:** ▱ *LENS* and ▱ *NGTH*
   Prove: $\overline{LS} \parallel \overline{GT}$

16. **Given:** ▱ *LENS* and ▱ *NGTH*
   Prove: $\angle E$ is supplementary to $\angle T$.
   16. Answers may vary. See back of book for sample.

pages 451–453 On Your Own

11. Pick 6 equally spaced lines on the paper. Place the paper so that the 1st button is on the 1st line and the last button is on the 6th line. Draw a line between the first and last buttons. The remaining buttons should be placed where the drawn line crosses the 4 ∥ lines.

13a. Sample:

   b. No; the pair of ▱s in part (a) is a counterexample.

14. 1. ▱*LENS* (Given)
   2. $\angle L \cong \angle ENS$ (Opp. ∠s of a ▱ are ≅.) 3. ▱*NGTH* (Given)
   4. $\angle T \cong \angle GNH$ (Opp. ∠s of a ▱ are ≅.) 5. $\angle GNH \cong \angle ENS$ (Vert. ∠s are ≅.) 6. $\angle L \cong \angle T$ (Transitive Prop. of ≅)

15. 1. ▱*LENS* (Given) 2. $\overline{LS} \parallel \overline{EH}$ (Def. of ▱) 3. ▱*NGTH* (Given)
   4. $\overline{GT} \parallel \overline{EH}$ (Def. of ▱)
   5. $\overline{LS} \parallel \overline{GT}$ (2 lines ∥ to a 3rd line are ∥.)

Exercises 17–24 Ask students to state what theorem or theorems they used in each problem.

LOGICAL REASONING Exercise 27b Remind students that they may have written a plan for this proof in Question 4.

Exercise 28 The proof of Theorem 9-4 involves drawing auxiliary segments $\overline{BG}$ and $\overline{DH}$ and showing $\triangle BGD \cong \triangle DHF$.

CRITICAL THINKING Exercises 29–30 Ask students to make a conjecture about the relationship between *RSTW* and *XYTZ*. (One is a dilation image of the other.)

26a. Rectangles, rhombuses, and squares; a rectangle has 2 lines of symmetry passing through the midpts. of opp. sides. A rhombus has 2 lines of symmetry passing through opp. vertices. A square has both kinds of lines of symmetry.

b. All □s have rotational symmetry because opp. sides are ≅, opp. angles are ≅, and the diagonals bisect each other.

27b. Sample:

Given: □*ABCD*. Prove:
∠*A* ≅ ∠*C*; ∠*B* ≅ ∠*D*. Draw
diagonal $\overline{BD}$. 1. □*ABCD* (Given)
2. $\overline{AB} \parallel \overline{CD}$ (Def. of □)
3. ∠*ABD* ≅ ∠*BDC* (If ∥ lines, then alt. int. ∠s are ≅.)
4. $\overline{BC} \parallel \overline{DA}$ (Def. of □)
5. ∠*ADB* ≅ ∠*CBD* (If ∥ lines, then alt. int. ∠s are ≅.)
6. $\overline{BD} \cong \overline{BD}$ (Reflexive Prop. of ≅) 7. △*ABD* ≅ △*CDB* (ASA)
8. ∠*A* ≅ ∠*C* (CPCTC) Similarly, use diagonal $\overline{AC}$ to prove ∠*B* ≅ ∠*D*.

29. 1. □*RSTW* and □*XYTZ* (Given)
2. ∠*R* ≅ ∠*T* (Opp. angles of a □ are ≅.) 3. ∠*T* ≅ ∠*X* (Opp. angles of a □ are ≅.) 4. ∠*R* ≅ ∠*X* (Transitive Prop. of ≅)

30. 1. □*RSTW* and □*XYTZ* (Given)
2. $\overline{RS} \parallel \overline{TW}$ (Def. of □)
3. $\overline{XY} \parallel \overline{TW}$ (Def. of □)
4. $\overline{RS} \parallel \overline{XY}$ (2 lines ∥ to a 3rd are ∥.)

452

Algebra **Find the value of the variable(s) in each parallelogram.**

17.

18.

$x = 15; y = 45$

19.

$x = 109; y = 88; z = 76$

20.

$x = 25; y = 115$

21.

$x = y = 6$

22.

$x = 10; y = 4$

23. $AC = 4x + 10$

$x = 0; y = 5$

24.

$x = 6; y = 4$

25. Writing If you know the measure of one angle of a parallelogram, explain how to find the measures of the remaining three angles. The opp. angles are ≅, so they have = measures. Consecutive angles are supplementary, so the sum of their measures is 180.

26. a. Transformations What types of parallelograms have reflectional symmetry? Explain. a–b. See margin.
b. Explain why all parallelograms have rotational symmetry.

27. a. Logical Reasoning Restate Theorem 9-2 (opposite angles of a parallelogram are congruent) in if-then form. If a quad. is a □, then opp. angles are ≅.
b. Prove Theorem 9-2. Include a figure and state what is given and what is to be proved. See margin.

28. The proof of Theorem 9-4 is outlined below. Supply the missing reason for each step.

Given: $\overleftrightarrow{AB} \parallel \overleftrightarrow{CD} \parallel \overleftrightarrow{EF}$ and $\overline{AC} \cong \overline{CE}$
Prove: $\overline{BD} \cong \overline{DF}$
Draw lines through *B* and *D* parallel to $\overleftrightarrow{AE}$ and intersecting $\overleftrightarrow{CD}$ and $\overleftrightarrow{EF}$ at *G* and *H*.
a. $\overleftrightarrow{AB} \parallel \overleftrightarrow{CD} \parallel \overleftrightarrow{EF}$ Given
b. *ABGC* and *CDHE* are parallelograms.
c. $\overline{BG} \cong \overline{AC}, \overline{DH} \cong \overline{CE}$
d. $\overline{AC} \cong \overline{CE}$ Given
e. $\overline{BG} \cong \overline{DH}$ Transitive Prop. of ≅
f. ∠2 ≅ ∠1, ∠1 ≅ ∠4, ∠4 ≅ ∠5, and ∠3 ≅ ∠6 If ∥ lines, then corres. ∠s are ≅.
g. ∠2 ≅ ∠5 Transitive Prop. of ≅
h. △*BGD* ≅ △*DHF* AAS
i. $\overline{BD} \cong \overline{DF}$ CPCTC

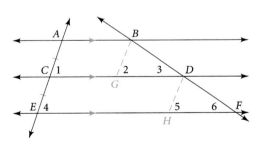

b. Def. of □
c. Opp. sides of a □ are ≅.

29. Given: □*RSTW* and □*XYTZ*
Prove: ∠*R* ≅ ∠*X*

30. Given: □*RSTW* and □*XYTZ*
Prove: $\overline{XY} \parallel \overline{RS}$
29–30. Answers may vary. See margin for samples.

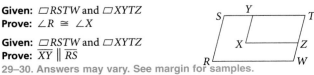

Transformations Exercises 31–33 refer to △*ABC* at the right and its image △*A′B′C′* under each transformation.

31. Reflect △*ABC* in $y = -2$. What type of quadrilateral is *ABA′C*? **kite**

32. Rotate △*ABC* 180° about the origin. What type of quadrilateral is *AC′BC*? **parallelogram**

33. Translate △*ABC* by ⟨4, 4⟩. What type of quadrilateral is *A′C′CB*? **trapezoid**

Chapter Project **Find Out by Doing**

Building a kite usually takes a lot of time, patience, and care. You can build a simple paper kite by following these directions.

Draw diagonals to find the center of an $8\frac{1}{2}$ by 11 in. sheet of paper. Then fold the paper, creasing only about a half inch past the center, to form the keel.

Bend each of the front corners of the paper out over to the keel. With a single staple, attach both corners to the keel and to each other about 1 in. from the front of the kite.

Attach one staple perpendicular to the keel as shown and tie one end of a spool of thread to it. You are ready to fly!

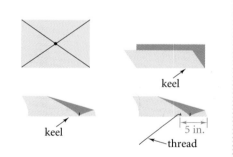

keel

keel

5 in.

thread

Exercises **MIXED REVIEW**

Sketch an example of each pair of angles. **34–39. See back of book for samples.**

34. supplementary angles

35. same-side interior angles

36. alternate interior angles

37. complementary angles

38. corresponding angles

39. vertical angles

40. **Coordinate Geometry** A triangle has coordinates $A(3, 0)$, $B(2, 5)$, and $C(-1, 3)$. Find the image of the triangle after a translation right 3 units and down 2 units followed by a reflection in the *x*-axis. **$A'(6, 2)$; $B'(5, -3)$; $C'(2, -1)$**

Getting Ready for Lesson 9-2

41. **a.** Find the coordinates of the midpoints of $\overline{AC}$ and $\overline{BD}$. What is the relationship between $\overline{AC}$ and $\overline{BD}$? **See above right.**
    b. Find the slopes of $\overline{BC}$ and $\overline{AD}$. How do they compare? **See above.**
    c. Are $\overline{AB}$ and $\overline{DC}$ parallel? Explain. **See below.**
    d. What type of figure is *ABCD*? **parallelogram**

41c. $\overline{AB} \parallel \overline{DC}$ because they are vertical.

41a. (2.5, 1.5), (2.5, 1.5); $\overline{AC}$ and $\overline{BD}$ bisect each other.

41b. $\frac{1}{3}$; $\frac{1}{3}$; the slopes are =.

453

PROBLEM OF THE DAY

The diagram shows a swimming pool with trees at each corner. Show how you can double the size of the pool, keeping it square without cutting down or moving the trees.

Problem of the Day is also available in Transparencies.

CONNECTING TO PRIOR KNOWLEDGE Have students identify parallelograms in buildings, bridges, artwork, etc. Ask students what they would need to know to prove the figures are parallelograms.

Students use geoboards to explore ways to determine whether a quadrilateral is a parallelogram. If geoboards are not available, students can use dot paper and a straightedge.

Review with students how to find the slope of a line on a geoboard or on dot paper by finding the ratio $\frac{rise}{run}$.

Lesson Planning Options

Prerequisite Skills

- Graphing in the coordinate plane
- Solving systems of linear equations

Assignment Options for Exercises On Your Own

Core 1–30
Extension 31

Use Mixed Review to maintain skills.

Resources

 Student Edition

Skills Handbook, pp. 663, 664, 667
Extra Practice, p. 642
Glossary/Study Guide

 Teaching Resources

Chapter Support File, Ch. 9
- Practice 9-2(two worksheets)
- Reteaching 9-2
- Alternative Activity 9-2
Classroom Manager 9-2
Glossary, Spanish Resources

 Transparencies
94

What You'll Learn

- Finding characteristics of quadrilaterals that indicate that they are parallelograms

...And Why

To solve problems in navigation and sailing

What You'll Need

- 11-by-11 peg geoboard
- straightedge

QUICK REVIEW

slope = $\frac{rise}{run}$

Connections Navigation . . . and more

9-2 Proving That a Quadrilateral Is a Parallelogram

WORK TOGETHER

By definition, a quadrilateral is a parallelogram if both pairs of opposite sides are parallel. Work with a partner and a geoboard to explore other ways to determine whether a quadrilateral is a parallelogram.

Figure 1   Figure 2

1. The segments in Figure 1 bisect each other. Connect the endpoints to form a quadrilateral. Find the slopes of opposite pairs of sides and determine what type of quadrilateral it is. -4 and $-\frac{2}{5}$; parallelogram

■ Make several quadrilaterals by joining the endpoints of pairs of bisecting segments on a geoboard. Classify the quadrilaterals you form.

2. Make a **conjecture** about quadrilaterals whose diagonals bisect each other. If diags. of a quad. bisect each other, the quad. is a ▱.

3. The segments in Figure 2 are congruent and parallel. Connect the endpoints to form a quadrilateral. Find the slopes of all four sides and determine what type of quadrilateral it is. $-\frac{2}{3}$ and $\frac{1}{2}$; parallelogram

■ Make several quadrilaterals by joining the endpoints of pairs of congruent and parallel segments on a geoboard. Classify the quadrilaterals you form.

4. Make a **conjecture** about quadrilaterals that have one pair of congruent and parallel sides. If a quad. has 1 pair of ≅ and ∥ sides, the quad. is a ▱.

CRITICAL THINKING Ask students if a figure with congruent diagonals is always a parallelogram. Then draw a kite with congruent diagonals as a counterexample.

MENTAL MATH Question 5 After students find the values of *x* and *y,* encourage them to evaluate each expression mentally to check that the two segments of each diagonal are congruent.

Example 1

You may want to start by discussing a plan for the proof: Show $\triangle AEB \cong \triangle CED$ and $\triangle BEC \cong \triangle DEA$. Then use CPCTC to show alternate interior angles are congruent. Then conclude that $\overline{AB} \parallel \overline{CD}$ and $\overline{BC} \parallel \overline{AD}$.

THINK AND DISCUSS

The results you obtained in the Work Together are the basis of Theorem 9-5 and Theorem 9-6.

Theorem 9-5

If the diagonals of a quadrilateral bisect each other, then the quadrilateral is a parallelogram.

Example 1

Use a flow proof to prove Theorem 9-5.

Given: $\overline{AC}$ and $\overline{BD}$ bisect each other at E.
Prove: $ABCD$ is a parallelogram.

Flow Proof

Who? Writing a flow proof is similar to writing a flow chart for a computer program. Ada Byron King, Countess of Lovelace (1815–1852), was the first programmer and the inventor of programming. In 1979, the U.S. Department of Defense named one of its computer languages ADA in her honor.

QUICK REVIEW

A parallelogram is a quadrilateral with both pairs of opposite sides parallel.

5. Try This Determine the value of the variables for which $LMNP$ is a parallelogram.

$x = 2.5; y = 12$

Additional Examples

FOR EXAMPLE 1 ....

Determine the values of the variables for which $QRST$ is a parallelogram.

$x = 3, y = 5$

Determine the values of the variables for which $KLMN$ is a parallelogram.

$x = 12, y = 9$

Discussion: *Name two pairs of congruent triangles in each parallelogram.*

FOR EXAMPLE 2 ....

Draw a parallelogram on grid paper with angles 60°, 60°, 120°, and 120°. Describe your steps.

Discussion: *Can two consecutive angles of a parallelogram be 60° each? Explain.*

455

Technology Options

For Exercise 23, students may draw the parallelogram using geometry software or a drawing program. For Exercises 25 and 30, students may use a graphing program to graph the parallelograms in the coordinate plane.

Prentice Hall Technology

Software
- Secondary Math Lab Toolkit™
- Integrated Math Lab 39
- Computer Item Generator 9-2

Internet
- See the Prentice Hall site. (http://www.phschool.com)

456

Theorem 9-6

If one pair of opposite sides of a quadrilateral are both congruent and parallel, then the quadrilateral is a parallelogram.

You can use Theorem 9-5 to show that Theorem 9-6 is true.

6a. $\angle 1 \cong \angle 4$ and $\angle 2 \cong \angle 3$; if ‖ lines, then alt. int. $\angle$s are $\cong$.

b. $\triangle ABE$ and $\triangle CDE$; ASA

d. The diags. of quad. *ABCD* bisect each other.

6. **Given:** $\overline{AB} \cong \overline{DC}$; $\overline{AB} \parallel \overline{DC}$
   a. Which numbered angles must be congruent? Why?
   b. Which triangles must be congruent? Why?
   c. Complete: $\overline{AE} \cong \blacksquare$ and $\overline{BE} \cong \blacksquare$. **CE; DE**
   d. What follows from part (c)?
   e. Why is *ABCD* a parallelogram?
   If the diags. of a quad. bisect each other, the quad. is a ▱.

Theorems 9-7 and 9-8 provide additional ways to prove that a quadrilateral is a parallelogram.

Theorem 9-7

If both pairs of opposite sides of a quadrilateral are congruent, then the quadrilateral is a parallelogram.

7. *Logical Reasoning* Write a paragraph proof of Theorem 9-7. Use quadrilateral *ABCD*, with $\overline{AB} \cong \overline{CD}$ and $\overline{BC} \cong \overline{DA}$. (*Hint:* Draw diagonal $\overline{BD}$ and use congruent triangles.)
   See margin p. 457.

Theorem 9-8

If both pairs of opposite angles of a quadrilateral are congruent, then the quadrilateral is a parallelogram.

You can use the fact that the sum of the measures of the interior angles of a quadrilateral is 360 to show that Theorem 9-8 is true.

8c. $\angle A$ and $\angle B$ are supplementary; $\angle B$ and $\angle C$ are supplementary.

8. **Given:** $\angle A \cong \angle C$ and $\angle B \cong \angle D$
   a. Let $m\angle A = x$ and $m\angle B = y$. Write an equation expressing the sum of the measures of the angles of quadrilateral *ABCD* in terms of x and y. $2x + 2y = 360$
   b. Solve for y in terms of x. $y = 180 - x$
   c. What is the relationship between $\angle A$ and $\angle B$? between $\angle B$ and $\angle C$? See left.
   d. What is the relationship between $\overline{AB}$ and $\overline{DC}$? between $\overline{BC}$ and $\overline{AD}$? Explain. $\overline{AB} \parallel \overline{DC}$, $\overline{BC} \parallel \overline{AD}$; if supplementary same-side interior $\angle$s, then lines are ‖.
   e. Classify quadrilateral *ABCD*. *ABCD* is a ▱.

9. **Try This** Based on the markings, decide if each figure must be a parallelogram. Justify your answer. b. No; the quad. could be an isosceles trap.

9a. Yes; if 1 pair of opp. sides of a quad. are both $\cong$ and ‖, then the quad. is a ▱.

a.   b.   c.

c. Yes; the 2nd pair of sides are ‖ because alt. int. $\angle$s are $\cong$. The quad. is a ▱ by def.

Have students make a list of the five ways to prove two quadrilaterals congruent. It should include the definition of parallelogram and Theorems 9-5 and 9-6. Some students may want to use the results of Question 8 to write a sixth way: If an angle is supplementary to both consecutive angles of a quadrilateral, then the quadrilateral is a parallelogram.

Exercises 1–8 Students apply the theorems presented in this lesson to determine whether or not the figures are parallelograms.

E x a m p l e   2   Relating to the Real World 🌐 ················

TACTILE LEARNING Students can make a parallel ruler using straws and brads. Then have them make their own map on graph paper, labeling a ship's position and its destination. They can make a compass using a protractor. Have them find the angle the ship must travel to reach its destination.

E x a m p l e   2   Relating to the Real World 🌐 ··············

Navigation A parallel rule is a navigational tool used to plot ship routes on charts. It is made of two rulers connected with congruent crossbars, such that $AB = DC$ and $AD = BC$. You place one ruler on a line connecting the ship's position to its destination point. Then you move the other ruler onto the chart's compass to find the angle of the route. Explain why this instrument works.

Because both the sections of the rulers and the crossbars are congruent, the rulers and crossbars form parallelogram $ABCD$. Since the figure is a parallelogram, the rulers are parallel. Therefore, the angle shown on the chart's compass is congruent to the angle the ship should travel.

10. Suppose $m\angle B = 60$. Find the measures of the other angles of parallelogram $ABCD$ formed by the parallel rule.
$m\angle A = m\angle C = 120, m\angle D = 60$

pages 455–457   Think and Discuss

7. Draw diagonal $\overline{BD}$. Since the opp. sides are ≅, $\triangle ABD \cong \triangle CDB$ by SSS. Then $\angle ABD \cong \angle CDB$ by CPCTC. If ≅ alt. int. $\angle$s, then lines are ∥, so $\overline{AB} \parallel \overline{CD}$. Similarly, $\angle ADB \cong \angle CBD$, and $\overline{BC} \parallel \overline{DA}$. By def., $ABCD$ is a ▱.

pages 457–459   On Your Own

1. Yes; if both pairs of opp. sides of a quad. are ≅, the quad. is a ▱.

2. No; the 2nd diagonal may not be bisected by the 1st.

3. Yes; if both pairs of opp. angles of a quad. are ≅, the quad. is a ▱.

4. No; the quad. may be an isosceles trapezoid.

5. Yes; both pairs of opp. sides are ∥ because alt. int. ∠s are ≅. The quad. is a ▱ by def.

6. Yes; if 1 pair of sides of a quad. is both ≅ and ∥, then the quad. is a ▱ by Thm. 9-6.

7. Yes; the quad. is a ▱ by def.

8. No; 1 pair of sides is ∥, but the other pair need not be ∥.

Based on the markings, decide if each figure must be a parallelogram. Justify your answer.   1–8. See margin.

1.   **2.**   **3.**   **4.**

5.   **6.**   **7.**   **8.**

457

Exercises 9–14 For each exercise, have students copy the figure, label the figure with the given information, and state any theorems they used to justify their answers.

ALGEBRA Exercises 15–17 Make sure that students do not assume the figures are parallel before finding the missing angle measures or side lengths.

ALTERNATIVE ASSESSMENT Exercises 18–20 After students complete these problems, have them work with a partner to use the properties of parallelograms to create their own algebra problems. Have students exchange problems within their groups and solve them.

STANDARDIZED TEST TIP Exercise 21 Students will quickly see that A and C are sufficient conditions. In order to see that D and E are also sufficient, students need to recognize that $\angle R$ supplementary to $\angle S$ implies $\overline{RW} \parallel \overline{ST}$.

OPEN-ENDED Exercise 23 Students may want to create these parallelograms using geoboards, straws, or other manipulatives.

State whether the information given about quadrilateral *RSTW* is sufficient to determine that it is a parallelogram.

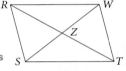

9. $\overline{RS} \parallel \overline{WT}, \overline{RS} \cong \overline{WT}$ **yes** **10.** $\overline{RS} \parallel \overline{WT}, \overline{ST} \cong \overline{RW}$ **no**

11. $\overline{RS} \cong \overline{WT}, \overline{ST} \cong \overline{RW}$ **yes** **12.** $\angle SRW \cong \angle WTS, \angle RST \cong \angle TWR$ **yes**

13. $\overline{RZ} \cong \overline{TZ}, \overline{SZ} \cong \overline{WZ}$ **yes** **14.** $\angle TSZ \cong \angle RSZ, \angle TWZ \cong \angle RWZ$ **no**

Algebra Find the value of *x*. Then tell whether *ABCD* must be a parallelogram. Explain your answer. 16. 31; no; consecutive ∠s are not supplementary and alt. int. ∠s are not ≅, so the sides are not parallel.

15.

60; yes; both pairs of opp. angles are ≅.

16.

17.

6; yes, both pairs of opp. sides are ≅.

Algebra Determine the values of the variables for which *ABCD* is a parallelogram.

18.

$x = 15; y = 25$

19.

$x = 3; y = 11$

20.

$x = 3; y = 4$

21. Standardized Test Prep Which of the following pairs of conditions will *not* be sufficient to prove that quadrilateral *RSTW* is a parallelogram? **B**

I. $\overline{RS} \parallel \overline{WT}$ **II.** $\overline{RS} \cong \overline{WT}$

III. $\overline{ST} \cong \overline{RW}$ **IV.** $\angle R$ is supplementary to $\angle S$.

A. I and II   **B.** I and III   **C.** II and III

D. I and IV   **E.** III and IV

22. a. Transformations Describe the transformation that maps $\overline{AB}$ to $\overline{A'B'}$. ⟨3, 2⟩

b. Suppose $\overline{C'D'}$ is the image of $\overline{CD}$ under the transformation in part (a). What kind of quadrilateral is $CDD'C'$? Explain. **See below.**

23. Open-ended Sketch two noncongruent parallelograms *ABCD* and *EFGH* such that $\overline{AC} \cong \overline{EG}$ and $\overline{BD} \cong \overline{FH}$. **See margin p. 459 for sample.**

24. Probability Two opposite angles of a quadrilateral measure 120. The measures of the other angles are multiples of 10. What is the probability that the quadrilateral is a parallelogram? $\frac{1}{6}$

22b. Parallelogram; at least 1 pair of opp. sides is both ≅ and ∥.

458

COORDINATE GEOMETRY Exercise 25 Have students copy the grid for each part of the problem.

Exercises 27–29 Have students work in groups to complete the proofs. Then have each group present one of the proofs to the class.

ESL Exercise 31 Help students understand "weaving." Bring in a piece of material in which the vertical and horizontal threads are visible to illustrate the meaning of the term. Help students compare and contrast the uses of weaving in the phrases "fabric weaving," "a car weaving in and out of its lane," and "a spider weaving a web."

DIVERSITY Exercise 31 Have students research the North American Indian art of basket weaving.

25. a. Coordinate Geometry Find the coordinates of point D so that $ABCD$ is a parallelogram. **(4, 0)**
  b. Find the coordinates of point E so that $ABEC$ is a parallelogram. **(6, 6)**
  c. Find the coordinates of point F so that $AFBC$ is a parallelogram. **(−2, 4)**

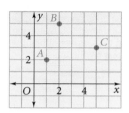

26. Writing Which pairs of theorems in Lessons 9-1 and 9-2 can be combined in if-and-only-if statements? Write the statements. **See margin.**

27–28. Answers may vary. See margin for sample.

Choose **Write a paragraph proof, a flow proof, or a two-column proof.**

27. Given: $\triangle TRS \cong \triangle RTW$
  Prove: $RSTW$ is a parallelogram.

28. Given: $\triangle PKJ \cong \triangle PML$
  Prove: $JKLM$ is a parallelogram.

29. Given: Parallelogram $ABCD$;
  E is the midpoint of $\overline{BC}$;
  F is the midpoint of $\overline{AD}$.
  a. Prove: $ABEF$ is a parallelogram.
  b. What theorem allows you to conclude that $\angle A \cong \angle BEF$? **Opp. angles of a ▱ are ≅.**
  c. What theorem allows you to conclude that $\overline{AB} \cong \overline{FE}$? **Opp. sides of a ▱ are ≅.**

a. See margin.

30. Coordinate Geometry The diagonals of quadrilateral $ABCD$ intersect at $E(-1, 4)$. Two vertices of $ABCD$ are $A(2, 7)$ and $B(-3, 5)$. What must the coordinates of C and D be in order to ensure that $ABCD$ is a parallelogram? **$C(-4, 1)$; $D(1, 3)$**

31. Weaving Fabric is made by weaving threads vertically (the warp) and horizontally (the weft), to form small rectangles. If the fabric is pulled vertically or horizontally, the fabric is rigid; that is, the rectangles keep their shape. **See below.**
  a. If the fabric is pulled along its diagonal (the bias), what happens to the weave of the fabric? What figures appear?
  b. How does this affect the shape of the fabric? **See below.**
  c. Research Sail makers have learned techniques to cut sails so that the fabric of the sail will not stretch as the force of the wind hits the sail. Research these techniques and prepare a short report summarizing your findings. **Check students' work.**

warp threads
bias
weft threads

a. ∥ threads remain ∥; the small rectangles are replaced with small nonrectangular ▱s.
b. The fabric stretches along one direction of threads and shrinks along the other.

23.

26. Thms. 9-1 and 9-7: A quad. is a ▱ if and only if the opp. sides are ≅. **Thms. 9-2 and 9-8:** A quad. is a ▱ if and only if the opp. ∠s are ≅. **Thms. 9-3 and 9-5:** A quad. is a ▱ if and only if the diagonals bisect each other.

27. 1. $\triangle TRS \cong \triangle RTW$ (Given)
  2. $\overline{RS} \cong \overline{TW}$; $\overline{ST} \cong \overline{WR}$ (CPCTC)
  3. $RSTW$ is a ▱. (If both pairs of opp. sides of a quad. are ≅, then the quad. is a ▱.)

28. 1. $\triangle PKJ \cong \triangle PML$ (Given)
  2. $\overline{PK} \cong \overline{PM}$; $\overline{PJ} \cong \overline{PL}$ (CPCTC)
  3. $\overline{JL}$ and $\overline{KM}$ bisect each other. (Def. of seg. bisector) **4.** $JKLM$ is a ▱. (If the diags. of a quad. bisect each other, then the quad. is a ▱.)

29a. Answers may vary. Sample:
  1. E is midpt. of $\overline{BC}$ and F is midpt. of $\overline{AD}$. (Given) **2.** $BE = \frac{1}{2}BC$; $AF = \frac{1}{2}AD$ (Def. of midpt.)
  3. ▱$ABCD$ (Given) **4.** $AD = BC$ (Opp. sides of a ▱ are ≅.)
  5. $\frac{1}{2}AD = \frac{1}{2}BC$ (Mult. Prop. of =)
  6. $AF = BE$ (Substitution)
  7. $\overline{AD} \parallel \overline{BC}$ (Opp. sides of a ▱ are ≅.) **8.** $ABEF$ is a ▱. (If 1 pair of opp. sides of a quad. is ≅ and ∥, then the quad. is a ▱.)

459

Exercises MIXED REVIEW

Exercises 32–35 Students review finding the areas of plane figures.

GETTING READY FOR LESSON 9-3 These exercises prepare students to find properties of special parallelograms.

Wrap Up

THE BIG IDEA Ask students: *If you know that one pair of opposite sides of a quadrilaterals is parallel, what additional information would be sufficient to prove that the quadrilateral is a parallelogram? Give as many answers as possible.*

RETEACHING ACTIVITY Students are given certain characteristics of quadrilaterals to prove that the quadrilaterals are parallelograms. (Reteaching worksheet 9-2)

Exercises CHECKPOINT

In this Checkpoint, your students will assess their own progress in Lessons 9-1 to 9-2.

Exercises 1–6 Students use the properties of parallelograms to find missing angle measures and side lengths.

Lesson Quiz

Lesson Quiz is also available in Transparencies.

State whether the information given about quadrilateral *EFGH* is sufficient to determine that it is a parallelogram.

1. $\overline{EF} \parallel \overline{HG}$, $\overline{EH} \parallel \overline{FG}$ sufficient

2. $\overline{ED} \cong \overline{DG}$, $\overline{HD} \cong \overline{DF}$ sufficient

3. $\angle FEH \cong \angle HGF$, $\angle EHG \cong \angle GFE$
sufficient

Determine the values of the variables for which *EFGH* is a parallelogram.

4. $m\angle E = 2x + 20$, $m\angle F = 5y$,
$m\angle G = 3x - 25$ $x = 45$, $y = 14$

460

Exercises MIXED REVIEW

Calculator Find the area of each figure. When the answer is not a whole number, round to the nearest tenth.

32.
115 cm²

33.
50.3 cm²

34.
104.5 in.²

35.
166.3 ft²

36. Locus Sketch the locus of points in space that are equidistant from two points. The locus is a plane that bisects and is ⊥ to the segment joining the 2 points.

Getting Ready for Lesson 9-3

State the definition for each of these special quadrilaterals.

37. a parallelogram

38. a rhombus

39. a rectangle

40. a square

37. A ▱ is a quad. with 2 pairs of ∥ sides.
38. A rhombus is a ▱ with 4 ≅ sides.
39. A rectangle is a ▱ with 4 rt. angles.
40. A square is a ▱ with 4 ≅ sides and 4 rt. angles.

FOR YOUR JOURNAL
Summarize four different ways you can prove that a quadrilateral is a parallelogram.

Exercises CHECKPOINT

Find the measures of the numbered angles for each parallelogram. $m\angle 1 = 106$; $m\angle 2 = 74$; $m\angle 3 = 26$

1.
$m\angle 1 = 59$; $m\angle 2 = 121$; $m\angle 3 = 59$

2.
$m\angle 1 = 43$; $m\angle 2 = 62$; $m\angle 3 = 62$

3.

Algebra Determine the values of the variables for which *ABCD* is a parallelogram.

4.
$x = 45$; $y = 60$

5.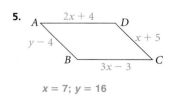
$x = 7$; $y = 16$

6.
$x = 1$; $y = 2$

7. Standardized Test Prep Which is *not* sufficient to prove that a quadrilateral is a parallelogram? **D**
   A. The diagonals bisect each other.
   B. Both pairs of opposite sides are congruent.
   C. Both pairs of opposite angles are congruent.
   D. The diagonals are perpendicular.
   E. A pair of opposite sides are congruent and parallel.

Math ToolboX — Technology

Exploring the Diagonals of Parallelograms

Before Lesson 9-3 ▶

Work in pairs or small groups.

Construct   Check students' work.

Use geometry software to construct a parallelogram. First construct segments $\overline{AB}$ and $\overline{BC}$. Construct a line through C parallel to $\overline{AB}$ and a line through A parallel to $\overline{BC}$. Label the point where the two lines intersect as D. Hide the lines and construct $\overline{AD}$ and $\overline{CD}$. Construct the diagonals of parallelogram $ABCD$ and their point of intersection E.

Measure the diagonals of the parallelogram so you can tell when they are congruent. Measure an angle formed by the diagonals so you can tell when the diagonals are perpendicular. Measure the angles formed by the diagonals and the sides of the parallelogram so you can tell when the diagonals bisect the angles of the parallelogram.

Investigate   Answers may vary. Samples are given.

- Measure an angle of the parallelogram so that when you manipulate the figure you can tell when it becomes a rectangle. Make note of any special properties of the diagonals of a rectangle. Manipulate the rectangle to check whether the properties hold. The diagonals are ≅ .

- Measure two adjacent sides of the parallelogram so you can tell when it is a rhombus. Make note of any special properties of the diagonals of a rhombus. Manipulate the rhombus to check whether the properties hold. The diagonals are perpendicular.

Conjecture   Answers may vary. Samples are given.

- Make as many conjectures as you can about the properties of the diagonals of rectangles and rhombuses. Diags. of a rect. are ≅; diags. of a rhombus are ⊥ bisectors of each other; diags. of a rhombus bisect the ∠s of the rhombus.
- Use what you know about squares to make **conjectures** about the diagonals of squares. All the properties of diags. listed above are true for the diags. of squares.

Extend

- Manipulate the diagonals so they are perpendicular. Make a **conjecture** about the type of parallelogram that is determined by perpendicular diagonals. In a ▱, perpendicular diags. determine a rhombus.

- Do the same for congruent diagonals and for diagonals that bisect the angles of the parallelogram. ≅ diags. determine a rectangle; diags. that bisect the angles of the ▱ determine a rhombus.

CONNECTING TO PRIOR KNOWLEDGE Copy the Venn diagram from page 93 omitting the labels. Ask students to add the labels: Quadrilaterals, Parallelograms, Rectangles, Squares, Rhombuses, Kites, and Trapezoids. Have them justify the placement of each by giving the definition of the figure.

Begin by reviewing the definition of each figure. Make sure students accurately draw each on grid paper. You may want to provide a handout with the table shown on page 462.

ERROR ALERT! Some students may check off a property in a category if they can find one example for which it holds. For example, they may check "all sides are ≅" for parallelograms because it is true for some parallelograms. **Remediation:** Make sure students understand that they should check off only properties true for all figures in that category.

Lesson Planning Options

Prerequisite Skills

- Recognizing special quadrilaterals

Assignment Options for Exercises On Your Own

To provide flexible scheduling, this lesson can be subdivided into parts.

1 Core 16–17, 19, 22–25
Extension 32

2 Core 1–15, 18, 20–21, 26–32
Extension 33–34

Use Mixed Review to maintain skills.

Resources

 Student Edition

Skills Handbook, pp. 646, 650, 659
Extra Practice, p. 642
Glossary/Study Guide

 Teaching Resources

Chapter Support File, Ch. 9
- Practice 9-3 (two worksheets)
- Reteaching 9-3
Classroom Manager 9-3
Glossary, Spanish Resources

 Transparencies
95, 99, 100

What You'll Learn
- Finding properties of rectangles, rhombuses, and squares

...And Why
To help in designing playgrounds and kites

What You'll Need
- centimeter grid paper
- scissors
- protractor
- ruler

9-3 Properties of Special Parallelograms

In Lesson 9-1, you explored the properties of parallelograms. Work in a group of three to explore the properties of rhombuses, rectangles, and squares.

- Each member should choose one of these special quadrilaterals and draw a large figure on grid paper.

- Using paper folding or a protractor and ruler, each member should measure and compare the sides, angles, and diagonals of his or her quadrilateral. Then he or she should share the results with the group.

- Use the results to complete a table like the one below. The properties of a parallelogram have been checked off.

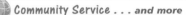

Property	Parallelogram	Rhombus	Rectangle	Square
All sides are ≅.		✔		✔
Opposite sides are ≅.	✔	✔	✔	✔
Opposite sides are ∥.	✔	✔	✔	✔
Opposite angles are ≅.	✔	✔	✔	✔
All angles are right ∡.			✔	✔
Diagonals bisect each other.	✔	✔	✔	✔
Diagonals are ≅.			✔	✔
Diagonals are ⊥.		✔		✔
Each diagonal bisects opposite angles.		✔		✔

∠AED are congruent and supplementary and therefore are right angles.

Theorem 9-9 Help students see that a diagonal of a rhombus bisects two opposite congruent angles resulting in four congruent angles.

ALTERNATIVE METHOD Question 1 Students can also prove △ABC ≅ △CDA by the SAS Postulate. Then ∠1 ≅ ∠4 and ∠2 ≅ ∠3 by CPCTC. Because △ABC and △CDA are isosceles, ∠1 ≅ ∠3 and ∠2 ≅ ∠4. By substitution, ∠1 ≅ ∠2 and ∠3 ≅ ∠4.

VISUAL LEARNING Copy ABCD and trace △ABE and △ADE in different colors. Mark corresponding sides and angles on the diagram as you read them in the proof.

TACTILE LEARNING Question 3 Have students prove Theorem 9-11 visually. Have them draw a rhombus, draw and label each diagonal d_1 and d_2 with a different color, cut the rhombus along its diagonals, and rearrange the resulting triangles to form a rectangle with base d_1 and height $\frac{d_2}{2}$.

Example 1

You may want to begin by discussing a plan for the proof: show △ABE and △ADE are congruent. Then ∠AEB and

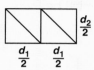

Part 1 Properties of Rhombuses

The properties you discovered in the Work Together are the basis for many of the theorems in this lesson.

Theorem 9-9

Each diagonal of a rhombus bisects two angles of the rhombus.

1. Answer the following questions to prove Theorem 9-9.
   a. ABCD is a rhombus. Why is △ABC ≅ △ADC? **SSS or SAS**
   b. What is the relationship between ∠1 and ∠2? between ∠3 and ∠4? Explain. **∠1 ≅ ∠2; ∠3 ≅ ∠4; CPCTC**

2. **Try This** If m∠B = 120, find the measures of the numbered angles. **30; 30; 30; 30**

Theorem 9-10

The diagonals of a rhombus are perpendicular.

Example 1

Write a paragraph proof of Theorem 9-10.

Given: ABCD is a rhombus.
Prove: $\overline{AC} \perp \overline{BD}$

Paragraph Proof

By the definition of rhombus, $\overline{AB} \cong \overline{AD}$. Because $\overline{AC}$ is a diagonal of a rhombus, it bisects ∠BAD. Therefore ∠1 ≅ ∠2. $\overline{AE} \cong \overline{AE}$ by the Reflexive Property of Congruence. By the SAS Postulate, △ABE ≅ △ADE. By CPCTC, ∠AEB ≅ ∠AED. Because ∠AEB and ∠AED are both congruent and supplementary, they are right angles. By the definition of perpendicular, $\overline{AC} \perp \overline{BD}$. ■

In Chapter 5, you found the area of a rhombus by using the formula for the area of a parallelogram, A = bh. Using Theorems 9-9 and 9-10, you can find another formula for the area of a rhombus. You will derive this formula in Exercise 17.

Theorem 9-11

The area of a rhombus is equal to half the product of the lengths of its diagonals.

$$A = \frac{1}{2}d_1 d_2$$

3. **Critical Thinking** Explain why you can use the area formula $A = \frac{1}{2}d_1 d_2$ to find the area of a square. **A square is a rhombus.**

Additional Examples

FOR EXAMPLE 1 ....

Write a two-column proof of Theorem 9-10. **See back of book.**

Discussion: *Are the diagonals of a square perpendicular? Explain.*

FOR EXAMPLE 2 ....

a. Find the measures of the numbered angles of the rhombus.
m∠1 = 34, m∠2 = 56, m∠3 = 56, m∠4 = 90

b. Find the area of the rhombus.
192 cm²

Discussion: *Explain why the four non-overlapping triangles formed by the diagonals of a rhombus are congruent.*

FOR EXAMPLE 3 ....

Refer to the diagram in Example 3. If the students use two 26-ft long pieces of rope as diagonals, find the possible dimensions of the rectangle they form. **Answers may vary. Sample: 10 ft by 24 ft**

Discussion: *Explain how you can use properties of a parallelogram and a rhombus to stake out a rhombus-shaped garden.*

Technology Options

464

Example 2

a. Find the measures of the numbered angles in the rhombus.

b. Find the area of the rhombus.

a. $m\angle 1 = 90$ Diagonals of a rhombus are perpendicular.
$m\angle 2 = 50$ If ∥ lines, then alt. int. ∠s are ≅.
$m\angle 3 = 50$ Each diagonal of a rhombus bisects two angles.
$m\angle 4 = 40$ Acute angles of a right △ are complementary.

b. $d_1 = 2(6) = 12$ Diagonals of a parallelogram bisect each other.
$d_2 = 2(5) = 10$
$A = \frac{1}{2}d_1 d_2$ Formula for the area of a rhombus
$= \frac{1}{2}(12)(10)$ Substitute the lengths of the diagonals.
$= 60$ Simplify.

The area of the rhombus is 60 cm².

 PROBLEM SOLVING

Look Back Explain how you could use triangles to find the area of the rhombus.

The diagonals divide the rhombus into 4 ≅ △s. Find the area of each △. Then multiply by 4 to get the area of the rhombus.

Part 2

Properties of Rectangles and Parallelograms

In the Work Together on page 462, you probably discovered the following properties of rectangles and parallelograms.

| **Theorem 9-12** | The diagonals of a rectangle are congruent. |

4. Answer the following questions to prove Theorem 9-12.
  a. *ABCD* is a rectangle. What parts of △*ABC* and △*DCB* must be congruent? Explain. See margin p. 465.
  b. Why is △*ABC* ≅ △*DCB*?
  c. Why is $\overline{AC} \cong \overline{BD}$? CPCTC
  b. SAS

The following theorems are suggested by the converses of Theorems 9-9, 9-10, and 9-12. You will write proofs of these theorems in the exercises.

Theorem 9-13	If one diagonal of a parallelogram bisects two angles of the parallelogram, then the parallelogram is a rhombus.
Theorem 9-14	If the diagonals of a parallelogram are perpendicular, then the parallelogram is a rhombus.
Theorem 9-15	If the diagonals of a parallelogram are congruent, then the parallelogram is a rectangle.

5. *Logical Reasoning* Suppose the diagonals of a parallelogram are both perpendicular and congruent. What type of special quadrilateral is it? Explain your reasoning. See margin p. 465.

Builders and construction workers use the properties of diagonals to "square off" rectangular foundations and other rectangular constructions.

Example 3 — Relating to the Real World 🌐 ·············

Community Service Volunteers are helping to build a rectangular play area in a city park. Explain how they can use properties of the diagonals of a parallelogram and a rectangle to stake the vertices of the play area.

The volunteers can use these two theorems to design the play area:

- Theorem 9-5: If the diagonals of a quadrilateral bisect each other, then the quadrilateral is a parallelogram.

- Theorem 9-15: If the diagonals of a parallelogram are congruent, then the parallelogram is a rectangle.

First, cut two pieces of rope of equal length for the diagonals. Then, fold each piece to find the midpoint of each diagonal. Next, position the ropes so that the ropes intersect at the midpoints. Any quadrilateral formed by connecting the endpoints of the two ropes will be a rectangle.

6. **Open-ended** The volunteers use two 20-ft-long pieces of rope as diagonals. Describe possible dimensions of the rectangle they can form.
Answers may vary. Sample: 12 ft by 16 ft

7. **Critical Thinking** Steven thinks that they can use this same method to stake off a square. Is he right? Explain why or why not.
Yes; if the ropes are ⊥ to each other, the endpoints of the rope determine a square.

Exercises — ON YOUR OWN

For each parallelogram (a) choose the best name and then (b) find the measures of the numbered angles.

1.
1a. rhombus

2.
2a. rectangle

3.
3a. rectangle

4.
4a. rhombus

5. **Carpentry** An open-backed bookcase has shelves 24 in. wide and 12 in. high. Diagonal braces help keep the shelves and the sides of the bookcase perpendicular to each other. Find the lengths of the braces.
26.8 in.

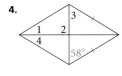

1b. $m\angle 1 = 38$; $m\angle 2 = 38$; $m\angle 3 = 38$; $m\angle 4 = 38$
2b. $m\angle 1 = 59$; $m\angle 2 = 31$; $m\angle 3 = 118$; $m\angle 4 = 31$
3b. $m\angle 1 = 56$; $m\angle 2 = 68$; $m\angle 3 = 112$; $m\angle 4 = 56$
4b. $m\angle 1 = 32$; $m\angle 2 = 90$; $m\angle 3 = 58$; $m\angle 4 = 32$

Exercises 6–9 Students use the properties of special parallelograms and the Pythagorean Theorem to find missing side lengths.

OPEN-ENDED Exercise 10 Make sure students understand that the diagonals of one of the rectangles should be congruent to the diagonals of the other.

STANDARDIZED TEST TIP **Exercise 11** Suggest students draw *RSTW* and label congruent sides and angles.

TRANSFORMATIONS Exercise 16 Students draw a segment and use reflections to create a rhombus.

Exercise 17 Students prove Theorem 9-11.

---

pages 465–468 On Your Own

18. Opp. sides of a square are ≅ and ‖; all angles are rt. angles; the 4 sides are ≅; the diagonals are ⊥ bisectors of each other; the diagonals are ≅; each diagonal bisects 2 angles of the square; the area = half the product of the lengths of the diagonals or = the square of the length of each side.

20. Yes; $7^2 + 24^2 = 25^2$, so $\triangle RST$ is a rt. $\triangle$. $\angle S$ is a rt. angle, and it follows that $\angle R$, $\angle T$, and $\angle W$ are also rt. angles. Therefore, $\square RSTW$ is a rectangle.

21. Yes; $2.5^2 + 6^2 = 6.5^2$, so the diagonals divide the $\square$ into 4 rt. $\triangle$s. Since the diagonals are ⊥, $\square JKLM$ is a rhombus.

26. Yes; since all rt. $\angle$s are ≅, the opp. angles are ≅, and the quad. is a $\square$. A $\square$ with all rt. $\angle$s is a rectangle.

27. Yes; 4 sides are ≅, so the opp. sides are ≅, and the quad. is a $\square$. A $\square$ with all sides ≅ is a rhombus.

28. Yes; a quad. with 4 ≅ sides is a $\square$, and a $\square$ with 4 ≅ sides and 4 rt. angles is a square.

📊 *Choose* Use mental math, pencil and paper, or a calculator to find *LB, BP,* and *LM* for each parallelogram.

LB = 10; BP = 5; LM = 8

6.

7.

8.
LB = 14; BP = 7; LM = $\frac{7\sqrt{5}}{2}$

9.
LB = 12; BP = 12; LM = $2\sqrt{11}$

LB = 15; BP = 15; LM = 17

10. *Open-ended* Sketch two noncongruent rectangles with congruent diagonals. **See below right for sample.**

11. *Standardized Test Prep* In quadrilateral *RSTW*, $\overline{RT}$ and $\overline{SW}$ bisect each other at *A* and $\overline{RA} \cong \overline{WA}$. *RSTW* must be a **C**
   I. parallelogram.
   II. rectangle.
   III. square.
   A. I only
   B. II only
   C. I and II
   D. II and III
   E. I, II, and III

Algebra Find the value of the variable(s) for each parallelogram.

12. $RZ = 2x + 5$, **30**
   $SW = 5x - 20$

13.
   $x = 45$; $y = 45$; $z = 30$

14. $m\angle 1 = 3y - 6$

   $x = 5$; $y = 32$; $z = 7.5$

15. $BD = 4x - y + 1$

   $x = 7.5$; $y = 3$

16. *Transformations* Draw $\overline{AB}$ and a line ℓ through *B* that is not perpendicular to $\overline{AB}$. Reflect $\overline{AB}$ in ℓ. Then reflect $\triangle A'AB$ in $\overline{AA'}$. What type of quadrilateral is $ABA'B'$? Explain. **See below right.**

17. Complete the following steps to derive the formula for the area of a rhombus.

   Given: Rhombus *ABCD*
   Prove: Area $= \frac{1}{2} \cdot BD \cdot AC$

   a. $\overline{AC} \perp$ ▨ because the diagonals of a rhombus are perpendicular. $\overline{BD}$
   b. Area of $\triangle ABD = \frac{1}{2} \cdot BD \cdot$ ▨ **AE**
   c. Area of $\triangle BCD = \frac{1}{2} \cdot BD \cdot$ ▨ **EC**
   d. Area of rhombus $ABCD = \frac{1}{2} \cdot BD \cdot$ ▨ $+ \frac{1}{2} \cdot BD \cdot$ ▨ **AE; EC**
   e. Area of rhombus $ABCD = \frac{1}{2} \cdot BD$ (▨ + ▨) **AE; EC**
   f. Area of rhombus $ABCD = \frac{1}{2} \cdot BD \cdot$ ▨ **AC**

18. *Writing* Summarize the properties of squares that follow from a square being a parallelogram, a rhombus, and a rectangle. **See margin.**

📊 19. *Calculator* In rhombus *EFGH*, the length of each side is 12 and $EG = 18$. Find *FH* to the nearest tenth. **15.9**

10. Sample:

16. Rhombus;
$\overline{AB} \cong \overline{BA'} \cong \overline{A'B'} \cong \overline{B'A}$

PROBLEM SOLVING HINT
Draw a diagram.

20. In □RSTW, RS = 7, ST = 24, and RT = 25. Is RSTW a rectangle? Explain.
    20–21. See margin p. 466.

21. In □JKLM, JL = 5, KM = 12, and JM = 6.5. Is JKLM a rhombus? Explain.

Find the area of each rhombus.

22.
    1200 ft²

23.
    24 m²

24.
    96 in.²

25.
    18 cm²

Logical Reasoning Decide whether each of these is a good definition. Justify your answer. 26–28. See margin p. 466 for reasoning.

26. A rectangle is a quadrilateral with four right angles. **yes**

27. A rhombus is a quadrilateral with four congruent sides. **yes**

28. A square is a quadrilateral with four right angles and four congruent sides. **yes**

Choose Write a two-column proof, a paragraph proof, or a flow proof.

29. **Theorem 9-13:** If one diagonal of a parallelogram bisects two angles of the parallelogram, then the parallelogram is a rhombus.

    Given: □ABCD; $\overline{AC}$ bisects ∠BAD and ∠BCD. 29–31. Answers
    Prove: ABCD is a rhombus. may vary. See margin for samples.

30. **Theorem 9-14:** If the diagonals of a parallelogram are perpendicular, then the parallelogram is a rhombus.

    Given: □ABCD; $\overline{AC} \perp \overline{BD}$
    Prove: ABCD is a rhombus.

31. **Theorem 9-15:** If the diagonals of a parallelogram are congruent, then the parallelogram is a rectangle.

    Given: □ABCD; $\overline{AC} \cong \overline{BD}$
    Prove: ABCD is a rectangle.

32. **Auto Repair** A car jack is shaped like a rhombus. As two of the opposite vertices get closer together, the other two opposite vertices get farther apart. The sides of a car jack are 17 cm long. When the horizontal distance between the vertices is 30 cm, what is the vertical distance between the other two vertices? **16 cm**

29. 1. $\overline{AC} \cong \overline{AC}$ (Reflexive Prop. of ≅) 2. $\overline{AC}$ bisects ∠BAD and ∠BCD. (Given) 3. ∠1 ≅ ∠2; ∠3 ≅ ∠4 (Def. of angle bisector) 4. △ABC ≅ △ADC (ASA) 5. $\overline{AB} \cong \overline{DA}$; $\overline{BC} \cong \overline{CD}$ (CPCTC) 6. □ABCD (Given) 7. $\overline{AB} \cong \overline{CD}$; $\overline{BC} \cong \overline{DA}$ (Opp. sides of a □ are ≅.) 8. $\overline{AB} \cong \overline{BC} \cong \overline{CD} \cong \overline{DA}$ (Transitive Prop. of ≅) 9. ABCD is a rhombus. (Def. of rhombus)

30. 1. □ABCD (Given) 2. $\overline{AE} \cong \overline{CE}$; $\overline{BE} \cong \overline{DE}$ (Diags. of a □ bisect each other.) 3. $\overline{AC} \perp \overline{BD}$ (Given) 4. ∠AEB, ∠BEC, ∠CED, and ∠DEA are rt. angles. (⊥ lines form 4 rt. angles.) 5. ∠AEB ≅ ∠BEC ≅ ∠CED ≅ ∠AED (All rt. angles are ≅.) 6. △AEB ≅ △CEB ≅ △AED ≅ △CED (SAS) 7. $\overline{AB} \cong \overline{BC} \cong \overline{CD} \cong \overline{DA}$ (CPCTC) 8. ABCD is a rhombus. (Def. of a rhombus)

31. In □ABCD, $\overline{AB} \cong \overline{DC}$ because opp. sides of a □ are ≅. $\overline{AD} \cong \overline{AD}$ by the Reflexive Prop. of ≅. Since $\overline{AC} \cong \overline{BD}$, △BAD ≅ △CDA by SSS and ∠BAD ≅ ∠CDA by CPCTC. ∠BAD and ∠CDA are consecutive angles of a □, so they are supplementary. Therefore, both angles are rt. ∠s and the angles opp. them are rt. ∠s. So □ABCD is a rectangle by def.

Exercises 33–34 Make sure students understand that these proofs depend on the quadrilateral's being a parallelogram. Have students show that a quadrilateral with one right angle is not always a rectangle, and a quadrilateral with two consecutive congruent sides is not always a rhombus.

Chapter Project **FIND OUT BY ANALYZING** Make sure students understand *effective area*. If possible, use a box to demonstrate. Also explain to students that a *rhomboid* is a parallelogram with noncongruent adjacent sides.

GETTING READY FOR LESSON 9-4 These exercises prepare students to find properties of trapezoids and kites.

Lesson Quiz

Lesson Quiz is also available in Transparencies.

1. Find the measures of ∠1 and ∠2.
$m\angle 1 = 90$,
$m\angle 2 = 40$

2. If *AE* = 10 in. and *ED* = 8 in., find the area of *ABCD*. **160 in.²**

Find the value of *x*.

3. $MQ = 2x - 1$,
$NQ = x + 3$
$x = 4$

4. $PQ = 2x + 3$,
$MO = 5x - 2$ $x = 8$

468

Wrap Up

THE BIG IDEA Ask students: *Describe the properties that a rectangle and rhombus have in common. What properties does a rectangle have that a rhombus does not? What properties does a rhombus have that a rectangle does not?*

RETEACHING ACTIVITY Students use the properties of rectangles, rhombuses, and squares to find missing angle measures. (Reteaching worksheet 9-3)

33. a. Given: ▱*ABCD*; ∠*B* is a right angle.
  Prove: *ABCD* is a rectangle. See margin p. 469.
  b. *Critical Thinking* State what you proved in part (a) as a theorem in if-then form.

If one ∠ of a ▱ is a rt. angle, then the ▱ is a rectangle.

34. a. Given: ▱*EFGH*; $\overline{EF} \cong \overline{FG}$ See margin
  Prove: *EFGH* is a rhombus. p. 469.
  b. *Critical Thinking* State what you proved in part (a) as a theorem in if-then form.

If 1 pair of adjacent sides of a ▱ are ≅, then the ▱ is a rhombus.

Chapter Project **Find Out by Analyzing**

Weight and area exposed to the wind are key factors in kite design. The greater the *effective area* facing the wind and the lighter the kite, the less wind you need to get the kite off the ground.

1. In Figure 1, a face of the square box kite is perpendicular to the wind. Describe the *effective area*. The effective area = the area of a face of the kite.

2. In Figure 2, a diagonal brace of the square box kite is perpendicular to the wind. Describe the *effective area*. See below.

3. Where on a box kite would you tie the string to get the greatest *effective area*? Explain. See below.

4. If you use two different lengths of wood for the diagonal braces of a box kite, you can make a *rhomboid* box kite. Explain why changing a square box kite to a rhomboid box kite can increase the *effective area*. See margin p. 469.

2. The effective area = √2 times the area of a face of the kite.

Figure 1

Figure 2

3. You should tie the string on a vertical stick. Then 1 of the diagonal braces is ⊥ to the wind, and the effective area is the greatest.

Sketch each pair of figures. 35–37. See margin p. 469 for samples.

35. congruent isosceles triangles   **36.** similar right triangles   **37.** congruent regular hexagons

38. *Open-ended* Give the lengths of the sides of an obtuse triangle.
Sample: 3 cm, 5 cm, and 7 cm

Getting Ready for Lesson 9-4

39. Sketch a quadrilateral with only two consecutive right angles. Classify the quadrilateral.   39–40. See right for samples.

40. Sketch a quadrilateral in which one diagonal is a perpendicular bisector of the other, but the second diagonal does not bisect the first. Classify the quadrilateral.

39. Sample:

trapezoid

40. Sample:

kite

Math ToolboX — Technology

Exploring Quadrilaterals within Quadrilaterals

Before Lesson 9-4 ▶

Work in pairs or small groups.

Construct

Use geometry software to construct a quadrilateral *ABCD*. Construct the midpoint of each side of *ABCD*. Construct segments joining the adjacent midpoints to form quadrilateral *EFGH*.
    Check students' work.

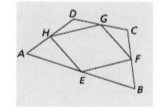

Investigate

Measure the lengths of the sides of *EFGH* and their slopes. Measure the angles of *EFGH*. What kind of quadrilateral does *EFGH* appear to be? **parallelogram**

Conjecture

Manipulate quadrilateral *ABCD* and make a conjecture about the quadrilateral whose vertices are the midpoints of a quadrilateral. Does your conjecture hold when *ABCD* is convex? Can you manipulate *ABCD* so that your conjecture doesn't hold? **The quad. whose vertices are midpts. of another quad. is a ▱; yes; no.**

Extend

- Draw the diagonals of *ABCD*. Describe *EFGH* when the diagonals are perpendicular and when they are congruent. **rectangle; rhombus**

- Construct the midpoints of *EFGH* and use them to construct quadrilateral *IJKL*. Construct the midpoints of *IJKL* and use them to construct quadrilateral *MNOP*. Compare the ratios of the lengths of the sides, perimeters, and areas of *MNOP* and *EFGH*. How are *MNOP* and *EFGH* related? **The ratio of lengths of sides and perimeters is $\frac{1}{2}$; the ratio of areas is $\frac{1}{4}$; MNOP ~ FGHE.**

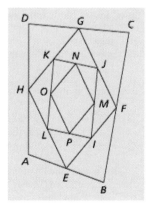

33a. Since *ABCD* is a ▱, opp. ∠s are ≅. So ∠*B* ≅ ∠*D*, therefore ∠*D* is a rt. angle. In a ▱, consecutive ∠s are supplementary. Therefore, ∠*A* and ∠*C* are each supplementary to ∠*B*. The supplement of a rt. angle is a rt. angle, so ∠*A* and ∠*C* are rt. ∠s. Therefore, *ABCD* is a rectangle by def.

34a. 1. ▱*EFGH* (Given) 2. $\overline{EF} \cong \overline{HG}$; $\overline{FG} \cong \overline{HE}$ (Opp. sides of a ▱ are ≅.) 3. $\overline{EF} \cong \overline{FG}$ (Given) 4. $\overline{EF} \cong \overline{HG} \cong \overline{FG} \cong \overline{HE}$ (Transitive Prop. of ≅) 5. *EFGH* is a rhombus. (Def. of rhombus)

Find Out by Analyzing

4. The greatest effective area is proportional to the length of the longer diagonal. If the faces of the kite are unchanged, then 1 diagonal of the rhombus is longer and 1 is shorter than the diagonals of the square.

page 468 Mixed Review

35.   36.   37.

CONNECTING TO PRIOR KNOWLEDGE Draw the following figures. Have students name them and describe how they are alike and how they are different.

WORK TOGETHER

Students use paper folding and cutting to make an isosceles trapezoid. Help students see that the fold line is a line of symmetry of the isosceles trapezoid. Ask students if the figure has any other symmetries.

THINK AND DISCUSS

VISUAL LEARNING Draw several trapezoids in different orientations and have students identify the legs and base angles.

Lesson Planning Options

Prerequisite Skills

- Recognizing trapezoids and kites
- Using formulas for distance and slope

Assignment Options for Exercises On Your Own

Core 1–19, 22–25
Extension 20–21, 26–27

Use Mixed Review to maintain skills.

Resources

Student Edition

Skills Handbook, pp. 650, 663
Extra Practice, p. 642
Glossary/Study Guide

Teaching Resources

Chapter Support File, Ch. 9
- Practice 9-4 (two worksheets)
- Reteaching 9-4
- Alternative Activity 9-4
Classroom Manager 9-4
Glossary, Spanish Resources

Transparencies
95

What You'll Learn
- Finding the properties of trapezoids and kites

...And Why
To solve problems in construction and design

What You'll Need
- lined paper
- scissors
- straightedge

QUICK REVIEW

An isosceles trapezoid is a trapezoid whose nonparallel sides are congruent.

3a. ∠*A* and ∠*B* are supplementary and ∠*C* and ∠*D* are supplementary because they are same-side interior ∠s formed by ∥ lines and a transversal.

c. *m*∠*B* = 78; *m*∠*C* = 78; *m*∠*D* = 102

Connections Architecture ... and more

9-4 Trapezoids and Kites

WORK TOGETHER

Work with a partner.

- Choose two lines on a piece of lined paper that are about 2 in. apart. Cut along these lines.

- Make a fold perpendicular to the cut lines so that each of the lines folds onto itself.

- Use a straightedge to draw a nonperpendicular segment from one parallel line to the other. Cut through the folded paper along that segment. Unfold the paper.

1. Classify the figure. **isosceles trapezoid**

2. **a.** Describe the relationship between the nonparallel sides of this figure. **Nonparallel sides are ≅.**
   b. Describe the relationship between the acute angles and the relationship between the obtuse angles. **The acute angles are ≅; the obtuse angles are ≅.**

THINK AND DISCUSS

In Chapter 5, you learned that the parallel sides of a trapezoid are the bases and the nonparallel sides are the legs. Each pair of angles adjacent to a base of a trapezoid are **base angles** of the trapezoid.

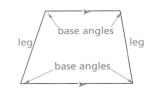

Your results in the Work Together activity are the basis of the following theorem.

Theorem 9-16   Base angles of an isosceles trapezoid are congruent.

3. **a.** In isosceles trapezoid *ABCD* at the right, what is the relationship between ∠*A* and ∠*B*? between ∠*D* and ∠*C*? Explain.
   b. What is the relationship between ∠*A* and ∠*C*? between ∠*D* and ∠*B*? Explain. **∠*A* and ∠*C* are suppl., and ∠*D* and ∠*B* are suppl.**
   c. If *m*∠*A* = 102, find *m*∠*B*, *m*∠*C*, **because of part (a) and** and *m*∠*D*. **because ∠*B* ≅ ∠*C*.**

Theorem 9-16 Students will prove this theorem in Exercise 24. Intuitively students should find this theorem believable since the base angles of an isosceles triangle are congruent.

ERROR ALERT! **Question 3** Some students may conclude that consecutive angles of an isosceles trapezoid are supplementary. **Remediation:** Help students see that unlike a parallelogram, a base angle of an isosceles trapezoid is supplementary to just one of its consecutive angles.

Example 1 Relating to the Real World ················

Copy the diagram onto the board or a transparency. As you review with students the three computational steps, highlight the angle being found on the diagram.

Make sure students understand that because the vertex angles of eight congruent triangles form a straight angle, the sum of their measures is 180, and each vertex angle measures $\frac{180}{8}$.

KINESTHETIC LEARNING Take students outside to sketch geometric patterns on buildings or houses. Have them describe the geometric objects that form the pattern.

Example 2 ·····································

ALTERNATIVE ASSESSMENT To help you assess students' understanding of the proof of Theorem 9-17, have them write a different proof using $\triangle ABD$ and $\triangle DCA$.

Example 1 Relating to the Real World ········

Architecture Part of the window of the World Financial Center in New York City is made from eight congruent isosceles trapezoids that create the illusion of a semicircle. What is the measure of the base angles of these trapezoids?

Each trapezoid is part of an isosceles triangle whose vertex angle is at the center of the circle and whose base angles are the acute base angles of the trapezoid.

The measure of $\angle 1$ is $\frac{180}{8}$, or 22.5.

The measure of each acute base angle is $\frac{180 - 22.5}{2}$, or 78.75.

The measure of each obtuse base angle of the trapezoid is $180 - 78.75$, or 101.25.

PROBLEM SOLVING HINT

Draw $\triangle ABC$ and $\triangle DCB$ as separate triangles and look for congruent parts.

4. a. *ABCD* is an isosceles trapezoid. How do $\triangle ABC$ and $\triangle DCB$ compare? Explain. $\triangle ABC \cong \triangle DCB$; SAS

 b. What must be true of the diagonals of isosceles trapezoid *ABCD*? Explain. **The diagonals are $\cong$; CPCTC.**

Theorem 9-17

The diagonals of an isosceles trapezoid are congruent.

Example 2 ··

Write a paragraph proof of Theorem 9-17.

Given: Isosceles trapezoid *ABCD* with $\overline{AB} \cong \overline{DC}$

Prove: $\overline{AC} \cong \overline{DB}$

Paragraph Proof

It is given that $\overline{AB} \cong \overline{DC}$. Because the base angles of an isosceles trapezoid are congruent, $\angle ABC \cong \angle DCB$. By the Reflexive Property of Congruence, $\overline{BC} \cong \overline{BC}$. Then by the SAS Postulate, $\triangle ABC \cong \triangle DCB$. Therefore $\overline{AC} \cong \overline{DB}$ by CPCTC.

Additional Examples

FOR EXAMPLE 1 ···························

Part of a spider's web is shown. Each trapezoid is isosceles. Find the measures of the base angles of *KLMN*. $m\angle M = m\angle N = 72$, $m\angle L = m\angle K = 108$

Discussion: *How are trapezoids KLMN and IJLK related?*

FOR EXAMPLE 2 ···························

Write a flow proof for Theorem 9-17. **See back of book.**

Discussion: *Describe another way to prove this theorem by using a different set of triangles.*

FOR EXAMPLE 3 ···························

Refer to the diagram in Example 3. If *LF* = 10 cm, *LA* = 10 cm, and *FG* = 22 cm, find the height of isosceles trapezoid *FLAG*. **8 cm**

Discussion: *Explain how to find the area of trapezoid FLAG.*

471

Example 3

Help students understand why $\triangle FLM \cong \triangle GAB$ by the AAS Theorem and why $FM = BG = 5$.

Question 5 Review the formula for the area of a trapezoid $A = \frac{1}{2}(b_1 + b_2)\, h$.

Question 6d Students should conclude that $\overline{OC} \perp \overline{BD}$. If students do not reach this conclusion, check that they calculated the slopes correctly and recognize that the products of the slopes is -1.

Theorem 9-18 Point out to students that the diagonals of a kite and a rhombus are both perpendicular. Therefore, knowing a quadrilateral has perpendicular diagonals is not a sufficient condition to conclude it is a kite, because it may be a rhombus.

In the Look Back question, help students see that T is equidistant from S and W and therefore must lie on the perpendicular bisector of $\overline{SW}$.

In the proof of Theorem 9-18, students justify why $\triangle STZ \cong \triangle WTZ$. By CPCTC, $\overline{SZ} \cong \overline{SW}$. Help students see that the diagonal of a kite whose endpoints are shared by noncongruent sides is always bisected by the other diagonal.

Technology Options

For Exercise 11, have students construct a kite using geometry software and measure its angles. Then have them investigate the relationships between consecutive angles and opposite angles as they manipulate the kite.

 Prentice Hall Technology

 Software
- Secondary Math Lab Toolkit™
- Computer Item Generator 9-4

CD-ROM
- Multimedia Geometry Lab 9

 Internet
- See the Prentice Hall site. (http://www.phschool.com)

472

You can use the lengths of the sides of an isosceles trapezoid to find the height of the trapezoid.

Example 3

Find the height of isosceles trapezoid $FLAG$.

Draw altitudes $\overline{LM}$ and $\overline{AB}$, creating rectangle $MLAB$, with $MB = 15$.
$\triangle FLM \cong \triangle GAB$ by AAS.

By CPCTC, $\overline{FM} \cong \overline{GB}$.
$FM = (25 - 15) \div 2 = 5$.

Use the Pythagorean Theorem to solve for LM.

$$5^2 + (LM)^2 = 13^2$$
$$25 + (LM)^2 = 169$$
$$(LM)^2 = 144$$
$$LM = 12$$

The height of isosceles trapezoid $FLAG$ is 12 cm.

5. What is the area of trapezoid $FLAG$? **240 cm²**

Another special quadrilateral that is not a parallelogram is a kite.

6. **a.** *Coordinate Geometry* Find the lengths of the sides of $OBCD$. **See below.**
   b. Classify $OBCD$. **kite**
   c. Find the slopes of $\overline{OC}$ and $\overline{BD}$. **1; −1**
   d. What is the relationship between $\overline{OC}$ and $\overline{BD}$? **$\overline{OC} \perp \overline{BD}$**

6a. $OB = OD = 2\sqrt{5}$; $CB = CD = 2$

Theorem 9-18 The diagonals of a kite are perpendicular.

7. Answer the following questions to prove Theorem 9-18.

   Given: Kite $RSTW$ with $\overline{RS} \cong \overline{RW}$ and $\overline{ST} \cong \overline{WT}$
   Prove: $\overline{RT} \perp \overline{SW}$

   a. What triangle is congruent to $\triangle RST$? Justify your answer. **$\triangle RWT$; SSS**
   b. Why is $\angle 1 \cong \angle 2$? **CPCTC**
   c. Why is $\triangle STZ \cong \triangle WTZ$? **SAS**
   d. Why is $\angle 3 \cong \angle 4$? **CPCTC**
   e. Why are $\angle 3$ and $\angle 4$ right angles? **See below.**
   f. Why is $\overline{RT} \perp \overline{SW}$? **Def. of $\perp$ lines**

8. **Try This** If $RS = 15$, $ST = 13$, and $SW = 24$, find RT. (*Hint:* Use Pythagorean triples.) **14**

7e. If 2 $\angle$s are $\cong$ and supplementary, then they are rt. $\angle$s.

PROBLEM SOLVING

Look Back Explain why Theorem 9-18 could easily be a corollary of Theorem 4-13: Converse of Perpendicular Bisector Theorem.
Since 2 pairs of adjacent sides are $\cong$, 2 vertices are equidistant from the endpoints of a diagonal. So, those vertices are on the $\perp$ bisector of the diagonal.

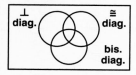
The following statements are suggested by the converses of the theorems in this lesson. Draw figures to show that the statements are false.

9. A quadrilateral with perpendicular diagonals is a kite or a rhombus.

10. A quadrilateral with congruent diagonals is an isosceles trapezoid or a rectangle.

11. A quadrilateral with diagonals that are congruent and perpendicular is a square.

9–11. See margin for samples.

pages 470–473   **Think and Discuss**

9.

10.

11.

Exercises   **ON YOUR OWN**

Find the measures of ∠1 and ∠2.

1.

2.

3.

4.

m∠1 = 77; *m*∠2 = 103   *m*∠1 = 108; *m*∠2 = 108   *m*∠1 = 90; *m*∠2 = 68   *m*∠1 = 69; *m*∠2 = 69

5. Find *UI*, *IT*, and *UT*, if *AS* = 16.

UI = 6; *IT* = 15; *UT* = 21

6. a. Find the height of an isosceles trapezoid with bases 30 cm and 70 cm long and legs 29 cm long.   21 cm

  b. Find the area of the trapezoid.   1050 cm²

7. The perimeter of a kite is 66 cm. The length of one of its sides is 3 cm less than twice the length of another. Find the length of each side of the kite.
12 cm, 12 cm, 21 cm, 21 cm

8. Design To make a beach umbrella, Taheisha cut eight panels from material with parallel stripes. The panels were congruent isosceles triangles with a vertex angle of 40° as shown at the right.

  a. Classify each yellow quadrilateral.   isos. trap.

  b. Find the measures of the interior angles of each yellow quadrilateral.
70, 110, 110, 70

473

Exercise 9 Suggest students trace the quadrilateral that is outlined and label the measures of the interior angles on the figure.

Exercise 10a Students may want to trace the kite they sketch and cut it out in order to use paper folding and rotation to find symmetries.

CRITICAL THINKING Exercise 11 Have students discuss their responses in groups and revise their answers if necessary.

OPEN-ENDED Exercise 17 Students may want to create these triangles using toothpicks as diagonals and string as the sides of the kite.

Exercise 18b Students will need to expand $(12 - x)^2$ to solve this problem.

Exercise 19 Make sure that students understand the directions.

---

pages 473–476 On Your Own

11a. No; If one pair of consecutive ∠s is supplementary, then another pair must be also because a pair of opp. ∠s of a kite is ≅. Therefore, the opp. sides are ∥, which means the figure is a ▱ and cannot be a kite.

b. Yes; if 2 ≅ angles are rt. angles, they are supplementary. The other 2 angles are also supplementary.

17.

19. $\overline{AA'} \cong \overline{AA''}$ and $\overline{BA'} \cong \overline{BA''}$, so it is a kite (unless $x = 60$, in which case the 4 sides are ≅ and it is a rhombus).

474

9. a. *Construction* At the right, a quadrilateral formed by the beams of the bridge is outlined. Classify the quadrilateral. Explain your reasoning. **See below right.**
   b. Find the measures of the other interior angles of the figure. **112; 68; 68**

10. a. *Transformations* Sketch a kite and describe its symmetries. **reflectional symmetry**
   b. *Critical Thinking* A classmate claims that the longer diagonal of a kite is a line of symmetry for the kite. Is he correct? Explain. **See below right.**

11. a. *Critical Thinking* Can two consecutive angles of a kite be supplementary? Explain.
   b. Can two opposite angles of a kite be supplementary? Explain. **a–b. See margin.**

12. *Standardized Test Prep* In quadrilateral *DEAL*, ∠*D* is supplementary to ∠*E*. Quadrilateral *DEAL* could be a __?__. **C**
   I. trapezoid   **II.** kite   **III.** rhombus
   A. I only   **B.** III only   **C.** I or III
   D. II or III   **E.** I, II, or III

112°

9a. Isosceles trapezoid; all the large rt. △s appear to be ≅ .
10b. No; the line of symmetry of a kite is the diagonal between the noncongruent angles.

Algebra **Find the value of the variable(s).**

13. $6x - 3$; $4x + 1$; $2x + 3$
1.5

14. $(x + 6)°$; $2x°$
28

15. $(3x + 5)°$; $y°$; $(2y - 20)°$; $(4x - 30)°$; $(2x - 4)°$
x = 35; y = 30

16. $AC = 4x, BD = 3y$; A ; D ; $3x - 5$; $x + y$; B ; C
x = 7.5; y = 10

17. *Open-ended* Sketch two kites that are not congruent, but such that the diagonals of one are congruent to the diagonals of the other. **See margin for sample.**

18. a. *Calculator* If $SW = 8$, find RT to the nearest tenth. **13.6**
   b. If $RT = 12$, find SW to the nearest tenth.
   (*Hint:* Let $TZ = x$, $RZ = 12 - x$, and $SZ = y$. Write two equations and then solve.) **10.0**

S ; 10 ; Z ; 6 ; R ; T ; 10 ; 6 ; W

19. *Transformations* Draw $\overline{AB}$. Rotate $\overline{AB}$ $x°$ about B, where $0 < x < 90$. Reflect △ABA' in $\overline{AB}$, labeling the image of A' as A''. What type of quadrilateral is $AA'BA''$? Explain. **See margin.**

20. a. *Geometry in 3 Dimensions* If a plane parallel to the base   **square** intersects a square pyramid, what shape is the cross section?
   b. If the plane is not parallel to the base, what shapes can the cross section have? **isosceles trapezoid, kite, triangle, pentagon, or a scalene quad.**

21.

21. Open-ended Charlie Brown is talking to Lucy about a "three-foot flat kite with a sail area of four and one-half square feet." Draw a kite with two 3-ft diagonals that has an area of $4\frac{1}{2}$ ft². Show the lengths of the segments of both diagonals. **See margin for sample.**

22. Critical Thinking If *KLMN* is an isosceles trapezoid, is it possible for $\overline{KM}$ to bisect $\angle LMN$ and $\angle LKN$? Explain.

No; if $\overline{KM}$ bisects $\angle LMN$ and $\angle LKN$, then $\triangle LMK \cong \triangle NMK$. Then 2 pairs of adj. sides are $\cong$ and *KLMN* is a kite or a rhombus, which is impossible.

23. Writing A *kite* is sometimes defined as a quadrilateral with two pairs of congruent adjacent sides. Compare this to the definition on page 91. Are parallelograms, trapezoids, rhombuses, rectangles, or squares special kinds of kites according to the changed definition? Explain. **Rhombuses and squares would be kites.**

24. Complete the following two-column proof of Theorem 9-16: The base angles of an isosceles trapezoid are congruent.

Given: *ABCD* is an isosceles trapezoid with $\overline{AB} \cong \overline{DC}$.

Prove: $\angle B \cong \angle C$ and $\angle BAD \cong \angle D$
Begin by drawing $\overline{AE} \parallel \overline{DC}$.

Statements	Reasons
1. *ABCD* is an isosceles trapezoid; $\overline{AB} \cong \overline{DC}$.	**1.** Given
a. ▨ $\parallel \overline{EC}$ *AD*	**2.** Definition of trapezoid
3. *AECD* is a ▱.	**b.** ? Def. of ▱
4. $\angle C \cong \angle 1$	**c.** ? If $\parallel$ lines, then corres. $\angle$s are $\cong$.
d. $\overline{DC} \cong$ ▨ *AE*	**5.** Opposite sides of a ▱ are $\cong$.
6. $\overline{AE} \cong \overline{AB}$	**e.** ? Property of $\cong$ Transitive
7. $\angle B \cong \angle 1$	**f.** ? Base $\angle$s of an isos. $\triangle$ are $\cong$.
8. $\angle B \cong \angle C$	**g.** ? Transitive Prop. of $\cong$
9. $\angle B$ and $\angle BAD$ are supplements; $\angle C$ and $\angle ADC$ are supplements.	**h.** ? If $\parallel$ lines, then same-side interior $\angle$s are supplementary.
10. $\angle BAD \cong \angle CDA$	**i.** Supplements of $\cong \angle$s are ? . congruent

25. a. Picture Framing Describe the shape of the four pieces of wood that are joined to form the picture frame at the right. **isosceles trapezoids**

b. Find the angle measures of each piece of wood. **45, 135, 135, 45**

475

Exercises 26–27 Have each student work with a partner to complete the proofs.

 Chapter Project **FIND OUT BY RESEARCHING** Check with your school library or local library to see if they have the books listed on page 488. If not, see if it is possible for them to borrow the books from another library, or ask for a list of references for books they have on making kites.

Exercises   MIXED REVIEW

JOURNAL You may also want students to describe the properties of kites.

PROBABILITY Exercises 28–30 Students find the geometric probability of a dart's landing in a certain area of a dart board.

GETTING READY FOR LESSON 9-5 These exercises prepare students to organize coordinate proofs.

Wrap Up

THE BIG IDEA Ask students: *How are a kite and a rhombus similar? different? How are a trapezoid and a rectangle similar? different?*

RETEACHING ACTIVITY Students use properties of trapezoids to find missing measurements. (Reteaching worksheet 9-4)

Reteaching 9-4

Practice 9-4

Practice 9-4
Mixed Exercises

Lesson Quiz

Lesson Quiz is also available in Transparencies.

1. The measure of ∠A is 112. Find the measures of ∠B, ∠C, and ∠D.

$m\angle B = 112$, $m\angle C = 68$, $m\angle D = 68$

2. $AB = 30$ cm, $DC = 44$ cm, and $AD = 25$ cm. Find the height of $ABCD$. **24 cm**

3. $m\angle XWZ = 96$. Find $m\angle WXV$ and $m\angle WVX$.

$m\angle WXV = 42$, $m\angle WVX = 90$

4. $XZ = 8$, $WV = 3$, and the perimeter of $WXYZ$ is 32. Find XY. **11**

476

Choose Write a two-column proof, a paragraph proof, or a flow proof. **26–27. Answers may vary. See margin p. 477 for samples.**

26. Given: Kite $ABCD$ with $\overline{AB} \cong \overline{AD}$ and $\overline{BC} \cong \overline{DC}$
Prove: Area of kite $ABCD = \frac{1}{2} \cdot AC \cdot BD$

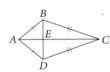

27. Given: Isosceles trapezoid $TRAP$ with $\overline{TR} \cong \overline{PA}$
Prove: $\angle 1 \cong \angle 2$

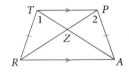

Chapter Project **Find Out by Researching**
To help decide what kind of kite you will design and build for this project, read about three different kinds of kites. Use the books listed on page 488 or other books or magazines. Summarize your research. Include the following in your report:
• a description of each kite   **Check students' work.**
• a list of materials needed to build each kite
• the wind conditions each kite is suited for

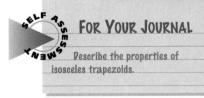

Exercises   MIXED REVIEW

Probability You randomly toss a dart at each dartboard. Find the probability the dart lands in a red area.

28. $\frac{1}{8}$

29. $\frac{3}{8}$

30. $\frac{1}{3}$

FOR YOUR JOURNAL
Describe the properties of isosceles trapezoids.

31. a. **Algebra** Write an algebraic expression for the area of a rectangle with width x and length $x + 7$. $x(x + 7)$ or $x^2 + 7x$
 b. If the perimeter of this rectangle is 38 cm, find its area. **78 cm²**

Getting Ready for Lesson 9-5

Coordinate Geometry Draw quadrilateral $QUAD$ with the given vertices. Then classify the quadrilateral.   **isosceles trapezoid**   **parallelogram**

32. $Q(-5, 0)$, $U(-3, 2)$, $A(3, 2)$, $D(5, 0)$

33. $Q(0, 0)$, $U(4, 0)$, $A(3, 2)$, $D(-1, 2)$

34. $Q(0, 0)$, $U(5, 5)$, $A(8, 4)$, $D(7, 1)$ **kite**

35. $Q(-3, 0)$, $U(0, 3)$, $A(3, 0)$, $D(0, -3)$ **square**

Math ToolboX

Students review the definition of *rational expression*. Then they practice simplifying, multiplying, and dividing them.

Review with students why the variable has restrictions and how to find the restrictions in each of the three examples.

Example 1

ERROR ALERT! Some students may try to cancel out part of sums. For example, they might try to cancel out the *x*'s or divide the 6 by 2. **Remediation:** Remind students that to simplify fractions, they can cancel out only common *factors* in the numerator and denominator.

Example 2

Point out that it is easier to factor the terms in the numerator and denominator and divide by common factors before multiplying.

Example 3

Make sure students remember how to find the reciprocal of a non-zero whole number.

ALTERNATIVE ASSESSMENT Have students work in groups. Assign each group five problems from each section to solve. Make sure that all problems are assigned. Then have each member of all groups present one of the problems to the class.

Math ToolboX — Algebra Review

Rational Expressions

After Lesson 9-4

A **rational expression** is an expression that can be written in the form $\frac{polynomial}{polynomial}$, where a variable is in the denominator. A rational expression is in simplest form if the numerator and denominator have no common factors except 1.

To multiply rational expressions $\frac{a}{b}$ and $\frac{c}{d}$, where b and $d \neq 0$, multiply the numerators and multiply the denominators. Then write the product in simplest form.

$$\frac{a}{b} \cdot \frac{c}{d} = \frac{ac}{bd}$$

To divide $\frac{a}{b}$ by $\frac{c}{d}$, where b, c, and $d \neq 0$, multiply by the reciprocal of $\frac{c}{d}$.

$$\frac{a}{b} \div \frac{c}{d} = \frac{a}{b} \cdot \frac{c}{d}$$

Example 1

Simplify $\frac{3x - 6}{x - 2}$.

$$\frac{3x - 6}{x - 2} = \frac{3(x - 2)}{x - 2}$$

$$= 3, x \neq 2$$

Example 2

Multiply $\frac{3x}{x - 1} \cdot \frac{2x - 2}{9x^2}$.

$$\frac{3x}{x - 1} \cdot \frac{2x - 2}{9x^2} = \frac{3x(2)(x - 1)}{(x - 1)(3x)(3x)}$$

$$= \frac{2}{3x}, x \neq 0 \text{ or } 1$$

Example 3

Divide $\frac{4x^5}{3}$ by $16x^7$.

$$\frac{4x^5}{3} \div 16x^7 = \frac{4x^5}{3} \cdot \frac{1}{16x^7}$$

$$= \frac{1}{12x^2}, x \neq 0$$

Simplify each expression.

1. $\frac{4x + 12}{x + 3}$ $4, x \neq -3$

2. $\frac{6c^3}{3c^4}$ $\frac{2}{c}, c \neq 0$

3. $\frac{3x - 9}{3x + 9}$ $\frac{x - 3}{x + 3}, x \neq -3$

4. $\frac{2a^6}{16a}$ $\frac{a^5}{8}, a \neq 0$

5. $\frac{28w + 12}{4}$ $7w + 3$

6. $\frac{m + 7}{m^2 - 49}$ $\frac{1}{m - 7}, m \neq -7 \text{ or } 7$

7. $\frac{5t^2}{25t^3}$ $\frac{1}{5t}, t \neq 0$

8. $\frac{6x^2 + 6x}{4x^2 + 4x}$

9. $\frac{4x^3 - 12x^2}{x - 3}$ $4x^2, x \neq 3$

10. $\frac{3s^2 + s}{s^3}$ $\frac{3s + 1}{s^2}, s \neq 0$

11. $\frac{v^2 + 2v + 1}{v + 1}$ $v + 1, v \neq -1$

12. $\frac{8r^7}{56r^2}$ $\frac{r^5}{7}, r \neq 0$

Find each product or quotient.

13. $\frac{3r^2}{4} \cdot \frac{20}{5r^3}$ $\frac{3}{r}, r \neq 0$

14. $\frac{x - 1}{x + 2} \div (2x - 2)$

15. $\frac{3c + 6}{5} \cdot \frac{25c}{c + 2}$

16. $\frac{4}{w^2} \div \frac{16}{w}$ $\frac{1}{4w}, w \neq 0$

17. $20x^2 \div \frac{4x}{3}$ $15x, x \neq 0$

18. $\frac{3x^2 + x}{2x} \cdot \frac{4x^2}{3x + 1}$

19. $\frac{9a^5}{2a} \div \frac{12a^3}{4}$ $\frac{3a}{2}, a \neq 0$

20. $\frac{x + 2}{x - 7} \div \frac{x}{x - 7}$

21. $\frac{t + 3}{t - 2} \cdot \frac{t^2 - 4}{5t + 15}$

22. $\frac{x^4 - x^3}{x - 1} \cdot \frac{2}{x^2}$

23. $\frac{a - 5}{a + 5} \div (2a - 10)$

24. $\frac{4r^2}{r^5} \cdot \frac{r^2}{2}$ $\frac{2}{r}, r \neq 0$

25. $9y^4 \div \frac{3y}{y + 1}$

26. $\frac{9w^3 - w}{2w - 1} \cdot \frac{1 - 2w}{w}$

27. $\frac{6c + 2}{c^2 + 1} \div \frac{2}{c - 1}$

28. $\frac{4m + 2}{m - 3} \cdot \frac{3 - m}{4m^2 - 1}$

14. $\frac{1}{2x + 4}, x \neq -2 \text{ or } 1$ 15. $15c, c \neq -2$ 18. $2x^2, x \neq -\frac{1}{3} \text{ or } 0$ 20. $\frac{x + 2}{x}, x \neq 0 \text{ or } 7$

21. $\frac{t + 2}{5}, t \neq -3 \text{ or } 2$ 22. $2x, x \neq 0 \text{ or } 1$ 23. $\frac{1}{2a + 10}, a \neq -5 \text{ or } 5$ 25. $3y^4 + 3y^3, y \neq -1 \text{ or } 0$

26. $1 - 9w^2, w \neq 0 \text{ or } \frac{1}{2}$ 27. $\frac{3c^2 - 2c - 1}{c^2 + 1}, c \neq 1$ 28. $\frac{2}{1 - 2m}, m \neq -\frac{1}{2}, \frac{1}{2}, \text{ or } 3$

Transparencies
11

26. 1. kite *ABCD* (Given)
2. $\overline{AC} \perp \overline{BD}$ (Diagonals of a kite are $\perp$.) 3. Area of $\triangle ABC = \frac{1}{2} \cdot AC \cdot BE$ ($A = \frac{1}{2}bh$)
4. Area of $\triangle CDA = \frac{1}{2} \cdot AC \cdot DE$ ($A = \frac{1}{2}bh$) 5. Area of *ABCD* = Area of $\triangle ABC$ + Area of $\triangle CDA$ (Area of a figure = the sum of areas of its nonoverlapping parts.) 6. Area of *ABCD* = $\frac{1}{2} \cdot AC \cdot (BE + DE)$ (Distributive Prop.)
7. Area of *ABCD* = $\frac{1}{2} \cdot AC \cdot BD$ (Segment Addition Post.)

27. Answers may vary. Sample:
1. Isosceles trapezoid *TRAP* (Given) 2. $\overline{TA} \cong \overline{PR}$ (Diagonals of an isos. trap. are $\cong$.)
3. $\overline{TR} \cong \overline{PA}$ (Given) 4. $\overline{RA} \cong \overline{RA}$ (Reflexive Prop. of $\cong$)
5. $\triangle TRA \cong \triangle PAR$ (SSS)
6. $\angle 1 \cong \angle 2$ (CPCTC)

477

PROBLEM OF THE DAY

Eight identical tables shaped as isosceles trapezoids fit together to make an octagonal table with a hole. Find the measures of the interior angles of the trapezoids.

112.5, 112.5, 67.5, 67.5

Problem of the Day is also available in Transparencies.

CONNECTING TO PRIOR KNOWLEDGE Have students graph each set of coordinates, connect the vertices, and classify the figure.

a. $A(-2, 2)$, $B(-5, 6)$, $C(-2, 6)$, $D(1, 2)$

b. $X(3, 4)$, $Y(5, -2)$, $Z(-5, -2)$, $W(-3, 4)$

WORK TOGETHER

Before students begin, review the formulas for slope and midpoint. Check that students correctly identify the slopes of vertical and horizontal lines.

TACTILE LEARNING Suggest that students make a cutout of a 10-unit square and trace it in different positions on the coordinate grid. Also suggest that students place each vertex of the square on an intersection of grid lines so the coordinates will be integers.

Lesson Planning Options

Prerequisite Skills

- Graphing in the coordinate plane
- Finding slopes and midpoints

Assignment Options for Exercises On Your Own

Core 1–20, 22–23, 25
Extension 21, 24, 26

Use Mixed Review to maintain skills.

Resources

Student Edition

Skills Handbook, pp. 660, 664
Extra Practice, p. 642
Glossary/Study Guide

Teaching Resources

Chapter Support File, Ch. 9
- Practice 9-5 (two worksheets)
- Reteaching 9-5
Classroom Manager 9-5
Glossary, Spanish Resources

Transparencies

5, 96, 101, 102

What You'll Learn
- Choosing convenient placement of coordinate axes on figures

...And Why
To use coordinate proofs to solve design problems

What You'll Need
- graph paper
- straightedge

Connections 🌐 Archaeology . . . *and more*

9-5 Organizing Coordinate Proofs

WORK TOGETHER

Work with a small group.

- Use graph paper to draw a number of coordinate planes with x- and y-coordinates from -12 to 12. On each, draw one or more squares with sides 10 units long. Draw the squares in different positions, with sides on one or both axes, parallel to the axes, or not parallel to either axis. Use more than one quadrant. Label each square $ABCD$.

- On each square, record the slope of each side, the slope of each diagonal, and the coordinates of the midpoints of the diagonals.

- Discuss which type of squares made your calculations easiest. **Generalize** your conclusions and explain your reasons.

THINK AND DISCUSS

In the Work Together, you saw that the position of a figure has an effect on how easy the figure is to work with. In coordinate proofs, it is generally easiest to use the origin as the center for the figure or to place a vertex at the origin and at least one side of the figure on an axis.

Example 1

Use the properties of each figure to find the missing coordinates.

a. rectangle $KLMN$

b. $\square OPQR$

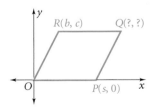

The x- and y-axes are horizontal and vertical lines of symmetry. The coordinates are $K(-a, b)$, $M(a, -b)$, and $N(-a, -b)$.

To go from point P to point Q keeping $OP = RQ$, go right b units and up c units. Point Q has coordinates $Q(s + b, c)$.

1. Try This When you place two sides of a figure on the coordinate axes, what are you assuming about the figure? **The 2 sides are $\perp$.**

Relate coordinate proofs to other styles of proofs students have used. Explain to students that in a coordinate proof, the figure is placed in the coordinate plane and algebraic arguments are used.

Example 1

In Part a, explain to students that, starting from the origin, point L is a units to the right and b units up. Since point M has the same horizontal distance and direction from the origin and the same vertical distance but opposite direction, it has coordinates $(a, -b)$. Have students give a similar explanation for the coordinates of points K and N.

Example 2 Relating to the Real World

The Math Toolbox on page 461 provides a way to use technology to investigate this property of quadrilaterals.

Make sure students see that because the coordinates of the quadrilateral were picked randomly, the results are true for all types of convex quadrilaterals.

Help students see that by picking the coordinates as multiples of 2, they avoid getting fractional values for the midpoints.

CONNECTING TO STUDENTS' WORLD Have students create designs for T-shirts using only quadrilaterals. Have them describe how they made them, using geometric terms to describe the shapes, angles, and lines.

It is often convenient to use coordinates that are multiples of 2 so that when you find midpoints you will not need to use fractions.

Example 2 Relating to the Real World

Design The assignment in art class is to create a T-shirt design by drawing any quadrilateral, connecting its midpoints to form another quadrilateral, and coloring the regions. Elena claims that everyone's inner quadrilateral will be a parallelogram. Is she correct? Explain.

Draw a quadrilateral on a coordinate plane. Locate one vertex at the origin and one side on the x-axis. Since you are finding midpoints, use coordinates that are multiples of 2. Find the coordinates of the midpoints T, W, V, and U, and the slopes of the sides of $TWVU$.

T = midpoint of $\overline{OI}$ = $\left(\frac{2a + 0}{2}, \frac{2b + 0}{2}\right)$ = (a, b)

W = midpoint of $\overline{IX}$ = $\left(\frac{2a + 2c}{2}, \frac{2b + 2d}{2}\right)$ = $(a + c, b + d)$

V = midpoint of $\overline{XR}$ = $\left(\frac{2c + 2e}{2}, \frac{2d + 0}{2}\right)$ = $(c + e, d)$

U = midpoint of $\overline{OR}$ = $\left(\frac{0 + 2e}{2}, \frac{0 + 0}{2}\right)$ = $(e, 0)$

slope of $\overline{TW}$ = $\frac{b - (b + d)}{a - (a + c)}$ = $\frac{d}{c}$

slope of $\overline{VU}$ = $\frac{d - 0}{(c + e) - e}$ = $\frac{d}{c}$ The slopes are equal, so the lines are parallel.

slope of $\overline{WV}$ = $\frac{(b + d) - d}{(a + c) - (c + e)}$ = $\frac{b}{a - e}$

slope of $\overline{TU}$ = $\frac{b - 0}{a - e}$ = $\frac{b}{a - e}$ The slopes are equal, so the lines are parallel.

Since both pairs of opposite sides of $TWVU$ are parallel, $TWVU$ is a parallelogram and Elena is correct!

PROBLEM SOLVING

Look Back Explain how you could prove that Elena is correct without using coordinate geometry.
See back of book.

2. Try This Use a different method to show that $TWVU$ is a parallelogram by finding the midpoints of the diagonals.

Midpoint of $\overline{TV}$ = $\left(\frac{a+c+e}{2}, \frac{b+d}{2}\right)$ = midpoint of $\overline{UW}$. So, the diagonals bisect each other and $TWVU$ is a $\square$. **9-5** Organizing Coordinate Proofs

---

FOR EXAMPLE 1

Use the properties of each figure to find the missing coordinates.

a. square $ABCD$

$A(-a, a)$, $D(-a, -a)$

b. rectangle $WXYZ$ $W(0, t)$, $Y(s, 0)$

Discussion: *What properties of squares and rectangles did you use?*

FOR EXAMPLE 2

Use a coordinate plane to show the diagonals of a square are perpendicular. **See back of book.**

Discussion: *Describe a different method to show the diagonals of a square are perpendicular.*

Exercises ON YOUR OWN

Give coordinates for points *W* and *Z* without using any new variables.

1. rectangle *W*(0, *h*); *Z*(*b*, 0)

2. square *W*(*a*, *a*); *Z*(*a*, 0)

3. square *W*(−*b*, *b*); *Z*(−*b*, −*b*)

4. parallelogram *W*(0, *b*); *Z*(*a*, 0)

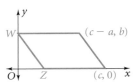

5. rhombus *W*(−*r*, 0); *Z*(0, −*t*)

6. isosceles trapezoid

W(−*b*, *c*); *Z*(0, *c*)

Find the coordinates of the midpoint of $\overline{WZ}$ and find *WZ* in the exercise named.

7. Exercise 1 $\left(\frac{b}{2}, \frac{h}{2}\right)$, $\sqrt{b^2 + h^2}$ **8.** Exercise 2 $\left(a, \frac{a}{2}\right)$, *a* **9.** Exercise 3 (−*b*, 0), 2*b*

10. Exercise 4 $\left(\frac{a}{2}, \frac{b}{2}\right)$, $\sqrt{a^2 + b^2}$ **11.** Exercise 5 $\left(-\frac{r}{2}, -\frac{t}{2}\right)$, $\sqrt{r^2 + t^2}$ **12.** Exercise 6 $\left(-\frac{b}{2}, c\right)$, *b*

13. a. *Open-ended* Choose values for *r* and *t* in Exercise 5. Find the slope and length of each side.   Sample: *r* = 3, *t* = 2; slopes are $\frac{2}{3}$ and $-\frac{2}{3}$; all lengths are $\sqrt{13}$.
  b. Does the figure satisfy the definition of a rhombus? Explain.
    Yes; the opp. sides have the same slope, so they are ∥. The 4 sides are ≅ .
14. Draw a square with sides 2*a* units long on the coordinate plane. Give coordinates for each vertex. **Answers may vary. See right for sample.**

14. (−*a*, *a*) *y* (*a*, *a*)

(−*a*, −*a*)   (*a*, −*a*)

15. a. Draw a square centered at the origin whose diagonals of length 2*b* units lie on the *x*- and *y*-axes. **See back of book.**
  b. Give the coordinates of the vertices of the square. (−*b*, 0), (0, *b*), (*b*, 0), (0, −*b*)
  c. Compute the length of a side of the square. *b*$\sqrt{2}$
  d. Find the slopes of two adjacent sides of the square. 1 and −1
  e. Do the slopes show that the sides are perpendicular? Explain. **Yes, because the product of the slopes is −1.**
16. a. Draw an isosceles triangle with base length 2*b* units and height 2*c*, placing one vertex on the origin.   **a–b. See back of book.**
  b. Draw an isosceles triangle with base length 2*b* units and height 2*c*, placing the base on the *x*-axis and the line of symmetry on the *y*-axis.
  c. Find the lengths of the legs of the triangle in part (a). $\sqrt{b^2 + 4c^2}$
  d. Find the lengths of the legs of the triangle in part (b). $\sqrt{b^2 + 4c^2}$
  e. How do the results of parts (c) and (d) compare? Explain.
    The lengths are =; the △ in (b) is ≅ to the △ in (a).

480

Exercise 17 Suggest students copy the figure and draw two vertical lines to make a rectangle and two triangles. This may help students see that the *x*-coordinate of *P* is *c − a*.

GEOMETRY IN 3 DIMENSIONS Exercise 20 Have students work in groups. Provide models of the coordinate axes to help students visualize the solids.

TRANSFORMATIONS Exercises 23–24 Suggest students do these exercises using geometry software or paper folding.

WRITING Exercise 25b Ask students to support their explanation with a diagram.

MAKING CONNECTIONS Exercise 26 Until the 1990s, most underwater archaeology was done in the Mediterranean Sea. With improved scuba equipment and mapping methods, divers have discovered wrecks of Spanish Armada ships off the coast of Ireland, Viking and Renaissance ships near Northern Europe, a Portuguese merchant ship off the coast of Kenya, and many other significant underwater archeological treasures.

Give the coordinates for point *P* without using any new variables.

17. isosceles trapezoid (*c − a, b*)

18. trapezoid with a right angle (*a*, 0)

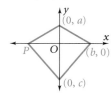

19. kite (*−b*, 0)

20. Geometry in 3 Dimensions Choose coordinates (*x, y, z*) for the vertices of a rectangular prism whose dimensions are *a, b,* and *c.* Use the origin as one of the vertices. **Sample: (0, 0, 0), (0, 0, c), (0, b, 0), (a, 0, 0), (0, b, c), (a, 0, c), (a, b, 0), (a, b, c)**

21. Geometry in 3 Dimensions A cube has edges 2*a* units long.
   a. Choose coordinates for the vertices, using the origin as one vertex.
   b. Choose coordinates for the vertices, using the origin as the center of the cube and making each of the cube's faces parallel to two of the three axes. **a–b. See margin.**

22. Draw a model for an equilateral triangle with sides 2*a* units long. Give coordinates of the vertices without introducing new variables. **See margin for sample.**

23. Transformations In Quadrant I draw $\overline{AB}$ that is not parallel to either axis. Let $\overline{A'B'}$ be its reflection over the *y*-axis. What type of quadrilateral is *BAA′B′*? Explain. **See margin.**

24. Transformations In Quadrant I draw $\overline{AB}$ that is parallel to the *y*-axis. Let $\overline{A'B'}$ be its reflection over the *y*-axis. What type of quadrilateral is *BAA′B′*? Explain. **See margin.**

25. a. What property of a rhombus makes it convenient to place its diagonals on the *x*- and *y*-axes? **See above right.**
   b. Writing Suppose a parallelogram is not a rhombus. Explain why it is inconvenient to place opposite vertices on the *y*-axis. **See margin.**

26. Archaeology Divers searching a shipwreck sometimes use gridded-plastic sheets to establish a coordinate system on the ocean floor. They record the coordinates of points where artifacts are found. Assume that divers search a square area and can go no farther than *b* units from their starting points. Draw a model for the area one diver can search. Assign coordinates to the vertices without using any new variables.
Answers may vary. See back of book for sample.

TECHNOLOGY HINT
You could do Exercises 23 and 24 with geometry software.

25a. The diagonals of a rhombus are ⊥.

21a. **(0, 0, 0), (0, 0, 2a), (0, 2a, 0), (2a, 0, 0), (0, 2a, 2a), (2a, 0, 2a), (2a, 2a, 0), (2a, 2a, 2a)**

   b. **(−a, −a, −a), (−a, −a, a) (−a, a, −a), (a, −a, −a), (−a, a, a), (a, −a, a), (a, a, −a), (a, a, a)**

22.

23.

Isosceles trapezoid; the *y*-axis is the ⊥ bisector of $\overline{AA'}$ and $\overline{BB'}$. In a plane, 2 lines ⊥ to a 3rd line are ∥, so $\overline{AA'} \parallel \overline{BB'}$. Also, *AB* = *A′B′*.

24.

Rectangle; the *y*-axis is the ⊥ bisector of $\overline{AA'}$ and $\overline{BB'}$. In a plane, 2 lines ⊥ to a 3rd line are ∥, so $\overline{AA'} \parallel \overline{BB'}$. Also, 2 lines ∥ to a 3rd line are ∥, so $\overline{AB} \parallel \overline{A'B'}$ and $\overline{AB} \perp \overline{AA'}$.

25b. The diagonals of a ▱ that is not a rhombus are not ⊥.

GETTING READY FOR LESSON 9-6 These exercises prepare students to use coordinate geometry in proofs.

Wrap Up

THE BIG IDEA Ask students: *What is the most convenient way to draw and label a square on a coordinate grid? a parallelogram?*

RETEACHING ACTIVITY Students find coordinates of figures on the coordinate plane. Then they prove statements about quadrilaterals using coordinate proofs. (Reteaching worksheet 9-5)

In this Checkpoint, your students will assess their own progress in Lessons 9-3 to 9-5.

A Point in Time

ESL Students may be confused by the term "relief sculpture." It may help to think of a "relief sculpture" as a carving that "releases" a work from its background.

You may wish to have students investigate the various types of relief sculpture such as *bas-relief*, *high relief*, and *intaglio*, the tools used by relief-sculptors, and Mayan, Southeast Asian, and Roman relief sculpture.

Lesson Quiz

Lesson Quiz is also available in Transparencies.

Draw each figure in the coordinate plane and give the coordinates of each vertex.

1. a square with sides *d* units long **Answers may vary. Sample:**

$(0, d)$ (d, d)

$(0, 0)$ $(d, 0)$

2. an isosceles trapezoid **Answers may vary. Sample:**

(a, b) $(s - a, b)$

$(0, 0)$ $(s, 0)$

3. a rectangle with its diagonals intersecting at the origin **See back of book.**

482

Find the area of each figure.

27. an equilateral triangle with altitude $6\sqrt{3}$ in. $36\sqrt{3}$ in.^{2}

28. a square with diagonals $5\sqrt{2}$ ft   25 ft^2

29. How much cardboard do you need to make a box 4 ft by 5 ft by 2 ft?   76 ft^2

Getting Ready for Lesson 9-6

30. a. Coordinate Geometry Graph the rhombus with vertices $A(2, 2)$, $B(7, 2)$, $C(4, -2)$, $D(-1, -2)$.

b. Connect the midpoints of consecutive sides to form a quadrilateral. What do you notice about the figure formed? The figure is a rectangle.

Find the value of the variable(s).

1.

$x = 51; y = 51$

2. 3

$3x + 5$ $5x - 1$

3.

58°

$x = 58; y = 32$

4.

$x = 2; y = 4$

5. Writing Summarize the characteristics of the diagonals of a rhombus that are not true for the diagonals of every parallelogram.

The diagonals of a rhombus are ⊥; each diagonal bisects 2 opp. angles of the rhombus.

A Point in Time

500 B.C.   500 A.D.   1500 A.D.

0   1000 A.D.   2000 A.

Egyptian Relief Sculpture

Many walls in ancient Egypt were decorated with relief sculptures. The relief sculpture in the photo was created in the year 255 B.C. First the artist sketched the scene on papyrus overlaid with a grid. Next the wall was marked with a grid the size of the intended sculpture. To draw each line, a tightly stretched string that had been dipped in red ochre was plucked, like a guitar string.

Using the grid squares as guides, the artist transferred the drawing to the wall. Then a relief sculptor cut the background away, leaving the scene slightly raised. Finally an artist painted the scene.

CONNECTING TO PRIOR KNOWLEDGE
Draw the following rectangle on a coordinate grid and have students find the slopes and the midpoints of the sides.

VISUAL LEARNING Suggest that partners draw different trapezoids. At least one partner should draw a trapezoid that is not isosceles. Make sure students understand that they are to find numerical coordinates for *M* and *N*.

What You'll Learn
- Proving theorems using figures in the coordinate plane

...And Why
To use coordinate geometry to design flags

What You'll Need
- graph paper
- straightedge

Connections ⊕ Flags . . . and more

9-6 Using Coordinate Geometry in Proofs

WORK TOGETHER

Work with a partner. Each of you should make your own figures.

- On graph paper, draw a trapezoid with one vertex at the origin and one base on the positive *x*-axis. Find the coordinates of each vertex.
- Find the coordinates of the midpoints *M* and *N* of the two nonparallel sides. Draw $\overline{MN}$.
- Find the slopes of $\overline{MN}$ and both bases of the trapezoid. Compare the slopes to find a relationship between $\overline{MN}$ and the bases.
- Compare the length of $\overline{MN}$ and the sum of the lengths of the bases.
- Compare your results with your partner. Make **conjectures** about the relationships between $\overline{MN}$ and the bases of a trapezoid.

THINK AND DISCUSS

The segment that joins the midpoints of the nonparallel sides of a trapezoid is the **midsegment of the trapezoid.** Your conjectures in the Work Together lead to the following theorem about the midsegment of a trapezoid.

Theorem 9-19

The midsegment of a trapezoid is (1) parallel to the bases and (2) half as long as the sum of the lengths of the bases.

Your main tools in coordinate geometry proofs are the formulas for slope, midpoint, and distance. Use these tools to prove Theorem 9-19 by answering the following questions.

Given: $\overline{MN}$ is the midsegment of trapezoid *TRAP*.
Prove: $\overline{MN} \parallel \overline{TP}$, $\overline{MN} \parallel \overline{RA}$, and $MN = \frac{1}{2}(TP + RA)$.

1. Find the coordinates of midpoints *M* and *N*.   **M(b, c); N(a + d, c)**

2. **a.** Find the slopes of the bases of the trapezoid. **0**
   b. Find the slope of $\overline{MN}$. **0**
   c. Compare the slopes.   The slopes are =.

3. **a.** Find the sum of the lengths of the bases. **2a + 2d − 2b**
   b. Find the length of $\overline{MN}$. **a + d − b**
   c. Compare the lengths.
   The midsegment is half the sum of the lengths of the bases.

Lesson Planning Options

Prerequisite Skills
- Graphing in the coordinate plane
- Finding distance, slope, and midpoints

Assignment Options for Exercises On Your Own

   Core 1–8, 12
   Extension 9–11

Use Mixed Review to maintain skills.

Resources

📖 **Student Edition**
Skills Handbook, pp. 660, 664
Extra Practice, p. 642
Glossary/Study Guide

▭ **Teaching Resources**
Chapter Support File, Ch. 9
- Practice 9-6 (two worksheets)
- Reteaching 9-6
Classroom Manager 9-6
Glossary, Spanish Resources

📽 **Transparencies**
5, 96

483

Students should be familiar with midsegments of triangles. Have them compare the properties of midsegments of triangles and midsegments of trapezoids.

CRITICAL THINKING Refer to trapezoid *RAPT* on page 483. Ask students: *If $\overline{TR}$ and $\overline{PA}$ were extended to form $\triangle TQP$, what could you say about $\overline{RQ}$ and $\overline{AQ}$?*

Example Relating to the Real World 🌐 ·······················

Discuss with students the placement of *MNPO*. Point out that placing two sides on the axes makes identifying the coordinates simpler by making use of as many zeros as

possible. Also point out that by using only the first quadrant, all the non-zero coordinates are positive.

DIVERSITY Have students bring in flags from their native countries and discuss the meaning or symbolism of each.

CRITICAL THINKING Question 4 Ask students if it would be enough to prove two consecutive sides congruent if they did not know *TWVU* was a parallelogram.

MAKING CONNECTIONS The study of flag design, history, symbolism, etiquette, terminology, and development is known as vexillology (from the Latin *vexillum*, meaning "flag").

Additional Examples

FOR EXAMPLE ·····························

Use coordinate geometry to prove that the quadrilateral formed by connecting the midpoints of the sides of a rhombus is a square.

Let *EFGH* be a rhombus. Choose convenient axes and coordinates, as shown. Let *J, K, L,* and *M* be the midpoints of the sides: *J(a, b),* *K(a, −b), L(−a, −b),* and *M(−a, b).* Show ∠*MJK* is a right angle.

Slope of $\overline{MJ} = 0$

Slope of $\overline{JK}$ is undefined.

$\overline{MJ}$ is horizontal and $\overline{JK}$ is vertical, thus they are perpendicular and *JKLM* is a square.

Discussion: *Explain why it is enough to prove just one angle is a right angle in order to prove that the quadrilateral formed by connecting the midpoints of a rhombus is a square.*

Example Relating to the Real World 🌐 ··············

Flags The flag at the left is constructed by connecting the midpoints of the sides of a rectangle. Use coordinate geometry to prove that the quadrilateral formed by connecting the midpoints of the sides of a rectangle is a rhombus.

Let *MNPO* be a rectangle. Choose convenient axes and coordinates, as shown in the figure at the right. Let *T, W, V,* and *U* be the midpoints of the sides of the rectangle.

Use the Midpoint Formula to find the coordinates of the midpoints:

$T(0, b)$ $W(a, 2b)$ $V(2a, b)$ $U(a, 0)$

From Lesson 9-5, you know that *TWVU* is a parallelogram. To prove that *TWVU* is a rhombus, show that consecutive sides are congruent.

$TW = \sqrt{(a - 0)^2 + (2b - b)^2} = \sqrt{a^2 + b^2}$

$WV = \sqrt{(2a - a)^2 + (b - 2b)^2} = \sqrt{a^2 + b^2}$

$TW = WV$, so parallelogram *TWVU* is a rhombus. ∎

4. *Critical Thinking* In the Example, explain why it is enough to prove just two consecutive sides congruent in order to prove that parallelogram *TWVU* is a rhombus. Opp. sides of a ▱ are ≅ . Use the Transitive Prop. of ≅ to prove all sides ≅.
5. *Try This* In the Example, use another method to prove that parallelogram *TWVU* is a rhombus. See back of book.

Exercises ON YOUR OWN

1. **Writing** The midpoints of $\overline{OR}$ and $\overline{ST}$ are W and Z, respectively. Which of the following figures would you prefer to use to find the coordinates of the midpoint of $\overline{WZ}$? Explain your choice.

   Answers may vary. Sample: C; you need to divide the coordinates by 2 twice to find the midpoint of $\overline{WZ}$.

   A.   **B.**   **C.**

Complete the coordinates for each figure. Then use coordinate geometry to prove the statement. 2–3, 5. See margin p. 486.

2. The diagonals of a parallelogram bisect each other (Theorem 9-3).

   Given: Parallelogram *ABCD*
   Prove: $\overline{AC}$ bisects $\overline{BD}$, and $\overline{BD}$ bisects $\overline{AC}$.

3. The diagonals of an isosceles trapezoid are congruent (Theorem 9-17).

   Given: Trapezoid *EFGH*, $\overline{FE} \cong \overline{GH}$
   Prove: $\overline{EG} \cong \overline{HF}$

4. The midpoint of the hypotenuse of a right triangle is equidistant from the vertices.

   Given: $\angle MON$ is a right angle, P is the midpoint of $\overline{MN}$.
   Prove: $MP = PN = OP$

   $P(b, a); MP = PN = OP = \sqrt{a^2 + b^2}$

5. The segments joining the midpoints of consecutive sides of an isosceles trapezoid form a rhombus.

   Given: Trapezoid *TRAP* with $\overline{TR} \cong \overline{AP}$, D, E, F, and G are midpoints of the indicated sides.
   Prove: *DEFG* is a rhombus.

   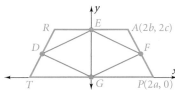

6. Compare your coordinate proof of Theorem 9-3 in Exercise 2 with the two-column proof on page 450. Which proof do you think is easier to understand? Explain. **Check students' work.**

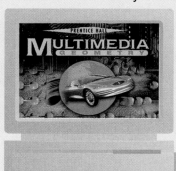
485

Exercise 9 Some students may not know what a "mobile" is. If possible, bring one in for students to see. Using the picture, ask students to name it in their native languages.

RESEARCH Exercise 9 Students should be able to find this information in an encyclopedia or physics textbook.

EXTENSION Exercise 9 If you have block scheduling or an extended class period, have students cut out a nonregular quadrilateral from a piece of lightweight cardboard. Have students try to balance the quadrilateral on the tip of a sharpened pencil.

Exercise 11 Students prove Theorem 4-18 from Lesson 4-8: The lines that contain the altitudes of a triangle are concurrent.

pages 485–487   On Your Own

2. $A(0, 0)$, $C(2a + 2b, 2c)$, $E(a + b, c)$; use the Midpoint Formula to find the midpts. of $\overline{AC}$, $(a + b, c)$, and $\overline{BD}$, $(a + b, c)$. Since the midpts. are the same, the diagonals bisect each other.

3. $E(-a, 0)$, $F(-b, c)$; use the Distance Formula to find the lengths of $\overline{EG}$, $\sqrt{(b + a)^2 + c^2}$, and of $\overline{HF}$, $\sqrt{(a + b)^2 + (-c)^2}$. The lengths are =, so the diagonals are $\cong$.

5. $T(-2a, 0)$, $R(-2b, 2c)$, $D(-a - b, c)$, $E(0, 2c)$, $F(a + b, c)$, $G(0, 0)$; $DE = EF = FG = GD = \sqrt{(a + b)^2 + c^2}$

7. $K(-b, a + c)$, $L(b, a + c)$, $M(b, c)$, $N(-b, c)$; slope of $\overline{KL}$ and slope of $\overline{MN}$ are 0. Slope of $\overline{LM}$ and slope of $\overline{NK}$ are undef. Lines with 0 slope and with undef. slope are $\perp$ to each other. Therefore, $KLMN$ is a rectangle.

8. The Triangle Midsegment Thm.—The segment connecting the midpts. of 2 sides of the triangle is ∥ to the 3rd side and is half its length; you can use the Midpoint Formula and the Distance Formula to prove the statement directly.

7. Use coordinate geometry to prove that the midpoints of the sides of a kite determine a rectangle.

   Given: Kite $DEFG$, $DE = EF$, $DG = GF$, K, L, M, and N are midpoints of the indicated sides.
   Prove: $KLMN$ is a rectangle. See margin.

8. *Open-ended* Give an example of a statement that you think is easier to prove with coordinate geometry than with a two-column proof. Explain your choice. See margin for sample.

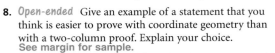

Alexander Calder

Alexander Calder (1898–1976) was an American sculptor who is considered the founder of modern kinetic art. Kinetic art, which is art that involves motion, is perhaps best seen in Calder's mobiles. His mobiles consist of a series of carefully balanced metal shapes hanging from wires. Calder's early mobiles are motorized. In his later ones, however, the shapes float gracefully and move in different directions with currents of air. Calder was inspired to make mobiles by watching circus performers. His initial attempts at kinetic art were motorized circus figures made of wire and wood.

9. *Research* For a mobile to be in balance, the artist must suspend the mobile from its center of gravity. The center of gravity, or *centroid*, is the point around which the weight of an object is evenly distributed. Choose an object from Calder's mobile. Research how you would find the center of gravity of the object. Check students' work.

10. The centroid of a triangle is the point where the medians meet. The centroid is $\frac{2}{3}$ of the distance from each vertex to the midpoint of the opposite side. Complete the following steps to find the centroid of the triangle at the right.

    a. Find the coordinates of points L, M, and N, the midpoints of the sides of the triangle. $L(1, 3)$, $M(5, 3)$, $N(4, 0)$
    b. Find the equations of lines $\overleftrightarrow{AM}$, $\overleftrightarrow{BN}$, and $\overleftrightarrow{CL}$. See below.
    c. Find the coordinates of point P, the of intersection of lines $\overleftrightarrow{AM}$ and $\overleftrightarrow{BN}$. $P\left(\frac{10}{3}, 2\right)$
    d. **Verify** that point P is the intersection of lines $\overleftrightarrow{AM}$ and $\overleftrightarrow{CL}$. $2 = -\frac{3}{7} \cdot \frac{10}{3} + \frac{24}{7}$ ✔
    e. Use the distance formula to **verify** that point P is $\frac{2}{3}$ of the distance from each vertex to the midpoint of the opposite side. Check students' work.

    b. $\overleftrightarrow{AM} : y = \frac{3}{5}x$; $\overleftrightarrow{BN} : y = -3x + 12$; $\overleftrightarrow{CL} : y = -\frac{3}{7}x + \frac{24}{7}$

CONNECTING TO STUDENTS' WORLD Exercise 13 Have students write a survey question with 4–6 possible responses. Have them survey at least 25 people. Then have them calculate the percent that chose each response and display their results in a bar graph.

PORTFOLIO Share with students the criteria you will use to assess their work in portfolios, as well as how you plan to use the results. Students should understand how the rubrics assess their work, how each piece in the portfolio counts, and how the scores they get in their portfolios will affect their overall evaluation.

THE BIG IDEA Ask students: *Describe the algebraic properties you use when writing a coordinate proof.*

RETEACHING ACTIVITY Students prove theorems using coordinate geometry. (Reteaching worksheet 9-6)

---

11. Given $\triangle ABC$ with altitudes p, q, and r, complete the following to show that p, q, and r intersect in a point. (This point is called the *orthocenter* of the triangle.) **b, d, f, g. See back of book.**
    a. The slope of $\overline{BC}$ is $\frac{c}{-b}$. What is the slope of line p? $\frac{b}{c}$
    b. Show that the equation of line p is $y = \frac{b}{c}(x - a)$.
    c. What is the equation of line q? $x = 0$
    d. Show that lines p and q intersect at $\left(0, \frac{-ab}{c}\right)$.
    e. The slope of $\overline{AC}$ is $\frac{c}{-a}$. What is the slope of line r? $\frac{a}{c}$
    f. Show that the equation of line r is $y = \frac{a}{c}(x - b)$.
    g. Show that lines r and q intersect at $\left(0, \frac{-ab}{c}\right)$.
    h. Give the coordinates of the orthocenter of $\triangle ABC$. $\left(0, -\frac{ab}{c}\right)$

12. *RSTW* is a rhombus. Give the coordinates of S and T. In part (c) give the coordinates in terms of a and c, without introducing any new variables.
    a. $S(3, 4)$; $T(8, 4)$
    b. $S(5, 12)$; $T(18, 12)$
    c. $S(a, \sqrt{c^2 - a^2})$; $T(a + c, \sqrt{c^2 - a^2})$

    d. Use your figure in part (c) for a coordinate proof that the diagonals of a rhombus are perpendicular.
    The slope of $\overline{SW}$ is $\frac{\sqrt{c^2 - a^2}}{a - c}$. The slope of $\overline{TR}$ is $\frac{\sqrt{c^2 - a^2}}{a + c}$ and $\frac{\sqrt{c^2 - a^2}}{a + c} \cdot \frac{\sqrt{c^2 - a^2}}{a - c} = -1$, so the lines are $\perp$.

1995 Cellular Phone Buyers

13. Data Analysis What percent of cellular phone buyers were younger than 25? **36%**

14. Writing Describe two ways to find what percent of cellular phone buyers were younger than 65. Use both methods. Are the answers the same? Explain. **See back of book.**

15. Critical Thinking Explain why the total of all cellular phone buyers is greater than 100%.
    The percent figure in each category is rounded to the nearest integer.

Reteaching 9-6
Practice 9-6
Practice 9-6
Mixed Exercises

Lesson Quiz

Lesson Quiz is also available in Transparencies.

Find the coordinates of the remaining vertices for each figure. Then use coordinate geometry to prove the statement. **See back of book.**

1. Given: Rectangle *CDEF*
   Prove: $\overline{CE} \cong \overline{DF}$

2. Given: Parallelogram *MNOP*
   Prove: $\overline{NO} \cong \overline{MP}$, $\overline{NM} \cong \overline{OP}$

Finishing The Chapter Project

PROJECT DAY You may wish to plan a project day during which students share their completed projects. Encourage groups to explain their processes as well as their products.

PROJECT NOTEBOOK Have students review their project work and bring their notebooks up to date.

- Have students review their kite designs. Ask them to share the different designs and models they tried and how each model or design performed.

- Ask students to share any insights they had when designing their kites, such as what made their kites perform better and what did not work.

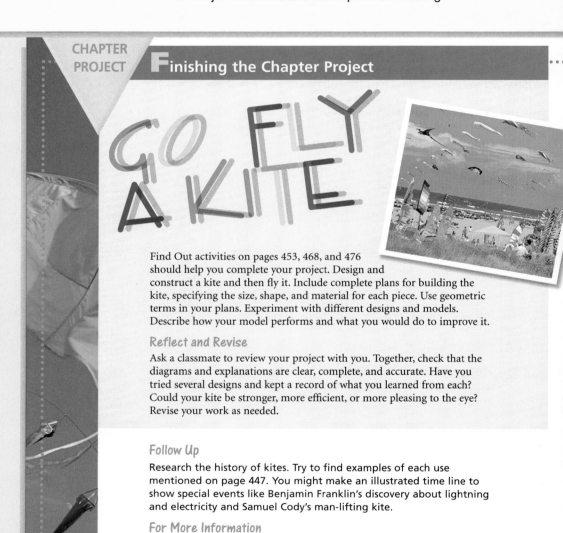

Finishing the Chapter Project

Find Out activities on pages 453, 468, and 476 should help you complete your project. Design and construct a kite and then fly it. Include complete plans for building the kite, specifying the size, shape, and material for each piece. Use geometric terms in your plans. Experiment with different designs and models. Describe how your model performs and what you would do to improve it.

Reflect and Revise

Ask a classmate to review your project with you. Together, check that the diagrams and explanations are clear, complete, and accurate. Have you tried several designs and kept a record of what you learned from each? Could your kite be stronger, more efficient, or more pleasing to the eye? Revise your work as needed.

Follow Up

Research the history of kites. Try to find examples of each use mentioned on page 447. You might make an illustrated time line to show special events like Benjamin Franklin's discovery about lightning and electricity and Samuel Cody's man-lifting kite.

For More Information

Baker, Rhoda, and Miles Denyer. *Flying Kites*. Edison, New Jersey: Chartwell Books, 1995.

Eden, Maxwell. *Kiteworks: Explorations in Kite Building & Flying*. New York: Sterling Publishing Co., 1989.

Kremer, Ron. *From Crystals to Kites*. Palo Alto, California: Dale Seymour Publications, 1995.

Morgan, Paul and Helene. *The Ultimate Kite Book*. New York: Simon & Schuster, 1992.

9 Wrap Up

Key Terms

base angles of a trapezoid (p. 470)
consecutive angles (p. 449)
midsegment of a trapezoid (p. 483)

How am I doing?

- State three ideas from this chapter that you think are important. Explain your choices.
- List the properties of different quadrilaterals.

Properties of Parallelograms   9-1

Opposite sides and opposite angles of a parallelogram are congruent. The diagonals of a parallelogram bisect each other.

If three or more parallel lines cut off congruent segments on one transversal, then they cut off congruent segments on every transversal.

Find the measures of the numbered angles for each parallelogram. 4. $m\angle 1 = 52$; $m\angle 2 = 25$; $m\angle 3 = 25$

1.

2.

3.

4.

2. $m\angle 1 = 71$; $m\angle 2 = 54$; $m\angle 3 = 55$

$m\angle 1 = 101$; $m\angle 2 = 79$; $m\angle 3 = 101$ 3. $m\angle 1 = 38$; $m\angle 2 = 43$; $m\angle 3 = 99$

Proving That a Quadrilateral Is a Parallelogram   9-2

A quadrilateral is a parallelogram if any of the following are true.

- The diagonals of the quadrilateral bisect each other.
- One pair of opposite sides of the quadrilateral are both congruent and parallel.
- Both pairs of opposite sides of the quadrilateral are congruent.
- Both pairs of opposite angles of the quadrilateral are congruent.

5. *Standardized Test Prep* Which quadrilaterals must be parallelograms? E

I.   **II.**   **III.**   **IV.**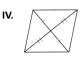

A. I only   **B.** III only   **C.** I and II   **D.** II and IV   **E.** I, II, and IV

489

ALGEBRA Exercises 6–8 Students can solve each system of equations simultaneously or by using substitution.

WRITING Exercise 17 Have students include a diagram along with the explanation.

Wrap Up pages 489–491

17. Pick 6 equally spaced lines on the lined paper. Place 1 corner of index card on the 1st line and the next corner on the 6th line. Mark the pts. where the remaining 4 lines intersect the edge of the index card. Repeat on the opp. edge of the index card. Then connect the marked pts. with ∥ lines.

Algebra **Determine the values of the variables for which *ABCD* is a parallelogram.**

6.

B — $7x - 1$ — C
$7x - 2$ ... $5x + 2$
A — $6x + y$ — D

$x = 2; y = 1$

7.

B $(3y - 20)°$ C
$(4y + 4)°$
A $4x°$ $(2x + 6)°$ D

$x = 29; y = 28$

8.

B $4x - 2$ $3x$ C
$3y - 3$ $3y - 1$
A D

$x = 4; y = 5$

Properties of Special Parallelograms, Trapezoids, and Kites   9-3, 9-4

The diagonals of a rhombus are perpendicular. Each diagonal of a rhombus bisects two angles of the rhombus. The area of a rhombus is half the product of the lengths of its diagonals, $A = \frac{1}{2}d_1d_2$.

The diagonals of a rectangle are congruent.

If one diagonal of a parallelogram bisects two angles of the parallelogram, it is a rhombus. If the diagonals of a parallelogram are perpendicular, it is a rhombus. If the diagonals of a parallelogram are congruent, it is a rectangle.

The nonparallel sides of a trapezoid are the legs. Each pair of angles adjacent to a base of a trapezoid are **base angles** of the trapezoid.

Base angles of an isosceles trapezoid are congruent. The diagonals of an isosceles trapezoid are congruent.

The diagonals of a kite are perpendicular.

Find the measures of the numbered angles for each quadrilateral.

9.

1 2 3 $56°$

10.

2 1 $60°$ 3

11.

2 $50°$ 1

12.

1 2 $65°$

$m\angle 1 = 124; m\angle 2 = 28; m\angle 3 = 62$ $m\angle 1 = 50; m\angle 2 = 130$

Find *AC* for each quadrilateral. 10. $m\angle 1 = 60; m\angle 2 = 90; m\angle 3 = 30$ $m\angle 1 = 90; m\angle 2 = 25$

13.

D — C 26 in.
$13\ in.$
E
A — B

14.

D — C 19 ft
$7\ ft$
E
$12\ ft$
A — B

15.

D — C 20 cm
E
$10\ cm$
A — B

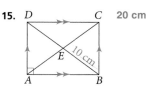

16. A rhombus has sides that are 10 ft long and a diagonal that is 16 ft long. Find its area.   **96 ft²**

17. *Writing* Explain how you could use a piece of lined paper to draw four lines on a blank index card that divide it into five equal sections.   **See margin.**

490

Remind students that the new mathematical terms in this chapter are defined in the Glossary/Study Guide in the back of the book.

Getting Ready For Chapter 10

Students may work these exercises independently or in small groups. The skills previewed will help prepare students to study similar triangles.

Organizing Coordinate Proofs   9-5

In coordinate proofs, it is usually easiest to use the origin as the center for the figure or to place a vertex at the origin and at least one side of the figure on an axis.

Give the coordinates of point *P* without using any new variables.

18. rectangle   **19.** rhombus   **20.** square   **21.** parallelogram

(a, b)

$(-a, 0)$

$(0, c)$

$(a - b, c)$

Using Coordinate Geometry in Proofs   9-6

The segment that joins the midpoints of the nonparallel sides of a trapezoid is the **midsegment of the trapezoid**. It is parallel to the bases and half as long as the sum of the lengths of the bases.

The formulas for slope, midpoint, and distance are used in coordinate proofs.

Choose coordinates for each figure. Then use coordinate geometry to prove the statement.   22–24. See margin.

22. The diagonals of a rectangle are congruent.
Given: Rectangle *ABCD*
Prove: $\overline{AC} \cong \overline{BD}$

23. The diagonals of a square are perpendicular.
Given: Square *FGHI*
Prove: $\overline{FH} \perp \overline{GI}$

24. Open-ended Show two different ways to draw an isosceles triangle for a coordinate proof.

Getting Ready for····················· CHAPTER 10

25–30. Answers may vary. Samples are given.

Write a fraction equivalent to the given fraction.

25. $\frac{4}{5}$ $\frac{8}{10}$ **26.** $\frac{9}{4}$ $\frac{27}{12}$ **27.** $\frac{6}{8}$ $\frac{3}{4}$ **28.** $\frac{1}{10}$ $\frac{2}{20}$ **29.** $\frac{4}{7}$ $\frac{16}{28}$ $\frac{6}{16}$ **30.** $\frac{3}{8}$

Solve each proportion.

31. $\frac{3}{4} = \frac{x}{8}$ 6   **32.** $\frac{2}{x} = \frac{8}{24}$ 6   **33.** $\frac{x}{9} = \frac{1}{3}$ 3   **34.** $\frac{10}{25} = \frac{2}{x}$ 5

22. Sample: $A(0, a)$, $B(b, a)$, $C(b, 0)$, $D(0, 0)$; $AC = \sqrt{a^2 + b^2}$, $BD = \sqrt{a^2 + b^2}$, so $AC = BD$, and $\overline{AC} \cong \overline{BD}$.

23. Sample: $F(0, a)$, $G(a, a)$, $H(a, 0)$, $I(0, 0)$. The slope of $\overline{FH}$ is -1. The slope of $\overline{GI}$ is 1. Since the product of the slopes is -1, $\overline{FH} \perp \overline{GI}$.

24. Sample:

491

Assessment

ENHANCED MULTIPLE CHOICE QUESTIONS are more complex than traditional multiple choice questions, which assess only one skill. Enhanced multiple choice questions assess the processes that students use, as well as the end results. The questions are written so that students use more than one strategy to solve the problem. Using multiple strategies is encouraged by the National Council of Teachers of Mathematics (NCTM). **Exercise 8** is an enhanced multiple choice question.

FREE RESPONSE QUESTIONS do not give answer choices. Some exercises have more than one possible answer. Students need to give only one correct response. **Exercises 1–2, 4–7, and 10–17** are free response questions.

WRITING EXERCISES allow students to describe how they think about and understand the concepts they have learned. **Exercise 9** is a writing exercise.

OPEN-ENDED PROBLEMS allow for more than one solution. Students must construct their own responses instead of choosing from possible answers. The students' responses will help you determine the depth of their understanding and any possible areas of difficulty. **Exercise 3** is an open-ended problem.

9 Assessment

Find AN in each parallelogram.

1.

A ... N
6 in.
9 in.
M 6 in. L

2.

N ... Q
9 cm
A 9 cm
6.5 cm
S ... R

3. *Open-ended* Sketch two noncongruent parallelograms ABCD and EFGH such that $\overline{AC} \cong \overline{BD} \cong \overline{EG} \cong \overline{FH}$. **See margin for sample.**

Algebra **Find the values of the variables for each parallelogram.**

4.

$z°$ 80° $x°$ $y°$
$x = 100; y = 50; z = 40$

5.
$x°$ $z°$ $y°$ 57°
$x = 57; y = 57; z = 66$

6.

$4x - 4$ $2x$ $2y + 2$ $3x + 2$
$x = 6; y = 5$

7.
$x°$ $y°$ $z°$ 36°
$x = 36; y = 108; z = 72$

8. *Standardized Test Prep* What is sufficient to prove that ABCD is a parallelogram? **E**

A ... B
D ... C

  I. $\overline{AC}$ bisects $\overline{BD}$.
  II. $\overline{AB} \cong \overline{DC}; \overline{AB} \parallel \overline{DC}$
  III. $\overline{AB} \cong \overline{DC}; \overline{BC} \cong \overline{AD}$
  IV. $\angle DAB \cong \angle BCD$ and $\angle ABC \cong \angle CDA$
  A. I and III   **B.** II and IV   **C.** II and III
  D. I and IV   **E.** II, III, and IV

9. *Writing* Explain why a square cannot be a kite. **Answers may vary. Sample: A square is a rhombus. So it has 4 ≅ sides. A kite has no opp. sides ≅.**

Find the measures of ∠1 and ∠2.

10.

30° 1 2 60°
$m\angle 1 = 90; m\angle 2 = 30$

11.

2 70° 1
$m\angle 1 = 70; m\angle 2 = 110$

12. *Transformations* Draw $\overline{AB}$ with midpoint M. Rotate $\overline{AB}$ x° about M, where $0 < x < 180$. What type of quadrilateral is $AA'BB'$? Explain. **Rectangle; the diagonals are ≅ and bisect each other.**

Find the area of each rhombus. If the answer is not an integer, round to the nearest tenth.

13.
4 ft 2 ft
16 ft²

14.
6 cm
31.2 cm²

Give the coordinates for points S and T without using any new variables. Then find the coordinates of the midpoint of $\overline{ST}$.

15.
T ... (a, b)
O
x
S ... (a, -b)
$S(-a, -b), T(-a, b); (-a, 0)$

16.
(c, d) T
O
S (b, 0)
$S(0, 0), T(b + c, d); \left(\frac{b + c}{2}, \frac{d}{2}\right)$

17. Use coordinate geometry to prove that the diagonals of a square are congruent.

  Given: ABCD is a square with vertices A(0, 0), B(a, 0), C(a, a), and D(0, a).
  Prove: AC = BD

D(0, a) C(a, a)
A B(a, 0)
$AC = a\sqrt{2}; BD = a\sqrt{2}$. So $AC = BD$.

Preparing For Standardized Tests

Standardized tests, such as those administered for state assessment, the SAT, or the ACT, include regular math questions, quantitative comparison questions, open-ended problems, and free response questions (which the SAT calls *grid-ins*).

MULTIPLE CHOICE QUESTIONS are followed by five answer choices, one of which is correct. **Exercises 1–6** are multiple choice questions.

QUANTITATIVE COMPARISON QUESTIONS ask students to compare two quantities. **Exercises 7 and 8** are quantitative comparison questions.

FREE RESPONSE QUESTIONS do not give answer choices. Students must provide one correct answer on their own. **Exercises 9 and 10** are free response questions.

OPEN-ENDED PROBLEMS allow for more than one solution. Students must construct their own responses instead of choosing a single answer. The responses students give will help you determine the depth of their understanding and what difficulties, if any, they are experiencing. **Exercise 11** is an open-ended problem.

STANDARDIZED TEST TIP Exercise 5 Students can save time by adding −4 to the *x*-coordinates and −1 to the *y*-coordinates of A, B, and C to find the image of △ABC instead of using a coordinate grid.

---

9 Preparing for Standardized Tests

For Exercises 1–8, choose the correct letter.

1. The diagonals of which quadrilateral are congruent?   **E**
- **A.** trapezoid
- **B.** rhombus
- **C.** parallelogram
- **D.** kite
- **E.** rectangle

2. For which value of *x* are lines *g* and *h* parallel?   **D**

- **A.** 5
- **B.** 12
- **C.** 18
- **D.** 25
- **E.** none of the above

3. What is the surface area of a sphere with radius 6 in.?   **C**
- **A.** 12π in.^{2}
- **B.** 36π in.^{2}
- **C.** 144π in.^{2}
- **D.** 216π in.^{2}
- **E.** 288π in.^{2}

4. Which trapezoid has an 8-in. midsegment?   **C**

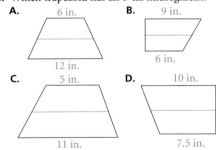

- **A.** 6 in. / 12 in.
- **B.** 9 in. / 6 in.
- **C.** 5 in. / 11 in.
- **D.** 10 in. / 7.5 in.
- **E.** none of the above

5. Transformations △ABC has vertices $A(3, 1)$, $B(4, -2)$, and $C(4, 7)$. Find the vertices of the image of △ABC under a translation 4 units left and 1 unit down.   **B**
- **A.** $A'(7, 2), B'(8, -1), C'(8, 8)$
- **B.** $A'(-1, 0), B'(0, -3), C'(0, 6)$
- **C.** $A'(7, 0), B'(8, -3), C'(8, 6)$
- **D.** $A'(-1, 2), B'(0, -1), C'(0, 8)$
- **E.** $A'(7, 0), B'(8, -1), C'(0, 6)$

6. How can you prove the triangles congruent?   **C**

- **A.** ASA
- **B.** SSS
- **C.** SAS
- **D.** HL
- **E.** The triangles are not congruent.

Compare the boxed quantity in Column A with the boxed quantity in Column B. Choose the best answer.

- **A.** The quantity in Column A is greater.
- **B.** The quantity in Column B is greater.
- **C.** The two quantities are equal.
- **D.** The relationship cannot be determined on the basis of the information supplied.

Column A ‖ **Column B**

7. | AE | | EC | **C**

8. | $m\angle ACD$ | | $m\angle CAD$ | **D**

Find each answer.

9. What is the area of the rhombus?
140 cm^2

10 cm · 7 cm

10. See margin p. 492 for sample.

10. Constructions Draw a segment with length *a*. Construct a rectangle with width *a* and length 2*a*.

11. Open-ended Give three numbers that could be the lengths of the sides of an acute triangle.
Sample: 5, 6, 7

Resources

📦 **Teaching Resources**

Chapter Support File, Ch. 9
- Standardized Test Practice
- Cumulative Review

📖 **Teacher's Edition**

See also p. 446E for assessment options

To accommodate flexible scheduling, some lessons are divided into parts. Assignment Options are given in the Lesson Planning Options for each lesson.

10-1 Ratio, Proportion, and Similarity (pp. 496–502)

Part **1** Ratio and Proportion in Similar Figures

Part **2** Using Proportions

Key Terms: Cross-Product Property, extended proportion, Golden Ratio, Golden Rectangle, proportion, scale, scale drawing

10-2 Proving Triangles Similar: AA, SAS, and SSS (pp. 504–510)

Part **1** Using the AA Similarity Postulate

Part **2** Using the SAS and SSS Similarity Theorems

Key Terms: Angle-Angle Similarity Postulate (AA~), indirect measurement , Side-Angle-Side Similarity Theorem (SAS~), Side-Side-Side Similarity Theorem (SSS~)

10-3 Similarity in Right Triangles (pp. 511–516)

Key Term: geometric mean

10-4 Proportions and Similar Triangles (pp. 517–523)

Part **1** Using the Side-Splitter Theorem

Part **2** Using the Triangle-Angle-Bisector Theorem

10-5 Perimeters and Areas of Similar Figures (pp. 524–529)

10-6 Areas and Volumes of Similar Solids (pp. 531–535)

Key Term: similar solids, similarity ratio

PACING OPTIONS

This chart suggests pacing only for the core lessons and their parts, and it is provided merely as a possible guide. It will help you determine how much time you have in your schedule to cover other features, such as the Chapter Project, Math Toolboxes, Wrap Up, and Assessment.

	1 Class Period	1 Class Period	1 Class Period	1 Class Period	1 Class Period	1 Class Period	1 Class Period	1 Class Period	1 Class Period
Traditional (40–45 min class periods)	10-1 **1**	10-1 **2**	10-2 **1**	10-2 **2**	10-3	10-4 **1**	10-4 **2**	10-5	10-6
Block Scheduling (90 min class periods)	10-1 **1 2**	10-2 **1 2**	10-3	10-4 **1 2**	10-5 10-6				

What Students Will Learn and Why

In this chapter, students will build on their knowledge of similarity, learned in Chapter 2, by learning how to use ratio and proportion with similar polygons. They also learn how to prove two triangles similar using the AA~ Postulate, and the SAS~ and SSS~ Theorems. Students apply these concepts to find distances using indirect measurement. Then students study similarity in right triangles and proportional relationships in triangles. Finally, they learn relationships among the similarity ratio, perimeter, and area of similar figures and among the similarity ratio, surface area, and volume of similar solids. The concepts presented in this chapter have uses in photography, architecture, and design.

Discussing the Chapter/Building on Experience

The concept map below relates chapter topics to real-world applications. You and your class may wish to add to the map or develop maps of your own. The center oval describes the topic of the chapter. The next level displays topics within the lessons. The outer ovals reflect applications of the content. As you and your class build a concept map, invite students to discuss applications with which they are familiar.

Interactive Questioning Tips

A question is interactive when there is "give and take" between the questioner (teacher or student) and the respondent. In Think and Discuss or when a critical thinking question is asked, it is important to encourage students to support their answers with facts. Ask "How do you know this?" to encourage logical reasoning. For example, in Lesson 10-1, Question 5, students are asked to explain why a particular solution *cannot* be the length of a Golden Rectangle.

Skills Practice

Every lesson provides skill practice with Try This exercises, Exercises On Your Own, and Exercises Mixed Review. The Student Edition includes Checkpoints (pp. 510, 529) and

Cumulative Review (p. 541). In the Teacher's Edition, the Lesson Planning Options section for each lesson lists Prerequisite Skills students should know for that lesson. At the back of the Student Edition is the Skills Handbook—mini-lessons on math your students may need to review. The Chapter Support File for Chapter 10 in the Teaching Resources box includes two Practice worksheets per lesson, a worksheet for two Checkpoints, and worksheets for Cumulative Review and Standardized Test Preparation.

Diverse Learning and Teaching Styles

In your Teacher's Edition, you will find suggestions as to how you can help students complete mathematical tasks in Chapter 10 by reinforcing various learning styles. Here are some examples.

- **Visual learning** identify corresponding parts of figures by tracing and rotating the figures to the same position (p. 500), use color coding to indicate pairs of congruent angles in a given triangle (p. 511)

- **Tactile learning** use geoboards to create similar rectangles (p. 524), use models of pairs of similar solids to measure corresponding dimensions (p. 532)

- **Auditory learning** understand properties of proportions by describing how the properties are related to the original proportion (p. 497), practice naming corresponding sides (p. 505)

- **Kinesthetic learning** identify which objects shaped like rectangles found outside are Golden Rectangles (p. 498)

Alternative Activity for Lesson 10-1

for use with Example 1, uses geometry software to explore similar triangles.

Alternative Activity for Lesson 10-2

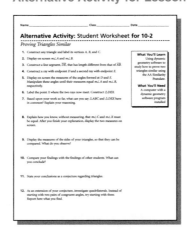

for use with Work Together, uses geometry software to explore the AA Similarity Postulate.

Alternative Activity for Lesson 10-5

for use with Work Together, uses geometry software to explore area and perimeter of similar polygons.

Cooperative Learning Tips

When used effectively, cooperative learning can help students develop interpersonal skills, learn to perform specific roles in a group, and learn to carry out specific responsibilities. The components of Chapter 10 provide a range of cooperative learning opportunities.

- In the Student Edition, the **Work Together** parts of lessons are specifically designed for cooperative learning activities.

- In the Teacher's Edition, you will find helpful hints for addressing diverse learning styles (see page C for Chapter 10). For every lesson, you will find a **Reteaching Activity**, which may involve cooperative learning.

Materials and Manipulatives

The authors expect all students to use scientific calculators. Calculator use is integrated throughout the course.

- calculator (10-1, 10-2, 10-5, 10-6)
- compass (10-1)
- geometry software (10-4)
- graph paper (10-1, 10-5)
- isometric dot paper (10-6)
- metric ruler (10-2)
- protractor (10-2)
- ruler (10-1)
- scissors (10-3)
- straightedge (10-1, 10-3)

TECHNOLOGY OPTIONS

Technology Tools		Chapter Project	10-1	10-2	10-3	10-4	10-5	10-6
Calculator		Assumed that students have scientific calculators at any time.						
Software	Secondary Math Lab Toolkit™		✔	✔	✔	✔	✔	✔
	Integrated Math Lab					✔	✔	
	Computer Item Generator		✔	✔	✔	✔	✔	✔
	Student Edition					✔		✔ᵀ
Video	Video Field Trip	✔						
CD-ROM	Multimedia Geometry Lab		✔	✔			✔	✔
Internet		See the Prentice Hall site. (http://www.phschool.com)						

✔ᵀ indicates Math Toolbox.

The Prentice Hall Geometry program offers you a rich variety of technology options. Be assured that all these options are provided as a means of enriching the program and are not essential for the successful completion of the course.

Assessment Options

The Prentice Hall Geometry Program provides you with many options. From these options, you may choose instructional materials and techniques appropriate for your students, or those necessary to meet your district's curriculum requirements. As the chart indicates, the program also supports your teaching efforts by offering you many choices for assessment.

ASSESSMENT OPTIONS

Assessment Support Materials	Chapter Project	10-1	10-2	10-3	10-4	10-5	10-6	Chapter End
Chapter Project	▲ ■ ●	▲ ■		▲ ■	▲ ■	▲ ■	▲ ■	▲ ■
Checkpoints			▲ ■ ●			▲ ■ ●		
Self-Assessment		▲ ■				▲ ■	▲ ■	▲ ■
Writing Assignment		▲	▲ ■	▲	▲	▲ ■	▲ ■	▲ ■ ●
Chapter Assessment								▲ ■ ●
Alternative Assessment	■	■	■		■	■	■	■ ●
Cumulative Review								▲ ■ ●
Standardized Test Prep		▲ ■	▲ ■	▲ ■	▲	▲	▲ ■	▲ ■ ●
Computer Item Generator	Can be used to create custom-made practice or assessment at any time.							

▲ = Student Edition   ■ = Teacher's Edition   ● = Teaching Resources

Checkpoints

Alternative Assessment

Chapter Assessment

Available in both Form A and Form B

Making the Right Connections

Mathematics is imbedded in nearly every walk of life. The National Council of Teachers of Mathematics (NCTM) encourages educators to recognize these connections and to emphasize them for the purpose of better educating students for success in life and in a global economy. The **Connections** chart below highlights these connections for Chapter 10.

CONNECTIONS

Lesson	Interdisciplinary Connections	Career Prep	Other Real World Connections	Math Integration	NCTM Standards
Chapter Project	Environmental Science	Research Computer Design	Nature Photographs Scale Models	Fractal Geometry	Algebra
10-1	History Art Geography	Architecture	Basketball Blueprints Leonardo DaVinci Leaning Tower of Pisa Money	Algebra Coordinate Geometry Data Analysis	Algebra Communication Connections Problem Solving
10-2	History	Architecture	National Parks Fire Tower Indirect Measurement	Algebra	Algebra Reasoning Communication Connections
10-3		Civil Engineering	Recreation Koch Snowflake Dental Services	Algebra Coordinate Geometry Data Analysis	Algebra Reasoning Communication Connections
10-4	Geography	Surveying	Sail Making Lakes Streets	Algebra Logical Reasoning Geometry in 3 Dimensions Transformational Geometry	Reasoning Communication Connections Problem Solving
10-5		Surveying	Community Service Remodeling School Enrollment	Algebra Data Analysis Transformational Geometry	Reasoning Communication Connections Problem Solving
10-6	Literature	Carpentry Package Design	Russian Dolls Paperweights Atomic Clocks Packaging	Coordinate Geometry Algebra	Reasoning Communication Connections Problem Solving

CONNECTING TO PRIOR LEARNING Ask students if they have ever seen a movie or a TV show in which a famous place was blown up, set on fire, or destroyed in some other way. Discuss how computers use properties of similar figures to generate scale models to create the scenes. Those properties of similarity will be investigated in this chapter.

CULTURAL CONNECTIONS The simplest fractal is called the Cantor bar, named after a nineteenth century German mathematician Georg Cantor. Have students construct a Cantor bar as follows: divide a line segment into three parts,

then remove the middle part. Repeat this procedure on the remaining two parts, then on the remaining four parts, and so on.

INTERDISCIPLINARY CONNECTIONS Fractal geometry has implications in physics, biology, geography, statistics, and art. Discuss with students the work of Benoit B. Mandlebrot, a French mathematician, who observed fractals in the fluctuations of the stock market, the distribution of galaxies, and the English shoreline.

Technology Options

Prentice Hall Technology

Video
Video Field Trip 10, "Fractally Speaking," an interview with Benoit Mandlebrot, one of the discoverers of the fractal world

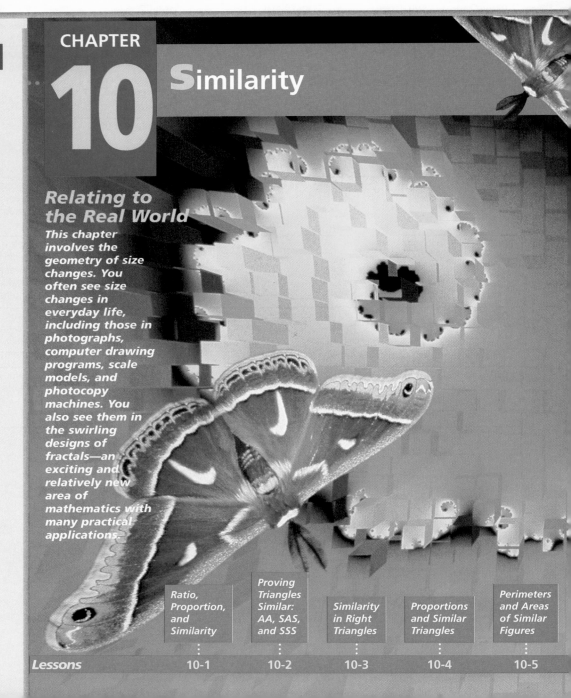

CHAPTER

10 **S**imilarity

Relating to the Real World

This chapter involves the geometry of size changes. You often see size changes in everyday life, including those in photographs, computer drawing programs, scale models, and photocopy machines. You also see them in the swirling designs of fractals—an exciting and relatively new area of mathematics with many practical applications.

Lessons	Ratio, Proportion, and Similarity	Proving Triangles Similar: AA, SAS, and SSS	Similarity in Right Triangles	Proportions and Similar Triangles	Perimeters and Areas of Similar Figures
	10-1	10-2	10-3	10-4	10-5

Launching the Project

PROJECT NOTEBOOK Encourage students to keep all project-related materials in a separate folder or notebook. See Chapter Project Manager and Scoring Rubric in Chapter Support File.

• Ask students to describe any patterns they may have seen on a fern, a pineapple, or a pinecone.

• Ask students to give examples of objects found in nature, other than those described on pages 494–495, that have repeating patterns.

TRACKING THE PROJECT You may wish to have students read Finishing the Chapter Project on page 536 to help them get an overview of the project. Set benchmark deadlines for students to show their work in progress.

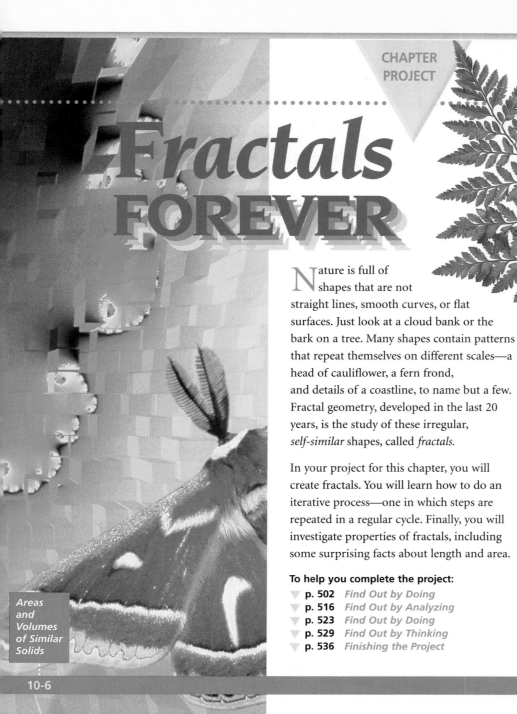

CHAPTER PROJECT

Fractals FOREVER

Nature is full of shapes that are not straight lines, smooth curves, or flat surfaces. Just look at a cloud bank or the bark on a tree. Many shapes contain patterns that repeat themselves on different scales—a head of cauliflower, a fern frond, and details of a coastline, to name but a few. Fractal geometry, developed in the last 20 years, is the study of these irregular, *self-similar* shapes, called *fractals*.

In your project for this chapter, you will create fractals. You will learn how to do an iterative process—one in which steps are repeated in a regular cycle. Finally, you will investigate properties of fractals, including some surprising facts about length and area.

To help you complete the project:

▼ **p. 502** *Find Out by Doing*
▼ **p. 516** *Find Out by Analyzing*
▼ **p. 523** *Find Out by Doing*
▼ **p. 529** *Find Out by Thinking*
▼ **p. 536** *Finishing the Project*

Areas and Volumes of Similar Solids

10-6

▼ Project Resources

 Teaching Resources
Chapter Support File, Ch. 10
• Chapter Project Manager and Scoring Rubric

Transparencies
103

▼ Using the Rubric

Sharing the scoring rubric for the project with your students will alert them to your expectations before they begin work on the project.

As students complete each Find Out question in the chapter, you may wish to have them evaluate their own work or a partner's work based on the scoring rubric. Students should have the opportunity to revise their work after it has been reviewed.

Name _____ Class _____ Date _____

Chapter Project Manager
Chapter 10 Fractals Forever

Getting Started Read about the project on page 495 of your textbook. As you work on the project, you will need several sheets of tracing paper (8½ × 11 in.) and a millimeter ruler. Keep all of your work for the project in a folder, along with this Project Manager.

Checklist and Suggestions

☐ snowflake drawings (page 502)   Measure and draw carefully.
☐ Stage 3 snowflake analysis (page 516)   Define perimeter with an equation.
☐ fractal trees (page 523)   Use patterns to draw the next-stage fractal tree.
☐ area estimation (page 529)   Compare the diagrams.
☐ report on fractals (page 536)   Check your work. Be sure someone else could follow your directions.

Scoring Rubric

3 Your drawings are accurate and neat. Your calculations are accurate. Your reasoning and explanations are correct and clearly expressed. Your report is complete and well organized.

2 Drawings and calculations are correctly chosen and used. There are minor errors in scale or computation. Reasoning and explanations are essentially correct, but may contain awkward or unclear passages.

1 Some drawings are inaccurate. There are many computational errors. Explanations are incomplete or incorrect.

0 Major elements of the project are incomplete or missing.

Your Evaluation of Project Evaluate your work, based on the *Scoring Rubric*.

Teacher's Evaluation of Project

495

CONNECTING TO PRIOR KNOWLEDGE Ask students if the following pairs of ratios are equivalent.

$$\frac{12}{32}, \frac{3}{8} \qquad \frac{2}{4}, \frac{8}{4} \qquad \frac{20}{32}, \frac{35}{56}$$

THINK AND DISCUSS

ESL Discuss with the use of the word *similar* in English compared to its use in mathematics. Point out that you may say "these two sweaters are similar" because they have the same color or pattern, not because they have same shape and their corresponding "dimensions" are proportional.

Example 1

Make sure students understand that the similarity ratio is dependent on the order of the similarity statement. $\triangle ABC \sim \triangle FED$ with similarity ratio $\frac{3}{4}$, but $\triangle FED \sim \triangle ABC$ with similarity ratio $\frac{4}{3}$.

Lesson Planning Options

Prerequisite Skills

- Simplifying ratios
- Solving quadratic equations

Assignment Options for Exercises On Your Own

To provide flexible scheduling, this lesson can be subdivided into parts.

1 Core 1–10, 13–18
Extension 29, 39

2 Core 11–12, 19–28, 30–36, 40
Extension 37–38

Use Mixed Review to maintain skills.

Resources

Student Edition

Skills Handbook, pp. 661, 662
Extra Practice, p. 643
Glossary/Study Guide

Teaching Resources

Chapter Support File, Ch. 10
- Practice 10-1 (two worksheets)
- Reteaching 10-1
- Alternative Activity 10-1
- Classroom Manager 10-1
- Glossary, Spanish Resources

Transparencies
7, 104

What You'll Learn
- Finding how to use ratio and proportion with similar polygons

...And Why
To use similarity in scale drawings, art, and architecture

What You'll Need
- ruler
- calculator
- graph paper
- compass
- straightedge

Connections 🌐 Architecture . . . *and more*

10-1 Ratio, Proportion, and Similarity

Part 1

THINK AND DISCUSS

Ratio and Proportion in Similar Figures

In Chapter 2 you learned that two polygons are *similar* if (1) corresponding angles are congruent **and** (2) corresponding sides are proportional. The ratio of the lengths of corresponding sides is the *similarity ratio*. You can write the ratio of a to b as $a : b$ or as $\frac{a}{b}$.

Example 1

Are the triangles similar? If they are, write a similarity statement and give the similarity ratio. If they are not, explain why they are not.

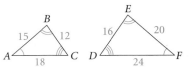

Three pairs of angles are congruent. To compare the ratios of corresponding side lengths, express the ratios in simplest form.

$$\frac{AC}{FD} = \frac{18}{24} = \frac{3}{4} \qquad \frac{AB}{FE} = \frac{15}{20} = \frac{3}{4} \qquad \frac{BC}{ED} = \frac{12}{16} = \frac{3}{4}$$

$\triangle ABC \sim \triangle FED$ with a similarity ratio $\frac{3}{4}$, or 3 : 4.

4 : 3 or $\frac{4}{3}$

1. What is the similarity ratio for the similarity $\triangle FED \sim \triangle ABC$?

2. **Try This** If the triangles at the left are similar, write a similarity statement and give the similarity ratio. If they are not, explain why they are not. $\triangle XYZ \sim \triangle MNP$; 2 : 3 or $\frac{2}{3}$

A **proportion** is a statement that two ratios are equal. You can read both

$$\frac{a}{b} = \frac{c}{d} \quad \text{and} \quad a : b = c : d$$

as "a is to b as c is to d." When three or more ratios are equal, you can write an **extended proportion**. For Example 1 you could write the following:

$$\frac{18}{24} = \frac{15}{20} = \frac{12}{16}$$

The following properties are helpful in solving proportions.

Properties of Proportions

$\frac{a}{b} = \frac{c}{d}$ is equivalent to

(1) $ad = bc$
(2) $\frac{b}{a} = \frac{d}{c}$
(3) $\frac{a}{c} = \frac{b}{d}$
(4) $\frac{a+b}{b} = \frac{c+d}{d}$

To help students understand the properties of proportions, give values for *a, b, c,* and *d* such that $\frac{a}{b} = \frac{c}{d}$ and have them substitute to check that the four properties are true.

AUDITORY LEARNING Students will better understand the properties of proportions if they describe how the properties are related to the original proportion. For example, the first property can be stated as "the product of the extremes is equal to the product of the means." The third property can be stated as "the ratio of the numerators of the proportion is equal to the ratio of the denominators of the proportion."

CRITICAL THINKING Question 3 Have students justify the remaining three properties of proportions.

Example 2 Relating to the Real World

Make sure students understand that a scale given with an equal sign, such as 1 in. = 16 ft, can be rewritten as $\frac{1}{16}$.

ERROR ALERT! Students may have difficulty setting up and solving proportions with complex fractions. **Remediation:** Show students how the proportions in Example 2 were set up and how the Cross-Product Property was used to simplify the equations. Then have students work in groups to answer Question 4, which involves similar proportions.

---

extremes
$$\frac{a}{b} = \frac{c}{d}$$
means

$$ad = bc$$

Who? As a 21-year-old architecture student, Maya Ying Lin won the design competition for the Vietnam War Memorial. She also designed the Civil Rights Memorial in Montgomery, Alabama.

The first property is called the **Cross-Product Property.** It can be stated as "The product of the extremes is equal to the product of the means."

3. To eliminate the denominators in $\frac{a}{b} = \frac{c}{d}$, by what would you multiply both sides of the equation? What would be the result? Use your answers to **justify** the Cross-Product Property. *bd; ad = bc; the product of the extremes, a and d, = the product of the means, b and c.*

Part 2 Using Proportions

A similarity ratio always compares dimensions in the same unit, such as meters. In a **scale drawing,** the **scale** compares each length in the drawing to the actual length being represented. The scale in a scale drawing can be in different units. A scale might be written as 1 in. to 100 mi, 1 in. = 12 ft, or 1 mm : 1 m.

Example 2 Relating to the Real World

Architecture What are the actual dimensions of the bedroom?

Use a ruler to find that the bedroom is $\frac{7}{8}$ in. by $\frac{5}{8}$ in. on the scale drawing.

$$\frac{1}{16} = \frac{\frac{7}{8}}{x} \qquad \frac{1}{16} = \frac{\frac{5}{8}}{y} \qquad \begin{array}{l}\leftarrow \text{drawing length (in.)}\\ \leftarrow \text{actual length (ft)}\end{array}$$

$$x = 16(\tfrac{7}{8}) \qquad y = 16(\tfrac{5}{8}) \qquad \text{Cross-Product Property}$$

$$x = 14 \qquad y = 10$$

The actual bedroom is 14 ft by 10 ft.

4. a. Try This What are the dimensions of the actual living room? **12 ft by 20 ft**

   b. What is the area of the actual living room? **240 ft²**

Bedroom

Living Room

Kitchen | Bath

Scale 1 in. = 16 ft

FOR EXAMPLE 1

Are the triangles similar? If they are, write a similarity statement and give the similarity ratio. If they are not, explain.

$\triangle YZX \sim \triangle HGF$; $\frac{2}{3}$

Discussion: *Sarah claims that* $\triangle YZX \sim \triangle HGF$. *Jerry claims that* $\triangle ZXY \sim \triangle GFH$. *Who is correct? Explain.*

FOR EXAMPLE 2

Refer to the diagram in Example 2. What are the actual dimensions of the kitchen? the bathroom? **8 ft by 8 ft; 8 ft by 6 ft**

Discussion: *What is the ratio of the area of the kitchen in the scale drawing to the area of the actual kitchen?*

Make sure students understand that *DFEA* is a square with side length 1. You may also want to explain why $EB = x - 1$ and review how to solve $x^2 - x = 1$.

Question 6 Help students understand that the ratio of the length to the width of any Golden Rectangle ≈ 1.618 : 1.

EXTENSION Have students research other real-world examples of Golden Rectangles in architecture and in art. For an example of its use in modern art, see the paintings of Piet Mondrian.

MAKING CONNECTIONS Have students find the ratio of pairs of consecutive terms in the Fibonacci Sequence 1, 1, 2, 3, 5, 8, 13, . . . Have them approximate each ratio to the nearest thousandth. They should discover that the ratios get closer and closer to the Golden Ratio.

A **Golden Rectangle** is a rectangle that can be divided into a square and a rectangle that is similar to the original rectangle. The ratio of the length of a Golden Rectangle to the width is called the **Golden Ratio.** To find the Golden Ratio, you can find the length x of a Golden Rectangle whose width is 1.

$ABCD \sim BCFE$	Definition of Golden Rectangle
$\dfrac{AB}{BC} = \dfrac{BC}{CF}$	Corresponding sides of ~ polygons are proportional.
$\dfrac{x}{1} = \dfrac{1}{x-1}$	Substitution
$x^2 - x = 1$	Cross-Product Property
$x^2 - x - 1 = 0$	Subtract 1 from each side.

Using the Quadratic Formula to solve this equation, you get $x = \dfrac{1 \pm \sqrt{5}}{2}$.

5. *Critical Thinking* Why does the answer $x = \dfrac{1 - \sqrt{5}}{2}$ not apply to this problem? **The ratio cannot be negative.**

6. a. *Calculator* Find the value of x to the nearest thousandth. 1.618
   b. What is the length of a Golden Rectangle whose width is 3 cm?
   c. What is the width of a Golden Rectangle whose length is 5 cm?
   b. 4.854 cm   c. 3.090 cm

The Golden Rectangle is considered pleasing to the human eye and has appeared in architecture and art since ancient times. It has intrigued artists including Leonardo da Vinci (1452–1519), who illustrated *The Divine Proportion,* a book about the Golden Rectangle. The Golden Rectangle also occurs frequently in nature and in the proportions of the human body.

498

WORK TOGETHER

Work with a partner to draw a Golden Rectangle using graph paper, a compass, and a straightedge.

- On graph paper draw a square *AEFD* with an even number of units on each side.
- Find the midpoint *M* of $\overline{AE}$.
- With radius *MF* draw an arc that intersects $\overrightarrow{AE}$ at point *B*.
- Construct the perpendicular to $\overleftrightarrow{AB}$ at point *B*.
- Let point *C* be the intersection of this perpendicular and $\overrightarrow{DF}$.
- Draw the rectangle *ABCD*.

a–c. Answers may vary. Samples are given.

7. **a.** Use *ME*, *EF*, and the Pythagorean Theorem to find *MF*. $2\sqrt{5}$
   b. Use *MF* to find *EB*. $2\sqrt{5} - 2$
   c. What are the dimensions of rectangle *ABCD*? $2 + 2\sqrt{5}$; 4
   d. **Verify** that *ABCD* is a Golden Rectangle. $\frac{AB}{BC} = \frac{1 + \sqrt{5}}{2}$ ✔

Exercises ON YOUR OWN

Algebra If $\frac{a}{b} = \frac{3}{4}$, which of the following must be true?

1. $4a = 3b$ T   **2.** $3a = 4b$ F

3. $\frac{a}{3} = \frac{b}{4}$ T   **4.** $\frac{4}{3} = \frac{b}{a}$ T

5. $\frac{4}{b} = \frac{3}{a}$ T   **6.** $ab = 3(4)$ F

7. $\frac{a + b}{b} = \frac{3 + 4}{4}$ T   **8.** $\frac{a + b}{a} = \frac{7}{3}$ T

9. $\frac{a + 3}{3} = \frac{b + 4}{4}$ T   **10.** $\frac{a}{b} = \frac{6}{8} = \frac{0.75}{1}$ T

11. *Models* The Leaning Tower of Pisa in Italy is about 180 ft tall. A souvenir paperweight of the Leaning Tower is 6 in. tall. What is the similarity ratio of the paperweight to the real tower? 1 : 360

12. Suppose the designer of the pyramid at the right wanted the base to be a 675-m square. The sides of the base of the pyramid that was built measure 0.675 m. What is the similarity ratio of the pyramid that was built to the one the designer had planned?
1 : 1000

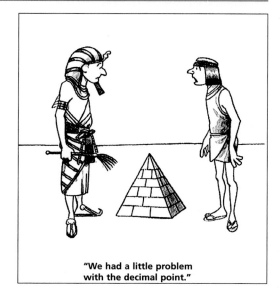

"We had a little problem with the decimal point."

499

Are the polygons similar? If they are, write a similarity statement and give the similarity ratio. If they are not, explain.

13. no; $\frac{36}{52} \neq \frac{20}{30}$

14. $QRST \sim XWZY$; $\frac{3}{4}$

15. $JKLM \sim OPQN$; $\frac{3}{5}$

16. $ABCD \sim FGHE$; $\frac{4}{5}$

17. No; the corres. angles are not $\cong$.

18. $\triangle ABC \sim \triangle FED$; $\frac{7}{5}$

Algebra Solve for x.

19. $\frac{x}{10} = \frac{15}{25}$ 6

20. $\frac{9}{24} = \frac{12}{x}$ 32

21. $\frac{11}{14} = \frac{x}{21}$ 16.5

22. $\frac{5}{x} = \frac{8}{11}$ $6\frac{7}{8}$

23. $\frac{x+3}{3} = \frac{10+4}{4}$ 7.5

24. $\frac{x+7}{7} = \frac{15}{5}$ 14

25. $\frac{4}{x} = \frac{x}{9}$ −6 or 6

26. $\frac{x}{2} = \frac{50}{x}$ −10 or 10

27. **Mental Math** A postcard is 6 in. by 4 in. A commercial printing shop will enlarge it to any size up to 3 ft on the longer dimension. What are the dimensions of the largest possible enlargement for this postcard? **3 ft by 2 ft**

PROBLEM SOLVING HINT
Draw a diagram.

28. **Open-ended** Measure the dimensions of the fronts of several boxes in your home, such as cereal boxes and laundry detergent boxes. Which box is closest to the shape of a Golden Rectangle? **Check students' work.**

29. **Coordinate Geometry** $\triangle ABC$ with vertices $A(2, 3)$, $B(2, 6)$, and $C(4, 6)$ is similar to $\triangle QRS$ with vertices $Q(6, 9)$, $R(6, 24)$, and S. Give two possibilities for the coordinates of vertex S. **(−4, 24), (16, 24)**

30. **Geography** A map of Louisiana is drawn to the scale 1 in. = 40 mi. On the map, the distance from Lake Charles to Baton Rouge is about $3\frac{1}{4}$ in. About how far apart are the two cities? **130 mi**

DIVERSITY Exercise 35 If possible, bring in or have students bring in currency from other countries. You may want to assign each group a country and have them research the currency from that country and its value in U.S. dollars.

TRANSFORMATIONS Exercise 39 This exercise helps students see the connections between dilations and similarity.

STANDARDIZED TEST TIP Exercise 40 Help students see that they can solve this problem by comparing the ratio of two adjacent sides in each rectangle with the ratio of adjacent sides of *ABCD*.

The polygons are similar. Find the values of the variables.

31.

$x = 6$; $y = 8$; $z = 10$

32.

$x = 16$; $y = 4.5$; $z = 7.5$

33.

$x = 20$; $y = 17.5$; $z = 7.5$

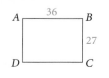 **34. Calculator** The switch plate for a standard electric light switch is in the shape of a Golden Rectangle. The longer side of a standard switch plate is about 114 mm. What is the length of the shorter side? Round your answer to the nearest millimeter. **70 mm**

35. Money From 1861 to 1928 the dollar bill measured $7\frac{7}{16}$ in. by $3\frac{1}{8}$ in. The dimensions of the current dollar bill are shown at the right. Are the two dollar bills similar rectangles? Explain. **See below.**

36. Geography Students on the campus of the University of Minnesota in Minneapolis built a model globe 42 ft in diameter on a scale of 1 : 1,000,000. About how tall would Mount Everest be on the model? (Mount Everest is about 29,000 ft tall.) **0.029 ft or 0.348 in.**

37. Data Collection On a single sheet of white paper, draw rectangles with the following dimensions: 3 in. by 3 in., 3 in. by 4 in., 3 in. by 5 in., and 3 in. by 6 in. Show the sheet to ten different people and ask them to select their first and second choices for most pleasing rectangles. Combine your findings with those of your classmates. Describe how your results do or do not confirm that the Golden Rectangle is the most pleasing rectangle. **Check students' work.**

38. a. Sports A basketball court is 84 ft by 50 ft. Choose a scale and draw a scale drawing of a basketball court. **a–b. Check students' work.**
   b. Writing Explain how you chose the scale for your drawing.

39. a. Transformations Draw *JKLM* with vertices $J(-2, -2)$, $K(6, -2)$, $L(6, 4)$, and $M(-2, 4)$. Then draw its image $J'K'L'M'$ under the dilation with center $O(0, 0)$ and scale factor $\frac{1}{2}$. **See margin.**
   b. How are *JKLM* and $J'K'L'M'$ related? Explain. **$JKLM \sim J'K'L'M'$ with similarity ratio 2:1**
   c. Is $J'K'L'M'$ an enlargement or reduction of *JKLM*? **reduction**

40. Standardized Test Prep Which rectangles are similar to rectangle *ABCD*? **E**

A. I only   **B.** II only   **C.** I and II   **D.** I and III   **E.** I, II, and III

35. No; the ratios of the corres. sides are not =; $\frac{17}{14} \neq \frac{25}{21}$.

$6\frac{1}{8}$ in.

$2\frac{5}{8}$ in.

pages 499–502   On Your Own

39a.

page 502   Mixed Review

42.

501

Lesson Quiz

Lesson Quiz is also available in Transparencies.

The following polygons are similar.

1. Write a similarity statement.
  PQRS ~ TUVW

2. Give the similarity ratio. $\frac{3}{4}$

3. Find *x*. 16

4. Find *y*. 9

Chapter Project   Find Out by Doing

In 1904, Swedish mathematician Helge von Koch created a fractal "snowflake." Draw one by starting with an equilateral triangle (Stage 0).

- Divide each side into three congruent segments.
- Draw an equilateral triangle on the middle segment of each side.
- Erase the middle segments on which you drew the smaller triangles.

You have now drawn Stage 1. Repeat the steps to create Stage 2. (Divide all twelve sides of Stage 1 into three congruent segments.) **Check students' work.**

Stage 0   Stage 1

Exercises MIXED REVIEW

Sketch a quadrilateral with the given property.

41. congruent diagonals
   See right.

42. perpendicular diagonals
   See margin p. 501 for sample.

43. only two parallel sides

44. An isosceles right triangle has a leg 9 in. long. How long is the hypotenuse? $9\sqrt{2}$ in.

41. Sample:

43. Sample:

Getting Ready for Lesson 10-2

What postulate or theorem can you use to prove the triangles congruent?

45.

SSS

46.

ASA

47.

SAS

A Point in Time

The Speed of Light

In **1675,** Danish astronomer Ole Römer used proportions to estimate the speed of light. He carefully measured the rotations of Jupiter's moons. With Earth at point *B*, a moon emerged from behind Jupiter 16.6 minutes later than when Earth was at point *A*. He reasoned that it must have taken 16.6 minutes for the light to travel from *A* to *B*. Using proportions, Römer estimated the speed of light is 150,000 mi/s, an estimate that compares favorably with today's accepted value of 186,282 mi/s.

Jupiter
sun
A   B
Earth
moon
not drawn to scale

Math ToolboX — Algebra Review

Transparencies 5

Direct Variation

Before Lesson 10-2

The perimeter p of an equilateral triangle depends on its side length s. The table shows perimeters for various side lengths. An equation that describes this relationship is $p = 3s$. This type of relationship is called a direct variation.

s	1	2	5	10
p	3	6	15	30

A **direct variation** is a relationship that can be described by an equation in the form $y = kx$, where $k \neq 0$. In the equation, k is called the **constant of variation.** You say that "y varies directly as x."

Example

Retail Sales Juan worked 16 hours last week at a department store and earned $92.00.

a. Assuming that his earnings e vary directly as the number of hours w he works, write an equation that relates these two variables.
b. How much will Juan earn if he works 12.5 hours in a week?

a.
$e = kw$ Write a direct variation equation.
$92 = k(16)$ Substitute for e and w.
$k = 5.75$ Solve for k.

The equation $e = 5.75w$ describes this direct variation.

b.
$e = 5.75w$ Use the equation from part (a).
$= 5.75(12.5)$ Substitute 12.5 for w.
$= 71.875$ Simplify.

Juan will earn $71.88 for working 12.5 hours.

Solve each problem.

1. **Taxes** The sales tax t on a purchase varies directly as the cost c of the items purchased. Write an equation relating these two variables if the sales tax rate is 6.5%. $t = 0.065c$

2. The circumference C of a circle varies directly as its diameter d. Write an equation that relates these two variables. $C = \pi d$

3. **Consumer Issues** Tandrell spends $16.48 for 12.3 gallons of gasoline.
   a. Write an equation that relates the total amount t spent on gasoline to the number of gallons purchased n. $t = 1.34n$
   b. How many gallons can Tandrell buy for $20.00? 14.9 gal

4. **Astronomy** An object that weighs 6 lb on Earth weighs 1 lb on the moon. If the weight w of an object on the moon varies directly as its weight on Earth e, write an equation relating these variables. $w = \frac{1}{6}e$

PROBLEM OF THE DAY

A cake has three circular tiers, each 4 in. high. The tiers have diameters of 30 in., 24 in., and 18 in. What is the surface area to be covered by frosting if there is no frosting between layers? 513π in.^{2} ≈ 1611.6 in.^{2}

Problem of the Day is also available in Transparencies.

CONNECTING TO PRIOR KNOWLEDGE Ask students to explain how to use the SSS Postulate, the SAS Postulate, the ASA Postulate, and the AAS Theorem to prove two triangles congruent.

WORK TOGETHER

Suggest that students begin by drawing two segments $\overline{AB}$ and $\overline{A'B'}$ of different lengths, then make A and A' the vertices of the 50° angle and B and B' the vertices of the 60° angles.

THINK AND DISCUSS

Angle-Angle Similarity Postulate Make sure students understand that this postulate is true for triangles but is not true for other polygons.

Lesson Planning Options

Prerequisite Skills

- Applying congruence postulates and theorems

Assignment Options for Exercises On Your Own

To provide flexible scheduling, this lesson can be subdivided into parts.

1 **Core** 11–19, 27–28
Extension 26

2 **Core** 1–10, 20–25, 29–30
Extension 31

Use Mixed Review to maintain skills.

Resources

Student Edition

Skills Handbook, pp. 646, 650
Extra Practice, p. 643
Glossary/Study Guide

Teaching Resources

Chapter Support File, Ch. 10
- Practice 10-2 (two worksheets)
- Reteaching 10-2
- Alternative Activity 10-2
Classroom Manager 10-2
Glossary, Spanish Resources

Transparencies
104, 107

What You'll Learn

10-2 **Proving Triangles Similar: AA, SAS, and SSS**

- Proving two triangles similar using the AA ~ Postulate and the SAS ~ and SSS ~ Theorems
- Using similarity in indirect measurement to find distances

...And Why

To find a missing length

What You'll Need

metric ruler, protractor, calculator

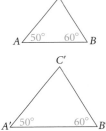

WORK TOGETHER

Work in groups.

- Draw two large triangles of different sizes, each with a 50° and a 60° angle. Label them as shown at the left below. Use a protractor to make sure that the angles are 50° and 60°.

- Measure the sides of each triangle to the nearest millimeter.

- Use a calculator to find the ratio of the lengths of each pair of corresponding sides.

1. What conclusion can you make about your triangles? The △s are ~.

2. Compare your results with those of other groups. Complete this **conjecture:**

   If two angles of one triangle are congruent to two angles of another triangle, then the triangles are __?__. similar

THINK AND DISCUSS

Part 1 **Using the AA Similarity Postulate**

In Chapter 8, you learned ways to show that two triangles are congruent. In this lesson you will learn three ways to show that two triangles are similar without relying on the definition of similarity. In the Work Together you discovered the following theorem.

Postulate 10-1

Angle-Angle Similarity Postulate (AA ~ Postulate)

If two angles of one triangle are congruent to two angles of another triangle, then the triangles are similar.

$$\triangle RST \sim \triangle LMP$$

Example 1

Explain why the triangles are similar. Write a similarity statement.

$\angle RSW \cong \angle VSB$ because vertical angles are congruent. $\angle R \cong \angle V$ because their measures are equal. $\triangle RSW \sim \triangle VSB$ by the Angle-Angle Similarity Postulate.

You can use similar triangles and measurements to compute distances that are difficult to measure directly. These methods are called **indirect measurement.** One method uses the fact that light reflects off a mirror at the same angle at which it hits the mirror.

Example 2 **Relating to the Real World** ⋯⋯⋯⋯⋯⋯⋯⋯⋯⋯

Geysers Ramon places a mirror on the ground 45 ft from the base of a geyser. He walks backward until he can see the top of the geyser in the middle of the mirror. At that point, Ramon's eyes are 6 ft above the ground and he is 7.5 ft from the mirror. Use similar triangles to find the height of the geyser.

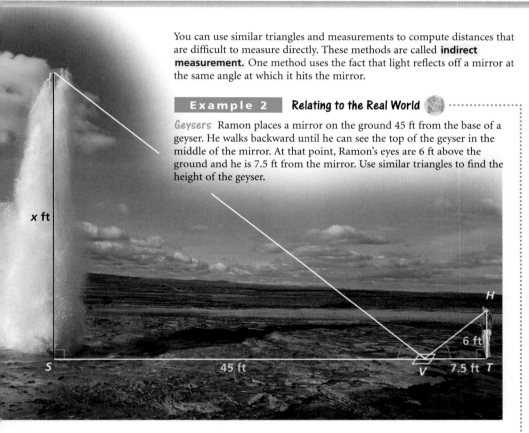

$\triangle HTV \sim \triangle JSV$ AA ~ Postulate

$\dfrac{HT}{JS} = \dfrac{TV}{SV}$ Corr. sides of ~ triangles are proportional.

$\dfrac{6}{x} = \dfrac{7.5}{45}$ Substitute.

$270 = 7.5x$ Cross-Product Property

$36 = x$ Divide each side by 7.5.

The geyser is 36 ft high.

3. **Try This** To find the height of a fire tower, Latisha places a mirror on the ground 40 ft from the base of the tower. Latisha's eyes are $5\frac{1}{2}$ ft above the ground. When Latisha stands 4 ft from the mirror, she can see the top of the tower. How tall is the fire tower? **55 ft**

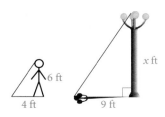

4. A lamppost casts a 9-ft shadow at the same time a person 6 ft tall casts a 4-ft shadow. Use similar triangles to find the height of the lamppost. **13.5 ft**

SAS Similarity Theorem Make sure students understand that the angle must be included between the sides that are proportional.

Point out that the proof of the SAS Similarity Theorem uses the SAS Congruence Theorem and the proof of the SSS Similarity Theorem uses the SSS Congruence Theorem.

Make sure students understand that if a triangle is similar to another triangle, then any triangle congruent to it is also similar to the other triangle.

Part 2 **Using the SAS and SSS Similarity Theorems**

The following two theorems follow from the AA Similarity Postulate.

Theorem 10-1
Side-Angle-Side
Similarity Theorem
(SAS ~ Theorem)

If an angle of one triangle is congruent to an angle of a second triangle, and the sides including the two angles are proportional, then the triangles are similar.

Given: $\angle A \cong \angle Q, \frac{AB}{QR} = \frac{AC}{QS}$

Prove: $\triangle ABC \sim \triangle QRS$

Outline of Proof of Theorem 10-1:

- Choose X on $\overline{QR}$ so that $AB = QX$. Draw $\overline{XY} \parallel \overline{RS}$. Use the AA ~ Postulate to show that $\triangle QXY \sim \triangle QRS$ and thus $\frac{QX}{QR} = \frac{QY}{QS}$.
- Combine this proportion with the given proportion and the fact that $AB = QX$ to show that $AC = QY$.
- Prove that $\triangle ABC \cong \triangle QXY$ and $\triangle ABC \sim \triangle QRS$.

Theorem 10-2
Side-Side-Side
Similarity Theorem
(SSS ~ Theorem)

If the corresponding sides of two triangles are proportional, then the triangles are similar.

Given: $\frac{AB}{QR} = \frac{BC}{RS} = \frac{AC}{QS}$

Prove: $\triangle ABC \sim \triangle QRS$

Outline of Proof of Theorem 10-2:

- Draw $\overline{XY}$ as in the proof for Theorem 10-1.
  Show that $\triangle QXY \sim \triangle QRS$ and thus $\frac{QX}{QR} = \frac{XY}{RS} = \frac{QY}{QS}$.
- Combine this proportion with the given proportion and the fact that $AB = QX$ to show that $BC = XY$ and $AC = QY$. Show that $\triangle ABC \cong \triangle QXY$ and $\triangle ABC \sim \triangle QRS$.

5. What postulate or theorem proves the pairs of triangles similar?

a.

SSS ~ Thm.

b.

SAS ~ Thm.

506

Example 3

ERROR ALERT! Students may have difficulty identifying the corresponding parts. **Remediation:** Help them see that since 12 is less than 16 and 18 is less than 24, the side with length 12 corresponds to the side with length 18 and the side with length 16 corresponds to the side with length 24.

EXTENSION Have students research how a pantograph is used to make similar figures.

Exercises 1–9 Check that students name the theorems and postulates correctly using the symbol ~ or the word "similarity."

Exercise 10 Completing the Work Together on page 504 will prepare students for the construction.

Example 3

Write a similarity statement and explain why the triangles are similar. Then find the length of $\overline{DE}$.

$\angle ABC \cong \angle EBD$ because vertical angles are congruent.

$\frac{AB}{EB} = \frac{12}{18} = \frac{2}{3}$ and $\frac{CB}{DB} = \frac{16}{24} = \frac{2}{3}$.

Therefore, $\triangle ABC \sim \triangle EBD$ by the SAS ~ Postulate.

$\frac{AC}{DE} = \frac{2}{3}$ Corr. sides of similar triangles are proportional.

$\frac{10}{DE} = \frac{2}{3}$ Substitution

$30 = 2 \cdot DE$ Cross-Product Property

$15 = DE$ Divide each side by 2.

The length of $\overline{DE}$ is 15.

    6. Find $m\angle E$ if $m\angle C = 49$ and $m\angle ABC = 39$.   92

pages 507–509   On Your Own

10.

Exercises   ON YOUR OWN

Can you prove the triangles similar? If so, write the similarity statement and name the postulate or theorem you used. $\triangle HFG \sim \triangle HKJ$; Alt. Interior Angles Thm. and AA ~ Post.

1. no

2.

3.

$\triangle ABC \sim \triangle FED$; SSS ~ Thm.

4. no

5. no

$\triangle APJ \sim \triangle ABC$; AA ~ Post.

6.

7.

8.

9. no

$\triangle MGK \sim \triangle MSP$; SAS ~ Thm. $\triangle AWV \sim \triangle AST$; SAS ~ Thm.

10. *Constructions* Draw any $\triangle ABC$. Use a straightedge and a compass to construct $\triangle RST$ so that $\triangle ABC \sim \triangle RST$ with similarity ratio 1 : 3.
See margin for sample.

507

11. **Standardized Test Prep** What is the value of x? **C**

    A. $5\frac{1}{3}$ **B.** 6   **C.** 6.75   **D.** 7   **E.** 8

12. **a.** *Critical Thinking* Are two isosceles triangles always similar? Explain. **No; the corres. angles need not be ≅.**

    b. Are two isosceles right triangles always similar? Explain.
    Yes; every isos. rt. △ is a 45°-45°-90° △, so all isos. rt. △s are ~ by AA~ Post.

Algebra **Solve for x.**

13. 9

14. 2.5

15.
$12\frac{5}{6}$

16. 12

17. 8

18. 15

19. **Open-ended** Name something that would be difficult to measure directly, and describe how you could measure it indirectly. **Check students' work.**

Indirect Measurement **Find the distance represented by x.**

20. 12 m

21.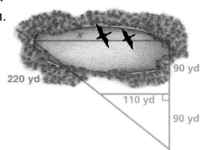

15 ft 9 in.   90 ft

22.

23.

24. **a.** Classify *RSTW*. **Trapezoid**
    b. Must any of the triangles shown be similar? Explain.
    △*RSZ* ~ △*TWZ* by **AA~ Post.**

25. **Mental Math** A yardstick casts a 1-ft shadow at the same time that a nearby tree casts a 15-ft shadow. How tall is the tree? **45 ft**

26. **a.** Write similarity statements involving two different pairs of similar triangles for the figure shown at the right. △*ABF* ~ △*ACD*, △*ECF* ~ △*EBD*
    b. **Algebra** Find the missing lengths.
    w = 8; *x* = 16.8; *y* = 19.2; *z* = 6

Skyscraper? *Nein!*

Hannalore Krause of Frankfurt, Germany, stopped the development of what was to be the tallest skyscraper in Europe because she wanted her apartment to get its fair amount of sunlight. To halt the construction she used a German law that specifies that every homeowner is entitled to sunlight.

Krause was offered 1.6 million dollars to drop her lawsuit, but she refused. The skyscraper, which would have cost about 400 million dollars, was to be built on a site that was only 60 m from Krause's apartment. Scheduled to be 265 m tall, it would have been slightly less than three-fourths the height of the Empire State Building.

Use the magazine article to answer Exercises 27 and 28.

27. **Writing** Explain how Hannalore Krause can use indirect measurement to estimate the length of the shadow of the building at a particular time of day.

27. Hannalore Krause can measure her shadow and use ~ △s to find the length of the shadow of the proposed building.

28. Suppose Hannalore is 1.75 m tall. When her shadow is 1 m long, about how long would the shadow of the proposed building be? **151 m**

Choose **Write a paragraph proof, a two-column proof, or a flow proof.**

29–30. Answers may vary. See margin for samples.

29. **Given:** $\overline{BC} \parallel \overline{DF}$
    Prove: △*BYC* ~ △*DYF*

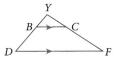

30. **Given:** $RT \cdot TQ = MT \cdot TS$
    Prove: △*RTM* ~ △*STQ*

31. **a.** Find the perimeters of the triangles at the right. **98 m; 98 m**
    b. Find the areas of the triangles at the right. **420 m²; 420 m²**
    c. **Critical Thinking** Can you conclude that two triangles with equal perimeters and equal areas are similar? Explain.
    No; corres. sides need not be proportional.

29. 1. $\overline{BC} \parallel \overline{DF}$ (Given) 2. ∠*YBC* ≅ ∠*YDF* (If ∥ lines, then corres. ∠s are ≅.) 3. ∠*DYF* ≅ ∠*DYF* (Reflexive Prop. of ≅) 4. △*BYC* ~ △*DYF* (AA~ Post.)

30. 1. $RT \cdot TQ = MT \cdot TS$ (Given) 2. $\frac{MT}{TQ} = \frac{RT}{TS}$ (Prop. of Proportions) 3. ∠*RTM* ≅ ∠*STQ* (Vert. ∠s are ≅.) 4. △*RTM* ~ △*STQ* (SAS~ Thm.)

page 510 Mixed Review

34.

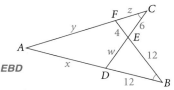

35.

36.

Checkpoint   page 510

7.

509

Reteaching 10-2
Practice 10-2
Practice 10-2

1. State the postulate or theorem you can use to prove the triangles are similar. **SAS Similarity Postulate**

2. Write a similarity statement.
   $\triangle QST \sim \triangle QPR$

3. Find *x*. **17.5**

510

Exercises MIXED REVIEW

Sketch each figure.

32. a regular hexagon   Sample:

33. opposite rays $\vec{RS}$ and $\vec{RB}$ Sample:

34. line ℓ intersecting plane P at point E See margin p. 509 for sample.

Draw a net for each space figure. 35–36. See margin p. 509 for samples.

35. a cube   36. a pyramid with a triangular base

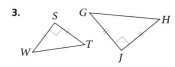

FOR YOUR JOURNAL

Write a brief paragraph explaining why two isosceles triangles with congruent vertex angles are always similar.

Getting Ready for Lesson 10-3

Solve each proportion. Leave your answers in simplest radical form.

37. $\frac{4}{x} = \frac{x}{5}$ $\pm 2\sqrt{5}$ 38. $\frac{3}{m} = \frac{m}{8}$ $\pm 2\sqrt{6}$ 39. $\frac{w}{2} = \frac{20}{w}$ $\pm 2\sqrt{10}$ 40. $\frac{a}{6} = \frac{27}{a}$ $\pm 9\sqrt{2}$

Exercises CHECKPOINT

Are the triangles similar? If so, write the similarity statement and name the postulate or theorem that proves they are similar.

1.

2.

3.

$\triangle ABC \sim \triangle XYZ$; **AA~ Post.** $\triangle LMN \sim \triangle RPQ$; **SSS~ Thm.** $\triangle WST \sim \triangle GJH$; **SAS~ Thm.**

The polygons are similar. Find the values of the variables.

4.   5.

$w = 4.5$; $x = \sqrt{29.25}$

6. In the movie *Ghostbusters*, a giant made of marshmallow roams the streets of New York City. Suppose that a man 6 ft 3 in. tall stands so that the tip of his shadow coincides with the tip of the giant's shadow. The man is 4 ft from the tip of the shadows and 24 ft from the marshmallow giant. How tall is the giant?
   43 ft 9 in.

7. *Open-ended* Sketch two figures that are similar and have a similarity ratio of 2 : 3. See margin p. 509 for sample.

CONNECTING TO PRIOR KNOWLEDGE Have students draw several right triangles and then draw the altitude to the hypotenuse of each triangle. Ask them to make a conjecture about the triangles formed.

WORK TOGETHER

Make sure that students draw the altitude to the hypotenuse, and not the median to the hypotenuse.

Question 4 Help students see that since all of the smaller triangles are similar to the larger triangle, they are similar to each other.

THINK AND DISCUSS

VISUAL LEARNING Copy △ABC three times and use color coding to indicate two pairs of congruent angles in △ABC and △ACD on the first copy, two pairs of congruent angles in △ABC and △CBD on the second copy, and two pairs of congruent angles in △ACD and △CBD on the third copy.

What You'll Learn
- Finding relationships among the lengths of the sides of a right triangle and the altitude to the hypotenuse

...And Why

To find distances by indirect measurement

What You'll Need
- straightedge
- scissors

10-3 *Connections* Recreation ... and more

Similarity in Right Triangles

WORK TOGETHER

Work with a partner.

- Draw one diagonal of a rectangular sheet of paper. Cut the paper on the diagonal to make two congruent right triangles.

- In one of the triangles, use paper folding to locate the altitude to the hypotenuse. Cut the triangle along the altitude to make two smaller right triangles.

- Label the angles of the three triangles as shown.

1. Compare the angles of the three triangles by placing the triangles on top of one another. Which angles have the same measure as ∠1? ∠4, ∠7

2. Which angles have the same measure as ∠2? ∠6, ∠8

3. Which angles have the same measure as ∠3? ∠5, ∠9

4. Based on your results, what is true about the three triangles? The △s are ~.

5. Use the diagram at the left to complete the similarity statement. △RST ~ △■ ~ △■ *RWS; SWT*

THINK AND DISCUSS

Your findings in the Work Together suggest the following theorem.

Theorem 10-3

The altitude to the hypotenuse of a right triangle divides the triangle into two triangles that are similar to the original triangle and to each other.

Given: Right △ABC, $\overline{CD}$ is the altitude to the hypotenuse.
Prove: △ABC ~ △ACD ~ △CBD

Proof of Theorem 10-3

Both smaller triangles are similar to △ABC by the AA Similarity Postulate because they each share an acute angle with △ABC and all three triangles are right triangles. Since both smaller triangles are similar to △ABC, their corresponding angles are congruent. Thus they are similar to each other.

Lesson Planning Options

Prerequisite Skills
- Simplifying radicals
- Using quadratic formula

Assignment Options for Exercises On Your Own

> **Core** 1–28, 32–35
> **Extension** 29–31

Use Mixed Review to maintain skills.

Resources

Student Edition
Skills Handbook, pp. 660, 661, 662
Extra Practice, p. 643
Glossary/Study Guide

Teaching Resources
Chapter Support File, Ch. 10
- Practice 10-3 (two worksheets)
- Reteaching 10-3
Classroom Manager 10-3
Glossary, Spanish Resources

Transparencies
105, 108

511

MAKING CONNECTIONS Just as the arithmetic mean has applications in geometry, the geometric mean has applications in algebra. Have students research these applications and present their findings to the class. Also have students research the harmonic mean and its applications in algebra and music.

Example 1 ....

Help students understand that the proportion can also be written $\frac{18}{x} = \frac{x}{4}$. Also check that students understand how $\sqrt{72}$ was simplified to $6\sqrt{2}$.

ERROR ALERT! Corollaries 1 and 2 Some students may not understand the meaning of "the lengths of the segments of the hypotenuse" and "the segment of the hypotenuse that is adjacent to that leg." **Remediation:** Copy $\triangle ABC$ and label the segments of the hypotenuse and the legs adjacent to the segments.

leg adjacent to $\overline{AD}$ leg adjacent to $\overline{DB}$

segments of the hypotenuse
$\overline{AD}$ and $\overline{DB}$

Additional Examples

FOR EXAMPLE 1 ....

Find the geometric mean of 6 and 20. Leave your answer in simplest radical form. $2\sqrt{30}$

FOR EXAMPLE 2 ....

Solve for x and y.
$2\sqrt{7}; 2\sqrt{3}$

FOR EXAMPLE 3 ....

A road from Taj's house and a road from Sonya's house meet at their school at a right angle. The public pool is 2 mi east of the school and 4 mi north of Sonya's house.

School   Taj's house   Pool

a. What is the distance from Taj's house to the pool? 1 mi

b. What is the distance from Sonya's house to school? $2\sqrt{5}$ mi

---

QUICK REVIEW

In the proportion
$$\frac{a}{b} = \frac{c}{d},$$
b and c are the means.

PROBLEM SOLVING

Look Back Give an alternate definition of geometric mean that does not involve a proportion.

For any 2 pos. numbers a and b, the geometric mean of a and b is $\sqrt{ab}$.

Proportions in which the means are equal occur frequently in geometry. For any two positive numbers a and b, the **geometric mean** of a and b is the positive number x such that $\frac{a}{x} = \frac{x}{b}$.

Example 1 ....

Algebra Find the geometric mean of 4 and 18.

$\frac{4}{x} = \frac{x}{18}$ Write a proportion.

$x^2 = 72$ Use the Cross-Product Property

$x = \sqrt{72}$ Find the positive square root.

$x = 6\sqrt{2}$ Write in simplest radical form.

6. a. Try This Find the geometric mean of 15 and 20. Leave your answer in simplest radical form. $10\sqrt{3}$

b. *Calculator* Find the answer to part (a) rounded to the nearest tenth. 17.3

Two important corollaries of Theorem 10-3 involve the geometric mean.

Corollary 1

The length of the altitude to the hypotenuse of a right triangle is the geometric mean of the lengths of the segments of the hypotenuse.

Proof of Corollary 1

Given: Right $\triangle ABC$,
$\overline{CD}$ is the altitude to the hypotenuse.
Prove: $\frac{AD}{CD} = \frac{CD}{DB}$

By Theorem 10-3, $\triangle CDB \sim \triangle ADC$. Since corresponding sides of similar triangles are proportional, $\frac{AD}{CD} = \frac{CD}{DB}$.

Corollary 2

The altitude to the hypotenuse of a right triangle intersects it so that the length of each leg is the geometric mean of the length of its adjacent segment of the hypotenuse and the length of the entire hypotenuse.

Proof of Corollary 2

Given: Right $\triangle ABC$,
$\overline{CD}$ is the altitude to the hypotenuse.
Prove: $\frac{AB}{AC} = \frac{AC}{AD}, \frac{AB}{CB} = \frac{CB}{DB}$

By Theorem 10-3, $\triangle ABC \sim \triangle ACD$. Their corresponding sides are proportional, so $\frac{AB}{AC} = \frac{AC}{AD}$. Similarly, $\triangle ABC \sim \triangle CBD$ and $\frac{AB}{CB} = \frac{CB}{DB}$.

512

Example 2

Discuss with students how to determine which theorem or corollary to apply to find a missing value. Since *x* is a leg, use Corollary 2, which gives the relationship between the legs and the segments of the hypotenuse. Since *y* is the altitude, use Corollary 1, which gives the relationship between the altitude and the segments of the hypotenuse.

Example 3   Relating to the Real World

Check that students understand that $AB = 500$ because 300, 400, and 500 are a Pythagorean triple, that $\overline{CD}$ is the altitude to $\overline{AB}$ because "walks straight across" means the shortest distance which is perpendicular to the ocean, and that the proportion $\frac{AD}{AC} = \frac{AC}{AB}$ applies Corollary 2.

Question 8 Students can use the results of Example 3 to find $DB = AB - AD = 320$.

Example 2

Solve for *x* and *y*.

Use Corollary 2 to solve for *x*.

$$\frac{4 + 5}{x} = \frac{x}{4}$$
$$x^2 = 36$$
$$x = 6$$

Use Corollary 1 to solve for *y*.

$$\frac{4}{y} = \frac{y}{5}$$
$$y^2 = 20$$
$$y = 2\sqrt{5}$$

7. **Try This** Solve for *x* and *y*. If the answers are not whole numbers, leave them in simplest radical form. **$x = 8; y = 4\sqrt{3}$**

You can use the Corollaries to Theorem 10-3 to find distances.

Example 3   Relating to the Real World

Recreation At the parking lot of a State Park, the 300-m path to the snack bar and the 400-m path to the boat rental shop meet at a right angle. Marla walks straight from the parking lot to the ocean. How far is Marla from the snack bar?

$\overline{CD}$, the perpendicular segment from point *C* to $\overline{AB}$, is the shortest path to the ocean. $\triangle ABC$ is a right triangle. Using Pythagorean triples, $AB = 500$. To find AD, apply Corollary 2.

$$\frac{AD}{AC} = \frac{AC}{AB} \qquad \text{Corollary 2}$$
$$\frac{AD}{300} = \frac{300}{500} \qquad \text{Substitute.}$$
$$500(AD) = 90{,}000 \qquad \text{Cross-Product Property}$$
$$AD = 180 \qquad \text{Divide each side by 500.}$$

Marla is 180 m from the snack bar.

8. How far did Marla walk from the parking lot to the ocean? **240 m**

10-3 Similarity in Right Triangles   **513**

Technology Options

For Exercise 21, students may use graphing software to graph the triangles. For Exercises 20 and 35, students may use a drawing program to draw the triangles.

Prentice Hall Technology

Software
- Secondary Math Lab Toolkit™
- Integrated Math Lab 41
- Computer Item Generator 10-3

Internet
- See the Prentice Hall site. (http://www.phschool.com)

ALTERNATIVE ASSESSMENT Have students work with a partner to choose 5 problems that represent the key topics of the lesson. Have them write the problem, the concept, and the solution for each.

ALGEBRA **Exercises 8–15** Ask students to justify their answers by naming the property they apply.

ALGEBRA **Exercises 16–19** Have students write the proportion they use to find *x*. Check especially Exercises 17–19 where students have to subtract or add to find one of the terms for the proportion.

Exercise 20 Students may want to draw sketches for part a, then adjust their sketches after finding *h* for part b.

Exercise 23 Students use the Pythagorean Theorem to find the length of the highway from Blare to Albany and Corollary 2 to find the distance from Blare to the proposed service station.

---

pages 514–516 On Your Own

20b.

c. Draw a 10 cm segment. At a pt. 2 cm from 1 endpt. draw a ⊥ segment 4 cm long. Draw segments connecting the other endpt. of the 4 cm segment with the endpts. of the 10 cm segment.

1. Complete: △*JKL* ~ △■ ~ △■
   JNK; KNL

Algebra **Find the geometric mean of each pair of numbers. If an answer is not a whole number, leave it in simplest radical form.**

2. 4 and 9 6 **3.** 4 and 10 **4.** 4 and 12 **5.** 3 and 48 12 **6.** 5 and 125 25 **7.** 11 and 1331
                    $2\sqrt{10}$ $4\sqrt{3}$ 121

Algebra **Refer to the figure to complete each proportion.**

8. $\frac{a}{c} = \frac{r}{\blacksquare}$ a **9.** $\frac{a}{c} = \frac{h}{\blacksquare}$ b **10.** $\frac{r}{h} = \frac{a}{\blacksquare}$ b **11.** $\frac{\blacksquare}{h} = \frac{h}{\blacksquare}$ r, s

12. $\frac{\blacksquare}{a} = \frac{a}{\blacksquare}$ **13.** $\frac{\blacksquare}{b} = \frac{b}{\blacksquare}$ **14.** $\frac{h}{a} = \frac{\blacksquare}{c}$ b **15.** $\frac{h}{a} = \frac{\blacksquare}{b}$ s
      c, r   c, s

Algebra **Solve for *x*. If an answer is not a whole number, leave it in simplest radical form.**

16. 9 **17.** 20 **18.** 10 **19.**
        6   *x*   4   *x*
                 40   21   *x* $6\sqrt{3}$
     x 4   ├──50──┤   3   9

20. a. The altitude to the hypotenuse of a right triangle divides the hypotenuse into segments 2 cm and 8 cm long. Find the length *h* of the altitude. **4 cm b–c. See margin.**

   b. Drawing Use the value you found for *h* in part (a), along with the lengths 2 cm and 8 cm, to draw the right triangle accurately.

   c. Writing Explain how you drew the triangle in part (b).

21. Coordinate Geometry $\overline{CD}$ is the altitude to the hypotenuse of right △*ABC*. The coordinates of *A*, *D*, and *B* are (4, 2), (4, 6), and (4, 15), respectively. Find all possible coordinates of point *C*. **(−2, 6), (10, 6)**

22. Algebra The altitude to the hypotenuse of a right triangle divides the hypotenuse into segments whose lengths are in the ratio 1 : 2. The length of the altitude is 8. How long is the hypotenuse? **$12\sqrt{2}$**

23. Civil Engineering Study the plan at the right. A service station will be built on the interstate highway and a road will connect it with Cray. How far from Blare should the service station be located so that the proposed road will be perpendicular to the interstate? How long will the new road be? **18 mi; 24 mi**

Exercise 28 One strategy for solving this problem is to apply Corollary 1 relating the altitude to the segments of the hypotenuse.

Exercise 31 Students will need to use the quadratic formula.

Exercise 32 Another proof of the Pythagorean Theorem is presented.

Exercise 33 Students should begin by making a sketch. They can find the hypotenuse by remembering the proportions of a 30°-60°-90° triangle. The altitude is the side opposite the 60° angle in a right triangle with hypotenuse of length 10.

Exercise 34 Students may want to begin by testing the validity of the corollary in right triangles with side lengths 3, 4, and 5 or 5, 12, and 13.

Algebra Find the values of the variables. If an answer is not a whole number, leave it in simplest radical form.

$x = 12\sqrt{5}$; $y = 12$; $z = 6\sqrt{5}$

24.

$x = 20$; $y = 12$; $z = 15$

25.

$x = 12$; $y = 3\sqrt{7}$; $z = 4\sqrt{7}$

26.

27.

$x = 4$; $y = 2\sqrt{13}$; $z = 3\sqrt{13}$

28. Standardized Test Prep The length of the altitude to the hypotenuse of a right triangle is 8. The length of the hypotenuse is 16. What is the length of one of the segments into which the altitude divides the hypotenuse? **A**

A. 8 **B.** $8\sqrt{2}$ **C.** 4 **D.** $4\sqrt{2}$ **E.** cannot be determined

Algebra Find the value of *x*. If an answer is not a whole number, leave it in simplest radical form.

> **PROBLEM SOLVING HINT**
> Use the Quadratic Formula. (See page 439.)

29. 3

30. 4

31. 4.5

32. Pythagorean Theorem You can use Corollary 2 of Theorem 10-3 to prove the Pythagorean Theorem. Complete the following proof.

Given: Right $\triangle ABC$ with altitude $\overline{CD}$
Prove: $c^2 = a^2 + b^2$

Statements	Reasons
1. Right $\triangle ABC$ with altitude $\overline{CD}$	a. __?__ Given
2. $\frac{c}{a} = \frac{a}{r}, \frac{c}{b} = \frac{b}{q}$	b. __?__ See margin.
c. $\blacksquare = a^2, \blacksquare = b^2$ _cr; cq_	d. __?__ Cross-Product Prop.
3. $cr + cq = a^2 + b^2$	e. __?__ Addition Prop. of =
4. $c(r + q) = a^2 + b^2$	f. __?__ Distributive Prop.
5. $r + q = c$	g. __?__ Segment Addition Post.
6. $c^2 = a^2 + b^2$	h. __?__ Substitution

33. The length of the shorter leg of a 30°-60°-90° triangle is 10 cm. What is the length of the altitude to the hypotenuse? $5\sqrt{3}$ cm

34. a. Lauren thinks she has found a new corollary: The product of the lengths of the two legs of a right triangle is equal to the product of the lengths of the hypotenuse and the altitude from the right angle. Draw a figure for this corollary and write the *Given* and *To Prove*.
b. Critical Thinking Is Lauren's corollary true? Explain. It is true.

a–b. See also margin.

35. Open-ended Draw a right triangle so that the altitude from the right angle to the hypotenuse bisects the hypotenuse.

35.
Sample:

32b. The altitude of the hypotenuse of a rt. $\triangle$ intersects it so that the length of each leg is the geometric mean of the length of its adjacent segment of the hypotenuse and the length of the entire hypotenuse.

34a. Given: Right $\triangle ABC$ with altitude $\overline{CD}$; **Prove:** $BC \cdot CA = AB \cdot CD$

b. Answers may vary. Sample: Yes; each product = twice the area of the $\triangle$.

page 516 Mixed Review

38. The number of people getting dental exams is increasing while the number of extractions is declining. As the total number of patients receiving dental services is increasing, the ratio of exams to extractions is increasing sharply.

39.

515

Chapter Project FIND OUT BY ANALYZING Students discover a pattern in the perimeters of Koch snowflakes. Have students work in groups to complete the questions.

Exercises MIXED REVIEW

ESL Exercises 36–38 Some students may be unfamiliar with the word "extraction." Explain that it means the removal of a tooth.

GETTING READY FOR LESSON 10-4 These exercises prepare students to apply the Side-Splitter Theorem.

Wrap Up

THE BIG IDEA Ask students to explain in their own words the relationships between the lengths of sides of a right triangle and the altitude to the hypotenuse.

RETEACHING ACTIVITY Students use the relationships between the lengths of the sides of a right triangle and the altitude to the hypotenuse to find missing lengths. (Reteaching worksheet 10-3)

Lesson Quiz

Lesson Quiz is also available in Transparencies.

1. Complete:
$\triangle ABC \sim$ __?__ $\sim$ __?__.
$\triangle ADB$; $\triangle BDC$

2. Find x. 4

3. Find y. $2\sqrt{5}$

4. Find z. $3\sqrt{5}$

516

Chapter Project *Find Out by Analyzing*

Use the Stage 3 Koch snowflake shown here and the earlier stages you made in the Find Out question on page 502.

• At each stage, is the snowflake equilateral? **yes**

• Suppose each side of the original triangle is one unit. Complete the table to find the perimeter of each stage.

Stage	Number of sides	Length of a side	Perimeter
0	3	1	3
1	■ 12	$\frac{1}{3}$	■ 4
2	48	$\frac{1}{9}$ ■	$5\frac{1}{3}$ ■
3	■ 192	$\frac{1}{27}$	$7\frac{1}{9}$ ■

• **Patterns** Can you **predict** the perimeter at Stage 4? **mult. by $\frac{4}{3}$; $9\frac{13}{27}$**

• **Inductive Reasoning** Will there be a stage with a perimeter greater than 100 units? Explain. **The perimeter exceeds 100 at Stage 13.**

Stage 3

Exercises MIXED REVIEW

Data Analysis Use the graph showing the percent of people in the United States who received dental services.

36. In which year did more people have an extraction than a dental exam? **1959**

37. Between which years did the percent of the population having a dental exam increase the most? **1979–1989**

38. **Critical Thinking** Compare the ratio of dental exams to extractions for each year. What trend do you see in dental services? **See margin p. 515.**

39. Draw a rectangular prism in two-point perspective.
See margin p. 515 for sample.

Percent of U.S. Population Receiving Dental Services

Getting Ready for Lesson 10-4

Find the length of the midsegment of each trapezoid or triangle.

40.

7 cm
16 cm
11.5 cm

41.
15 mm
7.5 mm

42.

8 ft
18 ft
13 ft

43.

13 in.
16 in.
14.5 in.

CONNECTING TO PRIOR KNOWLEDGE Draw the following triangle and ask students to explain which pairs of angles are congruent.

Question 1 Students should discover that the equivalency of the ratios does not depend on the shape of the triangle or the distance between the parallel lines.

VISUAL LEARNING Copy the diagram and the proportion. Color code the segment name in the proportion and the segment in the diagram to help students visualize the relationship.

What You'll Learn
• Investigating proportional relationships in triangles

...And Why
To find lengths of material needed to make a sail and to determine distances on a city map

What You'll Need
• geometry software

Connections 🌐 *Sail Making . . . and more*

10–4 Proportions and Similar Triangles

W O R K   T O G E T H E R

🖳 Work with a partner. Use geometry software.

■ Construct $\triangle ABC$ and a point D on $\overline{AB}$.

■ Construct a line through D parallel to $\overline{AC}$.

■ Construct the intersection E of the parallel line with $\overline{BC}$.

■ Measure $\overline{BD}$, $\overline{DA}$, $\overline{BE}$, and $\overline{EC}$.

■ Calculate the ratios $\frac{BD}{DA}$ and $\frac{BE}{EC}$.

1. **Patterns** Compare the ratios $\frac{BD}{DA}$ and $\frac{BE}{EC}$ as you move the parallel line $\overleftrightarrow{DE}$ and as you change the shape of the triangle. $\frac{BD}{DA} = \frac{BE}{EC}$

T H I N K   A N D   D I S C U S S

Part 1 Using the Side-Splitter Theorem

In the Work Together you discovered the following relationship.

Theorem 10-4
Side-Splitter Theorem

If a line is parallel to one side of a triangle and intersects the other two sides, then it divides those sides proportionally.

Proof of Theorem 10-4

Given: $\triangle QXY$ with $\overleftrightarrow{RS} \parallel \overleftrightarrow{XY}$
Prove: $\frac{XR}{RQ} = \frac{YS}{SQ}$

Statements	Reasons
1. $\overleftrightarrow{RS} \parallel \overleftrightarrow{XY}$	1. Given
2. $\angle 1 \cong \angle 3$, $\angle 2 \cong \angle 4$	2. If $\parallel$ lines, then corr. $\angle$s are $\cong$.
3. $\triangle QXY \sim \triangle QRS$	3. AA $\sim$ Postulate
4. $\frac{XQ}{RQ} = \frac{YQ}{SQ}$	4. Corresponding sides of $\sim$ triangles are proportional.
5. $XQ = XR + RQ$, $YQ = YS + SQ$	5. Segment Addition Postulate
6. $\frac{XR + RQ}{RQ} = \frac{YS + SQ}{SQ}$	6. Substitution
7. $\frac{XR}{RQ} = \frac{YS}{SQ}$	7. A Property of Proportions

---

Lesson Planning Options

Prerequisite Skills

• Using geometry software to construct triangles, parallel lines, and angle bisectors

Assignment Options for Exercises On Your Own

To provide flexible scheduling, this lesson can be subdivided into parts.

▼1 **Core** 2–3, 6–7, 10–11, 27–31, 35
Extension 24

▼2 **Core** 1, 4–5, 8–9, 12–23, 25–26, 34
Extension 32–33

Use Mixed Review to maintain skills.

Resources

📖 **Student Edition**
Skills Handbook, pp. 646, 650
Extra Practice, p. 643
Glossary/Study Guide

📁 **Teaching Resources**
Chapter Support File, Ch. 10
• Practice 10-4 (two worksheets)
• Reteaching 10-4
Classroom Manager 10-4
Glossary, Spanish Resources

🏛 **Transparencies**
105, 109

517

Corollary to Theorem 10-4 Help students understand that the parallel lines divide the transversals into proportional segments, not congruent segments.

Example 1 Relating to the Real World ·················

Make sure students understand that the pieces of the sail are cut and sewn so the bases of the pieces are parallel.

ESL To help students understand the phrases "sail maker," "chalk outline," and "cutting floor," have them use the appropriate dictionary to learn how to express them in their native languages.

DIVERSITY Have students who have sailed in a sailboat share their experiences with the class.

CRITICAL THINKING Ask students how they could use the Side-Splitter Theorem to find y.

Additional Examples

FOR EXAMPLE 1 ·····························

Find the length of *x* and *y* on the sail. **4.5 ft; 2 ft**

Discussion: *What theorem or corollary did you apply to find x? to find y?*

FOR EXAMPLE 2 ·····························

Find the value of *x*. **4.5**

Discussion: *What theorem or corollary did you apply to find x?*

518

2. **Try This** Use the Side-Splitter Theorem to find the value of *x* in each diagram.
a. **8**
b.

The following corollary can be easily derived from the Side-Splitter Theorem. You will prove this corollary in Exercise 24.

| **Corollary to Theorem 10-4** | If three parallel lines intersect two transversals, then the segments intercepted on the transversals are proportional. $\frac{a}{b} = \frac{c}{d}$ | |

Example 1 Relating to the Real World ············

Sail Making Sail makers use computers to create a pattern for every sail they make. Then they draw a chalk outline on the cutting floor. After they cut out the panels of the sail, they sew them together to form the sail. The panel seams are parallel. Find the lengths *x* and *y*.

$$\frac{2}{x} = \frac{1.5}{1.5}$$ Use the Side-Splitter Theorem.

$$x = 2$$

$$\frac{3}{2} = \frac{y}{1.5}$$ Use the Corollary to Theorem 10-4.

$$3(1.5) = 2y$$ Use the Cross-Product Property.

$$\frac{3(1.5)}{2} = y$$ Divide each side by 2.

$$2.25 = y$$ Simplify.

Length *x* is 2 ft and length *y* is 2.25 ft. ■

3. **Try This** Solve for *x* and *y*. *x* = 18; *y* = 27.5

Check that students construct point *D* correctly so that when they manipulate the triangle in Question 4, *D* remains the point of intersection of the angle bisector and $\overline{CB}$.

Explain to students that in the proof of the Triangle-Angle-Bisector Theorem, $\overleftrightarrow{BE}$ must be drawn in order to apply the Side-Splitter Theorem.

Example 2

ERROR ALERT! Some students may confuse the Triangle-Angle-Bisector Theorem with Corollary 2 of Theorem 10-3 and write $\frac{PR}{PS} = \frac{PS}{PQ}$. **Remediation:** Reinforce that Theorem 10-3 and its corollaries apply to right triangles, and that the Triangle-Angle-Bisector Theorem states that the two segments formed by the angle bisector are proportional to the other two sides of the triangle.

Part 2

WORK TOGETHER

▷ Work with a partner. Use geometry software.

- Construct △*ABC* and the bisector of ∠*A*. Label point *D*, the intersection of the bisector and $\overline{CB}$.
- Measure $\overline{BD}$, $\overline{BA}$, $\overline{CD}$, and $\overline{CA}$.
- Calculate the ratios $\frac{CD}{DB}$ and $\frac{CA}{BA}$.

4. **Patterns** Compare the ratios as you change the triangle.
$$\frac{CD}{DB} = \frac{CA}{BA}$$

THINK AND DISCUSS

Using the Triangle-Angle-Bisector Theorem

In the Work Together you discovered the following relationship.

Theorem 10-5 Triangle-Angle-Bisector Theorem	If a ray bisects an angle of a triangle, then it divides the opposite side into two segments that are proportional to the other two sides of the triangle.

Proof of Theorem 10-5

Given: △*ABC*, $\overrightarrow{AD}$ bisects ∠*CAB*.
Prove: $\frac{CD}{DB} = \frac{CA}{BA}$

Draw $\overleftrightarrow{BE} \parallel \overline{DA}$.

Extend $\overline{CA}$ to meet $\overleftrightarrow{BE}$ at point *F*.
By the Side-Splitter Theorem, $\frac{CD}{DB} = \frac{CA}{AF}$. By the Corresponding Angles Theorem, ∠3 ≅ ∠1. Since $\overrightarrow{AD}$ bisects ∠*CAB*, ∠1 ≅ ∠2. By the Alternate Interior Angles Theorem, ∠2 ≅ ∠4. Using the Transitive Property of Congruence, you know that ∠3 ≅ ∠4. By the Converse of the Isosceles Triangle Theorem, *AF* = *AB*. Substituting *BA* for *AF*, $\frac{CD}{DB} = \frac{CA}{BA}$.

Example 2

Find the value of *x*.

$$\frac{PS}{SR} = \frac{PQ}{RQ} \qquad \text{Use the Triangle-Angle-Bisector Theorem.}$$
$$\frac{x}{6} = \frac{8}{5} \qquad \text{Substitute.}$$
$$x = \frac{6 \cdot 8}{5} = 9.6$$

5. **Answers may vary. Sample:**

5. Use the diagram in Example 2 and the properties of proportions to write four equivalent proportions.

Technology Options

For Exercise 32, students may draw the dilations using geometry software. For Exercise 33, students may draw and measure the triangles using geometry software.

Prentice Hall Technology

Software
- Secondary Math Lab Toolkit™
- Integrated Math Lab 42
- Computer Item Generator 10-4

Internet
- See the Prentice Hall site. (http://www.phschool.com)

519

Exercises ON YOUR OWN

Use the figure at the right to complete each proportion.

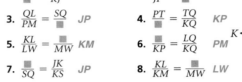

1. $\dfrac{RS}{\blacksquare} = \dfrac{JR}{KJ}$ **KS**

2. $\dfrac{KJ}{JP} = \dfrac{KS}{\blacksquare}$ **SQ**

3. $\dfrac{QL}{PM} = \dfrac{SQ}{\blacksquare}$ **JP**

4. $\dfrac{PT}{\blacksquare} = \dfrac{TQ}{KQ}$ **KP**

5. $\dfrac{KL}{LW} = \dfrac{\blacksquare}{MW}$ **KM**

6. $\dfrac{\blacksquare}{KP} = \dfrac{LQ}{KQ}$ **PM**

7. $\dfrac{\blacksquare}{SQ} = \dfrac{JK}{KS}$ **JP**

8. $\dfrac{KL}{KM} = \dfrac{\blacksquare}{MW}$ **LW**

Algebra Solve for x.

9. **6**

10. **7.5**

11. **7.5**

12. **4.8**

13. $3\frac{1}{3}$

14. **35**

15. **3.6**

16. **8**

17. **Geography** In Washington, D.C., 17th, 18th, 19th, and 20th Streets are parallel streets that intersect Pennsylvania Avenue and I Street.
   a. How long (to the nearest foot) is Pennsylvania Avenue between 19th Street and 18th Street? **559 ft**
   b. How long (to the nearest foot) is Pennsylvania Avenue between 18th Street and 17th Street? **671 ft**

The United States Capitol viewed from Pennsylvania Avenue

18. The legs of a right triangle are 5 cm and 12 cm long. Find the lengths, to the nearest tenth, of the segments into which the bisector of the right angle divides the hypotenuse. **3.8 cm, 9.2 cm**

PROBLEM SOLVING HINT
Draw a diagram.

pages 520–523 On Your Own

23a.

19. *Standardized Test Prep* In a triangle, the bisector of an angle divides the opposite side into two segments with lengths 6 cm and 9 cm. Which of the following can be the lengths of the other two sides of the triangle? **D**
   I. 4 cm and 6 cm   **II.** 20 cm and 30 cm   **III.** 12 cm and 18 cm
   A. I only   **B.** II only   **C.** I and II   **D.** II and III   **E.** I, II, and III

Algebra **Solve for x.**

20.
20

21. **2.5**

22. **9**

23. *Critical Thinking* Sharell draws $\triangle ABC$. She finds that the bisector of $\angle C$ bisects the opposite side.
   a. Sketch $\triangle ABC$ and the bisector. **See margin for sample.**
   b. What type of triangle is $\triangle ABC$? Explain your reasoning.

   b. Isosceles; use the Triangle-Angle-Bisector Thm.

24. Answer the following questions to prove the Corollary to the Side-Splitter Theorem.

   Given: $\overleftrightarrow{AW} \parallel \overleftrightarrow{BX} \parallel \overleftrightarrow{CY}$
   Prove: $\dfrac{AB}{BC} = \dfrac{WX}{XY}$

   Begin by drawing $\overleftrightarrow{WC}$, intersecting $\overline{BX}$ at point Z.
   a. Apply the Side-Splitter Theorem to $\triangle ACW$: $\dfrac{\blacksquare}{\blacksquare} = \dfrac{WZ}{ZC}$. **AB; BC**

   b. Apply the Side-Splitter Theorem to $\triangle CWY$: $\dfrac{WZ}{ZC} = \dfrac{\blacksquare}{\blacksquare}$. **WX; XY**
   c. Substitute to prove the corollary. $\dfrac{AB}{BC} = \dfrac{WX}{XY}$

25. An angle bisector of a triangle divides the opposite side of the triangle into segments 5 cm and 3 cm long. One side of the triangle is 7.5 cm long. Find all possible lengths for the third side of the triangle. **4.5 cm; 12.5 cm**

26. *Surveying* The perimeter of the triangular lot at the right is 50 m. The surveyor's tape bisects an angle. Find lengths x and y. (*Hint:* You can use a system of linear equations. See Skills Handbook page 667.)
   $x = 18$; $y = 12$

521

27a. If a line that intersects 2 sides of a △ divides them proportionally, then the line is ∥ to the 3rd side.

b. Answers may vary.
Sample:

Given: $\frac{QR}{RX} = \frac{QS}{SY}$

Prove: $\overline{RS} \parallel \overline{XY}$

Plan for Proof: To prove that $\overline{RS} \parallel \overline{XY}$, show that $\angle 3 \cong \angle 1$. To prove that $\angle 3 \cong \angle 1$, prove that $\triangle QRS \sim \triangle QXY$ by the SAS ~ Thm.

35. Measure *AC, CE* and *BD.* Using the Side-Splitter Thm., $\frac{AC}{CE} = \frac{AB}{BD}$. Then, $AB = \frac{BD \cdot AC}{CE}$.

27. a. *Logical Reasoning* Write the converse of the Side-Splitter Theorem.
   b. Draw a diagram, state the *Given* and *To Prove* for the converse, and write a Plan for Proof. a–b. See margin.

Determine whether the red segments are parallel. Explain each answer. You can use the result of Exercise 27.

28.

yes; $\frac{6}{10} = \frac{9}{15}$

29.

yes; $\frac{15}{12} = \frac{20}{16}$

30.

no; $\frac{12}{28} \neq \frac{10}{24}$

31.

yes; $\frac{45}{63} = \frac{55}{77}$

32. *Technology* Claire used geometry software to draw the red triangle. She dilated it with center (0, 0) and scale factor $\frac{3}{2}$ to get the blue triangle. Then she dilated the blue triangle with center (0, 0) and scale factor $\frac{1}{3}$ to get the green triangle.
   a. What is the scale factor of the dilation of the red triangle to the green one? $\frac{1}{2}$
   b. The scale factor of the dilation of the green triangle to the red one is 2. What is the scale factor of the dilation of the green triangle to the blue one? 3

33. *Geometry in 3 Dimensions* In the pyramid at the right, $\overleftrightarrow{FG} \parallel \overleftrightarrow{AB}$ and $\overleftrightarrow{GH} \parallel \overleftrightarrow{BC}$, $AF = 2$, $FE = 4$, and $BG = 3$.
   a. Find *GE*. 6
   b. If *EH* = 5, find *HC*. 2.5
   c. If *FG* = 3, find the perimeter of $\triangle ABE$. 19.5

34. The legs of a right triangle are 6 cm and 8 cm long. The bisector of the right angle divides the **a. Check students' work.** hypotenuse into two segments.
   a. Draw a sketch of the right triangle with its angle bisector.
   b. Find the lengths of these segments to the nearest tenth. 4.3 cm, 5.7 cm

35. *Writing* Describe how you could use the figure at the right to find the length of the oil spill indirectly. What measurements and calculations would you use?
Answers may vary. See margin for sample.

522

Chapter Project   *Find Out by Doing*

Fractals have three important properties:

- You can form them by repeating steps in a process called *iteration*.
- You can continue until the steps become too small to draw. Even then the steps could continue in your mind—there are an infinite number of iterations.
- At each stage, a portion of the figure is a reduced copy of the entire figure at the previous stage. This property is called *self-similarity*.
- The diagrams below show Stages 0, 1, and 2 for a fractal tree. Make larger copies of these stages and draw the next stage.

1 unit

Stage 0   Stage 1   Stage 2

Exercises   M I X E D   R E V I E W

Transformations $\triangle ABC$ has vertices $A(3, -1)$, $B(0, -8)$, and $C(-2, 4)$. **Find the coordinates of the vertices of its image under each transformation.**

36. reflection in the *x*-axis

37. rotation 90° counterclockwise about the origin

38. translation 4 units right and 6 units up
     A'(7, 5), B'(4, −2), C'(2, 10)

39. reflection in the line $y = -x$
     A'(1, −3), B'(8, 0), C'(−4, 2)

36. A'(3, 1), B'(0, 8), C'(−2, −4)

37. A'(1, 3), B'(8, 0), C'(−4, −2)

40. On Museum Wharf in Boston, Massachusetts, there is a sandwich shop shaped like a giant milk bottle. It is 40 ft tall and has a circumference of 58 ft at its base. What is the approximate circumference of a similar bottle with a height of 24 cm?   34.8 cm

Getting Ready for Lesson 10-5

Find the area and perimeter of each figure.

41.   49 in.²; 28 in.
    7 in.

42.   32 m², 24 m
    4 m
    8 m

43.   6 cm
    8 cm
    24 cm²; 24 cm

44.   10 ft
    $25\sqrt{3}$ ft²; 30 ft

10-4 Proportions and Similar Triangles   523

523

PROBLEM OF THE DAY

The images show the front and side views of an object. What would a three-dimensional view of the object look like?

 side

 front

Problem of the Day is also available in Transparencies.

CONNECTING TO PRIOR KNOWLEDGE Draw a triangle, rectangle, and trapezoid, labeling the base(s) and height of each. Have students find the areas.

If students use centimeter graph paper, the largest scale factor they can choose is 5. Provide graph paper with smaller squares to accommodate similar figures with large scale factors.

TACTILE LEARNING Students can use geoboards to create the similar rectangles. Because geoboards have fewer "squares" than graph paper, you may want to have students start with a 2-unit by 3-unit rectangle and restrict the choice of scale factors.

Question 3 Students may need to simplify ratios in order to recognize the relationship between the ratios of the perimeters and the ratios of the areas.

Lesson Planning Options

Prerequisite Skills

- Finding the areas of polygons

Assignment Options for Exercises On Your Own

Core 1–7, 9–21, 23
Extension 8, 22

Use Mixed Review to maintain skills.

Resources

Student Edition

Skills Handbook, p. 648, 659
Extra Practice, p. 643
Glossary/Study Guide

Teaching Resources

Chapter Support File, Ch. 10
- Practice 10-5 (two worksheets)
- Reteaching 10-5
- Alternative Activity 10-5
Classroom Manager 10-5
Glossary, Spanish Resources

Transparencies

18, 19, 106, 110

Connections Community Service . . . and more

10-5 Perimeters and Areas of Similar Figures

What You'll Learn

- Finding the relationships between the similarity ratio and the perimeters and areas of similar figures

...And Why

To determine the perimeter or area of a figure when you know the perimeter or area of a similar figure

What You'll Need

- graph paper
- calculator

WORK TOGETHER

Work with a partner to investigate perimeters and areas of similar rectangles.

In the corner of a sheet of graph paper, draw a 3 unit-by-4 unit rectangle as shown at the right.

Choose three scale factors from the set {2, 3, 4, . . . , 10}. Using the three scale factors and point *A* as the center, draw three dilations of the rectangle. Label them Rectangles I, II, and III.

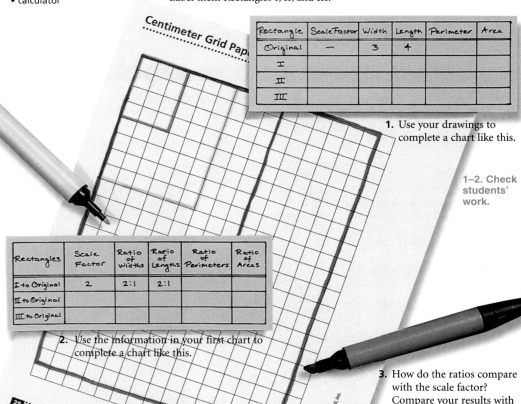

Rectangle	Scale Factor	Width	Length	Perimeter	Area
Original	–	3	4		
I					
II					
III					

1. Use your drawings to complete a chart like this.

1–2. Check students' work.

Rectangles	Scale Factor	Ratio of Widths	Ratio of Lengths	Ratio of Perimeters	Ratio of Areas
I to Original	2	2:1	2:1		
II to Original					
III to Original					

2. Use the information in your first chart to complete a chart like this.

3. How do the ratios compare with the scale factor? Compare your results with the results of other groups.
See margin p. 527.

THINK AND DISCUSS

Rectangle I is similar to Rectangle II with a similarity ratio of $1 : k$. You can use algebra to simplify the ratio of their perimeters and the ratio of their areas.

$$\frac{\text{Perimeter of Rect. I}}{\text{Perimeter of Rect. II}} = \frac{2l + 2w}{2(kl) + 2(kw)}$$
$$= \frac{2l + 2w}{k(2l + 2w)} = \frac{1}{k}$$

$$\frac{\text{Area of Rect. I}}{\text{Area of Rect. II}} = \frac{lw}{(kl)(kw)}$$
$$= \frac{lw}{(k^2)(lw)} = \frac{1}{k^2}$$

4. How do these algebraic results compare with the results you obtained in the Work Together? **The results agree.**

5. **Try This** Triangle I is similar to Triangle II with a similarity ratio of $1 : 2$. Find each ratio.

   a. $\dfrac{\text{Perimeter of Triangle I}}{\text{Perimeter of Triangle II}}$ $\frac{1}{2}$ b. $\dfrac{\text{Area of Triangle I}}{\text{Area of Triangle II}}$ $\frac{1}{4}$

6. **Try This** Trapezoid I is similar to Trapezoid II with a similarity ratio of $2 : 3$. Find each ratio.

   $\frac{2}{3}$ a. $\dfrac{\text{Perimeter of Trapezoid I}}{\text{Perimeter of Trapezoid II}}$ b. $\dfrac{\text{Area of Trapezoid I}}{\text{Area of Trapezoid II}}$ $\frac{4}{9}$

7. Any two circles are similar. If the radii of two circles are r and kr, find the ratios of their circumferences and their areas. $\frac{1}{k}$; $\frac{1}{k^2}$

The results you obtained above for rectangles, triangles, trapezoids, and circles are generalized for all similar figures in the following theorem.

Theorem 10-6
Perimeters and Areas of Similar Figures

If the similarity ratio of two similar figures is $a : b$, then (1) the ratio of their perimeters is $a : b$, and (2) the ratio of their areas is $a^2 : b^2$.

Example 1

⊞ **Calculator** The area of the smaller regular pentagon is about 27.5 cm². Find the area A of the larger regular pentagon.

Any two regular pentagons are similar. The ratio of the lengths of the corresponding sides is $\frac{4}{10}$, or $\frac{2}{5}$. The ratio of the area is $\frac{2^2}{5^2}$, or $\frac{4}{25}$.

$$\frac{4}{25} = \frac{27.5}{A}$$
$A \approx 25$ ☒ 27.5 ⊟ 4 ▤ 171.875

The area of the larger pentagon is about 172 cm².

8. **Try This** What is the area of a regular pentagon with sides 16 cm long? Round your answer to the nearest square centimeter. **440 cm²**

4 cm   10 cm

Example 2 Relating to the Real World

It is assumed that the number of bushels of corn harvested varies directly with the area of the plot of land.

Explain to students that the lengths of the plots are ℓ and 2.5ℓ for some $\ell > 0$, not 1 and 2.5. Likewise, the widths of the plots are w and $2.5w$ for some $w > 0$.

DIVERSITY Some students, especially those in rural areas, may be surprised to learn that some people living in cities cannot plant gardens because they do not have enough land around the apartment or house they live in. However, these people can often lease space in a community garden in which to grow their own vegetables and flowers.

Example 3

ERROR ALERT! Students may simplify $\frac{a^2}{b^2} = \frac{25}{49}$ by dividing the numerators and denominators by two instead of taking the square roots of the numerators and denominators.
Remediation: Review the meaning of an exponent and have students practice solving equations such as $a^2 = 25$ and $b^2 = 49$.

EXTENSION Have students work in groups to answer the following question: *By what amount would the side lengths of a regular n-gon be multiplied to produce a similar figure whose area is twice the area of the original figure? three times the area?*

Technology Options

For Exercise 13, students may use geometry software to draw the triangles. For Exercise 17, students may use geometry software to graph the quadrilateral and find the image under the dilation.

Prentice Hall Technology

 Software
• Secondary Math Lab Toolkit™
• Computer Item Generator 10-5

 CD-ROM
• Multimedia Geometry Lab 10

 Internet
• See the Prentice Hall site.
(http://www.phschool.com)

526

Example 2 Relating to the Real World

Community Service During the summer, a group of high school students used a plot of town land to grow 13 bushels of vegetables, which they gave to shelters for the homeless. Their project was so successful that next summer the town will let them use a larger, similar plot of land where each dimension is two and a half times the dimension of the original plot. How much can they expect to grow?

The ratio of the dimensions is 2.5 : 1, so the ratio of the areas of the two plots is $(2.5)^2 : 1^2$, or 6.25 : 1. With 6.25 times as much land they can expect to raise 6.25 times as much, or about 81 bushels.

9. Try This The similarity ratio of the dimensions of two similar pieces of window glass is 3 : 5. If the smaller piece costs $2.50, what should be the cost of the larger piece? $6.95

When you know the ratio of the areas of two similar figures, you can work backward to find the ratio of their perimeters.

Example 3

The areas of two similar triangles are 50 cm² and 98 cm². What is the ratio of their perimeters?

First find the similarity ratio $a : b$.

$\frac{a^2}{b^2} = \frac{50}{98}$ The ratio of the areas is $a^2 : b^2$.

$\frac{a^2}{b^2} = \frac{25}{49}$ Simplify $\frac{50}{98}$.

$\frac{a}{b} = \frac{5}{7}$ Find the square root of each side.

The ratio of the perimeters equals the similarity ratio 5 : 7.

10. Try This The areas of two similar rectangles are 1875 ft² and 135 ft². Find the ratio of their perimeters. $5\sqrt{5} : 3$

Exercises   O N   Y O U R   O W N

Exercises 1–3 Check that students write the ratio of the first figure to the second one, even when the first figure is larger than the second one.

DATA ANALYSIS Exercise 8a Ask students to draw a more appropriate pictograph.

RESEARCH Exercise 8b *USA Today* is a good source of pictographs.

TRANSFORMATIONS Exercise 10 Have students calculate the area by finding the similarity ratio and setting up a proportion. Then have them check their answer by copying the diagram, drawing $\overline{W'S'}$, and finding the area of each quadrilateral as the sum of the areas of two triangles.

Exercise 11 Make sure students read this problem carefully. The area of the smaller square, not the side length, is 4. Remind students to pay close attention to the units given.

Exercises   O N   Y O U R   O W N

For each pair of similar figures, give the ratio of the perimeters and the ratio of the areas of the first figure to the second one.

1. $\frac{1}{2}; \frac{1}{4}$

2 in.   4 in.

2. $\frac{4}{3}; \frac{16}{9}$

8 cm   6 cm

3. $\frac{2}{3}; \frac{4}{9}$

14 m   21 m

What is the similarity ratio of each pair of similar figures?

4. two circles with areas $2\pi\ cm^2$ and $200\pi\ cm^2$ $\frac{1}{10}$

5. two regular octagons with areas $4\ ft^2$ and $16\ ft^2$ $\frac{1}{2}$

6. two triangles with areas $80\ m^2$ and $20\ m^2$ 2

7. two trapezoids with areas $49\ cm^2$ and $9\ cm^2$ $\frac{7}{3}$

8a. The similarity ratio is 1 : 2, so the ratio of the areas is 1 : 4.

8. a. *Data Analysis* A reporter used the pictograph at the right to show that the number of houses with more than two televisions has doubled in the past few years. Why is such a pictograph misleading?

b. *Research* Find examples in magazines or newspapers in which areas of similar figures give misleading information. **Check students' work.**

9. *Remodeling* It costs the Johnsons $216 to have a 9 ft-by-12 ft wooden floor refinished. At that rate, how much would it cost them to have a 12 ft-by-16 ft wooden floor refinished? **$384**

10. *Transformations* $R'S'T'W'$ is the image of $RSTW$ under a dilation with center $(1, 1)$. How do the areas of $RSTW$ and $R'S'T'W'$ compare? Explain. **The ratio of the areas is 1 : 9; the scale factor is 3.**

11. *Drawing* Draw a square with an area of $4\ in.^2$. Draw a second square with an area that is four times as large. What is the ratio of their perimeters? **2 : 1**

12. The area of a regular decagon is $50\ cm^2$. What is the area of a regular decagon with sides four times the length of the smaller decagon? **800 cm²**

13. In $\triangle RST$, $RS = 20$ m, $ST = 25$ m, and $RT = 40$ m.
   a. *Open-ended* Choose a convenient scale. Then use a compass and a metric ruler to draw $\triangle R'S'T' \sim \triangle RST$.
   b. *Constructions* Construct an altitude of $\triangle R'S'T'$ and measure its length. Find the area of $\triangle R'S'T'$. **a–c. See margin.**
   c. *Estimation* Estimate the area of $\triangle RST$.

14. The area of the smaller triangle shown at the right is $24\ cm^2$. Solve for x and y. $x = 4\sqrt{2}$ cm; $y = 6\sqrt{2}$ cm

8 cm   12 cm

---

page 524 Work Together

3. The ratios of lengths, widths, and perimeters = the scale factor; the ratio of areas = the square of the scale factor.

pages 527–529 On Your Own

13a. Answers may vary. Sample: Use 1 : 1000 scale.

10 m

b. Answers may vary. For sample in part (a): 10 mm; 200 mm²

c. Estimates may vary slightly. Sample: 200 m²

16a. The lengths of the sides of the 2nd polygon are k times the lengths of the sides of the 1st polygon.

17a.

21a.

b. For sample in part (a): 91 mm; 320 mm^2

c. 455 yd; 8000 yd^2

23. Answers may vary. Sample: The proposed playground is more than adequate. The number of students is approximately double the earlier number. The area of the proposed playground is 4 times as large as the area of the orig. playground.

528

15. The areas of two similar rectangles are 27 in.^{2} and 48 in.^{2}. The longer side of the larger rectangle is 16 in. long. What is the length of the longer side of the smaller rectangle? **12 in.**

16. a. Transformations If a dilation with scale factor k maps a polygon onto a second polygon, what is the relationship between the lengths of the corresponding sides of the polygons? **See margin.**
   b. Complete: A dilation with scale factor k maps any polygon to a similar polygon whose area is ▓ times as large. k^2

17. a. Transformations Graph $ABCD$ with vertices $A(4, 0)$, $B(-2, 4)$, $C(-4, 2)$, and $D(0, -2)$. Then graph its image $A'B'C'D'$ under the dilation with center $(0, 0)$ and scale factor $\frac{3}{2}$. **See margin.**
   b. The area of $ABCD$ is 22 square units. What is the area of $A'B'C'D'$? **49.5 units^2**

Find the ratio of the perimeters and the ratio of the areas of the blue figure to the red one.

18. $\frac{5}{2}$; $\frac{25}{4}$ **19.** $\frac{8}{3}$; $\frac{64}{9}$ **20.** $\frac{3}{2}$; $\frac{9}{4}$

21a–c. See margin for samples.
21. a. Surveying A surveyor measured one side and two angles of a field as shown in the diagram. Use a ruler and a protractor to draw a similar triangle.
   b. Measure the sides and an altitude of your triangle and find its perimeter and area.
   c. Estimation Estimate the perimeter and area of the field.

22. a. Find the area of a regular hexagon with sides 2 cm long. Leave your answer in simplest radical form. $6\sqrt{3}$ cm^2
   b. Use your answer to part (a) and the ratio of the areas of similar polygons to find the areas of these regular hexagons. **See above.**

22b. $54\sqrt{3}$ cm^2; $\frac{27\sqrt{3}}{2}$ cm^2; $96\sqrt{3}$ cm^2

23. Writing The enrollment at an elementary school is going to increase from 200 students to 395 students. The local parents' group is planning to increase the playground area from 100 ft by 200 ft to a larger area that is 200 ft by 400 ft. What would you tell the parents' group when they ask your opinion about whether the new playground area will be large enough? **See margin.**

JOURNAL Have students share their journal entries with a partner. Partners should critique the entries for clarity, accuracy, and thoroughness. Then allow students to revise their entries.

GETTING READY FOR LESSON 10-6 These exercises prepare students to find the relationship between the similarity ratio and the ratio of areas and volumes of similar solids.

Wrap Up

THE BIG IDEA Ask students to write a word problem which can be solved by using the ratio of areas or perimeters.

RETEACHING ACTIVITY Students find the ratio of perimeters and areas of similar figures. (Reteaching worksheet 10-5)

Exercises | **CHECKPOINT**

In this Checkpoint, your students will assess their own progress in Lessons 10-3 to 10-5.

ALGEBRA Exercises 1–4 Have students explain how they found their answers by stating the theorem, postulate, or corollary they applied.

Exercises 5–8 Remind students that they can simplify the ratios of the areas before taking the square roots of the numerators and denominators.

Chapter Project *Find Out by Thinking*

What is the area of the Koch snowflake? At each stage you increase the area by adding more and more equilateral triangles. Suppose the area of Stage 0 is 1 square unit. Copy the diagrams and explain why the area of the Koch snowflake will never be greater than 2 square units.

Stage 0
1 square unit of area

The entire snowflake at each stage will be inside the regular hexagon. The area of the hexagon is 2 units^2, so the area of the snowflake is always < 2 units^2.

Exercises | **MIXED REVIEW**

Find the length of the hypotenuse of a right triangle with the given legs. Leave your answers in simplest radical form.

24. 8 cm, 9 cm
$\sqrt{145}$ cm

25. 3 in., 5 in.
$\sqrt{34}$ in.

26. 10 mm, 5mm
$5\sqrt{5}$ mm

27. Drawing Use a protractor to draw a regular octagon.
Check students' work.

Getting Ready for Lesson 10-6

Find the volume and surface area of each space figure.

28. cube with a 3-in. side
27 in.^{3}; 54 in.^{2}

29. 3 m-by-5 m-by-9 m rectangular prism
135 m^3; 174 m^2

 FOR YOUR JOURNAL

In your own words, explain the relationship among the similarity ratio of two similar polygons, the ratio of their perimeters, and the ratio of their areas. Include an example.

Exercises | **CHECKPOINT**

Algebra **Find the values of the variables.**

1.

$x = 15;\ z = 10\sqrt{3}$

2.
7.5
8, 12, 5, x

3.
$4\sqrt{5}$
y, 5, 16

4.

x, 2, 3, y, 5, 6
$x = 1\frac{2}{3};\ y = 3\frac{3}{5}$

Find the ratios of the perimeters of these similar figures.

5. two triangles with areas 4 ft^2 and 16 ft^2 $\frac{1}{2}$

6. two kites with areas 100 cm^2 and 25 cm^2 2

7. two squares with areas 63 m^2 and 7 m^2 3

8. two hexagons with areas 18 in.^{2} and 128 in.^{2} $\frac{3}{8}$

9. Standardized Test Prep In $\triangle ABC$, $\overrightarrow{BD}$ bisects $\angle B$. Which of the following is true? **D**

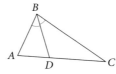

A. $\frac{AD}{CD} = \frac{CD}{DB}$

B. $\frac{AB}{CB} = \frac{CB}{DB}$

C. $\frac{AB}{AC} = \frac{AC}{AD}$

D. $\frac{AB}{BC} = \frac{AD}{DC}$

E. all of the above

Lesson Quiz

Lesson Quiz is also available in Transparencies.

1. Two similar trapezoids have areas 81 cm^2 and 196 cm^2, respectively. What is the similarity ratio? $\frac{9}{14}$

2. It costs $36 to have a carpet 12 ft by 10 ft cleaned. At that rate, how much would it cost to have a carpet 15 ft by 15 ft cleaned? $67.50

3. The area of a regular octagon is 72 cm^2. What is the area of a regular octagon with sides three times the length of the smaller octagon? **648 cm^2**

529

ERROR ALERT! Exercise 6 Because of the positions of the solids in the diagram, some students may choose the 80-m side and the 45-m side as corresponding sides and conclude that the rectangular prisms cannot be similar. **Remediation:** Point out that since the 80-m side and the 60-m side appear to be the longest sides, students should try them as corresponding sides.

ALTERNATIVE ASSESSMENT Exercises 14–17 These exercises can help you assess students' ability to apply Theorem 10-7 to solve real-world problems. Have students work in groups. Have them write one or two sentences explaining how they solved each problem.

MAKING CONNECTIONS Exercise 15 An atomic clock is based on the changes in the energy states of atoms. It is highly accurate because it is not affected by external conditions, such as air pressure and magnetic fields. The most accurate atomic clock is located at the National Institute of Standards and Technology in Boulder, Colorado. It is accurate to one- 10 billionths of a second per day. Watches and clocks are now being made that tell time by picking up radio signals from this atomic clock.

EXTENSION Exercise 15 Have students research how an atomic clock works.

pages 533–535 On Your Own

15. Answers may vary. Sample: No; if the dimensions of the box are $\frac{1}{10}$ of the orig. dimensions, then the new clock's weight should be $\frac{1}{1000}$ of the orig. weight.

19d. Paul Bunyan's weight is 1000 times the weight of an average person, but his bones can only support 600 times the weight of an average person.

page 535 Mixed Review

20.

21.

6. Is there a value of x for which the rectangular solids at the right are similar? Explain. See right.

7. The volumes of two spheres are 729 in.^{3} and 81 in.^{3}. Find the ratio of their radii. $\sqrt[3]{9}$: 1 or 3 : $\sqrt[3]{3}$

8. A carpenter is making a copy of an antique blanket chest that has the shape of a rectangular solid. The length, width, and height of the copy will be 4 in. greater than the original dimensions. Will the chests be similar? Explain. See right.

9. Estimation The volume of a spherical balloon with radius 3.1 cm is about 125 cm^3. Estimate the volume of a similar balloon with radius 6 cm. about 1000 cm^3

x m 60 m
40 m 30 m
80 m 45 m

6. 60; solve for *x*: $\frac{80}{60} = \frac{40}{30} = \frac{x}{45}$.

8. No; unless the chest is a cube, the increase in the lengths of the sides is not proportional.

Copy and complete the table for two similar solids.

	Similarity Ratio	Ratio of Surface Areas	Ratio of Volumes
10.	1 : 2	1 ▪ : ▪ 4	1 ▪ : ▪ 8
11.	3 : 5	9 ▪ : ▪ 25	27 ▪ : ▪ 125
12.	7 ▪ : ▪ 9	49 : 81	343 ▪ : ▪ 729
13.	5 ▪ : ▪ 8	25 ▪ : ▪ 64	125 : 512

14. A clown's face on a balloon is 4 in. high when the balloon holds 108 in.^{3} of air. How much air must the balloon hold for the face to be 8 in. high? 864 in.^{3}

15. Critical Thinking A company recently announced that it had developed the technology to reduce the size of *atomic clocks,* which are used in electronic devices that transmit data. The company claims that the smaller clock will be $\frac{1}{10}$ the size of existing atomic clocks and $\frac{1}{100}$ the weight. Do these ratios make sense? Explain.
See margin.

16. Packaging A cylinder 4 in. in diameter and 6 in. high holds 1 lb of oatmeal. To the nearest ounce, how much oatmeal will a similar 10-in. high cylinder hold? 74 oz

17. Estimation A teapot 4 in. tall and 4 in. in diameter holds about 1 quart of tea. About how many quarts would this teapot-shaped building hold?
Answers may vary. Sample: about 27,000 qt

534

---

18. *Literature* In *Gulliver's Travels* by Jonathan Swift, Gulliver first traveled to Lilliput. The average height of a Lilliputian was one twelfth Gulliver's height.

144 coats

  a. How many Lilliputian coats could be made from the material in Gulliver's coat? (*Hint:* Use the ratio of surface areas.)

  b. How many Lilliputian meals would be needed to make a meal for Gulliver? (*Hint:* Use the ratio of volumes.) **1728 meals**

  c. *Research* Visit your local library and read about Gulliver's voyage to Brobdingnag in *Gulliver's Travels.* Describe the size of the people and objects in this land. Use ratios of areas and volumes to describe Gulliver's life there.
  Check students' work.

19. Giants such as King Kong, Godzilla, and Paul Bunyan cannot exist because their bone structure could not support them. The legendary Paul Bunyan is ten times as tall as the average human.

  a. The strength of bones is proportional to the area of their cross-section. How many times stronger than the average person's bones would Paul Bunyan's bones be? **100 times**

  b. Weights of objects made of the same material are proportional to their volumes. How many times the average person's weight would Paul Bunyan's weight be? **1000 times**

  c. Human leg bones can support about 6 times the average person's weight. How many times the average person's weight could Paul Bunyan's legs support? **600 times**

  d. Use your answers to parts (b) and (c) to explain why Paul Bunyan's legs could not support his weight. **See margin p. 534.**

  e. *Writing* Explain why massive animals such as elephants have such thick legs. **The increase in the diameter of the legs must be greater than the average increase in other dimensions.**

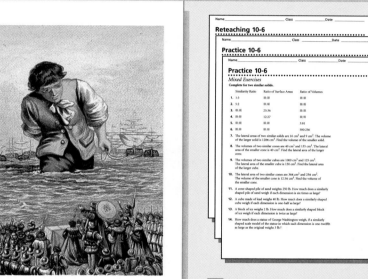

Exercises   MIXED REVIEW

Coordinate Geometry **Draw the image of each figure for the given transformation. 20–21. See margin p. 534.**

20. 90° rotation clockwise about the origin

21. reflection in the line $y = x$

22. What is the area of a 30°-60°-90° triangle with a shorter leg that is 4 cm long? Leave your answer in simplest radical form. $8\sqrt{3}$ cm²

Lesson Quiz

Lesson Quiz is also available in Transparencies.

For Exercises 1–3, two similar prisms have widths 6 in. and 9 in.

1. What is the similarity ratio? $\frac{2}{3}$

2. What is the ratio of the surface areas? $\frac{4}{9}$

3. What is the ratio of the volumes? $\frac{8}{27}$

4. The volume of a sphere is about 268 cm³. Estimate the volume of a sphere with a radius two times that of the smaller sphere. **about 2144 cm³**

535

Finishing the Chapter Project

PROJECT DAY You may wish to plan a project day on which students share their completed projects. Encourage groups to explain their processes as well as their products.

PROJECT NOTEBOOK Have students review their project work and bring their notebooks up to date.

- Have students review their fractal designs and their directions for creating them.
- Ask groups to share any insights they found when completing the project, such as the properties of side lengths or areas of fractals.

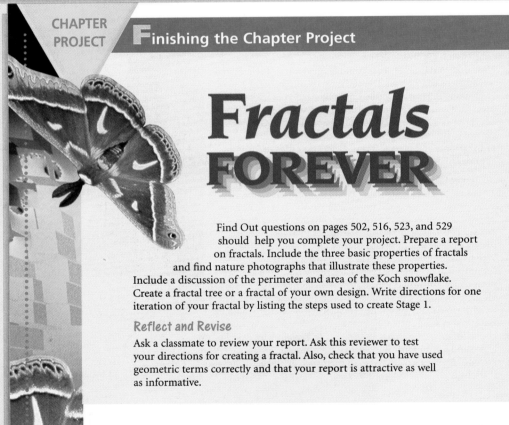

Finishing the Chapter Project

Fractals FOREVER

Find Out questions on pages 502, 516, 523, and 529 should help you complete your project. Prepare a report on fractals. Include the three basic properties of fractals and find nature photographs that illustrate these properties. Include a discussion of the perimeter and area of the Koch snowflake. Create a fractal tree or a fractal of your own design. Write directions for one iteration of your fractal by listing the steps used to create Stage 1.

Reflect and Revise

Ask a classmate to review your report. Ask this reviewer to test your directions for creating a fractal. Also, check that you have used geometric terms correctly and that your report is attractive as well as informative.

Follow Up

In studying the Koch snowflake, you noticed that the total perimeter increases beyond any fixed number (it is infinite), while the area remains less than some fixed number (it is finite). Find or create another fractal with this property and include it in your report.

For More Information

Coes, III, Loring. "Building Fractal Models with Manipulatives." *Mathematics Teacher* (November 1993): 646–651.

Peitgen, Heinz-Otto, et al. *Fractals for the Classroom: Strategic Activities Volume One.* New York: Springer-Verlag, 1991.

Peterson, Ivers. *The Mathematical Tourist.* New York: W.H. Freeman, 1988.

Wrap Up

HOW AM I DOING? Have students work in six groups. Ask each group to make a short presentation explaining the key concepts from one of the lessons in the chapter. Each presentation must include a visual aid and a sample problem.

KEY TERMS The numbers in parentheses direct students to the pages where the terms are used or defined. Students should be able to (1) write a simple explanation of each term, (2) illustrate the term with a diagram, or (3) show an example that uses the term.

ERROR ALERT! **Exercises 1–3** Some students may incorrectly identify corresponding sides based on the positions of the figures. **Remediation:** Have students trace the figures separately on small pieces of paper and rotate them so they are in the same position. Also remind students, that the longest sides correspond to each other and the shortest sides correspond to each other.

10 Wrap Up

Key Terms

Angle-Angle Similarity
 Postulate (AA~) (p. 504)
constant of variation (p. 503)
Cross-Product Property (p. 497)
direct variation (p. 503)
extended proportion (p. 496)
geometric mean (p. 512)
Golden Ratio (p. 498)
Golden Rectangle (p. 498)

indirect measurement (p. 505)
proportion (p. 496)
scale (p. 497)
scale drawing (p. 497)
Side-Angle-Side Similarity
 Theorem (SAS~) (p. 506)
Side-Side-Side Similarity
 Theorem (SSS~) (p. 506)
similar solids (p. 531)

similarity ratio (p. 532)

How am I doing?

- State three ideas from this chapter that you think are important. Explain your choices.
- Describe the properties of similar figures.

Resources

Student Edition
Extra Practice, p. 643
Glossary/Study Guide

Teaching Resources
Study Skills Handbook
Glossary, Spanish Resources

Ratio, Proportion, and Similarity   10-1

A **proportion** is a statement that two ratios are equal.
$\frac{a}{b} = \frac{c}{d}$ is equivalent to:

(1) $ad = bc$ (2) $\frac{b}{a} = \frac{d}{c}$ (3) $\frac{a}{c} = \frac{b}{d}$ (4) $\frac{a+b}{b} = \frac{c+d}{d}$

In a **scale drawing,** the **scale** compares each length in the drawing to the actual length being represented.

A **Golden Rectangle** is a rectangle that can be divided into a square and a rectangle that is similar to the original rectangle. The lengths of the adjacent sides of a Golden Rectangle are in a ratio called the **Golden Ratio,** which is $1 : \frac{1 + \sqrt{5}}{2}$.

The polygons below are similar. Find the values of the variables.

1.

2. 9

3. $x = 12;\ y = 15$

Proving Triangles Similar: AA, SAS, and SSS   10-2

If two angles of one triangle are congruent to two angles of another triangle, then the two triangles are similar by the **Angle-Angle Similarity Postulate** (**AA~**). If an angle of one triangle is congruent to an angle of a second triangle, and the sides including the two angles are proportional, then the triangles are similar by the **Side-Angle-Side Similarity Theorem (SAS~).**

537

STANDARDIZED TEST TIP **Exercise 7** Remind students that right triangles have congruent right angles, so they need only one other pair of congruent angles to use the AA ~ Postulate.

ALTERNATIVE ASSESSMENT **Exercise 10** To assess students' understanding of the relationships between the sides of a right triangle, the altitude to the hypotenuse, and the segments of the hypotenuse, have students work in groups to write an indirect measurement problem requiring the use of these relationships in the solution.

WRITING **Exercise 11** Students may need to review Lesson 4-4 for the definition of *midsegment of a triangle*.

If the corresponding sides of two triangles are proportional, then the triangles are similar by the **Side-Side-Side Similarity Theorem (SSS~)**.

Are the triangles similar? If so, write the similarity statement and name the postulate or theorem that proves they are similar.

4.

5. no

6.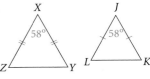

△*ABC* ~ △*FDE*; **AA**~ **Post.**

△*XYZ* ~ △*JKL*; **SAS**~ **Thm.**

7. Standardized Test Prep Two right triangles have an acute angle with the same measure. What is the most direct way to prove that the triangles are similar? **C**

  A. SSS~   **B.** SAS~   **C.** AA~   **D.** SSA~   **E.** cannot be proven

Similarity in Right Triangles   10-3

The **geometric mean** of two positive numbers a and b is the positive number x such that $\frac{a}{x} = \frac{x}{b}$.

When the altitude is drawn to the hypotenuse of a right triangle:

- the two triangles formed are similar to the original triangle and to each other;
- the length of the altitude is the geometric mean of the lengths of the segments of the hypotenuse; and
- the length of each leg is the geometric mean of the lengths of the hypotenuse and the segment of the hypotenuse that is adjacent to that leg.

Find the values of the variables. When an answer is not a whole number, leave it in simplest radical form.

8.

$x = 15; y = 12; z = 20$

9.

$x = 2\sqrt{21}; y = 4\sqrt{3}; z = 4\sqrt{7}$

10.

$x = 2\sqrt{3}; y = 6; z = 4\sqrt{3}$

Proportions and Similar Triangles   10-4

If a line is parallel to one side of a triangle and intersects the other two sides, then it divides those sides proportionally. If three parallel lines intersect two transversals, then the segments intercepted on the transversals are proportional. The bisector of an angle of a triangle divides the opposite side into two segments that are proportional to the sides of the triangle.

11. Writing Explain why a line that intersects the legs of a trapezoid and is parallel to the bases divides the legs proportionally.

11. Answers may vary. Sample: The legs of the trapezoid are transversals intersected by 3 ∥ lines, so they are divided proportionally.

Getting Ready for Chapter 11

Students may work these exercises independently or in small groups. The skills previewed will help prepare students to study right triangle trigonometry.

Find the value of x.

12. 7.5

13. 5.5

14. 37.5

Perimeters, Areas, and Volumes of Similar Figures and Solids   10-5, 10-6

If the similarity ratio of two similar plane figures is $a : b$, then the ratio of their perimeters is $a : b$, and the ratio of their areas is $a^2 : b^2$.

Similar solids have the same shape and all their corresponding dimensions are proportional. If the similarity ratio of two similar solids is $a : b$, then the ratio of their surface areas is $a^2 : b^2$, and the ratio of their volumes is $a^3 : b^3$.

For each pair of similar figures, find the ratio of the area of the first figure to the area of the second.

15.

4 : 9

16. 9 : 4

17. 1 : 4

For each pair of similar solids, find the ratio of the volume of the first figure to the volume of the second.

18. 27 : 64

19.

64 : 27

20. 125 : 343

21. Open-ended Sketch two similar figures whose areas are in the ratio 16 : 25. Include dimensions. **See margin for sample.**

Getting Ready for.. ► CHAPTER

11

Find the ratios $\frac{BC}{AB}$, $\frac{AC}{AB}$, and $\frac{BC}{AC}$. Leave your answers in simplest radical form.

22. $\frac{3}{5}; \frac{4}{5}; \frac{3}{4}$

23. $\frac{\sqrt{2}}{2}; \frac{\sqrt{2}}{2}; 1$

24. $\frac{\sqrt{3}}{2}; \frac{1}{2}; \sqrt{3}$

Wrap Up   pages 537–539

21.

539

ENHANCED MULTIPLE CHOICE QUESTIONS are more complex than traditional multiple choice questions, which assess only one skill. Enhanced multiple choice questions assess the processes that students use, as well as the end results. The questions are written so that students use more than one strategy to solve the problem. Using multiple strategies is encouraged by the National Council of Teachers of Mathematics (NCTM). **Exercise 10** is an enhanced multiple choice question.

FREE RESPONSE QUESTIONS do not give answer choices. Some exercises have more than one possible answer. Students need to give only one correct response. **Exercises 1–9, 12–15, and 17–19** are free response questions.

WRITING EXERCISES allow students to describe how they think about and understand the concepts they have learned. **Exercise 16** is a writing exercise.

OPEN-ENDED PROBLEMS allow for more than one solution. Students must construct their own responses instead of choosing from possible answers. The students' responses will help you determine the depth of their understanding and any possible areas of difficulty. **Exercise 11** is an open-ended problem.

Resources

Teaching Resources

Chapter Support File, Ch. 10
- Cumulative Review
- Standardized Test Practice

Teacher's Edition

See also p. 494E for assessment options

Software

Computer Item Generator

Assessment   page 540

11. 4 : 3

16. Height of a tree; stretch out your arm with the thumb pointing up. Walk away from the tree until the top of the tree lines up with the top of the thumb and the base of the tree lines up with the base of the thumb. Measure the distance to the tree, the length of your arm, and the length of your thumb. Solve the proportion.

Cumulative Review   page 541

9. A median of a △ is a segment whose endpoints are a vertex and the midpoint of the side opp. the vertex. An altitude of a △ is a ⊥ segment from a vertex to a line containing the side opp. the vertex.

11.

540

Solve each proportion.

1. $\frac{4}{5} = \frac{x}{20}$ 16   **2.** $\frac{6}{x} = \frac{10}{7}$ 4.2   **3.** $\frac{x}{3} = \frac{8}{12}$ 2

Are the triangles similar? If so, write the similarity statement and name the postulate or theorem that you can use to prove they are similar.

△*PRQ* ~ △*TWV*; SSS~

4.

5. no

6. A meter stick is held perpendicular to the ground. It casts a shadow 1.5 m long. At the same time, a telephone pole casts a shadow that is 9 m long. How tall is the telephone pole? **6 m**

Find the geometric mean of each pair of numbers. If the answer is not a whole number, leave it in simplest radical form.

7. 10, 15 $5\sqrt{6}$ **8.** 4, 9 6   **9.** 6, 12 $6\sqrt{2}$

10. *Standardized Test Prep* Which proportion is true for the triangle below? **A**

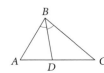

A. $\frac{AB}{BC} = \frac{AD}{DC}$ **B.** $\frac{AD}{BD} = \frac{BD}{CD}$ **C.** $\frac{AB}{AC} = \frac{AC}{AD}$

D. $\frac{AB}{BC} = \frac{AD}{BD}$ **E.** $\frac{AC}{BC} = \frac{CB}{DC}$

---

11. *Open-ended* Draw an isosceles triangle △*ABC*. Then draw a triangle △*DEF* so that △*ABC* ~ △*DEF*. State the similarity ratio of △*ABC* to △*DEF*. See margin for sample.

Find the value of x.

12.

13. 10

14. 10

15.

$5\frac{5}{11}$

16. *Writing* Describe an object whose height or length would be difficult to measure directly. Then describe a method for measuring the object that involves using similar triangles. See margin for sample.

For each pair of similar figures, find the ratio of the area of the first figure to the area of the second.

17. 49 : 64

18. 9 : 4

19. The two solids are similar. Find the ratio of the volume of the first figure to the volume of the second. 64 : 125

Cumulative Review

Item	Review Topic	Chapter		Item	Review Topic	Chapter
1	Symmetry	3		6, 7	Similarity in Right Triangles	10
2	Volumes of Similar Solids	10		8	Properties of Parallelogram	9
3	Surface Area	6		9	Triangles	3
4	Proving Triangles Congruent	8		10	Area	5
5	Special Quadrilaterals	2		11	Basic Constructions	1

10 Cumulative Review

For Exercises 1–7, choose the correct letter.

1. Which figure has exactly one line of symmetry?

 A.   B. D

 C.   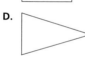 D.

E. none of them

2. What is the ratio of the volumes of similar solids whose similarity ratio is 4 : 9? **E**
   A. $\sqrt{2} : \sqrt{3}$ **B.** 2 : 3   **C.** 4 : 9
   D. 16 : 81   **E.** 64 : 729

3. What is the surface area of the cylinder? **B**

6 in.
12 in.

   A. 96π in.²   **B.** 144π in.²   **C.** 192π in.²
   D. 216π in.²   **E.** 432π in.²

4. Which triangle is *not* necessarily congruent to the given triangle? **B**

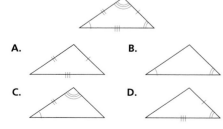

   A.   **B.**

   C.   **D.**

   E. All of the triangles are congruent.

5. What is the most precise name of the figure? **C**

   A. quadrilateral
   B. parallelogram
   C. rectangle
   D. rhombus
   E. square

Compare the boxed quantity in Column A with the boxed quantity in Column B. Choose the best answer.

   A. The quantity in Column A is greater.
   B. The quantity in Column B is greater.
   C. The two quantities are equal.
   D. The relationship cannot be determined on the basis of the information supplied.

Column A	Column B

6. | x | y | **B**

7. | $m\angle ACD$ | $m\angle B$ | **C**

Find each answer.

8. Which special quadrilaterals have perpendicular diagonals? **rhombuses and kites**

9. **Writing** Explain the difference between a median and an altitude of a triangle.
See margin p. 540.

10. How many nonoverlapping circles with 1-in. radius can you fit on a 4-in. square? Find the area of the square not covered by circles.
$4; (16 - 4\pi)$ in.²

11. **Constructions** Draw an angle of about 150°. Construct its angle bisector.
See margin p. 540 for sample.

541

11 Right Triangle Trigonometry

To accommodate flexible scheduling, some lessons are divided into parts.
Assignment Options are given in the Lesson Planning Options for each lesson.

11-1   The Tangent Ratio (pp. 544–549)

    Part ▼**1** Using the Tangent Ratio

    Part ▼**2** Using the Inverse Tangent Function

    Key Term: tangent

11-2   The Sine and Cosine Ratios (pp. 551–555)

    Key Terms: cosine, identity, sine

11-3   Angles of Elevation and Depression (pp. 556–561)

    Key Terms: angle of depression, angle of elevation

11-4   Vectors and Trigonometry (pp. 563–567)

    Key Term: vector

11-5   Adding Vectors (pp. 568–572)

    Key Term: resultant

11-6   Trigonometry and Area (pp. 573–577)

    Part ▼**1** Finding Areas of Regular Polygons

    Part ▼**2** Finding the Area of a Triangle Given SAS

PACING OPTIONS

This chart suggests pacing only for the core lessons and their parts, and it is
provided merely as a possible guide. It will help you determine how much
time you have in your schedule to cover other features, such as the Chapter
Project, Math Toolboxes, Wrap Up, and Assessment.

	1 Class Period	1 Class Period	1 Class Period	1 Class Period	1 Class Period	1 Class Period	1 Class Period	1 Class Period	1 Class Period
Traditional (40–45 min class periods)	11-1 ▼1 ▼2	11-2	11-3	11-4	11-5	11-6 ▼1 ▼2			
Block Scheduling (90 min class periods)	11-1 ▼1 ▼2	11-2 11-3	11-4	11-5	11-6 ▼1 ▼2				

What Students Will Learn and Why

In this chapter, students will build on their knowledge of right triangles, learned in Chapter 5, by learning to calculate tangent ratios, sine ratios, and cosine ratios of right triangles. They learn to use these ratios to determine unknown measures in right triangles. Students then apply these skills by using angles of elevation and depression and trigonometric ratios to solve problems. They also learn how to describe vectors using ordered pair notation, how to describe the magnitude and direction of vectors, and how to solve problems that involve vector addition. Finally, students use trigonometry to find the area of regular polygons and acute triangles. Trigonometry is used by engineers, astronomers, surveyors, and others to measure distance indirectly. Vectors are used to model real-world situations involving velocity and to find the speed and direction of an object that has two forces acting on it.

Discussing the Chapter/Building on Experience

The concept map below relates chapter topics to real-world applications. You and your class may wish to add to the map or develop maps of your own. The center oval describes the topic of the chapter. The next level displays topics within the lessons. The outer ovals reflect applications of the content. As you and your class build a concept map, invite students to discuss applications with which they are familiar.

Interactive Questioning Tips

A question is interactive when there is "give and take" between the questioner and the respondent. In Think and Discuss or when a critical thinking question is asked, it is important to encourage all students to participate. It can be helpful to bring students to the chalkboard so they can illustrate their answers and support their thinking. For example, in Lesson 11-5, students are asked to explain why the term resultant, meaning the sum of two vectors, makes sense.

Skills Practice

Every lesson provides skills practice with Try This exercises, Exercises On Your Own, and Exercises Mixed Review. The

Student Edition includes Checkpoints (pp. 561, 572) and Preparing for Standardized Tests (p. 583). In the Teacher's Edition, the Lesson Planning Options section for each lesson lists Prerequisite Skills students should know for that lesson. At the back of the Student Edition is the Skills Handbook—mini-lessons on math your students may need to review. The Chapter Support File for Chapter 11 in the Teaching Resources box includes two Practice worksheets per lesson, a worksheet for two Checkpoints, and worksheets for Cumulative Review and Standardized Test Preparation.

Diverse Learning and Teaching Styles

In your Teacher's Edition, you will find suggestions as to how you can help students complete mathematical tasks in Chapter 11 by reinforcing various learning styles. Here are some examples.

- **Visual learning** make a poster that displays a right triangle and the three trigonometric ratios (p. 552), use different colors to indicate angles of elevation and depression (p. 556)

- **Tactile learning** take turns moving a marble by blowing through straws (p. 570)

- **Auditory learning** use a mnemonic device to differentiate between the three trigonometric ratios (p. 552)

- **Kinesthetic learning** use the method in Example 2 to go outside and measure distances indirectly (p. 545), measure the length of shadows to determine the sun's elevation (p. 560)

Alternative Activity for Lesson 11-1

for use with Work Together and Example 1, uses geometry software to explore ratios of sides in similar right triangles.

Alternative Activity for Lesson 11-2

for use with Example 1, uses geometry software to investigate sine and cosine ratios in right triangles.

Alternative Activity for Lesson 11-6

for use with Example 3, uses geometry software to study formulas for the area of triangle.

Cooperative Learning Tips

When used effectively, cooperative learning can help students develop interpersonal skills, learn to perform specific roles in a group, and learn to carry out specific responsibilities. The components of Chapter 11 provide a range of cooperative learning opportunities.

- In the Student Edition, the **Work Together** parts of lessons are specifically designed for cooperative learning activities.

- In the Teacher's Edition, you will find helpful hints for addressing diverse learning styles (see page C for Chapter 11). For every lesson, you will find a *Reteaching Activity,* which may involve cooperative learning.

Materials and Manipulatives

The authors expect all students to use scientific calculators. Calculator use is integrated throughout the course.

- calculator (11-1, 11-2, 11-3, 11-4, 11-5, 11-6)
- centimeter ruler (11-1, 11-2)
- graph paper (11-2, 11-5)
- marble (11-5)
- protractor (11-1)
- straws (11-5)

TECHNOLOGY OPTIONS

Technology Tools		Chapter Project	11-1	11-2	11-3	11-4	11-5	11-6
Calculator		Assumed that students have scientific calculators at any time.						
Software	Secondary Math Lab Toolkit™		✔	✔	✔	✔	✔	✔
	Integrated Math Lab		✔	✔				
	Computer Item Generator		✔	✔	✔	✔	✔	✔
	Student Edition			✔ᵀ				
Video	Video Field Trip	✔						
CD-ROM	Multimedia Geometry Lab		✔	✔			✔	✔
Internet		See the Prentice Hall site. (http://www.phschool.com)						

✔ᵀ indicates Math Toolbox.

The Prentice Hall Geometry program offers you a rich variety of technology options. Be assured that all these options are provided as a means of enriching the program and are not essential for the successful completion of the course.

Assessment Options

The Prentice Hall Geometry Program provides you with many options. From these options, you may choose instructional materials and techniques appropriate for your students, or those necessary to meet your district's curriculum requirements. As the chart indicates, the program also supports your teaching efforts by offering you many choices for assessment.

ASSESSMENT OPTIONS

Assessment Support Materials	Chapter Project	11-1	11-2	11-3	11-4	11-5	11-6	Chapter End
Chapter Project	▲ ■ ●	▲ ■			▲ ■		▲ ■	▲ ■
Checkpoints				▲ ■ ●		▲ ■ ●		
Self-Assessment		▲ ■			▲ ■		▲ ■	▲ ■
Writing Assignment		▲ ■	▲	▲	▲ ■	▲	▲ ■	▲ ■ ●
Chapter Assessment								▲ ■ ●
Alternative Assessment		■	■	■	■	■	■	▲ ■ ●
Cumulative Review								●
Standardized Test Prep		▲ ■	▲ ■					▲ ■ ●
Computer Item Generator	Can be used to create custom-made practice or assessment at any time.							

▲ = Student Edition   ■ = Teacher's Edition   ● = Teaching Resources

Checkpoints

Alternative Assessment

Chapter Assessment

Available in both Form A and Form B

Making the Right Connections

Mathematics is imbedded in nearly every walk of life. The National Council of Teachers of Mathematics (NCTM) encourages educators to recognize these connections and to emphasize them for the purpose of better educating students for success in life and in a global economy. The **Connections** chart below highlights these connections for Chapter 11.

CONNECTIONS

Lesson	Interdisciplinary Connections	Career Prep	Other Real World Connections	Math Integration	NCTM Standards
Chapter Project	Physics Astronomy		Navigation Measuring Heights Stars	Algebra	Communication Connections Problem Solving
11-1	History Language Arts	Engineering Construction	Suspension Bridges Backpacking Pyramids Katoomba Scenic Railway	Algebra Coordinate Geometry	Algebra Connections Communication Problem Solving
11-2	Astronomy History	Farming	Escalators Agriculture Orbits of Planets Sports	Algebra	Algebra Connections Communication Problem Solving
11-3	Meteorology	Surveying Aviation Engineering	Navigation Blimp Flag Pole	Algebra Coordinate Geometry Data Analysis	Coordinate Geometry Connections Communication Problem Solving
11-4	Science	Aviation Veterinary Science	Air Travel Golden Retrievers Homing Pigeons Honeybees European Eel	Algebra Coordinate Geometry	Coordinate Geometry Connections Communication Problem Solving
11-5	Physics Meteorology	Aviation	Navigation Boat Travel Air Travel Hurricanes	Coordinate Geometry Probability Geometry in 3 Dimensions	Coordinate Geometry Connections Communication Problem Solving
11-6	History	Architecture Surveying Industrial Design	Castle del Monte Land Plots Measuring Devices	Geometry in 3 Dimensions	Connections Communication Problem Solving

CONNECTING TO PRIOR LEARNING Draw three noncongruent right triangles. Label the lengths of the legs on one, the lengths of the shorter leg and the hypotenuse on the second, and the lengths of the longer leg and hypotenuse on the third. Discuss how the Pythagorean Theorem can be used to find the length of the third side of each triangle. Then draw a fourth right triangle and label the length of one side and the measure of one angle. Discuss that, in this chapter, students will learn how to find the lengths of the other two sides from this information.

CULTURAL CONNECTIONS In ancient Egypt, every year after the Nile River overflowed its banks and washed out farm boundaries, the Egyptians fixed new boundaries by surveying. Surveying is the technique of measuring angles and triangles to determine the position of points or boundaries. A surveyor maps boundaries with an instrument called a transit.

INTERDISCIPLINARY CONNECTIONS Distances of the stars can be determined from trigonometric parallax. If the position of a nearby star is measured from two points on opposite sides of the Earth's orbit, a small angular displacement is

Technology Options

Prentice Hall Technology

Video
Video Field Trip 11, "Playing with Numbers," a look at how teachers apply trigonometry in the world of amusement parks

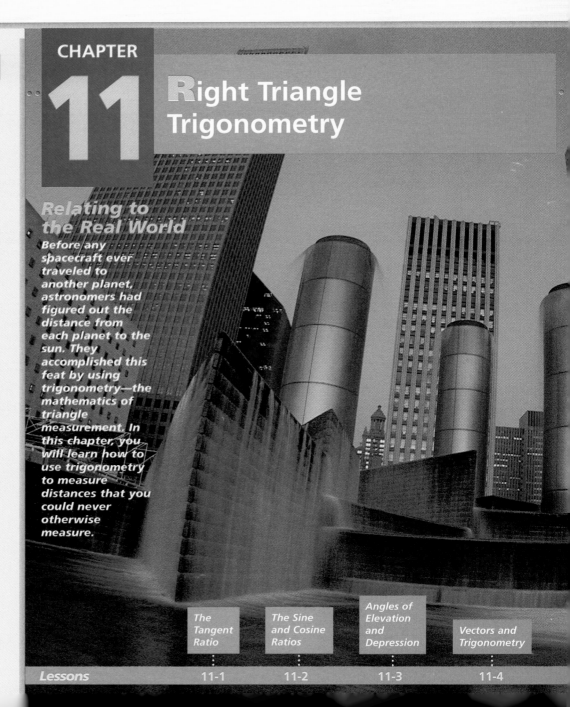

CHAPTER **11** **R**ight Triangle Trigonometry

Relating to the Real World

Before any spacecraft ever traveled to another planet, astronomers had figured out the distance from each planet to the sun. They accomplished this feat by using trigonometry—the mathematics of triangle measurement. In this chapter, you will learn how to use trigonometry to measure distances that you could never otherwise measure.

The Tangent Ratio	The Sine and Cosine Ratios	Angles of Elevation and Depression	Vectors and Trigonometry

Lessons   11-1   11-2   11-3   11-4

seen. Using the Earth's orbit as the base line, the distance of the star can be found from the angular size of the parallax. Interested students might like to make a presentation on finding star distances.

ABOUT THE PROJECT Students construct clinometers and use them to measure the heights of objects in the school yard. Then students use their clinometers to measure the angle of elevation of the star Polaris.

Launching the Project

PROJECT NOTEBOOK Encourage students to keep all project-related materials in a separate folder or notebook. See Chapter Project Manager and Scoring Rubric in Chapter Support File.

- Ask students to give some examples of distances that must have been measured indirectly, such as the distance from Earth to Mercury and the distance to the center of the earth.
- Ask students to describe some fields in which indirect measurement is used. Examples might be surveying, astronomy, and navigation.

TRACKING THE PROJECT You may wish to have students read Finishing the Chapter Project on page 578 to help them get an overview of the project. Set benchmark deadlines for students to show their work in progress.

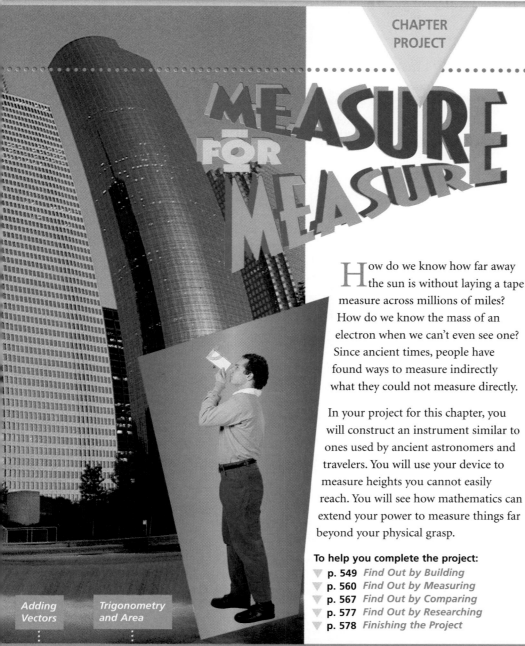

CHAPTER PROJECT

MEASURE FOR MEASURE

How do we know how far away the sun is without laying a tape measure across millions of miles? How do we know the mass of an electron when we can't even see one? Since ancient times, people have found ways to measure indirectly what they could not measure directly.

In your project for this chapter, you will construct an instrument similar to ones used by ancient astronomers and travelers. You will use your device to measure heights you cannot easily reach. You will see how mathematics can extend your power to measure things far beyond your physical grasp.

To help you complete the project:

▼ **p. 549** *Find Out by Building*
▼ **p. 560** *Find Out by Measuring*
▼ **p. 567** *Find Out by Comparing*
▼ **p. 577** *Find Out by Researching*
▼ **p. 578** *Finishing the Project*

Adding Vectors

Trigonometry and Area

11-5   11-6

▼ Project Resources

Teaching Resources
Chapter Support File, Ch. 11
● Chapter Project Manager and Scoring Rubric

Transparencies
111

▼ Using the Rubric

Sharing the scoring rubric for the project with your students will alert them to your expectations before they begin work on the project.

As students complete each Find Out question in the chapter, you may wish to have them evaluate their own work or a partner's work based on the scoring rubric. Students should have the opportunity to revise their work after it has been reviewed.

543

CONNECTING TO PRIOR KNOWLEDGE Draw two similar triangles and label the vertices. Have students use corresponding sides to write as many proportions as possible.

WORK TOGETHER

ERROR ALERT! Some students will confuse the leg opposite an angle with the leg adjacent to an angle. **Remediation:** Draw several right triangles in different positions. Have students practice naming the legs opposite and adjacent to each acute angle.

THINK AND DISCUSS

Help students see that because the tangent ratio is defined for the acute angles of a right triangle, the tangent ratio can be found for all angles between 0° and 90°. In more advanced courses, students may learn how to find the tangent ratio for angles with measures greater than 90°.

Lesson Planning Options

Prerequisite Skills

- Understanding of ratios
- Graphing lines in the coordinate plane

Assignment Options for Exercises On Your Own

To provide flexible scheduling, this lesson can be subdivided into parts.

1 **Core** 1–4, 9–12, 23–24
Extension 25–27

2 **Core** 5–8, 13–20, 28–34
Extension 21–22, 35

Use Mixed Review to maintain skills.

Resources

 Student Edition
Skills Handbook, p. 646
Extra Practice, p. 644
Glossary/Study Guide

Teaching Resources
Chapter Support File, Ch. 11
- Practice 11-1 (two worksheets)
- Reteaching 11-1
- Alternative Activity 11-1
- Classroom Manager 11-1
- Glossary, Spanish Resources

 Transparencies
5, 11, 112, 115

What You'll Learn
- Calculating tangents of acute angles in right triangles
- Using tangents to determine side lengths in triangles

...And Why
To calculate distances that cannot be measured directly

What You'll Need
- protractor
- centimeter ruler
- calculator

1. Answers may vary slightly: 10°: 0.18, 20°: 0.36, 30°: 0.58, 40°: 0.84, 50°: 1.19, 60°: 1.73, 70°: 2.75, 80°: 5.67

2. The ratio is the same for all rt. △s with the given angle.

When? The word *trigonometry* was first used in a publication in 1595 by German clergyman and mathematician Bartholomaus Pitiscus (1561–1613).

Connections 🌐 Hiking ... and more

11-1 The Tangent Ratio

WORK TOGETHER

- Work in small groups. Your teacher will assign each group a different angle measure from the set {10°, 20°, . . . , 80°}.

- Have each member of your group draw a right triangle containing the assigned angle. Make the triangles different sizes. Label your triangle △*PAW*, where ∠*P* is the assigned angle.

- Use a ruler to measure and label the lengths of the legs of △*PAW* to the nearest millimeter.

1. *Calculator* Use a calculator to compute the ratio $\frac{\text{leg opposite } \angle P}{\text{leg adjacent to } \angle P}$. Round your answer to two decimal places. **See left.**

2. Compare the results of Question 1 within your group. Make a **conjecture** based on your comparison. **See left.**

3. Compare your results with those of other groups. What do you notice? For each given angle, the ratio does not depend on the size of the △.

THINK AND DISCUSS

Part 1 *Using the Tangent Ratio*

The word *trigonometry* comes from the Greek words meaning "triangle measurement." In the Work Together, you made a discovery about a ratio of the lengths of sides of a right triangle. This ratio is called the tangent ratio.

tangent of ∠*A* = $\frac{\text{leg opposite } \angle A}{\text{leg adjacent to } \angle A}$

This equation can be abbreviated:

$$\tan A = \frac{\text{opposite}}{\text{adjacent}}$$

Example 1

Write the tangent ratios for ∠*U* and ∠*T*.

$\tan U = \frac{\text{opposite}}{\text{adjacent}} = \frac{TV}{UV} = \frac{4}{3}$

$\tan T = \frac{\text{opposite}}{\text{adjacent}} = \frac{UV}{TV} = \frac{3}{4}$

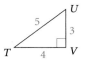

4. **a.** **Try This** Write the tangent ratios for ∠*K* and ∠*J*. $\frac{3}{7}; \frac{7}{3}$
   b. How is tan *K* related to tan *J*?
   tan *K* is the reciprocal of tan *J*.

Example 1 ....

Point out to students that one of the tangent ratios is greater than 1 and the other is less than 1. Ask students if this is always true of the acute angles of a right triangle.

Question 4 Ask students to describe the relationship between ∠J and ∠K. Students should observe that the tangent ratios of complementary angles are reciprocals.

ALTERNATIVE ASSESSMENT To assess students' understanding of why tangent ratios for congruent angles are equal, ask them to use △TOW and △T'O'W' to explain why tan W = tan W'.

Example 2 **Relating to the Real World** ....

ESL Students may be confused by this meaning of the term "compass" thinking that it refers to the instrument they use for constructions. If possible, bring in a directional compass and demonstrate how to take readings from it.

Make sure students understand how $\tan 86° = \frac{x}{50}$ was derived and why $x = 50(\tan 86°)$.

Help students check that their calculators are in degree mode before they use the tan key. Also show students how to use the table of trigonometric functions on page 674.

KINESTHETIC LEARNING If you have block scheduling or an extended class period, take students outside to measure distances indirectly using the method described in Example 2.

You discovered in the Work Together that the tangent ratio for a given acute angle does not depend on the size of the triangle. Why is this true? Consider the two right triangles shown below.

By the AA Similarity Postulate, the two triangles are similar.

Because the triangles are similar, these corresponding sides are in proportion.

$$\frac{OW}{O'W'} = \frac{TO}{T'O'}$$

Applying a property of proportions yields the tangent ratios for ∠T and ∠T'.

$$\frac{OW}{TO} = \frac{O'W'}{T'O'}$$

You can use the tangent ratio to measure distances that would be difficult to measure directly.

Example 2 **Relating to the Real World** ....

Hiking You are hiking in the Rocky Mountains. You come to a canyon and follow these steps to estimate its width.

Step 1: Point your compass at an object on the opposite edge of the canyon and note the reading.

Step 2: Turn 90° and walk off a distance in a straight line along the edge of the canyon.

Step 3: Turn and point the compass at the object again, taking another reading.

You subtract your readings in Steps 1 and 3 to find that $m\angle 1 = 86$. The distance you walked in Step 2 was 50 ft. What is the width of the canyon?

50 ft   1   86°   not to scale

$$\tan 86° = \frac{x}{50} \qquad \text{Use the tangent ratio.}$$
$$x = 50(\tan 86°) \qquad \text{Solve for } x.$$

50 ☒ 86 TAN ▤ 715.03331

The canyon is about 700 ft wide.

GRAPHING CALCULATOR HINT

The keystrokes for a scientific calculator are shown at the right. On a graphing calculator, enter
50 ☒ TAN 86 ENTER .

Additional Examples

FOR EXAMPLE 1 ....

Refer to the triangle in Example 1. If $UV = 5$ and $VT = 12$, find the tangent ratios for ∠U and ∠V.

$\tan U = \frac{12}{5}$; $\tan T = \frac{5}{12}$

Discussion: *If UV = 6 and UT = 10, explain how to find the tangent ratios for ∠U and ∠V.*

FOR EXAMPLE 2 ....

Find the value of g to the nearest tenth.

11.8

C   5   D
g   23°
E

FOR EXAMPLE 3 ....

Find the measure to the nearest degree of the acute angles that the line $y = 2x - 4$ makes with a horizontal line. **63°**

Discussion: *Describe a line for which the measure of the acute angle that the line makes with a horizontal line is 90. Describe a line for which the measure of the acute angle that the line makes with a horizontal line is 0.*

Question 5 In part b, make sure students correctly set up the equation with *w* in the denominator. You might want to review how to solve such equations. In part c, students may write different equations depending on which angle they use.

Explain to students that given an acute angle, they can use the tan function to find the tangent ratio. Given the tangent ratio, they can use the $\tan^{-1}$ function to find the angle. Then help students locate the $\tan^{-1}$ key on their calculator and give several problems for them to solve using it.

CRITICAL THINKING Question 7 Students should discover that the tangent of a 45° angle is 1.

Technology Options

For Exercise 25, students may make the table and graph using graphing software or graphing calculators.

Prentice Hall Technology

Software
- Secondary Math Lab Toolkit™
- Integrated Math Lab 43
- Computer Item Generator 11-1

CD-ROM
- Multimedia Geometry Lab 11

Internet
- See the Prentice Hall site. (http://www.phschool.com)

546

---

5. Try This Find the value of *w* to the nearest tenth.

a. 10, 54°, *w*, 13.8

b. *w*, 1.0, 28°, 1.9

c. 2.5, *w*, 57°, 33°, 3.8

Part 2 Using the Inverse Tangent Function

Consider △*BHX* at the left. Suppose you want to find m∠*X*. You can use the tangent ratio to do so. You know that $\tan X = \frac{6}{8} = 0.75$. To find m∠*X*, use the *inverse tangent* function on your calculator.

$$\tan X = 0.75$$
$$m\angle X = \tan^{-1}(0.75) \quad \text{"}\tan^{-1}\text{" means "inverse tangent."}$$

0.75 [TAN⁻¹] *36.869898*   Use the inverse tangent function on a calculator.

So m∠*X* ≈ 37.

GRAPHING CALCULATOR HINT

On most calculators, you find the inverse tangent of 0.75 by entering .75 [2nd] [TAN] or .75 [TAN⁻¹]. On a graphing calculator, enter [2nd] [TAN] .75 [ENTER].

6. Find m∠*J* to the nearest degree.
a. $\tan J = 0.5$ 27 **b.** $\tan J = 0.34$ 19 **c.** $\tan J = 100$ 89

7. Critical Thinking Given that $\tan C = 1$, explain how to find m∠*C* without using a calculator.
45; if the tangent ratio is 1, the △ is isosceles.

8. Find m∠*Y* to the nearest degree. 68

Example 3 shows how the tangent ratio is related to slope.

Example 3

Algebra Find the measure of the acute angle that the line $y = 3x + 2$ makes with a horizontal line.

The line $y = 3x + 2$ has a slope of 3. Notice that the ratio $\frac{\text{rise}}{\text{run}}$ is the same as $\frac{\text{leg opposite } \angle A}{\text{leg adjacent to } \angle A}$. So $\tan A = 3$, and $m\angle A = \tan^{-1}(3)$.

3 [TAN⁻¹] *71.565051*
$m\angle A \approx 71.6$

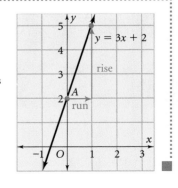

9. Try This Find the measure of the acute angle that each line makes with a horizontal line. Round your answer to the nearest tenth.
a. $y = \frac{1}{2}x + 6$ 26.6 **b.** $y = 6x - 1$ 80.5

MAKING CONNECTIONS **Exercise 21** The Katoomba Scenic Railway is 1020 feet long. Railway cars are attached to two steel cables 22 mm in diameter which are pulled by a 220-hp electric winding machine. The ride takes 1 min 40 sec. The railway carries about 420,000 passengers a year.

Exercises   **O N   Y O U R   O W N**

Express tan A and tan B as ratios.

1. $\frac{1}{2}$; 2

2. $\frac{2}{3}$; $\frac{3}{2}$

3. 1; 1

4. 3; $\frac{1}{3}$

Find each missing value. Round your answer to the nearest tenth.

5. tan ▓° = 3.5   74.1

6. tan 34° = $\frac{▓}{20}$ 13.5

7. tan 2° = $\frac{4}{▓}$ 114.5

8. tan ▓° = 90   89.4

Find the value of x. Round lengths of segments to the nearest tenth and angle measures to the nearest degree.

9. 11.2

10. 12.3

11. 14.4

12. 2.5

13. 32

14. 58

15. 48

16. 65

17. 1.6

18. 63

19. 21.4

20. 58

21. Engineering The *grade* of a road or railway is the ratio $\frac{\text{rise}}{\text{run}}$, usually expressed as a percent. For example, a railway with a grade of 5% rises 5 ft for every 100 ft of horizontal distance. The world's steepest railway is the Katoomba Scenic Railway in the Blue Mountains of Australia. It has a grade of 122%. At what angle does this railway go up?   about 51°

22. The lengths of the diagonals of a rhombus are 2 in. and 5 in. Find the measures of the angles of the rhombus to the nearest degree.
44° and 136°

pages 547–549   **On Your Own**

25a.

x	tan x°		x	tan x°
5	0.1		50	1.2
10	0.2		55	1.4
15	0.3		60	1.7
20	0.4		65	2.1
25	0.5		70	2.7
30	0.6		75	3.7
35	0.7		80	5.7
40	0.8		85	11.4
45	1			

b.

Exercise 23 Make sure students understand how the right triangle shown on the diagram is formed and how to find the length of its base.

WRITING Exercise 24 Suggest that students make a chart showing the tangent ratios for the special right triangles. They can add the sine and cosine ratios to the chart after the next lesson.

Exercise 26 Students should not assume that the two triangles shown are right triangles but, using the SAS Congruence Postulate, can easily deduce it.

OPEN-ENDED Exercise 35 You may want to share with students the following method for calculating Pythagorean triples: For any positive numbers x and y with $x > y$, the three numbers $x^2 - y^2$, $2xy$, and $x^2 + y^2$ form a Pythagorean triple.

Chapter Project **FIND OUT BY BUILDING** In this activity, students follow the directions to make a clinometer. You may want to make one ahead of time for the class to use as a model. Have students work in groups with all students making their own clinometers.

Find Out by Building

$\angle 1$ and $\angle 2$ are complementary, and $\angle 2$ and $\angle 3$ are complementary, so $m\angle 1 = m\angle 3$.

line of sight

1
2   horizon line
3
edge of string protractor

page 549 Mixed Review

36a. If a quadrilateral has $\cong$ diagonals, then the quadrilateral is a $\square$.

37a. If a flag is a United States flag, then it contains the colors red, white, and blue.

38a. If diagonals of a quadrilateral are $\perp$ bisectors of each other, then the quadrilateral is a rhombus.

39a. If you live on an island, then you live in Hawaii.

41a–b.

23. Pyramids All but two of the pyramids built by the ancient Egyptians have faces inclined at 52° angles. (The remaining two have faces inclined at $43\frac{1}{2}°$.) Suppose an archaeologist discovers the ruins of a pyramid. Most of the pyramid has eroded, but she is able to determine that the length of a side of the square base is 82 m. How tall was the pyramid, assuming its faces were inclined at 52°? Round your answer to the nearest meter. **52 m**

52°

82 m

24. Writing Explain why tan 60° = $\sqrt{3}$. Include a diagram with your explanation. **For any length of the short leg s, the length of the leg opposite the 60° angle is $s\sqrt{3}$. So tan 60° = $\frac{s\sqrt{3}}{s} = \sqrt{3}$.**

25. a. Coordinate Geometry Use a calculator to complete the table of values at the right. Give your answers to the nearest tenth.
   b. Plot the points $(x, \tan x°)$ on the coordinate plane. Connect them with a smooth curve. **a–b. See margin p. 547.**
   c. What happens to the tangent ratio as the measure of the angle approaches 0? as it approaches 90? **See below.**
   d. Use the graph to estimate each value. **Estimates may vary slightly. Samples are given.**
   tan $\blacksquare°$ = 7 **82**   tan 68° = $\blacksquare$ **2.5**   tan $\blacksquare°$ = 3.5 **74**
   c. The ratio approaches 0; the ratio increases rapidly.

x	$\tan x°$
5	▨
10	▨
⋮	⋮
85	▨

Find w, then x. Round lengths of segments to the nearest tenth and angle measures to the nearest degree.

26.

43°
x
w 5

$w = 5$; $x = 4.7$

27.

10
56°   34°
w x

$w = 6.7$; $x = 8.1$

28.

10
w
6
$x°$
9

$w = 15$; $x = 53$

29.

3
7   $w°$
$x°$ 5

$w = 59$; $x = 36$

Algebra Find the measure of the acute angle that each line makes with a horizontal line. Round your answer to the nearest tenth.

30. $y = 5x - 7$ **78.7**   **31.** $y = \frac{4}{3}x - 1$ **53.1**   **32.** $3x - 4y = 8$ **36.9**   **33.** $-2x + 3y = 6$
33.7

34. Construction The roadway of a suspension bridge is supported by cables, as shown. The cables extend from the roadway to a point on the tower 50 ft above the roadway. The cables are set at 10-ft intervals along the roadway. Find the angles from the roadway to the top of the tower for the six cables nearest the tower. Round your answers to the nearest tenth.
78.7°, 68.2°, 59.0°, 51.3°, 45°, 39.8°

35. Open-ended Select a Pythagorean triple other than a multiple of 3, 4, 5. Find the measures of the acute angles of the right triangle associated with your Pythagorean triple. Round each measure to the nearest tenth.
Sample: 5, 12, 13 triple; 22.6 and 67.4

Exercises 36–39 Students review writing converses of statements and evaluating their truth values.

JOURNAL Suggest that students include diagrams with their explanations. You also might ask if their explanations are dependent on the angle's measuring 60.

GETTING READY FOR LESSON 11-2 These exercises prepare students to calculate sines and cosines of acute angles.

Wrap Up

THE BIG IDEA Ask students: *Describe a right triangle in which the tangent ratios of its two acute angles are equal.*

RETEACHING ACTIVITY Students calculate the measure of the acute angles that lines make with the *x*-axis. (Reteaching worksheet 11-1)

Chapter Project   Find Out by Building

Use the diagram at the right to build a *clinometer*, an angle-measuring device similar to instruments used by navigators for hundreds of years. You will need a protractor, string, tape, a piece of heavy cardboard, a small weight, and a straw.

To use the clinometer, look through the straw at the object you want to measure (the top of a building, for example). Have someone else read the angle marked by the hanging string.

• Why is the angle measure indicated by the string on the protractor the same as $m\angle 1$? (*Hint:* The string is always perpendicular to the horizon.) See margin p. 548.

line of sight

Look through the straw.

horizon line

Exercises MIXED REVIEW

In Exercises 36–39: (a) Write the converse of each conditional. (b) Determine the truth value of the statement and its converse. 36 a–39a. See margin p. 548.

36. If a quadrilateral is a parallelogram, then the quadrilateral has congruent diagonals. b. false; false

37. If a flag contains the colors red, white, and blue, then the flag is a United States flag. b. false; true

38. If a quadrilateral is a rhombus, then its diagonals are perpendicular bisectors of one another. b. true; true

39. If you live in Hawaii, then you live on an island. b. true; false

40. *Locus* Sketch the locus of points in a plane that are equidistant from the diagonals of a kite. See right.

41. a. *Constructions* Draw a triangle. Then construct the perpendicular bisectors of two of its sides. a–b. See margin p. 548 for sample.
b. Draw the circle that circumscribes the triangle. (*Hint:* The intersection of the perpendicular bisectors is its center.)

SELF ASSESSMENT

FOR YOUR JOURNAL

Two different right triangles each have an angle that measures 60. Explain why tan 60° is the same for both of these triangles.

40.

Getting Ready for Lesson 11-2

For each triangle, find the ratios $\dfrac{\text{leg opposite } \angle B}{\text{hypotenuse}}$ and $\dfrac{\text{leg adjacent to } \angle B}{\text{hypotenuse}}$.

42.

15, 8, $\sqrt{161}$

$\dfrac{8}{15}; \dfrac{\sqrt{161}}{15}$

43.

10, $3\sqrt{29}$, 19

$\dfrac{10}{19}; \dfrac{3\sqrt{29}}{19}$

44.
$2\sqrt{78}$, 7, 19

$\dfrac{7}{19}; \dfrac{2\sqrt{78}}{19}$

45.

15, 9, 12

$\dfrac{9}{15}$ or $\dfrac{3}{5}$; $\dfrac{12}{15}$ or $\dfrac{4}{5}$

Reteaching 11-1

Practice 11-1

Practice 11-1
Mixed Exercises

Lesson Quiz

Lesson Quiz is also available in Transparencies.

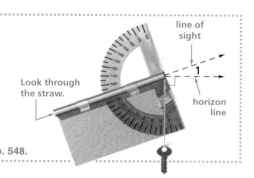

G, 2, $\sqrt{29}$, I, 5, H

1. Write the tangent ratio for $\angle G$. $\dfrac{5}{2}$

2. Write the tangent ratio for $\angle H$. $\dfrac{2}{5}$

N, M, O

3. If $MN = 8$ and $m\angle M = 36$, find NO to the nearest tenth. 5.8

4. If $MO = \sqrt{65}$ and $NO = 4$, find $m\angle M$ to the nearest degree. 30

549

Students construct a triangle and calculate the sine of one of its acute angles. Then they manipulate the triangle and observe how this affects the sine. In the Extend, students repeat the investigation calculating the cosine and tangent ratios.

Using geometry software allows students to calculate the sine of an angle in many triangles without having to draw each triangle individually and measure the sides.

Check that students construct the figures correctly. When moving point D, $\overleftrightarrow{ED}$ should remain perpendicular to $\overrightarrow{AB}$. When moving point C, it should remain on $\overrightarrow{AE}$.

Conjecture

ERROR ALERT! Students may have trouble reading the table of trigonometric functions. **Remediation:** Explain what is represented by each column, row, and intersection of a row and column. Then have students practice finding different values in the table.

ADDITIONAL PROBLEM Have students make a table that shows $m\angle A$ and the ratios $\dfrac{\text{leg opposite } \angle A}{\text{hypotenuse}}$, $\dfrac{\text{leg adjacent to } \angle A}{\text{hypotenuse}}$, and $\dfrac{\text{leg opposite } \angle A}{\text{leg adjacent to } \angle A}$. Include values of 10, 20, 30, ..., 80 for $m\angle A$. Ask them to describe any relationships they observe among the ratios.

Materials and Manipulatives

- Geometry software

 Transparencies
11

Math Toolbox   page 550

Investigate

$m\angle A$	$\dfrac{DE}{AE}$
10	0.17
20	0.34
30	0.5
40	0.64
50	0.77
60	0.87
70	0.94
80	0.98

Extend

$m\angle A$	$\dfrac{DA}{AE}$	$m\angle A$	$\dfrac{DE}{DA}$
10	0.98	10	0.18
20	0.94	20	0.36
30	0.87	30	0.58
40	0.77	40	0.84
50	0.64	50	1.19
60	0.5	60	1.73
70	0.34	70	2.75
80	0.17	80	5.67

Math ToolboX   Technology

Exploring Trigonometric Ratios

Before Lesson 11-2

Work in pairs or small groups.

Construct

Use geometry software to construct $\overrightarrow{AB}$ and $\overrightarrow{AC}$ so that $\angle A$ is acute. Through a point D on $\overrightarrow{AB}$ construct a line perpendicular to $\overrightarrow{AB}$ that intersects $\overrightarrow{AC}$ in point E. Moving point D enlarges or reduces $\triangle ADE$. Moving point C changes the size of $\angle A$. **Check students' work.**

Investigate

- Measure $\angle A$ and then find the lengths of the sides of the triangle. Calculate the ratio $\dfrac{\text{length of leg opposite } \angle A}{\text{length of hypotenuse}}$, which is $\dfrac{DE}{AE}$. **Check students' work.**

- Move point D to change the size of the right triangle without changing the size of $\angle A$. Does the ratio change as the size of the triangle changes?   **no**

- Move point C to change the size of $\angle A$. How does the ratio change as the size of $\angle A$ changes? What value does the ratio approach as $m\angle A$ approaches 0? as $m\angle A$ approaches 90?   **As $m\angle A$ increases, so does the ratio; 0; 1**

- Make a table that shows $m\angle A$ and the ratio $\dfrac{\text{length of leg opposite } \angle A}{\text{length of hypotenuse}}$. In your table, include values of 10, 20, 30, . . . , 80 for $m\angle A$. **See margin for table.**

Conjecture

Compare your table with the table of trigonometric ratios on page 674. Do your values for $\dfrac{\text{length of leg opposite } \angle A}{\text{length of hypotenuse}}$ match the values in one of the columns of the table? What is the name of this ratio in the table?
The values match those in the sine column; sine.

Extend

- Repeat the investigation for the ratio $\dfrac{\text{length of leg adjacent to } \angle A}{\text{length of hypotenuse}}$, which is $\dfrac{DA}{EA}$.

- Repeat the investigation for the ratio $\dfrac{\text{length of leg opposite } \angle A}{\text{length of leg adjacent to } \angle A}$, which is $\dfrac{ED}{DA}$.

- **The smaller the measure of the angle, the closer DA is to AE; the values are between 0 and 1.**

- **The greater the measure of the angle, the greater is the ratio; the values are positive and can be arbitrarily large.**

See margin for tables.

PROBLEM OF THE DAY

A rectangle with integral side lengths has an area numerically equivalent to three times its perimeter. What are its possible dimensions? **7 by 42, 8 by 24, 9 by 18, 10 by 15, or 12 by 12**

Problem of the Day is also available in Transparencies.

CONNECTING TO PRIOR KNOWLEDGE Draw several right triangles. For each acute angle, have students find the ratios of the following lengths.

$$\frac{\text{leg opposite the angle}}{\text{hypotenuse}} \quad \text{and} \quad \frac{\text{leg adjacent the angle}}{\text{hypotenuse}}$$

Example 1

Discuss with students each step taken to find the cosine and sine of the angles in parts a–d: writing the definition, identifying the legs, and substituting side lengths.

Make sure students understand why their observations in Question 1 can be expressed as $\sin x° = \cos (90 - x)°$ by having them substitute several values for x, noticing the angles are complements and the ratios are equal.

CRITICAL THINKING Questions 2–3 Ask students to summarize what they learned about the sine and cosine ratios of the special right triangles.

What You'll Learn
- Calculating sines and cosines of acute angles in right triangles
- Using sine and cosine to determine unknown measures in right triangles

...And Why

To understand how the ratios were used to calculate the sizes of orbits of planets

What You'll Need
- centimeter ruler
- graph paper
- calculator

Connections 🌐 Astronomy . . . and more

11-2 The Sine and Cosine Ratios

THINK AND DISCUSS

The tangent ratio, as you've seen, involves both legs of a right triangle. The sine and cosine ratios involve one leg and the hypotenuse.

sine of $\angle A = \dfrac{\text{leg opposite } \angle A}{\text{hypotenuse}}$

cosine of $\angle A = \dfrac{\text{leg adjacent to } \angle A}{\text{hypotenuse}}$

These equations can be abbreviated:

$$\sin A = \frac{\text{opposite}}{\text{hypotenuse}}$$

$$\cos A = \frac{\text{adjacent}}{\text{hypotenuse}}$$

Example 1

Refer to $\triangle GRT$ at the left. Find each ratio.

a. $\sin T$ 　　b. $\cos T$
c. $\sin G$ 　　d. $\cos G$

a. $\sin T = \dfrac{\text{opposite}}{\text{hypotenuse}} = \dfrac{8}{17}$ 　　b. $\cos T = \dfrac{\text{adjacent}}{\text{hypotenuse}} = \dfrac{15}{17}$

c. $\sin G = \dfrac{\text{opposite}}{\text{hypotenuse}} = \dfrac{15}{17}$ 　　d. $\cos G = \dfrac{\text{adjacent}}{\text{hypotenuse}} = \dfrac{8}{17}$

1a. The leg adjacent to $\angle G$ is opposite $\angle T$.

1. a. Explain why $\sin T = \cos G = \frac{8}{17}$. **See left.**
    b. The word *cosine* is derived from the words *complement's sine*. Which angle in $\triangle GRT$ is the complement of $\angle T$? of $\angle G$? $\angle G$; $\angle T$
    c. Explain why the derivation of the word *cosine* makes sense. **The cosine of an angle is the sine of the complementary angle.**

Another way of describing the pattern in Question 1 is to say that $\sin x° = \cos (90 - x)°$ for values of x between 0 and 90. This type of equation is called an **identity** because it is always true for the allowed values of the variable. You will discover other identities in the exercises.

2. Refer to $\triangle PQR$ at the left. Find each ratio.
    a. $\sin P$ $\frac{\sqrt{2}}{2}$ 　　b. $\cos P$ $\frac{\sqrt{2}}{2}$
    c. $\sin R$ $\frac{\sqrt{2}}{2}$ 　　d. $\cos R$ $\frac{\sqrt{2}}{2}$

3. Refer to $\triangle TSN$ at the right. Find each ratio.
    a. $\sin S$ $\frac{\sqrt{3}}{2}$ 　　b. $\cos S$ $\frac{1}{2}$
    c. $\sin T$ $\frac{1}{2}$ 　　d. $\cos T$ $\frac{\sqrt{3}}{2}$

Lesson Planning Options

Prerequisite Skills
- Understanding of ratios

Assignment Options for Exercises On Your Own

  Core 1–16, 20–23
  Extension 17–19

Use Mixed Review to maintain skills.

Resources

📖 **Student Edition**
Skills Handbook, p. 646
Extra Practice, p. 644
Glossary/Study Guide

Teaching Resources
Chapter Support File, Ch. 11
- Practice 11-2 (two worksheets)
- Reteaching 11-2
- Alternative Activity 11-2
Classroom Manager 11-2
Glossary, Spanish Resources

Transparencies
5, 11, 112, 116

551

AUDITORY LEARNING Some students will confuse the definitions of the three trigonometric ratios. Suggest the mnemonic device **SOHCAHTOA**, or **S**ome **O**ld **H**orse **C**aught **A H**orse **T**aking **O**ats **A**way for: **S**ine equals **O**pposite over **H**ypotenuse; **C**osine equals **A**djacent over **H**ypotenuse; **T**angent equals **O**pposite over **A**djacent.

VISUAL LEARNING Have students make a poster which displays a right triangle and the three trigonometric ratios.

Example 2 *Relating to the Real World* ···················

Make sure students understand the diagram. Begin by asking them to identify the two planets and to describe what each side of the triangle represents. Then have them identify which side of the triangle is the hypotenuse and which leg is opposite ∠1.

Students may want to calculate how many miles Mercury is from the sun by multiplying 0.38 by 93 million miles.

CRITICAL THINKING Ask students to describe two ways to find the distance from Earth to Mercury.

ERROR ALERT! **Question 5b and c** Some students will have difficulty solving equations with *x* in the denominator. **Remediation:** Review techniques for solving, such as cross multiplying, multiplying by the LCD, or taking the reciprocal of both sides.

Additional Examples

FOR EXAMPLE 1 ···················

Refer to the triangle in Example 1. Let $TG = 25$, $GR = 7$, and $TR = 24$. Find each ratio.

a. sin T $\frac{7}{25}$ **b.** cos T $\frac{24}{25}$
c. sin G $\frac{24}{25}$ **d.** cos G $\frac{7}{25}$

Discussion: *In $\triangle ABC$, if tan $A = \frac{\sqrt{7}}{3}$ and sin $A = \frac{\sqrt{7}}{4}$, can you find cos A?*

FOR EXAMPLE 2 ···················

Find the height of the building to the nearest foot. **41 ft**

Discussion: *Describe another way to find the height of the building that uses a different trigonometric ratio.*

FOR EXAMPLE 3 ···················

Refer to the diagram in Example 3. If $LO = 6$ and $OF = 3$, find $m\angle O$ to the nearest degree. **60**

Discussion: *Describe another way to find $m\angle O$ that uses a different trigonometric ratio.*

552

Who? Vera Rubin (1928–) used techniques of indirect measurement to determine the speeds at which stars in far-off galaxies travel.

What? 1 AU (astronomical unit) is defined as the average distance from Earth to the sun (about 93 million miles).

GRAPHING CALCULATOR HINT

On a scientific calculator, enter 22.3 [SIN]. On a graphing calculator, enter [SIN] 22.3 [ENTER].

The trigonometric ratios have been known for centuries. People in many cultures have used them to solve problems—especially problems involving distances that cannot be measured directly.

Example 2 **Relating to the Real World** ···········

Astronomy The Polish astronomer Nicolaus Copernicus (1473–1543) developed a method for determining the size of the orbits of planets closer to the sun than Earth. The key to his method was determining when the planets were in the position shown in the diagram, and then measuring ∠1. If $m\angle 1 = 22.3$ for Mercury, how far is Mercury from the sun in astronomical units (AU)?

$$\sin 22.3° = \frac{x}{1} \quad \text{Use the sine ratio.}$$
$$0.38 \approx x \quad \text{Use a calculator to find sin 22.3°.}$$

So Mercury is about 0.38 AU from the sun.

4. Try This If $m\angle 1 = 46.1$ for Venus, how far is Venus from the sun? **about 0.72 AU**

5. Find the value of *x* to the nearest tenth.

a.   b.   c.

When you know the lengths of a leg and the hypotenuse of a right triangle, you can use inverse sine or inverse cosine functions on a calculator to find the measures of the acute angles.

Example 3
· · · · · · · · · · · · · · ·

Find $m\angle L$ to the nearest degree.

$\cos L = \frac{2.5}{4.0}$ Use the cosine ratio.

$= \frac{5}{8}$ Simplify the right side.

$m\angle L = \cos^{-1}\left(\frac{5}{8}\right)$ Use inverse cosine.

(5 ÷ 8) cos⁻¹ *51.317813*

So $m\angle L \approx 51$.

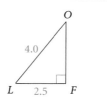

6. Try This Find the value of *x*. Round your answer to the nearest degree.

a. **41**   b. **68**   c.

W O R K   T O G E T H E R

7. Copy the table at the right. Complete it by using a centimeter ruler to measure the triangles at the left to the nearest millimeter. Because the hypotenuse of each triangle is 10 cm, you shouldn't need a calculator to compute the ratios.   **Answers may vary slightly. See margin p. 554 for table.**

8. Algebra Graph the ordered pairs $(x, \sin x°)$ on the coordinate plane for values of *x* in the domain $0 < x < 90$. Connect the points with a smooth curve.   **8–9. See margin p. 554.**

9. Algebra Graph the ordered pairs $(x, \cos x°)$ on the same coordinate plane. Again, connect the points with a smooth curve.

10. Transformations What transformation maps one of the curves onto the other?   reflection in *x* = 45

x	sin *x*°	cos *x*°
10	■	■
20	■	■
30	■	■
40	■	■
50	■	■
60	■	■
70	■	■
80	■	■

553

page 553   Work Together

7.

x	sin x°	cos x°
10	0.17	0.98
20	0.34	0.94
30	0.50	0.87
40	0.64	0.77
50	0.77	0.64
60	0.87	0.50
70	0.94	0.34
80	0.98	0.17

8–9.

pages 554–555   On Your Own

5. Yes; the other acute angle is the complement of the 1st. You can use the sine, cosine, and tangent ratios to find the length of the other sides.

17. $\sin A = \dfrac{\text{opposite}}{\text{hypotenuse}}$,

$\cos A = \dfrac{\text{adjacent}}{\text{hypotenuse}}$;

$\sin A \div \cos A$

$= \dfrac{\text{opposite}}{\text{hypotenuse}} \div \dfrac{\text{adjacent}}{\text{hypotenuse}}$

$= \dfrac{\text{opposite}}{\text{adjacent}} = \tan A$

for any $\angle A$ $0 < m\angle A < 90$

554

Exercises	**ON YOUR OWN**	

Express sin M and cos M as ratios. $\frac{1}{2}; \frac{\sqrt{3}}{2}$

1. $\frac{7}{25}; \frac{24}{25}$

2. $\frac{4\sqrt{2}}{9}; \frac{7}{9}$

3.

4. Escalators The world's longest escalator is in the subway system of St. Petersburg, Russia. The escalator has a vertical rise of 195 ft 9.5 in. and rises at an angle of 10.4°. How long is the escalator? Round your answer to the nearest foot. **1085 ft**

5. Writing Leona Halfmoon said that if she had a diagram that showed the measure of one acute angle and the length of one side of a right triangle, she could find the measure of the other acute angle and the lengths of the other sides. Is she right? Explain. **See margin.**

Find the value of x. Round lengths of segments to the nearest tenth and angle measures to the nearest degree.

6. 11.5

7. 8.3

8. 17.9

9. 21

10. 51

11. 46

12. 66

13. 106.5

14. 3.4

15. Standardized Test Prep In $\triangle ABC$, $m\angle B = 90$. Find sin C. **D**

A. $\frac{BC}{AC}$ **B.** $\frac{BC}{AB}$ **C.** $\frac{AB}{BC}$ **D.** $\frac{AB}{AC}$ **E.** $\frac{AC}{AB}$

16. Agriculture Jane is planning to build a new grain silo with a radius of 15 ft. She reads that the recommended slope of the roof is 22°. She wants the roof to overhang the edge of the silo by 1 ft. What should the slant height of the roof be? Give your answer in feet and inches. **about 17 ft 3 in.**

17. Critical Thinking Use what you know about trigonometric ratios to show that the following equation is an identity. **See margin.**

$$\tan A = \sin A \div \cos A$$

EXTENSION Exercise 18 Have students use the definitions of sine and cosine and the Pythagorean Theorem to prove their conjectures are true.

Exercises MIXED REVIEW

Exercise 28 Students are given the circumferences of two spheres and asked to find the ratio of their volumes. Point out that the simplified ratio of the volumes does not contain π.

GETTING READY FOR LESSON 11-3 These exercises prepare students to identify and use angles of elevation and depression to solve problems.

THE BIG IDEA Ask students: *Explain how you decide which trigonometric ratio to use to solve a problem.*

RETEACHING ACTIVITY Students use sine and cosine to determine unknown measures in right triangles. (Reteaching worksheet 11-2)

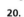

18. a. *Open-ended* Pick three values of *x* between 0 and 90. For each value, evaluate the expression $(\sin x°)^2 + (\cos x°)^2$. **1; 1; 1**
   b. *Patterns* Use your results from part (a) to make a **conjecture**.

18b. For any value of *x* between 0 and 90, $(\sin x°)^2 + (\cos x°)^2 = 1.$

19. *Astronomy* Copernicus had to devise a method different from the one in Example 2 in order to find the size of the orbits of planets farther from the sun than Earth. His method involved noting the number of days between the times that the planets were in the positions labeled A and B in the diagram. Using this time and the number of days in each planet's year, he calculated the measures of the angles labeled 1 and 2.
   a. For Mars, $m\angle 1 = 55.2$ and $m\angle 2 = 103.8$. How far is Mars from the sun in astronomical units (AU)? **about 1.51 AU**
   b. For Jupiter, $m\angle 1 = 21.9$ and $m\angle 2 = 100.8$. How far is Jupiter from the sun in astronomical units (AU)? **about 5.19 AU**

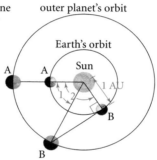

Find *w* and then *x*. Round lengths of segments to the nearest tenth and angle measures to the nearest degree.

20.

$w = 3; x = 41$

21.

$w = 37; x = 7.5$

22.

$w = 68.3; x = 151.6$

23.

$w = 59; x = 20.0$

Exercises MIXED REVIEW

Find the value of each variable. When an answer is not a whole number, round to the nearest tenth.

24. $\square ABCD$

$a = 105; b = 75$

25. rhombus *QRST*

$a = 90; b = 40; c = 50$

26. rectangle *JKLM*

$a = 30; b = 5$

27. kite *WXYZ*

$a = 90; b = 12.6; c = 3$

28. *Sports* The circumference of a softball is 12 in. The circumference of a field hockey ball is 9 in. How many times larger than the volume of the field hockey ball is the volume of the softball? **about 2.37 times larger**

Getting Ready for Lesson 11-3
Refer to rectangle *ABCD* to complete the statements.

29. $\angle 1 \cong \blacksquare \ \angle 7$

30. $\angle 5 \cong \blacksquare \ \angle 11$

31. $\angle 3 \cong \blacksquare \ \angle 6$

32. $m\angle 1 + m\angle 5 = \blacksquare$ **90**

33. $m\angle 10 + m\angle 3 = \blacksquare$ **180**

34. $\angle 10 \cong \blacksquare$ $\angle 8$

Name ___ Class ___ Date ___
Reteaching 11-2

Name ___ Class ___ Date ___
Practice 11-2

Name ___ Class ___ Date ___
Practice 11-2
Mixed Exercises
Express sin *P* and cos *P* as ratios.

Find the value of *x*. Round lengths of segments to the nearest tenth and angle measures to the nearest degree.

Lesson Quiz

Lesson Quiz is also available in Transparencies.

1. Express sin *K* as a ratio. $\dfrac{3\sqrt{5}}{9}$

2. Express cos *K* as a ratio. $\dfrac{6}{9}$

3. If $m\angle G = 25$ and $GE = 10$, find *ED* to the nearest tenth. **4.2**

4. If $GD = 8$ and $GE = 13$, find $m\angle G$ to the nearest degree. **52**

555

Can you move two lines of the "house" to make it face the other direction?

Problem of the Day is also available in Transparencies.

CONNECTING TO PRIOR KNOWLEDGE Draw two parallel lines cut by a transversal. Label the angles formed with the numbers 1–8. Then ask students to identify congruent angles. Have them justify their answers.

THINK AND DISCUSS

ESL Relate the meaning of *angle of depression* to depressions in terrain or the Great Depression. Relate the meaning of and *angle of elevation* to an elevator or land elevation.

VISUAL LEARNING Use different colors to indicate angles of elevation and angles of depression.

ERROR ALERT! Some students will label the angle of elevation or depression as the angle made with a vertical line instead of a horizontal line. **Remediation:** Draw several examples of objects at two different heights and have students practice drawing the angles of elevation and depression.

Lesson Planning Options

Prerequisite Skills

- Using trigonometric ratios

Assignment Options for Exercises On Your Own

Core 1–9, 12–14
Extension 10–11

Use Mixed Review to maintain skills.

Resources

 Student Edition

Skills Handbook, p. 646
Extra Practice, p. 644
Glossary/Study Guide

 Teaching Resources

Chapter Support File, Ch. 11
- Practice 11-3 (two worksheets)
- Reteaching 11-3
Classroom Manager 11-3
Glossary, Spanish Resources

 Transparencies

113

Connections Surveying . . . and more

11-3 Angles of Elevation and Depression

What You'll Learn

- Identifying angles of elevation and depression
- Using angles of elevation and depression and trigonometric ratios to solve problems

...And Why

To calculate distances indirectly in a variety of real-world settings

What You'll Need

- calculator

1. The horizontal lines are ∥, so alt. interior ∠s are ≅.

THINK AND DISCUSS

Suppose a person in a hot-air balloon sees a person at an angle 38° *below* a horizontal line. This angle is an **angle of depression.** At the same time, the person on the ground sees the hot-air balloon at an angle 38° *above* a horizontal line. This angle is an **angle of elevation.**

Horizontal line
Angle of depression
Angle of elevation
Horizontal line

1. Refer to the diagram. What property of parallel lines ensures that the angle of elevation is congruent to the angle of depression?
   See left.

Example 1

Describe each angle as it relates to the objects in the diagram.

a. ∠1   **b.** ∠4

a. angle of depression from the peak to the hiker
b. angle of elevation from the hut to the hiker
   2a. angle of elevation from the hiker to the peak

2. **Try This** Describe each angle as it relates to the diagram in Example 1.
   a. ∠2   **b.** ∠3
   2b. angle of depression from the hiker to the hut

Surveyors use two main instruments to measure angles of elevation and depression. They are the *transit* and the *theodolite.* On both instruments, the surveyor sets the horizon line perpendicular to the direction of gravity. Using gravity to find the horizon line ensures accurate measures even on sloping surfaces.

horizon line

pull of gravity

Example 1

Make sure that students understand the need to state from where and to where (i.e., "from the peak to the hiker" or "from the hut to the hiker") when describing an angle of elevation or depression.

MAKING CONNECTIONS One of the tools surveyors use to measure distance is an electronic distance measurement device (EDM). An electromagnetic impulse is transmitted from one point to another, from where it is reflected back to the original point. The time the signal travels and the known speed of the impulse are used to calculate the distance between points.

Example 2   Relating to the Real World

MAKING CONNECTIONS Delicate Arch is one of 90 arches that have been discovered in the park. These giant stone arches are carved from the red sandstone of the Colorado plateau by the erosive forces of frost, wind, and rain. The red sandstone dates to the Jurassic Period, the age of dinosaurs.

Question 3 Discuss with students the most convenient ratio to use in solving this problem. Then ask students to describe alternative methods.

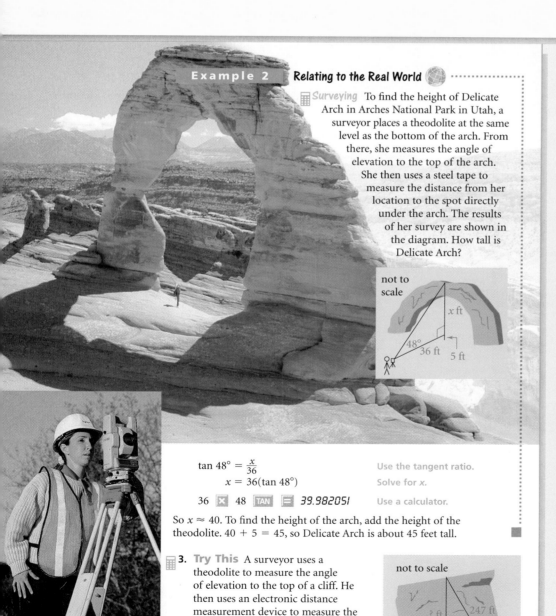

Example 2   Relating to the Real World

Surveying To find the height of Delicate Arch in Arches National Park in Utah, a surveyor places a theodolite at the same level as the bottom of the arch. From there, she measures the angle of elevation to the top of the arch. She then uses a steel tape to measure the distance from her location to the spot directly under the arch. The results of her survey are shown in the diagram. How tall is Delicate Arch?

$\tan 48° = \frac{x}{36}$ Use the tangent ratio.

$x = 36(\tan 48°)$ Solve for x.

36 ✕ 48 TAN ▤ 39.982051   Use a calculator.

So $x \approx 40$. To find the height of the arch, add the height of the theodolite. $40 + 5 = 45$, so Delicate Arch is about 45 feet tall. ▪

3. Try This A surveyor uses a theodolite to measure the angle of elevation to the top of a cliff. He then uses an electronic distance measurement device to measure the distance from the theodolite to the top of the cliff. His measurements are shown in the diagram. How tall is the cliff? Round your answer to the nearest foot. **about 234 ft**

Additional Examples

FOR EXAMPLE 1

Describe ∠1 and ∠2 as they relate to the objects in the diagram.

∠1 is the angle of depression from the plane to the tower; ∠2 is the angle of elevation from the tower to the plane.

Discussion: *How are ∠1 and ∠2 related? Explain.*

FOR EXAMPLE 2

Refer to the diagram above. The angle of depression from the plane to the tower is 25° and the plane is 1000 ft above the tower. What is the horizontal distance from the plane to the tower? **≈ 2145 ft**

Discussion: *Describe another way you could solve this problem.*

FOR EXAMPLE 3

Refer to the diagram above. The angle of depression is 15° and the horizontal distance from the plane to the tower is 5,200 ft. How high above the tower is the plane? **≈ 1393 ft**

Example 3 Relating to the Real World 🌐 ··················

Help students understand that the distance from the airplane to the airport is different from the *horizontal* distance from the airplane to the airport. Ask students which distance is greater and why.

Explain to students that the airport's having an altitude of 1007 ft does not mean it is 1007 ft above ground. The airport is 1107 ft above sea level. Also make sure that students understand why the plane is 1707 ft above the airport, not 2714 ft.

Exercises 1 and 2 Students should state whether each angle is an angle of elevation or an angle of depression, and from what object to what object.

DIVERSITY Exercise 3 This is a good opportunity to discuss disabilities with students. Students may be surprised to learn that while some people are born with disabilities caused by cerebral palsy, spina bifida, and Down's syndrome, about three-fourths of the disabled Americans today are so because of accidents, diseases, and war.

Technology Options

For Exercise 13, students may use a drawing program to draw the diagrams and a word-processing program to write their problems.

Prentice Hall Technology

 Software
- Secondary Math Lab Toolkit™
- Computer Item Generator 11-3

Internet
- See the Prentice Hall site. (http://www.phschool.com)

Too low   Slightly low

On correct
approach path

Slightly high   Too high

How? Most airports place lights near the runway that signal the pilot if the angle of descent is too great or too small. The lights shown here are red when viewed from above and white when viewed from below. Each of the four lights is tilted at a different angle.

Example 3 Relating to the Real World 🌐 ···········

 Aviation If you live near an airport, you have probably noticed that airplanes follow certain paths as they prepare for landing. These paths are called *approaches*. The approach to runway 17 of the Ponca City Municipal Airport in Oklahoma calls for the pilot to begin a 3° descent starting from an altitude of 2714 ft. How many miles from the runway is an airplane at the beginning of this approach?

3° angle of descent
2714 ft
not to scale   Altitude of airport: 1007 ft

The airplane is 2714 − 1007, or 1707 ft above the level of the airport. Use trigonometry to find the desired distance.

1707 ft

$\sin 3° = \dfrac{1707}{x}$ Use the sine ratio.

$x = \dfrac{1707}{\sin 3°}$ Solve for *x*.

1707 ⊟ 3 SIN ⊟ *32616.2*   Use a calculator to find *x*.

⊟ 5280 ⊟ *6.1773105*   Convert feet to miles by dividing by 5280.

An airplane is about 6.2 miles from the runway at the beginning of the approach to runway 17 at Ponca City.

Describe each angle as it relates to the objects in the diagram. 1–2. See margin p. 559.

1. a. ∠1
b. ∠2
c. ∠3
d. ∠4

2. a. ∠1
b. ∠2
c. ∠3
d. ∠4

Jim   Kelley

3. Engineering The Americans with Disabilities Act states that wheelchair ramps can have a slope no greater than $\frac{1}{12}$. Find the maximum angle of elevation of a ramp with this slope. Round your answer to the nearest tenth. **4.8°**

558

ERROR ALERT! Exercise 4 Students may have difficulty if they try to find the height of the building directly.
Remediation: Help students see that the height of the smaller building equals the height of the taller building minus the height of the right triangle shown.

Exercises 4–5 Discuss with students that the phrase "not to scale" shown in the diagram means that the lengths and heights of objects are not proportional.

Exercise 7 Make sure students understand that the distance of 1503 m is the length of the hypotenuse of the triangle created by the meteorologist, the weather balloon, and the point on the ground directly below the weather balloon.

Exercise 8 Make sure students understand how to label the "angle of elevation of the sun" in their diagrams.

Exercise 9 Help students draw a diagram for this problem or have them work on it in groups. Make sure students understand that they are to find the horizontal distance from the blimp to the stadium.

Solve each problem. Round your answer to the nearest unit unless instructed otherwise.

4. Two office buildings are 51 m apart. The height of the taller building is 207 m. The angle of depression from the top of the taller building to the top of the shorter building is 15°. Find the height of the shorter building. **193 m**

15°
51 m
207 m
not to scale

5. A surveyor is 980 ft from the base of the world's tallest fountain at Fountain Hills, Arizona. The angle of elevation to the top of the column of water is 29.7°. His angle measuring device is at the same level as the base of the fountain. Find the height of the column of water to the nearest 10 ft. **560 ft**

not to scale
29.7°
980 ft

6. On the observation platform in the crown of the Statue of Liberty, Miguel is approximately 250 ft above ground. He sights a ship in New York harbor and measures the angle of depression as 18°. Find the distance from the ship to the base of the statue. **769 ft**

7. A meteorologist measures the angle of elevation of a weather balloon as 41°. A radio signal from the balloon indicates that it is 1503 m from her location. How high is the weather balloon above the ground? **986 m**

8. The world's tallest unsupported flagpole is a 282-ft-tall steel pole in Surrey, British Columbia. The shortest shadow cast by the pole during the year is 137 ft long. What is the angle of elevation of the sun when the shortest shadow is cast? **64°**

9. A blimp is flying to cover a football game. The pilot sights the stadium at a 7° angle of depression. The blimp is flying at an altitude of 400 m. How many kilometers is the blimp from the point 400 m above the stadium? Round your answer to the nearest tenth. **3.3 km**

PROBLEM SOLVING HINT

Draw a diagram using the given information. Then decide which trigonometric ratio you can use to solve the problem.

pages 558–560 On Your Own

1a. angle of elevation from the submarine to the boat

b. angle of depression from the boat to the submarine

c. angle of elevation from the boat to the lighthouse

d. angle of depression from the lighthouse to the boat

2a. angle of elevation from Jim to the waterfall

b. angle of elevation from Kelley to the waterfall

c. angle of depression from the waterfall to Jim

d. angle of depression from the waterfall to Kelley

KINESTHETIC LEARNING Exercise 10 If possible, take students outside right before noon. Drive a stick upright into the ground in full sun. At noon have students measure the length of the stick's shadow and the height of the stick that is above ground. Then have them calculate the elevation of the sun.

CRITICAL THINKING Exercise 11 You may also want to ask students how they could find the height of the tower.

ESL Exercise 11 Explain to students what "guy wires" are and why and how they are used.

ALTERNATIVE ASSESSMENT Exercise 13 Have students create their own problems using trigonometric ratios. Have them write each problem on an index card and the worked out solution on the back. Use them as a review or testing.

STANDARDIZED TEST TIP Exercise 14 Students may want to let $m\angle Y = 60$ and $m\angle Z = 30$. This satisfies $m\angle Y > m\angle Z$ and students can use the side lengths 1, $\sqrt{3}$, and 2 to calculate the trigonometric ratios quickly.

Chapter Project **FIND OUT BY MEASURING** Before assigning this activity, decide whether you want all students to measure the height of the same object. Also, tell students that each solution should be accompanied by a diagram showing the distances and angle they measured.

10a. Measure the length of the stick. Then measure the length of the shortest shadow. The ratio of the length of the stick to the length of the shadow is the tangent ratio of the angle of elevation of the sun at noon.

11. The ground is one leg of a rt. △ and the wire is the hypotenuse. Measure the distance from the ground end of the wire to the base of the tower. Then divide this length by the cosine ratio of the angle formed by the wire and the ground.

page 561 Mixed Review

18.

All Adults

Bluegrass Buyers

19b. 55–64; 55–64 year olds have a higher share of bluegrass sales than their share of population.

See margin.

10. a. *Navigation* A simple method for finding a north-south line is shown in the diagram. How could you use this method to also find the angle of elevation of the sun at noon?

    b. *Research* For locations in the continental United States, the relationship between the latitude ℓ and angle of elevation a of the sun at noon on the first day of summer is $a = 90° - \ell + 23\frac{1}{2}°$. Find the latitude of your town and determine the angle of elevation of the sun on the first day of summer.
    Check students' work.

Put a stick in the ground before noon and mark the end of its shadow every 15 minutes. When the shadows begin to lengthen, stop marking the shadows. The mark closest to the stick is directly north of the stick.

11. *Critical Thinking* A television tower is located on a flat plot of land. The tower is supported by several guy wires. Explain how you could find the length of any of these wires. Assume that you are able to measure distances along the ground as well as angles formed by wires and the ground. **See margin.**

12. *Meteorology* One method that meteorologists use to find the height of a layer of clouds above the ground is to shine a bright spotlight directly up onto the cloud layer and measure the angle of elevation from a known distance away. Find the height of the cloud layer in the diagram to the nearest 10 m. **1080 m**

13. a. *Open-ended* Draw and label a diagram that shows a real-world example of an angle of elevation and an angle of depression.
    b. *Writing* Write a word problem that uses the angle of depression from your diagram. Include a detailed solution to your problem.

a–b. Answers may vary. See back of book for sample.

14. *Standardized Test Prep* In the diagram, $m\angle Y > m\angle Z$. Which statement is *not* true? **E**
    A. $\sin Y > \cos Y$ **B.** $\cos Y < \cos Z$ **C.** $\tan Y > \sin Y$
    D. $\tan Z > \cos Y$ **E.** $\cos Z > \sin Y$

Chapter Project **Find Out by Measuring**

Use your clinometer to measure the angle of elevation to an object such as the roof of your school or the top of a flagpole. Then determine how far away you are from the object that you measured. Use what you've learned about trigonometry to find the height of the object. Be sure to add your own height to the height you come up with!

Check students' work.

Exercises **MIXED REVIEW**

Data Analysis **Refer to the graph to answer the questions.** 15–18. Answers may vary slightly.

15. What percent of adults are 18–24 years old? about 13.5%

16. What percent of bluegrass purchases did adults 18–24 make? about 18.5%

17. Which age group contains the least number of people? 55–64

18. Create two circle graphs using the data from the double bar graph. See margin.

19. a. Which age group buys more bluegrass: 35–44-year-olds or 55–64-year-olds? 35–44
   b. Which of these two age groups likes bluegrass more? Explain. 55–64; See margin for explanation.

20. **Coordinate Geometry** Find the equation of the line that passes through $(3, 7)$ and is parallel to the line $y = \frac{3}{2}x - 5$. $y = \frac{3}{2}x + \frac{5}{2}$

Getting Ready for Lesson 11-4

Transformations **Find the image of each point under a translation with the given translation vector.**

21. $(2, 7); \langle 1, -9 \rangle$ $(3, -2)$

22. $(-3, 0); \langle 6, -1 \rangle$ $(3, -1)$

23. $(4, -7); \langle 5, 0 \rangle$ $(9, -7)$

24. $(-5, 12); \langle -8, -11 \rangle$ $(-13, 1)$

Who Buys Bluegrass Music?
from a survey of adults who bought bluegrass music in the last year

0% 5% 10% 15% 20% 25%
18–24
25–34
35–44
45–54
55–64
65+

■ all adults
■ bluegrass buyers

Source: *International Bluegrass Music Association, Owensboro, KY*

Exercises **CHECKPOINT**

1. **Standardized Test Prep** Which value is greatest? C
   A. sin 30°   **B.** cos 45°   **C.** tan 60°
   D. sin 10°   **E.** cos 70°

2. **Architecture** The Leaning Tower of Pisa leans about 5.5° from vertical. How far from the base of the tower will an object dropped from the tower land? about 17 ft

3. A captain of a sailboat sights the top of a lighthouse at a 17° angle of elevation. A navigation chart shows the height of the lighthouse to be 120 m. How far is the sailboat from the lighthouse? about 393 m

Find the value of x. Round lengths of segments to the nearest tenth and angle measures to the nearest degree.

4. 15.0

5. 61

6. 20.8

5.5°

Lesson Quiz

Lesson Quiz is also available in Transparencies.

1. Describe ∠1 and ∠2 as they relate to the objects in the diagram.

∠1 is the angle of elevation from the boat to the lighthouse beacon; ∠2 is the angle of depression from the lighthouse beacon to the boat.

2. Refer to the diagram above. The captain of the boat knows that the lighthouse on the coast is 100 m tall. If she measures the angle of elevation to be 2°, how far is the boat from the coast? ≈ 2864 m

561

Students review how to transform literal equations by solving for one variable in terms of the other.

Example 1

Explain to students that it must be stated that $r \neq 0$ because division by zero is not defined.

Example 2

ERROR ALERT! A common error made by students is dividing $2\pi rh$ and A by $2\pi r$ first, then subtracting $2\pi r^2$. **Remediation:** Review the steps for solving an equation: Add or subtract first, then multiply or divide. Use a simpler example like solving $y = 2x + 1$ for x to show that the steps are not interchangeable.

ALTERNATIVE ASSESSMENT Have students work in five groups. Assign each group three of the problems to solve. Then have them present their worked-out solutions to the class.

Transparencies
15, 16

Math ToolboX — Algebra Review

Literal Equations

Before Lesson 11-4

A **literal equation** is an equation involving two or more variables. Formulas are special types of literal equations. You solve for one variable in terms of the others when you transform a literal equation.

Example 1

The formula for the volume of a cylinder is $V = \pi r^2 h$. Find a formula for the height in terms of the radius and volume.

$$V = \pi r^2 h$$
$$\frac{V}{\pi r^2} = \frac{\pi r^2 h}{\pi r^2} \qquad \longleftarrow \text{ Divide each side by } \pi r^2, r \neq 0.$$
$$\frac{V}{\pi r^2} = h \qquad \longleftarrow \text{ Simplify.}$$

The formula for the height is $h = \dfrac{V}{\pi r^2}$.

Example 2

The formula for the surface area of a cylinder is $A = 2\pi rh + 2\pi r^2$. Solve for h.

$$A = 2\pi rh + 2\pi r^2$$
$$A - 2\pi r^2 = 2\pi rh + 2\pi r^2 - 2\pi r^2 \qquad \longleftarrow \text{ Subtract } 2\pi r^2 \text{ from each side.}$$
$$A - 2\pi r^2 = 2\pi rh \qquad \longleftarrow \text{ Simplify.}$$
$$\frac{A - 2\pi r^2}{2\pi r} = \frac{2\pi rh}{2\pi r} \qquad \longleftarrow \text{ Divide each side by } 2\pi r, r \neq 0.$$
$$\frac{A - 2\pi r^2}{2\pi r} = h \qquad \longleftarrow \text{ Simplify.}$$

The formula for the height is $h = \dfrac{A - 2\pi r^2}{2\pi r}$.

Solve each equation for the variable in red.

1. $P = 2w + 2\ell \quad w = \dfrac{P - 2\ell}{2}$

2. $\tan A = \dfrac{y}{x} \quad x = \dfrac{y}{\tan A}$

3. $A = \dfrac{1}{2}bh \quad b = \dfrac{2A}{h}$

4. $C = 2\pi r \quad r = \dfrac{C}{2\pi}$

5. $A = \dfrac{1}{2}(b_1 + b_2)h$ See below.

6. $V = \ell wh \quad h = \dfrac{V}{\ell w}$

7. $A = \dfrac{1}{2}ap \quad a = \dfrac{2A}{p}$

8. $m\angle C + m\angle D = 180$

9. $A = \pi r^2 \quad r = \sqrt{\dfrac{A}{\pi}}$

10. $S = 180(n - 2) \quad n = \dfrac{S + 360}{180}$

11. $V = \dfrac{1}{3}\ell wh \quad w = \dfrac{3V}{\ell h}$

12. $a^2 + b^2 = c^2 \quad b = \sqrt{c^2 - a^2}$

13. $\cos A = \dfrac{b}{c} \quad b = c \cos A$

14. $V = \dfrac{1}{3}\pi r^2 h \quad r = \sqrt{\dfrac{3V}{\pi h}}$

15. $S = \pi r^2 + \pi r\ell \quad \ell = \dfrac{S - \pi r^2}{\pi r}$

5. $b_2 = \dfrac{2A}{h} - b_1$ 8. $m\angle C = 180 - m\angle D$

CONNECTING TO PRIOR KNOWLEDGE Draw a triangle in the coordinate plane and its image under a translation. Have students give the vector that describes the translation. Repeat this using several different triangles.

THINK AND DISCUSS

Help students see that both the vectors used to describe translations and the real-world examples shown have magnitude and direction.

Point out that magnitude is not distance only. For example, magnitude can be weight, speed, or acceleration.

Question 2 Draw the following diagram and discuss the abbreviations. Also discuss the angles formed by the lines.

Connections 🌐 **Air Travel . . . and more**

11-4 Vectors and Trigonometry

THINK AND DISCUSS

A **vector** is any quantity that has *magnitude* (size) and *direction*. In Chapter 3, you used vectors to describe translations. In this lesson you will explore some other applications of vectors. Here are a few.

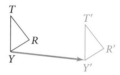

This vector describes the translation $\triangle TRY \rightarrow \triangle T'R'Y'$.

Magnitude: 25 mi/h
Direction: Straight up

Magnitude:
1.62 m/s²
Direction:
Toward center of the moon

Magnitude:
34 yd
Direction:
Straight through the uprights

1b. Yes; the description includes magnitude and direction.

1. *Critical Thinking* Does the sentence contain enough information to describe a vector? Explain. **No; the description gives the direction**
   a. A car heads northwest. **but no magnitude.**
   b. A hiker walks south at 5 miles per hour. **See left.**
   c. The wind blows at 45 kilometers per hour.
   No; the description gives magnitude but no direction.
2. Two sisters, Altheia and Chenice, drive from point A to point B. In describing their trip, Altheia says, "We ended up 71 miles northwest of where we started." Chenice says, "We ended up 50 miles west and 50 miles north of where we started." Explain why both sisters' descriptions of their trip are accurate. **Both descriptions allow you to find the pt. where the trip ended.**

Question 2 suggests two different ways that you can describe a vector.

- *Use its size and direction.* The magnitude of $\overrightarrow{AB}$ is 71 (about $50\sqrt{2}$), and its direction is northwest (or 45° north of west).

- *Use its horizontal and vertical change.* The ordered pair notation $\langle -50, 50 \rangle$ describes $\overrightarrow{AB}$, where -50 represents the horizontal change from A to B, and 50 represents the vertical change.

563

Point out the symbol used to indicate a vector. Make sure students differentiate it from the symbol used to indicate a ray.

Remind students that in ordered pair notation, a negative sign is used to indicate a horizontal change to the left or a vertical change down.

with a beginning (initial point) and end (terminal point). The arrow indicates which point is the initial point and which is the terminal point. Assure students that the context of the problem will clarify whether the arrow is a vector or a ray.

ESL Some students may have difficulty understanding the difference between "south of east" and "east of south." It may be helpful to display a poster with diagrams illustrating the difference. Also include diagrams illustrating "east of north" and "north of east."

Example 1

VISUAL LEARNING Help students understand that the *x*-coordinate is positive and the *y*-coordinate is negative because the direction from the origin to point *L* is right and down.

ERROR ALERT! Some students will have difficulty knowing if an arrow signifies a vector or a ray. **Remediation:** Help students understand that a vector is a directed line segment

Example 2 Relating to the Real World

Discuss with students why the lengths of the legs of the right triangle are 40 and 25.

Additional Examples

FOR EXAMPLE 1

Describe *ON* by using ordered pair notation. Give the coordinates to the nearest tenth. ⟨−1, 1.7⟩

Discussion: *Explain how you determine if the x- and y-coordinates are positive or negative.*

FOR EXAMPLE 2

A tour bus driver drove to a point 20 mi east and 32 mi south of the point at which he started. Find the distance from the starting point and the direction traveled.

37.7 mi in the direction 58° south of east

QUICK REVIEW

In the diagram, *I* is the *initial point* of $\overrightarrow{IT}$ and *T* is its *terminal point.*

Example 1

▦ **Coordinate Geometry** Describe $\overrightarrow{OL}$ by using ordered pair notation. Give the coordinates to the nearest tenth.

Use the sine and cosine ratios to find the values of *x* and *y*.

$\cos 50° = \frac{x}{65}$	$\sin 50° = \frac{y}{65}$	Use sine and cosine.
$x = 65(\cos 50°)$	$y = 65(\sin 50°)$	Solve for the variable.
≈ 41.8	≈ 49.8	Use a calculator.

The *y*-coordinate of the ordered pair is negative since *L* is in the fourth quadrant. So $\overrightarrow{OL} = \langle 41.8, -49.8 \rangle$.

In many applications of vectors, the direction of the vector is described in relation to north, south, east, and west. Here are a few examples.

25° south of east   35° east of north   42° south of west

3. Try This Sketch a vector that has a direction of 30° west of north. See margin p. 566 for sample.

Example 2 Relating to the Real World

▦ **Air Travel** A helicopter lands at a point 40 km west and 25 km south of the point at which it took off. Find the distance that the helicopter flew and the direction of its flight.

Start by drawing a diagram of the vector. To find the distance flown *c*, use the Pythagorean Theorem.

$40^2 + 25^2 = c^2$	Substitute 40 and 25 for the lengths of the legs.
$2225 = c^2$	Simplify the left side.
$c \approx 47$	Take the square root.

To find the direction of the helicopter's flight, find the angle that the vector makes with west.

$\tan x° = \frac{25}{40}$ Use the tangent ratio.

❲ 25 ➗ 40 ❳ TAN⁻¹ *32.005383*   Use a calculator.

The helicopter flew about 47 km at 32° south of west.

▦ **4. Try This** A small plane lands at a point 246 mi east and 76 mi north of the point at which it took off. Find the distance that the plane flew and the direction of its flight. **about 257 mi; 17° north of east**

Exercises 1–4 Suggest that students draw triangles like those shown in Example 1, labeling the legs x and y. Check that they remember to indicate direction with a negative sign, if appropriate, in their ordered pairs.

Exercises 5–8 Make sure students understand their answers should be phrases like "50° north of east."

DIVERSITY Exercise 9 The Greeks were responsible for originating our modern Olympics. The Olympic games originated in ancient Greece in 776 B.C., if not earlier, as a way of saluting their gods. In addition to the sports festival, there were music and oratory competitions and theatrical performances. The Olympics were abolished in the early Christian era (A.D. 386) because of their explicitly pagan overtones. They were revived in 1896.

Coordinate Geometry Describe each vector by using ordered pair notation. Give the coordinates to the nearest unit.

1.

⟨−22, 46⟩

2.

⟨602, 669⟩

3.

⟨−307, −54⟩

4.

⟨38, −65⟩

Describe the direction of each vector.

5.

15° south of west

6.

40° east of south

7.

20° west of south

8.

44° north of west

Biology Solve each problem. Round your answers to the nearest unit, unless otherwise directed.

9. Homing pigeons are capable of returning to their home upon release. Homing pigeons carried news of Olympic victories to various cities in ancient Greece. Suppose one such pigeon took off from Athens and landed in Sparta, which is 73 mi west and 64 mi south of Athens. Find the distance and direction of its flight. **about 97 mi; 41° south of west**

10. Honeybees describe vectors through movement. A bee that discovers a new source of pollen flies back to the hive and does a "dance" for the other bees. The movements of this dance tell other bees how to get to the pollen. Suppose a bee describes a source of pollen 1000 ft away and 60° counterclockwise from the direction of the sun. Draw a diagram of this vector. Include labels for the sun, the hive, and the pollen. **See margin p. 566.**

11. During its adult life, a European eel travels from the Belgian coast to breeding grounds in the Sargasso Sea. This part of the Atlantic Ocean is about 2300 mi south and 4800 mi west of Belgium. Find the distance and direction of the eel's journey. Round the distance to the nearest 100 mi. **5300 mi at 26° south of west**

12. The owners of a golden retriever named Ginger took her from her home to a location 17 mi north and 29 miles east. There, they somehow lost her. Ginger, however, managed to find her way home after 3 days. Find the distance and direction of her journey home (assuming she took the shortest route). **34 mi at 30° south of west**

Technology Options

For Exercises 9–12, students can use a graphing program or a drawing program to draw the diagrams.

Prentice Hall Technology

Software
- Secondary Math Lab Toolkit™
- Computer Item Generator 11-4

Internet
- See the Prentice Hall site. (http://www.phschool.com)

565

WRITING Exercise 13 Ask students to explain how the cartoon illustrates the similarities and differences between $\vec{AB}$ and $\vec{BA}$.

ALTERNATIVE ASSESSMENT Exercise 14 This exercise can help you assess students' understanding of direction. Ask them to support their answer with a diagram and another example.

Exercise 15 Students may need to review the terms *dilation* and *scale factor* which can be found in Lesson 3-7 or the glossary.

CRITICAL THINKING Exercises 17–19 If a sentence does not contain enough information, ask students to rewrite it so it does.

PATTERNS Exercises 24 and 25 Have students compare their definitions and revise them, if necessary.

pages 563–564 Think and Discuss

3.

pages 565–567 On Your Own

10.

14. Yes; since 35° and 55° are complementary angles, both statements describe the same direction.

15. The directions of both vectors are the same. The ratio of the magnitude of the image to the magnitude of the orig. vector is *k*.

13. Writing How are the vectors $\vec{AB}$ and $\vec{BA}$ alike? How are they different? **Vectors *AB* and *BA* have the same magnitude but opp. directions.**

14. Critical Thinking Valerie described the direction of a vector as 35° south of east. Pablo described it as 55° east of south. Could the two be describing the same vector? Explain. **See margin.**

15. Transformational Geometry Point A' is the image of A under a dilation with scale factor k and center O. How are the direction and magnitude of $\vec{OA}$ related to the direction and magnitude of $\vec{OA'}$? **See margin.**

16. Open-ended Name four other vectors with the same magnitude as $\langle -7, -24 \rangle$.
Sample: $\langle 7, 24 \rangle$, $\langle 24, -7 \rangle$, $\langle 20, 15 \rangle$, $\langle -15, -20 \rangle$

Critical Thinking Does each sentence contain enough information to describe a vector? Explain your answer.

17. The angle of elevation of a baseball hit by Frank Thomas is 35°. **No; the description gives the direction but no magnitude.**

18. A rocket is launched upward with an initial thrust of 400,000 lb. **Yes; the description includes magnitude and direction.**

19. A cheetah runs at 71 miles per hour. **No; the description gives magnitude but no direction.**

Find the magnitude and direction of each vector.

20.

about 707 mi; 25° west of south

21.

20 mi/h
50 mi/h

See above.

22.

1000 km
4700 km

about 4800 km; 12° north of west

23.

0.12 in./h
0.19 in./h

See above.

21. about 54 mi/h; 22° north of east

23. about 0.22 in./h; 32° north of east

"Well, lemme think. ... You've stumped me, son. Most folks only wanna know how to go the other way."

24. Patterns Use the diagrams below to write a definition of *equal vectors*.

All of these vectors are equal.   None of these vectors are equal.

25. Patterns Use the diagrams below to write a definition of *parallel vectors*.

All of these vectors are parallel.   None of these vectors are parallel.

24. Vectors are = if they have = magnitudes and the same direction.
25. Vectors are ∥ if they have the same or opp. directions.

566

FIND OUT BY COMPARING Have students measure different objects from the ones in Lesson 11-3. It may be easier to let one group measure at a time. This will allow you to keep a better eye on what is going on and it will avoid the confusion of students getting in each other's way.

Exercises   MIXED REVIEW

JOURNAL Check that students' diagrams and tables include how to describe vectors using ordered pair notation and how to describe the magnitude and direction of vectors.

GETTING READY FOR LESSON 11-5 These exercises prepare students to add vectors.

Wrap Up

THE BIG IDEA Ask students: *Explain the difference between a vector, a line segment, and a ray.*

RETEACHING ACTIVITY Students describe vectors using ordered pair notation. (Reteaching worksheet 11-4)

---

26. *Air Travel* A plane takes off on a runway in the direction 10° east of south. When it reaches 5000 ft, it turns right 45°. It cruises at this altitude for 60 mi. It then turns left 160°, descends, and lands. Match each velocity vector with the appropriate portion of the flight.

A. The plane ascends.
B. The plane cruises.
C. The plane descends.

I. C

II. B

III. A

 Find Out by Comparing

Repeat the activity on page 560, but this time work in groups to estimate the height of a single object on your school grounds. Have each person in your group measure the angle of elevation from a different distance. Then compare results within the group. Write a brief report explaining the variations in your estimates of the object's height. Decide as a group on a single estimate of the object's height. Check students' work.

27. Neither; you need information about at least 1 acute angle or at least 1 other side.

Exercises   MIXED REVIEW

Is each pair of triangles *congruent, similar,* or *neither*? Justify your answers. 27. See above.

27.   **28.**   **29.**

similar; AA~   congruent; AAS

FOR YOUR JOURNAL

Create a diagram or table that summarizes what you learned in this lesson.

30. *Sports* A cylindrical hockey puck is 1 in. high and 3 in. in diameter. What is its volume? Round your answer to the nearest tenth. about 7.1 in.³

31. A circle has radius 7 m. Two radii form a 100° angle. What is the length of the minor arc? Round your answer to the nearest tenth. 12.2 m

Getting Ready for Lesson 11-5

32. a. Find A', the image of $A(4, 3)$ under the translation $\langle 2, 5 \rangle$. $A'(6, 8)$
   b. Find A'', the image of A' under the translation $\langle -5, 6 \rangle$. $A''(1, 14)$
   c. What single translation maps A to A''? $\langle -3, 11 \rangle$

Lesson Quiz

Lesson Quiz is also available in Transparencies.

1. Find the magnitude and direction of the vector. Round to the nearest whole unit. 43 mi/h in the direction of 55° north of east

2. Describe the vector using ordered pair notation. Give the coordinates to the nearest unit.
$\langle -65, 55 \rangle$

567

CONNECTING TO PRIOR KNOWLEDGE Draw a triangle with vertices $A(1, 2)$, $B(6, 1)$, and $C(3, 5)$. Then have students find its image under the translation $\langle -2, -3 \rangle$ followed by the translation $\langle -1, 5 \rangle$. Ask them to give one translation vector that would produce the same image.

THINK AND DISCUSS

Make sure students understand that $\vec{u}$, $\vec{v}$, and $\vec{w}$ represent vectors in ordered pair notation and do not represent lengths.

Example 1

Review with students their definitions of equal vectors from Exercise 24 of Lesson 11-4. Then point out that the head-to-tail method is possible because $\vec{c}$ is "equal" to its image under a translation.

Lesson Planning Options

Prerequisite Skills

- Describing vectors

Assignment Options for Exercises On Your Own

> **Core** 1–16, 20
> **Extension** 17–19

Use Mixed Review to maintain skills.

Resources

 Student Edition

Skills Handbook, pp. 646, 660
Extra Practice, p. 644
Glossary/Study Guide

 Teaching Resources

Chapter Support File, Ch. 11
- Practice 11-5 (two worksheets)
- Reteaching 11-5
Classroom Manager 11-5
Glossary, Spanish Resources

 Transparencies

5, 114, 117, 118

What You'll Learn

- Solving problems that involve vector addition

...And Why

To find the speed and direction of an object that has two forces acting on it

What You'll Need

- graph paper
- a marble
- three straws
- calculator

1. Answers may vary. Sample: The trip from Houston to Memphis is the result of the trip from Houston to New Orleans followed by the trip from New Orleans to Memphis.

 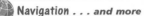
11-5 Adding Vectors

THINK AND DISCUSS

Until now, you've named vectors by using the initial point and terminal point ($\overrightarrow{AB}$, for example). You can also name vectors by using a single lowercase letter, such as $\vec{u}$.

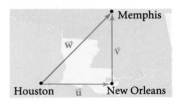

The map shows vectors representing a flight from Houston to Memphis with a stopover in New Orleans. The vector from Houston to Memphis is called the *sum* of the other two vectors. You write this as $\vec{u} + \vec{v} = \vec{w}$.

1. **Critical Thinking** The sum of two vectors is called a **resultant**. Use the example of the trip from Houston to Memphis to explain why this name makes sense. **See left.**

Example 1

Coordinate Geometry Refer to the diagram at the left. Find $\vec{e}$, the sum of $\vec{a}$ and $\vec{c}$.

Draw $\vec{a}$ with its initial point at the origin. Then draw $\vec{c}$ so that its initial point is the terminal point of $\vec{a}$. Finally, draw a vector from the initial point of $\vec{a}$ to the terminal point of $\vec{c}$. This vector is $\vec{e}$, the resultant.

The method of adding vectors shown in Example 1 is called the *head-to-tail method*. (Do you see why?) You can describe the head-to-tail method mathematically by using ordered pair notation.

$$\begin{aligned} \vec{a} + \vec{c} &= \langle 4, 3 \rangle + \langle -1, 2 \rangle &&\text{Express } \vec{a} \text{ and } \vec{c} \text{ in ordered pair notation.} \\ &= \langle 4 + (-1), 3 + 2 \rangle &&\text{Add the } x\text{- and } y\text{-coordinates.} \\ &= \langle 3, 5 \rangle &&\text{Simplify.} \end{aligned}$$

A look back at the diagram confirms that $\langle 3, 5 \rangle$ is indeed the resultant.

> **Adding Vectors**
>
> For $\vec{a} = \langle x_1, y_1 \rangle$ and $\vec{c} = \langle x_2, y_2 \rangle$, $\vec{a} + \vec{c} = \langle x_1 + x_2, y_1 + y_2 \rangle$.
>
> Example: For $\vec{a} = \langle -3, 2 \rangle$ and $\vec{c} = \langle 1, 5 \rangle$, $\vec{a} + \vec{c} = \langle -2, 7 \rangle$.

The diagram at the right shows that you can add vectors in any order. That is, $\vec{u} + \vec{v} = \vec{v} + \vec{u}$. Notice also that the four vectors shown in red form a quadrilateral. This quadrilateral is a parallelogram because its opposite sides are congruent. The result $\vec{w}$ is a diagonal of this parallelogram. This characteristic of vector addition is called the *parallelogram rule*.

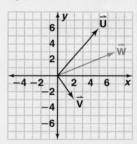

Vector sums can show the result of actions that take place one after the other, such as a trip from Houston to Memphis by way of New Orleans. Vector sums can also show the result of two forces that act at the same time on an object. An example of this is the two forces that act on a boat—the forces of its engine and the current. As shown in the diagram, the force of the current combines with the force of the engine to give the boat its velocity.

A boat traveling in this direction and at this speed . . . hits this current . . . and ends up traveling in this direction and at this speed.

Example 2 Relating to the Real World 🌐 ·················

📐 Navigation A ferry shuttles people from one side of a river to the other. The speed of the ferry in still water is 25 mi/h, and the river flows directly south at 7 mi/h. Suppose the ferry heads directly west. What are the ferry's resulting speed and direction?

25 mi/h
7 mi/h $x°$
c
N
W—E
S

The diagram shows the sum of the two vectors. To find the ferry's speed, use the Pythagorean Theorem to find the length of the resultant.

$c^2 = 25^2 + 7^2$ The lengths of the legs are 25 and 7.
$c^2 = 674$ Simplify.
$c \approx 25.96151$ Use a calculator to take the square root.

To find the ferry's direction, use trigonometry.

$\tan x° = \frac{7}{25}$ Use the tangent ratio.

$x = \tan^{-1}\left(\frac{7}{25}\right)$

$x \approx 15.642246$ Use a calculator.

The ferry's speed is about 26 mi/h, and its direction is about 16° south of west.

📐 **2. Try This** Use the diagram to find the angle at which the ferry must head upriver in order to travel directly across the river.

25 mi/h
7 mi/h
$x°$

about 16° north of west

569

Exercises 23 and 24 Students will need to calculate the heights before they can find the areas.

GETTING READY FOR LESSON 11-6 These exercises prepare students to use trigonometry to find the areas of regular polygons.

Wrap Up

THE BIG IDEA Ask students to describe three ways to find the sum of two vectors.

RETEACHING ACTIVITY Students solve problems that involve vector addition. (Reteaching worksheet 11-5)

In this Checkpoint, your students will assess their own progress in Lessons 11-4 to 11-5.

Exercise 2 Suggest that students copy the diagram and draw the vector sum as a way to check their answers.

Exercise 3 Check that students do not confuse the direction "east of south" with "south of east."

Lesson Quiz

Lesson Quiz is also available in Transparencies.

1. Find the sum of vectors ⟨3, 5⟩ and ⟨−2, 1⟩. Draw a diagram to support your answer. **⟨1, 6⟩; See back of book.**

2. The cruising speed of an airplane is 400 mi/h. Suppose the airplane cruising directly north encounters a wind blowing directly west at 30 mi/h. What is the airplane's resulting speed and direction? **≈ 401 mi/h in the direction 4° west of north**

Flying into a Hurricane

When most pilots hear a forecast for gale force winds, they don't think, "Time to fly." Then again, most pilots don't work for the National Oceanic and Atmospheric Administration. NOAA operates two WP-3D airplanes that fly directly into hurricanes. These four-engine turboprops, which carry eight crew members and up to ten scientists, are loaded with data-collection equipment. Some of this equipment is in the WP-3D's long "snout," which also serves as a lightning rod. In a routine flight, the WP-3D is struck by lightning 3 or 4 times. Surprisingly, small burn holes are the only damage from these strikes. To help overcome temporary blindness caused by lightning flashes, the pilots set the cockpit lights at the brightest level.

TIMELESS MAGAZINE **72**

20. In still air, the WP-3D flies at 374 mi/h. Suppose that a WP-3D flies due west into a hurricane and encounters a 95-mi/h wind blowing due south. What are the resulting speed and direction of the plane? **about 386 mi/h at 14° south of west**

Find the area of each figure to the nearest tenth.

21. 12 cm
452.4 cm²

22. 5 in., 11 in., 7 in.
17.5 in.²

23. 80 m
5542.6 m²

24. 7 km, 6 km, 9 km
45.3 km²

25. *Open-ended* Draw a figure in one-point perspective. **See back of book for sample.**

Getting Ready for Lesson 11-6

The hexagon at the right is regular. Name each point or segment.

26. the center **G**

27. a radius $\overline{GD}$

28. an apothem $\overline{GH}$

1. Find the magnitude of vectors $\vec{a}$ and $\vec{c}$. Round your answers to the nearest tenth. **$\vec{a}$: 6.4; $\vec{c}$: 4.5**

2. Find the sum $\vec{a} + \vec{c}$. Give your answer in ordered pair notation. **⟨−2, −9⟩**

3. *Air Travel* A twin-engine plane has a speed of 300 mi/h in still air. Suppose this plane travels directly south and encounters a 50 mi/h wind blowing due east. Find the resulting speed and direction of the plane. Round your answers to the nearest unit. **304 mi/h at 9° east of south**

4. *Open-ended* Sketch two vectors $\vec{u}$ and $\vec{v}$ and their sum $\vec{w}$ on graph paper. Give the ordered pair notation for each vector. **See back of book for sample.**

CONNECTING TO PRIOR KNOWLEDGE Draw a regular hexagon on the board. Label the apothem 5 cm and the radius 5.6 cm and have students calculate the area.

THINK AND DISCUSS

VISUAL LEARNING Copy the diagram and the definitions onto a poster and display it for the class.

Example 1

Help students see that $\triangle XCY \cong \triangle ZCY$ by the HL Theorem. Therefore, $m\angle XCY = m\angle ZCY$ (or $m\angle XCY = \frac{1}{2}m\angle XCZ$) and $XY = ZY$ (or $XY = \frac{1}{2}XZ$).

Make sure students understand the keystrokes used to evaluate the expression and do not insert parentheses around "80 ÷ 36."

What You'll Learn
- Using trigonometry to find the areas of regular polygons
- Using the sine ratio to find the areas of acute triangles

...And Why

To solve problems involving angle measures and areas

What You'll Need
- calculator

Connections **Architecture . . . and more**

11-6 Trigonometry and Area

THINK AND DISCUSS

Part 1 Finding Areas of Regular Polygons

In Chapter 5, you learned to find the area of a regular polygon by using the formula $A = \frac{1}{2}ap$, where a is the apothem and p is the perimeter. By using the trigonometric ratios together with this formula, you can solve other types of problems. Before you do so, however, take a minute to review the parts of a regular polygon in the diagram below.

the center of the circumscribed circle — center

apothem — the distance from the center to a side

an angle formed by two consecutive radii — central angle

radius — the distance from the center to a vertex

Example 1

Find the area of a regular pentagon with side 8 cm.

To use the formula $A = \frac{1}{2}ap$, you need the perimeter and apothem. The perimeter is $5 \cdot 8$, or 40. To find the apothem, use trigonometry.

The measure of central angle $\angle XCZ$ is $\frac{360}{5}$, or 72.
$m\angle XCY = \frac{1}{2}m\angle XCZ$, so $m\angle XCY = 36$.

$XY = \frac{1}{2}XZ$, so $XY = 4$.

$\tan 36° = \frac{4}{a}$ Use the tangent ratio.

$a = \frac{4}{\tan 36°}$ Solve for a.

Now substitute into the area formula.

$A = \frac{1}{2}ap$

$= \frac{1}{2} \cdot \frac{4}{\tan 36°} \cdot 40$ Substitute for a and p.

$= \frac{80}{\tan 36°}$ Simplify.

 80 ÷ 36 TAN = *110.11055*   Use a calculator.

The area of a regular pentagon with side 8 cm is about 110 cm².

1. Try This Find the area of a regular octagon with a perimeter of 80 in. Give your answer to the nearest tenth. 482.8 in.²

 CALCULATOR HINT

Do all the rounding at the end of your solution. This method gives a more accurate answer than you would get by rounding several times before the final computation.

8 cm

Lesson Planning Options

Prerequisite Skills
- Finding trigonometric ratios

Assignment Options for Exercises On Your Own

To provide flexible scheduling, this lesson can be subdivided into parts.

1. **Core** 1–8, 19–20, 22
   Extension 17–18

2. **Core** 9–16
   Extension 21

Use Mixed Review to maintain skills.

Resources

Student Edition
Skills Handbook, p. 659
Extra Practice, p. 644
Glossary/Study Guide

Teaching Resources
Chapter Support File, Ch. 11
- Practice 11-6 (two worksheets)
- Reteaching 11-6
- Alternative Activity 11-6
Classroom Manager 11-6
Glossary, Spanish Resources

Transparencies
18, 114

573

Example 2 Relating to the Real World

Review with students that eight congruent central angles are formed by the radii of the octagon and that their sum is 360°. Therefore, the measure of one of the central angles is $\frac{360}{8}$.

Make sure that students understand why the length of the side is 2x and how the step $8 \cdot 2x$ becomes $16 \cdot 16(\sin 22.5°)$.

ERROR ALERT! Because this problem requires many steps, some students will have difficulty determining what information needs to be found and organizing the information in a useful way. **Remediation:** Work through each step of the problem with students. Point out that in order to use the area formula, they need to find the apothem and the perimeter. To find the perimeter, they need to know the side length. It may help to draw a box around the solution to each part.

Question 2 Review with students the term *horizontal cross section*.

Additional Examples

FOR EXAMPLE 1

Find the area of a regular octagon with side length 12 cm to the nearest tenth. **695.3 cm²**

FOR EXAMPLE 2

The floor of a gazebo is a regular pentagon. Its radius is 8 ft. Find the area of the floor to the nearest whole number. **152 ft²**

FOR EXAMPLE 3

A landscaper designs a triangular garden. Two edges of the garden have lengths 12 ft and 10 ft. The angle between the edges is 54°. Find the area of the garden to the nearest whole number. **49 ft²**

The Castel del Monte, situated on a hill in southern Italy, contains many regular octagons. It was built in the 1200s as a hunting residence for Frederick II, the king of Sicily.

Example 2 Relating to the Real World

Architecture The radius of the castle's inner courtyard is 16 m. Find the area of the courtyard.

Use trigonometry to find the apothem and the perimeter. The measure of the central angle of an octagon is $\frac{360}{8}$, or 45. So $m\angle C = \frac{1}{2}(45) = 22.5$.

$$\cos 22.5° = \frac{a}{16} \qquad\qquad \sin 22.5° = \frac{x}{16}$$
$$a = 16(\cos 22.5°) \qquad\qquad x = 16(\sin 22.5°)$$

Now use x to find the perimeter p.

$p = 8 \cdot \text{length of side}$
$\quad = 8 \cdot 2x$ The length of each side is 2x.
$\quad = 16 \cdot 16(\sin 22.5°)$ Simplify and substitute for x.
$\quad = 256(\sin 22.5°)$ Simplify.

Finally, substitute into the area formula, $A = \frac{1}{2}ap$.

$A = \frac{1}{2} \cdot 16(\cos 22.5°) \cdot 256(\sin 22.5°)$ Substitute for a and p.
$\quad = 2048(\cos 22.5°)(\sin 22.5°)$ Simplify.
$\quad = 724.07734$ Use a calculator.

The area of the courtyard of the Castel del Monte is about 724 m².

2. **Try This** All of the eight small towers around the castle are also regular octagons. The radius of each is 7.3 m. Find the area of a horizontal cross section of each tower to the nearest square meter. **151 m²**

The examples and exercises in this lesson will be restricted to triangles in which the included angle is acute. However, you may want to tell students that there is a method for finding the sine ratio of an obtuse angle so the area formula applies to all triangles.

Example 3 **Relating to the Real World** ················

KINESTHETIC LEARNING If you have block scheduling or an extended class period, take students outside. Have them work in groups of five. Have three students be vertices of a triangle. Use twine to make the sides. Have the other two students measure two of the sides with a tape measure and the included angle with a compass. Then have the groups calculate the area of the triangle they formed.

Technology Options

For Exercise 26, students may use construction software to construct the parallel lines.

Prentice Hall Technology

Software
- Secondary Math Lab Toolkit™
- Computer Item Generator 11-6

CD-ROM
- Multimedia Geometry Lab 11

Internet
- See the Prentice Hall site. (http://www.phschool.com)

Part 2 **Finding the Area of a Triangle Given SAS**

Suppose you want to find the area of $\triangle ABC$, but you know only the lengths b and c, and $m\angle A$. To use the formula Area $= \frac{1}{2}bh$, you need to know the height. You can find the height by using trigonometry.

$$\sin A = \frac{h}{c} \qquad \text{Use the sine ratio.}$$
$$h = c(\sin A) \qquad \text{Solve for } h.$$

Now substitute for h in the formula Area $= \frac{1}{2}bh$.

$$\text{Area} = \frac{1}{2}bc(\sin A)$$

Theorem 11-1
Area of a Triangle Given SAS

The area of a triangle is one half the product of the lengths of two sides and the sine of the included angle.

Area of triangle $= \frac{1}{2} \cdot$ side length $\cdot$ side length $\cdot$ sine of included angle

The proof of this theorem for the case in which the given angle is obtuse requires a more complete definition of sine. You will study this definition in later math courses.

Example 3 **Relating to the Real World** ················

Surveying When surveyed, two adjacent sides of a triangular plot of land measured 412 ft and 386 ft. The angle between the sides was 71°. Find the area of the plot.

Area $= \frac{1}{2} \cdot$ side length $\cdot$ side length $\cdot$ sine of included angle

$$= \frac{1}{2} \cdot 412 \cdot 386 \cdot \sin 71° \qquad \text{Substitute the given information.}$$
$$= 75183.855 \qquad \text{Use a calculator.}$$
$$\approx 75{,}200 \text{ ft}^2$$

3. Try This Two adjacent sides of a triangular building plot measure 120 ft and 85 ft. The angle between them measures 85°. Find the area of the land. Round your answer to the nearest square foot.   **5081 ft^2**

Exercises **ON YOUR OWN**

Find the area of each polygon. Give your answers to the nearest tenth.

1. equilateral triangle with apothem 4 in. **83.1 in.^{2}**

2. regular octagon with apothem 6 cm **119.3 cm^2**

3. regular hexagon with radius 10 ft **259.8 ft^2**

4. regular dodecagon with apothem 10 ft **321.5 ft^2**

5. regular decagon with radius 4 in. **47.0 in.^{2}**

6. regular pentagon with apothem 7 cm **178.0 cm^2**

7. regular 15-gon with side length 12 yd **2540.5 yd^2**

8. regular decagon with perimeter 80 cm **492.4 cm^2**

575

ESL **Exercise 17** Some students may think a "hexagonal nut" is a type of edible nut like a peanut or a walnut. Help them understand that a "hexagonal nut" is a small block of metal that is used in conjunction with a bolt to fasten something. If possible, bring some nuts and bolts to class to illustrate.

Exercise 18 Steps a–f help students derive a formula for the area of a regular *n*-gon.

CONNECTING TO STUDENTS' WORLD Exercise 20 Have students investigate the shapes and dimensions of other street signs and calculate their areas.

Exercise 21 Make sure students understand how to solve for one of the legs of a triangle given the area formula.

WRITING Exercise 22 Suggest that students draw a regular polygon and describe why the statement is true for that polygon. Then they can generalize their explanation to other polygons.

Chapter Project **FIND OUT BY RESEARCHING** Allow students several days to complete this activity. Make sure students understand where to find the star Polaris.

pages 575–577 On Your Own

18a. The segments connecting *C* with the vertices of the polygon form $n \cong$ angles. The sum of the measures of these angles is 360, so the measure of each angle is $\frac{360}{n}$. The apothem is the angle bisector for each of these angles, so $m\angle C = \frac{1}{2}\left(\frac{360}{n}\right) = \frac{180}{n}$.

f. The area of a regular polygon with apothem 1 approaches π as the number of sides increases.

21. 320 ft

300 ft
65°

22. Each apothem is the altitude of an isosceles △, so it is also the angle bisector and the median.

page 577 Mixed Review

26.

Find the area of each triangle. Give your answers to the nearest tenth.

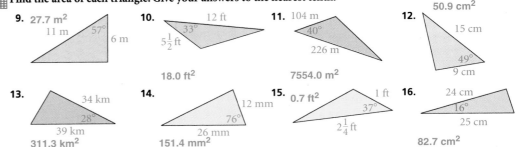

9. 27.7 m² — 11 m, 57°, 6 m
10. 18.0 ft² — 12 ft, 33°, $5\frac{1}{2}$ ft
11. 104 m, 40°, 226 m — 7554.0 m²
12. 50.9 cm² — 15 cm, 49°, 9 cm
13. 311.3 km² — 34 km, 28°, 39 km
14. 151.4 mm² — 12 mm, 76°, 26 mm
15. 0.7 ft² — 1 ft, 37°, $2\frac{1}{4}$ ft
16. 82.7 cm² — 24 cm, 16°, 25 cm

17. *Industrial Design* Refer to the diagram of the hexagonal nut. Round each answer to the nearest unit.
  a. Find the area of the circular space in the nut. 50 mm²
  b. Find the area of the hexagon minus the area of the circle. 116 mm²
  c. *Geometry in 3 Dimensions* Find the volume of the nut. 232 mm³

4 mm, 8 mm, 2 mm

18. Suppose a circle is inscribed in a regular *n*-gon with center *C* and apothem 1, as shown in the diagram.
  a. Explain why $m\angle C = \frac{1}{2}\left(\frac{360}{n}\right) = \frac{180}{n}$. See margin.
  b. Explain why $s = \tan C$. b–d. See right.
  c. Explain why the perimeter of the *n*-gon is $2n(\tan C)$.
  d. Explain why the area of the *n*-gon is $n\left(\tan \frac{180}{n}\right)$.
  e. *Open-ended* Pick a value for *n* between 0 and 10. Use a calculator to find the area of the *n*-gon. Then find the area of regular polygons with 10*n* sides and 100*n* sides. Sample: *n* = 9: 3.276; 3.143; 3.142
  f. What do you notice about your answers to part (e)? Explain. See margin.

C, 1, *s*

18b. *s* is the leg opp. $\angle C$, so $\tan C = \frac{s}{1} = s$.
  c. The length of each side is 2*s*. So the perimeter is $n \cdot 2s = 2n(\tan C)$.
  d. The area of a regular *n*-gon is $\frac{1}{2}ap = n(\tan \frac{180}{n})$.

19. *Architecture* The Pentagon, in Arlington, Virginia, is one of the world's largest office buildings. It is a regular pentagon, and the length of each of its sides is 921 ft. Find the amount of space covered by the Pentagon. Round your answer to the nearest thousand square feet. 1,459,000 ft²

20. The standard length of a side of a stop sign is 1 ft $\frac{1}{4}$ in. Find the area of this stop sign to the nearest tenth of a square foot. 5.0 ft²

21. *Surveying* A surveyor wants to mark off a triangular parcel with an area of 1 acre. One boundary of the triangle extends 300 ft along a straight road. A second boundary extends at an angle of 65° from one end of this boundary. Draw a triangle to represent the piece of land and determine the length of the second boundary line to the nearest foot. (1 acre = 43,560 ft²) See margin.

22. *Writing* Explain why each apothem of a regular polygon bisects a central angle and a side of the polygon. See margin.

MARKET ST 1 ft 1/4 in. STOP

576

Geometry at Work

To become a surveyor requires a background in mathematics and the ability to work with computers. Job opportunities are available in construction planning and in urban and regional planning.

Encourage students to investigate these topics:
- geodetic, hydrographic, and plane surveying
- the use of aerial photography, the NAVSTAR Global Positioning System (GPS), and electronic distance measurement equipment (EDM)
- basic surveying methods such as trilateration

Chapter Project   *Find Out by Researching*

Find the star Polaris in the evening sky. Use your clinometer to measure the angle of elevation to Polaris. The angle that you measure should be approximately equal to your latitude. Use a map to find your latitude. How accurate was your estimate?

Big Dipper
Little Dipper
Polaris

Check students' work.

Exercises   MIXED REVIEW

Find the length of each midsegment.

23.   **24.** 4 cm   **25.**

10 in.
5 in.

16 cm
10 cm

17 m
8.5 m

26. *Constructions* Draw a line and a point not on the line. Construct a line parallel to the first line through the point. **See margin p. 576.**

27. *Geometry in 3 Dimensions* Find the volume and lateral surface area of a cylindrical can with radius 4.0 cm and height 5.6 cm. Give your answers to the nearest tenth. **281.5 cm³; 140.7 cm²**

![self assessment] **PORTFOLIO**

For your portfolio, select one or two items from your work for this chapter. Here are some possibilities.
- an interesting example of indirect measurement
- work that shows originality
Explain why you have included each selection.

Geometry at Work

Surveyor

Surveyors calculate the locations, shapes, and areas of plots of land. A survey begins with a benchmark—a reference point whose latitude, longitude, and elevation are known. The surveyor uses a device called a *transit* to measure the angles of the plot of land and the distances of key points from the benchmark. Using trigonometry, the surveyor finds the latitude, longitude, and elevation of each key point in the survey. These points are located on a map and an accurate sketch of the plot is drawn. Finally, the area is calculated. One method involves dividing the plot into triangles and measuring the

lengths of two sides and the included angle of each. The formula $A = \frac{1}{2}ab(\sin C)$ gives the area of each triangle. The area of the entire plot is the sum of the areas of the triangles.

Mini Project: On a flat area outside your school, place four objects to mark the vertices of an irregular quadrilateral. Calculate the area of the quadrilateral. Explain your method, and tell how you measured the sides and angles of the figure.

Reteaching 11-6

Practice 11-6

Practice 11-6
Mixed Exercises

Find the area of each polygon. Give your answers to the nearest tenth.
1. an equilateral triangle with apothem 5.8 cm
2. a square with radius 17 ft
3. a regular hexagon with apothem 19 mm
4. a regular pentagon with radius 9 m
5. a regular octagon with radius 20 in.
6. a regular hexagon with apothem 11 cm
7. a regular decagon with apothem 10 in.
8. a square with radius 9 cm

Find the area of each triangle. Give your answers to the nearest tenth.
9. 10. 11.
12. 13. 14.
15. 16. 17.

Find the area of each regular polygon.
18. a triangular dog pen with apothem 4 m
19. a hexagonal swimming pool cover with radius 5 ft
20. an octagonal floor of a gazebo with apothem 6 ft
21. a square deck with radius 2 m
22. a hexagonal patio with apothem 4 ft

Lesson Quiz

Lesson Quiz is also available in Transparencies.

Give each answer to the nearest tenth.

1. Find the area of a regular pentagon with apothem 6 cm. **130.8 cm²**

2. Find the area of a regular decagon with radius 3 m. **26.5 m²**

3. Two sides of a triangle measure 7 in. and 12 in. The angle between the two sides is 35°. Find the area of the triangle. **24.1 in.²**

4. Two sides of a triangle measure 50 ft and 70 ft. The angle between the two sides is 58°. Find the area of the triangle. **1484.1 ft²**

Finishing The Chapter Project

PROJECT DAY You may wish to plan a project day during which students share their completed projects. Encourage groups to explain their processes as well as their products.

PROJECT NOTEBOOK Have students review their project work and bring their notebooks up to date.

- Have students present their displays. Ask each student to explain one measurement.
- Ask students to share any insights they found when completing the project, such as how the clinometer is used to find an angle of elevation.

SCORING RUBRIC

3 Student's display is complete. It includes a clinometer and suggestions to improve it. All measurements, calculations, diagrams, and explanations are accurate and presented in an organized manner.

2 Student's display is complete. It includes a clinometer and suggestions to improve it. The measurements, calculations, diagrams, and explanations contain minor errors but are presented in an organized manner.

1 Student's display is complete. It includes a clinometer and suggestions to improve it. The measurements, calculations, diagrams, and explanations contain errors or are not presented in an organized manner.

0 Major elements are incomplete or missing.

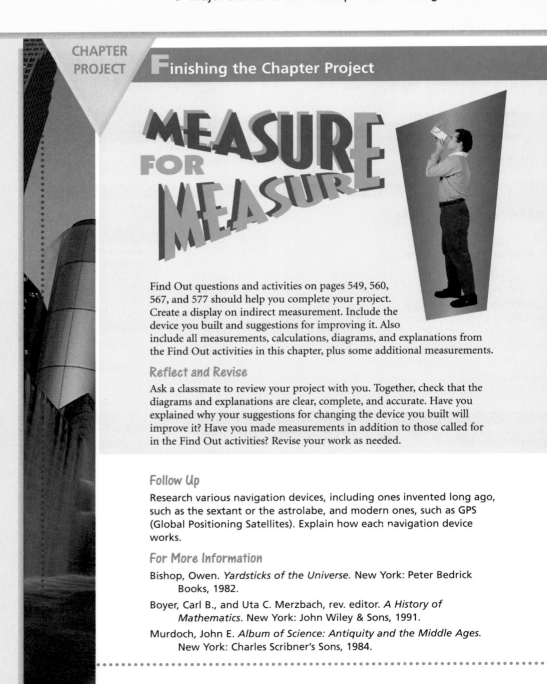

Finishing the Chapter Project

MEASURE FOR MEASURE

Find Out questions and activities on pages 549, 560, 567, and 577 should help you complete your project. Create a display on indirect measurement. Include the device you built and suggestions for improving it. Also include all measurements, calculations, diagrams, and explanations from the Find Out activities in this chapter, plus some additional measurements.

Reflect and Revise

Ask a classmate to review your project with you. Together, check that the diagrams and explanations are clear, complete, and accurate. Have you explained why your suggestions for changing the device you built will improve it? Have you made measurements in addition to those called for in the Find Out activities? Revise your work as needed.

Follow Up

Research various navigation devices, including ones invented long ago, such as the sextant or the astrolabe, and modern ones, such as GPS (Global Positioning Satellites). Explain how each navigation device works.

For More Information

Bishop, Owen. *Yardsticks of the Universe.* New York: Peter Bedrick Books, 1982.

Boyer, Carl B., and Uta C. Merzbach, rev. editor. *A History of Mathematics.* New York: John Wiley & Sons, 1991.

Murdoch, John E. *Album of Science: Antiquity and the Middle Ages.* New York: Charles Scribner's Sons, 1984.

578

Wrap Up

Exercises 1–4 Students should leave their answers as ratios.

Exercises 5–8 Ask students to write the equation they used to solve each problem. This will help you assess where students are having difficulty in setting up the equations or in solving them.

HOW AM I DOING? Have students work in small groups. Ask each group to make a short presentation explaining how to use one of the trigonometric ratios to solve problems. Each presentation should include a visual aid and two worked-out examples.

KEY TERMS The numbers in parentheses direct students to the pages where the terms are used or defined. Students should be able to (1) write a simple explanation of each term, (2) illustrate the term with a diagram, or (3) show an example that uses the term.

---

11 Wrap Up

Key Terms

angle of depression (p. 556)
angle of elevation (p. 556)
cosine (p. 551)
identity (p. 551)
literal equation (p. 562)
resultant (p. 568)
sine (p. 551)
tangent (p. 544)
vector (p. 563)

How am I doing?

- List the three trigonometric ratios described in this chapter. Include a diagram.
- State two ways you can describe a vector and explain how to convert from one description to the other.

Resources

Student Edition
Extra Practice, p. 644
Glossary/Study Guide

Teaching Resources
Study Skills Handbook
Glossary, Spanish Resources

The Sine, Cosine, and Tangent Ratios   11-1, 11-2

In right triangle $\triangle ABC$, **sine** of $\angle A = \sin A = \dfrac{\text{leg opposite } \angle A}{\text{hypotenuse}}$.

$\quad$ **cosine** of $\angle A = \cos A = \dfrac{\text{leg adjacent to } \angle A}{\text{hypotenuse}}$,

$\quad$ and **tangent** of $\angle A = \tan A = \dfrac{\text{leg opposite } \angle A}{\text{leg adjacent to } \angle A}$.

You can use the inverses of the trigonometric ratios to find the measure of an angle of a right triangle.

There are many trigonometric **identities**, including $\sin x° = \cos (90 - x)°$.

Express $\sin A$, $\cos A$, and $\tan A$ as ratios.

1.

2.

3.

4.

1. $\dfrac{4}{5}; \dfrac{3}{5}; \dfrac{4}{3}$ 2. $\dfrac{\sqrt{19}}{10}; \dfrac{9}{10}; \dfrac{\sqrt{19}}{9}$

3. $\dfrac{\sqrt{3}}{2}; \dfrac{1}{2}; \dfrac{\sqrt{3}}{1}$ 4. $\dfrac{8}{17}; \dfrac{15}{17}; \dfrac{8}{15}$

Find the value of x. Round lengths of segments to the nearest tenth and angle measures to the nearest degree.

5. 51

6. 16.5

7. 33

8. 13.8

9. *Standardized Test Prep* In which triangle is $m\angle X$ the greatest? **D**

A.

B.

C.

D.

E.

Angles of Elevation and Depression 11-3

An angle below a horizontal line is an **angle of depression**. An angle above a horizontal line is an **angle of elevation**.

Solve each problem.

not to scale

10. Two hills are 2 mi apart. The elevation of the taller hill is 2707 ft. The angle of depression from the top of the taller hill to the top of the shorter hill is 7°. Find the elevation of the shorter hill to the nearest foot. (1 mi = 5280 ft) **1410 ft**

11. A surveyor is 305 ft from the base of the new courthouse. Her angle measuring device is 5 ft above the ground. The angle of elevation to the top of the building is 42°. Find the height of the courthouse to the nearest foot. **280 ft**

12. **Writing** Explain why the angle of depression ∠1 and the angle of elevation ∠2 in the diagram are congruent.
The horizontal lines are ∥, so alt. interior ∠s are ≅.

Vectors and Trigonometry 11-4

A **vector** is any quantity that has magnitude and direction.

Describe each vector by using ordered pair notation. Give the coordinates to the nearest unit.

13. y ⟨126, 82⟩
   150
   33°

14. y ⟨37, −93⟩
   100
   22°

15. y ⟨−22, 34⟩
   40
   57°

16. ⟨−206, −283⟩
   y
   350
   36°

Find the magnitude and direction of each vector. 18. about 206 km at 14° west of south
   about 175 m/h at 31° east of north

17. N
   75 mi
   W   E
   150 mi
   S
   about 168 mi at 27° east of south

18. 50 km N
   W   E
   200 km
   S

19. N
   225 mi/h
   W   E
   450 mi/h
   S
   about 503 mi/h at 27° north of west

20. N
   150 m/h
   W   E
   90 m/h
   S

21. **Open-ended** Write three vectors with the same direction as ⟨3, 4⟩.
   Explain how you found your answers. **Answers may vary. Sample: ⟨6, 8⟩, ⟨7.5, 10⟩, ⟨30, 40⟩;**
   multiply each coordinate by the same positive number.

Critical Thinking Does each sentence contain enough information to describe a vector? Explain.

22. A person bicycles at 15 miles per hour. **No; the description gives magnitude but no direction.**

23. A butterfly flies 60 km northeast. **Yes; the description includes magnitude and direction.**

24. A manatee migrates 100 km to the Atlantic coast.
No; the description gives magnitude but no direction.

580

Getting Ready for Chapter 12

Students may work these exercises independently or in small groups. The skills previewed will help prepare students to study chords, secants, and tangents of circles.

Adding Vectors   11-5

Wrap Up   pages 579–581

36.

The sum of two vectors is a **resultant**. You can add vectors by using the head-to-tail method or by using ordered pair notation. Vector sums can show the result of actions that take place one after the other or the result of two forces that act at the same time on an object.

Coordinate Geometry **Find the sum of each pair of vectors. Give your answers in ordered pair notation.**

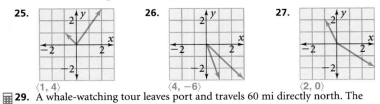

25. $\langle 1, 4 \rangle$ 26. $\langle 4, -6 \rangle$ 27. $\langle 2, 0 \rangle$ 28. $\langle 1, -1 \rangle$

29. A whale-watching tour leaves port and travels 60 mi directly north. The tour then travels 5 mi due east.
   a. In what direction should the boat head to return to port? **5° west of south**
   b. How long will the return trip take if the boat averages 20 mi/h? **about 3 h**

Trigonometry and Area   11-6

You can use trigonometry to find the area of regular polygons. You can also use trigonometry to find the area of a triangle when you know the lengths of two sides and the measure of the included angle.

Area of triangle $= \frac{1}{2} \cdot$ side length $\cdot$ side length $\cdot$ sine of included angle

Find the area of each polygon. Round your answers to the nearest tenth.

30. regular decagon with radius 5 ft **73.5 ft²**   31. regular pentagon with apothem 8 cm **232.5 cm²**

32.
   12 in.
   64°
   15 in.
   80.9 in.²

33.
   15 cm
   45°
   19 cm
   100.8 cm²

34.
   65°
   15 ft   13 ft
   88.4 ft²

35.
   12 m
   78°
   70.4 m²   12 m

Getting Ready for... CHAPTER

12

36. *Open-ended* Draw a circle. Then draw two central angles, one twice the measure of the other. **See margin for sample.**

Find the area and circumference of a circle with the given radius or diameter. Leave your answer in terms of π.

37. $r = 5$ in.   38. $d = 8$ cm   39. $r = 11$ m   40. $d = 4$ ft
   25π in.²; 10π in. 16π cm²; 8π cm 121π m²; 22π m 4π ft²; 4π ft

581

ENHANCED MULTIPLE CHOICE QUESTIONS are more complex than traditional multiple choice questions, which assess only one skill. Enhanced multiple choice questions assess the processes that students use, as well as the end results. The questions are written so that students use more than one strategy to solve the problem. Using multiple strategies is encouraged by the National Council of Teachers of Mathematics (NCTM). There are no enhanced multiple choice questions on this assessment.

FREE RESPONSE QUESTIONS do not give answer choices. Some exercises have more than one possible answer. Students need to give only one correct response. **Exercises 1–12, 14–18, and 20–24** are free response questions.

WRITING EXERCISES allow students to describe how they think about and understand the concepts they have learned. **Exercise 13** is a writing exercise.

OPEN-ENDED PROBLEMS allow for more than one solution. Students must construct their own responses instead of choosing from possible answers. The students' responses will help you determine the depth of their understanding and any possible areas of difficulty. **Exercise 19** is an open-ended problem.

Resources

Teaching Resources

Chapter Support File, Ch. 11
• Chapter Assessment, Forms A and B
• Alternative Assessment Chapter Assessment, Spanish Resources

Teacher's Edition

See also p. 542E for assessment options

Software
Computer Item Generator

Assessment   page 582

13. The acute ∠s of a rt. △ are complementary, so, in rt. △ABC, if $m\angle A = x$, $m\angle B = 90 - x$. So $\sin x° = \frac{BC}{AB} = \cos(90 - x)°$.

19.

582

---

11 Assessment

Express sin B, cos B, and tan B as ratios.

1.

$\frac{\sqrt{57}}{11}$; $\frac{8}{11}$; $\frac{\sqrt{57}}{8}$

2.

2. $\frac{\sqrt{33}}{7}$; $\frac{4}{7}$; $\frac{\sqrt{33}}{4}$

⊞ Find the value of x. Round lengths of segments to the nearest tenth and angle measures to the nearest degree.

3.

41

4.

18.7

5.

9.5

6.

28

⊞ Algebra Find the measure of the acute angle that each line makes with a horizontal line. Round your answer to the nearest tenth.

7. $y = 3x - 2$ 71.6
8. $y = x + 1$ 45
9. $y = \frac{1}{2}x + 5$ 26.6
10. $x - 2y = 6$ 26.6

⊞ Solve each problem.

11. A surveyor measuring the tallest tree in a park stands 100 ft from it. His angle-measuring device is 5 ft above the ground. The angle of elevation to the top of the tree is 48°. How tall is the tree? **about 116 ft**

12. A hot-air balloon is competing in a race. After 20 min, the balloon is at an altitude of 300 m. The pilot can still see the starting point at a 25° angle of depression. How many meters is the balloon from the starting point on the ground? **about 710 m**

13. Writing Explain why $\sin x° = \cos(90 - x)°$. Include a diagram with your explanation. **See margin.**

⊞ Describe each vector using ordered pair notation. Round the coordinates to the nearest unit.

14.

⟨95, −44⟩

15.

⟨−133, −346⟩

16. A family went on vacation to a beach 120 mi east and 30 mi south of their home. Find the distance and the direction the beach is from their home.
about 124 mi at 14° south of east

Find the sum of each pair of vectors. Give your answers in ordered pair notation.

17.

⟨1, 8⟩

18.

⟨4, 1⟩

19. Open-ended Draw two vectors with different directions on a coordinate grid. Then draw their resultant and describe the sum using ordered pair notation. **See margin for sample.**

⊞ Find the area of each polygon. Round your answer to the nearest tenth.

20.

22.1 in.²

21.

279.1 mm²

22. a regular hexagon with apothem 5 ft **86.6 ft²**

23. a regular pentagon with radius 3 cm **21.4 cm²**

24. a regular decagon with perimeter 90 in. **623.2 in.²**

Preparing for Standardized Tests

Standardized tests, such as those administered for state assessment, the SAT, or the ACT, include regular math questions, quantitative comparison questions, open-ended problems, and free response questions (which the SAT calls *grid-ins*).

MULTIPLE CHOICE QUESTIONS are followed by five answer choices, one of which is correct. **Exercises 1–7** are multiple choice questions.

QUANTITATIVE COMPARISON QUESTIONS ask students to compare two quantities. **Exercises 8 and 9** are quantitative comparison questions.

FREE RESPONSE QUESTIONS do not give answer choices. Students must provide one correct answer on their own. **Exercises 10 and 12** are free response questions.

OPEN-ENDED PROBLEMS allow for more than one solution. Students must construct their own responses instead of choosing a single answer. The responses students give will help you determine the depth of their understanding and what difficulties, if any, they are experiencing. **Exercise 11** is an open-ended problem.

STANDARDIZED TEST TIP **Exercise 3** Students can use the Pythagorean Theorem to find the length of the hypotenuse but it is not necessary. Help students observe that because the hypotenuse is the longest side, all the answer choices are less than 1 except tan A.

---

11 Preparing for Standardized Tests

For Exercises 1–9, choose the correct letter.

1. In which transformation is the image *not* necessarily congruent to the preimage? **D**
   A. rotation
   B. reflection
   C. translation
   D. dilation
   E. glide translation

2. Which quadrilaterals have congruent diagonals?
   I. square
   II. trapezoid **A**
   III. parallelogram
   IV. kite

   A. I only
   B. III only
   C. I and II only
   D. III and IV only
   E. I, II, and IV only

3. Which is greatest in the triangle below? **C**

   A. sin A
   B. cos A
   C. tan A
   D. sin B
   E. cos B

4. What is the surface area of a rectangular prism with length 9 cm, width 8 cm, and height 10 cm? **D**
   A. 27 cm^2
   B. 240 cm^2
   C. 242 cm^2
   D. 484 cm^2
   E. 720 cm^2

5. For what value of x will the two triangles be similar? **A**

   A. 2
   B. 4
   C. 8
   D. $10\frac{2}{3}$
   E. 12

6. Which information *cannot* be used to prove two triangles congruent? **E**
   A. SSS
   B. SAS
   C. ASA
   D. AAS
   E. AAA

7. What is the locus of points in a plane a given distance from a given line? **E**
   A. a line
   B. a circle
   C. a cylinder
   D. a ray
   E. two parallel lines

Compare the boxed quantity in Column A with the boxed quantity in Column B. Choose the best answer.

A. The quantity in Column A is greater.
B. The quantity in Column B is greater.
C. The two quantities are equal.
D. The relationship cannot be determined on the basis of the information supplied.

Column A	Column B
8. sin 30°	cos 30° **B**
9. the magnitude of $\vec{c} + \vec{a}$	the magnitude of $\vec{a} + \vec{c}$ **C**

Find each answer.
10–12. See back of book for samples.

10. *Aviation* Pilots often refer to the angle of an object outside the plane in terms of a clock face. Thus, an object at 12 o'clock is straight ahead, an object at 3 o'clock is 90° to the right, and so on.
    a. Suppose that two pilots flying in the same direction spot the same object. One reports it at 1 o'clock, the other at 2 o'clock. Draw a diagram showing the possible locations of the two planes and the object.
    b. Suppose that at the same time one pilot sights the object, she sights the other plane at 9 o'clock. Draw a diagram of the positions of the planes and the object.

11. *Open-ended* Draw a triangle. Measure two sides and the angle between them. Then find the area of the triangle.

12. *Constructions* Construct a square with side length a.

Resources

📕 **Teaching Resources**
Chapter Support File, Ch. 11
• Standardized Test Practice
• Cumulative Review

📖 **Teacher's Edition**
See also p. 542E for assessment options

583

To accommodate flexible scheduling, some lessons are divided into parts. Assignment Options are given in the Lesson Planning Options for each lesson.

12-1 Circles in the Coordinate Plane (pp. 586–591)
  Part **1** Writing the Equation of a Circle
  Part **2** Using the Equation of a Circle
  Key Term: standard form of an equation of a circle

12-2 Properties of Tangents (pp. 593–599)
  Part **1** Tangents to Circles
  Part **2** Circumscribing Circles
  Key Terms: circumscribed about, inscribed in, point of tangency, tangent to a circle

12-3 Properties of Chords and Arcs (pp. 600–606)
  Part **1** Congruent Arcs and Chords
  Part **2** Chords Equidistant from the Center of a Circle
  Key Term: chord

12-4 Inscribed Angles (pp. 607–613)
  Part **1** Measuring Inscribed Angles
  Part **2** Angles Formed by Tangents and Chords
  Key Terms: circumscribed about, inscribed in, inscribed angle, intercepted arc

12-5 Angles Formed by Chords, Secants, and Tangents (pp. 614–619)
  Key Term: secant

12-6 Circles and Lengths of Segments (pp. 621–626)

PACING OPTIONS

This chart suggests pacing only for the core lessons and their parts, and it is provided merely as a possible guide. It will help you determine how much time you have in your schedule to cover other features, such as the Chapter Project, Math Toolboxes, Wrap Up, and Assessment.

	1 Class Period	1 Class Period	1 Class Period	1 Class Period	1 Class Period	1 Class Period	1 Class Period	1 Class Period	1 Class Period
Traditional (40–45 min class periods)	12-1 **1**	12-1 **2**	12-2 **1**	12-2 **2**	12-3 **1** **2**	12-4 **1**	12-4 **2**	12-5	12-6
Block Scheduling (90 min class periods)	12-1 **1** **2**	12-2 **1** **2**	12-3 **1** **2**	12-4 **1** **2**	12-5	12-6			

What Students Will Learn and Why

In this chapter, students will use their knowledge of congruent triangles and similar triangles, learned in Chapters 8 and 10, to discover characteristics of circles. Students learn how to write the equation of a circle and how to use the equation of a circle to solve real-world problems. Students learn properties of tangents, chords, and arcs. Then they find the measure of inscribed angles, the arcs they intercept, and angles formed by chords, secants, and tangents. Finally, students learn to find the lengths of segments associated with circles. The principles students learn in this chapter have applications in photography, architecture, and communications.

Discussing the Chapter/Building on Experience

The concept map below relates chapter topics to real-world applications. You and your class may wish to add to the map or develop maps of your own. The center oval describes the topic of the chapter. The next level displays topics within the lessons. The outer ovals reflect applications of the content. As you and your class build a concept map, invite students to discuss applications with which they are familiar.

1 Class Period	1 Class Period	1 Class Period	1 Class Period	1 Class Period	1 Class Period	1 Class Period	1 Class Period	1 Class Period	1 Class Period	1 Class Period

Interactive Questioning Tips

A question is interactive when there is "give and take" between the questioner (teacher or student) and the respondent. In Think and Discuss or when a critical thinking question is asked, it is important to get all of the students thinking. Encourage students to agree or disagree with their classmates, and remind them that there is often more than one correct answer. For example, in Lesson 12-6, Example 2, students are asked to explain why a segment perpendicular to a chord is contained in a diameter of the circle.

Skills Practice

Every lesson provides skill practice with Try This exercises,

Exercises On Your Own, and Exercises Mixed Review. The Student Edition includes Checkpoints (pp. 606, 619) and Cumulative Review (p. 632). In the Teacher's Edition, the Lesson Planning Options section for each lesson lists Prerequisite Skills students should know for that lesson. At the back of the Student Edition is the Skills Handbook—mini-lessons on math your students may need to review. The Chapter Support File for Chapter 12 in the Teaching Resources box includes two Practice worksheets per lesson, a worksheet for two Checkpoints, and worksheets for Cumulative Review and Standardized Test Preparation.

Diverse Learning and Teaching Styles

In your Teacher's Edition, you will find suggestions as to how you can help students complete mathematical tasks in Chapter 12 by reinforcing various learning styles. Here are some examples.

- **Visual learning** draw diagrams for Theorems 12-5, 12-6, and 12-7 (p. 601), construct a circle and chords (p. 609), shade the interior angles formed by chords, secants, and tangents to visualize the arcs they intercept (615)

- **Tactile learning** experiment with MIRA™ (p. 600)

- **Auditory learning** learn verbal cues to help remember the definitions of circumscribe and inscribe (p. 596), practice naming segments or chords, secant segments, exterior secant segments, and tangent segments (p. 621)

- **Kinesthetic learning** make a bulletin board display showing many colorful circles and their equations (p. 590)

Alternative Activity for Lesson 12-1

for use with Think and Discuss, uses a graphing calculator to graph circles.

Alternative Activity for Lesson 12-4

for use with Work Together, uses geometry software to explore properties of inscribed angles and their intersected arcs.

Alternative Activity for Lesson 12-5

for use with Work Together, uses geometry software to explore properties of secants and their intercepted arcs.

Cooperative Learning Tips

When used effectively, cooperative learning can help students develop interpersonal skills, learn to perform specific roles in a group, and learn to carry out specific responsibilities. The components of Chapter 12 provide a range of cooperative learning opportunities.

- In the Student Edition, the Work Together parts of lessons are specifically designed for cooperative learning activities.

- In the Teacher's Edition, you will find helpful hints for addressing diverse learning styles (see page C for Chapter 12). For every lesson, you will find a Reteaching Activity, which may involve cooperative learning.

Materials and Manipulatives

The authors expect all students to use scientific calculators. Calculator use is integrated throughout the course.

- centimeter ruler (12-2, 12-3)
- compass (12-2, 12-3, 12-4, 12-5, 12-6)
- graph paper (12-1)
- MIRA™ (12-3)
- protractor (12-3, 12-4, 12-5)
- ruler (12-4, 12-6)
- straightedge (12-2)

TECHNOLOGY OPTIONS

Technology Tools		Chapter Project	12-1	12-2	12-3	12-4	12-5	12-6
Calculator		Assumed that students have scientific calculators at any time.						
Software	Secondary Math Lab Toolkit™		✔	✔	✔	✔	✔	✔
	Integrated Math Lab				✔		✔	
	Computer Item Generator		✔	✔	✔	✔	✔	✔
	Student Edition				✔	✔		✔T
Video	Video Field Trip	✔						
CD-ROM	Multimedia Geometry Lab		✔	✔	✔	✔		
Internet		See the Prentice Hall site. (http://www.phschool.com)						

✔T indicates Math Toolbox.

The Prentice Hall Geometry program offers you a rich variety of technology options. Be assured that all these options are provided as a means of enriching the program and are not essential for the successful completion of the course.

Assessment Options

The Prentice Hall Geometry Program provides you with many options. From these options, you may choose instructional materials and techniques appropriate for your students, or those necessary to meet your district's curriculum requirements. As the chart indicates, the program also supports your teaching efforts by offering you many choices for assessment.

ASSESSMENT OPTIONS

Assessment Support Materials	Chapter Project	12-1	12-2	12-3	12-4	12-5	12-6	Chapter End
Chapter Project	▲■●	▲■		▲■		▲■		▲■
Checkpoints			▲■●			▲■●		
Self-Assessment		▲■			▲■	▲■	▲■	▲■
Writing Assignment	▲■	▲■	▲	▲■	▲■	▲■	▲■●	
Chapter Assessment								▲■●
Alternative Assessment	■	■	■	■	■	■	▲■●	
Cumulative Review								▲■●
Standardized Test Prep		▲■				▲■	▲	▲■●
Computer Item Generator	Can be used to create custom-made practice or assessment at any time.							

▲ = Student Edition   ■ = Teacher's Edition   ● = Teaching Resources

Checkpoints

Alternative Assessment

Chapter Assessment

Available in both Form A and Form B

Making the Right Connections

Mathematics is imbedded in nearly every walk of life. The National Council of Teachers of Mathematics (NCTM) encourages educators to recognize these connections and to emphasize them for the purpose of better educating students for success in life and in a global economy. The **Connections** chart below highlights these connections for Chapter 12.

CONNECTIONS

Lesson	Interdisciplinary Connections	Career Prep	Other Real World Connections	Math Integration	NCTM Standards
Chapter Project	Art History	Design	Jewelry Stone Carvings Clothing Islamic Art	Coordinate Geometry	Connections Communication Problem Solving
12-1	Meteorology History	Engineering Telecommunications	Cellular Telephones Earth Weather	Algebra Geometry in 3 Dimensions Coordinate Geometry	Communication Connections Coordinate Geometry Problem Solving
12-2	Astronomy	Machinery Construction Design	Air Conditioning Eclipse Clocks	Coordinate Geometry Algebra	Communication Connections Reasoning Problem Solving
12-3	Art	Archeology Transportation	Compact Disc Transporting Milk	Coordinate Geometry Logical Reasoning	Communication Connections Reasoning Problem Solving
12-4		Photography	Technology Motion Pictures	Logical Reasoning	Communication Connections Reasoning Problem Solving
12-5	History Astronomy	Photography	Space Travel Surveys	Algebra Logical Reasoning	Communication Connections Reasoning Problem Solving
12-6	Astronomy	Architecture Engineering Aerospace Engineering	Space Exploration Wankel Engine	Logical Reasoning	Communication Connections Reasoning Problem Solving

CONNECTING TO PRIOR LEARNING Have students use a compass to draw a circle. Using the same compass setting, have them mark six points on the circle equidistant from each other. Then have them draw chords connecting consecutive points to form a hexagon. Discuss the relationship between an angle of the hexagon and the arc of the circle it intercepts.

CULTURAL CONNECTIONS The symbol of the Olympic Games is five entwined circles, each ring representing a continent. Students might research the history of the Olympic rings and present a visual/verbal report on the meaning and the significance of the symbol.

INTERDISCIPLINARY CONNECTIONS While artists use circles to create patterns and designs, astronomers and physicists also study circles, particularly circular motion. Ancient scholars believed that the planets traveled in perfect circular motion about the Earth. Have students research how this theory was eventually proven false.

ABOUT THE PROJECT Students explore techniques used for centuries to produce circular art. They then apply the techniques to create their own designs.

Technology Options

Prentice Hall Technology

Video
Video Field Trip 12, "A Touch of Glass," a visit to a glass blowing factory

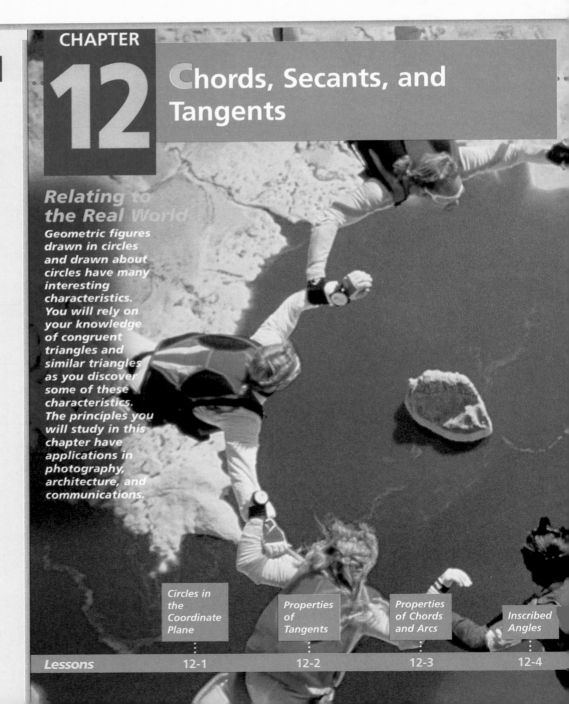

CHAPTER

12 Chords, Secants, and Tangents

Relating to the Real World

Geometric figures drawn in circles and drawn about circles have many interesting characteristics. You will rely on your knowledge of congruent triangles and similar triangles as you discover some of these characteristics. The principles you will study in this chapter have applications in photography, architecture, and communications.

Circles in the Coordinate Plane	Properties of Tangents	Properties of Chords and Arcs	Inscribed Angles
Lessons 12-1	12-2	12-3	12-4

PROJECT NOTEBOOK Encourage students to keep all project-related materials in a separate folder or notebook. **See Chapter Project Manager and Scoring Rubric in Chapter Support File.**

- Ask students to describe designs, emblems, or logos they have seen that use circles. Students should be familiar with the Olympic rings or emblems on different automobiles made from circles and arcs.

- Have students list other real-world examples of objects that are made of intertwined circles, such as chains, necklaces, and key rings.

TRACKING THE PROJECT You may wish to have students read Finishing the Chapter Project on page 627 to help them get an overview of the project. Set benchmark deadlines for students to show their work in progress.

CHAPTER PROJECT

GO FOR A SPIN

For centuries, artists have used the simple elegance of the circle in their designs. Some have crafted intertwining patterns that like the circle itself have no beginning and no end. Some have disturbed the symmetry of the circle to create optical illlusions.

In your chapter project, you will explore some of the techniques used through the ages to produce circular art such as the painting at the left by Alma Thomas. You will then apply your discoveries to create a dizzying design. You will see why some artists find that "going in circles" may be the best way to reach their objective.

To help you complete the project:

▽ **p. 591** *Find Out by Doing*
▽ **p. 605** *Find Out by Exploring*
▽ **p. 618** *Find Out by Constructing*
▽ **p. 627** *Finishing the Project*

Angles Formed by Chords, Secants, and Tangents
12-5

Circles and Lengths of Segments
12-6

▼ Project Resources

Teaching Resources
Chapter Support File, Ch. 12
- Chapter Project Manager and Scoring Rubric

Transparencies
119

▼ Using the Rubric

Sharing the scoring rubric for the project with your students will alert them to your expectations before they begin work on the project.

As students complete each Find Out question in the chapter, you may wish to have them evaluate their own work or a partner's work based on the scoring rubric. Students should have the opportunity to revise their work after it has been reviewed.

585

CONNECTING TO PRIOR KNOWLEDGE On a coordinate grid, draw a circle. Label the coordinates of the center and a point on the circle. Have students find the length of the radius.

WORK TOGETHER

ALTERNATIVE METHOD Questions 3 and 4 Have students solve $x^2 + y^2 = 25$ for y ($y = \sqrt{25 - x^2}$ or $y = -\sqrt{25 - x^2}$). Then have them use the table feature on graphing calculators to determine points that satisfy the equation. Students can also use the graphing calculator to graph the points.

THINK AND DISCUSS

Theorem 12-1 Help students understand that x and y are variables and h, k, and r are constants.

586

What You'll Learn

• Writing the equation of a circle
• Using the equation of a circle to solve real-world problems

...And Why

To investigate situations in which equations of circles can be used, such as expressing the range of cellular telephone towers

What You'll Need

• graph paper

Connections ⊕ Communications . . . and more

12-1 Circles in the Coordinate Plane

WORK TOGETHER

Work with a small group. Consider the equation $x^2 + y^2 = 25$.

1. What are the values of y when $x = 0$? **−5, 5**

2. What are the values of x when $y = 4$? **−3, 3**

3. Make a table of at least eight ordered pairs (x, y) that satisfy the equation $x^2 + y^2 = 25$. Then graph the ordered pairs. **See margin p. 589.**

4. **a.** The points you graphed lie on a circle. What is the center of the circle? What is the radius? **(0, 0); 5**
   b. What is the square of the radius? **25**
   c. What connection do you see between the square of the radius and the equation of the circle?
   The value of $x^2 + y^2$ is = to the square of the radius.

5. Find the center and radius of each circle.
   a. $x^2 + y^2 = 9$ **(0, 0); 3**
   b. $x^2 + y^2 = 36$ **(0, 0); 6**
   c. $x^2 + y^2 = 121$ **(0, 0); 11**

THINK AND DISCUSS

Part 1 **Writing the Equation of a Circle**

You can use the Distance Formula to find an equation of a circle with center (h, k) and radius r. Let (x, y) be any point on the circle. The radius is the distance from (h, k) to (x, y).

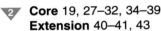

$r = \sqrt{(x - h)^2 + (y - k)^2}$ Distance Formula
$r^2 = (x - h)^2 + (y - k)^2$ Square both sides.

This proves the following theorem.

Theorem 12-1
Equation of a Circle

The **standard form of an equation of a circle** with center (h, k) and radius r is $(x - h)^2 + (y - k)^2 = r^2$.

Example 1 ·

Write the standard equation of the circle with center $(5, -2)$ and radius 7.

Use the equation of a circle with $(h, k) = (5, -2)$ and $r = 7$.

$(x - 5)^2 + [(y - (-2)]^2 = 7^2$ Substitute.
$(x - 5)^2 + (y + 2)^2 = 49$ Simplify.

Example 1

ERROR ALERT! Some students may have trouble substituting negative values into the equation. **Remediation:** Remind students that subtracting a negative number is the same as adding its opposite.

EXTENSION Some graphing software allows students to graph circles. Give students opportunity to use the software throughout the lesson to check graphs and equations.

ERROR ALERT! Question 7 Some students will use the wrong signs for the coordinates of the center. **Remediation:** Remind students that the equation of a circle in standard form has minus signs. Help them see that $(x - 7)^2 + (y + 2)^2 = 64$ is equivalent to $(x - 7)^2 + [y - (-2)]^2 = 64$.

CRITICAL THINKING Question 8 Ask students if the following are equations of circles. If an equation describes a circle, have them find the center and radius.

a. $x^2 + y^2 = 144$ **b.** $x^2 - y^2 = 9$ **c.** $y^2 + x^2 = 49$

Example 2 **Relating to the Real World**

Have students use the distance formula to verify the radius is 10. Point out that the equation is left in standard form with the binomials not expanded.

TRANSFORMATIONS Question 10 Help students see that the translation vector describing the translation of $\odot A$ to $\odot B$ is the same translation vector describing the translation of point A to point B.

6a. $(x - 3)^2 + (y - 5)^2 = 36$
b. $(x + 2)^2 + (y + 1)^2 = 2$

7a. $(7, -2)$; 8
b. $(2, 3)$; 10

9. $\odot B$: $(x - 16)^2 + (y - 10)^2 = 100$;
   $\odot O$: $x^2 + y^2 = 144$

6. Try This Write the equation of each circle.
   a. center $(3, 5)$; $r = 6$ **b.** center $(-2, -1)$; $r = \sqrt{2}$

7. Try This Find the center and radius of each circle.
   a. $(x - 7)^2 + (y + 2)^2 = 64$ **b.** $(x - 2)^2 + (y - 3)^2 = 100$

8. What is the standard form of the equation of a circle with center at the origin and radius r? $x^2 + y^2 = r^2$

Part 2 **Using the Equation of a Circle**

You can use equations of circles to model real-world situations.

Example 2 **Relating to the Real World**

Communications When you make a call from a cellular phone, a tower receives the call. In the graph, the center of each circle is the location of a cellular telephone tower. The equation of a circle can describe the receiving and transmitting range of a tower. Find the equation that describes the position and the range of Tower A.

The center of $\odot A$ is $(4, 20)$, and the radius is 10. Use the equation of a circle with $(h, k) = (4, 20)$ and $r = 10$.

$(x - 4)^2 + (y - 20)^2 = 10^2$ Substitute.
$(x - 4)^2 + (y - 20)^2 = 100$ Simplify. ■

9. Find the equation of the positions and ranges of the other two towers. **See above left.**

10. Transformations $\odot B$ is a translation of $\odot A$. Use ordered pair notation to describe the translation vector.
$\langle 12, -10 \rangle$

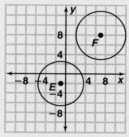

Additional Examples

FOR EXAMPLE 1 ....

Write the standard equation of the circle with center $(3, -4)$ and radius 6. $(x - 3)^2 + (y + 4)^2 = 36$

FOR EXAMPLE 2 ....

In the graph, the center of each circle is the location of a broadcasting tower for a radio station. Find the equation that describes the position and range of tower F.

$(x - 7)^2 + (y - 8)^2 = 25$

Discussion: *Describe the transformation that takes $\odot F$ onto $\odot E$.*

FOR EXAMPLE 3 ....

Write an equation of a circle with center $(1, 2)$ that passes through the point $(3, -4)$.
$(x - 1)^2 + (y - 2)^2 = 40$

Discussion: *Describe the center and the radius of a circle that is entirely in the second quadrant.*

587

Technology Options

For Exercises 15–18 and Exercise 41, students may use graphing software or a graphing calculator to graph the circles.

Prentice Hall Technology

 Software
- Secondary Math Lab Toolkit™
- Computer Item Generator 12-1

 CD-ROM
- Multimedia Geometry Lab 12

 Internet
- See the Prentice Hall site. (http://www.phschool.com)

If you know the center of a circle and a point on the circle, you can write an equation of the circle.

Example 3 ··

Write an equation of the circle with center $(1, -3)$ that passes through the point $(4, 2)$.

The radius is the distance from the center to any point on the circle.

$$r = \sqrt{(1 - 4)^2 + (-3 - 2)^2} \quad \text{Use the Distance Formula.}$$
$$= \sqrt{(-3)^2 + (-5)^2} \quad \text{Simplify.}$$
$$= \sqrt{9 + 25} = \sqrt{34}$$

Use the equation of a circle with $(h, k) = (1, -3)$ and $r = \sqrt{34}$.

$$(x - 1)^2 + (y - (-3)^2) = (\sqrt{34})^2 \quad \text{Substitute.}$$
$$(x - 1)^2 + (y + 3)^2 = 34 \quad \text{Simplify.}$$

11. Does the graph of $(x - 1)^2 + (y + 3)^2 \leq 34$ include points inside or points outside the circle shown in Example 3? **inside**

12. Try This A diameter of a circle has endpoints $(-3, 7)$ and $(5, 5)$. Write an equation of the circle. $(x - 1)^2 + (y - 6)^2 = 17$

1. $(x - 2)^2 + (y + 8)^2 = 81$ 2. $x^2 + (y - 3)^2 = 49$ 3. $(x - 0.2)^2 + (y - 1.1)^2 = 0.16$

Exercises   ON YOUR OWN

Write an equation of each circle. 1–3. See above.

1. center $(2, -8)$; $r = 9$ **2.** center $(0, 3)$; $r = 7$ **3.** center $(0.2, 1.1)$; $r = 0.4$

4. center $(5, -1)$; $r = 12$ **5.** center $(-6, 3)$; $r = 8$ **6.** center $(-9, -4)$; $r = \sqrt{5}$
   $(x - 5)^2 + (y + 1)^2 = 144$ $(x + 6)^2 + (y - 3)^2 = 64$ $(x + 9)^2 + (y + 4)^2 = 5$

Match each equation or inequality with a graph.

7. $(x - 1)^2 + (y - 3)^2 = 9$ **B**

8. $(x + 1)^2 + (y - 1)^2 > 4$ **D**

9. $x^2 + y^2 = 4$ **C**

10. $(x - 2)^2 + y^2 < 9$ **A**

A.

B.

C.

D.

Find the center and the radius of each circle.

11. $(x + 7)^2 + (y - 5)^2 = 16$ (−7, 5); 4

12. $(x - 3)^2 + (y + 8)^2 = 100$ (3, −8); 10

13. $(x - 0.3)^2 + y^2 = 0.04$ (0.3, 0); 0.2

14. $(x + 5)^2 + (y + 2)^2 = 48$ (−5, −2); $4\sqrt{3}$

15–17. See margin for graph.

Graph each circle. Label its center and state its radius. 18. See margin p. 590 for graph.

15. $x^2 + y^2 = 36$ 6

16. $x^2 + (y - 4)^2 = 16$ 4

17. $(x + 2)^2 + y^2 = 9$ 3

18. $(x + 4)^2 + (y - 1)^2 = 25$ 5

19. a. Transformations The circle with equation $(x + 5)^2 + (y - 3)^2 = 64$ is a translation image of $x^2 + y^2 = 64$. Use ordered pair notation to describe the translation vector. ⟨−5, 3⟩

   b. Transformations The circle $x^2 + y^2 = 64$ is the dilation image of $x^2 + y^2 = 1$. What is the center and scale factor of the dilation? (0, 0); 8

   c. Writing Write *true* or *false*. Every circle in the coordinate plane is a transformation image of $x^2 + y^2 = 1$. Explain. **See margin.**

20. a. Weather Consider a point on the edge of a cup of an anemometer. Describe the locus of points that this point passes through as the cup spins in the wind. **circle**

   b. Locus Suppose the distance from the center of the anemometer to a point on the edge of a cup is 6 in. Write an equation for the locus of points you described in part (a). Use the center of the anemometer as the origin.
   $x^2 + y^2 = 36$

The speed at which the cups of an anemometer spin indicates the speed of the wind.

Write an equation of each circle.
See below.

21.

22. $x^2 + (y - 3)^2 = 4$

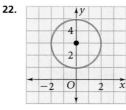

23. $(x - 2)^2 + (y - 2)^2 = 16$

24.

25.

26.

$(x + 3)^2 + y^2 = 16$
21. $x^2 + y^2 = 9$

$(x + 2)^2 + (y - 3)^2 = 9$

$(x + 1)^2 + (y + 2)^2 = 9$

12-1 Circles in the Coordinate Plane   **589**

page 586   Work Together

3.

x	y
0	5
5	0
−5	0
0	−5
3	4
−4	3
−3	−4
4	−3

pages 588–591   On Your Own

15.   6

16.   4

17.   3

589

18. 5

19c. True; a transformation consisting of a translation and a dilation can move the center of the ⊙ to any pt. and make the ⊙ any size.

41.

$x^2 + y^2 = 36$; $x^2 + (y - 3)^2 = 9$; $x^2 + (y + 3)^2 = 9$

page 591 Mixed Review

45. $\angle AEB \cong \angle DEC$ because vertical $\angle$s are $\cong$. Then $\triangle ABE \cong \triangle DCE$ by AAS, and $\overline{BE} \cong \overline{CE}$, $\overline{AE} \cong \overline{DE}$ by CPCTC. $\overline{AC} \cong \overline{DB}$ by the Segment Addition Post. $\overline{BC} \cong \overline{BC}$ by Reflexive Prop. of $\cong$. Then $\triangle ABC \cong \triangle DCB$ by SSS.

590

Write an equation of the circle with the given center passing through the given point.
$(x + 2)^2 + (y - 6)^2 = 16$

27. center $(-2, 6)$; through $(-2, 10)$ **28.** center $(1, 2)$; through $(0, 6)$ $(x - 1)^2 + (y - 2)^2 = 17$

29. center $(7, -2)$; through $(1, -6)$ **30.** center $(-10, -5)$; through $(-5, 5)$
$(x - 7)^2 + (y + 2)^2 = 52$ $(x + 10)^2 + (y + 5)^2 = 125$

31. Transformations The graph of $x^2 + y^2 = 100$ is translated so that its center is $(3, -5)$. What is the equation of the image? See above.

32. Critical Thinking Determine whether each equation is an equation of a circle. If it is not, explain why. a. yes

a. $(x - 1)^2 + (y + 2)^2 = 9$ **b.** $x + y = 9$ See above.
c. $x + (y - 3)^2 = 9$ **d.** $x^2 + (y - 1)^2 = 9$ yes
No; x is not squared. 33a–c. See below.

33. a. Write the equation of the equator with the center of Earth as the origin. The equator's radius is about 3960 mi long.

b. Find the length of a 1° arc on the equator to the nearest tenth.

c. At the equator, a 1° arc in latitude is 60 nautical miles long. How many miles are in a nautical mile? Round to the nearest tenth.

d. History Columbus planned his trip to the east by going west. He thought each 1° arc was 45 miles long. He estimated that the trip would take 21 days. Use your answer to part (b) to find a better estimate. about 32 days
33a. $x^2 + y^2 = 15{,}681{,}600$ b. 69.1 mi c. 1.2 mi

Write an equation of a circle with diameter $\overline{AB}$. 34–36. See below right.

34. $A(0, 0)$, and $B(8, 6)$ **35.** $A(3, 0)$, and $B(7, 6)$ **36.** $A(1, 1)$, and $B(5, 5)$

37. $A(-1, 0)$, and $B(-5, -3)$ **38.** $A(-3, 1)$, and $B(0, 9)$ **39.** $A(-2, 3)$, and $B(6, -7)$
$(x + 3)^2 + (y + 1.5)^2 = 6.25$ $(x + 1.5)^2 + (y - 5)^2 = 18.25$ $(x - 2)^2 + (y + 2)^2 = 41$

31. $(x - 3)^2 + (y + 5)^2 = 100$
32b. No; the variables are not squared.

PEANUTS® by Charles M. Schulz

40. Snoopy can't draw a square with a compass. But he could construct a square and use it to find the length $5\sqrt{2}$ in. Then he could draw a circle with that length as the radius. Explain how.

The diagonals of the square have length $5\sqrt{2}$ in.

41. Open-ended On graph paper, make a design that includes at least three circles. Write the equations of your circles. See margin for sample.

42. Find the circumference and the area of the circle whose equation is $(x - 9)^2 + (y - 3)^2 = 64$. Leave your answers in terms of π. 16π units; 64π units^2

34. $(x - 4)^2 + (y - 3)^2 = 25$
35. $(x - 5)^2 + (y - 3)^2 = 13$
36. $(x - 3)^2 + (y - 3)^2 = 8$

---

43. *Geometry in 3 Dimensions* The equation of a sphere is similar to the equation of a circle. The equation of a sphere with center (h, j, k) and radius r is $(x - h)^2 + (y - j)^2 + (z - k)^2 = r^2$.

a. $M(-1, 3, 2)$ is the center of a sphere passing through $T(0, 5, 1)$. What is the radius of the sphere? $\sqrt{6}$

b. Write an equation of the sphere. $(x + 1)^2 + (y - 3)^2 + (z - 2)^2 = 6$

Chapter Project   Find Out by Doing

For many centuries, artists throughout the world have used ropelike patterns called *knots* on jewelry, clothing, stone carvings, and other items. You can create a knot design using graph paper and a compass. Use a pencil because you will need to erase portions of your drawing.

- Mark the origin at the center of a sheet of graph paper, but do not draw any axes. Draw four circles with centers $(0, 5)$, $(5, 0)$, $(0, -5)$, and $(-5, 0)$ and with radius $5\sqrt{2}$. Using the same centers draw four circles with radius $4\sqrt{2}$.

- Connect the four centers to form a square. (shown in red)

- Draw segments through the intersections of the smaller and larger circles. (shown in green)

- Erase arcs to make bands that appear to weave in and out. Color your design. **Check students' work.**

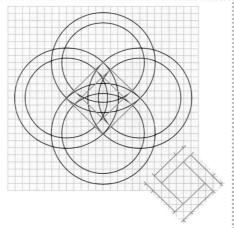

Exercises   MIXED REVIEW

Use the given information. Explain how to prove △ABC ≅ △DCB.

44. Given: $\angle BCA \cong \angle CBD$, $\overline{BD} \cong \overline{CA}$ $\overline{BC} \cong \overline{BC}$; use SAS Post.

45. Given: $\angle ABE \cong \angle DCE$, $\overline{AB} \cong \overline{DC}$ See margin p. 590.

46. A cube has surface area 96 in.². What is the surface area of a cube with sides twice as long? **384 in.²**

47. The volume of a cube is 64 in.³. What is the volume of a cube with sides twice as long? **512 in.³**

Getting Ready for Lesson 12-2
Find the complement and supplement of each angle.

48. 48°   **49.** 73°   **50.** 21°   **51.** 87°
42°; 132°   17°; 107°   69°; 159°   3°; 93°

Students learn how to describe the location of a point using polar coordinates and how to graph points with polar coordinates.

Help students see how finding polar coordinates is similar to finding the magnitude and direction of a vector which they learned in Lesson 11-4.

Example 1

ERROR ALERT! Some students may measure angles in the clockwise direction. **Remediation:** Help students understand that in the polar coordinate system angles are measured in the counterclockwise direction starting from the polar axis.

Example 2

Help students understand that the radius of each circle in the diagram increases by 1 unit.

ADDITIONAL PROBLEMS

1. Graph $S(2, 60°)$. Find the polar coordinates of a point T such that $m\angle SOT = 90$. Answers may vary. Sample: (3, 150°)

2. Graph $Q(3, 210°)$. Find the polar coordinates of a point R such that $m\angle QOR = 180$. Answers may vary. Sample: (5, 30°)

Transparencies
12, 123

Polar Coordinates

Extends Lesson 12-1

The polar-coordinate system locates a point using its distance from the origin, or **pole,** and the measure of a central angle formed by the polar axis and a ray from the pole through the point. The coordinates of A are $(2, 60°)$ because A is 2 units from the pole O and the measure of the angle formed by the polar axis and $\overrightarrow{OA}$ is 60.

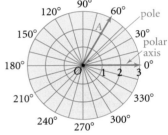

Example 1

What are the polar coordinates of P, Q, R, and S?

The coordinates of P are $(3, 90°)$.

The coordinates of Q are $(2, 210°)$.

The coordinates of R are $(4, 45°)$.

The coordinates of S are $(3.5, 285°)$.

Example 2

Graph the points $T(2, 30°)$, $V(1, 135°)$, and $W(3, 330°)$.

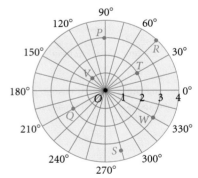

Find the polar coordinates of each point.

1. A (3, 120°)   2. B (2, 75°)   3. C (5, 315°)
4. D (4, 285°)   5. E (2, 240°)   6. F (3, 330°)

Graph each point.

7. $G(5, 180°)$ 8. $H(4, 60°)$
9. $I(3, 45°)$ 10. $J(1, 225°)$
11. $K(3.5, 150°)$ 12. $L(5, 270°)$

13. Explain how you can use the polar coordinates of X and Y to find the measure of $\angle XOY$.

Read the measures of the central ∠s for points X and Y from the graph, and subtract the measures.

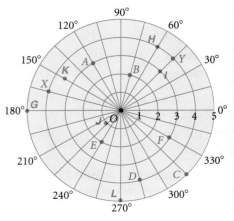

PROBLEM OF THE DAY

How can you place 21 marbles in four boxes so that each box contains an odd number of marbles? **Answers may vary. Sample given.**

Problem of the Day is also available in Transparencies.

CONNECTING TO PRIOR KNOWLEDGE Draw several different right triangles on the board. Label the lengths of two sides of each and have students find the length of the third side.

Check that students do not draw a segment that intersects a circle at one point rather than drawing a line that touches a circle at one point.

MAKING CONNECTIONS The term *tangent* comes from the Latin verb *tangere* which means "to touch."

ESL Students may be confused by using *tangent* in a new way. Try to use the phrases "tangent of an angle" and "tangent to a circle" to help reinforce the difference.

Connections *Machine Shops . . . and more*

What You'll Learn

- Finding the relationship between a radius and a tangent, and between two tangents drawn from the same point
- Circumscribing a circle

...And Why

To use tangents to circles in real-world situations, such as working in a machine shop

What You'll Need

- compass
- straightedge
- centimeter ruler

12-2 Properties of Tangents

WORK TOGETHER

Work in a group.

- Use a compass to draw a circle. Label the center *O*.
- Use a straightedge to draw a line that intersects the circle in only one point. Label the point *B*.
- Draw $\overline{OB}$.

1. What seems to be true about the angle formed by the radius and the line that you drew? Compare results within your group. **The radius and the line form a rt. angle.**

THINK AND DISCUSS

Part 1 Tangents to Circles

In Chapter 11, you studied *the tangent of an angle in a right triangle.* Now you will study properties of *a tangent to a circle.*

A **tangent to a circle** is a line in the plane of the circle that intersects the circle in exactly one point.

The point where a circle and a tangent intersect is the **point of tangency**.

$\overrightarrow{BA}$ is a tangent ray and $\overline{BA}$ is a tangent segment. The word *tangent* may refer to a tangent line, a tangent ray, or a tangent segment.

Your observation in the Work Together suggests the following theorem.

Theorem 12-2

If a line is tangent to a circle, then it is perpendicular to the radius drawn to the point of tangency.

If $\overleftrightarrow{AB}$ is tangent to $\odot O$ at P, then $\overleftrightarrow{AB} \perp \overline{OP}$.

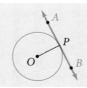

2. How many lines can you draw that are tangent to a circle at a given point on the circle? **1**

Lesson Planning Options

Prerequisite Skills

- Using the Pythagorean Theorem
- Expanding binomials

Assignment Options for Exercises On Your Own

To provide flexible scheduling, this lesson can be subdivided into parts.

1 **Core** 1–12, 17, 22–23
Extension 13, 25

2 **Core** 14–16, 18–19
Extension 20, 21, 24

Use Mixed Review to maintain skills.

Resources

Student Edition

Skills Handbook, p. 650
Extra Practice, p. 645
Glossary/Study Guide

Teaching Resources

Chapter Support File, Ch. 12
- Practice 12-2 (two worksheets)
- Reteaching 12-2
Classroom Manager 12-2
Glossary, Spanish Resources

Transparencies
120

593

Read through the proof of Theorem 12-2 with students. Make sure students understand why assuming $\overline{OP}$ is not perpendicular to n makes it possible to draw a segment $\overline{OL}$ that is perpendicular. Also make sure students understand why they can pick a point K such that $\overline{LK} \cong \overline{LP}$.

Example 1 ··································

Check that students understand why $SQ = r + 4$. Also review with students how to expand a binomial.

Example 2 **Relating to the Real World** ·················

ERROR ALERT! Some students will think $\angle EAD$ is a right angle and $\overline{ED}$ is the hypotenuse of $\triangle AED$. **Remediation:** Label all four right angles of $EBCD$ and remind students that the supplement of a right angle is a right angle.

Additional Examples

FOR EXAMPLE 1 ·······················

Refer to the diagram in Example 1. $\overline{PQ}$ is tangent to $\odot S$ at P. If $PQ = 8$ and $TQ = 5$, find the length of the radius of $\odot S$. **3.9**

FOR EXAMPLE 2 ·······················

Find the distance between the centers of the pulleys.

20 in. $\approx$ 20.4 in.

10 in.   6 in.

Discussion: *Explain how you can solve this problem in a different way.*

n P

n P L K

Who? Alma Thomas (1891–1978) used geometric designs in many of her paintings. In *A Joyful Scene of Spring* (p. 585), Thomas used wedges of color to represent the many circular gardens planted throughout Washington, D.C.

Indirect Proof of Theorem 12-2

Given: n is tangent to $\odot O$ at P.

Prove: $n \perp \overline{OP}$

Step 1: Assume that n is not perpendicular to $\overline{OP}$.

Step 2: If n is not perpendicular to $\overline{OP}$, some other segment $\overline{OL}$ must be perpendicular to n. Also there is a point K on n such that $\overline{LK} \cong \overline{LP}$. $\angle OLK \cong \angle OLP$ because perpendicular lines form congruent adjacent angles. $\overline{OL} \cong \overline{OL}$. So, $\triangle KLO \cong \triangle PLO$ by SAS. By CPCTC, $\overline{OK} \cong \overline{OP}$, which means K and P are both on $\odot O$ by the definition of a circle. For two points on n to also be on $\odot O$ contradicts the given fact that n is tangent to $\odot O$ at P. So the assumption that n is not perpendicular to $\overline{OP}$ must be false.

Step 3: Therefore, $n \perp \overline{OP}$ must be true.

You can use the Pythagorean Theorem to solve problems involving tangents.

Example 1 ····················

$\overline{PQ}$ is tangent to $\odot S$ at P. Find the length of a radius of $\odot S$.

Since $\overline{PQ}$ is tangent to $\odot S$ at P, $\triangle PQS$ is a right triangle with hypotenuse $\overline{SQ}$. $\overline{PS}$ and $\overline{ST}$ are radii of $\odot S$.

$$PS^2 + PQ^2 = SQ^2 \qquad \text{Pythagorean Theorem}$$
$$r^2 + 6^2 = (r + 4)^2 \qquad PS = ST = r;\ ST + TQ = SQ$$
$$r^2 + 36 = r^2 + 8r + 16 \qquad \text{Simplify.}$$
$$20 = 8r \qquad \text{Subtract } r^2 \text{ and 16 from each side.}$$
$$r = 2.5 \qquad \text{Divide each side by 8.}$$

P 6 Q
r T 4
r
S

Tangents are formed by belts and ropes that pass over pulleys and wheels.

Example 2 **Relating to the Real World** ··············

Machine Shop A belt fits tightly around two circular pulleys. Find the distance between the centers of the pulleys.

30 in.   8 in.

14 in.

ALTERNATIVE ASSESSMENT To assess students' understanding of indirect proof, have students work in groups to write an indirect proof of Theorem 12-3. Then have them compare their proofs with those of other groups.

ALTERNATIVE METHOD Have students draw two intersecting lines on a sheet of paper. Then have them use a compass to draw a circle on another sheet of paper that is small enough to fit between the lines. Have them cut out the circle and place it between the lines so it is tangent to both lines, mark the points of tangency, and measure the distances from the point of intersection to the points of tangency.

Label the diagram. Draw a segment parallel to $\overline{CB}$ from D to $\overline{AB}$. Label the intersection E.

$EBCD$ is a rectangle. $\triangle AED$ is a right triangle with $ED = 30$ in. and $AE = 14 - 8 = 6$ in.

Use the Pythagorean Theorem to find the distance between the centers, AD.

$AE^2 + ED^2 = AD^2$	Pythagorean Theorem
$6^2 + 30^2 = AD^2$	Substitute.
$936 = AD^2$	Simplify.
$30.594117 = AD$	Use a calculator.

The distance between the centers is about 30.6 in.

3–4. See margin p. 596.

3. Explain why $EBCD$ in Example 2 is a rectangle.

4. Explain why $\triangle AED$ in Example 2 is a right triangle.

5. **Try This** In the diagram at the right, $\overline{PQ}$ is tangent to $\odot O$ at P. Find the radius of $\odot O$. **8 in.**

The converse of Theorem 12-2 is also true. You can use the Converse of Theorem 12-2 to determine if a segment is tangent to a circle. You can also use the converse to construct a tangent to a circle.

Theorem 12-3
Converse of Theorem 12-2

If a line in the same plane as a circle is perpendicular to a radius at its endpoint on the circle, then the line is tangent to the circle.

If $\overleftrightarrow{AB} \perp \overline{OP}$ at P, then $\overleftrightarrow{AB}$ is tangent to $\odot O$.

6. In the diagram at the right, is $\overline{LM}$ tangent to $\odot N$ at L? Explain.

Yes; $7^2 + 24^2 = 25^2$, so $\triangle NLM$ is a rt. $\triangle$ and $\angle L$ is a rt. angle.

Have each member of your group construct a circle and select a point outside the circle. From the point, draw two tangent segments to the circle.

7. **a.** Measure the tangent segments. What do you notice? Compare results within your group. **The segments have = lengths.**
   b. Write a **conjecture** based on your results. **2 segments with a common endpt. outside a $\odot$ and tangent to that $\odot$ are $\cong$.**

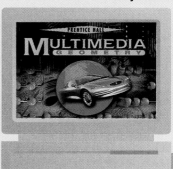

pages 593–595 Think and Discuss

3. Answers may vary. Sample: The radii are ∥ because, in a plane, 2 lines ⊥ to a 3rd line are ∥. Then *EBCD* is a ▱ with 2 rt. angles. So it is a rectangle.

4. ∠*AED* is supplementary to right angle ∠*BED*, so it is also a right angle. So ∠*AED* is a right △.

pages 596–599 On Your Own

9a.

10. 1. $\overline{BA}$ and $\overline{BC}$ are tangent to ⊙*O* at *A* and *C*, respectively. (Given)
2. $\overline{BA} \perp \overline{OA}$, $\overline{BC} \perp \overline{OC}$ (A line tangent to a ⊙ is ⊥ to the radius drawn to the pt. of tangency.)
3. △*OAB* and △*OCB* are rt. △s. (Def. of rt. △) 4. $\overline{OA} \cong \overline{OC}$ (All radii of a ⊙ are ≅.) 5. $\overline{OB} \cong \overline{OB}$ (Reflexive Prop. of ≅)
6. △*OAB* ≅ △*OCB* (HL Thm.)
7. $\overline{BA} \cong \overline{BC}$ (CPCTC)

12a.

THINK AND DISCUSS

Circumscribing Circles

In the figure at the left, the sides of the triangle are tangent to the circle. The triangle is **circumscribed about** the circle. The circle is **inscribed in** the triangle.

Theorem 12-4 allows you to investigate figures that circumscribe a circle. You will prove this theorem in Exercise 10.

Theorem 12-4

Two segments tangent to a circle from a point outside the circle are congruent.

If $\overline{AB}$ and $\overline{CB}$ are tangent to ⊙*O* at *A* and *C*, respectively, then $\overline{AB} \cong \overline{CB}$.

Example 3

⊙*O* is inscribed in △*ABC*. Find the perimeter of △*ABC*.

$AD = AF = 10$ cm   Two segments tangent to a circle from
$BD = BE = 15$ cm   a point outside the circle are congruent.
$CF = CE = 8$ cm

$AD + AF + BD + BE + CF + CE =$ the perimeter
$10 + 10 + 15 + 15 + 8 + 8 = 66$
The perimeter is 66 cm.

8. a. **Try This** ⊙*O* is inscribed in △*PQR*. Copy the diagram and label each length you know based on Theorem 12-4.
   b. △*PQR* has a perimeter 88 cm. Find *QY*.

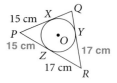

Exercises   **ON YOUR OWN**

Assume that lines that appear to be tangent are tangent. *O* is the center of each circle. Find the value of *x*.

1.   2.   3.   4.

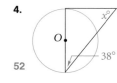

63   30   72   52

In each diagram, $\overline{PQ}$ is tangent to $\odot O$ at P. Find the value of x.

5.

13

6.

4.8

7.

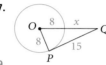

9

8. Air Conditioning Mr. Gonzales is replacing a cylindrical air-conditioning duct in a building. He estimates the radius of the duct by folding a ruler to form two 6-in. tangents to the duct. The tangents form an angle. Mr. Gonzales measures the angle bisector from the vertex to the duct. It is about $2\frac{3}{4}$ in. long. What is the radius of the air-conditioning duct? about 5 in.

9. a. Coordinate Geometry Draw several circles tangent to both coordinate axes. See margin p. 596 for sample.
 b. Writing Describe the locus of the centers of all such circles. the lines bisecting the angles formed by the axes
 c. Algebra Write the equation(s) of the locus of points you described in part (b). $y = x$, $y = -x$

10. Choose Write a two-column proof, paragraph proof, or flow proof of Theorem 12-4. See margin p. 596 for sample.
 Given: $\overline{BA}$ and $\overline{BC}$ are tangent to $\odot O$ at A and C, respectively.
 Prove: $\overline{BA} \cong \overline{BC}$

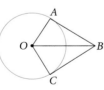

11. Standardized Test Prep $\overline{BD}$ and $\overline{CK}$ are diameters of $\odot A$. $\overline{BP}$ and $\overline{QP}$ are tangents to $\odot A$. Which of the following is *not* true? **D**
 A. $m\angle QPA = 25$ **B.** $m\angle BAP = 65$ **C.** $m\angle CDA = 57.5$
 D. $m\angle DAQ = 25$ **E.** $m\angle CAB = 115$

12a. See margin p. 596 for sample.

12. a. Constructions Use a compass to draw a circle. Draw a diameter of the circle. Use the construction of a perpendicular through a point on a line to construct tangents at the endpoints of the diameter.
 b. What seems to be true of the tangents? **Justify** your answer. The tangents are ∥; in a plane, 2 lines ⊥ to a 3rd are ∥.

13. A plumber installs a pipe with diameter 6 in. in a corner. The board securing the pipe in place is 1 in. thick. The shortest length of board she can use forms an isosceles right triangle with the two walls.
 a. What is the length (to the nearest tenth) of the side of the board tangent to the pipe? 14.5 in.
 b. What is the outside length of the board to the nearest tenth? 16.5 in.

17. 1. $\overline{BC}$ is tangent to $\odot A$ at D. (Given) **2.** $\overline{BC} \perp \overline{AD}$ (A tangent to a $\odot$ is $\perp$ to the radius drawn to the pt. of tangency.) **3.** $\overline{DB} \cong \overline{DC}$ (Given) **4.** $\overline{AD}$ is the $\perp$ bisector of $\overline{BC}$. (Def. of $\perp$ bisector) **5.** $\overline{AB} \cong \overline{AC}$ (A pt. on the $\perp$ bisector of a segment is equidistant from the endpts. of the segment.)

18. 1. $\odot A$ and $\odot B$ with common tangents $\overline{DF}$ and $\overline{CE}$ (Given) **2.** $\overline{GC} \cong \overline{GD}$, $\overline{GE} \cong \overline{GF}$ (2 segments tangent to a $\odot$ from a pt. outside the circle are $\cong$.) **3.** $\frac{GC}{GE} = \frac{GD}{GF}$ (Division Prop. of =) **4.** $\angle CGD \cong \angle EGF$ (Vertical $\angle$s are $\cong$.) **5.** $\triangle GDC \sim \triangle GFE$ (SAS $\sim$)

19. They are $\cong$; $\overline{CE} \cong \overline{FE}$ and $\overline{FE} \cong \overline{DE}$ because 2 segments tangent to a $\odot$ from a pt. outside the $\odot$ are $\cong$; $\overline{CE} \cong \overline{DE}$ by Transitive Prop. of $\cong$.

20a.

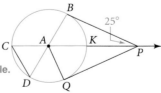

 b. Draw the diagonals of the small square. The large square contains $8 \cong \triangle$s. The small square contains 4 of them.

Exercises 17–18 Have students work with partners or in small groups. Suggest they begin by writing a plan for each proof. Make sure students do not assume anything about the segments from the appearance of the diagrams.

MAKING CONNECTIONS Exercise 21 The maximum duration of an eclipse of the sun is 7 min, 31 sec and there can be at most five solar eclipses per year.

CONNECTING TO STUDENTS' WORLD Exercise 21 Have students research other facts about a solar or lunar eclipse and share them with the class.

EXTENSION Exercise 21 Challenge students to draw a pair of circles for which there is exactly one common tangent, exactly two common tangents, exactly three common tangents, and exactly four common tangents.

21. **Blue segments are common external tangents to the sun and the moon; green segments are common internal tangents to the sun and the moon; red segments are common external tangents to the sun and Earth.**

22b. $\frac{x}{2}$; $m\angle 1$ is twice $m\angle 4$. Since $\triangle OAB$ is isosceles, $\angle 2 \cong \angle 3$. So $m\angle 3 = \frac{180 - x}{2} = 90 - \frac{x}{2}$. Since $\angle 3$ and $\angle 4$ are complementary, $m\angle 4 = 90 - (90 - \frac{x}{2}) = \frac{x}{2}$.

23.

24a.

In each diagram, a polygon circumscribes a circle. Find the perimeter of each polygon.

14.
8 cm 16 cm 6 cm 9 cm 78 cm

15.
14.2 in. 1.8 in. 3.7 in. 3.4 in. 3.6 in.

16.
68 cm 17 cm 7 cm 6 cm 12 cm 15 cm

Choose Write a two-column proof, paragraph proof, or flow proof.

17–18. Answers may vary. See margin p. 597 for samples.

17. **Given:** $\overline{BC}$ is tangent to $\odot A$ at D.
    $\overline{DB} \cong \overline{DC}$
    Prove: $\overline{AB} \cong \overline{AC}$

18. **Given:** $\odot A$ and $\odot B$ with common tangents $\overline{DF}$ and $\overline{CE}$
    Prove: $\triangle GDC \sim \triangle GFE$

19. **Critical Thinking** $\overline{EF}$ is tangent to both $\odot A$ and $\odot B$ at F. $\overline{CD}$ is tangent to $\odot A$ at C and to $\odot B$ at D. What can you conclude about $\overline{CE}$, $\overline{DE}$, and $\overline{FE}$? **Justify** your answer. **See margin p. 597.**

20. Leonardo da Vinci wrote, "When each of two squares touch the same circle at four points, one is double the other."
    a. Sketch a figure to illustrate this statement. **See margin p. 597 for sample.**
    b. **Justify** the statement. **See margin p. 597.**

21. **Solar Eclipse** Common tangents to two circles may be internal or external. If a line were drawn through the centers of the two circles, a *common internal tangent* would intersect the line and a *common external tangent* would *not* intersect the line. In the diagram of a solar eclipse, which are common tangents to the sun and the moon? to the sun and Earth? State whether the tangents are internal or external. **See margin.**

Sun Earth Moon

22. **a.** $\overline{AC}$ is tangent to $\odot O$ at A and $m\angle 1 = 70$. Find $m\angle 4$. **35**
    b. Let $m\angle 1 = x$. Find $m\angle 4$ in terms of x. What is the relationship between $\angle 1$ and $\angle 4$? Explain. **See margin p. 598.**

23. *Coordinate Geometry* Graph the equation $x^2 + y^2 = 9$. Then draw a segment from $(0, 5)$ tangent to the circle. Find the length of the segment. **See margin p. 598 for diagram; 4**

24. **a.** *Open-ended* Draw a quadrilateral circumscribed about a circle. **See margin p. 598 for sample.**
    b. *Patterns* Compare the sums of the lengths of the opposite sides. Repeat the experiment with another circle and quadrilateral. Make a **conjecture** based on your observations. **See below.**

25. *Clock Making* Mr. Franklin is building a case for a clock. The case will be in the shape of a regular hexagon. The diameter of the circular face is 10 in. Find the inside perimeter of the clock case. **about 34.6 in.**

24b. The sums of lengths of opp. sides are =.

Exercises MIXED REVIEW

Find sin A and cos A. Leave your answers in simplest radical form. 26. $\frac{\sqrt{5}}{5}$; $\frac{2\sqrt{5}}{5}$

26.

27.
$\frac{13}{17}$, $\frac{2\sqrt{30}}{17}$

28.
$\frac{3}{5}$, $\frac{4}{5}$

29. **a.** Sketch a quadrilateral whose diagonals are congruent and bisect each other. What kind of quadrilateral did you sketch? **rectangle**
    b. *Coordinate Geometry* Decide where you would place coordinate axes on the quadrilateral if you were using it in a coordinate proof. Sketch your axes. **Answers may vary. Sample: See right.**

Getting Ready for Lesson 12-3

Choose Use mental math, paper and pencil, or a calculator. Find the value of x. If your answer is not an integer, round to the nearest tenth.

30. **5**

31. **8.1**

32. **7.2 3.4**

PROBLEM OF THE DAY

If the ratio of the lengths of the edges of a right rectangular prism is 1:2:3 and the total surface area is 352 cm², find the volume. **384 cm³**

Problem of the Day is also available in Transparencies.

CONNECTING TO PRIOR KNOWLEDGE Draw a circle and label four points on it. Have students name all the major and minor arcs.

WORK TOGETHER

TACTILE LEARNING Make sure students understand how to use MIRA™. Allow students time to experiment with it before beginning this activity.

ALTERNATIVE METHOD If MIRA™ is not available, students can use paper folding to reflect $\overset{\frown}{AB}$. Make sure students fold the circle onto itself though its center. Similarly, students can use paper folding to construct a perpendicular to $\overline{GH}$.

Lesson Planning Options

Prerequisite Skills

- Finding the measures of arcs
- Using the Pythagorean Theorem

Assignment Options for Exercises On Your Own

To provide flexible scheduling, this lesson can be subdivided into parts.

1 Core 9, 14–19, 21, 23–24, 26
Extension 20, 27

2 Core 1–8, 10–13, 22
Extension 25

Use Mixed Review to maintain skills.

Resources

Student Edition

Skills Handbook, pp. 646, 650
Extra Practice, p. 645
Glossary/Study Guide

Teaching Resources

Chapter Support File, Ch. 12
- Practice 12-3 (two worksheets)
- Reteaching 12-3
Classroom Manager 12-3
Glossary, Spanish Resources

Transparencies
12, 121

What You'll Learn

- Finding the lengths of chords and measures of arcs of a circle
- Locating the center of a circle using chords

...And Why

To find the radius of a circle in real-life situations such as archaeology

What You'll Need

compass, MIRA™, protractor, centimeter ruler

▶ **TECHNOLOGY HINT**
The Work Together could be done using geometry software.

QUICK REVIEW

The measure of a minor arc is the measure of its corresponding central angle. The measure of a major arc is 360 minus the measure of its related minor arc.

QUICK REVIEW

Congruent arcs have the same measure and are in the same circle or in congruent circles.

5. Yes; a diameter is a segment with endpts. on the ⊙.

Connections — Archaeology . . . and more

12-3 Properties of Chords and Arcs

WORK TOGETHER

Have each member of your group use a compass to draw a large circle. Label its center O. Create $\overset{\frown}{AB}$ by labeling two points A and B on your circle.

- Construct an arc congruent to $\overset{\frown}{AB}$ by placing a MIRA on ⊙O and moving it until the circle maps on itself and you see the images of A and B. Label the images A' and B'. Draw radii $\overline{OA}$, $\overline{OB}$, $\overline{OA'}$, and $\overline{OB'}$.

1. **a.** Use a protractor to measure $\angle AOB$ and $\angle A'OB'$. Compare results. **The measures are = .**
   b. Write a **conjecture** about the central angles of congruent arcs. **Central angles of ≅ arcs are ≅ .**

- Draw $\overline{AB}$ and $\overline{A'B'}$.
   AB and A′B′ are = .

2. **a.** Measure $\overline{AB}$ and $\overline{A'B'}$. Compare results within your group.
   b. Write a **conjecture** about the segments joining the endpoints of congruent arcs. **Segments joining the endpts. of ≅ arcs are ≅ .**

- Use a compass to draw another circle. Label its center M. Label two points G and H on your circle. Draw $\overline{GH}$. While keeping an edge of the MIRA on point M, construct a diameter perpendicular to $\overline{GH}$ by moving the MIRA until the image of G maps onto H. Draw the MIRA line. Label its intersection with $\overline{GH}$ as F and label its intersection with the circle as J so that F is between J and M.

3. Measure $\overline{GF}$ and $\overline{HF}$. What do you notice? Compare results. **GF = FH**

4. Find $m\overset{\frown}{GJ}$ and $m\overset{\frown}{HJ}$. What do you notice? Compare results. **$m\overset{\frown}{GJ} = m\overset{\frown}{HJ}$**

THINK AND DISCUSS

Part 1 Congruent Arcs and Chords

In the Work Together, you created segments with endpoints on a circle. These segments are **chords** of the circle. The diagram shows arc $\overset{\frown}{PQ}$ and its related chord $\overline{PQ}$.

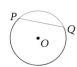

5. Is a diameter a chord? Explain why or why not.

6. Is a radius a chord? Explain why or why not.
   No; 1 endpt. of a radius is not on the ⊙.

THINK AND DISCUSS

Review with students why congruent arcs must be in the same circle or in congruent circles. Also point out that a chord is related to the *minor arc* it intercepts.

VISUAL LEARNING Students will benefit from drawing diagrams for Theorems 12-5, 12-6, and 12-7. Suggest they draw and label different parts of the circles with different colors.

LOGICAL REASONING Question 7 Point out that students can use Theorem 12-5 to justify Theorem 12-6.

Example 1

ERROR ALERT! Some students may think that $\overline{TC}$ and $\overline{TE}$ are radii of the circle so $\overline{TC} \cong \overline{TE}$. **Remediation:** Review the definition of radius and emphasize that one endpoint must be the *center* of the circle.

CRITICAL THINKING Ask students how they could use $\sin^{-1}$ or $\cos^{-1}$ to find $m\angle A$.

Your observations in the Work Together suggest the following theorems. You will prove Theorem 12-7 in Exercise 18.

Theorem 12-5	In the same circle or in congruent circles, (1) congruent central angles have congruent arcs; and (2) congruent arcs have congruent central angles.
Theorem 12-6	In the same circle or in congruent circles, (1) congruent chords have congruent arcs; and (2) congruent arcs have congruent chords.
Theorem 12-7	A diameter that is perpendicular to a chord bisects the chord and its arc.

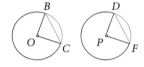

7. Logical Reasoning In the diagram at the left, $\odot O \cong \odot P$.
  a. Given that $\overline{BC} \cong \overline{DF}$, **justify** Theorem 12-6, part (1), by explaining why $\overset{\frown}{BC} \cong \overset{\frown}{DF}$.
  b. Given that $\overset{\frown}{BC} \cong \overset{\frown}{DF}$, **justify** Theorem 12-6, part (2), by explaining why $\overline{BC} \cong \overline{DF}$. a–b. See margin p. 603.

A segment that contains the center of a circle is part of a diameter. So, you may use Theorem 12-7 for a segment that is part of a diameter and is perpendicular to a chord.

QUICK REVIEW

The distance from a point to a line is the length of the perpendicular segment from the point to the line.

Example 1

Chord $\overline{CE}$ is 24 in. long and 5 in. from the center of $\odot A$.

a. Find the radius of $\odot A$.
b. Find $m\overset{\frown}{CE}$.

a. Copy the diagram and draw radius $\overline{AC}$ as shown at the left.

$TC = \frac{1}{2}(24) = 12$ The diameter $\perp$ to a chord bisects the chord.
$AC^2 = 5^2 + 12^2 = 169$ Use the Pythagorean Theorem.
$AC = 13$ in.

b. Extend $\overline{AT}$ to intersect the circle at D as shown below.

$\frac{1}{2}m\overset{\frown}{CE} = m\overset{\frown}{CD}$ A diameter $\perp$ to a chord bisects the chord and its arc.
$m\overset{\frown}{CE} = 2m\overset{\frown}{CD}$
$m\overset{\frown}{CD} = m\angle CAT$ The measure of a minor arc = the measure of its central angle.
$m\overset{\frown}{CE} = 2m\angle CAT$ Substitution
$\tan \angle CAT = \frac{12}{5} = 2.4$ $\tan \angle A = \frac{\text{opp.}}{\text{adj.}} = \frac{CT}{AT}$
$m\angle CAT \approx 67.380135$ Use a calculator to find $\tan^{-1}(2.4)$.
$m\overset{\frown}{CE} \approx 2 \boxed{\times} 67.380135$
$m\overset{\frown}{CE} \approx 134.8$

Additional Examples

FOR EXAMPLE 1

Refer to the diagram in Example 1. Let chord $\overline{CE}$ be 30 in. long and 6 in. from the center of $\odot A$.

a. Find the radius of $\odot A$. $\approx$ **16.2 in.**

b. Find $m\overset{\frown}{CE}$. $\approx$ **136.4**

FOR EXAMPLE 2

Trace the bottom of a can. Use the method described in Example 2 to find the center of the can. **Answers may vary. Sample:**

FOR EXAMPLE 3

Refer to the diagram in Example 3. If $AO = 13$ in. and $EO = 5$ in., find CD. Explain your reasoning.
$AE = 12$ **in. by the Pythagorean Theorem. Because a diameter (or part of a diameter) that is perpendicular to a chord bisects it,** $AB = 2AE = 24$. **Because chords that are equidistant from the center of the same circle are congruent,** $CD = AB = 24$ **in.**

601

Question 8 Have students model the steps given in Example 1 to find the radius and arc measure.

AUDITORY LEARNING Have students work in pairs. Have partners take turns reading their justifications aloud. Reading their justifications aloud will help students assess whether their reasoning is clear and organized.

Example 2 **Relating to the Real World**

CONNECTING TO STUDENTS' WORLD Have students bring in a jar or other circular object. Have them trace part of it, then construct the center of the circle.

Theorem 12-9 Give several examples of pairs of congruent chords including pairs that are parallel to each other and pairs that are not.

Technology Options

For Exercise 17, students may use geometry software to draw the diagram. For Exercise 26, students may use graphing software or graphing calculators to graph the line and circle.

Prentice Hall Technology

 Software
- Secondary Math Lab Toolkit™
- Integrated Math Lab 45
- Computer Item Generator 12-3

 Internet
- See the Prentice Hall site. (http://www.phschool.com)

---

8. a. Try This Find the radius of $\odot C$ to the nearest tenth. **13.0**

b. Find $m\overset{\frown}{AB}$ to the nearest tenth. **115.1**

You can use the following theorem to reconstruct a circle from an arc.

Theorem 12-8 | The perpendicular bisector of a chord contains the center of the circle.

9. Logical Reasoning Use the Converse of the Perpendicular Bisector Theorem (Theorem 4-13 on page 219) to **justify** Theorem 12-8. See margin p. 603.

See margin p. 603.

Example 2 **Relating to the Real World**

Archaeology An archaeologist found pieces of a jar. She wants to find the radius of the rim of the jar to help guide her as she reassembles the pieces. How can she find the center and radius of the rim?

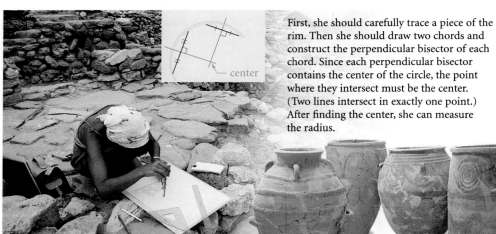

First, she should carefully trace a piece of the rim. Then she should draw two chords and construct the perpendicular bisector of each chord. Since each perpendicular bisector contains the center of the circle, the point where they intersect must be the center. (Two lines intersect in exactly one point.) After finding the center, she can measure the radius.

Part 2 **Chords Equidistant from the Center of a Circle**

The following theorem shows the relationship between two congruent chords and their distances from the center of a circle.

Theorem 12-9 | In the same circle or in congruent circles, (1) chords equidistant from the center are congruent; and (2) congruent chords are equidistant from the center.

Example 3

Although this proof has nine statements, students should not have difficulty following the reasoning. Challenge students to rewrite the proof by drawing $\overline{OB}$ and $\overline{OD}$ and showing $\triangle BOE \cong \triangle DOF$.

Exercises   ON YOUR OWN

ALTERNATIVE ASSESSMENT Have students choose five exercises, excluding proofs, that cover all the concepts in this lesson. Have them write each exercise, the concepts needed to answer it, and a detailed answer.

Exercises 1–8 You may want to point out to students that in some figures they will need to draw auxiliary lines. They will apply the important fact that all radii of a circle are congruent.

Example 3

Prove Theorem 12-9, part (1).

Given: $\odot O$, $\overline{OE} \perp \overline{AB}$, $\overline{OF} \perp \overline{CD}$, $\overline{OE} \cong \overline{OF}$
Prove: $\overline{AB} \cong \overline{CD}$

Begin by drawing $\overline{OA}$ and $\overline{OC}$.

Statements	Reasons
1. $\overline{OA} \cong \overline{OC}$	1. All radii of a circle are $\cong$.
2. $\overline{OE} \cong \overline{OF}$	2. Given
3. $\overline{OE} \perp \overline{AB}$, $\overline{OF} \perp \overline{CD}$	3. Given
4. $\angle AEO$ and $\angle CFO$ are right angles.	4. Definition of right angles
5. $\triangle AEO \cong \triangle CFO$	5. HL Theorem
6. $AE = CF$	6. CPCTC
7. $AE = \frac{1}{2}AB$, $CF = \frac{1}{2}CD$	7. A diameter $\perp$ to a chord bisects the chord.
8. $\frac{1}{2}AB = \frac{1}{2}CD$	8. Substitution
9. $AB = CD$, or $\overline{AB} \cong \overline{CD}$	9. Multiplication Property of Equality ■

Exercises   ON YOUR OWN

⊞ **Calculator** Find the value of *x*. If your answer is not an integer, round it to the nearest tenth.

1.

2.

3.

4.

5.

6.

7.

8.

Answers may vary slightly. Sample: 5.9 cm
9. a. The photo at the right shows part of a compact disc. Trace the disc. Find its radius in centimeters.
b. Writing Explain how you found the radius of the compact disc.
Answers may vary. Sample: Draw 2 nonparallel chords. Construct the ⊥ bisector of each chord. The intersection of the ⊥ bisectors is the center of the ⊙. Measure the radius.

---

pages 600–603   Think and Discuss

7a. $\overline{OB} \cong \overline{PD}$ and $\overline{OC} \cong \overline{PF}$ because radii of $\cong$ ⊙s are $\cong$. $\triangle OBC \cong \triangle PDF$ by the SSS Post. Then $m\angle BOC = m\angle DPF$ by CPCTC. But $m\widehat{BC} = m\angle BOC$ and $m\widehat{DF} = m\angle DPF$ so by substitution, $m\widehat{BC} = m\widehat{DF}$, or $\widehat{BC} \cong \widehat{DF}$.

b. $m\widehat{BC} = m\angle O$ and $m\widehat{DF} = m\angle P$. Since $\widehat{BC} \cong \widehat{DF}$, it follows that $\angle O \cong \angle P$. $\triangle OBC \cong \triangle PDF$ by SAS. Then $\overline{BC} \cong \overline{DF}$ by CPCTC.

9. The center of a ⊙ is equidistant from the endpts. of any chord. By the Converse of the Perpendicular Bisector Thm., the center must lie on the ⊥ bisector of the chord.

ESL **Exercises 10–13** To reinforce the vocabulary from this chapter, have students take turns with a partner stating the theorem they used to solve each problem.

Exercises 11–12 Students can avoid extra work if they recognize the triangles are 45°-45°-90° and 30°-60°-90° triangles, respectively.

ERROR ALERT! Exercise 14 Some students may not understand that the radii of a sphere and of a circle on the sphere be different. **Remediation:** Cut an orange through the center and again in a different parallel plane. Show that the circular cross section through the center is larger than the other circular cross section.

Exercise 19 If you had students do this exercise already in class, make sure that they use different objects for their homework.

Exercise 20 You may want to have students solve this problem in small groups. One approach is to find the area of the shaded region shown in the diagram below:

$\frac{1}{2}\pi(29.5)^2 -$ [area of triangle + 2(area of sectors)].

The volume of the milk equals the area times 470.

---

pages 603–605 On Your Own

21. 1. $\overline{CE} \perp \overline{BD}$ (Given) 2. $\overline{BF} \cong \overline{FD}$ (A diameter $\perp$ to a chord bisects the chord.) 3. $\overline{CE}$ is the $\perp$ bisector of $\overline{BD}$. (Def. of $\perp$ bisector) 4. $\overline{BC} \cong \overline{DC}$ (A point on the $\perp$ bisector of a segment is equidistant from the endpts. of the segment.) 5. $\overarc{BC} \cong \overarc{DC}$ ($\cong$ chords have $\cong$ arcs.)

22. 1. $\overarc{BC} \cong \overarc{DE}$ (Given) 2. $\overline{BC} \cong \overline{DE}$ ($\cong$ arcs have $\cong$ chords.) 3. $\overline{AF} \perp \overline{BC}, \overline{AG} \perp \overline{DE}$ (Given) 4. $\overline{AF} \cong \overline{AG}$ ($\cong$ chords are equidistant from the center.) 5. $\angle AFG \cong \angle AGF$ (Base $\angle$s of an isos. $\triangle$ are $\cong$.)

Find $m\overarc{AB}$.

10.
108

11.
90

12.
120

13.

about 123.9

14. **Geometry in 3 Dimensions** Sphere O with radius 13 cm is intersected by a plane 5 cm from its center forming $\odot A$. Find the radius of $\odot A$. **12 cm**

15. A plane intersects a sphere that has radius 10 in. forming $\odot B$ with radius 8 in. How far is the plane from the center of the sphere? **6 in.**

16. A plane intersects a sphere 12 in. from the sphere's center forming $\odot C$ with radius 18 in. What is the radius of the sphere? Round to the nearest tenth. **21.6 in.**

17. Two concentric circles have radii of 4 cm and 8 cm. A segment tangent to the smaller circle is a chord of the larger circle. What is the length of the segment? **$8\sqrt{3}$ cm**

PROBLEM SOLVING HINT
Draw a diagram.

18. Supply the reasons for each statement in this proof of Theorem 12-7.

Given: $\odot O$ with diameter $\overline{ED} \perp \overline{AB}$ at C
Prove: $\overline{AC} \cong \overline{BC}$ and $\overarc{AD} \cong \overarc{BD}$

Begin by drawing $\overline{OA}$ and $\overline{OB}$.

Statements		Reasons	
1. $\overline{OA} \cong \overline{OB}$		a. __?__	All radii of a $\odot$ are $\cong$.
2. $\overline{ED} \perp \overline{AB}$		b. __?__	Given
3. $\angle ACO$ and $\angle BCO$ are right angles.		c. __?__	Def of $\perp$ lines
4. $\overline{OC} \cong \overline{OC}$	Reflexive Prop. of $\cong$	d. __?__	
5. $\triangle AOC \cong \triangle BOC$	HL	e. __?__	
6. $\overline{AC} \cong \overline{BC}$	CPCTC	f. __?__	
7. $\angle AOC \cong \angle BOC$	CPCTC	g. __?__	
8. $\overarc{AD} \cong \overarc{BD}$		h. __?__	

h. $\cong$ central angles have $\cong$ arcs.

19. **Constructions** Use a circular object such as a can or a saucer to draw a circle. Construct the center of the circle. **Check students' work.**

20. **Transporting Milk** The diameter of the base of a cylindrical milk tank is 59 in. The height of the tank is 470 in. A delivery person estimates that the depth of the milk in the tank is 20 in. Find the number of gallons of milk in the tank to the nearest gallon. (231 in.^{3} = 1 gal) **1661 gal**

604

Choose **Write a two-column proof, paragraph proof, or flow proof.**

21. Given: $\odot A$ with $\overline{CE} \perp \overline{BD}$
Prove: $\widehat{BC} \cong \widehat{DC}$

21–22. Answers may vary. See margin p. 604 for samples.

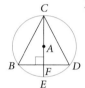

22. Given: $\odot A$ with $\widehat{BC} \cong \widehat{DE}$, $\overline{AF} \perp \overline{BC}$, $\overline{AG} \perp \overline{DE}$
Prove: $\angle AFG \cong \angle AGF$

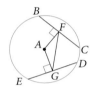

23. a. Use the diagram at the right. Complete each statement. Given that $\overline{AB}$ is a diameter of the circle and $\overline{AB} \perp \overline{CD}$, then ▩ ≅ ▩, and ▩ ≅ ▩. *EC; ED; BC; BD*

b. Given that $\overline{AB}$ is the perpendicular bisector of $\overline{CD}$, then $\overline{AB}$ contains the __?__ . *center of the ⊙*

c. Which theorems are illustrated in parts (a) and (b)? **See margin.**

d. *Open-ended* Draw a figure or figures to illustrate the other theorems presented in this lesson. **See margin.**

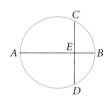

24. $\odot A$ and $\odot B$ are congruent. $AB = 8$ in. $\overline{CD}$ is a chord of both circles. $CD = 6$ in. How long is a radius? **5 in.**

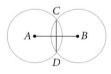

25. *Writing* Explain why the phrase "in the same circle or in congruent circles" is essential to Theorems 12-5, 12-6, and 12-9. **See margin.**

26. *Coordinate Geometry* Find the length of the chord of the circle $x^2 + y^2 = 25$ that is determined by the line $x = 3$. **8**

27. a. *Critical Thinking* The diameter of a circle is 20 cm. Two chords in the circle are 6 cm and 16 cm. In how many ways can you draw the chords so that they are parallel to the same diameter? (*Hint:* Draw a diagram.) **2**

b. What are the possible distances between the chords to the nearest tenth of a centimeter? **3.5 cm and 15.5 cm**

Chapter Project **Find Out by Exploring**

Stare at these circular patterns for a few seconds. Notice how they seem to pulsate. In contrast to the ancient art form you explored in the Find Out activity on page 591, op art is a twentieth-century phenomenon. **See margin.**

• Use geometric terms to describe how Figures A and B are related.

• Create your own op art by transforming a *target* design like Figure A. Use geometric terms to describe your design. **Check students' work.**

Figure A   Figure B

23c. A diameter ⊥ to a chord bisects the chord and its arc; the ⊥ bisector of a chord contains the center of the ⊙.

d. Sample: Theorem 12-5

25. The thms. are not true for angles, chords, or arcs that are in noncongruent ⊙s.

Find Out By Exploring

Both figures are made from 9 circles with the same center. In Figure A, the smallest circle and alternate rings are black. In Figure B, vertical and horizontal tangents to the smallest circle are drawn. Then tangents at 45° angles to the first ones are drawn. Alternating sections of the 6 outer rings are black as well as the smallest ring.

Checkpoint   page 606

10a.

Exercises 28–33 Ask students to justify their reasoning by writing an equation or inequality.

GETTING READY FOR LESSON 12-4 Students review how to find measures of arcs formed by central angles. These exercises prepare students to find measures of arcs formed by inscribed angles.

Wrap Up

THE BIG IDEA Ask students to summarize what they learned about chords and their associated arcs in this lesson.

RETEACHING ACTIVITY Students find the lengths of chords and measures of arcs of a circle. (Reteaching worksheet 12-3)

In this Checkpoint, your students will assess their own progress in Lessons 12-1 to 12-3.

Exercises 1–3 Make sure students find the length of the radius, not the diameter.

Exercises 4–6 Check that students do not think an inscribed circle bisects a tangent at the point of tangency.

OPEN-ENDED Exercise 10 If students use a right triangle, one of the quadrilaterals will be a square and the other two will be kites.

Lesson Quiz

Lesson Quiz is also available in Transparencies.

For Exercises 1–2, if your answer is not an integer, round to the nearest tenth.

1. Find the value of *x*. 12.5

2. Find the value of *y*. 12.5

3. Use a circular object such as a can to draw a circle. Construct the center of the circle. **Answers may vary. Sample: See back of book.**

606

Exercises   MIXED REVIEW

Determine whether a triangle with the given side lengths is acute, right, or obtuse.

28. 4, 4, 4   **29.** 3, 5, 6   **30.** 6, 8, 10   **31.** 2, 3, 4   **32.** 7, $\sqrt{63}$, 10   **33.** 5, 8, $\sqrt{70}$
acute   obtuse   right   obtuse   acute   acute

34. You want to find out how tall a tree in a park is. Your shadow length is $\frac{3}{4}$ of your height. The tree's shadow is 57 ft long. How tall is the tree? **76 ft**

Getting Ready for Lesson 12-4

Find the measure of each arc in $\odot O$.

35. $\overarc{AB}$ **36.** $\overarc{BC}$ **37.** $\overarc{AD}$
80   100   125

Exercises   CHECKPOINT

Coordinate Geometry The points are endpoints of the diameter of a circle. Write the equation of the circle.

1. (3, 1) and (0, 0)
$(x - 1.5)^2 + (y - 0.5)^2 = 2.5$

2. (−2, 5) and (9, −3)
$(x - 3.5)^2 + (y - 1)^2 = 46.25$

3. (−4, −8) and (1, 0)
$(x + 1.5)^2 + (y + 4)^2 = 22.25$

In each diagram, the polygon circumscribes a circle. Find the perimeter of the polygon.

4. **76 cm**
9 cm
13 cm   16 cm

5. **48 in.**
|←13 in.→|
10 in.   14 in.
8 in.

6. **51 m**
5 m
11 m   7.5 m
5 m
7 m

Find the value of *x*.

7. 24
15   9
x

8. 5
5
x

9. 8
30
x
17

10. a. *Open-ended* Draw a triangle circumscribed about a circle. Then draw the radii to each tangent. **See margin p. 605 for sample.**
  b. How many convex quadrilaterals are in the figure you drew in part (a)? **3**
  c. What is the name of these special quadrilaterals? **Justify** your answer. **Kites; the sides inside the ⊙ are ≅ because they are radii of the same ⊙; the sides outside the ⊙ are ≅ because they are tangent segments to a ⊙ drawn from a pt. outside the ⊙.**

TECHNOLOGY HINT
This exercise could be done using geometry software.

CONNECTING TO PRIOR KNOWLEDGE Draw a circle and several central angles. Label the angle measures and have students give the measures of the intercepted arcs.

What You'll Learn

• Finding the measure of inscribed angles and the arcs they intercept

...And Why

To use the relationships between inscribed angles and arcs in real-world situations, such as motion pictures

What You'll Need

compass, protractor, ruler

1a. Answers may vary. The results should reflect $m\angle 1 = m\angle 2 = m\angle 3$; $m\widehat{AB} = 2m\angle 1$

1c. $m\angle 1 = m\angle 2 = m\angle 3$

 TECHNOLOGY HINT

The Work Together could be done using geometry software.

Connections 🌐 **Motion Pictures . . . and more**

12-4 Inscribed Angles

W O R K T O G E T H E R

Have each member of your group draw two large circles. Label the centers X and Y. Draw the following diagrams on the circles.

1. **a.** *Patterns* In ⊙X, use a protractor to measure ∠AXB and each numbered angle. Determine $m\widehat{AB}$. Record your results and look for patterns. Compare results within your group. **b.** $m\widehat{AB} = 2m\angle 1$
   b. Write a **conjecture** about the relationship between $m\angle 1$ and $m\widehat{AB}$.
   c. Write a **conjecture** about the measures of ∠1, ∠2, and ∠3.

2. **a.** *Patterns* Use a protractor to measure the numbered angles in ⊙Y. Record your results and look for patterns. Compare your results.
   b. Write a **conjecture** about an angle whose vertex is on a circle and whose sides intersect the endpoints of a diameter of the circle.
   2a. Answers may vary. The results should reflect $m\angle 4 = m\angle 5 = m\angle 6 = 90$. **b.** See margin p. 610.

T H I N K A N D D I S C U S S

Part 1 Measuring Inscribed Angles

At the left, the vertex of ∠C is on ⊙O, and the sides of ∠C are chords of the circle. ∠C is an **inscribed angle**. $\widehat{AB}$ is the **intercepted arc** of ∠C.

A polygon is **inscribed in** a circle if all its vertices lie on the circle. △DEF is inscribed in ⊙Q. ⊙Q is **circumscribed about** △DEF.

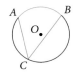

3. In the diagram at the left, which arc does ∠A intercept? $\widehat{BCD}$

4. Which angle intercepts $\widehat{DAB}$? ∠C

5. Is quadrilateral ABCD inscribed in the circle or is the circle inscribed in ABCD? **ABCD is inscribed in the ⊙.**

6. **a.** Which angles appear to intercept major arcs? ∠B, ∠C
   b. What kind of angles do these appear to be? **obtuse**

607

ERROR ALERT! Theorem 12-10 Some students may confuse "The measure of an inscribed angle is half the measure of its intercepted arc" with "The measure of an intercepted arc is half the measure of its inscribed angle." **Remediation:** Have students estimate the angle measures and arc measures as a way to check that their answers are reasonable.

Example 1

ESTIMATION Begin by having students estimate the values of a and b. Explain that $\widehat{PT}$ appears to be more than one fourth of the circle and $\angle PRS$ appears to be less than 90°.

Additional Examples

FOR EXAMPLE 1

Refer to the diagram in Example 1. If $m\angle PQT = 70$ and $m\widehat{TS} = 25$, find the values of a and b. **a = 140, b = 82.5**

FOR EXAMPLE 2

a. Name a pair of congruent inscribed angles. **Sample: $\angle FAD$ and $\angle FBD$**

b. Name a right angle. **$\angle FBC$**

c. Name a pair of supplementary angles. **Samples: $\angle FED$ and $\angle FBD$, $\angle EFB$ and $\angle EDB$**

FOR EXAMPLE 3

Find the values of x, y, and z if $\overline{AB}$ is a diameter.
$x = 90$, $y = 32$, $z = 32$

608

Your observations in the Work Together suggest the following theorem.

Theorem 12-10 **Inscribed Angle Theorem**	The measure of an inscribed angle is half the measure of its intercepted arc. $m\angle B = \frac{1}{2}m\widehat{AC}$

There are three cases of this theorem to consider.

Case I: The center is on a side of the angle.   Case II: The center is inside the angle.   Case III: The center is outside the angle.

Case I is proved below. You will prove Case II in Exercise 13.

Proof of Theorem 12-10, Case I
Given: $\odot O$ with inscribed $\angle ABC$ and diameter $\overline{BC}$
Prove: $m\angle ABC = \frac{1}{2}m\widehat{AC}$

Draw radius $\overline{OA}$. By the Exterior Angle Theorem, $m\angle 1 + m\angle 2 = m\angle AOC$. Since $OA = OB$, $\triangle AOB$ is isosceles and $m\angle 1 = m\angle 2$. Therefore, by substitution, $2(m\angle 1) = m\angle AOC$, or $m\angle 1 = \frac{1}{2}m\angle AOC$. Since $m\angle AOC = m\widehat{AC}$, $m\angle 1 = \frac{1}{2}m\widehat{AC}$ by substitution.

Example 1

Find the values of a and b in the diagram at the right.

Use the Inscribed Angle Theorem.

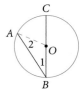

$$m\angle PQT = \frac{1}{2}m\widehat{PT}$$
$$60 = \frac{1}{2}a \qquad \text{Substitution}$$
$$a = 120 \qquad \text{Multiply each side by 2.}$$
$$m\angle PRS = \frac{1}{2}m\widehat{PS} \qquad \text{Inscribed Angle Theorem}$$
$$m\angle PRS = \frac{1}{2}(m\widehat{PT} + m\widehat{TS}) \qquad \text{Arc Addition Postulate}$$
$$b = \frac{1}{2}(120 + 30) \qquad \text{Substitution}$$
$$b = \frac{1}{2}(150) = 75 \qquad \text{Simplify.}$$

7. Try This Find $m\angle PQR$ if $m\widehat{PTR} = 230$. **115**

In the Work Together, you investigated the first two of the following three corollaries that follow from the Inscribed Angle Theorem. You will justify the corollaries in Exercises 14, 20, and 21.

Corollary 1	Two inscribed angles that intercept the same arc are congruent.
Corollary 2	An angle inscribed in a semicircle is a right angle.
Corollary 3	The opposite angles of a quadrilateral inscribed in a circle are supplementary.

Example 2

💻 **Technology** Dolores constructed ⊙A and the chords shown with geometry software.

a. As Dolores moves E on $\overset{\frown}{CED}$ between C and D, which pairs of inscribed angles will remain congruent to each other?
b. Which inscribed angle will remain a right angle?
c. Which pairs of inscribed angles will remain supplementary in quadrilateral $EFGD$?

a. $\angle CFE \cong \angle CDE$ Corollary 1
    $\angle ECD \cong \angle EGD$

b. $\angle CED$ is a right angle.   Corollary 2

c. $\angle DEF$ and $\angle FGD$ are supplementary.   Corollary 3
    $\angle EFG$ and $\angle GDE$ are supplementary.

8. Try This Find the value of each variable.
a.

$v = 84;\ w = 42;$
$x = 36;\ y = 108;$
$z = 42$

96°, v°, w°, x°, y°, z°, 72°

b.

107°, z°, x°, y°, 98°

$x = 53.5;\ y = 41;\ z = 85.5$

609

Theorem 12-11 Emphasize that ∠C is formed by a chord and a tangent, not by two tangents, and that the vertex of ∠C is on the circle, not in the exterior.

Example 3 ·······························

In order to find x and y, students must recognize that $\overline{QL}$ is a diameter. Help students see that $\angle KJL$ and $\angle Q$ intercept the same arc. Therefore, $m\angle Q = \frac{1}{2}m\widehat{JL} = z$.

Exercises 1–4 Students may not recognize that the polygons in Exercises 2 and 4 are neither inscribed nor circumscribed. Remind them that each side of a polygon circumscribed about a circle must touch the circle at only one point and that a polygon inscribed in a circle must touch the circle at each vertex.

---

page 607   Work Together

2b. If the vertex of an angle is on a ⊙ and the sides of the angle intersect the endpts. of a diameter of the ⊙, then the angle is a rt. angle.

pages 610–613   On Your Own

13. 1. ∠ABC is inscribed in ⊙O. (Given) **2.** $m\angle ABP = \frac{1}{2}m\widehat{AP}$ and $m\angle PBC = \frac{1}{2}m\widehat{PC}$ (Inscribed Angle Thm., Case I)

3. $m\angle ABP + m\angle PBC = \frac{1}{2}m\widehat{AP} + \frac{1}{2}m\widehat{PC}$ (Addition Prop. of =) **4.** $m\angle ABP + m\angle PBC = \frac{1}{2}(m\widehat{AP} + m\widehat{PC})$ (Distributive Prop.)

5. $m\angle ABP + m\angle PBC = m\angle ABC$ (Angle Addition Post.)

6. $m\widehat{AC} = m\widehat{AP} + m\widehat{PC}$ (Arc Addition Post.) **7.** $m\angle ABC = \frac{1}{2}m\widehat{AC}$ (Substitution)

Part 2   Angles Formed by Tangents and Chords

In the diagram, B and C are fixed points, and point A moves along the circle. From the Inscribed Angle Theorem, you know that as A moves, $m\angle A$ remains the same, and that $m\angle A = \frac{1}{2}m\widehat{BC}$. As the last diagram suggests, this is also true when A and C coincide.

   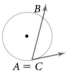

| **Theorem 12-11** | The measure of an angle formed by a chord and a tangent that intersect on a circle is half the measure of the intercepted arc. $m\angle C = \frac{1}{2}m\widehat{BDC}$ | |

Example 3 ·······························

Find the values of x, y, and z.

$x = 90$ — An angle inscribed in a semicircle is a rt. ∠.

$y = 90 - 35 = 55$ — The acute ∠s of a rt. △ are complementary.

$z = \frac{1}{2}m\widehat{JL}$ — Theorem 12-11

$\frac{1}{2}m\widehat{JL} = m\angle Q = 35$ — Inscribed Angle Theorem

$z = 35$ — Substitution

9. Try This $\overrightarrow{AB}$ is a tangent. $m\angle BAC = 38$. Find $m\angle D$.

38

Tell whether each polygon is *inscribed in* or *circumscribed about* the circle. If neither, explain why.

1.

inscribed in

2.

neither

3.

circumscribed about

4.

neither

610

Find the value of each variable.

5.

116°
58
$a°$

6.

180
$a°$

7. $a = 218; b = 109$

60°
$b°$
82°
$a°$

8.
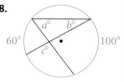
$a°$ $b°$
60° $c°$ 100°

$a = 50; b = 30; c = 100$

9.

$a°$ $c°$ 95°
$b°$

$a = 85; b = 47.5; c = 90$

10.

$a°$ $b°$
52° $c°$
84°

$a = 26; b = 64; c = 42$

11.

$b°$
68° 100°
71°
$a°$ $c°$

$a = 112; b = 124; c = 42$

12.

$c°$
44°
$b°$ $a°$
166°

$a = 22; b = 75; c = 150$

Choose **Write a two-column proof, paragraph proof, or flow proof.** 13–16. Answers may vary. See margin for samples.

13. Prove the Inscribed Angle Theorem, Case II.

Given: $\odot O$ with inscribed $\angle ABC$
Prove: $m\angle ABC = \frac{1}{2}m\widehat{AC}$

Plan for Proof: Use the Inscribed Angle Theorem, Case I, to show that $m\angle ABP = \frac{1}{2}m\widehat{AP}$ and $m\angle PBC = \frac{1}{2}m\widehat{PC}$.

14. Prove Corollary 1 to the Inscribed Angle Theorem.

Given: $\odot O$, $\angle A$ intercepts $\widehat{BC}$, and $\angle D$ intercepts $\widehat{BC}$.
Prove: $\angle A \cong \angle D$

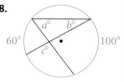

15. Given: In $\odot O$, $m\widehat{AD} = m\widehat{BC}$.
Prove: $\triangle ABD \cong \triangle BAC$

16. Given: In $\odot O$, $m\widehat{BC} = m\widehat{ED}$.
Prove: $\triangle EFB \sim \triangle CFD$

17. a. *Critical Thinking* A parallelogram is inscribed in a circle. What kind of parallelogram must it be? **rectangle**
b. Explain why your statement in part (a) is true. **See margin.**

18. Copy the diagram at the right on your paper. Draw chord $\overline{RQ}$. Explain why $m\widehat{PR} = m\widehat{QS}$.
See margin.

14. 1. $\angle A$ intercepts $\widehat{BC}$. (Given)
2. $m\angle A = \frac{1}{2}m\widehat{BC}$ (Measure of an inscribed $\angle$ is half the measure of its intercepted arc.) **3.** $\angle D$ intercepts $\widehat{BC}$. (Given)
4. $m\angle D = \frac{1}{2}m\widehat{BC}$ (Measure of an inscribed $\angle$ is half the measure of its intercepted arc.)
5. $m\angle A = m\angle D$, or $\angle A \cong \angle D$ (Substitution)

15. 1. $m\widehat{AD} = m\widehat{BC}$ (Given)
2. $m\angle ABD = \frac{1}{2}m\widehat{AD}$ and $m\angle BAC = \frac{1}{2}m\widehat{BC}$ (Measure of an inscribed $\angle$ is half the measure of its intercepted arc.)
3. $m\angle BAC = m\angle ABD$ (Substitution) **4.** $\overline{AD} \cong \overline{BC}$ ($\cong$ arcs have $\cong$ chords.)
5. $\angle ACB \cong \angle BDA$ (2 inscribed angles that intercept the same arc are $\cong$.) **6.** $\triangle ABD \cong \triangle BAC$ (AAS)

16. 1. $m\widehat{BC} = m\widehat{ED}$ (Given)
2. $\angle BEC \cong \angle EBD$ (2 inscribed angles that intercept $\cong$ arcs are $\cong$.) **3.** $\angle BFE \cong \angle CFD$ (Vertical $\angle$s are $\cong$.) **4.** $\triangle EFB \sim \triangle CFD$ (AA$\sim$)

17b. Opp. angles are $\cong$ and supplementary. So they are rt. angles.

18. $\angle PQR \cong \angle QRS$ because they are alt. int. $\angle$s and $\overline{PQ} \parallel \overline{RS}$. The arcs are $\cong$ because they are intercepted by $\cong$ inscribed angles.

20. $m\widehat{BDC} = 180$ and $m\angle A = \frac{1}{2}m\widehat{BDC}$. So $m\angle A = 90$ and $\angle A$ is a rt. angle.

21b. $m\widehat{DAB} + m\widehat{BCD} = 360$.

$m\angle A = \frac{1}{2}m\widehat{BCD}$ and

$m\angle C = \frac{1}{2}m\widehat{DAB}$, so

$m\angle A + m\angle C = \frac{1}{2} \cdot 360 = 180$.

$\angle A$ and $\angle C$ are supplementary.

23. $\angle ACB$ is inscribed in a semicircle so it is a rt. angle. Then $\overleftrightarrow{BC}$ is ⊥ to radius $\overline{AC}$ and passes through its endpt. on the ⊙. Therefore, $\overleftrightarrow{BC}$ is tangent to ⊙A.

28a. The angles captured by each camera are ≅.

b. No; the cameras capture the scene from diff. locations.

30. Construct the ⊥ bisector to the hypotenuse to find the center of the ⊙. Use half the length of the hypotenuse as a radius to construct the ⊙.

32a. Sample:

19. *Constructions* Explain how you would construct the tangent to a circle at any point on the circle. **Draw the diameter through the given pt. Construct the line ⊥ to the diameter through this pt.**

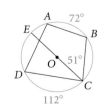

20. *Logical Reasoning* In the diagram at the right, $\angle A$ is inscribed in a semicircle. Write a justification of Corollary 2 of the Inscribed Angle Theorem. **See margin.**

21. In the diagram at the right, quadrilateral $ABCD$ is inscribed in ⊙O.
   a. Find the sum of the measures of the arcs intercepted by $\angle A$ and $\angle C$. **360**
   b. *Logical Reasoning* Explain why Corollary 3 to the Inscribed Angle Theorem must be true. **See margin.**

22. *Critical Thinking* Decide whether the following statements are true or false. Give a counterexample for each false statement.
   a. If two angles inscribed in a circle are congruent, then they intercept the same arc. **False; the inscribed angles can intercept congruent arcs.**
   b. If a right angle is an inscribed angle, then it is inscribed in a semicircle. **true**
   c. A circle can always be circumscribed about a quadrilateral whose opposite angles are supplementary. **true**

23. *Constructions* The diagrams below show the construction of a tangent to a circle from a point outside the circle. Explain why $\overleftrightarrow{BC}$ must be tangent to ⊙A. (*Hint:* Copy the third diagram and draw $\overline{AC}$.) **See margin.**

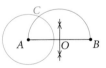

Given: ⊙A and point B
Construct the midpoint of $\overline{AB}$. Label the point O.

Construct a semicircle with radius OA and center O. Label its intersection with ⊙A as C.

Draw $\overleftrightarrow{BC}$.

Find each indicated measure for ⊙O.

24. a. $m\widehat{BC}$ **96**
   b. $m\angle B$ **55**
   c. $m\angle C$ **77**
   d. $m\widehat{AB}$ **154**

25. a. $m\widehat{EA}$ **30**
   b. $m\widehat{BC}$ **78**
   c. $m\angle A$ **95**
   d. $m\angle B$ **105**
   e. $m\angle BCD$ **85**
   f. $m\angle D$ **75**

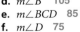

26. a. $m\angle A$ **40**
   b. $m\widehat{CE}$ **50**
   c. $m\angle C$ **40**
   d. $m\angle D$ **40**
   e. $m\angle ABE$ **65**

27. a. $m\widehat{DC}$ **64**
   b. $m\widehat{BD}$ **116**
   c. $m\angle BCD$ **58**
   d. $m\angle BDA$ **58**
   e. $m\angle ABD$ **58**
   f. $m\angle A$ **64**
   g. $m\angle CDE$ **32**

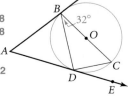

612

Exercises 33–34 Students review finding the lengths of midsegments of trapezoids.

 JOURNAL Have students include both inscribed and central angles in their descriptions.

GETTING READY FOR LESSON 12-5 These exercises prepare students to find arcs formed by intersecting chords.

Wrap Up

THE BIG IDEA Ask students to summarize the theorems and corollaries in this lesson.

RETEACHING ACTIVITY Students find the measure of inscribed angles and the arcs they intercept. (Reteaching worksheet 12-4)

---

28. a. *Motion Pictures* A director wants to capture the same scene on film from three different viewpoints. Explain why the cameras in the positions shown will record the same scene.
   b. *Critical Thinking* Will the scenes look the same when they are shown? Explain.
   a–b. See margin p. 612.

29. a. *Patterns* Sketch a trapezoid inscribed in a circle. Repeat several times using different circles. **Check students' work.**
   b. Make a **conjecture** about the kind of trapezoid that can be inscribed in a circle.
   See below.

30. *Writing* Explain how to construct a circle circumscribed about a right triangle. See margin p. 612.

31. *Mental Math* Draw a circle and inscribe an irregular five-pointed star. Find the sum of the measures of the five inscribed angles.   **180**

32. a. *Constructions* Draw two segments. Label their lengths x and y. Construct the geometric mean of x and y by following these steps.   See margin p. 612.
   Step 1: On a line, construct $\overline{RS}$ with length x and $\overline{ST}$ with length y for sample. such that S is between R and T.
   Step 2: Bisect $\overline{RT}$. Label the midpoint O. Use the length RO to construct a semicircle with diameter $\overline{RT}$.
   Step 3: Construct the perpendicular to $\overline{RT}$ at S. Label the point of intersection of the perpendicular with the semicircle as Q.
   b. What kind of triangle is $\triangle RQT$? **rt. triangle**
   c. *Critical Thinking* Why is QS the geometric mean of x and y? **Since $\overline{QS}$ is the altitude to the hypotenuse of a rt. $\triangle$, QS is the geometric mean of RS and ST.**

Camera 1

Camera 2

Camera 3

Scene

Exercises   M I X E D   R E V I E W

Find the length of the midsegment of a trapezoid with the given bases.

33. $b_1 = 3$ cm, $b_2 = 7$ cm   **34.** $b_1 = 8$ in., $b_2 = 13$ in.
   5 cm   **10.5 in.**

35. What is the measure of an interior angle of a regular pentagon?   **108**

Getting Ready for Lesson 12-5

O is the center of each circle. Find the measure of $\widehat{AB}$.

36.
   110
   70°

37.
   130
   50°

38.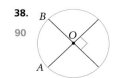
   90

29b. If a trapezoid is inscribed in a $\odot$, then it is an isosceles trapezoid.

Lesson Quiz

Lesson Quiz is also available in Transparencies.

95°

F

58° H

K J A

84°

I

Find each measure for $\odot A$.

1. $m\widehat{KJ}$ **21**

2. $m\widehat{JI}$ **96**

3. $m\angle JHI$ **48**

4. $m\angle KFH$ **100.5**

PROBLEM OF THE DAY

If you folded the pattern into a cube, how many semicircles would have diameters that coincide? **two**

Problem of the Day is also available in Transparencies.

CONNECTING TO PRIOR KNOWLEDGE Have students draw a circle, an inscribed angle, and a central angle that intercept the same arc. Have students explain how the measures of the angles can be calculated knowing the measure of the arc.

Encourage students to draw the circles and segments with a sharp pencil or fine-point pen so that the points where the segments intersect the circle are clear.

Question 1 Review the directions with students. Make sure they understand that they need to draw and measure central angles to find *x* and *y*.

Question 4 Help students see that a secant segment must have at least one endpoint in the exterior of a circle.

Lesson Planning Options

Prerequisite Skills

• Finding the measures of central angles and their intercepted arcs

Assignment Options for Exercises On Your Own

Core 1–14, 16–17
Extension 15, 18

Use Mixed Review to maintain skills.

Resources

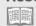 **Student Edition**

Skills Handbook, pp. 650, 656
Extra Practice, p. 645
Glossary/Study Guide

Teaching Resources

Chapter Support File, Ch. 12
• Practice 12-5 (two worksheets)
• Reteaching 12-5
• Alternative Activity 12-5
Classroom Manager 12-5
Glossary, Spanish Resources

 Transparencies
12, 122, 125

614

What You'll Learn

• Finding the measures of angles formed by chords, secants, and tangents

...And Why

To use measures of angles in real-world applications such as photography

What You'll Need

• protractor
• compass

 TECHNOLOGY HINT

The Work Together could be done using geometry software.

2. $m\angle 1 = \frac{1}{2}(x + y)$

3. $m\angle 1 = \frac{1}{2}(x - y)$

Connections Photography . . . and more

12-5 Angles Formed by Chords, Secants, and Tangents

■ Have each member of your group draw four circles. Label the centers *M*, *N*, *P*, and *Q*. Draw segments intersecting inside and outside the circles as shown below.

1. Copy and complete the chart below. In each diagram, use a protractor to measure ∠1, and find *x*° and *y*° by measuring central angles.

Circle	*m∠1*	*x*	*y*	*x + y*	*x − y*
⊙M					
⊙N					
⊙P					
⊙Q					

Check students' work.

2. In ⊙M, what do you notice about *m∠1* and the sum or the difference of the measures of the arcs? Compare results within your group.

3. In ⊙N, ⊙P, and ⊙Q, what do you notice about *m∠1* and the sum or the difference of the measures of the arcs? Compare results within your group.

A **secant** is a line that intersects a circle at two points. $\overrightarrow{AB}$ is a secant ray, and $\overline{AB}$ is a secant segment. The word *secant* may refer to a secant line, secant ray, or secant segment.

4. Does a secant always contain a chord of a circle? Explain.
   Yes; the segment connecting the pts. where the secant intersects the ⊙ is a chord.

VISUAL LEARNING Some students may want to shade the interior of the angles formed by chords, secants, and tangents as a way to visualize the arcs they intercept.

ERROR ALERT! **Theorems 12-12 and 12-13** Some students may be confused when to add and when to subtract. **Remediation:** Draw a circle and segments as shown below. Measure ∠1 and ∠2 and show that the angle whose vertex is in the interior is larger (therefore, add) than the angle whose vertex is in the exterior of the circle (therefore, subtract).

AUDITORY LEARNING It may help students to repeat the phrase "interior add, exterior subtract" several times to help them remember the difference between Theorem 12-12 and Theorem 12-13.

Students are asked to write a plan for the proof of Theorem 12-13 as it applies to two secants in Exercise 14.

The proof of Theorem 12-12 uses the Exterior Angle Theorem. You may want to review the theorem by drawing several triangles and having students identify exterior angles and then write their measures as sums of measures of interior angles.

The diagrams below show arcs intercepted by chords, secants, and tangents.

  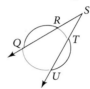

Chords $\overline{AC}$ and $\overline{BD}$ intercept two pairs of opposite arcs: $\overarc{AB}$ and $\overarc{DC}$, $\overarc{AD}$ and $\overarc{BC}$.

Tangents $\overrightarrow{KJ}$ and $\overrightarrow{KL}$ intercept $\overarc{JL}$ and $\overarc{JPL}$.

Secants $\overrightarrow{SQ}$ and $\overrightarrow{SU}$ intercept $\overarc{RT}$ and $\overarc{QU}$.

Your observations in the Work Together suggest the following theorems.

Theorem 12-12

The measure of an angle formed by two chords that intersect inside a circle is half the sum of the measures of the intercepted arcs.

$m\angle 1 = \frac{1}{2}(x + y)$

Theorem 12-13

The measure of an angle formed by two secants, two tangents, or a secant and a tangent drawn from a point outside the circle is half the difference of the measures of the intercepted arcs.

$m\angle 1 = \frac{1}{2}(x - y)$ $m\angle 1 = \frac{1}{2}(x - y)$ $m\angle 1 = \frac{1}{2}(x - y)$

Proof of Theorem 12-12
Given: $\odot O$ with intersecting chords $\overline{AC}$ and $\overline{BD}$
Prove: $m\angle 1 = \frac{1}{2}(m\overarc{AB} + m\overarc{CD})$
Begin by drawing $\overline{AD}$.

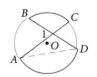

Statements	Reasons
1. $m\angle D = \frac{1}{2}m\overarc{AB}$, $m\angle A = \frac{1}{2}m\overarc{CD}$	1. Inscribed Angle Theorem
2. $m\angle 1 = m\angle D + m\angle A$	2. Exterior Angle Theorem
3. $m\angle 1 = \frac{1}{2}m\overarc{AB} + \frac{1}{2}m\overarc{CD}$	3. Substitution
4. $m\angle 1 = \frac{1}{2}(m\overarc{AB} + m\overarc{CD})$	4. Distributive Property

QUICK REVIEW
The Exterior Angle Theorem says that the measure of each exterior angle of a triangle equals the sum of the measures of the two remote interior angles.

FOR EXAMPLE 1 ....
Find the value of each variable.

a.

a. 45

b.

b. 60

c.

c. 40

FOR EXAMPLE 2 ....
Refer to Example 2. If the angle the camera makes with the tangents of the fountain is 55°, what is the measure of the arc of the circular basin of the fountain that will be in the photograph? **125**

615

Example 1

ERROR ALERT! In part a, some students may think that $x = 46$. **Remediation:** Point out that the chords do not intersect in the center of the circle, so the angles formed are not central angles.

ALTERNATIVE ASSESSMENT Question 5 Have students work in groups to make up problems like those in parts a–c. Have them write each problem on an index card with the solution on the back. Then have them exchange cards with another group and check each other's answers. Save the cards to use in a "math bee" or another review game.

Example 2 Relating to the Real World

Some students may think that there is not enough information given to solve this problem. Help them see that only one piece of information is missing; once you know $m\widehat{AB}$, you can find $m\widehat{AEB}$.

ESL Make sure students understand the words *fountain* and *basin.* Ask students to share examples of decorative fountains they have seen.

CONNECTING TO STUDENTS' WORLD Have students research the viewing angles of cameras. Have them bring in manuals for cameras they or their parents own, gather information from newspaper advertisements, or visit a store that sells cameras.

Technology Options

For Exercise 10, students may use a drawing program of geometry software to create a figure using tangents and secants. Then they can use the software to find the measures of the angles.

Prentice Hall Technology

 Software
- Secondary Math Lab Toolkit™
- Integrated Math Lab 46
- Computer Item Generator 12-5

Internet
- See the Prentice Hall site. (http://www.phschool.com)

Example 1

Find the value of each variable.

a.   **b.**   **c.**

$$x = \tfrac{1}{2}(46 + 90)$$
$$x = 68$$

$$y = \tfrac{1}{2}(110 - 30)$$
$$y = 40$$

$$20 = \tfrac{1}{2}(95 - z)$$
$$40 = 95 - z$$
$$z = 55$$

5. Try This Find the value of each variable.

a.   **b.**   **c.**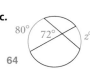

You can find the measures of arcs of a circle intercepted by tangents if you know the measure of the angle formed by the tangents.

Example 2 Relating to the Real World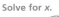

Photography Using a zoom lens, a photographer focuses his camera on a fountain. His camera is at the vertex of the angle formed by tangents to the fountain. He estimates this angle is 40°. What is the measure of the arc of the circular basin of the fountain that will be in his photograph?

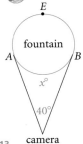

Let $m\widehat{AB} = x$. Then $m\widehat{AEB} = 360 - x$.

$$40 = \tfrac{1}{2}(m\widehat{AEB} - m\widehat{AB}) \qquad \text{Theorem 12-13}$$
$$40 = \tfrac{1}{2}[(360 - x) - x] \qquad \text{Substitution}$$
$$40 = \tfrac{1}{2}(360 - 2x) \qquad \text{Simplify.}$$
$$40 = 180 - x \qquad \text{Distributive Property}$$
$$x = 140 \qquad \text{Solve for } x.$$

An arc of 140° will be in the photograph.

616

Exercises   ON YOUR OWN

Exercises 1–8 Ask students to write the equation they solved as well as the answer to each problem. This will help you determine if their errors are in setting up the equations or in solving them.

DIVERSITY Exercise 9 Have students research space travel and space research done in other countries, and cooperative space explorations among countries. Also have students research the contributions of women in these areas. Have students share what they learn with the class.

Exercise 9a This exercise is similar to Example 2. Have students copy the diagram in Exercise 9, label the arcs, then model the solution steps in Example 2.

OPEN-ENDED Exercise 10 Encourage students to be creative in drawing a design made from tangents and secants.

STANDARDIZED TEST TIP Exercise 11 Some students may not see the significance of the phrase "the center of ⊙O is inside ∠ABC" and ignore it. Emphasize that standardized test questions are usually written concisely. The statement would likely not be given unless it was significant.

WRITING Exercise 12 Have students draw several different examples to test their conjectures, making sure that in at least one of their drawings neither chord is a diameter.

---

7. Step away; as she steps away, the measure of the angle between the tangents decreases and the measure of the arc increases.

6. In Example 2, what is m$\widehat{AEB}$? **220**

7. *Critical Thinking* To capture a greater arc of the circular basin in the photo, should the photographer step closer to or farther away from the fountain? Explain.

8. What should the angle at the camera be in order to photograph a 70° arc of the basin? **110°**

pages 617–618 On Your Own

12. The sum of the measures of the opp. arcs is 180; the measure of an ∠ formed by 2 chords inside a ⊙ is half the sum of the measures of the intercepted arcs.

Exercises   ON YOUR OWN

Assume that lines that appear tangent are tangent. Find the value of each variable.

1.
46

2.
50

3.

x = 60; y = 70

4.
60

5.

x = 100; y = 30

6.

x = 115; y = 74

7.

x = 50; y = 97.5

8.

x = 108; y = 72

9. **a.** *Space Travel* An astronaut directly over the equator estimates that the angle formed by the two tangents to the equator is 20°. What arc of the equator is visible to the astronaut? **160°**
   b. The radius of Earth is about 3960 mi. About how far is the spaceship from Earth? **about 18,800 mi**

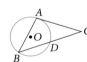

10. *Open-ended* Create a figure using tangents and secants. Find the measures of the angles and arcs in your figure. **Check students' work.**

11. *Standardized Test Prep* $\overline{AC}$ is tangent to ⊙O, m$\widehat{AD}$ = 90, and the center of ⊙O is inside ∠ABC. What is m∠C? **A**
    A. less than 45   **B.** 45   **C.** between 45 and 60
    D. between 60 and 90   **E.** none of the above

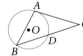

12. *Writing* Two chords intersect in a circle forming right angles. What is the sum of the measures of a pair of opposite arcs? **Justify** your answer. **See margin.**

13. **a.** *Algebra* $\overline{CA}$ and $\overline{CB}$ are tangents to ⊙O. Write an expression for m$\widehat{ADB}$ in terms of x. **360 − x**
    b. *Algebra* Write an expression for m∠C in terms of x. **180 − x**
    c. *Algebra* Write an expression for m$\widehat{AB}$ in terms of y. **180 − y**

617

Exercise 14 Students may need help recognizing that ∠*ABE* is an exterior angle of △*EBC*.

Exercise 15 Explain to students that, in this problem, *A* and *B* are fixed points, whereas *X*, *Y*, and *Z* are "variable" points.

Chapter Project ▽ **FIND OUT BY CONSTRUCTING** Help students see how they can use diameters of a circle to draw a square and the diagonals of a square to draw a circle. Students may want to use construction tools in geometry software to create this or other designs.

Exercises   **MIXED REVIEW**

DIVERSITY Exercises 19–21 Be aware that students' definitions of family will differ. Be especially conscious of students who may live in nontraditional family settings.

14. Since they are inscribed ∠s , $m\angle ABE = \frac{1}{2}m\widehat{AE}$ and

$m\angle BED = \frac{1}{2}m\widehat{BD}$. Apply the Exterior Angle Thm. to △*BCE* to prove that $m\angle C = \frac{1}{2}(m\widehat{AE} - m\widehat{BD})$.

15b. The ship is in safe waters if the measure of the angle is ≤ 30.

Checkpoint   **page 619**

5. A secant extends outside the ⊙, a chord does not.

14. Write a Plan for Proof for Theorem 12-13 as it applies to two secants drawn from a point outside a circle. **Answers may vary. See margin for samples.**
   Given: ⊙*O* with secants $\overline{CA}$ and $\overline{CE}$ intersecting at *C*.
   Prove: $m\angle ACE = \frac{1}{2}(m\widehat{AE} - m\widehat{BD})$

15. *Critical Thinking* A navigational map shows that the waters near lighthouses *A* and *B* are dangerous. The unsafe area is within $\widehat{AXB}$, a 300° arc. $m\angle X = 30; 30 < m\angle Y < 180; 0 < m\angle Z < 30$
   a. *X* represents locations of a ship on ⊙*O*. *Y* represents locations of a ship inside ⊙*O*. *Z* represents locations of a ship outside ⊙*O*. What is the measure of ∠*X*? What is the possible range of measures of ∠*Y*? of ∠*Z*?
   b. Using the angle a ship makes with the lighthouses, how can a ship's navigator be sure the ship is in safe waters? **See margin.**

Find the value of each variable.

16.
17.

$x = 80; y = 95$ $x = 80; y = 50; z = 90$

18. The angles of a quadrilateral measure 85, 76, 94, and 105. A circle is inscribed in the quadrilateral. What are the measures of the arcs between each two consecutive points of tangency? **95; 104; 86; 75**

Chapter Project ▽ **Find Out by Constructing** . . . .

Follow the steps below to create a pattern commonly found in 14th-century Islamic art and furniture. **Check students' work.**

    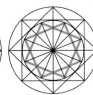

Step 1: In a circle, inscribe two squares rotated 45° from each other.

Step 2: Inscribe a circle in the squares.

Step 3: In each square, draw the diagonals.

Step 4: Bisect the central angles of the smaller circle.

Step 5: Inscribe two squares as shown. Then color to make the desired design.

618

JOURNAL Have students share their journal entries with a partner. Have them critique one another's entries for thoroughness, accuracy, clarity, and organization.

GETTING READY FOR LESSON 12-6 These exercises prepare students to prove relationships about lengths of segments of chords, secants, and tangents.

Wrap Up

THE BIG IDEA Ask students to explain the difference between finding the measure of an angle formed by a chord and a tangent and the measure of an angle formed by two tangents.

RETEACHING ACTIVITY Students find the measures of angles formed by chords, secants, and tangents. (Reteaching worksheet 12-5)

Exercises CHECKPOINT

In this Checkpoint, your students will assess their own progress in Lessons 12-4 to 12-5.

WRITING Exercise 5 Check that students show a secant can be a ray, a line, or a segment.

Exercises MIXED REVIEW

Data Analysis Use the graph showing the number of living siblings, including step-siblings and half-siblings, adults of different ages have.

19. About what percent of 45–64-year-olds have four or more siblings? **35%**

20. About what percent of 25–44-year-olds have two or more siblings? **80%**

21. Which age group is least likely to have only one sibling? **25–44**

Number of Living Siblings

Source: *American Demographics*

Getting Ready for Lesson 12-6

Each pair of figures is similar. Complete each statement.

22.

$$\frac{AB}{EF} = \frac{\blacksquare}{FG}$$ **BC**

23.

F, T, U, G, H

$$\frac{TF}{\blacksquare} = \frac{\blacksquare}{GH}$$

HF; UT

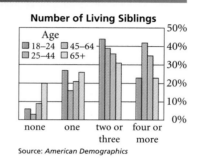

FOR YOUR JOURNAL

Summarize what you have learned in this lesson. Draw a diagram showing the angles formed by chords, secants, and tangents. Explain how to find the measure of each angle.

Exercises CHECKPOINT

Assume that lines that appear tangent are tangent. Find the value of each variable.

1.

58
170°
56°
x°

2.

100°
60°
a°
b°
c°
d°
84°

$a = 30; b = 42; c = 80; d = 116$

3.

30
95°
35°
x°

4.

125°
a°
b°
c°
140°

$a = 140; b = 70; c = 47.5$

5. **Writing** Explain the difference between a chord and a secant. Include a diagram. **See margin p. 618.**

6. **Standardized Test Prep** In the circle at the right, which measure is greatest? **D**
  A. $m\angle C$ **B.** $m\angle EBD$ **C.** $m\angle ABE$
  D. $m\widehat{BF}$ **E.** $m\angle BDF$

68°
40°
A, B, C, E, F, D

Lesson Quiz

Lesson Quiz is also available in Transparencies.

A, D, I, B, E, F, C, G, H

C is a point of tangency.

1. If $m\widehat{AI} = 60$ and $m\widehat{EC} = 100$, find $m\angle ABI$. **80**

2. If $m\angle G = 30$ and $m\widehat{AD} = 90$, find $m\widehat{FC}$. **30**

3. If $m\widehat{ECI} = 170$ and $m\widehat{EC} = 50$, find $m\angle IHC$. **35**

619

Students explore the relationship between chord segments and the relationship between secant segments and external secant segments. These relationships will be presented formally in Lesson 12-6.

Using the geometry software allows students to manipulate their constructions so they can observe that the relationship between the segments does not depend on which segments they drew.

ERROR ALERT! Some students may measure the wrong segments or calculate the wrong products and, thus, reach the wrong conclusions. **Remediation:** Have students compare their results with those of other pairs or groups. Have them discuss any discrepancies.

ADDITIONAL PROBLEM Have students take turns drawing circles similar to those on page 620. Ask them to label the measurements of three of the four segments. Then have their partners or other group members find the length of the fourth segment.

Math ToolboX   Technology

Exploring Chords and Secants

Before Lesson 12-6

Work in pairs or small groups.

Construct

Construct a circle with center A and two chords $\overline{BC}$ and $\overline{DE}$ that intersect each other at F.   **Check students' work.**

Investigate

Measure the segments $\overline{BF}$, $\overline{FC}$, $\overline{EF}$, and $\overline{FD}$. Use the calculator program of your software to find the products $BF \cdot FC$ and $EF \cdot FD$. Manipulate your construction and observe the products. What do you discover?
The 2 products are = .

Conjecture

Make a conjecture about the products of the lengths of the segments formed by the intersection of two chords in a circle.
The products of the lengths of segments formed by the intersection of 2 chords in a ⊙ are = .

Construct

Construct another circle and two secants that intersect in a point outside the circle. Label your construction as shown in the diagram.
Check students' work.

Investigate

Measure the segments $\overline{DG}$, $\overline{DF}$, $\overline{DE}$, and $\overline{DB}$. Calculate the products $DG \cdot DF$ and $DE \cdot DB$. Manipulate your construction and observe the products. What do you discover? **The 2 products are = .**

Conjecture

Make a **conjecture** about the products of the lengths of the segments formed by the intersection of two secants. **When 2 secants, such as $\overleftrightarrow{GF}$ and $\overleftrightarrow{EB}$ above, intersect at a point D outside the circle, $DG \cdot DF = DE \cdot DB$.**

Extend

Manipulate your construction so that secant $\overleftrightarrow{DG}$ becomes a tangent. What happens to the products you calculated? Can you explain how this special case is related to the case of two secants? **The product of the lengths of the segments formed by the secant is = to the square of the length of the tangent segment. When $\overline{DF}$ becomes tangent, pts. F and G coincide. So $DF \cdot DG = DF^2 = DG^2$.**

CONNECTING TO PRIOR KNOWLEDGE Copy the triangles onto the board and ask students to explain why they are similar and then to write three proportions relating to the sides of the triangles.

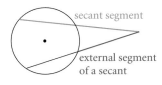

WORK TOGETHER

Question 2 Some students may have trouble measuring the length *t* because they have difficulty determining the exact point of tangency. Recommend that students use sharp pencils or fine-tipped pens to draw the circles and tangents. Advise them to draw large circles.

THINK AND DISCUSS

AUDITORY LEARNING Copy the three diagrams. Label the points where the segments intersect the circle or each other and have students practice naming segments of chords, secant segments, exterior secant segments and tangent segments.

Connections Architecture . . . and more

12-6 Circles and Lengths of Segments

What You'll Learn
- Finding the lengths of segments associated with circles

...And Why
To use the lengths of segments associated with circles in real-world applications such as architecture

What You'll Need
- ruler
- compass

TECHNOLOGY HINT
The Work Together could be done using geometry software.

WORK TOGETHER

Have members of your group draw two large circles. Draw and label segments as shown. Note that segment *t* is tangent to ⊙Q.

1. In ⊙P, measure lengths *a*, *b*, *c*, and *d*. Then find $a \cdot b$ and $c \cdot d$. What do you notice? Compare results within your group. $ab = cd$

2. **a.** In ⊙Q, measure lengths *w*, *x*, *y*, and *z*. Then find $(w + x)w$ and $(y + z)y$. What do you notice? Compare results within your group.
   b. Measure length *t*. Find t^2. What do you notice about t^2 and $(w + x)w$ and $(y + z)y$? Compare results within your group.
   a. $(w + x)w = (y + z)y$ **b.** t^2 is = to each product.

THINK AND DISCUSS

In the Work Together, you measured segments associated with circles. The diagram below will give you the vocabulary you need to refer to these segments.

segment of a chord

secant segment

external segment of a secant

tangent segment

Your observations in the Work Together suggest the following theorems.

Theorem 12-14

If two chords intersect inside a circle, then the product of the lengths of the segments of one chord equals the product of the lengths of the segments of the other chord.

$$a \cdot b = c \cdot d$$

621

EXTENSION The *power of a point* in the exterior of a circle is the product of the lengths of a secant segment and its external secant segment for any secant drawn from that point. Have students draw several secant segments from the same point and calculate the power of the point for each of the segments. Students should discover that the products are the same.

Example 1

ERROR ALERT! Some students may apply Theorem 12-14 to secant and tangent segments writing $8 \cdot 5 = y \cdot 4$ in part b, and $16 \cdot 8 = z^2$ in part c. **Remediation:** Display diagrams of the three theorems along with their equations. It may help students to write the theorem and the equation for each problem.

Question 3 Have students begin by identifying the lengths of the segments of the chords, the secant segment, the external secant segment, and the tangent segment.

Additional Examples

FOR EXAMPLE 1

Find the value of each variable.

a.

a. 12.6

b.

b. 10.9

c.

c. 12.5

FOR EXAMPLE 2

A chord perpendicular to a diameter divides the diameter into segments 12 in. and 3 in. long. How long is the chord? **12 in.**

622

Theorem 12-15

If two secant segments are drawn from a point outside a circle, the product of the lengths of one secant segment and its external segment equals the product of the lengths of the other secant segment and its external segment.

$(w + x)w = (y + z)y$

Theorem 12-16

If a tangent and a secant are drawn from a point outside a circle, then the product of the lengths of the secant segment and its external segment equals the square of the length of the tangent segment.

$(y + z)y = t^2$

Following is a proof of Theorem 12-14. You will prove Theorems 12-15 and 12-16 in Exercises 12 and 13.

Proof of Theorem 12-14

Given: $\odot O$ with chords $\overline{AC}$ and $\overline{BD}$ intersecting at E
Prove: $AE \cdot EC = DE \cdot EB$

Draw $\overline{AB}$ and $\overline{CD}$. $\angle AEB \cong \angle CED$ because vertical angles are congruent. $\angle C \cong \angle B$ because they are inscribed angles that intercept the same arc. So, $\triangle AEB \sim \triangle DEC$ by the Angle-Angle Similarity Postulate. Because lengths of corresponding sides of similar figures are proportional, $\frac{AE}{DE} = \frac{EB}{EC}$. Therefore, $AE \cdot EC = DE \cdot EB$.

Example 1

Find the value of each variable.

a.

b.

c.

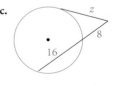

a. $8x = 20 \cdot 6$
   $8x = 120$
   $x = 15$

b. $(8 + 5)5 = (y + 4)4$
   $65 = 4y + 16$
   $49 = 4y$
   $y \approx 12.3$

c. $(16 + 8)8 = z^2$
   $192 = z^2$
   $13.9 \approx z$

3. **Try This** Find the value of x and y in the diagram at the left. If your answers are not integers, round them to the nearest tenth.

   $x = 7.1; y = 4$

Example 2 Relating to the Real World

Make sure students understand why 70 was added to 321.4 to find the diameter. Also make sure students see that the radius is half the diameter, not half of *x*.

DIVERSITY The history of bridges may fascinate some students. Have students research the longest bridge, the oldest bridge, or the fastest bridge ever built. Have them highlight the contributions made by bridge builders in India, Turkey, Japan, England, France, and Canada.

KINESTHETIC LEARNING If you have block scheduling or an extended class period, take students to the gymnasium. Use a circle on the basketball court. Have one student stand outside the circle holding two pieces of string. Have two other students stand on the circle, each holding an end of one of the

pieces of string. Then have other students measure the lengths of the tangent segments and secant segments formed by the string. Have students calculate the appropriate products and discuss whether their results support Theorem 12-5 or Theorem 12-6. Have the students standing on the circle move to different positions and repeat the activity.

Exercises ON YOUR OWN

ALTERNATIVE ASSESSMENT Exercises 1–6 You can use these exercises to assess students' understanding of Theorems 12-14, 12-15, and 12-16 by their ability to find the missing lengths. Have students work in groups of three and take turns recording the solutions to the problems.

You can use the theorems in the lesson to solve real-world problems.

Example 2 Relating to the Real World

Architecture The arch of a pedestrian bridge that crosses the San Antonio River is an arc of a circle. Find the radius of the circle.

The 300-ft chord is bisected by the perpendicular from the midpoint of the arch. Draw a sketch showing the chords of a circle. Then find the value of the unknown segment of the diameter.

$$70x = 150 \cdot 150$$
$$70x = 22{,}500$$
$$x \approx 321.4$$
$$\text{diameter} \approx 70 + 321.4 = 391.4 \text{ ft}$$
$$\text{radius} \approx 195.7 \text{ ft}$$

The radius is about 196 ft.

4. Critical Thinking Explain why the chord that contains the 70-ft segment is a diameter of the circle. The ⊥ bisector of a chord contains the center of the ⊙.

Technology Options

For Exercise 21c, students may perform the constructions using construction tools in geometry software.

Prentice Hall Technology

💾 **Software**
- Secondary Math Lab Toolkit™
- Computer Item Generator 12-6

🔄 **Internet**
- See the Prentice Hall site. (http://www.phschool.com)

Exercises ON YOUR OWN

▦ *Choose* Use mental math, paper and pencil, or a calculator. Find the value of each variable using the given chords, secants, and tangents. If your answer is not an integer, round it to the nearest tenth.

1.
11.5

2.
13.8

3.
7.8

4.
3.5

5.

x = 25.8; y = 12.4

6.
x = 5.3; y = 2.9

623

12-6 Circles and Lengths of Segments **623**

Exercise 7 Help students see that this problem is similar to Example 2 and have them model the solution steps.

Exercise 8 Have students compare their methods of solving this problem. This exercise provides a good opportunity to review problem-solving strategies.

Exercise 12 Students must recognize that a diameter perpendicular to a chord bisects the chord in order to solve this problem.

ERROR ALERT! Exercise 13 Some students may think that there is not enough information to solve this problem.
Remediation: Suggest students copy the diagram and draw the chords. Then hint that they should use the Pythagorean Theorem and Theorem 12-7.

Exercise 15 Make sure students correctly label the distance from the space craft to Jupiter on their diagrams.

pages 623–625 On Your Own

9. 1. $\overline{AC}$ and $\overline{BC}$ are secants of ⊙O. (Given) 2. ∠CAE ≅ ∠CBD (2 inscribed ∠s that intercept the same arc are ≅.) 3. ∠ACE ≅ ∠DCB (Reflexive Prop. of ≅) 4. △AEC ~ △BDC (AA~) 5. $\frac{EC}{DC} = \frac{AC}{BC}$ (In similar figures, corres. sides are proportional.) 6. BC · EC = AC · DC (Prop. of Proportions)

10. 1. $\overline{AC}$ is a tangent and $\overline{BC}$ is a secant of ⊙O. (Given) 2. $m\angle ABC = \frac{1}{2}m\widehat{AD}$ (The measure of an inscribed ∠ is half the measure of its intercepted arc.) 3. $m\angle DAC = \frac{1}{2}m\widehat{AD}$ (The measure of an ∠ formed by a chord and a tangent that intersect on a ⊙ is half the measure of the intercepted arc.) 4. m∠ABC = m∠DAC (Transitive Prop. of =) 5. ∠ACB ≅ ∠DCA (Reflexive Prop. of ≅) 6. △BAC ~ △ADC (AA~) 7. $\frac{AC}{DC} = \frac{BC}{AC}$ (In similar figures, corres. sides are proportional.) 8. BC · DC = AC^2 (Prop. of Proportions)

7. *Geology* This natural arch, in Arches National Park, Utah, is an arc of a circle. Find the diameter of the circle. **about 271 ft**

8. Two chords of a circle intersect. The segments of the first chord are 16 cm and 18 cm long. The lengths of the segments of the second chord are in the ratio 2 : 1. Find the lengths of the segments of the second chord. **24 cm and 12 cm**

Choose Write a two-column proof, paragraph proof, or flow proof. 9–10. Answers may vary. See margin for samples.

9. Prove Theorem 12-15.

Given: ⊙O with secants $\overline{AC}$ and $\overline{BC}$ (Chords $\overline{AE}$ and $\overline{BD}$ are drawn for you.)
Prove: BC · EC = AC · DC

Plan for Proof: In order to use the properties of proportions, prove △AEC ~ △BDC.

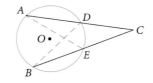

10. Prove Theorem 12-16.

Given: ⊙O with tangent $\overline{AC}$ and secant $\overline{BC}$ (Chords $\overline{AB}$ and $\overline{AD}$ are drawn for you.)
Prove: BC · DC = AC^2

Plan for Proof: In order to use the properties of proportions, prove △BAC ~ △ADC.

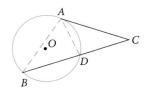

Find the diameter of ⊙O given the chords, secants, and tangents. Round your answer to the nearest tenth.

11. **26.7**

12. **16.7**

13. **14.1**

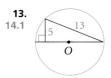

14. *Standardized Test Prep* $\overline{AB}$ is tangent to ⊙O at A. $\overline{AB} \perp \overline{EB}$. AB = BF. BC = 1 and CE = 7. Find AF. **C**
   A. 2   **B.** $3\frac{1}{2}$ **C.** 4
   D. $4\frac{1}{3}$ **E.** none of the above

15. *Space Exploration* The line of sight from an object above a planet to the horizon of the planet is a tangent line. The *Galileo* orbiter is a spacecraft that circles 133,300 mi above Jupiter. Jupiter's diameter is 88,700 mi. What is the distance from the *Galileo* orbiter to Jupiter's horizon? Round your answer to the nearest hundred miles. **172,000 mi**

Jupiter's horizon from *Galileo's* line of sight

Galileo

WRITING **Exercise 16** You may want to ask students to write the correct equation.

OPEN-ENDED **Exercise 17** Suggest that students choose points near the center of the circle and points near the boundary of the circle.

RESEARCH **Exercise 21** You may want to ask students to research which car companies have experimented with using Wankel engines, what the advantages and disadvantages of a Wankel engine are, who invented the Wankel engine, and when it was invented.

Exercise 22 Suggest that students draw a diagram.

16. *Writing* To find the value of x, a student wrote the equation $(7.5)6 = x^2$. What error did the student make? **See margin.**

17. **a.** *Open-ended* Draw a circle. Place a point inside the circle. Draw a chord through the point. Measure the segments of the chord that you drew. Find the product of the lengths.
    b. Choose three other points. Find the product of the lengths of the segments of a chord through each of these points. **a–b. Check students' work.**
    c. *Patterns* Use your answers to parts (a) and (b) to make a conjecture. What point inside a circle has the greatest product of the lengths of segments of chords?

16. The student should have used the length of the whole secant, 13.5, instead of the length of the internal segment, 7.5.

23a. If a tangent and a secant are drawn from a pt. outside a $\odot$, then the product of the lengths of the secant segment and its external segment = the square of the length of the tangent segment.

17c. The center has the greatest product of the lengths of the segments of chords passing through it.

Find the value of x and y using the given chords, secants, and tangents. If your answer is not an integer, round to the nearest tenth.

18.

19.

20.

$x = 10.7$; $y = 10$ **$x = 8.9$; $y = 2$**   **$x = 10.9$; $y = 2.3$**

21. **a.** *Engineering* The basis of a design of a rotor for a Wankel engine is an equilateral triangle. Each side of the triangle is a chord of an arc of a circle. The center of each circle is a vertex of the triangle. In the diagram at the right, each side of the equilateral triangle is 8 in. long. Find the value of x to the nearest tenth. **1.1 in.**
    b. *Research* Rotary engines are used in some snowmobiles. Find other uses of rotary engines. **Check students' work.**
    c. *Constructions* Construct an equilateral triangle. Then construct the arcs to draw a rotor. **See below right.**

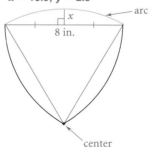

22. *Calculator* The diameter of a circle is 24 cm. A chord perpendicular to the diameter is 5 cm from the center of the circle. What is the length of the chord? Round your answer to the nearest tenth. **21.8 cm**

23. Following is a proof of the Pythagorean Theorem that uses a theorem presented in this lesson. Supply the missing reasons.

21c.

Given: $\odot O$ with tangent $\overline{PQ}$
Prove: $a^2 + b^2 = c^2$

Statements	Reasons
1. $PQ^2 = (QR)(QS)$	a. _?_
2. $b^2 = (c - a)(c + a)$	b. _?_
3. $b^2 = c^2 - a^2$	c. _?_ Distributive Prop.
4. $a^2 + b^2 = c^2$	d. _?_ Addition Prop. of =
a. See margin.	b. Substitution

Wrap Up

THE BIG IDEA Ask students to summarize how to find the lengths of chord segments, secant segments, and tangent segments.

Reteaching 12-6
Practice 12-6
Practice 12-6
Mixed Exercises

Exercises **MIXED REVIEW**

Find the value of *x* to the nearest tenth.

24.

13, 16, $x°$

35.7

25.

$x°$, 40.3, 17, 11

26. a. Calculator A ball has circumference 60 cm. What is its radius? Round your answer to the nearest millimeter. **9.5 cm or 95 mm**

b. What is the length of an edge of the smallest box that could contain this ball? **19.1 cm**

Lesson Quiz

Lesson Quiz is also available in Transparencies.

C is a point of tangency.

1. If *AB* = 10, *BC* = 8, and *IB* = 5, find *BE*. **16**

2. If *HI* = 24 and *EI* = 16, find *HC*. **13.9**

3. If *DF* = 12, *FG* = 8, and *CG* = 6, find *AG*. **20.7**

Geometry at Work

Aerospace Engineer

Aerospace engineers design and build all types of spacecraft, from the low-orbit space shuttle to interplanetary probes. Much of today's aerospace work involves communications satellites that relay TV, telephone, computer, and other signals to receivers around the world. The portion of Earth's surface that can communicate with a satellite increases as the height of the orbit increases.

The figure shows a satellite 12,000 miles above Earth, which has a radius of about 3960 miles. $\overset{\frown}{AB}$ is the arc of Earth that is in the range of the satellite. You can find $m\overset{\frown}{AB}$ by finding $m\angle AEB$, which is twice $m\angle AES$.

cosine of $\angle AES = \frac{AE}{SE} = \frac{3960}{3960 + 12,000} \approx 0.2481$

$m\angle AES \approx \cos^{-1}(0.2481) \approx 75.63$

$m\overset{\frown}{AB} = m\angle AEB \approx 2 \cdot 75.63 \approx 151.3$

The arc of Earth in the range of the satellite is about 151.3°.

12,000 mi

3960 mi

Earth

Mini Project: A geosynchronous orbit is used by communications satellites. Research geosynchronous orbits. Find the height of a geosynchronous orbit and find the arc of Earth that is in the range of a satellite in a geosynchronous orbit.

Finishing the Chapter Project

PROJECT DAY You may wish to plan a project day on which students share their completed projects. Encourage groups to explain their processes as well as their products.

PROJECT NOTEBOOK Have students review their project work and bring their notebooks up to date.

- Have students review both their designs and their instructions to draw them.
- Ask groups to share the techniques they used to create their designs, any experimentations with other designs, and how they made improvements in their designs.

Finishing the Chapter Project

CHAPTER PROJECT

GO FOR A SPIN

Find Out questions and activities on pages 591, 605, and 618 will help you complete your project. Using one or more of the techniques you explored, create your own design. First decide how the design will be used. Some possibilities are a poster, a school logo, and a tile pattern for a floor. State the purpose of your design, give instructions for drawing it, and explain the geometric concepts incorporated in it.

Reflect and Revise

Ask a classmate to review your project. Together, check that the diagrams and explanations are clear and accurate. Can you improve your design? Can someone follow your instructions? Revise your work as needed.

Follow Up

Leonardo da Vinci explored regions bounded by arcs. He showed that the first region at the right could be cut apart and reassembled into a rectangle. Read about da Vinci's efforts and try the other figures yourself.

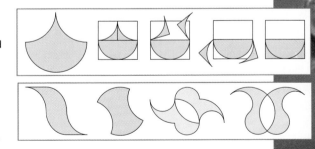

For More Information

Bain, George. *Celtic Art: The Methods of Construction.* New York: Dover, 1973.

Horemis, Spyros. *Optical and Geometrical Patterns and Designs.* New York: Dover, 1970.

Wills, Herbert. *Leonardo's Dessert.* Reston, Virginia: National Council of Teachers of Mathematics, 1985.

627

HOW AM I DOING? Divide the class into six groups with each group reviewing a different lesson. Ask each group to make a short presentation explaining the key ideas of the lesson. Each presentation must include a visual aid and a sample problem.

KEY TERMS The numbers in parentheses direct students to the pages where the terms are used or defined. Students should be able to (1) write a simple explanation of each term, (2) illustrate the term with a diagram, or (3) show an example that uses the term.

STANDARDIZED TEST TIP Exercise 7 Students can save valuable time by realizing that they do not need to graph any circles, but need only consider the radii.

Resources

 Student Edition
Extra Practice, p. 645
Glossary/Study Guide

Teaching Resources
Study Skills Handbook
Glossary, Spanish Resources

12 **W**rap Up

Key Terms

chord (p. 600)
circumscribed about
  (pp. 596, 607)
inscribed in
  (pp. 596, 607)
inscribed angle (p. 607)

intercepted arc (p. 607)
point of tangency (p. 593)
secant (p. 614)
standard form of an equation
  of a circle (p. 586)
tangent to a circle (p. 593)

How am I doing?

• State three ideas from this chapter that you think are important. Explain your choices.

• Describe the properties of different segments of a circle.

Circles in the Coordinate Plane   12-1

The **standard form of an equation of a circle** with center (h, k) and radius r is $(x - h)^2 + (y - k)^2 = r^2$.

If you know the center and a point on a circle, you can find an equation of the circle. Find the radius by using the Distance Formula to find the distance from the center to the given point. Then substitute the coordinates of the center for (h, k) and the radius for r in the standard form of the equation of a circle.

Find an equation of a circle with the given center and radius.
$(x - 2)^2 + (y - 5)^2 = 9$
1. center $= (2, 5); r = 3$

$(x + 3)^2 + (y - 1)^2 = 5$
2. center $= (-3, 1); r = \sqrt{5}$

$(x - 9)^2 + (y + 4)^2 = 12.25$
3. center $= (9, -4); r = 3.5$

Find an equation of the circle with the given center passing through the given point.
$x^2 + (y - 1)^2 = 80$
4. center $(0, 1)$, through $(4, 9)$

$(x + 2)^2 + (y - 3)^2 = 85$
5. center $(-2, 3)$, through $(4, -4)$

$(x - 10)^2 + (y - 7)^2 = 468$
6. center $(10, 7)$, through $(-8, -5)$

7. Standardized Test Prep Which circle has the least area? E

A. $(x - 1)^2 + (y - 3)^2 = 4$ **B.** $(x + 2)^2 + y^2 = 7$ **C.** $x^2 + (y - 5)^2 = 9$

D. $x^2 + y^2 = 10$ **E.** $(x + 3)^2 + (y + 2)^2 = 3$

Properties of Tangents   12-2

A **tangent to a circle** is a line, ray, or segment in the plane of the circle that intersects the circle in exactly one point, the **point of tangency**.

If a line is tangent to a circle, then the line is perpendicular to the radius drawn to the point of tangency. If a line is perpendicular to a radius at its endpoint on the circle, then the line is tangent to the circle.

Two segments tangent to a circle from a point outside the circle are congruent.

628

Each polygon circumscribes a circle. Find the perimeter of the polygon.

8.
7 in. 8 in.
5 in. 9 in.

58 in.

9.
17 mm
8 mm
6 mm
7 mm 19 mm

84 mm

10.
1.8 cm
2.9 cm
1.2 cm
1.8 cm

9.6 cm

11. Writing The word *tangent* is used in different ways in Chapters 11 and 12. Explain each use. Include diagrams in your explanation.
See margin.

Properties of Chords and Arcs   12-3

In the same circle or in congruent circles,
- congruent central angles intercept congruent arcs;
- congruent arcs have congruent central angles;
- congruent chords have congruent arcs;
- congruent arcs have congruent chords;
- chords equidistant from the center are congruent; and
- congruent chords are equidistant from the center.

A diameter that is perpendicular to a chord bisects the chord and its arc. The perpendicular bisector of a chord contains the center of the circle.

chords

 Calculator **Find the value of x. Round to the nearest tenth.**

12.
11
x
14

4.3

13.
12
7
x

19.5

14.
45°
x
9

6.4

15.
9
5
x 5

4.5

16. Open-ended Draw two circles with different radii. Draw a chord in the smaller circle and a congruent chord in the larger circle. Are the arcs of these chords congruent? Explain.
No; the arcs have different radii so they cannot be congruent.

Inscribed Angles   12-4

The vertex of an **inscribed angle** lies on a circle. Its sides **intercept** an arc of the circle. All the vertices of an **inscribed polygon** lie on a circle.

The measure of an inscribed angle is half the measure of its intercepted arc. The measure of an angle formed by a chord and a tangent that intersect on a circle is half the measure of the intercepted arc.

Two inscribed angles that intercept the same arc are congruent. The opposite angles of a quadrilateral inscribed in a circle are supplementary.

2x°
x°
2y°
y°

inscribed angle

11. In Ch. 11, a tangent of an angle is the ratio of the length of the opp. leg of a rt. △ to the length of the adjacent leg. In Ch. 12, a tangent line to a ⊙ is a line in the plane of the ⊙ that intersects the ⊙ at exactly 1 pt.

629

ALTERNATIVE ASSESSMENT **Exercises 17–28** Have
students work in groups. Assign each group one problem from
each section to solve. Then have them create and solve three
problems that incorporate the concepts from each lesson.

Remind students that the new mathematical terms in this
chapter are defined in the Glossary/Study Guide in the back of
the book.

Assessment   page 631

8a–b.

b. **The center lies on the angle
bisector.**

11.

**21. A rhombus inscribed in a ⊙ is a
square. Opp. ∠s of a quad.
inscr. in a ⊙ are suppl.
(Corollary 3). Opp ∠s of a
rhombus are ≅. So all the ∠s
must be right ∠s. All the sides
of a rhombus are ≅, so the
rhombus must be a square.**

630

**Assume that lines that appear tangent are tangent. Find the value of
each variable.** **18.** $a = 118$; $b = 49$; $c = 144$; $d = 98$ $a = 90$; $b = 90$; $c = 70$; $d = 65$

17.   **18.**   **19.**   **20.**

$a = 40$; $b = 140$; $c = 90$ $a = 34$; $b = 68$

Angles Formed by Chords, Secants, and Tangents   12-5

The measure of an angle formed by two intersecting chords in a
circle is half the sum of the measures of the intercepted arcs.

A **secant** is a line, ray, or segment that intersects a circle at two
points.

The measure of an angle formed by two secants, two tangents,
or a secant and a tangent drawn from a point outside a circle is
half the difference of the measures of the intercepted arcs.

$$m\angle 1 = \tfrac{1}{2}(x + y) \qquad m\angle B = \tfrac{1}{2}(y - x)$$

**Assume that lines that appear tangent are tangent. Find the value of
each variable.**

21.   **22.**   **23.**   **24.**

$a = 95$; $b = 85$

$x = 57$; $y = 44.5$; $z = 129$; $v = 51$

Circles and Lengths of Segments   12-6

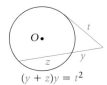

$a \cdot b = c \cdot d \qquad (w + x)w = (y + z)y \qquad (y + z)y = t^2$

**Find the value of each variable using the given chords, secants, and
tangents. If your answer is not an integer, round to the nearest tenth.**

25.   **26.**   **27.**   **28.**
9.5   4   17.1   8.4

12 Assessment

Find the center and radius of each circle.

1. $(x + 3)^2 + (y - 2)^2 = 9$ (−3, 2); 3

2. $(x - 5)^2 + (y - 9)^2 = 225$ (5, 9); 15

3. $(x - 2)^2 + (y - 4)^2 = 4$

Write the equation of each circle.

3.

4.

$x^2 + (y + 1)^2 = 4$

5. Find the circumference and area of the circle whose equation is $(x - 2)^2 + (y - 7)^2 = 81$. Round to the nearest tenth. 56.5 units;

254.5 units^2

Assume that lines that appear tangent are tangent. Find the value of x.

6.

94

7.

8. a. **Open-ended** Draw a circle with two congruent chords that form an inscribed angle.
   b. **Constructions** Construct the bisector of the inscribed angle. What do you notice?
   a–b. See margin for sample.

Find the value of x. If your answer is not an integer, round to the nearest tenth.

9.

7.2

10.

9.8

11. **Coordinate Geometry** Graph the circle $(x - 4)^2 + (y - 3)^2 = 25$. State the center and the radius of the circle.

See margin for graph; (4, 3); 5.

Find m⌢AB.

12.

65

13.

120

14. **Standardized Test Prep** In the figure at the right, a square is circumscribed about ⊙A. Find the area of the square. D
   A. 192 cm^2 B. 64 cm^2
   C. 256 + 16√3 cm^2 D. 256 cm^2
   E. It cannot be determined from the information given.

Assume that lines that appear tangent are tangent. Find the value of each variable. If your answer is not an integer, round to the nearest tenth.

15.

a = 110; b = 70

16.

a = 44; b = 71

17.

x = 26; y = 41.5

18.

10.5

19.

5.9

20.

8

21. **Writing** What is special about a rhombus inscribed in a circle? **Justify** your answer.
   See margin.

631

Item	Review Topic	Chapter		Item	Review Topic	Chapter
1	Triangles	2		10, 13	Circles	12
2, 15	Coordinate Plane	1		11	Medians of Triangles	4
3	Proving Triangles Congruent	8		12	Vectors	11
3	Parallel Lines	7		14	Proportions	10
4, 21	Area	5		16	Symmetry	3
5	Volume	6		17, 19	Constructions	1
6	Using Logical Reasoning	4		18	Proofs	9
7	Transformations	3		19	Areas of Similar Figures	10
8	Perpendicular Lines	2		20	Using Similar Triangles	10
9, 17	Quadrilaterals	9		21	Right Triangle Trigonometry	11

Resources

Teaching Resources

Chapter Support File, Ch. 12
- Cumulative Review
- Standardized Test Practice

Teacher's Edition

See also p. 584E for assessment options

632

---

12 Cumulative Review

For Exercises 1–15, choose the correct letter.

1. What is the best description of the triangle below? **E**

A. acute scalene **B.** right
C. equilateral **D.** obtuse scalene
E. isosceles right

2. What are the coordinates of the midpoint of $\overline{QS}$ with endpoints $Q(-2, -5)$ and $S(3, -8)$? **B**
A. $(-2.5, 6.5)$ **B.** $(0.5, -6.5)$ **C.** $(0.5, 1.5)$
D. $(-2.5, 1.5)$ **E.** $(-3.5, -5.5)$

3. Which theorem or postulate can you *not* use to prove $\triangle ABC \cong \triangle CDA$? **A**

A. HL **B.** ASA **C.** AAS
D. SAS **E.** SSS

4. What is the area of an isosceles right triangle with hypotenuse length $5\sqrt{2}$ in.? **B**
A. 5 in.^{2} **B.** 12.5 in.^{2} **C.** 25 in.^{2}
D. $25\sqrt{2}$ in.^{2} **E.** $(10 + 5\sqrt{2})$ in.^{2}

5. What is the volume of the figure? **E**

3 ft

6 ft   4 ft

A. 288 ft^3 **B.** 72 ft^3 **C.** 72π ft^3
D. $(13 + 72\pi)$ ft^3 **E.** $(72 + 18\pi)$ ft^3

6. Which of the following statements can be derived from the biconditional statement "The day is long if and only if it is summer"? **E**
A. If the day is long, then it is summer.
B. If it is summer, then the day is long.
C. If the day is not long, then it is not summer.
D. If it is not summer, then the day is not long.
E. all of the above

7. Which is a reflection of the figure in the x-axis? **B**

A. **B.**

C. **D.**

E. none of the above

8. Which line(s) is(are) perpendicular to the line $y = 4x - 1$? **D**
I. $y = 4x + 7$ **II.** $y = \frac{1}{4}x + 3$
III. $y = -\frac{1}{4}x - 5$ **IV.** $x + 4y = 16$
A. I only **B.** II only **C.** I and II
D. III and IV **E.** I, II, III, and IV

9. Which statement is true for both a rhombus and a kite? **D**
A. Opposite angles are congruent.
B. The diagonals are congruent.
C. Opposite sides are congruent.
D. The diagonals are perpendicular.
E. Opposite sides are parallel.

10. What is the value of x to the nearest tenth? **C**

A. 5 **B.** 9 **C.** 13.6 **D.** 15 **E.** 20.6

11. Which triangle is drawn with its medians? **B**

A. **B.**

C. **D.**

E. none of the above

Compare the boxed quantity in Column A with the one in Column B. Choose the best answer.

A. The quantity in Column A is greater.
B. The quantity in Column B is greater.
C. The two quantities are equal.
D. The relationship cannot be determined on the basis of the information supplied.

Column A	Column B	
12. the magnitude of $\langle 5, 1\rangle$	the magnitude of $\langle -4, 2\rangle$	A
13. the measure of an inscribed angle of a circle that intercepts a 78° arc	the measure of a central angle of a circle that intercepts a 78° arc	B

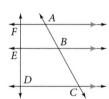

14. $\dfrac{AB}{FE}$	$\dfrac{BC}{ED}$	C

15. the distance between $(7, 3)$ and $(10, -2)$	the distance between $(3, -1)$ and $(0, 4)$	C

Find each answer. 16–17. See margin for samples.

16. *Open-ended* Sketch a figure with two lines of symmetry.

17. *Constructions* Draw a segment. Construct a kite whose diagonals are congruent to the segment you drew.

18. *Writing* What information is provided by a flow proof that is not in a two-column proof? See margin.

19. *Constructions* Copy the trapezoid. Construct a trapezoid similar to it whose perimeter is twice that of the original figure. What is the ratio of the area of the smaller figure to the area of the larger figure?

See margin for diagram; 1:4.

20. You are 5 ft 6 in. tall. When your shadow is 6 ft long, the shadow of a sculpture is 30 ft long. How tall is the sculpture? 27 ft 6 in.

21. A diagonal of a rectangular field makes a 70° angle with the side of the field that is 100 ft long. What is the area of the rectangle? 27,475 ft²

16.

17.

18. Answers may vary. Sample: A flow proof clearly shows the structure of the proof. That is, it shows how the given statements lead to other statements and, finally, to the statement to be proved.

19.

20.

21.

22.

23.

F   G

Extra Practice

Find the next two terms in each sequence.   ■ Lesson 1-1

1. 12, 17, 22, 27, 32, . . . 37, 42 **2.** 1, 1.1, 1.11, 1.111, 1.1111, . . . **3.** 5000, 1000, 200, 40, . . . 8, $\frac{8}{5}$
                                                          1.111 11, 1.111 111

4. 1, 12, 123, 1234, . . . **5.** 3, 0.3, 0.03, 0.003, . . . **6.** 1, 4, 9, 16, 25, . . . 36, 49
  12,345, 123,456   0.0003, 0.000 03

Write *true* or *false*.   ■ Lessons 1-2 and 1-3

7. *A, D, F* are coplanar. true **8.** $\overleftrightarrow{AC}$ and $\overleftrightarrow{FE}$ are coplanar. false

9. *A, B, E* are collinear. false **10.** *D, A, B, E* are coplanar. true

11. $\overleftrightarrow{FC} \parallel \overleftrightarrow{EF}$ false **12.** plane *ABC* $\parallel$ plane *FDE* true

13. $\overleftrightarrow{BC}$ and $\overleftrightarrow{DF}$ are skew lines. true **14.** $\overleftrightarrow{AD}$ and $\overleftrightarrow{EB}$ are skew lines. false

Use the figure at the right for Exercises 15–19.   ■ Lessons 1-4 and 1-5

15. If *BC* = 12 and *CE* = 15, then *BE* = ■. 27

16. ■ is the angle bisector of ■. $\overline{CG}; \angle ACB$

17. *BC* = 3*x* + 2 and *CD* = 5*x* − 10. Solve for *x*. 6

18. *m*∠*BCG* = 60, *m*∠*GCA* = ■, *m*∠*BCA* = ■ 60; 120

19. *m*∠*ACD* = 60 and *m*∠*DCH* = 20. Find *m*∠*HCA*. 40

Draw a diagram larger than the given one. Then do the construction.   ■ Lesson 1-6

20. Construct the perpendicular bisector of $\overline{AB}$. 20–23.
                                                               See
21. Construct ∠*A* so that *m*∠*A* = *m*∠1 + *m*∠2. margin.

22. Construct the angle bisector of ∠1.

23. Construct $\overline{FG}$ so that *FG* = *AB* + *CD*.

A •————————• B

C •
          • D

Algebra **Find the value of *x*.**   ■ Lesson 1-7

24. 24

$(3x − 14)°$ $(2x + 10)°$

25. 15

$2x°$
$4x°$

26. 25

$2x°$ $(5x + 5)°$

■ **In Exercises 27–32: (a) Find the distance between the points to the nearest tenth. (b) Find the coordinates of the midpoint of the segment with the given endpoints.**   ■ Lesson 1-8

27. *A*(2, 1), *B*(3, 0) a. 1.4 b. (2.5, 0.5) **28.** *R*(5, 2), *S*(−2, 4) a. 7.3 b. (1.5, 3) **29.** *Q*(−7, −4), *T*(6, 10) a. 19.1 b. (−0.5, 3)

30. *C*(−8, −1), *D*(−5, −11) a. 10.4 b. (−6.5, −6) **31.** *J*(0, −5), *N*(3, 4) a. 9.5 b. (1.5, −0.5) **32.** *Y*(−2, 8), *Z*(3, −5) a. 13.9 b. (0.5, 1.5)

Chapter 2 Extra Practice

25.
Top / Front / Right
Front / Right

26.
Top / Front / Right
Front / Right

27.
Top / Front / Right
Front / Right

28.
Top / Front / Right
Front / Right

CHAPTER 2

Extra Practice

Classify each triangle by its sides and angles. To do so, use a ruler to measure lengths of sides and a protractor to measure angles.   ■ **Lessons 2-1 and 2-2**

1. scalene, obtuse

2. isosceles, obtuse

3. isosceles, acute

4. scalene, right

Algebra Find the value of each variable.

5. $106°$, $94°$, $(x + 5)°$, 100, $135°$, $x°$

6. $x = 25;$ $y = 19$; $54°$, $130°$, $2x°$, $4y°$

7. 65; $(x + 8)°$, $(x - 3)°$, $45°$

8. $x = 110;$ $y = 102;$ $z = 82$; $z°$, $x°$, $70°$, $90°$, $78°$, $y°$

Graph the given points. Use the slope formula and/or the distance formula to determine the most precise name for quadrilateral *ABCD*.   ■ **Lessons 2-3 and 2-4**

9. $A(3, 5)$, $B(6, 5)$, $C(2, 1)$, $D(1, 3)$ trapezoid

10. $A(-1, 1)$, $B(3, -1)$, $C(-1, -3)$, $D(-5, -1)$ rhombus

11. $A(2, 1)$, $B(5, -1)$, $C(4, -4)$, $D(1, -2)$
parallelogram

12. $A(-4, 5)$, $B(-1, 3)$, $C(-3, 0)$, $D(-6, 2)$
square

Identify the following in $\odot P$. 13–17. Answers may vary. Samples are given. ■ **Lesson 2-5**

13. three minor arcs $\overset{\frown}{ED}$, $\overset{\frown}{AE}$, $\overset{\frown}{BA}$

14. two major arcs $\overset{\frown}{BED}$, $\overset{\frown}{CAE}$

15. two adjacent arcs $\overset{\frown}{ED}$, $\overset{\frown}{AE}$

16. two radii $\overline{PE}$, $\overline{PA}$

17. an acute central angle $\angle APB$

18. two diameters $\overline{BE}$, $\overline{AD}$

$\triangle SAT \cong \triangle GRE$. Complete the congruence statements.   ■ **Lesson 2-6**

19. $\angle S \cong \blacksquare \ \angle G$

20. $\overline{GR} \cong \blacksquare \ \overline{SA}$

21. $\angle E \cong \blacksquare \ \angle T$

22. $\overline{AT} \cong \blacksquare \ \overline{RE}$

23. $\triangle ERG \cong \blacksquare \ \triangle TAS$

24. $\overline{EG} \cong \blacksquare \ \overline{TS}$

Create an isometric drawing and an orthographic drawing for each foundation plan. 25–28. See margin.   ■ **Lesson 2-7**

25.
| 3 | 3 |
| 1 | 2 |
Right / Front

26.
| 4 | 1 |
| 1 | |
Right / Front

27.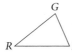
| 4 | 3 | 1 |
| | 2 | |
Right / Front

28.
| | 2 |
| 3 | 1 |
Right / Front

Chapter 3 Extra Practice

1.

2.

3.

4.

5.

6.

7.

8.

23a. line, rotational, point   b. yes

24a. line   b. yes

25a. line   b. yes

26a. line, point   b. yes

CHAPTER 3

Extra Practice

Coordinate Geometry Given points $S(6, 1)$, $U(2, 5)$, and $B(-1, 2)$, draw $\triangle SUB$ and its reflection image in the given line. 1–8. See margin.

■ Lesson 3-1

1. $y = 5$ **2.** $x = 7$ **3.** $y = -1$ **4.** the x-axis

5. $y = x$ **6.** $x = -1$ **7.** $y = 3$ **8.** the y-axis

In Exercises 9–14, refer to the figure at the right.

■ Lesson 3-2

9. What is the image of C **E** under the translation $\langle 4, -2 \rangle$?

10. What vector describes the translation $F \longrightarrow B$? $\langle -2, 4 \rangle$

11. What is the image of H **C** under the translation $\langle -2, 4 \rangle$?

12. What vector describes the translation $D \longrightarrow H$? $\langle 4, -2 \rangle$

13. What is the image of C **G** under the translation $\langle -2, -4 \rangle$?

14. What vector describes the translation $B \longrightarrow A$? $\langle -8, 0 \rangle$

Copy each figure and point P. Rotate the figure the given number of degrees about P. Label the vertices of the image.

■ Lesson 3-3

15. $60°$ **16.** $90°$ **17.** $180°$ **18.** $45°$

The blue figure is the image of the black figure. State whether the mapping is a reflection, rotation, translation, glide reflection, or dilation.

■ Lessons 3-4 and 3-7

19.   **20.**   **21.**   **22.**

rotation   dilation   translation   glide reflection

In Exercises 23–26: (a) State what kind of symmetry each figure has. (b) State whether each figure tessellates. 23–26. See margin.

■ Lessons 3-5 and 3-6

23.   **24.**   **25.**   **26.**

636

Chapter 4 Extra Practice

1. If 2 angles are ≅, then they are vert.; if 2 angles are not vert., then they are not ≅; if 2 angles are not ≅, then they are not vert.

2. If the side lengths of figures are proportional, then they are similar; if figures are not similar, then their side lengths are not proportional; if the side lengths of figures are not proportional, then they are not similar.

3. If a car has no doors, then it is blue; if a car is not blue, then it has doors; if a car has doors, then it is not blue.

8. 1. $\square BGKM$ (Given) 2. $m\angle B + m\angle G + m\angle K + m\angle M = 360$ (Sum of the measures of the int. $\angle$s of an n-gon $= (n - 2)180$.) 3. $m\angle B = m\angle G = m\angle K = m\angle M$ (Given) 4. $4(m\angle B) = 360$ (Substitution) 5. $m\angle B = 90$ (Division Prop. of $=$) 6. $m\angle G = m\angle K = m\angle M = 90$ (Substitution) 7. $\angle B$, $\angle G$, $\angle K$, and $\angle M$ are rt. angles. (Def. of rt. angle) 8. $\square BGKM$ is a rectangle (Def. of rectangle)

16.

17.

18.

For each statement, write the converse, the inverse, and the contrapositive. 1–3. See margin.

■ Lesson 4-1

1. If two angles are vertical angles, then they are congruent.

2. If figures are similar, then their side lengths are proportional.

3. If a car is blue, then it has no doors.

Find the value of each variable.

■ Lessons 4-2 and 4-4

4.

$x = 57;$
$y = 66$

5.

6.

7. 65

8. Rewrite this paragraph proof as a two-column proof.
Given: $\square BGKM$, $m\angle B = m\angle G = m\angle K = m\angle M$
Prove: $\square BGKM$ is a rectangle. See margin.

■ Lesson 4-3

By the Polygon Interior Angle-Sum Thm., $m\angle B + m\angle G + m\angle K + m\angle M = 360$. We are given that $m\angle B = m\angle G = m\angle K = m\angle M$, so by Substitution, $4(m\angle B) = 360$. Dividing each side by 4 yields $m\angle B = 90$. By Substitution, $m\angle G = m\angle K = m\angle M = 90$. So $\angle B$, $\angle G$, $\angle K$, and $\angle M$ are rt. angles. $\square BGKM$ is a rectangle by definition.

Write the first step of an indirect proof of each statement.

■ Lesson 4-5

9. $\triangle ABC$ is a right triangle.
Assume $\triangle ABC$ is not a rt. $\triangle$.

10. Points J, K, and L are collinear.
Assume pts. J, K, and L are not collinear.

11. Lines ℓ and m are parallel.
Assume lines ℓ and m are not $\parallel$.

List the sides of each triangle in order from shortest to longest.

■ Lesson 4-6

12.
NR, RS, SN

13.
JB, BP, PJ

14.
QM, DQ, MD

15.
$\overline{CT}$, $\overline{TA}$, $\overline{AC}$

Sketch and label each locus. 16–18. See margin.

■ Lesson 4-7

16. all points in a plane 2 cm from $\overrightarrow{AB}$

17. all points in space 1.5 in. from point Q

18. all points in a plane 3 cm from a circle with radius 2 cm

Is $\overline{AB}$ an angle bisector, altitude, median, or perpendicular bisector?

■ Lesson 4-8

19.
altitude

20. ⊥ bisector

21.
angle bisector

22.
median

637

Extra Practice

Find the perimeter and area of each figure. ■ **Lessons 5-1 and 5-2**

1.
14 in.
7 in.
42 in.; 98 in.²

2.
13 m | 12 m | 17 m
|← 17 m →|
47 m; 102 m²

3.
1 cm
3 cm | 2 cm
2 cm
10 cm; 5 cm²

4.
13 ft
11 ft | 12 ft
50 ft; 143 ft²

Algebra Find the value of *x*. If your answer is not a whole number, ■ **Lessons 5-3 and 5-4**
leave it in simplest radical form.

5.
15
12 | *x*
9

6.
5√3
60°
5
x

7. 3√5
9 | *x*
6

8.
3√2
x | 6

Find the area of each trapezoid or regular polygon. You may leave ■ **Lessons 5-5 and 5-6**
your answer in simplest radical form.

9.
6 cm
72 cm²

10.
10 in.
12 in.
16 in.
156 in.²

11.
5 mm
25√3 / 4 mm²

12.
4 ft
32√3 ft²

In Exercises 13–16: (a) Find the circumference of each circle. (b) Find ■ **Lesson 5-7**
the length of the arc shown in red. Leave your answers in terms of π.

13.
120°
6 cm
a. 6π cm b. 2π cm

14.
150° | 20 ft
a. 20π ft b. 5π/3 ft

15.
9 cm
a. 18π cm b. 9π/2 cm

16.
5 in.
225°
a. 10π in. b. 25π/4 in.

Find the area of each shaded sector or segment. Leave your answers ■ **Lesson 5-8**
in terms of π.

(12π − 9√3) in.²   81π/8 cm²   (4π − 8) m²

17. 49π/3 ft²

240° | 7 ft

18.
30° | 30°
6 in.

19.
135°
←18 cm→

20.
4 m

Chapter 6 Extra Practice

13. $\frac{500\pi}{3}$ cm^3; 100π cm^2

14. $\frac{256\pi}{3}$ in.^{3}; 64π in.^{2}

15. $\frac{4\pi}{3}$ ft^3; 4π ft^2

16. $\frac{\pi}{6}$ in.^{3}; π in.^{2}

17. $\frac{243\pi}{2}$ m^3; 81π m^2

CHAPTER 6

Extra Practice

Name the space figure that can be formed by folding each net.   ■ **Lesson 6-1**

1. cube

2.
triangular prism

3.
cylinder

4.
rectangular prism

In Exercises 5–25, you may leave your answers in terms of π.
Find the lateral area and surface area of each figure.   ■ **Lessons 6-2 and 6-3**

5. 6 ft, 4 ft, 3 ft
84 ft^2; 108 ft^2

6. 2 cm, 7 cm
28π cm^2; 36π cm^2

7. 10 in., 4 in.
40π in.^{2}; 56π cm^2

8. 12 in.
$108\sqrt{3}$ in.^{2}; $144\sqrt{3}$ in.^{2}

Find the volume of each figure.   ■ **Lessons 6-4 and 6-5**

9. 3 mm, 4 mm, 4 mm
16 mm^3

10. 5 mm, 5 mm, 5 mm, 7 mm
175 mm^3

11. 5 m, 6 m
15π m^3

12. 3 in., 5 in.
45π in.^{3}

Find the volume and surface area of a sphere with the given radius or
diameter.   **13–17. See margin.**   ■ **Lesson 6-6**

13. $r = 5$ cm   **14.** $d = 8$ in.   **15.** $d = 2$ ft   **16.** $r = 0.5$ in.   **17.** $d = 9$ m

Find the volume of each composite space figure.   ■ **Lesson 6-7**

18. 135 m^3 3 m, 3 m, 6 m, 6 m, 5 m
135 m^3

19. 6 ft, 4 ft, 3 ft
64π ft^3

20. 6 cm, 4 cm
128 cm^3

21. 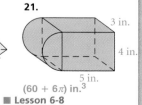 3 in., 4 in., 5 in.
$(60 + 6\pi)$ in.^{3}

Darts are thrown at random at each of the boards shown. If a dart
hits the board, find the probability that it will land in the shaded area.   ■ **Lesson 6-8**

22.
$\frac{1}{4}$

23.
$\frac{1}{3}$

24.
$1 - \frac{\pi}{4}$

25. 75°
$\frac{7}{24}$

1. $m\angle 1 = 134$, if ∥ lines, then same-side int. ∠s are supplementary; $m\angle 2 = 46$, Angle Addition Post. (or, if ∥ lines, then alt. int. ∠s are ≅).

2. $m\angle 1 = 125$, if ∥ lines, then corres. ∠s are ≅; $m\angle 2 = 55$, if ∥ lines, then same-side int. ∠s are supplementary (or Angle Addition Post.).

3. $m\angle 1 = 58$, if ∥ lines, then alt. int. ∠s are ≅; $m\angle 2 = 122$, Angle Addition Post. (or, if ∥ lines, then same-side int. ∠s are supplementary).

4. $m\angle 1 = 64$, if ∥ lines, then alt. int. ∠s are ≅; $m\angle 2 = 116$, if ∥ lines, then same-side int. ∠s are supplementary.

6. $r \parallel s$; if ≅ corres. ∠s, then lines are ∥.

7. $c \parallel d$; if supplementary same-side int. ∠s , then lines are ∥.

9. $r \parallel s$; if ≅ corres. ∠s , then lines are ∥.

13.

14.

15.

16.

640

21.

22.

23. The measure of an exterior angle with vertex *C* is clearly less than $m\angle A + m\angle B$.

Find $m\angle 1$ and then $m\angle 2$. State the theorems or postulates that justify your answers. 1–4. See margin.   ■ Lesson 7-1

1.

2.

3.

4.

Refer to the diagram. Use the given information to determine which lines, if any, must be parallel. If any lines are parallel, use a theorem or postulate to tell why. 6–7, 9. See margin.   ■ Lesson 7-2

5. $\angle 9 \cong \angle 14$ none

6. $\angle 1 \cong \angle 9$

7. $\angle 2$ is supplementary to $\angle 3$.

8. $\angle 7 \cong \angle 14$ none

9. $m\angle 6 = 60$, $m\angle 13 = 120$

10. $\angle 4 \cong \angle 13$ none

11. $\angle 3$ is supplementary to $\angle 10$. none

12. $\angle 10 \cong \angle 15$
$c \parallel d$; if ≅ alt. int. ∠s, then lines are ∥ .

Use the segments at the right for each construction.   ■ Lesson 7-3

13. Construct a square with side length *a*. 13–16. See margin.

14. Construct an isosceles right triangle with legs of length *b*.

15. Construct a trapezoid with bases of lengths *a* and *b*.

16. Construct a right triangle in which the length of a leg is *b* and the length of the hypotenuse is *a*.

Is each object drawn in one- or two-point perspective?   ■ Lesson 7-4

17.
1-pt.

18.
2-pt.

19.
2-pt.

20.
1-pt.

Draw a sketch to illustrate each property of spherical geometry.   ■ Lesson 7-5

21. Two distinct lines intersect in two points. 21–23. See margin for samples.

22. A triangle can have three right angles.

23. The measure of an exterior angle of a triangle is less than the sum of the measures of the remote interior angles.

Chapter 8 Extra Practice

10. $\overleftrightarrow{OL} \parallel \overleftrightarrow{MN}$, so $\angle OLN \cong \angle MNL$. $\overline{LN} \cong \overline{LN}$ by Reflexive Prop. of $\cong$. Since $\overline{LO} \cong \overline{MN}$, $\triangle MLN \cong \triangle ONL$ by SAS, and $\angle MLN \cong \angle ONL$ by CPCTC.

11. $\overline{OS} \cong \overline{OS}$ by Reflexive Prop. of $\cong$. Since $\angle T \cong \angle E$ and $\angle TSO \cong \angle EOS$, $\triangle TSO \cong \triangle EOS$ by AAS, and $\overline{TO} \cong \overline{ES}$ by CPCTC.

12. $\overline{BI} \cong \overline{BI}$ by Reflexive Prop. of $\cong$. Since $\angle MBI \cong \angle RIB$ and $\angle MIB \cong \angle RBI$, $\triangle MBI \cong \triangle RIB$ by ASA, and $\overline{MB} \cong \overline{RI}$ by CPCTC.

CHAPTER 8

Extra Practice

Can you prove that the triangles are congruent? If so, write the congruence and tell whether you would use SSS, SAS, ASA, or AAS. If not, write *not possible.*

■ Lessons 8-1 and 8-2

1.

$\triangle ALE \cong \triangle LAP$; SAS

2. $\triangle CAN \cong \triangle GLO$; SSS

3. not possible

4.

$\triangle NYT \cong \triangle WSJ$; ASA

5.

$\triangle BOI \cong \triangle TOW$; SAS

6.

$\triangle QUD \cong \triangle AUD$; AAS

What additional information would you need to prove the triangles congruent by the HL Theorem?

■ Lesson 8-3

7.

$\overline{ED} \cong \overline{RF}$

8.

$\angle E$ and $\angle T$ are rt. $\angle s$

9.

$\overline{KS} \cong \overline{PJ}$

Explain how you would use SSS, SAS, ASA, AAS, or HL with CPCTC to prove each statement.   10–12. See margin.

■ Lesson 8-4

10. $\angle MLN \cong \angle ONL$

11. $\overline{TO} \cong \overline{ES}$

12. $\overline{MB} \cong \overline{RI}$

Name a pair of overlapping congruent triangles in each diagram. State whether the triangles are congruent by SSS, SAS, ASA, AAS, or HL.

■ Lesson 8-5

13.

$\triangle QRM \cong \triangle RQS$; SSS

14.
$\triangle ANO \cong \triangle MPO$; AAS

15. $\triangle FAD \cong \triangle EBC$; AAS
$\overline{AF} \cong \overline{BE}$

641

Chapter 9 Extra Practice

6. Yes; if diags. of a quad. bisect each other, then the quad. is a ▱.

7. Yes; Triangle Angle-Sum Thm., if both pairs of opp. ∠s of a quad. are ≅, then the quad. is a ▱.

12. parallelogram;
$m\angle 1 = 45$; $m\angle 2 = 45$;
$m\angle 3 = 80$; $m\angle 4 = 55$

21. Given: Square *DRSQ* with *K, L, M, N* midpts. of $\overline{DR}$, $\overline{RS}$, $\overline{SQ}$, and $\overline{QD}$, respectively. Prove: *KLMN* is a square.

K(a, a), *L(a, −a)*, *M(−a, −a)*, and *N(−a, a)* are midpts. of the sides of the square. $KL = LM = MN = NK = 2a$. The slopes of $\overline{KL}$ and $\overline{MN}$ are undefined. The slopes of $\overline{LM}$ and $\overline{NK}$ are 0, so adjacent sides are ⊥ to each other. Since all angles are rt. angles, the quad. is a rectangle. A rectangle with all ≅ sides is a square.

642

Extra Practice

Algebra **Find the values of the variables in each parallelogram.**　■ **Lesson 9-1**

1.
$x = 12$; $y = 84$

2.
$x = 1$; $y = 7$

3.
$x = 30$; $y = 55$

4.
$x = 8$; $y = 25$

Based on the markings, decide whether each figure is a parallelogram. **Justify your answers.** 6–7. See margin.　■ **Lesson 9-2**

5.
yes; def. of ▱

6.

7.

8. no

For each parallelogram, determine the most precise name and find the measures of the numbered angles.　■ **Lesson 9-3**

11. rectangle; $m\angle 1 = 116$; $m\angle 2 = 64$; $m\angle 3 = 32$; $m\angle 4 = 58$

9.

10.

11. 116°

12. See margin.

square; $m\angle 1 = 45$; $m\angle 2 = 45$　　10. rhombus; $m\angle 1 = 50$; $m\angle 2 = 90$; $m\angle 3 = 40$; $m\angle 4 = 40$

Find $m\angle 1$ and $m\angle 2$.　■ **Lesson 9-4**

13. 70°

14. 110°

15. 110°

16. 67°

$m\angle 1 = 110$; $m\angle 2 = 70$　　$m\angle 1 = 110$; $m\angle 2 = 25$　　$m\angle 1 = 70$; $m\angle 2 = 70$　　$m\angle 1 = 90$; $m\angle 2 = 23$

Give coordinates for points *D* and *S* without using any new variables.　■ **Lesson 9-5**

17. rectangle

18. parallelogram

19. rhombus

20. square

$D(0, b)$, $S(a, 0)$　　$D(0, b)$, $S(−a, 0)$　　$D(−c, 0)$, $S(0, −b)$　　$D(0, 2a)$, $S(0, −2a)$

21. For the figure in Exercise 20, use coordinate geometry to prove that the midpoints of the sides of a square determine a square. See margin.　■ **Lesson 9-6**

Extra Practice

Algebra Solve for *x*.

■ Lesson 10-1

1. $\frac{2}{3} = \frac{x}{15}$ 10 **2.** $\frac{4}{9} = \frac{16}{x}$ 36 **3.** $\frac{x}{4} = \frac{6}{12}$ 2 **4.** $\frac{2}{x} = \frac{3}{9}$ 6 **5.** $\frac{3}{4} = \frac{x}{6}$ 4.5 **6.** $\frac{3}{7} = \frac{9}{x}$ 21

Can you prove that the triangles are similar? If so, write the similarity statement and tell whether you would use AA~, SAS~, or SSS~.

7.
$\triangle QCT \sim \triangle MCP$; SAS~

8.
$\triangle XYZ \sim \triangle ENW$; AA~

9.
not ~

Algebra **Find the value of each variable. If an answer is not a whole number, leave it in simplest radical form.**

■ Lessons 10-3 and 10-4

10.
$x = \sqrt{5}$; $y = 2$; $z = 2\sqrt{5}$

11. 14.4
$x = \sqrt{70}$;

12. 4
$x = \sqrt{70}$;

13.
$x = \sqrt{70}$;
$y = \sqrt{21}$; $z = \sqrt{30}$

14. 11.7

15.
$x = 65$; $y = 60$; $z = 156$

16.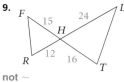

17.
$18\frac{2}{3}$

Find the ratio of the perimeters and the ratio of the areas of the blue figure to the red one.

■ Lesson 10-5

18.
5 : 8; 25 : 64

19.
4 : 3; 16 : 9

20.
5 : 16; 25 : 256

Copy and complete for two similar solids.

■ Lesson 10-6

	Similarity Ratio	Ratio of Surface Areas	Ratio of Volumes
21.	2 : 3	4 ■ : ■ 9	8 ■ : ■ 27
22.	5 ■ : ■ 8	25 : 64	125 ■ : ■ 512
23.	3 ■ : ■ 4	9 ■ : ■ 16	27 : 64

643

Chapter 11 Extra Practice

11a. $\langle -49, 142 \rangle$, $\langle 38, 47 \rangle$

  b. $\langle -11, 189 \rangle$

12a. $\langle -118, -55 \rangle$, $\langle 86, 110 \rangle$

  b. $\langle -32, 55 \rangle$

13a. $\langle -54, 72 \rangle$, $\langle -95, -33 \rangle$

  b. $\langle -149, 39 \rangle$

14a. $\langle -21, -56 \rangle$, $\langle 27, -64 \rangle$

  b. $\langle 6, -120 \rangle$

644

Find the value of x. Round lengths of segments to the nearest tenth and angle measures to the nearest degree.

■ **Lessons 11-1 and 11-2**

1.
5.6

2.
11.0

3.
9.4

4.
7.2

5.
29

6.
49

7.
50

8.
49

Solve each problem. Round your answers to the nearest foot.

■ **Lesson 11-3**

9. A couple is taking a balloon ride. After 25 minutes aloft, they measure the angle of depression from the balloon to its launch place as 16°. They are 180 ft above ground. Find the distance from the balloon to its launch place. **653 ft**

10. A surveyor is 300 ft from the base of an apartment building. The angle of elevation to the top of the building is 24°, and her angle-measuring device is 5 ft above the ground. Find the height of the building. **139 ft**

Coordinate Geometry In Exercises 11–14: (a) Describe each vector by using ordered pair notation. Give the coordinates to the nearest unit. (b) Find the ordered pair notation for the sum of each pair of vectors. **11–14. See margin.**

■ **Lessons 11-4 and 11-5**

11.

12.

13.

14.

Find the area of each polygon. Give your answers to the nearest tenth.

■ **Lesson 11-6**

15.
30.1 ft²

16.
78.0 in.²

17.
43.2 cm²

18.
20 m²

19. regular hexagon with apothem 3 ft **31.2 ft²**

20. regular octagon with radius 5 ft **70.7 ft²**

Chapter 12 Extra Practice

1. $x^2 + y^2 = 16$
2. $(x + 1)^2 + (y - 4)^2 = 25$
3. $(x - 9)^2 + (y + 3)^2 = 49$

Write an equation of each circle. 1–3. See margin.   ■ **Lesson 12-1**

1. center $(0, 0)$; $r = 4$ 2. center $(-1, 4)$; through $(-1, 9)$ 3. center $(9, -3)$; $r = 7$

4. center $(-4, 0)$; through $(2, 1)$ 5. center $(-6, -2)$; through $(-8, 1)$ 6. center $(0, 5)$; $r = 3$
   $(x + 4)^2 + y^2 = 37$ $(x + 6)^2 + (y + 2)^2 = 13$ $x^2 + (y - 5)^2 = 9$

Assume that lines that appear to be tangent are tangent. P is the   ■ **Lesson 12-2**
center of each circle. Find the value of x.

7. 65

8. 10

9. 6

10. $2\sqrt{3}$

Find the value of each variable. If your answer is not an integer, round   ■ **Lessons 12-3 and 12-4**
it to the nearest tenth.   14. $a = 55$; $b = 72$; $c = 178$; $d = 89$

11.

14.8

12.

5.2

13.

5.3

14.

15.

16.

17.

18. 20
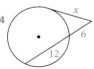

$a = 154$; $b = 76$ 16. $a = 38$; $b = 52$; $c = 104$; $d = 90$ $a = 105$; $b = 100$

Assume that lines that appear to be tangent are tangent. Find the   ■ **Lessons 12-5 and 12-6**
value of each variable. If your answer is not an integer, round it to the
nearest tenth.   19. $x = 193$; $y = 60.5$

19.

20. 5.6

21. 10.4

22. 70

23.

$x = 112.5$; $y = 67.5$

24. 11.5

25. 42.5

26.
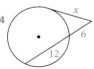
$x = 5.6$; $y = 11.9$

645

Problem Solving Strategies

You may find one or more of these strategies helpful in solving a word problem.

STRATEGY	WHEN TO USE IT
Draw a Diagram	You need help in visualizing the problem.
Guess and Test	Solving the problem directly is too complicated.
Look for a Pattern	The problem describes a relationship.
Make a Table	The problem has data that need organizing.
Solve a Simpler Problem	The problem is complex or has numbers that are too unmanageable to use at first.
Use Logical Reasoning	You need to reach a conclusion from some given information.
Work Backward	The answer can be arrived at by undoing various operations.

Problem Solving: Draw a Diagram

■Example **Antoine is 1.91 m tall. He measures his shadow and finds that it is 2.34 m long. He then measures the length of the shadow of a flagpole and finds that it is 13.2 m long. How tall is the flagpole?**

Start by drawing a diagram showing the given information. The diagram shows that the problem can be solved by using a proportion.

$\dfrac{1.91}{2.34} = \dfrac{x}{13.2}$ ⟵ Write a proportion.

$x \approx 10.77$ ⟵ Solve for x.

The flagpole is about 10.8 m tall.

EXERCISES

1. Five people meet and shake hands with one another. How many handshakes are there in all? **10 handshakes**

2. Three tennis balls fit snugly in a standard cylindrical container. Which is greater, the circumference of a ball or the height of the container? **circumference**

3. Three lines that each intersect a circle can determine at most 7 regions within the circle, as shown in the diagram. What is the greatest number of regions that can be determined by 5 lines? **16 regions**

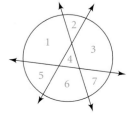

4. A triangle has vertices $(1, 3)$, $(2, 3)$, and $(7, 5)$. Find its area. **1 unit²**

646

Problem Solving: Guess and Test

Have you ever weighed yourself on a balance scale at a doctor's office? You start by guessing your weight, then you see if the scale balances. If it doesn't, you slide the weights back and forth until the scale does balance. This is an example of the *Guess and Test* strategy, a strategy that is helpful for solving many types of problems.

■Example   **You are offered two payment plans for a CD club. Plan 1 involves paying a $20 membership fee and $7 per CD. Plan 2 involves paying no membership fee and $10 per CD. What is the least number of CDs you would have to buy to make Plan 1 the less expensive plan?**

	Plan 1	Plan 2
Guess 4 CDs.	$20 + 7(4)$	$10(4)$
	$48 > 40$	← Too low. Guess higher.
Guess 7 CDs.	$20 + 7(7)$	$10(7)$
	$69 < 70$	← Plan 1 is less expensive!

You need to check 6 CDs, however, to be sure that 7 CDs is the *least* number you would have to buy to make Plan 1 less expensive.

$$20 + 7(6) \qquad 10(6)$$
$$62 > 60 \qquad ← \text{Plan 1 is more expensive.}$$

You need to buy at least 7 CDs to make Plan 1 the less expensive plan.

EXERCISES

1. Find three consecutive even integers whose product is 480. 6, 8, 10

2. The combined age of a father and his twin daughters is 54 years. The father was 24 years old when the twins were born. How old is each of the three people? Each daughter is 10 years old; the father is 34 years old.

3. What numbers can x represent in the rectangle? See below.

4. You are offered two payment plans for a video rental store. Plan 1 involves paying a $30 membership fee and $2 per rental. Plan 2 involves paying $3.50 per rental. What is the least number of videos you would have to rent to make Plan 1 the less expensive plan? 21 videos

x

$4 - x$

5. Ruisa bought 7 rolls of film to take 192 pictures on a field trip. Some rolls had 36 exposures and the rest had 24 exposures. How many rolls of each type did Ruisa buy? 2 rolls with 36 exposures and 5 rolls with 24 exposures

6. The sum of five consecutive integers is 5. Find the integers. −1, 0, 1, 2, 3

7. Paul buys a coupon for $20 that allows him to see movies for half price at a local theater over the course of one year. The cost of seeing a movie is normally $7.50. What is the least number of movies Paul would have to see to pay less than the normal price? at least 6

3. any real number between 0 and 4

Problem Solving: Make a Table and Look for a Pattern

There are two important ways that making a table can help you solve a problem. First, a table is a handy method of organizing information. Second, once the information is in a table, it is easier to find patterns.

■Example **The squares at the right are made of toothpicks. How many toothpicks are in the square with 7 toothpicks on a side?**

Make a table to organize the information.

No. of toothpicks on a side	1	2	3	4
Total no. of toothpicks in square	4	12	24	40

+8   +12   +16

Notice the pattern in the increases in the total number of toothpicks in each figure. The total number in the 5th square is 40 + 20, or 60. The number in the 6th is 60 + 24, or 84, and the number in the 7th is 84 + 28, or 112.

EXERCISES

1. The triangles are made up of toothpicks. How many toothpicks are in Figure 10? **165 toothpicks**

Figure 1   Figure 2   Figure 3

2. In each figure, the vertices of the smallest square are midpoints of the sides of the next larger square. Find the area of the ninth shaded square. $\frac{1}{256}$ in.²

      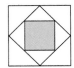

1 in.

3. This pattern is known as the Sierpinski triangle. Find the total number of shaded triangles in Figure 8. **3280 triangles**

   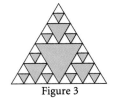

Figure 1   Figure 2   Figure 3

648

Problem Solving: Solve a Simpler Problem

Looking at a simpler version of a problem can be helpful in suggesting a problem-solving approach.

■Example   **A fence along the highway is 570 meters long. There is a fence post every 10 meters. How many fence posts are there?**

You may be tempted to divide 570 by 10, getting 57 as an answer, but looking at a simpler problem suggests that this answer isn't right. Suppose there are just 10 or 20 meters of fencing.

10 m
two fence posts

20 m
three fence posts

These easier problems suggest that there is always *one more* fence post than one tenth the length. So for a 570 meter fence, there are $\frac{570}{10} + 1$, or 58 fence posts.

EXERCISES

1. A farmer wishes to fence in a square lot with dimensions 70 yards by 70 yards. He will install a fence post every 10 yards. How many fence posts will he need? **28 posts**

2. Janette is planning to walk from her house to her friend Barbara's house. How many different paths can she take to get there? Assume that she walks only east and south. **84 paths**

Janette's house

N
W—E
S

Barbara's house

3. A square table can seat four people. For a banquet, a long rectangular table is formed by placing 14 such tables edge-to-edge in a straight line. How many people can sit at the long table? **30 people**

4. Find the sum of the whole numbers from 1 to 999. **499,500**

5. How many trapezoids are in the figure below? (*Hint:* Solve several simpler problems, then look for a pattern.) **25 trapezoids**

6. At a business luncheon, 424 handshakes took place. No two people shook hands with each other more than once. What is the least number of people in attendance at the luncheon? **30 people**

7. On his fiftieth birthday, the President was honored with a 21-gun salute. The sound of each gunshot lasted 1 second, and 4 seconds elapsed between shots. How long did the salute last? **101 s**

Problem Solving: Use Logical Reasoning

Some problems can be solved without the use of numbers. They can be solved by the use of logical reasoning, given some information.

Example **Anna, Bill, Carla, and Doug are siblings. Each lives in a different state beginning with W. Use these clues to determine where each sibling lives:**
(1) Neither sister lives in a state containing two words.
(2) Bill lives west of his sisters.
(3) Anna doesn't cross the Mississippi River when she visits Doug.

Make a table to organize what you know. Use an initial for each name.

State	A	B	C	D
West Virginia	✗	✗	✗	
Wisconsin		✗		
Wyoming		✗		
Washington	✗	✓	✗	✗

◄—— From Clue 1, you know that neither Anna nor Carla lives in West Virginia.

◄—— Using Clues 1 and 2, you know that Bill must live in Washington if he lives west of his sisters.

Use logical reasoning to complete the table.

State	A	B	C	D
West Virginia	✗	✗	✗	✓
Wisconsin	✓	✗	✗	✗
Wyoming	✗	✗	✓	✗
Washington	✗	✓	✗	✗

◄—— Doug lives in West Virginia because none of his siblings do.

◄—— From Clue 3, you know that Anna must live in Wisconsin.

◄—— Carla, therefore, lives in Wyoming.

EXERCISES

1. Harold has a dog, a canary, a goldfish, and a hamster. Their names are J.T., Izzy, Arf, and Blinky. Izzy has neither feathers nor fins. Arf can't bark. J.T. weighs less than the four-legged pets. Neither the goldfish nor the dog has the longest name. Arf and Blinky don't get along well with the canary. What is each pet's name?   Izzy is the dog; J.T. is the canary; Arf is the goldfish; Blinky is the hamster

2. At the state basketball championship tournament, 42 basketball games are played to determine the winner of the tournament. After each game, the loser is eliminated from the tournament. How many teams are in the tournament? 43 teams

3. The sophomore class has 124 students. Of these students, 47 are involved in muscial activities: 25 in band and 36 in choir. How many students are involved in both band and choir? 14 students

4. Tina's height is between Kimiko's and Ignacio's. Ignacio's height is between Jerome's and Kimiko's. Tina is taller than Jerome. List the people in order from shortest to tallest. Jerome, Ignacio, Tina, Kimiko

650

Problem Solving: Work Backward

In some situations it is easier to start with the end result and work backward to find the solution. You work backward in order to solve linear equations. The equation $2x + 3 = 11$ means "double x and add 3 to get 11." To find x, you "undo" those steps in reverse order.

$2x + 3 = 11$

$\quad 2x = 8 \quad$ ←— Subtract 3 from each side.

$\quad\quad x = 4 \quad$ ←— Divide each side by 2.

Another time it is convenient to work backward is when you want to "reverse" a set of directions.

■**Example**　**To get from the library to the school, go 3 blocks east, then 5 blocks north, then 2 blocks west. How do you go from the school to the library?**

To reverse the directions, start at the school and work backward. Go 2 blocks east, 5 blocks south, and 3 blocks west.

EXERCISES

1. To go from Bedford to Worcester, take Route 4 south, then Route 128 south, then Route 90 west. How do you get from Worcester to Bedford? **Route 90 east, Route 128 north, Route 4 north**

2. Sandy spent $\frac{1}{10}$ of the money in her purse for lunch. She then spent $23.50 for a gift for her brother, then half of what she had left on a new CD. If Sandy has $13 left in her purse, how much money did she have in it before lunch? **$55**

3. Algae are growing on a pond's surface. The area covered doubles each day. It takes 24 days to cover the pond completely. After how many days will the pond be half covered with algae? **23 d**

4. Don sold $\frac{1}{5}$ as many raffle tickets as Carlita. Carlita sold 3 times as many as Ranesha. Ranesha sold 7 fewer than Russell. If Russell sold 12 tickets, how many did Don sell? **3 tickets**

5. At 6% interest compounded annually, the balance in a bank account will double about every 12 years. If such an account has a balance of $16,000 now, how much was deposited when the account was opened 36 years ago? **$2000**

6. Solve the puzzle that Yuan gave to Inez: I am thinking of a number. If I triple the number and then halve the result, I get 12. What number am I thinking of? **8**

7. Carlos paid $14.60 for a taxi fare from a hotel to the airport, including a $2.00 tip. Green Cab Co. charges $1.20 per passenger plus $0.20 for each additional $\frac{1}{5}$ mile. How many miles is the hotel from the airport? **11.4 mi**

651

1–2. Answers may vary slightly.

1. 39 mm; 51 mm

2. $m\angle A = 48$; $m\angle B = 97$;
   $m\angle C = 35$

3.
   3.7 cm
   34°
   4.8 cm

4.
   43° 102°
   5.4 cm

5.
   68°
   $2\frac{1}{4}$ in. $2\frac{1}{4}$ in.
   112° 112°
   $2\frac{1}{4}$ in. $2\frac{1}{4}$ in.
   68°

6. Sample:
   48°   48°
   2 in.

7. $3\frac{1}{2}$ in.   134° $3\frac{1}{2}$ in.

652

Using a Ruler and Protractor

Knowing how to use a ruler and protractor is crucial for success in Geometry.

■**Example**   Draw a triangle that has sides of length 5.2 cm and 3.0 cm and a 68° angle between these two sides.

The angle opens to the left, so read angle measures from the top scale.

Centimeters

Step 1: Use a ruler to draw a segment 5.2 cm long.

Step 2: Place the crosshairs of a protractor at one endpoint of the segment. Make a small mark at the 68° position along the protractor.

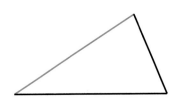

Step 3: Align the ruler along the small mark and the endpoint you used in Step 2. Place the zero point of the ruler at the endpoint. Draw a segment 3.0 cm long.

Step 4: Complete the triangle by connecting the endpoints of the first segment and the second.

EXERCISES

1. Measure sides $\overline{AB}$ and $\overline{BC}$ to the nearest millimeter.

2. Measure each angle of $\triangle ABC$ to the nearest degree.

1–7. See margin.

3. Draw a triangle that has sides of length 4.8 cm and 3.7 cm and a 34° angle between these two sides.

4. Draw a triangle that has 43° and 102° angles and a side of length 5.4 cm between these two angles.

5. Draw a rhombus that has sides of length $2\frac{1}{4}$ in. and 68° and 112° angles.

6. Draw an isosceles trapezoid that has a pair of 48° base angles and a base of length 2 in. between these two base angles.

7. Draw an isosceles triangle that has two congruent sides $3\frac{1}{2}$ in. long and a 134° vertex angle.

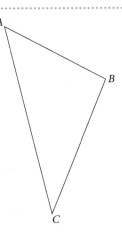

A

B

C

Measurement Conversions

To convert from one unit of measure to another, you multiply by a conversion factor. A *conversion factor* is a fraction equal to 1 that has different units in the numerator and the denominator. An example of a conversion factor is $\frac{1 \text{ ft}}{12 \text{ in.}}$. Other conversion factors are given in the table on page 668.

Example 1 **Complete.**

     a. 88 in. = ▧ ft   **b.** 5.3 m = ▧ cm

     c. 3700 mm = ▧ cm   **d.** 90 in. = ▧ yd

a. $88 \text{ in.} \cdot \frac{1 \text{ ft}}{12 \text{ in.}} = \frac{88}{12} \text{ ft} = 7\frac{1}{3} \text{ ft}$ **b.** $5.3 \text{ m} \cdot \frac{100 \text{ cm}}{1 \text{ m}} = 5.3(100) \text{ cm} = 530 \text{ cm}$

c. $3700 \text{ mm} \cdot \frac{1 \text{ cm}}{10 \text{ mm}} = 370 \text{ cm}$ **d.** $90 \text{ in.} \cdot \frac{1 \text{ ft}}{12 \text{ in.}} \cdot \frac{1 \text{ yd}}{3 \text{ ft}} = \frac{90}{36} \text{ yd} = 2\frac{1}{2} \text{ yd}$

Area is always in square units, and volume is always in cubic units.

1 yd = 3 ft $1 \text{ yd}^2 = 9 \text{ ft}^2$ $1 \text{ yd}^3 = 27 \text{ ft}^3$

Example 2 **Complete.**

     a. $300 \text{ in.}^2 = ▧ \text{ ft}^2$ **b.** $200,000 \text{ cm}^3 = ▧ \text{ m}^3$

a. $1 \text{ ft} = 12 \text{ in.}$, so $1 \text{ ft}^2 = (12 \text{ in.})^2$ or 144 in.^2 **b.** $1 \text{ m} = 100 \text{ cm}$, so $1 \text{ m}^3 = (100 \text{ cm})^3$ or $1,000,000 \text{ cm}^3$

     $300 \text{ in.}^2 \cdot \frac{1 \text{ ft}^2}{144 \text{ in.}^2} = 2\frac{1}{12} \text{ ft}^2$ $200,000 \text{ cm}^3 \cdot \frac{1 \text{ m}^3}{1,000,000 \text{ cm}^3} = 0.2 \text{ m}^3$

EXERCISES

Complete.

1. $40 \text{ cm} = ▧ \text{ m}$ 0.4   **2.** $1.5 \text{ kg} = ▧ \text{ g}$ 1500   **3.** $60 \text{ cm} = ▧ \text{ mm}$ 600

4. $200 \text{ in.} = ▧ \text{ ft}$ $16\frac{2}{3}$ **5.** $28 \text{ yd} = ▧ \text{ in.}$ 1008   **6.** $1.5 \text{ mi} = ▧ \text{ ft}$ 7920

7. $42 \text{ fl oz} = ▧ \text{ qt}$ $1\frac{5}{16}$ **8.** $430 \text{ mg} = ▧ \text{ g}$ 0.43   **9.** $34 \text{ L} = ▧ \text{ mL}$ 34,000

10. $1.2 \text{ m} = ▧ \text{ cm}$ 120   **11.** $43 \text{ mm} = ▧ \text{ cm}$ 4.3   **12.** $3600 \text{ s} = ▧ \text{ min}$ 60

13. $15 \text{ g} = ▧ \text{ mg}$ 15,000   **14.** $12 \text{ qt} = ▧ \text{ c}$ 48   **15.** $0.03 \text{ kg} = ▧ \text{ mg}$ 30,000

16. $14 \text{ gal} = ▧ \text{ qt}$ 56   **17.** $4500 \text{ lb} = ▧ \text{ t}$ $2\frac{1}{4}$ **18.** $234 \text{ min} = ▧ \text{ h}$ 3.9

19. $12 \text{ mL} = ▧ \text{ L}$ 0.012   **20.** $2 \text{ pt} = ▧ \text{ fl oz}$ 32   **21.** $20 \text{ m/s} = ▧ \text{ km/h}$ 72

22. $3 \text{ ft}^2 = ▧ \text{ in.}^2$ 432   **23.** $108 \text{ m}^2 = ▧ \text{ cm}^2$ 1,080,000   **24.** $2100 \text{ mm}^2 = ▧ \text{ cm}^2$ 21

25. $1.4 \text{ yd}^2 = ▧ \text{ ft}^2$ 12.6   **26.** $0.45 \text{ km}^2 = ▧ \text{ m}^2$ 450,000   **27.** $1300 \text{ ft}^2 = ▧ \text{ yd}^2$ $144\frac{4}{9}$

28. $1030 \text{ in.}^2 = ▧ \text{ ft}^2$ $7\frac{11}{72}$ **29.** $20,000,000 \text{ ft}^2 = ▧ \text{ mi}^2$ about 0.72   **30.** $1000 \text{ cm}^3 = ▧ \text{ m}^3$ 0.001

31. $1.4 \text{ ft}^3 = ▧ \text{ in.}^3$ 2419.2   **32.** $3.56 \text{ cm}^3 = ▧ \text{ mm}^3$ 3560   **33.** $0.013 \text{ km}^3 = ▧ \text{ m}^3$ 13,000,000

653

1. $23\frac{1}{2}$ ft to $24\frac{1}{2}$ ft

2. $123\frac{1}{2}$ cm to $124\frac{1}{2}$ cm

3. $339\frac{1}{2}$ mL to $340\frac{1}{2}$ mL

4. $5\frac{1}{4}$ mi to $5\frac{3}{4}$ mi

5. 73.15 cm to 73.25 cm

6. $33\frac{1}{2}$ yd² to $34\frac{1}{2}$ yd²

7. 5.35 mi to 5.45 mi

8. 6 ft $4\frac{3}{4}$ in. to 6 ft $5\frac{1}{4}$ in.

9. 8.7 cm to 9.1 cm

Measurement, Rounding Error, and Reasonableness

There is no such thing as an *exact* measurement. Measurements are always approximate. No matter how precise it is, a measurement actually represents a range of values.

The possible difference between a measurement and the actual value is called the error. The *error* is equal to half the unit of greatest precision.

■Example 1   **Chris's height, to the nearest inch, is 5 ft 8 in. Find the range of values this measurement represents.**

The height is given to the nearest inch, so the error is $\frac{1}{2}$ in. Chris's height, then, is between 5 ft $7\frac{1}{2}$ in. and 5 ft $8\frac{1}{2}$ in., or it is 5 ft 8 in. $\pm$ $\frac{1}{2}$ in. Within this range are all measures that, when rounded to the nearest inch, equal 5 ft 8 in.

As you calculate with measurements, error can accumulate.

■Example 2   **Jean drives 18 km to work each day. The distance is given to the nearest kilometer.**
  a. Find the range of values this measurement represents.
  b. Find the error in the round-trip distance.

a. The driving distance is between 17.5 and 18.5 km, or 18 $\pm$ 0.5 km.

b. Double the lower limit, 17.5, and the upper limit, 18.5. Thus, the round trip can be anywhere between 35 and 37 km, or 36 $\pm$ 1 km. The error for the round trip is twice the error of a single leg of the trip.

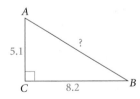

So that your answers will be reasonable, keep precision and error in mind as you calculate. For example, in finding AB, the length of the hypotenuse of $\triangle ABC$, it would be inappropriate to give the answer as 9.6566 if the sides are given to the nearest tenth. Round your answer to 9.7.

EXERCISES

Each measurement is followed by its unit of greatest precision. Find the   1–9. See margin.
range of values that each measurement represents.

1. 24 ft (ft)   **2.** 124 cm (cm)   **3.** 340 mL (mL)   **4.** $5\frac{1}{2}$ mi ($\frac{1}{2}$ mi)

5. 73.2 cm (mm)   **6.** 34 yd² (yd²)   **7.** 5.4 mi (0.1 mi)   **8.** 6 ft 5 in. (0.5 in.)

9. The lengths of the sides of *TJCM* are given to the nearest millimeter. Find the range of values for the figure's perimeter.

10. To the nearest degree, two angles of a triangle are 49° and 73°. What is the range of values for the measure of the third angle?   **57 to 59**

11. The lengths of the legs of a right triangle are given as 131 m and 162 m. You use a calculator to find the length of the hypotenuse. The calculator display reads *208.33867*. What should your answer be?   **208 m**

5. Median; the mode does not represent most of the data; the mean is significantly affected by the single highest salary.

Mean, Median, and Mode

Measures of central tendency, such as mean, median, and mode, are numbers that describe a set of data.

■**Example** **Eighteen students were asked to measure the angle formed by the three objects in the diagram. Their answers, in order from least to greatest, are as follows:**

65, 66, 66, 66, 66, 66, 66, 67, 67, 67, 67, 67, 68, 68, 69, 70, 74, 113

Find the mean, median, and mode of the data.

Oak tree

Flagpole

Statue

To find the *mean* (sometimes called the average), add the numbers and divide by the number of items.

$$\text{Mean} = \frac{\text{sum of the 18 measures}}{18} = \frac{1258}{18} = 69\frac{8}{9}$$

The *median* is the middle number when the items are placed in order. (When there is an even number of items, take the mean of the two middle numbers.) Here, the two middle numbers—the ninth and the tenth numbers on the list—are both 67. So the median is 67.

The *mode* is the number that appears most frequently. A set of data may have more than one mode or no modes. There are more 66's than any other number, so the mode is 66.

EXERCISES

Find the mean, median, and mode of each set of data.

1. 353.6; 301; no mode
2. $3.53; $3.56; no mode

1. Numbers of students per school in Newtown: 234, 341, 253, 313, 273, 301, 760

2. Amounts spent for lunch: $4.50, $3.26, $5.02, $3.58, $1.25, $3.05, $4.24, $3.56, $3.31

3. Salaries at D. B. Widget & Co.: $15,000; $18,000; $18,000; $21,700; $26,500; $27,000; $29,300; $31,100; $43,000; $47,800; $69,000; $140,000
$40,533; $28,150; $18,000

4. Population of towns in Brower County: 567, 632, 781, 902, 1034, 1100, 1598, 2164, 2193, 3062, 3074, 3108, 3800, 3721, 4104
2123; 2164; no mode

5. In Exercise 3, which measure or measures of central tendency do you think best represent the data? Explain. See margin.

6. Find the mean, median, and mode of the exam scores at the right.

6. 75.3; 78; 85

Final Exam Scores

34, 47, 53, 56, 57, 62, 62, 64, 67, 70, 74, 74, 74, 78, 82, 85, 85, 85, 85, 86, 88, 92, 93, 93, 94, 95, 97

7. $67\frac{6}{17}$; 67; 66

7. In the example, the student who reported the angle measure as 113 most likely made an error. If this measure is dropped from the list, what are the mean, median, and mode of the remaining 17 scores?

8. In the example, if the smallest measurement were 51 instead of 65, would the mean decrease? Would the median? Would the mode? yes; no; no

9. In the example, if the two students who measured the angle at 68 both reduced their measurements to 67, would the mode be affected? How?
Yes; the mode would be 67.

655

1.

Sales of Rock Music

5. No; you cannot tell how the temperature changed between the measurements.

6. Answers may vary. Sample: A line graph; the line graph shows change over time more clearly.

▮ Bar Graphs and Line Graphs

Data displayed in a table can be very useful, but a table is not as easy to interpret as a graph. A bar graph and a line graph can show the same data, but sometimes one type of graph will have advantages over the other.

▮**Example** Make a bar graph and a line graph showing the data in the table at the left.

Revenue of HJL Co.

Year	Revenue
1993	$39,780
1994	$40,019
1995	$51,772
1996	$63,444
1997	$79,855

Bar graphs are useful when you wish to compare amounts. In the example, the tallest bar is clearly twice the height of the shortest bar. At a glance, it is evident that in four years the revenue approximately doubled.

Line graphs allow you to see how a set of data changes over time. In the example, the slope of the line shows that revenue has increased at a steady rate since 1994.

Did revenue increase from 1993 to 1994? You can't tell by looking at either graph; for that information, you would have to look back at the table.

EXERCISES

1. Create a bar graph and a line graph to display the data in the table. Show years along the horizontal axis and sales along the vertical axis. See margin for sample.

Sales of Rock Music (in millions of dollars)

Year	1989	1990	1991	1992	1993	1994
Sales	$2833	$2722	$2726	$2852	$3034	$4236

Source: *Recording Industry Association of America*

For Exercises 2–6, refer to the line graph at the right. 3. 8 A.M.–2 P.M.

2. What was the lowest temperature recorded between 6 A.M. and 6 P.M.? 10°F

3. During which time periods did the temperature appear to increase?

4. Estimate the temperature at 11 A.M. and at 5 P.M. 28°F; 42°F

5. Can you tell from the graph what the actual maximum and minimum temperatures were between 6 A.M. and 6 P.M.? Explain. 5–6. See margin.

6. The same data could be presented in a bar graph. Which presentation is better for these data, a line graph or a bar graph? Why?

Temperatures in Grand Island, Nebraska, on February 2

656

Circle Graphs page 657

4. Age of Cars on the Road

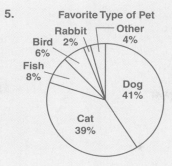

> 15 yr 10%
< 1 yr 6%
10–15 yr 20%
1–5 yr 34%
5–10 yr 30%

5. Favorite Type of Pet

Rabbit 2% — Other 4%
Bird 6%
Fish 8%
Dog 41%
Cat 39%

6. Number of People in Family

> 7 3%
7 6%
2 7%
6 13%
3 17%
5 24%
4 30%

Circle Graphs

A circle graph is used for presenting data as a fraction of a total.

■Example   **Create a circle graph to display the data in the table.**

Plans of Cranston High School Graduates

Attend 4-yr college	59%
Attend 2-yr college	21%
Attend technical college	8%
Enter work force	8%
Undecided/Other	4%

To find the angle for each wedge, or sector, recall that there are 360° in the whole circle. So to find, for example, the angle for 21%, calculate as follows:

21% of 360° = 0.21 · 360°
        ≈ 76°

The number of degrees in the wedge for 59% is greater than 180°. To create this wedge, draw a semicircle (to represent 50%) and add to the semicircle a wedge representing 9%.

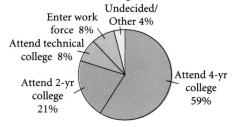

Plans of Cranston High School Graduates

Undecided/Other 4%
Enter work force 8%
Attend technical college 8%
Attend 2-yr college 21%
Attend 4-yr college 59%

EXERCISES

In Exercises 1–3, refer to the Example.

1. Find the measure of the angle for each of the five categories in the circle graph. 212; 76; 29; 29; 14

2. What is the ratio of graduates who plan to attend some type of college to those who don't or who are undecided? 22 : 3

3. Suppose there are 358 graduates of Cranston High School. Make a table showing the number of students in each category.

3.

4-yr college	211
2-yr college	75
Tech. college	29
Work	29
Undecided/Other	14

Create a circle graph to display each set of data. 4–6. See margin.

4. Age of Cars on the Road

Less than 1 yr	6%
1–5 yr	34%
5–10 yr	30%
10–15 yr	20%
Over 15 yr	10%

Source: *The Unofficial U.S. Census*

5. Favorite Type of Pet

Dog	41%
Cat	39%
Fish	8%
Bird	6%
Rabbit	2%
Other	4%

6. Number of People in Family

2	7%
3	17%
4	30%
5	24%
6	13%
7	6%
>7	3%

Box-and-Whisker Plots

A *box-and-whisker plot* is a way to display data on a number line. It provides a picture of how tightly the data cluster around the median and how wide a range the data have. The diagram below shows the various points associated with a box-and-whisker plot.

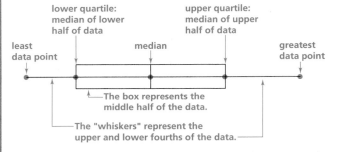

lower quartile: median of lower half of data

upper quartile: median of upper half of data

least data point

median

greatest data point

The box represents the middle half of the data.

The "whiskers" represent the upper and lower fourths of the data.

Example The heights, in inches, of 23 students are as follows:

58, 61, 63, 63, 63, 64, 64, 65, 65, 65, 67, 68, 68, 68, 69, 70, 70, 70, 72, 72, 72, 74, 75

Draw a box-and-whisker plot.

The heights vary from 58 in. to 75 in. The median is 68. The lower quartile (the median of the lower eleven heights) is 64. The upper quartile (the median of the upper eleven heights) is 70.

58   64   68   70   75

EXERCISES

1. All of the physical education students at Martin Luther King, Jr., High School were timed sprinting the 100-meter dash. The box-and-whisker plot below summarizes the data. Use it to find the following:
   a. Median 16.6   **b.** Lower quartile 15.1   **c.** Upper quartile 19.4

   12.4   15.1   16.6   19.4   23.7

2. Make a box-and-whisker plot for the following set of data, which lists the weights, in pounds, of the students trying out for the wrestling team at South Side High School.

   104   130   144   155   171

   104, 121, 122, 130, 130, 131, 140, 144, 147, 147, 148, 155, 160, 163, 171

658

Evaluating and Simplifying Expressions

You *evaluate* an expression with variables by substituting a number for each variable. Then simplify the expression using the order of operations.

Be especially careful with exponents and negative signs. For example, the expression $-x^2$ always yields a negative or zero value, and $(-x)^2$ is always positive or zero.

Order of Operations

1. Perform any operation(s) inside grouping symbols.
2. Simplify any term with exponents.
3. Multiply and divide in order from left to right.
4. Add and subtract in order from left to right.

■**Example 1** Evaluate each expression for $r = 4$.
   a. $-r^2$ b. $-3r^2$ c. $(-3r)^2$

a. $-r^2 = -(4)^2 = -16$
b. $-3r^2 = -3(4)^2 = -3(16) = -48$
c. $(-3r)^2 = (-3 \cdot 4)^2 = (-12)^2 = 144$

To simplify an expression, you combine like terms and eliminate any parentheses.

■**Example 2** Simplify each expression.
   a. $5r - 2r + 1$ b. $\pi(3r - 1)$ c. $(r + \pi)(r - \pi)$

a. Combine like terms: $5r - 2r + 1 = 3r + 1$
b. Use the distributive property: $\pi(3r - 1) = 3\pi r - \pi$
c. Multiply polynomials: $(r + \pi)(r - \pi) = r^2 - \pi^2$

EXERCISES

Evaluate each expression for $x = 5$ and $y = -3$.

1. $-2x^2$ −50
2. $-y + x$ 8
3. $-xy$ 15
4. $(x + 5y) \div x$ −2
5. $x + 5y \div x$ 2
6. $(-2y)^2$ 36
7. $(2y)^2$ 36
8. $(x - y)^2$ 64
9. $\frac{x + 1}{y}$ −2
10. $y - (x - y)$ −11
11. $-y^x$ 243
12. $\frac{2(1 - x)}{y - x}$ 1
13. $x \cdot y - x$ −20
14. $x - y \cdot x$ 20
15. $\frac{y^3 - x}{x - y}$ −4
16. $-y(x - 3)^2$ 12

17. Which expression gives the area of the shaded region of the figure at the right? **B**
   A. $\pi(R - S)^2$ B. $\pi(R^2 - S^2)$
   C. $\pi(S^2 - R^2)$ D. $\pi R^2 - 2\pi S$

Simplify.
18. $6x - 4x + 8 - 5$ $2x + 3$
19. $2(\ell + w)$ $2\ell + 2w$
20. $3x - 5 + 2x$ $5x - 5$
21. $-(4x + 7)$ $-4x - 7$
22. $-4x(x - 2)$ $-4x^2 + 8x$
23. $3x - (5 + 2x)$ $x - 5$
24. $2t^2 + 4t - 5t^2$ $-3t^2 + 4t$
25. $(r - 1)^2$ $r^2 - 2r + 1$
26. $(1 - r)^2$ $r^2 - 2r + 1$
27. $(y + 1)(y - 3)$ $y^2 - 2y - 3$
28. $4h + 3h - 4 + 3$ $7h - 1$
29. $\pi r - (1 + \pi r)$ −1
30. $(x + 4)(2x - 1)$ $2x^2 + 7x - 4$
31. $2\pi h(1 - r)^2$ $2\pi hr^2 - 4\pi hr + 2\pi h$
32. $3y^2 - (y^2 + 3y)$ $2y^2 - 3y$
33. $-(x + 4)^2$ $-x^2 - 8x - 16$

Simplifying Radicals

A radical expression is in its *simplest form* when all three of the following statements are true.

1. The expression under the radical sign contains no perfect square factors (other than 1).
2. The expression under the radical sign does not contain a fraction.
3. The denominator does not contain a radical expression.

■Example 1   **Simplify.**

a. $\sqrt{\dfrac{4}{9}}$ b. $\sqrt{12}$

a. $\sqrt{\dfrac{4}{9}} = \dfrac{\sqrt{4}}{\sqrt{9}} = \dfrac{2}{3}$ b. $\sqrt{12} = \sqrt{4} \cdot \sqrt{3} = 2\sqrt{3}$

■Example 2   **Find the length of the diagonal of rectangle *HJKL*.**

$c^2 = 7^2 + 1^2$ ◄─── Use the Pythagorean Theorem.
$c^2 = 50$ ◄─── Simplify the right side.
$c = \sqrt{50}$ ◄─── Find the square root of each side.
$ = \sqrt{25 \cdot 2}$
$ = 5\sqrt{2}$ ◄─── Simplify the radical.

■Example 3   **Simplify $\dfrac{1}{\sqrt{3}}$.**

$\dfrac{1}{\sqrt{3}} \cdot \dfrac{\sqrt{3}}{\sqrt{3}} = \dfrac{\sqrt{3}}{3}$ ◄─── Multiply by $\dfrac{\sqrt{3}}{\sqrt{3}}$, or 1, to eliminate the radical in the denominator.

EXERCISES

Simplify each radical expression.

1. $\sqrt{27}$ $3\sqrt{3}$ **2.** $\sqrt{24}$ $2\sqrt{6}$ **3.** $\sqrt{150}$ $5\sqrt{6}$ **4.** $\sqrt{\dfrac{1}{9}}$ $\dfrac{1}{3}$ **5.** $\sqrt{\dfrac{72}{9}}$ $2\sqrt{2}$

6. $\dfrac{\sqrt{228}}{\sqrt{16}}$ $\dfrac{\sqrt{57}}{2}$ **7.** $\sqrt{\dfrac{2}{5}}$ $\dfrac{\sqrt{10}}{5}$ **8.** $\sqrt{\dfrac{27}{75}}$ $\dfrac{3}{5}$ **9.** $\dfrac{3}{\sqrt{8}}$ $\dfrac{3\sqrt{2}}{4}$ **10.** $\dfrac{6\sqrt{18}}{\sqrt{48}}$ $\dfrac{3\sqrt{6}}{2}$

Find the value of *x*. Leave your answer in simplest radical form.

11. x $5\sqrt{10}$

12.

13. $4\sqrt{14}$

14. $3\sqrt{5}$

15. $4\sqrt{10}$

16. $2\sqrt{51}$

17. $2\sqrt{29}$

18. $3\sqrt{61}$

660

Simplifying Ratios

The ratio of the shorter leg to the longer leg of this right triangle is 4 to 6. This ratio can be written in several ways:

4 to 6 $\frac{4}{6}$ 4 : 6

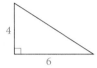

You simplify ratios the same way you simplify fractions, by dividing out common factors from the numerator and denominator.

■Example   Simplify each ratio.

   a. 4 to 6   **b. 3ab : 27ab**   **c.** $\frac{4a + 4b}{8a + 8b}$

a. $4 \text{ to } 6 = \frac{4}{6}$

   $= \frac{2 \cdot \cancel{2}}{3 \cdot \cancel{2}}$ ◄── Divide out the common factor 2.

   $= \frac{2}{3}$

b. $3ab : 27ab = \frac{\cancel{3ab}^{\,1}}{\cancel{27ab}_{\,9}}$ ◄── Divide out the common factor 3ab.

   $= \frac{1}{9}$

c. $\frac{4a + 4b}{a + b} = \frac{4\cancel{(a + b)}}{\cancel{a + b}}$ ◄── Factor the numerator. The denominator cannot be factored.
   $= 4$ Divide out the common factor (a + b).

EXERCISES

Simplify each ratio.

13. $\frac{x - 3}{3x - 2}$

1. 25 to 15 $\frac{5}{3}$ **2.** 6 : 9 $\frac{2}{3}$ **3.** $\frac{7}{14x}$ $\frac{1}{2x}$ **4.** 0.8 to 2.4 $\frac{1}{3}$

5. $\frac{12c}{14c}$ $\frac{6}{7}$ **6.** $22x^2$ to $35x$ $\frac{22x}{35}$ **7.** $0.5ab : 8ab$ $\frac{1}{16}$ **8.** $\frac{4xy}{0.25x}$ 16y

9. $1\frac{1}{2}x$ to $5x$ $\frac{3}{10}$ **10.** $\frac{x^2 + x}{2x}$ $\frac{x + 1}{2}$ **11.** $\frac{1}{4}r^2$ to $6r$ $\frac{r}{24}$ **12.** $0.72t : 7.2t^2$ $\frac{1}{10t}$

13. $(2x - 6) : (6x - 4)$ **14.** $12xy : 8xy$ $\frac{3}{2}$ **15.** $(9x - 9y)$ to $(x - y)$ **16.** $\frac{\pi r}{r^2 + \pi r}$

   See above.   9 $\frac{\pi}{r + \pi}$

Express each ratio in simplest form.

17. shorter leg : longer leg $\frac{5}{12}$ **18.** hypotenuse to shorter leg $\frac{13}{5}$

19. $\frac{\text{shorter leg}}{\text{hypotenuse}}$ $\frac{5}{13}$ **20.** hypotenuse : longer leg $\frac{13}{12}$

21. longer leg to shorter leg $\frac{12}{5}$ **22.** $\frac{\text{longer leg}}{\text{hypotenuse}}$ $\frac{12}{13}$

Write an expression in simplest form for $\frac{\text{area of shaded figure}}{\text{area of blue figure}}$ **.**

23.   **24.**   **25.**
$\frac{2}{\pi}$ $\frac{5}{14}$ $\frac{1}{9}$

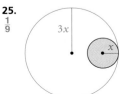

Solving Proportions

An equation in which both sides are ratios is called a *proportion*. A proportion can be written in three equivalent ways:

$\frac{a}{b} = \frac{c}{d}$ *a* is to *b* as *c* is to *d*

Because the product of the *means* (in this case, *b* and *c*) is equal to the product of the *extremes* (*a* and *d*), you can solve proportions by cross-multiplying.

■Example 1   Solve for *n*.

a. $\frac{n}{8} = \frac{5}{2}$ b. $\frac{(n+1)}{4} = \frac{5}{9}$

a. $\frac{n}{8} = \frac{5}{2}$

   $2n = 8 \cdot 5$ ◄— Cross-multiply. —►

   $2n = 40$ ◄— Simplify and solve for *n*. —►

   $n = 20$

b. $\frac{(n+1)}{4} = \frac{5}{9}$

   $9(n+1) = 4 \cdot 5$

   $9n + 9 = 20$

   $9n = 11$

   $n = \frac{11}{9}$

■Example 2   A map has the scale 1 in. = 4 mi. What actual distance does $3\frac{1}{4}$ in. represent on the map?

$\frac{1 \text{ in.}}{4 \text{ mi}} = \frac{3.25 \text{ in.}}{x \text{ mi}}$ ◄— Write a proportion.

$x \cdot 1 = 4(3.25)$ ◄— Cross-multiply.

$x = 13$ ◄— Solve for *x*.

$3\frac{1}{4}$ inches represents 13 miles.

EXERCISES

Solve each proportion.

1. $\frac{5}{2} = \frac{x}{7}$ 17.5

2. $\frac{x+2}{3} = \frac{8}{15}$ −0.4

3. $\frac{8}{x} = \frac{x}{2}$ −4 or 4

4. $\frac{9}{w} = \frac{16}{144}$ 81

5. $\frac{18}{x} = 6$ 3

6. $\frac{13t}{26} = \frac{40}{16}$ 5

7. $\frac{8}{11} = \frac{12}{x}$ 16.5

8. $\frac{3}{4} = \frac{x}{48}$ 36

9. $\frac{52}{p} = \frac{2}{3}$ 78

10. $12 = \frac{36}{p}$ 3

11. $\frac{7}{3} = \frac{28}{t+9}$ 3

12. $\frac{5}{7} = \frac{10}{y+2}$ 12

13. $\frac{a+5}{9} = \frac{14}{4}$ 26.5

14. $\frac{x+10}{6} = \frac{3}{2}$ −1

15. $\frac{2}{c+1} = \frac{9}{8c+1}$ 1

16. $\frac{m+4}{7} = \frac{15-m}{12}$ 3

17. A map has the scale 1 cm = 1200 km. What actual distance does 10.4 cm represent on the map? **12,480 km**

18. A model airplane has the scale 1 : 72. The wingspan of the model is 11.5 in. What is the wingspan, in feet, of the actual plane? **69 ft**

19. An architect builds a model of an apartment complex with the scale 1 in. = 5 ft. Find the area of a rectangular patio that measures 5 in.-by-7.25 in. on the model. **906.25 ft²**

662

16.

17.

18.

19.

20.

21.

22.

23.

24.

Solving Linear Equations and Inequalities

An equation or inequality is *linear* if its variables are raised only to the power of 1. So $5x - 3 = 2$ is linear, but $x^2 - x + 1 = 0$ is not. To solve an equation, use the properties of equality and properties of real numbers (see page 672) to find all the values of the variable that satisfy the equation.

Example 1   Solve each equation.
   a. $5x - 3 = 2$ **b.** $1 - 2(x + 1) = x$

a. $5x - 3 = 2$
   $5x = 5$ ← Add 3 to each side.
   $x = 1$ ← Divide each side by 5.

b. $1 - 2(x + 1) = x$
   $1 - 2x - 2 = x$ ← Use the Distributive Property.
   $-1 - 2x = x$ ← Simplify the left side.
   $-1 = 3x$ ← Add $2x$ to each side.
   $-\frac{1}{3} = x$ ← Divide each side by 3.

To solve a linear inequality, use properties of inequality (see page 672). Remember that when you multiply or divide both sides by a negative number, you reverse the order of the inequality.

Example 2   Solve. Graph the solution on a number line.
   a. $2x - 1 \geq 5$ **b.** $1 - x > -1$

a. $2x - 1 \geq 5$
   $2x \geq 6$ ← Add 1 to each side.
   $x \geq 3$ ← Divide each side by 2.

Solid bullet at 3 means that 3 is a solution.

b. $1 - x > -1$
   $-x > -2$ ← Subtract 1 from each side.
   $x < 2$ ← Divide each side by -1. Reverse the order of the inequality.

Open bullet at 2 means that 2 is *not* a solution.

EXERCISES

Solve each equation.

1. $3n + 2 = 17$ 5
2. $3n - 4 = -6$ $-\frac{2}{3}$
3. $2x + 4 = 10$ 3

4. $3(n - 4) = 15$ 9
5. $5a - 2 = -12$ -2
6. $4 - 2y = 8$ -2

7. $-6z + 1 = 13$ -2
8. $\frac{m}{-2} - 3 = 1$ -8
9. $\frac{2}{3}(n + 1) = -\frac{1}{4}$ $-1\frac{3}{8}$

10. $7 = -2(4n - 4.5)$ 0.25
11. $2(1 - 3n) = 2n + 4$ $-\frac{1}{4}$
12. $5k + 2(k + 1) = 23$ 3

13. $\frac{5}{7}p - 10 = 30$ 56
14. $6 - (3t + 4) = -17$ $6\frac{1}{3}$
15. $(w + 5) - (2w + 5) = 5$ -5

Solve each inequality. Graph the solution on a number line. 16–24. See margins for graphs.

16. $2n < 8$ $n < 4$
17. $6 - x \leq 4$ $x \geq 2$
18. $\frac{1}{2}n \leq -\frac{3}{8}$ $n \leq -\frac{3}{4}$

19. $5t + 3 \geq 23$ $t \geq 4$
20. $3 - z \geq 7$ $z \leq -4$
21. $y - 4 > 2 + 3y$ $y < -3$

22. $-6m - 4 < 32$ $m > -6$
23. $2(k - 4) \leq -12$ $k \leq -2$
24. $5 - (n - 3) \geq -4n$ $n \geq -2\frac{2}{3}$

22.

Slope and Intercepts

The slope of a line is a number that describes how steep it is. A line with a positive slope goes upward from left to right, and a line with a negative slope goes downward from left to right. The *slope* of a line is defined as

$\frac{\text{vertical change (rise)}}{\text{horizontal change (run)}}$ or, more formally, as follows:

The slope m of a line through the points (x_1, y_1) and (x_2, y_2) is $m = \frac{y_2 - y_1}{x_2 - x_1}$.

■Example 1   **Find the slope of the hypotenuse of $\triangle ABC$.**

Let $(x_1, y_1) = (-2, 3)$ and let $(x_2, y_2) = (4, -1)$.

Then $m = \frac{y_2 - y_1}{x_2 - x_1} = \frac{-1 - 3}{4 - (-2)} = \frac{-4}{6} = -\frac{2}{3}$

An intercept is the x- or y-value where the line crosses an axis.

■Example 2   **For the line $2y - x = 4$, find the following:**
a. the x-intercept   **b. the y-intercept**

a. To find the x-intercept, let $y = 0$.

$2y - x = 4$
$2(0) - x = 4$
$x = -4$

The x-intercept is -4.

b. To find the y-intercept, let $x = 0$.

$2y - x = 4$
$2y - 0 = 4$
$y = 2$

The y-intercept is 2.

Thus, the graph of $2y - x = 4$ passes through $(-4, 0)$ and $(0, 2)$.

Lines with positive or negative slopes have both x- and y- intercepts. However, horizontal and vertical lines have only one intercept. The slope of a horizontal line is zero, and the slope of a vertical line is undefined.

EXERCISES

Find the slope of the line through each pair of points.

1. $(5, 1), (2, 7)$ -2 **2.** $(-2, 3), (4, -7)$ $-\frac{5}{3}$ **3.** $(0, 5), (5, 0)$ -1 **4.** $(-4, -2), (-5, 8)$ -10

5. $(5, 7), (-2, 7)$ 0 **6.** $(0, 0), (4, -3)$ $-\frac{3}{4}$ **7.** $(3, -2), (3, 9)$ undef.   **8.** $(\frac{1}{2}, -2), (-\frac{3}{2}, 1)$ $-\frac{3}{2}$

Find the x- and y-intercepts for each linear equation.

9. $3x - y = 1$ $\frac{1}{3}; -1$ **10.** $2y + x = 2$ $2; 1$ **11.** $y = -1$ no intercept; -1 **12.** $-4x - y = 8$ $-2; -8$

13. $5x + 5y = 5$ $1; 1$ **14.** $y = x$ $0; 0$ **15.** $x = -4$ $-4;$ no intercept   **16.** $\frac{1}{2}x - \frac{1}{4}y = \frac{3}{4}$ $1\frac{1}{2}; -3$

17. $1 = x - 2y$ $1; -\frac{1}{2}$ **18.** $y = 4x - 5$ $1\frac{1}{4}; -5$ **19.** $0.9y - 0.5x = 2$ $-4; 2\frac{2}{9}$ **20.** $y = -2x - 31$ $-15\frac{1}{2}; -31$

21. The vertices of a triangle are $(-3, -1), (-3, 5),$ and $(6, -1)$. Find the slope of each side of the triangle. undef.; $-\frac{2}{3}$; 0

22. Graph the line with y-intercept 3 and no x-intercept. Find its slope. See margin for graph; 0.

Graphing Linear Equations and Inequalities   page 665

1.

2.

3.

4.

5.

6.

7.

8.

9.

10.

11.

12.

13.

14.

15.

16.

17.

18.

19.

20.

Graphing Linear Equations and Inequalities

Examples 1 and 2 give two methods for graphing a linear equation.

■Example 1   **Graph the equation $3x - y = 4$.**

Make a table by selecting several x-values and substituting each in the equation to find the corresponding y-value. Only two points are needed to graph a line, but finding a third is a good check for accuracy. Plot the points and draw the line.

x	0	1	2
y	-4	-1	2

■Example 2   **Graph the equation $2y - 3x = 2$.**

You can use a table as in Example 1, or you can use the slope-intercept form $y = mx + b$. In this form, m is the slope and b is the y-intercept. To write the equation in slope-intercept form, solve for y.

$$2y - 3x = 2$$
$$2y = 3x + 2 \quad \longleftarrow \text{Subtract } 3x \text{ from each side.}$$
$$y = \tfrac{3}{2}x + 1 \quad \longleftarrow \text{Multiply each side by } \tfrac{1}{2}.$$

So the slope m is $\tfrac{3}{2}$, and the y-intercept b is 1. Plot $(0, 1)$. From there, use the fact that $\tfrac{\text{rise}}{\text{run}} = \tfrac{3}{2}$ to move up 3 units and right 2 units. Plot a second point there. Draw a line connecting the two points.

■Example 3   **Graph the inequality $y > x - 1$.**

Start by graphing the equation $y = x - 1$. Points on this line are *not* solutions of the inequality. You show this by using a dashed line. (In general, use a dashed line for $<$ or $>$ and a solid line for $\le$ or $\ge$.) To find which side of the line contains solutions of the inequality, test a point not on the line.

$$(0) > (0) - 1 \quad \longleftarrow \text{Test } (0, 0) \text{ in the inequality } y > x - 1.$$
$$0 > -1 \quad \longleftarrow \text{The point makes the inequality true, so shade the region containing } (0, 0).$$

EXERCISES

Graph each equation. 1–12. See margin.

1. $2x + y = 3$

2. $3y - x = 6$

3. $2x + 3y = 12$

4. $y = \tfrac{2}{3}x + 5$

5. $y = -\tfrac{1}{3}x$

6. $x - 2y = 4$

7. $x = 4$

8. $y = -2x - 1$

9. $y = -3$

10. $y = \tfrac{3}{4}x - 3$

11. $3x + y = 9$

12. $4x - 6y = 6$

Graph each inequality. 13–20. See margin.

13. $x + y \le 4$

14. $y > x + 2$

15. $y < x - 3$

16. $y \ge x + 9$

17. $2x + y \le 5$

18. $y \le 5$

19. $y - 3 < 2x + 2$

20. $x < 0$

665

11. $h = \frac{3V}{\ell w}$

15. $\ell = \frac{S - \pi r^2}{\pi r} = \frac{S}{\pi r} - r$

16. $b_1 = \frac{2A - hb_2}{h} = \frac{2A}{h} - b_2$

19. $\ell = \frac{2S - 2B}{p}$

20. $h = \frac{S - 2\pi r^2}{2\pi r} = \frac{S}{2\pi r} - r$

Solving Literal Equations

An equation with two or more variables is called a *literal equation*. These equations appear frequently in geometry, often as formulas. You can solve a literal equation for any of its variables.

■**Example 1** The formula $p = 2(\ell + w)$ gives the perimeter p of a rectangle with length ℓ and width w. Solve the equation for ℓ.

$p = 2(\ell + w)$
$p = 2\ell + 2w$ ← Use the Distributive Property.
$p - 2w = 2\ell$ ← Subtract $2w$ from each side.
$\frac{p - 2w}{2} = \ell$ ← Divide each side by 2.

■**Example 2** The formula $A = \frac{1}{2}(b_1 + b_2)h$ gives the area A of a trapezoid with bases b_1 and b_2 and height h. Solve for h.

$A = \frac{1}{2}(b_1 + b_2)h$
$2A = h(b_1 + b_2)$ ← Multiply each side by 2.
$\frac{2A}{b_1 + b_2} = h$ ← Divide each side by $(b_1 + b_2)$.

■**Example 3** The formula for converting from degrees Celsius C to degrees Fahrenheit F is $F = \frac{9}{5}C + 32$. Solve for C.

$F = \frac{9}{5}C + 32$
$F - 32 = \frac{9}{5}C$ ← Subtract 32 from each side.
$\frac{5}{9}(F - 32) = C$ ← Multiply each side by $\frac{5}{9}$.

EXERCISES

Solve each equation for the variable in red. 11, 15–16, 19–20. See margin.

1. Perimeter of rectangle: $p = 2w + 2\ell$ $w = \frac{p - 2\ell}{2}$ **2.** Volume of prism: $V = \ell wh$ $w = \frac{V}{\ell h}$

3. Surface area of sphere: $S = 4\pi r^2$ $r = \frac{1}{2}\sqrt{\frac{S}{\pi}} = \frac{\sqrt{\pi S}}{2\pi}$ **4.** Lateral area of cylinder: $A = 2\pi rh$ $r = \frac{A}{2\pi h}$

5. Area of kite or rhombus: $A = \frac{1}{2}d_1 d_2$ $d_2 = \frac{2A}{d_1}$ **6.** Area of circle: $A = \pi r^2$ $r = \sqrt{\frac{A}{\pi}} = \frac{\sqrt{\pi A}}{\pi}$

7. Area of regular polygon: $A = \frac{1}{2}ap$ $a = \frac{2A}{p}$ **8.** Volume of cylinder: $V = \pi r^2 h$ $h = \frac{V}{\pi r^2}$

9. Area of triangle: $A = \frac{1}{2}bh$ $h = \frac{2A}{b}$ **10.** Tangent of $\angle A$: $\tan A = \frac{y}{x}$ $x = \frac{y}{\tan A}$

11. Volume of rectangular pyramid: $V = \frac{1}{3}\ell wh$ **12.** Circumference of circle: $C = 2\pi r$ $r = \frac{C}{2\pi}$

13. Cosine of $\angle A$: $\cos A = \frac{b}{c}$ $b = c \cos A$ **14.** Volume of cone: $V = \frac{1}{3}\pi r^2 h$ $r = \sqrt{\frac{3V}{\pi h}} = \frac{\sqrt{3\pi hV}}{\pi h}$

15. Surface area of right cone: $S = \pi r^2 + \pi r\ell$ **16.** Area of trapezoid: $A = \frac{1}{2}(b_1 + b_2)h$

17. Volume of pyramid: $V = \frac{1}{3}Bh$ $B = \frac{3V}{h}$ **18.** Pythagorean Theorem: $a^2 + b^2 = c^2$ $b = \sqrt{c^2 - a^2}$

19. Surface area of regular pyramid: $S = B + \frac{1}{2}p\ell$ **20.** Surface area of right cylinder: $S = 2\pi r^2 + 2\pi rh$

666

Systems of Linear Equations

Normally, there are many ordered pairs that satisfy a given equation. For example, $(3, 4)$, $(4, 5)$, $(5, 6)$, and infinitely many other pairs all satisfy the equation $y = x + 1$. To solve a system of two linear equations, however, you need to find ordered pairs that satisfy both equations at once. Ordinarily, there is just one such ordered pair; it is the point where the equations of the two lines intersect.

One method you can always use to solve a system of linear equations is the substitution method.

■Example **Solve the system.** $2x - y = -10$
$$-3x - 2y = 1$$

Solve one of the equations for a variable. Looking at the two equations, it seems easiest to solve the first equation for y.

$2x - y = -10$
$\quad -y = -2x - 10$ ← Subtract $2x$ from each side.
$\quad\quad y = 2x + 10$ ← Multiply each side by -1.

Now substitute $2x + 10$ for y in the other equation.

$\quad\quad\quad -3x - 2y = 1$ ← Write the other equation.
$-3x - 2(2x + 10) = 1$ ← Substitute $(2x + 10)$ for y.
$\quad -3x - 4x - 20 = 1$ ← Use the distributive property.
$\quad\quad\quad\quad -7x = 21$ ← Simplify the left side and add 20 to each side.
$\quad\quad\quad\quad\quad x = -3$ ← Divide each side by -7.

So $x = -3$. To find y, substitute -3 for x in either equation.

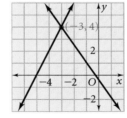

$\quad 2x - y = -10$ ← Write one of the equations.
$2(-3) - y = -10$ ← Substitute -3 for x.
$\quad -6 - y = -10$ ← Simplify.
$\quad\quad -y = -4$ ← Add 6 to each side.
$\quad\quad\quad y = 4$ ← Multiply each side by -1.

So the solution is $x = -3$ and $y = 4$, or $(-3, 4)$. If you graph $2x - y = -10$ and $-3x - 2y = 1$, you will find that the lines intersect at $(-3, 4)$.

EXERCISES

Solve each system.

1. $x + y = 3$ $(4, -1)$
   $x - y = 5$

2. $y - x = 4$ no solution
   $x + 3 = y$

3. $y = 1$ $(4, 1)$
   $5x - 2y = 18$

4. $4y - x = -3$ infinitely many solutions
   $2x - 6 = 8y$

5. $8x - 1 = 4y$
   $3x = y + 1$ $\left(\frac{3}{4}, 1\frac{1}{4}\right)$

6. $2x + 2y = -4$
   $-x + 3y = 6$ $(-3, 1)$

7. $12y - 3x = 11$
   $x - 2y = -2$ $\left(-\frac{1}{3}, \frac{5}{6}\right)$

8. $5x + 7y = 1$
   $4x - 2y = 16$
   $(3, -2)$

9. Give an example of a system of linear equations with no solution. What do you know about the slopes of the lines of such a system?
   Check students' work; they are $=$ or both undef.

667

Measures

United States Customary	Metric
Length	
12 inches (in.) = 1 foot (ft)	10 millimeters (mm) = 1 centimeter (cm)
36 in. = 1 yard (yd)	100 cm = 1 meter (m)
3 ft = 1 yard	1000 mm = 1 meter
5280 ft = 1 mile (mi)	1000 m = 1 kilometer (km)
1760 yd = 1 mile	
Area	
144 square inches (in.²) = 1 square foot (ft²)	100 square millimeters (mm²) = 1 square centimeter (cm²)
9 ft² = 1 square yard (yd²)	10,000 cm² = 1 square meter (m²)
43,560 ft² = 1 acre (a)	10,000 m² = 1 hectare (ha)
4840 yd² = 1 acre	
Volume	
1728 cubic inches (in.³) = 1 cubic foot (ft³)	1000 cubic millimeters (mm³) = 1 cubic centimeter (cm³)
27 ft³ = 1 cubic yard (yd³)	1,000,000 cm³ = 1 cubic meter (m³)
Liquid Capacity	
8 fluid ounces (fl oz) = 1 cup (c)	1000 milliliters (mL) = 1 liter (L)
2 c = 1 pint (pt)	1000 L = 1 kiloliter (kL)
2 pt = 1 quart (qt)	
4 qt = 1 gallon (gal)	
Mass	
16 ounces (oz) = 1 pound (lb)	1000 milligrams (mg) = 1 gram (g)
2000 pounds = 1 ton (t)	1000 g = 1 kilogram (kg)
	1000 kg = 1 metric ton (t)
Temperature	
32°F = freezing point of water	0°C = freezing point of water
98.6°F = normal body temperature	37°C = normal body temperature
212°F = boiling point of water	100°C = boiling point of water

Time	
60 seconds (s) = 1 minute (min)	365 days = 1 year (yr)
60 minutes = 1 hour (h)	52 weeks (approx.) = 1 year
24 hours = 1 day (da)	12 months = 1 year
7 days = 1 week (wk)	10 years = 1 decade
4 weeks (approx.) = 1 month (mo)	100 years = 1 century

Symbols

. . .	and so on	p. 5
+	plus (addition)	p. 6
=	is equal to, equality	p. 6
n^2	square of n	p. 6
( )	parentheses for grouping	p. 8
−	minus (subtraction)	p. 8
×, ·	times (multiplication)	p. 8
−a	opposite of a	p. 9
a^n	nth power of a	p. 10
P(event)	probability of the event	p. 11
$\overleftrightarrow{AB}$	line through points A and B	p. 13
$\overline{AB}$	segment with endpoints A and B	p. 18
$\overrightarrow{AB}$	ray with endpoint A and through point B	p. 18
∥	is parallel to	p. 18
>	is greater than	p. 22
<	is less than	p. 22
≥	is greater than or equal to	p. 22
≤	is less than or equal to	p. 22
AB	length of $\overline{AB}$	p. 25
$\lvert a \rvert$	absolute value of a	p. 25
≅	is congruent to	p. 25
∠A	angle with vertex A	p. 26
∠ABC	angle with sides $\overrightarrow{BA}$ and $\overrightarrow{BC}$	p. 26
m∠A	measure of angle A	p. 26
°	degree(s)	p. 26
⌐	right angle symbol	p. 27
⊥	is perpendicular to	p. 33
m	slope of a linear function	p. 54
b	y-intercept of a linear function	p. 54
x_1, x_2	specific values of the variable x	p. 54
d	distance	p. 54
$\sqrt{x}$	nonnegative square root of x	p. 54
(a, b)	ordered pair with x-coordinate a and y-coordinate b	p. 54
△ABC	triangle with vertices A, B, and C	p. 69
$a : b$, $\frac{a}{b}$	ratio of a to b	p. 72
n-gon	polygon with n sides	p. 80
□$ABCD$	parallelogram with vertices A, B, C, and D	p. 91
⊙A	circle with center A	p. 96
d	diameter	p. 96
r	radius	p. 96
%	percent	p. 97

$\overset{\frown}{AB}$	arc with endpoints A and B	p. 98
$\overset{\frown}{ABC}$	arc with endpoints A and C and containing B	p. 98
$m\overset{\frown}{AB}$	measure of $\overset{\frown}{AB}$	p. 98
∼	is similar to	p. 103
A'	image of A, A prime	p. 125
→	maps to	p. 125
$\begin{bmatrix} 1 & 2 \\ 3 & 4 \end{bmatrix}$	matrix	p. 131
$\overrightarrow{AB}$	vector with initial point A and terminal point B	p. 133
$\langle x, y \rangle$	ordered pair notation for a vector	p. 133
{ }	set brackets	p. 166
⊿	angles	p. 197
≠	is not equal to	p. 210
≇	is not congruent to	p. 210
≯	is not greater than	p. 214
≮	is not less than	p. 214
A	area	p. 243
s	length of a side	p. 243
b	base length	p. 244
h	height	p. 244
≈	is approximately equal to	p. 250
b_1, b_2	bases of a trapezoid	p. 269
a	apothem	p. 274
p	perimeter	p. 274
π	pi, ratio of the circumference of a circle to its diameter	p. 279
C	circumference	p. 279
B	area of a base	p. 309
h	length of an altitude	p. 309
L.A.	lateral area	p. 309
S.A.	surface area	p. 310
V	volume	p. 315
ℓ	slant height	p. 316
⚠	triangles	p. 422
±	plus or minus	p. 439
d_1, d_2	lengths of diagonals	p. 463
tan A	tangent of ∠A	p. 544
sin A	sine of ∠A	p. 551
cos A	cosine of ∠A	p. 551
$\vec{v}$	vector **v**	p. 568
[ ]	brackets for grouping	p. 586

Formulas

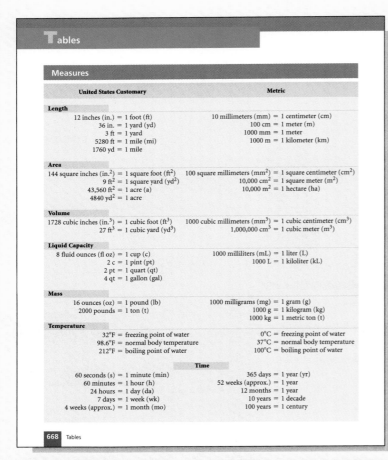

Square — $A = s^2$

Rectangle — $A = bh$

Parallelogram — $A = bh$

Triangle — $A = \frac{1}{2}bh$

Trapezoid — $A = \frac{1}{2}h(b_1 + b_2)$

Regular Polygon — $A = \frac{1}{2}ap$

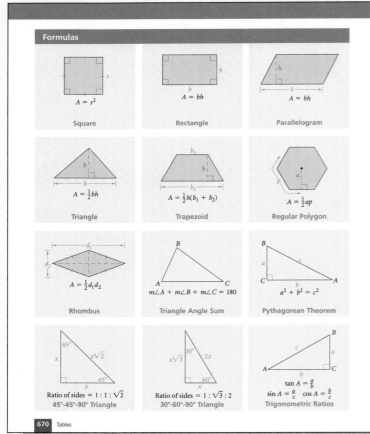

Rhombus — $A = \frac{1}{2}d_1 d_2$

Triangle Angle Sum — $m\angle A + m\angle B + m\angle C = 180$

Pythagorean Theorem — $a^2 + b^2 = c^2$

45°-45°-90° Triangle — Ratio of sides = $1 : 1 : \sqrt{2}$

30°-60°-90° Triangle — Ratio of sides = $1 : \sqrt{3} : 2$

Trigonometric Ratios — $\tan A = \frac{a}{b}$ $\sin A = \frac{a}{c}$ $\cos A = \frac{b}{c}$

Circle — $C = \pi d$ or $C = 2\pi r$ $A = \pi r^2$

Arc — Length of $\overset{\frown}{AB} = \frac{m\overset{\frown}{AB}}{360} \cdot 2\pi r$

Sector of a Circle — Area sector $AOB = \frac{m\overset{\frown}{AB}}{360} \cdot \pi r^2$

Equation of Circle — $r^2 = (x - h)^2 + (y - k)^2$

Distance and Midpoint — $d = \sqrt{(x_2 - x_1)^2 + (y_2 - y_1)^2}$ $M = \left(\frac{x_1 + x_2}{2}, \frac{y_1 + y_2}{2}\right)$

Slope — $m = \frac{\text{rise}}{\text{run}} = \frac{y_2 - y_1}{x_2 - x_1}$

Slope-Intercept Form of Linear Equation — $y = mx + b$

Right Prism — L.A. $= ph$ S.A. $=$ L.A. $+ 2B$ $V = Bh$

Right Cylinder — L.A. $= 2\pi rh$ or L.A. $= \pi dh$ S.A. $=$ L.A. $+ 2B$ $V = Bh$ or $V = \pi r^2 h$

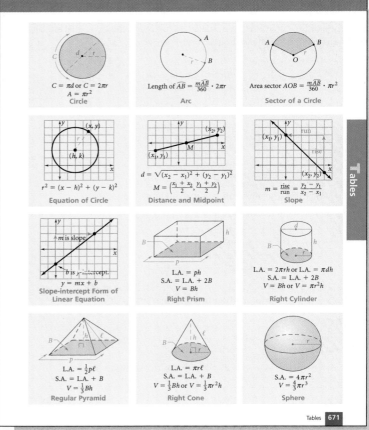

Regular Pyramid — L.A. $= \frac{1}{2}p\ell$ S.A. $=$ L.A. $+ B$ $V = \frac{1}{3}Bh$

Right Cone — L.A. $= \pi r\ell$ S.A. $=$ L.A. $+ B$ $V = \frac{1}{3}Bh$ or $V = \frac{1}{3}\pi r^2 h$

Sphere — S.A. $= 4\pi r^2$ $V = \frac{4}{3}\pi r^3$

T668

Properties of Real Numbers

Unless otherwise stated, *a*, *b*, *c*, and *d* are real numbers.

Identity Properties

Addition $\quad a + 0 = a$ and $0 + a = a$

Multiplication $\quad a \cdot 1 = a$ and $1 \cdot a = a$

Commutative Properties

Addition $\quad a + b = b + a$

Multiplication $\quad a \cdot b = b \cdot a$

Associative Properties

Addition $\quad (a + b) + c = a + (b + c)$

Multiplication $\quad (a \cdot b) \cdot c = a \cdot (b \cdot c)$

Inverse Properties

Addition
The sum of a number and its *opposite*, or *additive inverse*, is zero.

$a + (-a) = 0$ and $-a + a = 0$

Multiplication
The *reciprocal*, or *multiplicative inverse*, of a rational number $\frac{a}{b}$ is $\frac{b}{a}$ $(a, b \neq 0)$.

$a \cdot \frac{1}{a} = 1$ and $\frac{1}{a} \cdot a = 1$ $(a \neq 0)$

Distributive Properties

$a(b + c) = ab + ac \qquad (b + c)a = ba + ca$
$a(b - c) = ab - ac \qquad (b - c)a = ba - ca$

Properties of Equality

Addition $\quad$ If $a = b$, then $a + c = b + c$.

Subtraction $\quad$ If $a = b$, then $a - c = b - c$.

Multiplication $\quad$ If $a = b$, then $a \cdot c = b \cdot c$.

Division $\quad$ If $a = b$ and $c \neq 0$, then $\frac{a}{c} = \frac{b}{c}$.

Substitution $\quad$ If $a = b$, then b can replace a in any expression.

Reflexive $\quad a = a$

Symmetric $\quad$ If $a = b$, then $b = a$.

Transitive $\quad$ If $a = b$ and $b = c$, then $a = c$.

Properties of Proportions

$\frac{a}{b} = \frac{c}{d}$ is equivalent to

(1) $ad = bc$ $\quad$ (2) $\frac{b}{a} = \frac{d}{c}$

(3) $\frac{a}{c} = \frac{b}{d}$ $\quad$ (4) $\frac{a + b}{b} = \frac{c + d}{d}$

Zero-Product Property

If $ab = 0$, then $a = 0$ or $b = 0$.

Properties of Inequality

Addition $\quad$ If $a > b$ and $c \geq d$, then $a + c > b + d$.

Multiplication $\quad$ If $a > b$ and $c > 0$, then $ac > bc$.
$\quad$ If $a > b$ and $c < 0$, then $ac < bc$.

Transitive $\quad$ If $a > b$ and $b > c$, then $a > c$.

Comparison $\quad$ If $a = b + c$ and $c > 0$, then $a > b$.

Properties of Exponents

For any nonzero numbers *a* and *b*, any positive number *c*, and any integers *m* and *n*,

Zero Exponent $\quad a^0 = 1$

Negative Exponent $\quad a^{-n} = \frac{1}{a^n}$

Product of Powers $\quad a^m \cdot a^n = a^{m+n}$

Quotient of Powers $\quad \frac{a^m}{a^n} = a^{m-n}$

Power to a Power $\quad (c^m)^n = c^{mn}$

Product to a Power $\quad (ab)^n = a^n b^n$

Quotient to a Power $\quad \left(\frac{a}{b}\right)^n = \frac{a^n}{b^n}$

Properties of Square Roots

For any nonnegative numbers *a* and *b*, and any positive number *c*,

Product of Square Roots $\quad \sqrt{a} \cdot \sqrt{b} = \sqrt{ab}$

Quotient of Square Roots $\quad \frac{\sqrt{a}}{\sqrt{c}} = \sqrt{\frac{a}{c}}$

Squares and Square Roots

Number n	Square n^2	Positive Square Root $\sqrt{n}$	Number n	Square n^2	Positive Square Root $\sqrt{n}$	Number n	Square n^2	Positive Square Root $\sqrt{n}$
1	1	1.000	51	2601	7.141	101	10,201	10.050
2	4	1.414	52	2704	7.211	102	10,404	10.100
3	9	1.732	53	2809	7.280	103	10,609	10.149
4	16	2.000	54	2916	7.348	104	10,816	10.198
5	25	2.236	55	3025	7.416	105	11,025	10.247
6	36	2.449	56	3136	7.483	106	11,236	10.296
7	49	2.646	57	3249	7.550	107	11,449	10.344
8	64	2.828	58	3364	7.616	108	11,664	10.392
9	81	3.000	59	3481	7.681	109	11,881	10.440
10	100	3.162	60	3600	7.746	110	12,100	10.488
11	121	3.317	61	3721	7.810	111	12,321	10.536
12	144	3.464	62	3844	7.874	112	12,544	10.583
13	169	3.606	63	3969	7.937	113	12,769	10.630
14	196	3.742	64	4096	8.000	114	12,996	10.677
15	225	3.873	65	4225	8.062	115	13,225	10.724
16	256	4.000	66	4356	8.124	116	13,456	10.770
17	289	4.123	67	4489	8.185	117	13,689	10.817
18	324	4.243	68	4624	8.246	118	13,924	10.863
19	361	4.359	69	4761	8.307	119	14,161	10.909
20	400	4.472	70	4900	8.367	120	14,400	10.954
21	441	4.583	71	5041	8.426	121	14,641	11.000
22	484	4.690	72	5184	8.485	122	14,884	11.045
23	529	4.796	73	5329	8.544	123	15,129	11.091
24	576	4.899	74	5476	8.602	124	15,376	11.136
25	625	5.000	75	5625	8.660	125	15,625	11.180
26	676	5.099	76	5776	8.718	126	15,876	11.225
27	729	5.196	77	5929	8.775	127	16,129	11.269
28	784	5.292	78	6084	8.832	128	16,384	11.314
29	841	5.385	79	6241	8.888	129	16,641	11.358
30	900	5.477	80	6400	8.944	130	16,900	11.402
31	961	5.568	81	6561	9.000	131	17,161	11.446
32	1024	5.657	82	6724	9.055	132	17,424	11.489
33	1089	5.745	83	6889	9.110	133	17,689	11.533
34	1156	5.831	84	7056	9.165	134	17,956	11.576
35	1225	5.916	85	7225	9.220	135	18,225	11.619
36	1296	6.000	86	7396	9.274	136	18,496	11.662
37	1369	6.083	87	7569	9.327	137	18,769	11.705
38	1444	6.164	88	7744	9.381	138	19,044	11.747
39	1521	6.245	89	7921	9.434	139	19,321	11.790
40	1600	6.325	90	8100	9.487	140	19,600	11.832
41	1681	6.403	91	8281	9.539	141	19,881	11.874
42	1764	6.481	92	8464	9.592	142	20,164	11.916
43	1849	6.557	93	8649	9.644	143	20,449	11.958
44	1936	6.633	94	8836	9.695	144	20,736	12.000
45	2025	6.708	95	9025	9.747	145	21,025	12.042
46	2116	6.782	96	9216	9.798	146	21,316	12.083
47	2209	6.856	97	9409	9.849	147	21,609	12.124
48	2304	6.928	98	9604	9.899	148	21,904	12.166
49	2401	7.000	99	9801	9.950	149	22,201	12.207
50	2500	7.071	100	10,000	10.000	150	22,500	12.247

Trigonometric Ratios

Angle	Sine	Cosine	Tangent	Angle	Sine	Cosine	Tangent
1°	0.0175	0.9998	0.0175	46°	0.7193	0.6947	1.0355
2°	0.0349	0.9994	0.0349	47°	0.7314	0.6820	1.0724
3°	0.0523	0.9986	0.0524	48°	0.7431	0.6691	1.1106
4°	0.0698	0.9976	0.0699	49°	0.7547	0.6561	1.1504
5°	0.0872	0.9962	0.0875	50°	0.7660	0.6428	1.1918
6°	0.1045	0.9945	0.1051	51°	0.7771	0.6293	1.2349
7°	0.1219	0.9925	0.1228	52°	0.7880	0.6157	1.2799
8°	0.1392	0.9903	0.1405	53°	0.7986	0.6018	1.3270
9°	0.1564	0.9877	0.1584	54°	0.8090	0.5878	1.3764
10°	0.1736	0.9848	0.1763	55°	0.8192	0.5736	1.4281
11°	0.1908	0.9816	0.1944	56°	0.8290	0.5592	1.4826
12°	0.2079	0.9781	0.2126	57°	0.8387	0.5446	1.5399
13°	0.2250	0.9744	0.2309	58°	0.8480	0.5299	1.6003
14°	0.2419	0.9703	0.2493	59°	0.8572	0.5150	1.6643
15°	0.2588	0.9659	0.2679	60°	0.8660	0.5000	1.7321
16°	0.2756	0.9613	0.2867	61°	0.8746	0.4848	1.8040
17°	0.2924	0.9563	0.3057	62°	0.8829	0.4695	1.8807
18°	0.3090	0.9511	0.3249	63°	0.8910	0.4540	1.9626
19°	0.3256	0.9455	0.3443	64°	0.8988	0.4384	2.0503
20°	0.3420	0.9397	0.3640	65°	0.9063	0.4226	2.1445
21°	0.3584	0.9336	0.3839	66°	0.9135	0.4067	2.2460
22°	0.3746	0.9272	0.4040	67°	0.9205	0.3907	2.3559
23°	0.3907	0.9205	0.4245	68°	0.9272	0.3746	2.4751
24°	0.4067	0.9135	0.4452	69°	0.9336	0.3584	2.6051
25°	0.4226	0.9063	0.4663	70°	0.9397	0.3420	2.7475
26°	0.4384	0.8988	0.4877	71°	0.9455	0.3256	2.9042
27°	0.4540	0.8910	0.5095	72°	0.9511	0.3090	3.0777
28°	0.4695	0.8829	0.5317	73°	0.9563	0.2924	3.2709
29°	0.4848	0.8746	0.5543	74°	0.9613	0.2756	3.4874
30°	0.5000	0.8660	0.5774	75°	0.9659	0.2588	3.7321
31°	0.5150	0.8572	0.6009	76°	0.9703	0.2419	4.0108
32°	0.5299	0.8480	0.6249	77°	0.9744	0.2250	4.3315
33°	0.5446	0.8387	0.6494	78°	0.9781	0.2079	4.7046
34°	0.5592	0.8290	0.6745	79°	0.9816	0.1908	5.1446
35°	0.5736	0.8192	0.7002	80°	0.9848	0.1736	5.6713
36°	0.5878	0.8090	0.7265	81°	0.9877	0.1564	6.3138
37°	0.6018	0.7986	0.7536	82°	0.9903	0.1392	7.1154
38°	0.6157	0.7880	0.7813	83°	0.9925	0.1219	8.1443
39°	0.6293	0.7771	0.8098	84°	0.9945	0.1045	9.5144
40°	0.6428	0.7660	0.8391	85°	0.9962	0.0872	11.4301
41°	0.6561	0.7547	0.8693	86°	0.9976	0.0698	14.3007
42°	0.6691	0.7431	0.9004	87°	0.9986	0.0523	19.0811
43°	0.6820	0.7314	0.9325	88°	0.9994	0.0349	28.6363
44°	0.6947	0.7193	0.9657	89°	0.9998	0.0175	57.2900
45°	0.7071	0.7071	1.0000	90°	1.0000	0.0000	

Postulates & Theorems

Chapter 1: Tools of Geometry

Postulate 1-1
Through any two points there is exactly one line. (p. 14)

Postulate 1-2
If two lines intersect, then they intersect in exactly one point. (p. 14)

Postulate 1-3
If two planes intersect, then they intersect in a line. (p. 14)

Postulate 1-4
Through any three noncollinear points there is exactly one plane. (p. 14)

Postulate 1-5
Ruler Postulate
The points of a line can be put into a one-to-one correspondence with the real numbers so that the distance between any two points is the absolute value of the difference of the corresponding numbers. (p. 25)

Postulate 1-6
Segment Addition Postulate
If three points A, B, and C are collinear and B is between A and C, then $AB + BC = AC$. (p. 26)

Postulate 1-7
Protractor Postulate
Let $\overrightarrow{OA}$ and $\overrightarrow{OB}$ be opposite rays in a plane. $\overrightarrow{OA}$, $\overrightarrow{OB}$, and all the rays with endpoint O that can be drawn on one side of $\overline{AB}$ can be paired with the real numbers from 0 to 180 in such a way that:
a. $\overrightarrow{OA}$ is paired with 0 and $\overrightarrow{OB}$ is paired with 180.
b. If $\overrightarrow{OC}$ is paired with x and $\overrightarrow{OD}$ is paired with y, then $m\angle COD = |x - y|$. (p. 27)

Postulate 1-8
Angle Addition Postulate
If point B is in the interior of $\angle AOC$, then $m\angle AOB + m\angle BOC = m\angle AOC$.
If $\angle AOC$ is a straight angle, then $m\angle AOB + m\angle BOC = 180$. (p. 28)

Properties of Congruence

Reflexive Property
$\overline{AB} \cong \overline{AB}$ and $\angle A \cong \angle A$
Symmetric Property
If $\overline{AB} \cong \overline{CD}$, then $\overline{CD} \cong \overline{AB}$.
If $\angle A \cong \angle B$, then $\angle B \cong \angle A$.
Transitive Property
If $\overline{AB} \cong \overline{CD}$ and $\overline{CD} \cong \overline{EF}$, then $\overline{AB} \cong \overline{EF}$.
If $\angle A \cong \angle B$ and $\angle B \cong \angle C$, then $\angle A \cong \angle C$. (p. 47)

Theorem 1-1
Vertical Angles Theorem
Vertical angles are congruent. (p. 48)

Theorem 1-2
Congruent Supplements Theorem
If two angles are supplements of congruent angles (or of the same angle), then the two angles are congruent. (p. 49)

Theorem 1-3
Congruent Complements Theorem
If two angles are complements of congruent angles (or of the same angle), then the two angles are congruent. (p. 49)

The Distance Formula
The distance d between two points $A(x_1, y_1)$ and $B(x_2, y_2)$ is $d = \sqrt{(x_2 - x_1)^2 + (y_2 - y_1)^2}$. (p. 54)

The Midpoint Formula
The coordinates of the midpoint M of $\overline{AB}$ with endpoints $A(x_1, y_1)$ and $B(x_2, y_2)$ are the following:
$M = \left(\frac{x_1 + x_2}{2}, \frac{y_1 + y_2}{2}\right)$ (p. 55)

Chapter 2: Investigating Geometric Figures

Theorem 2-1
Triangle Angle-Sum Theorem
The sum of the measures of the angles of a triangle is 180. (p. 68)

Theorem 2-2
Exterior Angle Theorem
The measure of each exterior angle of a triangle equals the sum of the measures of its two remote interior angles. (p. 70)
  Corollary
  The measure of an exterior angle of a triangle is greater than the measure of either of its remote interior angles. (p. 70)

Theorem 2-3
Polygon Interior Angle-Sum Theorem
The sum of the measures of the interior angles of an n-gon is $(n - 2)180$. (p. 77)

Theorem 2-4
Polygon Exterior Angle-Sum Theorem
The sum of the measures of the exterior angles of a polygon, one at each vertex, is 360. (p. 78)

Slopes of Parallel Lines
The slopes of two nonvertical parallel lines are equal. Two lines with the same slope are parallel. Vertical lines are parallel. (p. 85)

Slopes of Perpendicular Lines
The product of the slopes of two perpendicular lines, neither of which is vertical, is -1. If the product of the slopes of two lines is -1, then the lines are perpendicular. A horizontal and a vertical line are perpendicular. (p. 85)

Theorem 2-5
Two lines parallel to a third are parallel to each other. (p. 85)

Theorem 2-6
In a plane, two lines perpendicular to a third line are parallel to each other. (p. 85)

Postulate 2-1
Arc Addition Postulate
The measure of the arc formed by two adjacent arcs is the sum of the measure of two arcs. (p. 98)

Chapter 3: Transformations: Shapes in Motion

Properties of a Reflection
A reflection reverses orientation. A reflection is an isometry. (p. 126)

Properties of a Translation
A translation is an isometry. A translation does not change orientation. (p. 132)

Properties of a Rotation
A rotation is an isometry. A rotation does not change orientation. (p. 139)

Theorem 3-1
A composition of reflections in two parallel lines is a translation. (p. 144)

Theorem 3-2
A composition of reflections in two intersecting lines is a rotation. (p. 144)

Theorem 3-3
In a plane, two congruent figures can be mapped onto one another by a composition of at most three reflections. (p. 146)

Theorem 3-4
Isometry Classification Theorem
There are only four isometries. They are reflection, translation, rotation, and glide reflection. (p. 147)

Chapter 4: Triangle Relationships

Theorem 4-1
Isosceles Triangle Theorem
If two sides of a triangle are congruent, then the angles opposite those sides are also congruent. (p. 189)
  Corollary
  If a triangle is equilateral, then it is equiangular. (p. 190)

Theorem 4-2
The bisector of the vertex angle of an isosceles triangle is the perpendicular bisector of the base. (p. 189)

Theorem 4-3
Converse of the Isosceles Triangle Theorem
If two angles of a triangle are congruent, then the sides opposite the angles are congruent. (p. 189)
  Corollary
  If a triangle is equiangular, then it is equilateral. (p. 190)

Theorem 4-4
If a triangle is a right triangle, then the acute angles are complementary. (p. 195)

Theorem 4-5
If two angles of one triangle are congruent to two angles of another triangle, then the third angles are congruent. (p. 195)

Theorem 4-6
All right angles are congruent. (p. 195)

Theorem 4-7
If two angles are congruent and supplementary, then each is a right angle. (p. 195)

Theorem 4-8
Triangle Midsegment Theorem
If a segment joins the midpoints of two sides of a triangle, then the segment is parallel to the third side and half its length. (p. 201)

Theorem 4-9
Triangle Inequality Theorem
The sum of the lengths of any two sides of a triangle is greater than the length of the third side. (p. 214)

Theorem 4-10
If two sides of a triangle are not congruent, then the larger angle lies opposite the larger side. (p. 215)

Theorem 4-11
If two angles of a triangle are not congruent, then the longer side lies opposite the larger angle. (p. 215)

Theorem 4-12
Perpendicular Bisector Theorem
If a point is on the perpendicular bisector of a segment, then it is equidistant from the endpoints of the segment. (p. 219)

Theorem 4-13
Converse of Perpendicular Bisector Theorem
If a point is equidistant from the endpoints of a segment, then it is on the perpendicular bisector of the segment. (p. 219)

Theorem 4-14
Angle Bisector Theorem
If a point is on the bisector of an angle, then it is equidistant from the sides of the angle. (p. 222)

Theorem 4-15
Converse of Angle Bisector Theorem
If a point in the interior of an angle is equidistant from the sides of the angle, then it is on the angle bisector. (p. 222)

Theorem 4-16
The perpendicular bisectors of the sides of a triangle are concurrent at a point equidistant from the vertices. (p. 227)

Theorem 4-17
The bisectors of the angles of a triangle are concurrent at a point equidistant from the sides. (p. 227)

Theorem 4-18
The lines that contain the altitudes of a triangle are concurrent. (p. 230)

Theorem 4-19
The medians of a triangle are concurrent. (p. 230)

Chapter 5: Measuring in the Plane

Postulate 5-1
The area of a square is the square of the length of a side.
$A = s^2$ (p. 243)

Postulate 5-2
If two figures are congruent, their areas are equal. (p. 243)

Postulate 5-3
The area of a region is the sum of the areas of its nonoverlapping parts. (p. 243)

Theorem 5-1
Area of a Rectangle
The area of a rectangle is the product of its base and height.
$A = bh$ (p. 244)

Postulates & Theorems

Theorem 5-2
Area of a Parallelogram
The area of a parallelogram is the product of any base and the corresponding height.
$A = bh$ (p. 249)

Theorem 5-3
Area of a Triangle
The area of a triangle is half the product of any base and the corresponding height.
$A = \frac{1}{2}bh$ (p. 251)

Theorem 5-4
Pythagorean Theorem
In a right triangle, the sum of the squares of the lengths of the legs is equal to the square of the length of the hypotenuse.
$a^2 + b^2 = c^2$ (p. 257)

Theorem 5-5
Converse of the Pythagorean Theorem
If the square of the length of one side of a triangle is equal to the sum of the squares of the lengths of the other two sides, then the triangle is a right triangle. (p. 258)

Theorem 5-6
45°-45°-90° Triangle Theorem
In a 45°-45°-90° triangle, both legs are congruent and the length of the hypotenuse is $\sqrt{2}$ times the length of a leg.
hypotenuse $= \sqrt{2} \cdot$ leg (p. 264)

Theorem 5-7
30°-60°-90° Triangle Theorem
In a 30°-60°-90° triangle, the length of the hypotenuse is twice the length of the shorter leg. The length of the longer leg is $\sqrt{3}$ times the length of the shorter leg.
hypotenuse $= 2 \cdot$ shorter leg
longer leg $= \sqrt{3} \cdot$ shorter leg (p. 265)

Theorem 5-8
Area of a Trapezoid
The area of a trapezoid is half the product of the height and the sum of the lengths of the bases.
$A = \frac{1}{2}h(b_1 + b_2)$ (p. 269)

Theorem 5-9
Area of a Regular Polygon
The area of a regular polygon is half the product of the apothem and the perimeter.
$A = \frac{1}{2}ap$ (p. 274)

Theorem 5-10
Circumference of a Circle
The circumference of a circle is π times the diameter.
$C = \pi d$ or $C = 2\pi r$ (p. 279)

Theorem 5-11
Arc Length
The length of an arc of a circle is the product of the ratio $\frac{\text{measure of the arc}}{360}$ and the circumference of the circle.
Length of $\overset{\frown}{AB} = \frac{m\overset{\frown}{AB}}{360} \cdot 2\pi r$ (p. 281)

Theorem 5-12
Area of a Circle
The area of a circle is the product of π and the square of the radius.
$A = \pi r^2$ (p. 285)

Theorem 5-13
Area of a Sector of a Circle
The area of a sector of a circle is the product of the ratio $\frac{\text{measure of the arc}}{360}$ and the area of the circle.
Area of sector $AOB = \frac{m\overset{\frown}{AB}}{360} \cdot \pi r^2$ (p. 286)

Chapter 6: Measuring in Space

Theorem 6-1
Lateral and Surface Areas of a Right Prism
The lateral area of a right prism is the product of the perimeter of the base and the height.
L.A. $= ph$
The surface area of a right prism is the sum of the lateral area and the areas of the two bases.
S.A. $=$ L.A. $+ 2B$ (p. 310)

Theorem 6-2
Lateral and Surface Areas of a Right Cylinder
The lateral area of a right cylinder is the product of the circumference of the base and the height of the cylinder.
L.A. $= 2\pi rh$ or L.A. $= \pi dh$
The surface area of a right cylinder is the sum of the lateral area and the areas of the two bases.
S.A. $=$ L.A. $+ 2B$ (p. 311)

Theorem 6-3
Lateral and Surface Areas of a Regular Pyramid
The lateral area of a regular pyramid is half the product of the perimeter of the base and the slant height.
L.A. $= \frac{1}{2}p\ell$
The surface area of a regular pyramid is the sum of the lateral area and the area of the base.
S.A. $=$ L.A. $+ B$ (p. 317)

Theorem 6-4
Lateral and Surface Areas of a Right Cone
The lateral area of a right cone is half the product of the circumference of the base and the slant height.
L.A. $= \frac{1}{2} \cdot 2\pi r\ell$ or L.A. $= \pi r\ell$
The surface area of a right cone is the sum of the lateral area and the area of the base.
S.A. $=$ L.A. $+ B$ (p. 318)

Theorem 6-5
Cavalieri's Principle
If two space figures have the same height and the same cross-sectional area at every level, then they have the same volume. (p. 324)

Theorem 6-6
Volume of a Prism
The volume of a prism is the product of the area of a base and the height of the prism.
$V = Bh$ (p. 324)

Theorem 6-7
Volume of a Cylinder
The volume of a cylinder is the product of the area of a base and the height of the cylinder.
$V = Bh$ or $V = \pi r^2 h$ (p. 325)

Theorem 6-8
Volume of a Pyramid
The volume of a pyramid is one third the product of the area of the base and the height of the pyramid.
$V = \frac{1}{3}Bh$ (p. 331)

Theorem 6-9
Volume of a Cone
The volume of a cone is one third the product of the area of the base and the height of the cone.
$V = \frac{1}{3}Bh$ or $V = \frac{1}{3}\pi r^2 h$ (p. 332)

Theorem 6-10
Surface Area of a Sphere
The surface area of a sphere is four times the product of π and the square of the radius of the sphere.
S.A. $= 4\pi r^2$ (p. 338)

Theorem 6-11
Volume of a Sphere
The volume of a sphere is $\frac{4}{3}$ the product of π and the cube of the radius of the sphere.
$V = \frac{4}{3}\pi r^3$ (p. 339)

Chapter 7: Reasoning and Parallel Lines

Postulate 7-1
Corresponding Angles Postulate
If two parallel lines are cut by a transversal, then corresponding angles are congruent. (p. 364)

Theorem 7-1
Alternate Interior Angles Theorem
If two parallel lines are cut by a transversal, then alternate interior angles are congruent. (p. 364)

Theorem 7-2
Same-Side Interior Angles Theorem
If two parallel lines are cut by a transversal, then the pairs of same-side interior angles are supplementary. (p. 364)

Postulate 7-2
Converse of Corresponding Angles Postulate
If two lines are cut by a transversal so that a pair of corresponding angles are congruent, then the lines are parallel. (p. 371)

Postulates & Theorems

T670

Theorem 7-3
Converse of Alternate Interior Angles Theorem
If two lines are cut by a transversal so that a pair of alternate interior angles are congruent, then the lines are parallel. (p. 372)

Theorem 7-4
Converse of Same-Side Interior Angles Theorem
If two lines are cut by a transversal so that a pair of same-side interior angles are supplementary, then the lines are parallel. (p. 372)

Postulate 7-3
Euclid's Parallel Postulate
Through a point not on a line, there is one and only one line parallel to the given line. (p. 394)

Postulate 7-4
Spherical Geometry Parallel Postulate
Through a point not on a line, there is no line parallel to the given line. (p. 394)

Chapter 8:   Proving Triangles Congruent

Postulate 8-1
Side-Side-Side Postulate (SSS Postulate)
If three sides of one triangle are congruent to three sides of another triangle, then the two triangles are congruent. (p. 406)

Postulate 8-2
Side-Angle-Side Postulate (SAS Postulate)
If two sides and the included angle of one triangle are congruent to two sides and the included angle of another triangle, then the two triangles are congruent. (p. 408)

Postulate 8-3
Angle-Side-Angle Postulate (ASA Postulate)
If two angles and the included side of one triangle are congruent to two angles and the included side of another triangle, then the two triangles are congruent. (p. 414)

Theorem 8-1
Angle-Angle-Side Theorem (AAS Theorem)
If two angles and a nonincluded side of one triangle are congruent to two angles and the corresponding nonincluded side of another triangle, then the triangles are congruent. (p. 416)

Theorem 8-2
Hypotenuse-Leg Theorem (HL Theorem)
If the hypotenuse and a leg of one right triangle are congruent to the hypotenuse and a leg of another right triangle, then the triangles are congruent. (p. 420)

Chapter 9:   Quadrilaterals

Theorem 9-1
Opposite sides of a parallelogram are congruent. (p. 448)

Theorem 9-2
Opposite angles of a parallelogram are congruent. (p. 449)

Theorem 9-3
The diagonals of a parallelogram bisect each other. (p. 450)

Theorem 9-4
If three (or more) parallel lines cut off congruent segments on one transversal, then they cut off congruent segments on every transversal. (p. 450)

Theorem 9-5
If the diagonals of a quadrilateral bisect each other, then the quadrilateral is a parallelogram. (p. 455)

Theorem 9-6
If one pair of opposite sides of a quadrilateral are both congruent and parallel, then the quadrilateral is a parallelogram. (p. 456)

Theorem 9-7
If both pairs of opposite sides of a quadrilateral are congruent, then the quadrilateral is a parallelogram. (p. 456)

Theorem 9-8
If both pairs of opposite angles of a quadrilateral are congruent, then the quadrilateral is a parallelogram. (p. 456)

Theorem 9-9
Each diagonal of a rhombus bisects two angles of the rhombus. (p. 463)

Theorem 9-10
The diagonals of a rhombus are perpendicular. (p. 463)

Theorem 9-11
The area of a rhombus is equal to half the product of the lengths of its diagonals (p. 463)

Theorem 9-12
The diagonals of a rectangle are congruent. (p. 464)

Theorem 9-13
If one diagonal of a parallelogram bisects two angles of the parallelogram, then the parallelogram is a rhombus. (p. 464)

Theorem 9-14
If the diagonals of a parallelogram are perpendicular, then the parallelogram is a rhombus. (p. 464)

Theorem 9-15
If the diagonals of a parallelogram are congruent, then the parallelogram is a rectangle. (p. 464)

Theorem 9-16
Base angles of an isosceles trapezoid are congruent. (p. 470)

Theorem 9-17
The diagonals of an isosceles trapezoid are congruent. (p. 471)

Theorem 9-18
The diagonals of a kite are perpendicular. (p. 472)

Theorem 9-19
Trapezoid Midsegment Theorem
The midsegment of a trapezoid is (1) parallel to the bases and (2) half as long as the sum of the lengths of the bases. (p. 483)

Chapter 10:   Similarity

Postulate 10-1
Angle-Angle Similarity Postulate
(AA ~ Postulate)
If two angles of one triangle are congruent to two angles of another triangle, then the triangles are similar. (p. 504)

Theorem 10-1
Side-Angle-Side Similarity Theorem
(SAS ~ Theorem)
If an angle of one triangle is congruent to an angle of a second triangle, and the sides including the two angles are proportional, then the triangles are similar. (p. 506)

Theorem 10-2
Side-Side-Side Similarity Theorem
(SSS ~ Theorem)
If the corresponding sides of two triangles are proportional, then the triangles are similar. (p. 506)

Theorem 10-3
The altitude to the hypotenuse of a right triangle divides the triangle into two triangles that are similar to the original triangle and to each other. (p. 511)

Corollary 1
The length of the altitude to the hypotenuse of a right triangle is the geometric mean of the lengths of the segments of the hypotenuse. (p. 512)
Corollary 2
The altitude to the hypotenuse of a right triangle intersects it so that the length of each leg is the geometric mean of the length of its adjacent segment of the hypotenuse and the length of the entire hypotenuse. (p. 512)

Theorem 10-4
Side-Splitter Theorem
If a line is parallel to one side of a triangle and intersects the other two sides, then it divides those sides proportionally. (p. 517)

Corollary
If three parallel lines intersect two transversals, then the segments intercepted on the transversals are proportional. (p. 518)

Theorem 10-5
Triangle-Angle-Bisector Theorem
If a ray bisects an angle of a triangle, then it divides the opposite side into two segments that are proportional to the other two sides of the triangle. (p. 519)

Theorem 10-6
Perimeters and Areas of Similar Figures
If the similarity ratio of two similar figures is $a : b$, then (1) the ratio of their perimeters is $a : b$, and (2) the ratio of their areas is $a^2 : b^2$. (p. 525)

Theorem 10-7
Areas and Volumes of Similar Solids
If the similarity ratio of two similar solids is $a : b$, then (1) the ratio of their areas is $a^2 : b^2$, and (2) the ratio of their volumes is $a^3 : b^3$. (p. 532)

Chapter 11:   Right Triangle Trigonometry

Theorem 11-1
Area of a Triangle Given SAS
The area of a triangle is one half the product of the lengths of two sides and the sine of the included angle.

Area of triangle =
$\frac{1}{2} \cdot$ side length $\cdot$ side length $\cdot$ sine of included angle
(p. 575)

Chapter 12:   Chords, Secants, and Tangents

Theorem 12-1
Equation of a Circle
The standard form of an equation of a circle with center (h, k) and radius r is
$(x - h)^2 + (y - k)^2 = r^2$. (p. 586)

Theorem 12-2
If a line is tangent to a circle, then it is perpendicular to the radius drawn to the point of tangency. (p. 593)

Theorem 12-3
Converse of Theorem 12-2
If a line in the same plane as a circle is perpendicular to a radius at its endpoint on the circle, then the line is tangent to the circle. (p. 595)

Theorem 12-4
Two segments tangent to a circle from a point outside the circle are congruent. (p. 596)

Theorem 12-5
In the same circle or in congruent circles, (1) congruent central angles have congruent arcs, and (2) congruent arcs have congruent central angles. (p. 601)

Theorem 12-6
In the same circle or in congruent circles, (1) congruent chords have congruent arcs, and (2) congruent arcs have congruent chords. (p. 601)

Theorem 12-7
A diameter that is perpendicular to a chord bisects the chord and its arc. (p. 601)

Theorem 12-8
The perpendicular bisector of a chord contains the center of the circle. (p. 602)

Theorem 12-9
In the same circle or in congruent circles, (1) chords equidistant from the center are congruent, and (2) congruent chords are equidistant from the center. (p. 602)

Theorem 12-10
Inscribed Angle Theorem
The measure of an inscribed angle is half the measure of its intercepted arc. (p. 608)

Corollary 1
Two inscribed angles that intercept the same arc are congruent. (p. 609)
Corollary 2
An angle inscribed in a semicircle is a right angle. (p. 609)
Corollary 3
The opposite angles of a quadrilateral inscribed in a circle are supplementary. (p. 609)

Theorem 12-11
The measure of an angle formed by a chord and a tangent that intersect on a circle is half the measure of the intercepted arc. (p. 610)

Theorem 12-12
The measure of an angle formed by two chords that intersect inside a circle is half the sum of the measures of the intercepted arcs. (p. 615)

Theorem 12-13
The measure of an angle formed by two secants, two tangents, or a secant and a tangent drawn from a point outside the circle is half the difference of the measures of the intercepted arcs. (p. 615)

Theorem 12-14
If two chords intersect inside a circle, then the product of the lengths of the segments of one chord equals the product of the lengths of the segments of the other chord. (p. 621)

Theorem 12-15
If two secant segments are drawn from a point outside a circle, the product of the lengths of one secant segment and its external segment equals the product of the lengths of the other secant segment and its external segment. (p. 622)

Theorem 12-16
If a tangent and a secant are drawn from a point outside a circle, then the product of the lengths of the secant segment and its external segment equals the square of the length of the tangent segment. (p. 622)

Constructions

Construction 1
Congruent Segments
Construct a segment congruent to a given segment. (p. 40)

Construction 2
Congruent Angles
Construct an angle congruent to a given angle. (p. 40)

Construction 3
Perpendicular Bisector
Construct the perpendicular bisector of a segment. (p. 42)

Construction 4
Angle Bisector
Construct the bisector of an angle. (p. 42)

Construction 5
Parallel through a Point Not on a Line
Construct a line parallel to a given line and through a given point not on the line. (p. 377)

Construction 6
Perpendicular through a Point on a Line
Construct the perpendicular to a given line through a given point on the line. (p. 378)

Construction 7
Perpendicular through a Point Not on a Line
Construct the perpendicular to a given line from a given point not on the line. (p. 379)

T671

A

Examples

Acute angle (p. 27) An acute angle is an angle whose measure is between 0 and 90.

Acute triangle (p. 71) An acute triangle has three acute angles.

Adjacent angles (p. 48) Adjacent angles have a common side and a common vertex but no common interior points.

∠1 and ∠2 are adjacent. ∠3 and ∠4 are *not* adjacent.

Adjacent arcs (p. 98) Adjacent arcs are on the same circle and have exactly one point in common.

$\overparen{AB}$ and $\overparen{BC}$ are adjacent arcs.

Alternate interior angles (p. 363) Given two lines and a transversal, the alternate interior angles are nonadjacent interior angles that lie on opposite sides of the transversal.

Example: ∠1 and ∠2 are alternate interior angles, as are ∠3 and ∠4.

Altitude See *cone, cylinder, parallelogram, prism, pyramid,* and *trapezoid.*

Altitude of a triangle (p. 229) An altitude of a triangle is a perpendicular segment from a vertex to the line containing the side opposite that vertex.

altitude

Angle (p. 26) An angle is formed by two rays with the same endpoint. The rays are the *sides* of the angle and the common endpoint is the *vertex* of the angle.

Example: This angle could be named ∠A, ∠BAC, or ∠CAB.

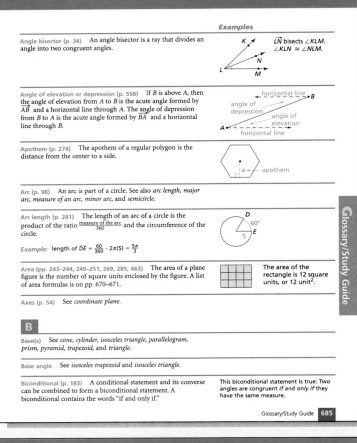

Examples

Angle bisector (p. 34) An angle bisector is a ray that divides an angle into two congruent angles.

$\overrightarrow{LN}$ bisects ∠KLM. ∠KLN ≅ ∠NLM.

Angle of elevation or depression (p. 556) If *B* is above *A*, then the angle of elevation from *A* to *B* is the acute angle formed by $\overrightarrow{AB}$ and a horizontal line through *A*. The angle of depression from *B* to *A* is the acute angle formed by $\overrightarrow{BA}$ and a horizontal line through *B*.

horizontal line, angle of depression, angle of elevation, horizontal line

Apothem (p. 274) The apothem of a regular polygon is the distance from the center to a side.

apothem

Arc (p. 98) An arc is part of a circle. See also *arc length, major arc, measure of an arc, minor arc,* and *semicircle.*

Arc length (p. 281) The length of an arc of a circle is the product of the ratio $\frac{\text{measure of the arc}}{360}$ and the circumference of the circle.

Example: length of $\overparen{DE}$ = $\frac{60}{360} \cdot 2\pi(5) = \frac{5\pi}{3}$

Area (pp. 243–244, 249–251, 269, 285, 463) The area of a plane figure is the number of square units enclosed by the figure. A list of area formulas is on pp. 670–671.

The area of the rectangle is 12 square units, or 12 unit².

Axes (p. 54) See *coordinate plane.*

B

Base(s) See *cone, cylinder, isosceles triangle, parallelogram, prism, pyramid, trapezoid,* and *triangle.*

Base angle See *isosceles trapezoid* and *isosceles triangle.*

Biconditional (p. 183) A conditional statement and its converse can be combined to form a biconditional statement. A biconditional contains the words "if and only if."

This biconditional statement is true: Two angles are congruent *if and only if* they have the same measure.

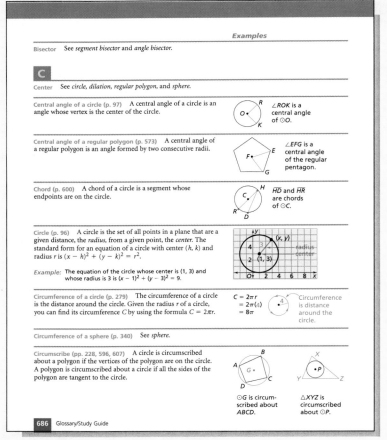

Examples

Bisector See *segment bisector* and *angle bisector.*

C

Center See *circle, dilation, regular polygon,* and *sphere.*

Central angle of a circle (p. 97) A central angle of a circle is an angle whose vertex is the center of the circle.

∠ROK is a central angle of ⊙O.

Central angle of a regular polygon (p. 573) A central angle of a regular polygon is an angle formed by two consecutive radii.

∠EFG is a central angle of the regular pentagon.

Chord (p. 600) A chord of a circle is a segment whose endpoints are on the circle.

$\overline{HD}$ and $\overline{HR}$ are chords of ⊙C.

Circle (p. 96) A circle is the set of all points in a plane that are a given distance, the *radius*, from a given point, the *center*. The standard form for an equation of a circle with center (*h, k*) and radius *r* is $(x - h)^2 + (y - k)^2 = r^2$.

Example: The equation of the circle whose center is (1, 3) and whose radius is 3 is $(x - 1)^2 + (y - 3)^2 = 9$.

Circumference of a circle (p. 279) The circumference of a circle is the distance around the circle. Given the radius *r* of a circle, you can find its circumference *C* by using the formula $C = 2\pi r$.

$C = 2\pi r$
$= 2\pi(4)$
$= 8\pi$

Circumference is distance around the circle.

Circumference of a sphere (p. 340) See *sphere.*

Circumscribe (pp. 228, 596, 607) A circle is circumscribed about a polygon if the vertices of the polygon are on the circle. A polygon is circumscribed about a circle if all the sides of the polygon are tangent to the circle.

⊙G is circumscribed about ABCD. △XYZ is circumscribed about ⊙P.

Examples

Collinear (p. 13) Collinear points lie on the same line.

Example: Points *A, B,* and *C* are collinear, but points *A, B,* and *Z* are noncollinear.

Complementary angles (p. 48) Two angles are complementary angles if the sum of their measures is 90.

Example: ∠HKI and ∠IKJ are complementary angles, as are ∠HKI and ∠EFG.

Composition of transformations (p. 135) A composition of two transformations is a transformation in which the second transformation is performed on the image of the first.

Example: If you reflect △ABC in line *m* to get △A'B'C' and then reflect △A'B'C' in line *n* to get △A"B"C", you perform a composition of transformations.

Concave polygon (p. 76) See *polygon.*

Concentric circles (p. 280) Concentric circles lie in the same plane and have the same center.

The two circles both have center *D* and are therefore concentric.

Conclusion (p. 182) In an *if-then* statement (conditional), the conclusion is the part that follows *then.*

In the statement, "If it rains, then I will go outside," the *conclusion* is "I will go outside."

Concurrent (p. 227) Concurrent lines are three or more lines that meet at one point. The point at which they meet is the *point of concurrency.*

Example: Point *E* is the point of concurrency of the bisectors of the angles of △ABC. The bisectors are concurrent.

Conditional (p. 182) A conditional is an *if-then statement.*

If you act politely, *then* you will earn respect.

Cone (p. 318)   A cone is a three-dimensional figure that has a circular *base*, a *vertex* not in the plane of the circle, and a curved lateral surface, as shown in the diagram. The *altitude* of a cone is the perpendicular segment from the vertex to the plane of the base. The *height* is the length of the altitude. A *right cone* is a cone in which the altitude contains the center of the base. The *slant height* of a right cone is the distance from the vertex to the edge of the base.

Congruence transformation (p. 124)   See *isometry*.

Congruent angles (p. 28)   Two angles are congruent if they have the same measure.

Example: $m\angle J = m\angle K$, so $\angle J \cong \angle K$.

Congruent arcs (p. 281)   Two arcs are congruent if they have the same measure and are in the same circle or congruent circles.

$\widehat{EF} \cong \widehat{FG}$ $\widehat{EF} \not\cong \widehat{LP}$

Congruent circles (p. 102)   Two circles are congruent if their radii are congruent.

⊙A and ⊙B have the same radius, so ⊙A ≅ ⊙B.

Congruent polygons (p. 102)   Two polygons are congruent if their corresponding sides are congruent and their corresponding angles are congruent.

$\triangle DEF \cong \triangle GHI$

Congruent segments (p. 25)   Two segments are congruent if they have the same length.

$\overline{AB} \cong \overline{CD}$

Conjecture (p. 5)   A conjecture is a conclusion reached by using inductive reasoning.

As you walk down the street, you see many people holding unopened umbrellas. You make the conjecture that the forecast must call for rain.

Consecutive angles (p. 449)   Consecutive angles of a polygon have a common side.

Example: In ▱JKLM, $\angle J$ and $\angle M$ are consecutive angles, as are $\angle J$ and $\angle K$. $\angle J$ and $\angle L$ are *not* consecutive.

Construction (p. 39)   A construction involves using only a straightedge and compass to make geometric figures. A *straightedge* is a ruler with no markings on it. A *compass* is a tool used to draw circles and arcs.

Example: The diagram shows the construction of a line perpendicular to a line ℓ through a point P on ℓ.

Contrapositive (p. 184)   The contrapositive of the conditional "if *p*, then *q*" is the conditional "if not *q*, then not *p*." A conditional and its contrapositive always have the same truth value.

Conditional: If a figure is a triangle, then it is a polygon.
Contrapositive: If a figure is not a polygon, then it is not a triangle.

Converse (p. 183)   The converse of the conditional "if *p*, then *q*" is the conditional "if *q*, then *p*."

Conditional: If you live in Cheyenne, then you live in Wyoming.
Converse: If you live in Wyoming, then you live in Cheyenne.

Convex polygon (p. 76)   See *polygon*.

Coordinate(s) of a point (pp. 25, 54)   The coordinate of a point on a number line is its distance and direction from the origin. The coordinates of a point on the coordinate plane are in the form (x, y), where x is the *x-coordinate* and y is the *y-coordinate*.

The coordinate of P is -3.

The coordinates of T are $(-4, 3)$.

Coordinate plane (p. 54)   The coordinate plane is formed by two number lines, called the *axes*, intersecting at right angles. The *x-axis* is the horizontal axis, and the *y-axis* is the vertical axis. The two axes meet at the *origin*, $O(0, 0)$. The axes divide the plane into four *quadrants*.

Coordinate proof (p. 201)   See *proof*.

Coplanar (p. 13)   Points and lines in the same plane are coplanar.

Example: Point C and $\overleftrightarrow{AB}$ are coplanar but points A, B, C, and Q are noncoplanar.

Corollary (p. 70)   A corollary is a statement that follows directly from a theorem.

Theorem: If two sides of a triangle are congruent, then the angles opposite those sides are congruent.
Corollary: If a triangle is equilateral, then it is equiangular.

Corresponding angles (p. 363)   Corresponding angles lie on the same side of the transversal *t* and in corresponding positions relative to ℓ and *m*.

Example: $\angle 1$ and $\angle 2$ are corresponding angles, as are $\angle 3$ and $\angle 4$, $\angle 5$ and $\angle 6$, and $\angle 7$ and $\angle 8$.

Cosine ratio (p. 551)   See *trigonometric ratios*.

Counterexample (p. 182)   A counterexample to a statement is a particular example or instance of the statement that is not true.

Statement: If you live in a state that begins with W, then you live in a state that does not border an ocean.
Counterexample: Washington

CPCTC (p. 426)   CPCTC is an abbreviation for "corresponding parts of congruent triangles are congruent."

Example: By the SAS Congruence Postulate, $\triangle KLM \cong \triangle QPR$. By CPCTC, you also know that $\angle L \cong \angle P$, $\angle M \cong \angle R$, and $\overline{LM} \cong \overline{PR}$.

Cube (p. 310)   A cube is a prism with all square faces.

Cylinder (p. 310)   A cylinder is a three-dimensional figure with two congruent circular *bases* that lie in parallel planes. An *altitude* of a cylinder is a perpendicular segment that joins the planes of the bases. Its length is the *height* of the cylinder. In a *right cylinder*, the segment joining the centers of the bases is an altitude. In an *oblique cylinder*, the segment joining the centers of the bases is not perpendicular to the planes containing the bases.

right cylinder   oblique cylinder

D

Decagon (p. 76)   A decagon is a polygon with ten sides.

Deductive reasoning (p. 46)   Deductive reasoning is a process of reasoning logically from given facts to a conclusion.

Based on the fact that the sum of any two even numbers is even, you can deduce that the product of an even number and any whole number is even.

Diagonal (p. 76)   See *polygon*.

Diameter (p. 96)   A diameter of a circle is a segment that contains the center of the circle and whose endpoints are on the circle. The term *diameter* can also mean the length of this segment.

$\overline{DM}$ is a diameter of ⊙C.

Dilation (p. 166)   A dilation, or *similarity transformation*, with *center C* and *scale factor n*, where $n > 0$, maps a point R to R' in such a way that R' is on $\overrightarrow{CR}$ and $CR' = n \cdot CR$. The center of a dilation is its own image. If $n > 1$, the dilation is an *enlargement*, and if $0 < n < 1$, the dilation is a *reduction*.

Example: $\overline{R'Q'}$ is the image of $\overline{RQ}$ under a dilation with center C and scale factor 3.

Distance from a point to a line (p. 221)   The distance from a point to a line is the length of the perpendicular segment from the point to the line.

Example: The distance from point P to line ℓ is *PT*.

Dodecagon (p. 76)   A dodecagon is a polygon with twelve sides.

E

Edge (p. 302)   See *polyhedron*.

Endpoint (p. 18)   See *ray* and *segment*.

Enlargement (p. 167)   See *dilation*.

Equiangular triangle (polygon) (pp. 71, 78)   An equiangular triangle (polygon) is a triangle (polygon) whose angles are all congruent.

Each angle of the pentagon is a 108° angle.

Equilateral triangle (polygon) (pp. 71, 78)   An equilateral triangle (polygon) is a triangle (polygon) whose sides are all congruent.

Each side of the quadrilateral is 1.5 cm long.

Euclidean geometry (p. 393)   Euclidean geometry is a geometry of the plane in which Euclid's Parallel Postulate is true.

Example: In Euclidean geometry, there is exactly one line parallel to line ℓ through point P.

Exterior angle of a polygon (p. 69)   An exterior angle of a polygon is an angle formed by a side and an extension of an adjacent side.

Example: $\angle KLM$ is an exterior angle of $\triangle JKL$.

F

Face (p. 302)   See *polyhedron*.

Flow proof (p. 372)   See *proof*.

Foundation drawing (p. 110)   A foundation drawing shows the base of a structure and the height of each part.

Example: The first drawing is a foundation drawing; the second is an isometric drawing based on the foundation drawing.

Frieze pattern (p. 137)   A frieze pattern, also known as a *strip pattern*, repeats itself along a straight line. A frieze pattern can be mapped onto itself by a *translation*.

G

Geometric mean (p. 512)   The geometric mean of two positive numbers a and b is the positive number x such that $\frac{a}{x} = \frac{x}{b}$.

The geometric mean of 6 and 24 is 12. $\frac{6}{x} = \frac{x}{24} \rightarrow x^2 = 144 \rightarrow x = 12$

Glide reflection (p. 146)   A glide reflection is a composition of three reflections in lines that intersect in more than one point. Equivalently, a glide reflection is a composition of a translation followed by a reflection in a line parallel to the translation vector.

Example: The blue G in the diagram is the glide reflection image of the black G.

Glide reflectional symmetry (p. 161)   A repeating pattern has glide reflectional symmetry if it can be mapped onto itself by a glide reflection.

Example: The tessellation shown can be mapped onto itself by a glide reflection in the given line and the given vector.

Golden rectangle, Golden ratio (p. 498)   A *golden rectangle* is a rectangle that can be divided into a square and a rectangle that is similar to the original rectangle. The *golden ratio* is the ratio of the length of a golden rectangle to its width. The value of the golden ratio is $\frac{1 + \sqrt{5}}{2}$, or about 1.62.

$ABCD$ is a rectangle. $ADFE$ is a square.

$ABCD \sim FEBC$

Great circle (p. 340)   A great circle is the intersection of a sphere and a plane containing the center of the sphere. A great circle divides a sphere into two *hemispheres*.

hemispheres — great circle

H

Half-turn (p. 154)   A rotation of 180° is called a half-turn.

Example: The blue R in the diagram is the image of the black R under a half-turn about the given point.

180°

Height   See *cone, cylinder, parallelogram, prism, pyramid, trapezoid,* and *triangle*.

Hemisphere (p. 340)   See *great circle*.

Heptagon (p. 76)   A heptagon is a polygon with seven sides.

Heron's formula (p. 253)   A formula for finding the area of a triangle given the lengths of its sides.

$A = \sqrt{s(s-a)(s-b)(s-c)}$, where s is the semiperimeter of the triangle.

Hexagon (p. 76)   A hexagon is a polygon with six sides.

Hypotenuse (p. 256)   See *right triangle*.

Hypothesis (p. 182)   In an *if-then statement* (conditional), the hypothesis is the part that follows *if*.

In the statement "If she leaves, then I will go with her," the *hypothesis* is "she leaves."

I

Identity (p. 551)   An identity is an equation that is true for all allowed values of the variable.

$\sin x° = \cos(90 - x)°$ for $0 < x < 90$

Image (p. 124)   See *transformation*.

Indirect measurement (p. 505)   Indirect measurement is used to measure things that are difficult to measure directly.

Example: By measuring the distances shown in the diagram and using properties of similar figures, you can find the height of the taller tower.
$\frac{240}{540} = \frac{x}{1192} \rightarrow x \approx 529.8$ ft

240 ft
540 ft
1192 ft

Indirect proof (p. 208)   See *indirect reasoning* and *proof*.

Indirect reasoning (p. 207)   In indirect reasoning, all possibilities are considered and then all but one are proved false. The remaining possibility must be true.

Eduardo spent more than $60 on two books at a store. Prove that at least one book costs more than $30.

Proof: Suppose neither costs more than $30. Then he spent no more than $60 at the store. Since this contradicts the given information, at least one book costs $30 or more.

Inductive reasoning (p. 5)   Inductive reasoning is a type of reasoning that reaches conclusions based on a pattern of specific examples or past events.

You see four people walk into a building. Each person emerges with a small bag containing hot food. You use inductive reasoning to conclude that this building contains a restaurant.

Initial point (p. 133)   See *vector*.

Inscribe (pp. 228, 596, 607)   A circle is inscribed in a polygon if the sides of the polygon are tangent to the circle. A polygon is inscribed in a circle if the vertices of the polygon are on the circle.

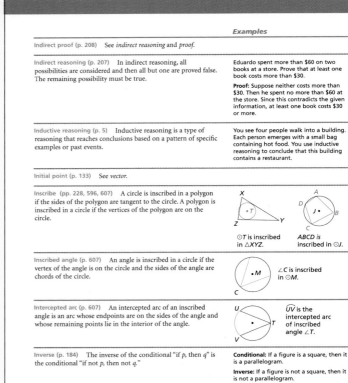

$\odot T$ is inscribed in $\triangle XYZ$.

$ABCD$ is inscribed in $\odot J$.

Inscribed angle (p. 607)   An angle is inscribed in a circle if the vertex of the angle is on the circle and the sides of the angle are chords of the circle.

$\angle C$ is inscribed in $\odot M$.

Intercepted arc (p. 607)   An intercepted arc of an inscribed angle is an arc whose endpoints are on the sides of the angle and whose remaining points lie in the interior of the angle.

$\overarc{UV}$ is the intercepted arc of inscribed angle $\angle T$.

Inverse (p. 184)   The inverse of the conditional "if p, then q" is the conditional "if not p, then not q."

Conditional: If a figure is a square, then it is a parallelogram.

Inverse: If a figure is not a square, then it is not a parallelogram.

Isometric drawing (p. 109) An isometric drawing of a three-dimensional object shows a corner view of the figure.

Isometry (p. 124) An isometry, also known as a *congruence transformation*, is a transformation in which the original figure and its image are congruent.

The four isometries are reflections, rotations, translations, and glide reflections.

Isosceles trapezoid (p. 91, 470) An isosceles trapezoid is a trapezoid whose legs are congruent.

Isosceles triangle (pp. 71, 188) An isosceles triangle is a triangle that has at least two congruent sides. In an isosceles triangle that is not equilateral, the two congruent sides are called *legs* and the third side is called the *base*. The two angles with the base as a side are *base angles* and the third angle is the *vertex angle*.

K

Kite (p. 91) A kite is a quadrilateral with two pairs of congruent adjacent sides and no opposite sides congruent.

L

Lateral area (pp. 309, 311, 316, 318) The lateral area of a prism or pyramid is the sum of the areas of the lateral faces. The lateral area of a cylinder or cone is the area of the curved surface. A list of lateral area formulas is on pages 670–671.

L.A. of pyramid $= \frac{1}{2}p\ell$
$= \frac{1}{2}(20)(6)$
$= 60 \text{ cm}^2$

Lateral face See *prism* and *pyramid*.

Leg See *isosceles triangle, right triangle,* and *trapezoid*.

Line (pp. 13, 393) In Euclidean geometry, you can think of a line as a series of points that extends in two directions without end. In spherical geometry, you can think of a line as a great circle of a sphere.

Locus (p. 220) A locus is the set of points that meet a stated condition.

Example: The blue figure is the locus of points in a plane 1 cm from $\overline{DC}$.

M

Major arc (p. 98) A major arc of a circle is any arc longer than a semicircle.

$\overset{\frown}{DEF}$ is a major arc of $\odot C$.

Map (p. 124) See *transformation*.

Matrix (p. 131) A matrix is a rectangular array of numbers. Each item in a matrix is called an *entry*.

The matrix $\begin{bmatrix} 1 & -2 \\ 0 & 13 \end{bmatrix}$ has dimensions 2×2. The number 1 is the entry in the first row and first column.

Measure of an angle (p. 26) Angles are measured in degrees. An angle can be measured with a *protractor*.

$m\angle ZAY = 80$, $m\angle YAX = 60$, and $m\angle ZAX = 140$.

Measure of an arc (p. 98) The measure of a minor arc is the measure of its central angle. The measure of a major arc is 360 minus the measure of its related minor arc.

$m\overset{\frown}{TY} = 70$
$m\overset{\frown}{TOY} = 290$

Median of a triangle (p. 229) A median of a triangle is a segment that joins a vertex of the triangle and the midpoint of the side opposite that vertex.

Midpoint of a segment (p. 33) A midpoint of a segment is the point that divides the segment into two congruent segments.

midpoint of $\overline{AB}$

Midsegment of a trapezoid (p. 483) The segment that joins the midpoints of the legs of a trapezoid is the midsegment of the trapezoid.

Midsegment of a triangle (pp. 201, 235) A midsegment of a triangle is a segment that joins the midpoints of two sides of the triangle.

Minor arc (p. 98) A minor arc of a circle is any arc shorter than a semicircle.

$\overset{\frown}{KC}$ is a minor arc of $\odot S$.

N

Negation (p. 184) A negation of a statement has the opposite meaning of the original statement.

Statement: The angle is obtuse.

Negation: The angle is not obtuse.

Net (p. 302) A net is a two-dimensional pattern that you can fold to form a three-dimensional figure.

Example: The net shown can be folded into a prism with pentagonal bases.

net

n-gon (p. 76) An n-gon is a polygon with n sides.

Nonagon (p. 76) A nonagon is a polygon with nine sides.

O

Oblique cylinder or prism See *cylinder* and *prism*.

Obtuse angle (p. 27) An obtuse angle is an angle whose measure is between 90 and 180.

147°

Obtuse triangle (p. 71) An obtuse triangle has one obtuse angle.

Octagon (p. 76) An octagon is a polygon with eight sides.

Opposite rays (p. 18) Opposite rays are collinear rays with the same endpoint. They form a line.

$\overrightarrow{UT}$ and $\overrightarrow{UN}$ are opposite rays.

Orientation (p. 126) Two figures have *opposite* orientation if a reflection is needed to map one onto the other. If a reflection is not needed to map one figure onto the other, the figures have the *same* orientation.

R Я The two R's have opposite orientation.

Origin (p. 54) See *coordinate plane*.

Orthographic drawing (p. 111) An orthographic drawing shows the top view, front view, and right-side view of a three-dimensional figure.

Example: The diagram shows an isometric drawing (upper right) and the three views that make up an orthographic drawing.

Top

Front

Right

P

Paragraph proof (p. 195) See *proof*.

Parallel lines (pp. 18, 363) Two lines are parallel if they lie in the same plane and do not intersect. The symbol ∥ means "is parallel to."

$\ell \parallel m$

These symbols indicate parallel lines.

Parallelogram (pp. 91, 249–250) A parallelogram is a quadrilateral with two pairs of parallel sides. You can choose any side to be the *base*. An *altitude* is any segment perpendicular to the line containing the base drawn from the side opposite the base. The *height* is the length of an altitude.

altitude

base

T675

Parallel planes (p. 19) Parallel planes are planes that do not intersect.

Planes *Y* and *Z* are parallel.

Pentagon (p. 76) A pentagon is a polygon with five sides.

Perimeter of a polygon (p. 242) The perimeter of a polygon is the sum of the lengths of its sides.

$p = 4 + 4 + 5 + 3$
$= 16$ in.

Perpendicular bisector (p. 34) The perpendicular bisector of a segment is a segment, ray, line, or plane that is perpendicular to the segment at its midpoint.

Example: $\overleftrightarrow{YZ}$ is the perpendicular bisector of $\overline{AB}$. It is perpendicular to $\overline{AB}$ and intersects it at its midpoint *M*.

Perpendicular lines (p. 33) Two lines are perpendicular if they intersect and form right angles. The symbol ⊥ means "is perpendicular to."

$m \perp n$

Perspective drawing (p. 385) Perspective drawing is a way of drawing objects on a flat surface so that they look the same way as they appear to the eye. In *one-point perspective*, there is one *vanishing point*. In *two-point perspective*, there are two vanishing points.

one-point perspective

two-point perspective

Pi (p. 279) Pi (π) is the ratio of the circumference of any circle to its diameter. The number π is irrational and can be approximated by $\pi \approx 3.14159$.

$\pi = \dfrac{C}{d}$

Plane (pp. 13, 393) In Euclidean geometry, you can think of a plane as a flat surface that extends in all directions without end. It has no thickness. In spherical geometry, you can think of a plane as the surface of a sphere.

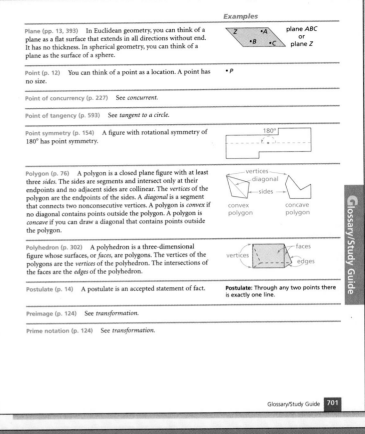

plane *ABC* or plane *Z*

Point (p. 12) You can think of a point as a location. A point has no size.

• *P*

Point of concurrency (p. 227) See *concurrent*.

Point of tangency (p. 593) See *tangent to a circle*.

Point symmetry (p. 154) A figure with rotational symmetry of 180° has point symmetry.

180°

Polygon (p. 76) A polygon is a closed plane figure with at least three *sides*. The sides are segments and intersect only at their endpoints and no adjacent sides are collinear. The *vertices* of the polygon are the endpoints of the sides. A *diagonal* is a segment that connects two nonconsecutive vertices. A polygon is *convex* if no diagonal contains points outside the polygon. A polygon is *concave* if you can draw a diagonal that contains points outside the polygon.

vertices
diagonal
sides
convex polygon
concave polygon

Polyhedron (p. 302) A polyhedron is a three-dimensional figure whose surfaces, or *faces*, are polygons. The vertices of the polygons are the *vertices* of the polyhedron. The intersections of the faces are the *edges* of the polyhedron.

vertices
faces
edges

Postulate (p. 14) A postulate is an accepted statement of fact.

Postulate: Through any two points there is exactly one line.

Preimage (p. 124) See *transformation*.

Prime notation (p. 124) See *transformation*.

Prism (p. 309) A prism is a polyhedron with two congruent, parallel faces, called the *bases*. The other faces are parallelograms and are called the *lateral faces*. An *altitude* of a prism is a perpendicular segment that joins the planes of the bases. Its length is the *height* of the prism. In a *right prism*, the lateral faces are rectangular and a lateral edge is an altitude. In an *oblique prism*, some or all of the lateral faces are nonrectangular.

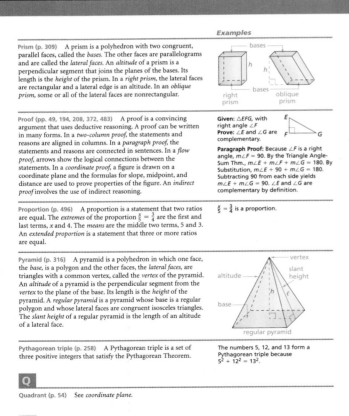

bases
right prism
bases
oblique prism

Proof (pp. 49, 194, 208, 372, 483) A proof is a convincing argument that uses deductive reasoning. A proof can be written in many forms. In a *two-column proof*, the statements and reasons are aligned in columns. In a *paragraph proof*, the statements and reasons are connected in sentences. In a *flow proof*, arrows show the logical connections between the statements. In a *coordinate proof*, a figure is drawn on a coordinate plane and the formulas for slope, midpoint, and distance are used to prove properties of the figure. An *indirect proof* involves the use of indirect reasoning.

Given: △*EFG*, with right angle ∠*F*
Prove: ∠*E* and ∠*G* are complementary.

Paragraph Proof: Because ∠*F* is a right angle, $m\angle F = 90$. By the Triangle Angle-Sum Thm., $m\angle E + m\angle F + m\angle G = 180$. By Substitution, $m\angle E + 90 + m\angle G = 180$. Subtracting 90 from each side yields $m\angle E + m\angle G = 90$. ∠*E* and ∠*G* are complementary by definition.

Proportion (p. 496) A proportion is a statement that two ratios are equal. The *extremes* of the proportion $\frac{x}{5} = \frac{3}{4}$ are the first and last terms, *x* and 4. The *means* are the middle two terms, 5 and 3. An *extended proportion* is a statement that three or more ratios are equal.

$\frac{x}{5} = \frac{3}{4}$ is a proportion.

Pyramid (p. 316) A pyramid is a polyhedron in which one face, the *base*, is a polygon and the other faces, the *lateral faces*, are triangles with a common vertex, called the *vertex* of the pyramid. An *altitude* of a pyramid is the perpendicular segment from the *vertex* to the plane of the base. Its length is the *height* of the pyramid. A *regular pyramid* is a pyramid whose base is a regular polygon and whose lateral faces are congruent isosceles triangles. The *slant height* of a regular pyramid is the length of an altitude of a lateral face.

vertex
slant height
altitude
base
regular pyramid

Pythagorean triple (p. 258) A Pythagorean triple is a set of three positive integers that satisfy the Pythagorean Theorem.

The numbers 5, 12, and 13 form a Pythagorean triple because $5^2 + 12^2 = 13^2$.

Quadrant (p. 54) See *coordinate plane*.

Quadrilateral (p. 76) A quadrilateral is a polygon with four sides.

R

Radius of a circle (p. 96) A radius of a circle is any segment with one endpoint on the circle and the other endpoint at the center of the circle. *Radius* can also mean the length of this segment.

$\overline{DE}$ is a radius of ⊙*D*.

Radius of a regular polygon (p. 274) The radius of a regular polygon is the distance from the center to a vertex.

radius

Ray (p. 18) A ray is a part of a line consisting of one *endpoint* and all the points of the line on one side of the endpoint.

endpoint of $\overrightarrow{AB}$

Rectangle (p. 91) A rectangle is a parallelogram with four right angles.

Reduction (p. 167) See *dilation*.

Reflection (p. 126) A reflection in line *r* is a transformation such that if a point *A* is on line *r*, then the image of *A* is itself, and if a point *B* is not on line *r*, then its image *B'* is the point such that *r* is the perpendicular bisector of $\overline{BB'}$.

Reflectional symmetry (p. 152) A figure has reflectional symmetry, or *line symmetry*, if there is a reflection that maps the figure onto itself.

A reflection in the given line maps the figure onto itself.

Regular polygon (pp. 78, 274) A regular polygon is a polygon that is both equilateral and equiangular. Its *center* is the center of the circumscribed circle.

ABCDEF is a regular hexagon. Point *X* is its center.

Regular pyramid (p. 316) See *pyramid*.

Glossary/Study Guide

T676

Remote interior angles (p. 69) For each exterior angle of a triangle, the two nonadjacent interior angles are called its remote interior angles.

∠1 and ∠2 are remote interior angles of ∠3.

Resultant (p. 568) The sum of two vectors is called a resultant.

$\vec{w}$ is the resultant of $\vec{u} + \vec{v}$.

Rhombus (p. 91) A rhombus is a parallelogram with four congruent sides.

Right angle (p. 27) A right angle is an angle whose measure is 90.

90° This symbol indicates a right angle.

Right cone (p. 318) See *cone*.

Right cylinder (p. 310) See *cylinder*.

Right prism (p. 309) See *prism*.

Right triangle (pp. 71, 256) A right triangle contains one right angle. The side opposite the right angle is the *hypotenuse* and the other two sides are the *legs*.

leg / hypotenuse / leg

Rotation (p. 139) A rotation of $x°$ about a point R is a transformation such that for any point V, its image is the point V' where $RV = RV'$ and $m\angle VRV' = x$. The image of R is itself. All rotations in this text are *counterclockwise* rotations.

Rotational symmetry (p. 154) A figure has rotational symmetry if there is a rotation of 180° or less that maps the figure onto itself.

The figure has 120° rotational symmetry.

S

Same-side interior angles (p. 363) Same-side interior angles lie on the same side of the transversal t and between ℓ and m.

Example: ∠1 and ∠2 are same-side interior angles, as are ∠3 and ∠4.

Scalar multiplication (p. 168) In scalar multiplication, each entry in a matrix is multiplied by the same number, the *scalar*.

$$2 \cdot \begin{bmatrix} 1 & 0 \\ -2 & 3 \end{bmatrix} = \begin{bmatrix} 2(1) & 2(0) \\ 2(-2) & 2(3) \end{bmatrix} = \begin{bmatrix} 2 & 0 \\ -4 & 6 \end{bmatrix}$$

Scale drawing (p. 497) In a scale drawing the *scale* compares each length in the drawing to the actual length being represented.

Scale: 1 in. = 30 ft

Scale factor (p. 166) The scale factor of a dilation is the number that describes the size change from an original figure to its image. See also *dilation*.

Example: The scale factor of the dilation that maps $\triangle ABC$ to $\triangle A'B'C'$ is $\frac{1}{2}$.

Scalene triangle (p. 71) A scalene triangle has no sides congruent.

Secant (p. 614) A secant is a line, ray, or segment that intersects a circle at two points.

$\overleftrightarrow{AB}$ is a secant of ⊙C.

Sector of a circle (p. 286) A sector of a circle is the region bounded by two radii and their intercepted arc.

sector AOB

Segment (p. 18) A segment is a part of a line consisting of two points, called *endpoints*, and all points between them.

endpoints of $\overline{DE}$

Segment bisector (p. 33) A segment bisector is a line, segment, ray, or plane that intersects a segment at its midpoint.

ℓ bisects $\overline{KJ}$.

Segment of a circle (p. 287) The part of a circle bounded by an arc and the segment joining its endpoints is a segment of a circle.

Example: The portion of the interior of the circle bounded by ∠ACB and outside is a segment of ⊙C.

segment of ⊙C

Semicircle (p. 98) A semicircle is half a circle.

semicircle

Side See *angle* and *polygon*.

Similarity ratio (p. 103) The ratio of the lengths of corresponding sides of similar polygons or solids is the similarity ratio.

$\triangle JKL \sim \triangle MNO$

Similarity ratio = $\frac{2}{5}$

Similarity transformation (p. 167) See *dilation*.

Similar polygons (p. 103) Two polygons are similar if corresponding angles are congruent and corresponding sides are proportional. The symbol ∼ means "is similar to."

$\frac{DE}{AB} = \frac{EF}{BC} = \frac{FD}{CA}$

$\triangle ABC \sim \triangle DEF$

Similar solids (p. 531) Similar solids have the same shape and all their corresponding dimensions are proportional.

Sine ratio (p. 551) See *trigonometric ratios*.

Skew (p. 19) Two lines are skew if they do not lie in the same plane.

$\overleftrightarrow{AB}$ and $\overleftrightarrow{EF}$ are skew.

Slant height See *cone* and *pyramid*.

Slope of a line (p. 83) The slope of a line in the coordinate plane is the ratio of vertical change to the corresponding horizontal change. If (x_1, y_1) and (x_2, y_2) are points on a nonvertical line, then the slope is $\frac{y_2 - y_1}{x_2 - x_1}$. The slope of a horizontal line is 0, and the slope of a vertical line is undefined.

Example: The line containing $P(-1, -1)$ and $Q(1, -2)$ has slope $\frac{-2 - (-1)}{1 - (-1)} = \frac{-1}{2} = -\frac{1}{2}$.

Space (p. 12) Space is the set of all points.

Sphere (pp. 337, 340) A sphere is the set of all points in space a given distance r, the *radius*, from a given point C, the *center*. A *great circle* is the intersection of a sphere and a plane containing the center of the sphere. The *circumference* of a sphere is the circumference of any great circle of the sphere.

great circle / radius / center

Spherical geometry (p. 393) In spherical geometry, a plane is considered to be the surface of a sphere and a line is considered to be a great circle of the sphere. In spherical geometry, through a point not on a given line, there is no line parallel to the given line.

In spherical geometry, lines are represented through great circles of a sphere.

Square (p. 91) A square is a parallelogram with four congruent sides and four right angles.

Straight angle (p. 27) A straight angle is an angle whose measure is 180.

$m\angle AOB = 180$

Supplementary angles (p. 48) Two angles are supplementary if the sum of their measures is 180.

Example: ∠MNP and ∠ONP are supplementary, as are ∠MNP and ∠QRS.

Surface area (pp. 309, 311, 316, 318, 338) The surface area of a prism, pyramid, cylinder, or cone is the sum of the lateral area and the areas of the bases. A list of surface-area formulas is on pages 670–671.

S.A. of prism = L.A. + 2B
= 66 + 2(28)
= 122 cm²

Symmetry (pp. 152–154) A figure has symmetry if there is an isometry that maps the figure onto itself. See *glide reflectional symmetry, point symmetry, reflectional symmetry, rotational symmetry,* and *translational symmetry*.

A regular pentagon has reflectional symmetry and 72° rotational symmetry.

Glossary/Study Guide

T677

Tangent ratio (p. 544) See *trigonometric ratios*.

Tangent to a circle (p. 593) A tangent to a circle is a line, segment, or ray in the plane of the circle that intersects the circle in exactly one point. That point is the *point of tangency*.

Example: Line ℓ is tangent to ⊙C at D.

Terminal point (p. 133) See *vector*.

Tessellation (pp. 159–160) A tessellation, or *tiling*, is a repeating pattern of figures that completely covers a plane without gaps or overlap. A *pure tessellation* is a tessellation that consists of congruent copies of one figure.

Theorem (p. 49) A conjecture that is proven is a theorem.

The theorem "Vertical angles are congruent" can be proven by using postulates, definitions, properties, and previously stated theorems.

Transformation (p. 124) A transformation is a change in the position, size, or shape of a figure. The given figure is called the *preimage* and the resulting figure is called the *image*. A transformation *maps* a figure onto its image. *Prime notation* is sometimes used to identify image points. In the diagram, X′ (read "X prime") is the image of X.

Preimage   Image

△XYZ → △X′Y′Z′

Translation (p. 132) A translation is a transformation that moves points the same distance and in the same direction. A transformation can be described by a vector.

Example: The blue triangle in the diagram is the image of the black triangle under the translation ⟨−5, −2⟩.

Translational symmetry (p. 161) A repeating pattern has translational symmetry if there is a translation that maps the pattern onto itself.

Example: The tessellation shown can be mapped onto itself by the given translation.

Transversal (p. 363) A transversal is a line that intersects two coplanar lines in two points.

t is a transversal of ℓ and m.

Trapezoid (pp. 91, 269, 470) A trapezoid is a quadrilateral with exactly one pair of parallel sides, the *bases*. The nonparallel sides are called the *legs* of the trapezoid. Each pair of angles adjacent to a base are *base angles* of the trapezoid. An *altitude* of a trapezoid is a perpendicular segment from one base to the line containing the other base. Its length is called the *height* of the trapezoid.

Example: In trapezoid ABCD, ∠ADC and ∠BCD are one pair of base angles, and ∠DAB and ∠ABC are the other.

Triangle (pp. 71, 251) A triangle is a polygon with three sides. You can choose any side to be the *base*. Then the *height* is the length of the altitude drawn to the line containing that base.

Trigonometric ratios (pp. 544, 551) In right triangle △ABC with acute angle ∠A:

$$\text{sine of } \angle A = \sin A = \frac{\text{leg opposite } \angle A}{\text{hypotenuse}}$$

$$\text{cosine of } \angle A = \cos A = \frac{\text{leg adjacent to } \angle A}{\text{hypotenuse}}$$

$$\text{tangent of } \angle A = \tan A = \frac{\text{leg opposite } \angle A}{\text{leg adjacent to } \angle A}$$

Truth value (p. 182) When you determine whether a conditional statement is true or false, you determine its truth value.

The truth value of the statement "If a figure is a triangle, then it has four sides." is **false**.

Two-column proof (p. 194) See *proof*.

Vector (pp. 133, 563) A vector is any quantity that has magnitude (size) and direction. You can represent a vector as an arrow that starts at one point, the *initial point*, and goes to a second point, the *terminal point*. A vector can be described by *ordered pair notation* ⟨x, y⟩, where x represents horizontal change from the initial point to the terminal point, and y represents vertical change from the initial point to the terminal point.

Vector $\overrightarrow{ON}$ has initial point O and terminal point N. The ordered pair notation for the vector is ⟨5, 2⟩.

Vertex See *angle, cone, polygon, polyhedron,* and *pyramid*. The plural form of vertex is *vertices*.

Vertex angle (p. 188) See *isosceles triangle*.

Vertical angles (p. 48) Two angles are vertical angles if their sides are opposite rays.

∠1 and ∠2 are vertical angles, as are ∠3 and ∠4.

Volume (p. 324) Volume is a measure of the space a figure occupies. A list of volume formulas is on pages 670–671.

The volume of this prism is 24 cubic units, or 24 unit³.

T678

CHAPTER 1

Lesson 1-1   pages 7–10

ON YOUR OWN 1. 80, 160   **3.** −3, 4   **5.** 3, 0   **7.** N, T
9. 720, 5040   **11.** $\frac{1}{36}, \frac{1}{49}$ **15.** The trip takes about 25 min.

23. a line parallel to the first two and midway between them   **25.** It's possible but not likely. As he grows older, his growth will slow down and eventually stop.

27a.

There will be about 15,000 radio stations.   **29.** 123454321
31. 75°
33a.

33b. 20^2, or 400; the sequence is the squares of successive counting numbers.   **33c.** n^2 **35a.** Women may soon outrun men in running competitions.   **35b.** The conclusion was based on continuing the trend shown in past records.   **35c.** The conclusions are based on fairly recent records for women, and those rates of improvement may not continue. The conclusion about the marathon is most suspect because records date only from 1955.
37a. Answers may vary. Sample: Leap years are divisible by 4.   **37b.** Answers may vary. Sample: 2020, 2100, 2400
37c. Leap years are divisible by 4 except years ending in 00, which are leap years only if they are divisible by 400.
39. 2

MIXED REVIEW 53a. *B* and *W*   **53b.** *N* and *T*

Toolbox   page 11

1. $\frac{3}{10}$ **5.** $\frac{9}{10}$ **9.** $\frac{1}{10}$ **13.** $\frac{1}{3}$ **15.** $\frac{2}{3}$ **17.** $\frac{2}{3}$

Lesson 1-2   pages 15–17

ON YOUR OWN 1. no   **3.** no   **5.** no   **7.** no   **9.** yes
11. C   **13.** yes   **15.** no   **17.** yes   **19.** yes   **21.** no
23. U   **25.** Answers may vary. Sample: plane *XWST* and plane *UVST*   **29.** An infinite number; infinitely many planes can intersect in one line.   **31.** C   **33.** 1; points *A*, *B*, and *C* are points on the 2 lines and these 3 points are

noncollinear, so exactly 1 plane contains them.   **35.** never
37. always   **39.** never   **41a.** $\frac{1}{4}$ **41b.** 1   **43.** collinear
45. noncollinear

MIXED REVIEW 49. 34   **51.** 20   **53.** 3   **55.** yes   **57.** no

Lesson 1-3   pages 20–22

ON YOUR OWN 1. $\overline{DF}$ **3.** $\overline{CF}, \overline{BE}$ **5.** plane *ABC* and plane *DEF*   **7.** $\overline{RS}, \overline{RT}, \overline{RW}, \overline{ST}, \overline{SW}, \overline{TW}$
9.   **11.**

13. false   **15.** true   **17.** true   **19.** true   **21.** never
23. always   **25.** always   **27.** always   **29.** always
35. The lines of intersection are parallel. Answers will vary. Sample: the ceiling and floor intersect a wall in two parallel lines.   **39.** E

MIXED REVIEW 41. −22, −29   **43.** by 2 points on the line or with a single lower-case letter   **45.** with the word *plane* followed either by a single capital letter or the names of at least 3 noncollinear points in the plane   **47.** 6
49. 3   **51.** 3   **53.** 9   **55.** 9   **57.**
61.

Toolbox   page 23

1. −9   **5.** 16   **9.** 6   **13.** $-\frac{7}{3}$ **17.** 4

Lesson 1-4   pages 28–31

ON YOUR OWN 1. 9   **3.** 11   **5.** false   **7.** false
9. $\overline{AB} \cong \overline{CD}, \overline{AC} \cong \overline{BD}$ **11.** 24   **13.** 13; 40; 24
15. 125   **17.** Answers may vary. Samples: **17a.** ∠*QVM*, ∠*PVN*   **17b.** ∠*QVP*, ∠*MVN*   **17c.** ∠*MQV*, ∠*QNP*
21–23. Estimates may vary slightly.   **21.** 60; acute
23. 135; obtuse   **27.** 15   **33.** 8   **35.** 7

MIXED REVIEW 37. 25   **39.** 30   **41.** coplanar
43. collinear   **45.**   **47.**

CHECKPOINT 1. 29, 31.5   **2.** 3.45678, 3.456789   **3.** −162, 486   **5.** yes   **6.** no   **7.** yes   **8.** yes   **9.** yes   **10.** H
11. $\overleftrightarrow{DC}, \overline{EF}, \overline{AB}$ **12.** Sample: $\overleftrightarrow{AB}, \overleftrightarrow{EH}$ **13.** Sample: plane *ABFE* ∥ plane *DCGH* or plane *HEFG* ∥ plane *ABCD*
14. Sample: ∠*EAB*; ∠*AEF*; ∠*EHG*   **15.** 17

Lesson 1-5   pages 35–38

ON YOUR OWN 1. b   **3.** 6   **5.** 5   **7.** *CM* (or *DM*)
9. 20; 40   **11.** *AOC*   **13.** $\overrightarrow{OB}$; ∠*AOC*   **15.** true
17. true   **19.** false   **21.** false
23.   **25.**

27.   **29.** Q   **31.** −4   **33.** 12   **35.** 4
37. 6   **39.** 20   **41a.** one; infinitely many   **41b.** one
41c. infinitely many   **47.** b
49. 15   **51.** 48   **53.** D

55. perpendicular; it intersects

MIXED REVIEW 57. Answers may vary. Sample: ∠*AOD*
59. ∠*BOE*   **61.** 3   **63.** ∠*APT* ≅ ∠*TPR*

Lesson 1-6   pages 43–44

ON YOUR OWN 1.

3.   **5.**

7. $m\angle 1 + m\angle 2$ **9.**

11.   **15.** The angle bisectors of the 3 angles of any triangle intersect in a single point.

17a. Sample: **17b.** 60

MIXED REVIEW 39.
41.   **43.** 5   **45.** 11.1   **47.** 9.8

CHECKPOINT 1. A good definition states precisely what a term is, using commonly understood or previously

19a–b. Answers may vary. Sample:
19c. Point *O* is the center of the circle.

MIXED REVIEW 21. 16   **23.** 8
25. 50   **27.** 45

Toolbox   page 45

INVESTIGATE   yes; $\overleftrightarrow{HG}$ intersects $\overline{EF}$, but it is not the ⊥ bisector of $\overline{EF}$.

SUMMARIZE   A figure created by *draw* has no constraints. A figure created by *construct* is dependent upon an existing object.
Since $\overleftrightarrow{DC}$ was constructed as the ⊥ bisector of $\overline{AB}$, it remains the ⊥ bisector through any manipulation. Since point *G* was constructed on $\overleftrightarrow{EF}$, the only restriction on $\overleftrightarrow{HG}$ during any manipulation is that it must contain point *G* which has to be on $\overleftrightarrow{EF}$.

EXTEND $\overrightarrow{KM}$ is always the angle bisector of ∠*JKL*. $\overrightarrow{OQ}$ is not always the bisector of ∠*NOP*.

Lesson 1-7   pages 50–52

ON YOUR OWN 1. Reflexive Prop. of ≅   **3.** Symmetric Prop. of ≅   **5.** Substitution Prop.   **7.** Mult. Prop. of =
9. Trans. Prop. of =   **13.** 9   **15.** 18   **17.** 10   **19a.** *B* can be any point on the positive *y*-axis, for example, (0, 5).
21. *x* = 14; *y* = 15   **23a.** 90   **23b.** 45   **23c.** Not possible; all vert. angles are ≅.   **25.** 30 and 60
27. ∠*EIG* and ∠*FIH* are right angles by the markings. ∠*EIF* ≅ ∠*GIH* because they are complements of the same angle.   **29.** Add. Prop. of =; Div. Prop. of =
31. Mult. Prop. of =; Distr. Prop.; Add. Prop. of =
33. Because ∠1 and ∠2 are supplementary, $m\angle 1 + m\angle 2 = 180$. Because ∠3 and ∠4 are supplementary, $m\angle 3 + m\angle 4 = 180$. So, $m\angle 1 + m\angle 2 = m\angle 3 + m\angle 4$. Because ∠2 ≅ ∠4, $m\angle 2 = m\angle 4$. Thus, by Subtraction Prop. of =, $m\angle 1 = m\angle 3$ and ∠1 ≅ ∠3.   **35.** No; guys with beards may not park on Mon.   **37.** No; parking is not allowed from 6:49 A.M. to 9:11 A.M. on Tues.

MIXED REVIEW 39.
41.   **43.** 5   **45.** 11.1   **47.** 9.8

---

defined terms.   **2a.**
2b.   **2c.**

3. $m\angle 1 + m\angle 2 = 90$ **4.** C
    $m\angle 3 + m\angle 4 = 90$

Lesson 1-8   pages 56–57

ON YOUR OWN 7. 6   **9.** 8   **11.** 23.3   **13.** 25
15. 12.0   **17.** (3, 1)   **19.** (6, 1)   **21.** $\left(3\frac{7}{8}, -3\right)$
23. (8, 18)   **25.** No; $AD = AB = 4.2$, $DC = CB = 3.2$.
29a. 19.2   **29b.** (−1.5, 0)   **31a.** 5.4   **31b.** (−1, 0.5)
33a. *A*(0, 0, 0), *B*(3, 0, 0), *C*(3, −3, 0), *D*(0, −3, 0)
E(0, 0, 5), *F*(3, 0, 5), *G*(0, −3, 5)
33b.

MIXED REVIEW 35. 72; 162   **37.** 66.5; 156.5   **39.** 12; 102

Wrap Up   pages 59–62

1. 17, 21; add 4 to the previous term to get the next term.
2. 63, 127; add consecutively increasing powers of 2 to the previous term to get the next term.   **3.** $\frac{5}{6}, \frac{6}{7}$; add 1 to the numerator and denominator of the preceding term to get the next term.   **4.** 5, −6; write the sequence of whole numbers and then change the signs of the even whole numbers.
5.   **6a.** 76   **6b.** The last two digits will always be 76.   **7.** If the points were collinear, an infinite number of planes would pass through them.   **8–13.** Answers may vary. Samples are given.   **8.** $\overleftrightarrow{QR}$ and $\overleftrightarrow{RS}$ **9.** $\overleftrightarrow{QR}$ and $\overleftrightarrow{SC}$ **10.** *Q*, *R*, and *S*
11. *Q*, *R*, *S*, *C*   **12.** plane *QRST* and plane *ABCD*
13. $\overleftrightarrow{AD}, \overleftrightarrow{CD}, \overleftrightarrow{TD}$ **14.** always   **15.** sometimes   **16.** never

17. always   **18.** always   **19.** never   **21.** 3 or −7   **22.** 18
23. 31   **24.** 20   **25.** $m\angle KJD + m\angle DJH = m\angle KJH$ by the Angle Add. Post.; $m\angle KJD = m\angle DJH$ by the markings; $\overrightarrow{JD}$ bisects ∠*KJH* by the definition of angle bisector.
26. *AB* = *CD* by the markings; *AC* = *BD* by the Seg. Add. Post.   **27.** ∠1 ≅ ∠4 by the markings; ∠1 ≅ ∠2 and ∠3 ≅ ∠4 because vert. angles are ≅; ∠2 ≅ ∠3 by the Trans. Prop. of ≅.   **29.** No; $\overrightarrow{BK}$ may not bisect $\overline{LJ}$.   **30.** 3
31. 1   **32.** D   **33.**

34a–b.   **42.** (0, 0)   **43.** 3.2

44a.   **44b.** *AB* = 3, *AC* = 5, *BC* ≈ 5.8
    44c. $\overline{BC}, \overline{AC}, \overline{AB}$

Preparing for Standardized Tests   page 65

1. D   **3.** E   **5.** E   **7.** B   **9.** D   **11.** D   **13.** $\left(\frac{15}{2}, 2\right)$

CHAPTER 2

Lesson 2-1   pages 71–74

ON YOUR OWN 1. acute isosceles   **3.** right scalene
9a. 60; the sum of measures is 180 and the 3 measures are =.   **9b.** 90; the sum of measures is 180 and the measure of the 3rd angle is 90.   **11.** 115.5   **13.** $t = 60$; $w = 60$ **15.** 83.1   **17.** *a* = 67; *b* = 58; *c* = 125; *d* = 23; *e* = 90   **19.** 103   **21.** C   **25.** 33°   **27.** 37, 78, 65; acute   **29.** > 180; measures of both angles at the equator = 90 and the angle at the pole has pos. measure.
31a. $\frac{1}{3}$ **31b.** $\frac{1}{7}$ **33a.** 900; 30, 60, 90   **33b.** right

MIXED REVIEW 35.   **37.** 10.0   **39.** 7
    41a. 60, 120, 60, 120
    41b. 360

T679

Page 714

INVESTIGATE 360

CONJECTURE The sum of measures of the exterior angles of a polygon is always 360.

EXTEND When the polygon "disappears," the angles become adjacent. The sum of their measures is 360.

Lesson 2-2   pages 79–81

ON YOUR OWN 1. convex dodecagon 3. convex octagon 5. 7.

9. octagon; $m\angle 1 = 135$; $m\angle 2 = 45$ 11. 140; 40
13. $\frac{180y - 360}{y}$; $\frac{360}{y}$ 15. 10 17. $\frac{360}{x}$ 19. 102
21. $y = 103$; $z = 70$ 23. $x = 69$; $w = 111$ 25. 113
27a. (20, 162), (40, 171), (60, 174), (80, 175.5), (100, 176.4), (120, 177), (140, 177.4), (160, 177.8), (180, 178), (200, 178.2)
27b.

Interior Angle Measure of Polygons

27c. very close to 180
27d. No; a regular polygon with all straight angles would have all its vertices on a straight line.

MIXED REVIEW 31. $\overrightarrow{RT}$ and $\overrightarrow{RK}$ 33. Answers may vary. Sample: $\angle BRT$ and $\angle BRK$ 35. 40.25 37. $x = 104$; $y = 35$ 39. 72 and 18 41. -1 43. 0

INVESTIGATE The value of m affects the steepness of the line.

Changing the value of b shifts the line vertically.

CONJECTURE Answers may vary. Samples: A line with

pos. value of m goes from the lower left to the upper right. The greater the abs. value of m the steeper the line. For neg. values of b, the line shifts down by the number of units = to the abs. value of b. The line passes through the origin if $b = 0$.

EXTEND The lines are ∥; the values of m are =; lines with equations that have = values of m are ∥.

a. b. c.

The lines are ⊥; the product of the values of m is -1; 2 lines with equations in which the product of values of m is -1 are ⊥.

Lesson 2-3   pages 86–88

ON YOUR OWN 1. k: pos.; ℓ: neg.; s: 0; t: undef.
3. No; lines with no slope are vert. Lines with slope 0 are horizontal. 5. undef.; 0; perpendicular 7. $-\frac{1}{8}$; 8; perpendicular 9. 0; 0; parallel 11. No; the slopes of the sides are $\frac{3}{5}$, $-\frac{5}{8}$, and $-\frac{8}{3}$. No 2 sides are ⊥.
13. perpendicular 15. parallel
17. parallel 19. perpendicular

Page 715

21a. 21b. $x = -5$ 21d. $y = 2$
21e. The lines are ⊥; a horizontal line is always ⊥ to a vert. line. 23. yes

25.
25a. $\overleftrightarrow{AB} \parallel \overleftrightarrow{FB}$, $\overleftrightarrow{BC} \perp \overleftrightarrow{FB}$, $\overleftrightarrow{AB} \perp \overleftrightarrow{BC}$
25b. $\overleftrightarrow{AB} \perp \overleftrightarrow{BC}$, $\overleftrightarrow{BC} \parallel \overleftrightarrow{CG}$, $\overleftrightarrow{AB}$ and $\overleftrightarrow{CG}$ are skew lines.
27. Answers may vary. Sample: No; the "lines" intersect twice. 29a. (1, 10), (2, 20), (3, 30), (4, 40), (5, 50), (6, 60), (7, 70), (8, 80), (9, 90), (10, 100)
29b. 29c. The slope is 1000.
29d. Sample: Yes; you can make the slope as steep as you want, but it will never be vertical.

MIXED REVIEW 31. 25.5 33. 22.5 and 67.5
35. $\overline{FG}$ and $\overline{EH}$, $\overline{EF}$ and $\overline{GH}$

CHECKPOINT 1. 2. 3. 4. 5. 6. 7. 8.

9. (1) Divide 360 by n to find the exterior angle measure. Subtract the result from 180.
(2) Multiply 180 by $n - 2$ and divide the result by n.
10. $-\frac{2}{5}$, $\frac{5}{2}$; perpendicular 11. 1; -1; perpendicular
12. $-\frac{5}{4}$, $\frac{4}{5}$ perpendicular 13. $\frac{2}{9}$, $\frac{2}{9}$; parallel

1. $y = 3x + 5$ 5. $y = -\frac{5}{4}x + 8$ 9. $y = -x + 7$

13. $y = 5x - 10$

Lesson 2-4   pages 93–95

ON YOUR OWN 1. parallelogram, rhombus, rectangle, square 3. trapezoid 5. true 7. false 9. false
17. kite 19. rectangle
21. some isosceles trapezoids some trapezoids
23. rectangle square
25. $x = 11$; $y = 21$; 13, 13, 15, 15 27. $b = 9$; $r = 5$; 6, 6, 6, 6 29. parallelogram, kite, rhombus, trapezoid, isos. trapezoid 31. parallelogram, rectangle, square, kite, trapezoid

MIXED REVIEW 33. 8.2
35a. 35b. 37. 33% 39. 75%

Lesson 2-5   pages 99–101

ON YOUR OWN 1, 3, 7. Answers may vary. 1. Sample: $\overline{BC}$, $\overline{CD}$ 3. Sample: $\overline{BCE}$, $\overline{BFE}$ 5. $\overline{BE}$, $\overline{CF}$ 7. Sample: $\angle BOC$ 9. $\angle BOC$, $\angle EOF$ 11. 10 cm 13. $12\sqrt{2}$ in.
15. 6.5 cm 17. $\frac{5\sqrt{3}}{2}$ in. 19. $\frac{4}{9}$ km 23. $(-2, 5)$; $\sqrt{5}$
25. $(-$ 27. $(3, -4.5)$; 8.5 29. 180 31. 52
33. 180 39a. 6°; 30°; 120° 39b. 2.5°; 5°; 10°
39c. 102.5 41a. 90 41b. 30 41c. 145 41d. 125
41e. 235 41f. 215 43a. 80 43b. 100 43c. 150
43d. 210 43e. 280 45. 160 47. Stay in the circle for a 220° arc before exiting.

MIXED REVIEW 51. 95 53. $t = 120$; $y = 60$ 55. 37

Page 716

Lesson 2-6   pages 105–108

ON YOUR OWN 1. A and H, B and G, C and E, F and D
3. $\overline{CM}$ 5. B 7. $\angle J$ 9. $\triangle CLM$ 11. HY 13. HY
15. $\angle R$ 17. $\frac{5}{2}$ 19. 50 21. 70 23. 7.5 cm
25. $\angle P \cong \angle S$; $\angle O \cong \angle I$; $\angle C \cong \angle D$; $\angle Y \cong \angle E$
27a. IDES 27b. LYPO 31. Yes; the ratios of radii, diameters, and circumferences of 2 circles are =.
33. $\triangle BEC \cong \triangle AED$ 35. $t = 2$ in.; $x = 15$ 37. 2.3 cm
39a. 7.2 cm; 9.6 cm; 12 cm 39b. 53; 90; 37 39c. 9 cm; 12 cm; 15 cm 41. $\frac{2}{4}$ 43a. yes; $\frac{8}{16} = \frac{10}{20}$ 43b. no; $\frac{4}{2} \neq \frac{5}{7}$

MIXED REVIEW
47. Trapezoid; slope of $\overline{BT}$ = slope of $\overline{AS}$. Trapezoid; slope of $\overline{AB} \neq$ slope of $\overline{ST}$.
49. 160 51. a rectangle

CHECKPOINT 1. (5.5, 3); 2.5 2. (1.5, 7); $\frac{\sqrt{13}}{}$
3. (0.5, 3.5); $\frac{\sqrt{170}}{2}$ 4. $(-5, -0.5)$; $\frac{\sqrt{117}}{2}$ 5. 65 6. 90
7. 25 8. 245 9. 115 10. 90 11. 25 12. 180 13. 180
14. 15. 16. 17. A

Lesson 2-7   pages 112–115

ON YOUR OWN
1a.

1	1
1	1
1	1

1b.
3a.

3	2
1	1

3b.

5a. 5b. front top right
7a.
7b. front right
13. triangle 15. isosceles triangle 17. B 19. D
21. front right 23. front top right
25. front top / front right

Page 717

Wrap Up   pages 117–119

1. 61; scalene acute 2. 35; isosceles obtuse 3. $x = 60$; $y = 60$; equilateral; equiangular 4. $x = 45$; $y = 45$; isosceles; right 5. D 6. 120; 60 7. 135; 45 8. 144; 36
9. 165; 15 10. 8; 14, 9, 7, 9 11. $m = 4$; $t = 5$; 7, 14, 14, 7
12. $a = 1$; $b = 2$; 6, 6, 6, 6 13. 5; 3; neither 14. 4; 4; parallel 15. $-\frac{1}{3}$; 3; perpendicular 16. 1; 1; parallel
17. (4, 3); 3 18. (1, -1); $\sqrt{5}$ 19. (-1, -3); $\sqrt{13}$
20. (5.5, 5); $\frac{3\sqrt{5}}{2}$ 21. 30 22. 120 23. 330 24. 120
25. $\overline{ML}$ 26. $\angle U$ 27. $\overline{ST}$ 28. ONMLK
30a. front right 30b. front right
32. 33.
34. 35.
36. 37.

Cumulative Review   page 121

1. D 3. E 5. C 7. B 9. D 11. (2.5, -2)
13. front right

CHAPTER 3

Lesson 3-1   pages 128–130

ON YOUR OWN
1. 3. BOX ℓ

5a. $\overline{PQ}$ and $\overline{P'Q'}$, $\overline{QR}$ and $\overline{Q'R'}$, $\overline{RS}$ and $\overline{R'S'}$, $\overline{SP}$ and $\overline{S'P'}$ 5b. isometry 5c. opposite 7a. $\overline{AR}$ and $\overline{A'R'}$, $\overline{RT}$ and $\overline{R'T'}$, $\overline{TA}$ and $\overline{T'A'}$ 7b. not isometry 7c. opposite
9a. $\overline{RI}$ and $\overline{R'I'}$, $\overline{IT}$ and $\overline{I'T'}$, $\overline{TR}$ and $\overline{T'R'}$ 9b. not isometry 9c. opposite
11. 15.
17. 21a. Answers may vary. Sample: The writing hand would not cover what was already written.

Write the mirror image of this sentence.

21b. Write the mirror image of this sentence. 23.
25a. S-Isomer
25b. Samples: gloves, shoes, scissors 27. First and third panels; the figures in the second panel are not ≅, and the fourth panel shows a slide. 29. No; the points farthest from the line of reflection move the farthest.
MIXED REVIEW 31. rectangle 33a. (-1, -1) 33b. 2
33c. $-\frac{1}{2}$ 33d. $y = -\frac{1}{2}x - \frac{3}{2}$

1. $\begin{bmatrix} 11 & 10 \\ 1 & 12 \end{bmatrix}$ 5. $\begin{bmatrix} 8 & 11.3 \\ 15 & 11.1 \end{bmatrix}$ 9. $\begin{bmatrix} 447 & 18 & 20 \\ 546 & 23 & 10 \\ 450 & 22 & 18 \\ 396 & 30 & 22 \end{bmatrix}$

Lesson 3-2 — pages 135–137

ON YOUR OWN **1.** ⟨1, −3⟩ **3.** ⟨1, −1⟩ **5.** ⟨4, −2⟩
7. C **9.** I **11.** H **13.**

15.

17. A' C' E'
$$\begin{bmatrix} -2 & -1 & -9 \\ 6 & 9 & -2 \end{bmatrix}$$

19. N' I' L' E'
$$\begin{bmatrix} -1 & -1 & -6 & -6 \\ -9 & -2 & 0 & -7 \end{bmatrix}$$

21. $U'(1, 16);\ G'(2, 12)$ **25.** (0, 0) **27a.** ⟨−4, −2⟩
27b.

MIXED REVIEW **29.** bisector **31a.**
31b. 2, −3; 2, 2
31c. The lines are ∥.
33. 300°
35. 450°

Lesson 3-3 — pages 141–143

1.

3.

5.

7. 110 **9.** 180 **11.** M **13.** $\overline{BC}$ **15.** I **17.** J
21. $\overline{MN} \cong \overline{M'N'},\ \overline{ME} \cong \overline{M'E},\ \overline{EN} \cong \overline{EN'},$
$\angle MEN \cong \angle M'EN',\ \angle MNE \cong \angle M'N'E,$

23.

25.

29. 108

MIXED REVIEW **31.** Sample:

35. Sample:

$\angle EMN \cong \angle EM'N',\ \angle MEM' \cong \angle NEN'$

CHECKPOINT **1.** (3, −4) **2.** (−4, 3) **3.** (1, 11)
4. (4, −3) **5.** (4, −1) **6.** (4, 3) **7.** Images and
preimages under translations, reflections, and rotations
are congruent to each other. Translations and rotations do
not affect orientation. Reflection reverses orientation.
8a. $\overline{AD}$ and $\overline{A'D'},\ \overline{AF}$ and $\overline{A'F'},\ \overline{DF}$ and $\overline{D'F'}$ **8b.** No;
the image is not ≅ to the preimage.

Lesson 3-4 — pages 147–150

ON YOUR OWN **1.** 60° **3.** 30° **5a.** III **5b.** IV
5c. II **5d.** I
7.

11.

13. translation **15.** rotation **17.** glide reflection
19. glide reflection **21.** rotation **23.** translation
25. reflection **27.** rotation **31.** Rotations and glide
reflections are equally likely to occur. They are more likely

---

to occur than translations and reflections.
MIXED REVIEW **33.** 79, 130 and 151 **35a.** true
35b. false **35c.** true **37.** Each figure maps onto itself.

Toolbox — page 151

INVESTIGATE All 6 polygons change in the same way;
yes.

Lesson 3-5 — pages 155–158

ON YOUR OWN
1.
3. rotational: 90°, point **5.** point
7. no symmetry **9.** reflectional
11. rotational **13.** any isosceles
but not equilateral △
15.
17.
19. reflectional, rotational
21. point **23.** reflectional,
rotational **25.** reflectional,
rotational **27.** reflectional,
point

31.
top view

33a.

Language	Horizontal Line	Vertical Line	Point
English	B, C, D, E, H, I, K, O, X	A, H, I, M, O, T, U, V, W, X, Y	H, I, N, O, S, X, Z
Greek	B, E, H, Θ, I, K, Ξ, Θ, Σ, Φ, X	Δ, Λ, Π, Θ, I, A, M, Ξ, O, Π, T, Y, Φ, X, Ψ, Ω	Z, H, Θ, I, N, Ξ, O, Φ, X

35. reflectional in y-axis **37.** point **45.** (3, −4)

MIXED REVIEW **47.** 1 **49.** $\frac{7}{3}$ **51.** 0; 3

CHECKPOINT **1.** rotational **2.** point **3.** reflectional,
point **4.** $C'(−4, 3),\ A'(−1, 6),\ L'(−3, 2)$

Lesson 3-6 — pages 163–165

ON YOUR OWN
1. **3.** **5.**

rotational, point, reflectional, glide
reflectional, and translational

9.

rotational, point, and translational

13. **15.**

17. **19.**

MIXED REVIEW **21.** equilateral, equiangular
23. scalene, right **25a.** $\overline{BD}$ **25b.** $\overline{BCE}$
25c. Sample: $\overline{ED}$ **25d.** Sample: $\overline{AE}$ **25e.** Sample:
$\angle BAE$ **25f.** Sample: $\overline{BE}$ and $\overline{ED}$ **27a.** 3; 10 **27b.** 2

Lesson 3-7 — pages 168–172

ON YOUR OWN
1.

5a. reduction **5b.** $\frac{1}{3}$ **7a.** enlargement **7b.** 1
9a. enlargement **9b.** $\frac{3}{2}$ **11a.** reduction **11b.** $\frac{2}{3}$
13. A' B' C' **15.** A' B' C' **17.** about 343
$$\begin{bmatrix} 3 & 9 & 15 \\ 0 & 6 & 3 \end{bmatrix} \qquad \begin{bmatrix} -4 & -8 & -6 \\ 0 & -6 & 0 \end{bmatrix}$$

19.

21. $M = M'$ **23a.** A' B' C' D'
$$\begin{bmatrix} -6 & 6 & 6 & -6 \\ -6 & -6 & 6 & 6 \end{bmatrix}$$
23b.

23c. The image of a
dilation with a
negative factor
is the image of a
dilation with a
positive factor with
the same absolute
value, rotated 180°
about the origin.

25. Q' R' T' W' **27.** Q' R' T' W'
$$\begin{bmatrix} -9 & -6 & 9 & 9 \\ 12 & -3 & 3 & 15 \end{bmatrix} \qquad \begin{bmatrix} -6 & -4 & 6 & 6 \\ 8 & -2 & 2 & 10 \end{bmatrix}$$
29a. vertex of V **29b.** $\frac{1}{2}$ **33.** 10; 12 **35.** 32; 7.5
37. True; the image and the preimage are similar.
39. False; a dilation does not change orientation.

MIXED REVIEW **41.** $x = 105;\ y = 75;\ z = 35$
43. $x = 85;\ y = 125$ **45.** trapezoid

47.

Wrap Up — pages 174–177

1. **2.**

6. **8.** **9.** E

11. $A'(7, 12),\ B'(6, 6),\ C'(3, 5)$ **12.** $R'(−4, 3),\ S'(−6, 6),$
$T'(−10, 8)$ **13.** (2, 8) **14.** (−2, −1) **15.** (11, −4)
16. **17.**

18. **19.**

20. (−2, 5) **21.** (−3, 0) **22.** (−1, −4) **23.** (0, 7)
24. (8, −2) **26a.** II **26b.** I **26c.** III
26d. IV **27a.** III **27b.** IV **27c.** II **27d.** I
28. $T'(−4, −9),\ A'(0, −5),\ M'(−1, −10)$ **29.** reflectional
30. 72° rotational **31.** 90° rotational, point
32a. rotational, point, reflectional,
translational, glide reflectional
33a. and **33b.** point, reflectional,
translational, glide reflectional
34a. and **34b.** rotational, point, reflectional,
translational, glide reflectional
35. M' A' T' H' **36.** A' N' D'
$$\begin{bmatrix} -15 & -30 & 0 & 15 \\ 20 & -45 & 0 & 10 \end{bmatrix} \qquad \begin{bmatrix} 14 & -8 & 0 \\ -2 & -6 & 4 \end{bmatrix}$$
37. W' I' T' H' **38.** F' U' N'
$$\begin{bmatrix} 12 & 6 & 9 & 0 \\ 15 & 18 & 24 & 21 \end{bmatrix} \qquad \begin{bmatrix} -2 & 2\frac{1}{2} & 2 \\ 0 & 0 & -2\frac{1}{2} \end{bmatrix}$$
39. Rotations, dilations and translations preserve
orientation. Reflections and glide reflections reverse
orientation. **40.** (2, 8) **41.** (1, 7) **42.** (5, 4)
43. isosceles, acute **44.** scalene, right **45.** isosceles,

---

obtuse **46.** scalene, acute

Preparing for Standardized Tests — page 179

1. E **3.** D **5.** A **7.** A **9.** C **11.** rotations, reflections,
translations, and glide reflections

CHAPTER 4

Lesson 4-1 — pages 185–187

ON YOUR OWN **1.** You send in a proof-of-purchase
label; they send you a get-well card. **3.** If $3x − 7 = 14$,
then $3x = 21$. **5.** If a triangle is isosceles, then it has two
congruent sides. **7.** 1 and 9 are not prime. **9.** Softball
and cricket are sports played with a ball and a bat.
11a. If you grow, then you will eat all of your vegetables.
11b. If you do not eat all of your vegetables, then you will
not grow. **11c.** If you do not grow, then you will not eat
all of your vegetables. **15a.** If 2 segments have the same
length, then they are ≅. **15b.** If 2 segments are not ≅,
then they have different lengths. **15c.** If 2 segments have
different lengths, then they are not ≅. **19a.** If you have a
passport, then you travel from the U.S. to Kenya.
19b. true; false **23a.** If the slopes of 2 nonvertical lines
are =, then they are ∥. **23b.** true; true **23c.** 2
nonvertical lines are ∥ if and only if their slopes are =.
29. If the sum of the digits of a number is divisible by 3,
then the number is divisible by 3; if a number is divisible
by 3, then the sum of the digits of the number is divisible
by 3. **33a.** If a polygon is regular, then all its sides are ≅.
33b. If not all the sides of a polygon are ≅, then the
polygon is not regular. **35a.** If a transformation is a rotation,
then it is an isometry. **35b.** If a transformation is not an
isometry, it is not a rotation.

MIXED REVIEW
37. **39.**

41. $A'(0, −3),\ B'(4, 6),\ C'(−6, −1)$ **43.** 35

Lesson 4-2 — pages 191–193

ON YOUR OWN **1.** $x = 80;\ y = 40$ **3.** $x = 4.5;\ y = 60$
5. $x = 92;\ y = 71$ **7.** $x = 64;\ y = 71$ **9.** The measure of

each base angle is 70. **11.** The 3rd vertex must be on the
⊥ bisector of the base, since $x = 3$. **13.** False; a
rectangle need not have 4 ≅ sides. **15.** true
17. (0, 5), (5, 0), (10, 10), (−5, 5), (5, −5)
19a. 25 **19b.** 40, 40, 100 **19c.** Isosceles; the △ has
2 ≅ angles. **21a.** isosceles **21b.** 900 ft; 1100 ft
21c. Answers may vary. Sample: The tower is the ⊥
bisector of the base. **23.** 2.5 **25.** 35 **27.** 60 **29.** 50
31. 120 **33.** 70 **35.** No; the base is the side opposite the
vertex angle. **37.** $m = 20;\ n = 45$ **39.** $m = 36;\ n = 27$

MIXED REVIEW **41.** (1, 5); $\sqrt{13}$ **43.** (0.5, 6.5); $\frac{1}{2}\sqrt{26}$
45. 24 sides **47.** $\overline{DF} \parallel \overline{EG}$ because in a plane, 2 lines ⊥
to a 3rd line are ∥.

Lesson 4-3 — pages 196–199

ON YOUR OWN **1.** Answers may vary. Samples:
$m\angle V = 45$ because acute angles of a rt. △ are
complementary; $UT = TV$ because if 2 ∠s of a △
are ≅, the sides opposite them are ≅. **3.** $ABCD$ is a
rectangle; sum of the measures of angles of a quadrilateral
= 360 so each angle is 90°. **5.** Answers may vary. Sample:
$MP = MN$ and $NO = PO$ because if 2 ∠s of a △ are ≅,
the sides opposite them are ≅. **7.** C **9.** E; assume (A) is
T. Then (B−F) are all T. But (B) is F if (C−F) are T. So the
assumption that (A) is T must be F and (A) is F. Assume
(B) is T. Then (C−F) are F. But (C) is T if (B) is T, so the
assumption that (B) is T must be F and (B) is F. Since (A)
and (B) are F, (C) is F. Since (A−C) are F, (D) is F. Since
(A−D) are F, (E) is F. Since (E) is T, (F) is F. **11a.** $\angle ONK$
11b. $\angle MNO$ **11c.** $\angle MON$ **13.** d, f, b, a, c, e
15. By Substitution, $m\angle 1 + m\angle 2 = m\angle 2 + m\angle 3$.
Subtracting = quantities from each side yields
$m\angle 1 = m\angle 3$. **17.** Given; Isosceles Triangle Thm.;
Isosceles Triangle Thm.; Transitive Prop. of ≅

MIXED REVIEW **19.** 147.6, 144, 54, 14.4
21a. **21b.** shift left 10 and
up 9; ⟨−10, 9⟩

Toolbox — page 200

CONJECTURE The midsegment is ∥ to a side of the △
and is half its length.

T681

EXTEND Opp. angles of the orig. △ and the midsegment △ have = measures; corr. angles in the 4 smaller △s have = measures.
The sides of the midsegment △ are each $\frac{1}{2}$ of the corr. side of the original △; the 4 △s are ≅; the 4 △s are ~ to the original △. The area of each smaller △ is $\frac{1}{4}$ the area of the original △; the perimeter of each smaller △ is $\frac{1}{2}$ the perimeter of the orig. △.

Lesson 4-4 pages 203–206

ON YOUR OWN   1. 9   **3.** 31   **5a.** $H(2, 0)$; $J(4, 2)$
5b. slope of $\overline{HJ} = 1$, slope of $\overline{EF} = 1$ ✔
5c. $HJ = 2\sqrt{2}$, $EF = 4\sqrt{2}$, $HJ = \frac{1}{2}EF$ **7a.** Answers may vary. Sample:

7b. Dilation with center F and scale factor $\frac{1}{2}$ **7c.** The triangles are ~.
9. 60   **11.** 10
13. 45   **15.** 154 cm   **17.** 2 cm; the length of a side of the largest square = the length of the diagonal of the middle square. The length of the diagonal of that square is twice the length of the sides of the smallest square.
MIXED REVIEW   19. 5   **21.** (−2, 6)   **23.** Lines m and n do not intersect.   **25.** △ABC is isosceles.   **27.** 180; it must be a straight angle.

CHECKPOINT   1a. If the measure of at least one of the angles of a triangle is 60, then the triangle is equilateral.   **1b.** true; false   **2a.** If all the angles of a polygon are ≅, then the polygon is regular.   **2b.** true; false   **3.** A converse reverses the hypothesis and the conclusion. The truth value of a converse does not depend on the truth value of the original statement. A contrapositive reverses and negates the hypothesis and the conclusion of the original statement. The truth values of a statement and its contrapositive are the same.   **4.** C   **5a.** 9   **5b.** 54, 54, 72   **5c.** Isosceles; has 2 ≅ angles.   **6.** False; a △ with angles 30°, 30°, 120° is an obtuse isosceles.   **7.** 36

Lesson 4-5 pages 209–211

ON YOUR OWN   1. Assume it is not raining outside.
3. Assume △PEN is scalene.   **5.** Assume $\overline{XY} \not\cong \overline{AB}$.
7. I and II   **9.** I and III   **11.** This bridge is a bascule.
13. Sumiko is not an air traffic controller.   **15.** Assume $\angle A \cong \angle B$. Then $\triangle ABC$ is isosceles with $BC = AC$. This contradicts the assumption. Therefore, $\angle A \neq \angle B$.   **17.** E
19. Assume that the driver had not applied the brakes. Then the wheels would not have locked and there would

be no skid marks. There are skid marks. Therefore, the assumption is false. The driver had applied the brakes.
21. Assume the polygon is a hexagon. Then the sum of measures of its interior angles is 720. But the sum of measures of the polygon's interior angles is 900, not 720. Therefore, the assumption is false. The polygon is not a hexagon.   **23.** Assume $m \angle P = 90$. By def., $m \angle Q > 90$. The sum of the angle measures of $\triangle PQR$ is > 180. By the Triangle Angle-Sum Thm., the sum of the angle measures of a △ is 180. Therefore, the assumption is false, and an obtuse △ cannot contain a rt. angle.   **25.** Mr. Pitt was in Maine on April 8 and stayed there at least until 12:05 A.M. Assume Mr. Pitt is the robber. Then he took < 55 min to travel from Maine to Charlotte. It is not possible to travel from Maine to Charlotte in 55 min or less. Therefore, Mr. Pitt is not the robber.   **27.** The hole in the roof; of 5 possibilities, 4 have been eliminated.
MIXED REVIEW   29. Answers may vary. Sample: $ABCD$ and $BCFG$ **31.** Answers may vary. Sample: $A, B, C,$ and D
33. B

$\overline{PR}, \overline{QR}, \overline{PQ}$

Toolbox page 212

1. $x \leq -1$ **5.** $a \leq 18$ **9.** $n \leq -3\frac{1}{2}$ **13.** $n \geq -119$
17. $b \geq 8$ **21.** $x < -5$ **25.** $a \geq -1$

Lesson 4-6 pages 216–218

ON YOUR OWN   1. no; $2 + 3 \not> 6$ **3.** Yes; the length of each segment is < the sum of the lengths of the other 2.
5. Yes; the length of each segment is < the sum of the lengths of the other 2.   **7.** Yes; the length of each segment is < the sum of the lengths of the other 2.
9. $\overline{MN}, \overline{ON}, \overline{OM}$ **11.** $\overline{TU}, \overline{UV}, \overline{TV}$ **13.** $\overline{AK}, \overline{AR}, \overline{KR}$
15. $\angle Q, \angle R, \angle S$ **17.** $\angle G, \angle H, \angle I$ **19.** $\angle A, \angle B, \angle C$
21. $\angle Z, \angle Y, \angle X$ **23.** $\frac{1}{2}$ **25b.** The directions of each pair of inequalities match.   **25c.** The 3rd side of the 1st triangle is longer than the 3rd side of the 2nd triangle.
27. The 2 cities may not be both straight ahead. For instance, Topeka might be 110 mi east, and Wichita might be 90 mi south.   **29.** $\overline{CD}$ **31.** $4 < z < 20$
33. $0 < z < 12$ **35a.** Given   **35b.** Isosceles Triangle Thm.   **35c.** Angle Addition Post.   **35d.** Substitution   **35e.** Exterior Angle Thm.   **35f.** Transitive Prop. of Inequality

---

Lesson 4-7 pages 223–225

ON YOUR OWN
1.

x 4 cm
5. $\overline{D} \quad a \quad \overline{E}$ **9.**
11.

5 cm / 3 cm / G 4.5 cm H
13. The locus is the two points at which the bisector of $\angle JKL$ intersects $\odot C$.   **15.** second base   **17a.** a circle   **17b.** a (smaller) circle
21. The locations that meet Paul's requirement are on the ⊥ bisector of the segment connecting their offices. The locations that meet Priscilla's requirement are within a circle centered at the downtown with radius 3 mi. The locations that meet both requirements lie along the portion of the ⊥ bisector that is within the circle.
23.

27.
29. pts. equidistant from the sides of $\angle A$
31. pts. equidistant from two parallel planes
33a.   **33b.**
33c.   **35.**
 side view
37.
side view
MIXED REVIEW   39. $\widehat{CBA}, \widehat{CAB}$

MIXED REVIEW   37. $S'(-2, -7), Y'(4, -3)$ **39.** 156; 24
41. The set of red pts. is 3 units from the set of blue pts.
41.

CHECKPOINT   1. $\overline{AB}, \overline{BC}, \overline{AC}$ **2.** $\overline{MN}, \overline{MO}, \overline{NO}$
3. $\overline{QR} \cong \overline{RS}, \overline{QS}$ **4.** Sample: If $x = |x|$, then $x \geq 0$; assume $x < 0$.   **5.** Assume February has at least 30 days.
6. Assume pentagon has at least 4 rt. angles.
7.   **8.**

Toolbox page 226

CONJECTURE Each set of lines intersects at a single pt.
EXTEND acute △; right △; obtuse △; The medians and angle bisectors always intersect inside the △. Altitudes intersect inside the △ for acute △s, at a vertex for rt. △s, and outside the △ for obtuse △s.

Lesson 4-8 pages 230–232

ON YOUR OWN   1. median   **3.** none of these
5. altitude   **7a.** $(-2, 0)$ **7b.** $(1, 3)$ **9a.** $(0, 0)$
9b. $(-4, 0)$ **11.** IA, IIC, IIIB, IVD   **13.** the pt. of concurrency of the ⊥ bisectors of segments connecting the 3 areas   **15a.** $x = 0, y = 0, y = x$
15b. $x = 6, y = 6, y = x$ **15c.** The line $y = x$; since the altitude from D bisects the base of isosceles $\triangle DEF$, the altitude is also the ⊥ bisector of the base.   **17a.** The triangle balances.   **17b.** The triangle balances.
MIXED REVIEW   19. right   **21.** right   **23.** Sample: $\overleftrightarrow{AB}$ and $\overleftrightarrow{DE}$ **25.** Sample: $\overline{AB}, \overline{BC}, \overline{BE}$

Wrap Up pages 234–237

1a. If you are south of the equator, then you are in Australia.   **1b.** true; false   **2a.** If the measure of an angle is > 90 and < 180, then the angle is obtuse.   **2b.** true; true   **2c.** An angle is obtuse if and only if its measure is > 90 and < 180.   **3a.** If it is cold outside, then it is snowing.   **3b.** true; false   **4a.** If the sides of a figure are ≅, then it is a square.   **4b.** true; false   **6.** $x = 4$; $y = 65$ **7.** $x = 60$; $y = 60$ **8.** $x = 55$; $y = 62.5$
9. $x = 65$; $y = 90$ **10.** d, c, a, b   **12.** Answers may vary.

Sample: $\angle ABC$ is a rt. angle by def. of complementary angles and the Angle Addition Post. $\angle A$ and $\angle C$ are complementary because acute angles of a rt. △ are complementary.   **13.** $\angle E \cong \angle F$ because base ∠s of an isosceles △ are ≅.   **14.** Answers may vary. Samples: $\angle HIG \cong \angle JIK$ because they are vert. angles. $\angle HIG \cong \angle G$ and $\angle JIK \cong \angle J$ because base ∠s of an isosceles △ are ≅.   **15.** 15   **16.** 12   **17.** 11
18. Assume that the room had been painted with oil-based paint. Then the brushes would be soaking in paint thinner, but they are not. So the assumption is false. The room must not have been painted with oil-based paint.
19. Assume that both numbers are odd. The product of 2 odd numbers is always odd, which contradicts the fact that their product is even. So the assumption that both numbers are odd is false, and at least 1 must be even.
20. Assume that a triangle has 2 or more obtuse angles. By def., the measure of each of these angles is > 90. Then the sum of angle measures of the △ is > 180. By the Triangle Angle-Sum Thm., the sum of angle measures of a △ is 180. Therefore the assumption was false, and a △ has no more than 1 obtuse angle.   **21.** Assume 1 angle of an equilateral △ is obtuse. Then its measure is > 90 and < 180. By the Isosceles Triangle Thm., the remaining angles are each ≅ to the 1st angle. By def. of ≅ angles and the Transitive Prop. of ≅, the measures of the 3 angles are =, and all the angles are obtuse. Then the sum of the measures of the angles is > 270. But the sum of the measures of angles of a △ is 180. Therefore the assumption is false. An equilateral △ cannot have an obtuse angle.   **22.** $\angle T, \angle R, \angle S$; $\overline{SR}, \overline{TS}, \overline{TR}$
23. $\angle C, \angle A, \angle B$; $\overline{AB}, \overline{BC}, \overline{AC}$
24. $\angle G, \angle O, \angle F$; $\overline{OF}, \overline{FG}, \overline{OG}$ **25.** B
27.   **28.**

30. $(-1, 0)$ **31.** $(0, -1)$

32. $(2, -3)$
33. 16 cm; 15 cm^2
34. 30.4 ft; 55.8 ft^2
35. 4 m; 0.75 m^2
36. 5   **37.** 13   **38.** 15

Cumulative Review page 239

1. E   **3.** A   **5.** B   **7.** A   **9.** C   **11.** D
13. Sample:

CHAPTER 5

Lesson 5-1 pages 245–248

ON YOUR OWN   1. about 40 in.   **3.** about 20 ft
5. 36 cm   **7.** 24 cm   **9.** 78 cm   **11.** 74 ft   **13.** 15 cm^2
15. 14 cm^2 **17.** 12 $units^2$ **19.** 15 $units^2$ **21b.** 38 units
21d. 54 $units^2$ **23.** 288 cm   **25.** 6 yd^2 **27a.** 3492 $in.^2$ or $24\frac{1}{4}$ ft^2 **27b.** $11\frac{3}{8}$ ft^2 **27c.** \$71.80   **27d.** \$9.43
33a. Samples: 10 ft by 90 ft, 200 ft; 15 ft by 60 ft, 150 ft
33b. 30 ft by 30 ft.   **35.** 310 cm^2 **37.** 24 cm^2 **39.** 16
41. 16
MIXED REVIEW   45. (5.5, 5)   **47.** (−4, 3)   **49.** If it is November, then it is Thanksgiving.   **51.** between 2 m and 8 m   **53.** 2 $units^2$ **55.** 8 $units^2$

Lesson 5-2 pages 252–254

ON YOUR OWN   1. 15 $units^2$ **3.** 6 $units^2$ **5.** 27 $units^2$
7. 4 in.   **9.** 240 cm^2 **11.** 20.3 cm^2 **13b.** 24.5 $units^2$
15b. 16 $units^2$ **17.** 0.24   **21.** 8 $units^2$ **23.** 8 $units^2$
25. 312.5 ft^2 **27.** 12,800 m^2 **29.** The areas of the △s are =; they have the same bases and = heights.
31. 126 m^2 **33.** 60 $units^2$ **35.** 4.5 $units^2$
MIXED REVIEW
37. $A'(1, 3), B'(-1, 3), C'(-1, 2) D'(1, 0)$
39. $A'(-1, -3), B'(-3, -3), C'(-3, -2) D'(-1, 0)$
41. $9 + 16 = 25$ **43.** $36 + 64 = 100$

Toolbox page 255

1. $5\sqrt{2}$ **3.** 8   **5.** $4\sqrt{3}$ **7.** $6\sqrt{2}$ **9.** 6   **11.** $6\sqrt{2}$

Lesson 5-3 pages 259–262

ON YOUR OWN   1. 10   **3.** $2\sqrt{89}$ **5.** $3\sqrt{2}$ **7.** $6\sqrt{2}$
9. 14 ft   **11.** obtuse   **13.** acute   **15.** obtuse   **17.** obtuse
19. acute   **21.** right   **25.** 7.6   **27.** 19.3   **29.** 11.3
31. 4.2 in.   **33.** $\frac{9\sqrt{3}}{2}$ m^2 **35.** 10.5 $in.^2$
37a. $|x_2 - x_1|$; $|y_2 - y_1|$
37b. $PQ^2 = (x_2 - x_1)^2 + (y_2 - y_1)^2$
37c. $PQ = \sqrt{(x_2 - x_1)^2 + (y_2 - y_1)^2}$ **39.** 50   **41.** 15
43. 84   **45.** 16   **47.** 12 cm   **49.** 17.9 cm   **51a.** 5 in.
51b. $\sqrt{29}$ in. or about 5.4 in.
51c. $d_2 = \sqrt{AC^2 + BC^2 + BD^2}$ **51d.** 34 in.
53. $\sqrt{61}$ **55.** $2\sqrt{38}$
MIXED REVIEW
59.   **61.**

Lesson 5-4 pages 266–268

ON YOUR OWN   1. $x = 8$; $y = 8\sqrt{2}$ **3.** $x = 24$; $y = 12\sqrt{3}$ **5.** $x = \sqrt{2}$; $y = 2$ **7.** $x = 4$; $y = 4\sqrt{3}$
9a. 55 ft   **9b.** 0.55 min or 33 sec   **11.** 9   **13.** $x = 9$; $y = 18$ **15.** $a = 6$; $b = 6\sqrt{2}$; $c = 2\sqrt{3}$; $d = 6$
17. $a = 4$; $b = 4$ **19.** C   **21.** 110.9 cm^2 **23.** 11.3 yd^2
25. $\frac{9\sqrt{3}}{2}$ $units^2$ **27b.** $2\sqrt{3}$ units   **27c.** $s\sqrt{3}$ units
MIXED REVIEW   29. 1   **31.** 7 $units^2$; 12.1 units
CHECKPOINT   1. 84 $in.^2$; 48 in.   **2.** 112 cm^2; 48 cm
3. 72 m^2; 40 m   **4.** 12   **5.** $x = 10$; $y = 10\sqrt{2}$
6. $x = 12\sqrt{3}$; $y = 24$ **7.** B
8. Sample:

Lesson 5-5 pages 271–273

ON YOUR OWN   1. 472 $in.^2$ **3.** 30 ft^2 **5.** 108,990 mi^2
7. 4 ft   **9.** $52\sqrt{3}$ ft^3 **11.** 128 cm^2 **13a.** $\frac{1}{2}hb_1$; $\frac{1}{2}hb_2$
15. 669 $in.^2$ **17.** 18 cm; 12 cm, 24 cm   **19.** 49.9 ft^2
21. 11.3 cm^2 **23.** 1.5 m^2

MIXED REVIEW   29. $25\sqrt{3}$ cm^2 **31.** $\frac{100\sqrt{3}}{3}$ m^2

Lesson 5-6 pages 276–278

ON YOUR OWN   1. 120; 60; 30   **3.** 60; 30; 60
5. 12,100 $in.^2$ **7.** 128 cm^2 **9.** 841.8 ft^2 **11.** 310.4 ft^2
15. 72 cm^2 **17.** $75\sqrt{3}$ ft^2 **21a.** (2.8, 2.8)
21b. 5.6 units^2 **21c.** 44.8 units^2 **23.** $24\sqrt{3}$ cm^2
25. $36\sqrt{3}$ $in.^2$
MIXED REVIEW
27.   **29.**   **31.** 25.13   **33.** 31.42

Lesson 5-7 pages 282–284

ON YOUR OWN   1. 15π cm   **3.** 3.7π cm   **5.** 56.55 in.
7. 1.57 yd   **9.** 28π cm; 3.5π cm   **11.** 36π m; 27π m
13a. 100 in.   **13b.** 50 in.   **13c.** $\frac{100}{3}\pi$ in.   **15.** 105 ft
17. 490π mi   **19.** 36.13 m   **21.** 3.93 m   **23.** 2π in.
25. 12.6
MIXED REVIEW
29.

31. about 1 $in.^2$
33. about 1 $in.^2$
CHECKPOINT   1. 110 cm^2 **2.** $72\sqrt{3}$ ft^2 **3.** $27\sqrt{3}$ ft^2
4. 50.27 in.   **5.** 12.57 m   **6.** 31.42 ft   **7.** 8.80 km
8. 56.55 mm   **9.** 4.5π mm

Lesson 5-8 pages 288–290

ON YOUR OWN   1. $400\pi^2$ **3.** $\frac{9}{64}\pi$ $in.^2$ **5.** 30 m
7. 6.25π $units^2$ **9.** 54.11 m^2 **11.** 11,310 ft^2
13. 64π cm^2 **15.** $\frac{169}{6}\pi^2$ m^2 **17.** 1,620,000 m^2
19. 18.27 ft^2 **21.** 925.41 ft^2 **23.** 12 in.
25. $(784 - 196\pi)$ $in.^2$ **27.** 4π m^2

29a.

29b. the area of $\frac{3}{4}$ circle with radius 10 ft and $\frac{1}{4}$ circle with radius 2 ft
29c. about 239 ft²

MIXED REVIEW 31. $90 **33.** $18\sqrt{3}$ cm² **35.** 72; isosceles, acute **37.** 68; scalene, acute **39.** 45; isosceles, right

Toolbox page 291

INVESTIGATE The ratios do not change with size.

CONJECTURE As the number of sides increases, each ratio comes closer to 1.

EXTEND Yes; the ratio of the perimeter to the circumference gets closer to 1 faster than the ratio of the areas.
about 63 cm; about 314 cm²

Wrap Up pages 293–296

1. 32 cm; 64 cm² **2.** 38 ft; 78 ft² **3.** 32 in.; 40 in²
5. 10 m² **6.** 90 in.² **7.** 33 ft² **8.** 16 **9.** $2\sqrt{113}$
10. 17 **11.** $x = 9\sqrt{3}$; $y = 18$ **12.** $x = 12\sqrt{2}$
13. $x = \frac{20\sqrt{3}}{3}$; $y = \frac{40\sqrt{3}}{3}$ **14.** E **15.** 18 m² **16.** 16 ft²
17. $96\sqrt{3}$ mm² **18.**

19.

20.

21.

20.8 in.²   128 mm²   127.3 cm²
4 in.   8 mm   7 cm

22. 8π in.²; $\frac{22}{9}\pi$ in. **23.** 14π m; $\frac{147}{3}\pi$ m
24. 6π mm; π mm **25.** 76.97 ft² **26.** 18.27 m²
27. 40.96 cm² **28.** 4.14 in.² **29.** 98.4 cm² **30.** 684 ft²

Preparing for Standardized Tests page 299

1. A **3.** E **5.** B **7.** C **9.** C **11.** No; if an altitude is outside the △, then the △ is obtuse and the altitude is from an acute angle vertex. The altitude from the other acute angle vertex is also outside the △.

CHAPTER 6

Lesson 6-1 pages 304–306

ON YOUR OWN 1. A, B, D **3.** B **5.** E **7.** A **9.** blue
11. brown **13a.**

15. 6 in. **17a.** A: icosahedron; B: octahedron; C: hexahedron; D: tetrahedron; E: dodecahedron
17b. tetrahedron, hexahedron; triangular pyramid, cube
17c. $12 = 8 + 6 - 2$

MIXED REVIEW 21. $\angle B$ **23.** 40π cm²

Toolbox page 307

1. B **3.** B **5.** 10 **7.** 51 **9.** 0.035 **11.** 230 **13.** 5
15. 30,000,000,000 **17.** $\frac{5}{18}$ **19.** 108

Lesson 6-2 pages 312–314

ON YOUR OWN 1. 38 units² **3.** 38 units²
5. 144 ft²; 216 ft² **7.** 288 in.²; 336 in.² **9a.** right hexagonal prism **9b.** $48\sqrt{3}$ cm² **9c.** 240 cm²
9d. $(240 + 48\sqrt{3})$ cm² **11.** 880 cm² **13.** 36,800 cm²
15. 20 cm
17a. $A(3, 0, 0)$, $B(3, 5, 0)$, $C(0, 5, 0)$, $D(0, 5, 4)$ **17b.** 5
17c. 3 **17d.** 4 **17e.** 94 units² **21.** 619.1 m²
23. 1726 cm² **25.** D **27a.** $r = 0.7$ cm, $h = 4$ cm
27b. a translation

MIXED REVIEW 29. 60 cm²
31. $B'(4, 2)$, $I'(0, -3)$, $G'(-1, 0)$
33. $B'(12, 2)$, $I'(8, -3)$, $G'(7, 0)$ **35.** 15.3 in.
37. 17.7 cm

Toolbox page 315

INVESTIGATE about 130 cm²; arbitrarily large

CONJECTURE either a large side length or a large height; $s = h \approx 4.6$ cm; length of side of base = height; cube

EXTEND 10 cm-by-10 cm-by-10 cm

Lesson 6-3 pages 319–322

ON YOUR OWN 1. 17 cm **3.** 12.8 m **5.** 264 in.²
7. 80 in.² **13.** 228.1 in.² **17.** 80.1 m² **19.** 43.5 cm²
21. 179.4 in.² **23.** 62.4 cm² **25.** They are =.
29. 5 cm; 4 cm

MIXED REVIEW 31. $AB = 5$, $BC = 6$, $AC = 5$; isosceles
33. $WX = \sqrt{82}$, $XY = 3\sqrt{5}$, $YW = \sqrt{13}$; scalene
35. If the sum of measures of 2 angles is 90, then they are complementary; true. **37.** 60 cubes **39.** 3 by 3 by 3

CHECKPOINT 1. 297.6 in.² **2.** 377.0 cm² **3.** 185.6 m²
4. 288.7 ft² **5.** 477.5 ft²

Lesson 6-4 pages 327–329

ON YOUR OWN 1. 904.8 in.³ **3.** 80 in.³ **5.** 125.7 cm³
7. 280.6 cm³ **9a.** 28 ft³ **9b.** 1747 lb
13. 79 million ft³ **15.** 16 ft **19a.** 5832 in.³
19b. 729 in.³ **21a.** 24 cm³ **21b.** 3 cm **23.** 140.6 in.³
25a. 16π units³ **25b.** 32π units³

MIXED REVIEW 27. $\overline{AC}, \overline{AB}, \overline{BC}$ **29.** $\overline{BC}, \overline{AB}, \overline{AC}$
31. 8 in.

Lesson 6-5 pages 333–336

ON YOUR OWN 1. 115.5 in.³ **3.** 122.5 in.³
5a. 120π ft³ **5b.** 60π ft³ **5c.** 240π ft³ **7.** 300 in.³
9. $\frac{16}{3}\pi$ ft³ **13.** The volumes are =; the volume of the large cone is $\frac{1}{3}$ the volume of the cylinder; the volume of each small cone is $\frac{1}{3}$ the volume of half the cylinder.
15. 15 in.³ **17a.** 5,920,000 ft³ **17b.** 267 ft
19. pyramid **21.** 3 **23.** 9

MIXED REVIEW
25a. $AB = 5$, $BC = 10$, $CD = 5$, $AD = 10$
25b. $AB = \frac{4}{3}$, $BC = -\frac{3}{4}$, $CD = \frac{4}{3}$, $AD = -\frac{3}{4}$
25c. rectangle **27.** 113.1 in.²; 37.7 in.
29. 19.6 ft²; 15.7 ft

Lesson 6-6 pages 340–343

ON YOUR OWN 1. 1794.5 cm² **3.** 23.8 in.²
5. 64π units²; $\frac{256}{3}\pi$ units³ **7.** 85 lb **9.** 288π cm²
11. $\frac{2048}{3}\pi$ cm³ **13.** No; the volume of the ice cream is $\frac{4}{3}$ times the volume of the cone. **15a.** 1207 ft³
15b. 10.8 $\frac{lb}{ft^3}$ **15c.** 4191 mi **17a.** 3 in. **17b.** 102.9 in.³
19. 2 : 3 **21a.** $6\sqrt{3}$ in.; $3\sqrt{3}$ in. **21b.** 371.7 in.³ **23.** A
25. The balls weigh 75 lb and 253 lb, respectively.

27a. Cube; the edge of the cube is about 1.61 times as long as the radius r of the sphere. The surface area of the cube, about $15.59 r^2$, is > surface area of the sphere, about $12.57 r^2$.

MIXED REVIEW 33. 261.3 m³

CHECKPOINT 1. 376 ft²; 480 ft² **2.** 659.7 cm²; 1256.6 cm³ **3.** 332.9 in.²; 377.0 in.³ **4.** 113.1 m²; 113.1 m³ **5.** C **6.** The remaining volume is $2\pi r^3$, which is $> \frac{4}{3}\pi r^3$ (volume of one ball).

Lesson 6-7 pages 346–347

ON YOUR OWN 1. 864π in.³ **3.** 10,368 in.³ **5.** 501 in.³
7a. **7b.** 1250π in.³ **9.** cone, hemisphere
13a.

13b. 19 ft; 34 ft **15.** 73 cm³

17a. 237 ft² **17b.** 1 can

MIXED REVIEW 19. Assume $\angle P \cong \angle N$. By the Converse of the Isos. Triangle Thm., $\overline{MN} \cong \overline{MP}$, which contradicts the hypothesis. Therefore, $\angle P \not\cong \angle N$.
21. $\frac{1}{6}$ **23.** $\frac{1}{2}$

Lesson 6-8 pages 350–352

ON YOUR OWN 1. $\frac{2}{5}$ or 40% **3.** about 61%
5. 40% **7a.** The erasure must start at least 15 min before the end of the tape.

7b. **9.** 4% **11.** about 1.9%
13. about 26%

MIXED REVIEW 15. U.S. **17.** 16 cm

Wrap Up pages 354–357

1.

2. D **3.** C **4.** A **5.** B **6.** 36 cm²
7. 66π m² **8.** 208 in.² **9.** 170π ft²
10. 172.8 ft²; 251.3 ft² **11.** 260 cm²; 360 cm² **12.** 37.7 in.²; 50.3 in.²
13. 320 m²; 576 m² **14.** 250 ft³
15. 54π cm³ **16.** 1764 in.³
17. 32π m³ **19.** 235.6 mm³
20. 149.3 ft³ **21.** 6 m³ **22.** 301.6 cm³

---

23. 314.2 in.²; 523.6 in.³ **24.** 153.9 cm²; 179.6 cm³
25. 50.3 ft²; 33.5 ft³ **26.** 8.0 ft²; 2.1 ft³ **27.** 8.6 in.³
28. 263.9 m³ **29.** 162 cm³ **30.** 280 in.³ **31.** $\frac{1}{2}$ or 50%
32. $\frac{3}{8}$ or 37.5% **33.** $\frac{1}{6}$ or about 16.7% **34.** No; you model probability by ratio of lengths of segments.
35. Sample: $\overline{AB}, \overline{EF}, \overline{CD}$ **36.** Sample: $\overline{AB}, \overline{BC}, \overline{BF}$

Cumulative Review page 359

1. E **3.** C **5.** D **7.** C

CHAPTER 7

Toolbox page 362

INVESTIGATE $m\angle 1 = m\angle 3 = m\angle 5 = m\angle 7$, $m\angle 2 = m\angle 4 = m\angle 6 = m\angle 8$

CONJECTURE Sample: 2 sets of 4 $\cong$ angles are formed.

EXTEND Yes; the angles formed by 3 $\parallel$ lines have a relation similar to the one for the angles formed by 2 $\parallel$ lines; 2
All the angles formed by these lines are rt. angles.

Lesson 7-1 pages 366–369

ON YOUR OWN 1. $\angle 1$ and $\angle 2$: corresponding, $\angle 3$ and $\angle 4$: alt. interior, $\angle 5$ and $\angle 6$: corresponding **3.** $\angle 1$ and $\angle 2$: corresponding, $\angle 3$ and $\angle 4$: same-side interior, $\angle 5$ and $\angle 6$: alt. interior **5.** 120 (If $\parallel$ lines, then corres. $\angle$s are $\cong$.); 60 (If $\parallel$ lines, then same-side. $\angle$s are supplementary.) **7.** 70 (If $\parallel$ lines, then same-side int. $\angle$s are supplementary.); 110 (If $\parallel$ lines, then same-side int. $\angle$s are supplementary.) **9.** If $\parallel$ lines, then alt. int. $\angle$s are $\cong$. **11.** If $\parallel$ lines, then alt. int. $\angle$s are $\cong$. **13.** If $\parallel$ lines, then corres. $\angle$s are $\cong$. **15a.** corresponding
15b. alt. interior **17a.** $\frac{1}{2}$ **19.** $\angle 1$ and $\angle 9$, $\angle 2$ and $\angle 10$, $\angle 5$ and $\angle 11$, $\angle 6$ and $\angle 12$ **21.** same-side interior angle, ℓ **23.** alt. interior, ℓ **25.** $\angle 3$, $\angle 9$ **27.** $\angle 7$, $\angle 10$
29a. $BERT$ is a $\square$. **29b.** def. of $\square$ **29c.** If $\parallel$ lines, then alt. int. $\angle$s are $\cong$. **31.** 70 **33.** 32 **35.** 20
37. $v = 42$, $w = 25$, $x = 76$, $y = 37$ **41.** Answers may vary. Sample: Perpendicular parking does not waste any space but makes it harder to park a car. Slanted parking makes it easier to park a car and makes the direction of traffic clear, but there are fewer parking spaces because some space in each corner is wasted.

MIXED REVIEW 43. $(-0.5, 3.5)$ **45.** $(-1.5, -2.5)$
47. 5 **49.** 1790 cm²; 1937 cm² **51.** If there are no clouds in the sky, then the sky is blue.

Toolbox page 370

1. $(-3, -7)$ **3.** no solution **5.** $(8, 17)$

Lesson 7-2 pages 373–376

ON YOUR OWN 1. $\overrightarrow{BE} \parallel \overrightarrow{CG}$; if $\cong$ corres. $\angle$s, then lines are $\parallel$. **3.** $\overrightarrow{IO} \parallel \overrightarrow{LM}$; if supplementary same-side int. $\angle$s, then lines are $\parallel$. **5.** $a \parallel b$; if $\cong$ corres. $\angle$s, then lines are $\parallel$. **7.** $a \parallel b$; if supplementary same-side int. $\angle$s, then lines are $\parallel$. **9.** $\ell \parallel m$; if $\cong$ alt. int. $\angle$s, then lines are $\parallel$. **11.** $a \parallel b$; if supplementary same-side int. $\angle$s, then lines are $\parallel$. **13.** no $\parallel$ lines **15.** Vertical $\angle$s are $\cong$, and if $\cong$ corres. $\angle$s, then lines are $\parallel$.

17.

| $a \parallel b$ |
| Given |

↓

| $\angle 7 \cong \angle 2$ |
| Alt. Interior $\angle$s Thm. |

| $\angle 7 \cong \angle 10$ |
| Given |

↓

| $\angle 2 \cong \angle 10$ |
| Transitive Prop. of $\cong$ |

↓

| $\ell \parallel m$ |
| Converse of Corres. $\angle$s Post. |

19. If corres. angles are $\cong$, then the lines are $\parallel$. **21.** D **23.** 50 **25.** 31 **27.** 20
29a. The $\triangle$s are $\sim$ and isosceles, so the 4 base angles are $\cong$. Then the alt. interior angles are $\cong$, so the lines are $\parallel$. **31.** Each line and the flat surface form a corres. angle that is congruent to the 60° angle of the drawing $\triangle$. Since the corres. angles are $\cong$, the lines are $\parallel$. **33.** Trapezoid; 2 distinct pairs of same-side int. angles are supplementary, so one pair of sides are $\parallel$. **35.** Rectangle; all the angles are rt. angles and 2 pairs of opp. sides are $\parallel$. **37.** 1. $\overline{A'B'}$ is the reflection of $\overline{AB}$ in line m. (Given) 2. $\overline{AA'} \perp m$ and $\overline{BB'} \perp m$ (Def. of reflection) 3. $\overline{AA'} \parallel \overline{BB'}$ (In a plane, 2 lines $\perp$ to 3rd are $\parallel$.)

MIXED REVIEW 39. 157.1 cm² **41.** 2.3 m²

Lesson 7-3 pages 380–383

ON YOUR OWN

1.   **3a.**

7.   **9.**

11a–b.   **13.**

15.

17c. $p \parallel m$; in a plane, 2 lines $\perp$ to 3rd are $\parallel$.

19a. ①-④: construct 2 $\perp$ lines. ⑤: construct a rt. △ with a hypotenuse that is twice the length of a leg. **19b.** ①-③: construct an equilateral △. ④-⑥: construct an angle bisector. **19c.** ①-③: construct an equilateral △. ④-⑤: construct the $\perp$ bisector of a side.

MIXED REVIEW 21. Cannot form a △; $2 + 3 = 5$
23. acute; $5^2 < 4^2 + 4^2$ **25a.** $\frac{16}{3}\pi$ cm **25b.** 64π cm²
25c. $\frac{64}{3}\pi$ cm³

CHECKPOINT 1. If $\parallel$ lines, then corres. $\angle$s are $\cong$.
2. If $\cong$ corres. $\angle$s, then lines are $\parallel$. **3.** If $\parallel$ lines, then same-side int. $\angle$s are supplementary. **4.** If $\cong$ alt. int. $\angle$s, then lines are $\parallel$. **5.** Vertical $\angle$s are $\cong$. **6.** If $\parallel$ lines, then alt. int. $\angle$s are $\cong$. **7.** If $\cong$ corres. $\angle$s, then lines are $\parallel$.
8. If $\parallel$ lines, then corres. $\angle$s are $\cong$. **9.** If supplementary same-side int. $\angle$s, then lines are $\parallel$.

10.   **11.**

12. C

Toolbox page 384

INVESTIGATE Above and to the left; inside $ABCD$; below and to the right.

Lesson 7-4 pages 388–391

ON YOUR OWN 1. 2-pt. perspective **3.** 2-pt. perspective **5.** IB, IIC, IIIA
7.

9.

13. The painting is in perspective. The edges of the road converge to a vanishing point.

MIXED REVIEW 21a. If it is July 4, then it is a national holiday in the United States. **21b.** false; true
23. a circle with center at $(12, -6)$ and radius 6
25. 270

Lesson 7-5 pages 395–397

ON YOUR OWN

1.   **3.**

7.   **11.**   **15.** true
17. true
19. false

T683

MIXED REVIEW
21. yes **23.** yes

25. $-\frac{2}{3}$ **27.** $\frac{1}{3}$ **29.** 36, 54

Wrap Up — pages 399–401
1. 120, If ∥ lines, then corres. ∠s are ≅; 120, Vertical ∠s are ≅. **2.** 75, If ∥ lines, then same-side int. ∠s are supplementary; 105, If ∥ lines, then alt. int. ∠s are ≅. **3.** 55, If ∥ lines, then same-side int. ∠s are supplementary; 90, If ∥ lines, then alt. int. ∠s are ≅. **6.** C **7.** 20 **8.** 20 **9.** 24 **10.**

11a. **11b.** $b\sqrt{3}$ **11c.** 30, 60, 90

15. **16.**
17. See diagram for Exercise 15.
18.
19. $x = 60$; $y = 30$ **20.** $x = 9$; $y = 9\sqrt{2}$; $z = 45$ **21.** $y = 4$; $z = 2\sqrt{3}$ **22.** $z = 45$ **23.** $x = 35$; $y = 10$; $z = 10$ **24.** $w = 88$; $x = 7$; $y = 52$; $z = 40$

Preparing for Standardized Tests — page 403
1. C **3.** D **5.** C **7.** B **9.** B

CHAPTER 8

Lesson 8-1 — pages 409–412
ON YOUR OWN **1.** $\overline{XZ}$ **3.** SAS **7.** △JKL ≅ △NMO; SSS **9.** not possible **11.** △PQR ≅ △NMO; SAS **13.** △XYP ≅ △QYP; SAS **17.** ∠s; SAS Post. **19.** 1. $\overline{AE}$ and $\overline{BD}$ bisect each other. (Given) 2. $\overline{AC} ≅ \overline{CE}$; $\overline{BC} ≅ \overline{CD}$ (Def. of segment bisector) 3. ∠ACB ≅ ∠ECD (Vertical ∠s are ≅.) 4. △ACB ≅ △ECD (SAS) **21a.** ≅ (equality) and ∼ (similarity) **23.** 1. $\overline{FG} ∥ \overline{KL}$ (Given) 2. ∠GFK ≅ ∠LKF (If ∥ lines, then alt. int. ∠s are ≅.) 3. $\overline{FG} ≅ \overline{KL}$ (Given) 4. $\overline{FK} ≅ \overline{FK}$ (Reflexive Prop. of ≅) 5. △FGK ≅ △KLF (SAS)

MIXED REVIEW **27.** 314.2 mm³; 282.7 mm² **29.** 34, 34

Toolbox — page 413
INVESTIGATE yes; no; yes
INVESTIGATE yes; yes; no; only when the segments coincide
CONJECTURE No; no; the above constructions demonstrate SSA △s that are not ≅ and AAA △s that are not ≅.
EXTEND no; no; yes

Lesson 8-2 — pages 416–419
ON YOUR OWN **1.** AAS **3.** AAS **5.** ASA **7.** not possible **9.** ∠D ≅ ∠H **11.** ∠M ≅ ∠P **15.** Def. of ∠s; SSS **19.** 1. $\overline{FG} ∥ \overline{JH}$ (Given) 2. ∠FGJ ≅ ∠HJG (If ∥ lines, then alt. int. ∠s are ≅.) 3. ∠F ≅ ∠H (Given) 4. $\overline{JG} ≅ \overline{JG}$ (Reflexive Prop. of ≅) 5. △FGJ ≅ △HJG (AAS) **21.** 1. ∠MON ≅ ∠QOP (Vertical ∠s are ≅.) 2. ∠N ≅ ∠P (Given) 3. $\overline{MO} ≅ \overline{QO}$ (Given) 4. △MON ≅ △QOP (AAS) **23.** The hypotenuse of a rt. △ is longer than each leg. So $FE > 5$ cm and $\overline{FE} ≅ \overline{AB}$.

MIXED REVIEW **25.** (2,0) **27.** $x = \frac{7\sqrt{3}}{3}$; $y = \frac{14\sqrt{3}}{3}$ **29.** $x = 4$; $y = 4\sqrt{2}$

Lesson 8-3 — pages 422–425
ON YOUR OWN **1.** E **3.** $\overline{XV} ≅ \overline{TV}$ or $\overline{RX} ≅ \overline{RT}$ **5.** △AQC and △GJC are rt. angles. **7.** $\overline{RT} ≅ \overline{NQ}$ **9.** You need to know which side is the hypotenuse. **11b.** −1; −1; 1 **11c.** They are rt. △s. **11d.** $\sqrt{26}$; $\sqrt{26}$ **11e.** △EGD and △EGF share a common leg $\overline{EG}$. Since the hypotenuses are ≅, the right △s are ≅ by HL Thm. **13.** 1. $\overline{OM}$ and $\overline{ON}$ are radii of ⊙O. (Given)

2. $\overline{OM} ≅ \overline{ON}$ (All radii of a ⊙ are ≅.) 3. ∠M and ∠N are rt. angles. (Given) 4. △LMO and △LNO are rt. ∠s. (Def. of rt. △s) 5. $\overline{OL} ≅ \overline{OL}$ (Reflexive Prop. of ≅) 6. △LMO ≅ △LNO (HL Thm.) **17.** All sides of a regular polygon are ≅. Since the △s are rt. △s, and the shorter legs are all ≅, by HL Thm., all the △s are ≅.
19.

MIXED REVIEW **21.** Angle Addition Post. **23.** If ∥ lines, then same-side int. ∠s are supplementary. **25.** If ∥ lines, then corres. ∠s are ≅. **27.** 7.64 m²

CHECKPOINT **1.** ASA **2.** SSS **3.** SAS **4.** not possible **5.** AAS **6.** HL **7b.** No; if 2 pairs of angles are ≅, the 3rd pair of angles is also ≅. Then the △s are ≅ by AAS or ASA. **8.** E **9.** If the hypotenuse and an acute angle of one right triangle are congruent to the hypotenuse and an acute angle of another right triangle, then the triangles are congruent. The HA Theorem is true. Since the right angles are congruent, the triangles are congruent by AAS.

Lesson 8-4 — pages 429–432
ON YOUR OWN **1.** Use ASA to prove △ABD ≅ △CBD. **3.** Use SAS to prove △STP ≅ △OTP. **5.** Use HL to prove △OER ≅ △OEP. **7.** Yes; the △s are ≅ by SSS, and the angles are ≅ by CPCTC. **9a.** Given **9b.** Given **9c.** Def. of angle bisector **9d.** Reflexive Prop. of ≅ **9e.** ASA **9f.** CPCTC **11a.** Given **11b.** Def. of ∥ lines **11c.** All rt. ∠s are ≅. **11d.** Given **11e.** Def. of segment bisector **11f.** Reflexive Prop. of ≅ **11g.** SAS **11h.** CPCTC **13.** It is given that $\overline{BA} ≅ \overline{BC}$ and $\overline{BD}$ bisects ∠ABC. ∠ABD ≅ ∠CBD by def. of ∠ bisector, and ∠A ≅ ∠C because base ∠s of an isosceles △ are ≅. Then △ABD ≅ △CBD by AAS. $\overline{AD} ≅ \overline{CD}$ by CPCTC. Therefore, $\overline{BD}$ bisects $\overline{AC}$ by def. of segment bisector. By the Angle Addition Post., m∠ADB + m∠CDB = 180. ∠ADB ≅ ∠CDB by CPCTC. So, the measure of each angle is ½(180) = 90. Therefore, $\overline{BD} ⊥ \overline{AC}$ by def. of ⊥ lines. **15a.** Use SAS on 2 legs and rt. angle. **15b.** $\overline{BF}$; CPCTC **15c.** You use the △s with ≅ hypotenuses and ≅ legs. By HL, △FAB ≅ △BCD. **17a.** $\overline{PA} ≅ \overline{PB}$; $\overline{AC} ≅ \overline{BC}$ **17b.** $\overline{CP} ≅ \overline{CP}$ by Reflexive Prop. of ≅. Then, △APC ≅ △BPC by SSS and ∠APC ≅ ∠BPC by CPCTC. Therefore, m∠APC = m∠BPC = 90 by Angle Addition Post., and $\overline{CP} ⊥ \overline{AB}$ by def. of ⊥ lines.

MIXED REVIEW **21.** 89% **23.** about 79°

25.

Lesson 8-5 — pages 436–438
ON YOUR OWN **1.** ∠M **3.** $\overline{XY}$ **5.** △STU, △TSR; SSS **7.** △PQT, △URS; AAS **9.** △WYX, △ZXY; HL **11.** Prove △QUB by ASA. So $\overline{QT} ≅ \overline{QU}$. Then use SAS to prove △QET ≅ △QEU. **13a.** Given **13b.** Reflexive Prop. of ≅ **13c.** ITE **13d.** SSS **13e.** TID **13f.** Given **13g.** All rt. ∠s are ≅. **13h.** AAS **13i.** $\overline{TD}$; $\overline{RO}$ **13j.** CPCTC **15.** B **17.** Since $\overline{TQ}$ bisects $\overline{PR}$, $\overline{PQ} ≅ \overline{RQ}$. Since $\overline{TQ} ⊥ \overline{PR}$, ∠PQT and ∠RQT are rt. ∠s. Also, $\overline{QT} ≅ \overline{QT}$, so △PQT ≅ △RQT by SAS. ∠PTQ ≅ ∠RTQ by CPCTC. Since $\overline{TQ}$ bisects ∠VQS, ∠VQT ≅ ∠SQT. So, △VQT ≅ △SQT by ASA, and $\overline{VQ} ≅ \overline{SQ}$ by CPCTC.

MIXED REVIEW **19.** isosceles rt. △ **21.** 8 units²; $(8 + 4\sqrt{2})$ units

Toolbox — page 439
1. 2, −7 **3.** −0.5, −3 **5.** −0.27, −3.06 **7.** −3, 9 **9.** −0.5, 0.75

Wrap Up — pages 441–443
1. SSS; △DMR ≅ △TMR **2.** not possible **3.** SAS; △MNQ ≅ △PNO **4.** The order of the vertices indicates the corresponding parts. **5.** D **6.** not possible **7.** AAS **8.** ASA **9.** 1. $\overline{PS} ≅ \overline{SQ}$ and $\overline{RQ} ≅ \overline{QS}$ (Given) 2. ∠PSQ and ∠RQS are rt. ∠s. (Def. of ⊥ lines) 3. ∠PSQ and ∠RQS are rt. ∠s. 4. $\overline{PQ} ≅ \overline{RS}$ (Given) 5. $\overline{QS} ≅ \overline{QS}$ (Reflexive Prop. of ≅) 6. △PSQ ≅ △RQS (HL Thm.) **10.** 1. U is the midpt. of $\overline{TV}$. (Given) 2. $\overline{TU} ≅ \overline{UV}$ (Def. of midpt.) 3. $\overline{XU} ⊥ \overline{TV}$ and $\overline{WV} ⊥ \overline{TV}$ (Given) 4. ∠XUT and ∠WVU are rt. ∠s. (Def. of ⊥ lines) 5. △TXU and △UWV are rt. ∠s. (Def. of rt. △s) 6. △TXU ≅ △UWV (HL Thm.) **11.** 1. $\overline{LN} ≅ \overline{KM}$ (Given) 2. ∠LNK and ∠LNM are rt. ∠s. (Def. of ⊥ lines.) 3. △KLN and △MLN are rt. ∠s. 4. $\overline{KL} ≅ \overline{ML}$ (Given) 5. $\overline{LN} ≅ \overline{LN}$ (Reflexive Prop. of ≅) 6. △KLN ≅ △MLN (HL Thm.) **13.** Use AAS to show △TVY ≅ △YWX. $\overline{TV} ≅ \overline{YW}$ by CPCTC. **14.** Use ASA to show △BCE ≅ △DCE. ∠B ≅ ∠D by CPCTC. **15.** Use HL to show △KLM ≅ △MNK. $\overline{KN} ≅ \overline{ML}$ by CPCTC. **16.** △ADB, △ACE; SSS **17.** △FIH, △GHI; SAS **18.** △PST, △RAT; ASA **19.** rectangle **20.** square **21.** parallelogram **22.** kite

23. The diagonals are ⊥ bisectors of each other. Each diagonal is an angle bisector of 2 of the angles of the rhombus. The area of the rhombus is half the product of the lengths of the diagonals.

Cumulative Review — page 445
1. E **3.** A **5.** B **7.** A **11.**

CHAPTER 9

Lesson 9-1 — pages 451–453
ON YOUR OWN **1.** m∠1 = 118; m∠2 = 62; m∠3 = 118 **3.** m∠1 = 81; m∠2 = 28; m∠3 = 71 **5.** 32 **7.** 16 **9.** ST = 7 cm; TW = 17 cm; WR = 7 cm **11.** Pick 6 equally spaced lines on the paper. Place the paper so that the 1st button is on the 1st line and the last button is on the 6th line. Draw a line between the first and last buttons. The remaining buttons should be placed where the drawn line crosses the 4 ∥ lines. **15.** 1. ∠LENS (Given) 2. $\overline{LS} ≅ \overline{EH}$ (Def. of ▱) 3. ∠NGTH (Given) 4. $\overline{GT} ≅ \overline{EH}$ (Def. of ▱) 5. $\overline{LS} ≅ \overline{GT}$ (2 lines ∥ to a 3rd line are ∥.) **17.** 60 **19.** x = 109; y = 88; z = 76 **21.** x = y = 6 **23.** x = 0; y = 5 **27a.** If a quad. is a ▱, then opp. angles are ≅.
27b. Given: ▱ABCD. Prove: ∠A ≅ ∠C; ∠B ≅ ∠D. Draw diagonal $\overline{BD}$. 1. ▱ABCD (Given) 2. $\overline{AB} ≅ \overline{CD}$ (Def. of ▱) 3. ∠ABD ≅ ∠BDC (If ∥ lines, then alt. int. ∠s are ≅.) 4. $\overline{BC} ≅ \overline{DA}$ (Def. of ▱) 5. ∠ADB ≅ ∠CBD (If ∥ lines, then alt. int. ∠s are ≅.) 6. $\overline{BD} ≅ \overline{BD}$ (Reflexive Prop. of ≅) 7. △ABD ≅ △CDB (ASA) 8. ∠A ≅ ∠C (CPCTC) Similarly, use diagonal $\overline{AC}$ to prove ∠B ≅ ∠D. **29.** 1. ▱RSTW and △XYTZ (Given) 2. ∠T ≅ ∠T (Opp. angles of a ▱ are ≅.) 3. ∠X ≅ ∠T (Opp. angles of a ▱ are ≅.) 4. ∠X ≅ ∠R (Transitive Prop. of ≅) **31.** kite **33.** trapezoid

MIXED REVIEW **41a.** (2.5, 1.5), (2.5, 1.5); $\overline{AC}$ and $\overline{BD}$ bisect each other. **41b.** $\frac{1}{3}$, $\frac{1}{3}$; the slopes are =. **41c.** $\overline{AB} ∥ \overline{DC}$ because they are vertical. **41d.** parallelogram

Lesson 9-2 — pages 457–460
ON YOUR OWN **1.** Yes; if both pairs of opp. sides of a quad. are ≅, then quad. is a ▱. **3.** Yes; if both pairs of opp. angles of a quad. are ≅, the quad. is a ▱. **5.** Yes; both pairs of opp. sides are ≅ because alt. int. ∠s are ≅. The quad. is a ▱ by def. **7.** Yes; the quad. is a ▱ by def. **9.** **11.** yes **13.** **15.** 60; yes; both pairs of opp. angles are ≅ **17.** 6; yes; both pairs of opp. sides are ≅ **19.** x = 3; y = 11 **21.** 8 **25a.** (4, 6) **25b.** (6, 6) **25c.** (−2, 4) **27.** 1. △TRS ≅ △RTW (Given) 2. $\overline{RS} ≅ \overline{TW}$; $\overline{ST} ≅ \overline{WR}$ (CPCTC) 3. RSTW is a ▱. (If both pairs of opp. sides of a quad. are ≅, then the quad. is a ▱.) **29a.** 1. E is midpt. of $\overline{BC}$, and F is midpt. of $\overline{AD}$. (Given) 2. $BE = \frac{1}{2}BC$; $AF = \frac{1}{2}AD$ (Def. of midpt.) 3. ▱ABCD (Given) 4. $AD = BC$ (Opp. sides of a ▱ are ≅.) 5. $\frac{1}{2}AD = \frac{1}{2}BC$ (Mult. Prop. of ≅) 6. $AF = BE$ (Substitution) 7. $\overline{AD} ∥ \overline{BC}$ (Opp. sides of a ▱ are ≅.) 8. ABEF is a ▱. (If 1 pair of opp. sides of a quad. is ≅ and ∥, then the quad. is a ▱.) **29b.** Opp. angles of a ▱ are ≅. **29c.** Opp. sides of a ▱ are ≅. **31a.** 1. threads remain ∥; the small rectangles are replaced with small nonrectangular ▱s. **31b.** The fabric stretches along one direction of threads and shrinks along the other.

MIXED REVIEW **33.** 50.3 cm² **35.** 166.3 ft² **37.** A ▱ is a quad. with 2 pairs of ∥ sides. **39.** A rectangle is a ▱ with 4 rt. angles.

CHECKPOINT **1.** m∠1 = 59; m∠2 = 121; m∠3 = 59 **2.** m∠1 = 43; m∠2 = 74; m∠3 = 106; m∠2 = 74; m∠3 = 26 **4.** x = 45; y = 60 **5.** x = 7; y = 16 **6.** x = 1; y = 2 **7.** D

Toolbox — page 461
INVESTIGATE Sample: The diagonals are ≅. Sample: The diagonals are ⊥.
CONJECTURE Sample: Diags. of a rectangle are ≅; diags. of a rhombus are ⊥ bisectors of each other; diags. of a rhombus bisect the angles of the rhombus. Sample: All the properties of the diags. of rectangles and rhombuses are true for the diags. of squares.
EXTEND In a ▱, perpendicular diags. determine a rhombus; ≅ diags. determine a rectangle; diags. that bisect the angles of the ▱ determine a rhombus.

Lesson 9-3 — pages 465–468
ON YOUR OWN **1a.** rhombus **1b.** m∠1 = 38; m∠2 = 38; m∠3 = 38; m∠4 = 38 **3a.** rectangle **3b.** m∠1 = 56; m∠2 = 68; m∠3 = 112; m∠4 = 56 **5.** 26.8 in. **7.** LB = 10; BP = 5; LM = 8 **9.** LB = 12; BP = 12; LM = 2√11 **11.** C **13.** x = 45; y = 45; z = 30 **15.** x = 7.5; y = 3 **17a.** BD **17b.** AE **17c.** EC **17d.** AE; EC **17e.** AE; EC **17f.** AC **19.** 15.9 **21.** 1.5² + 6² = 6.5², so the diagonals divide the ▱ into 4 rt. △s. Since the diagonals are ⊥, JKLM is a rhombus. **23.** 24 m² **25.** 18 cm² **27.** Yes; 4 sides are ≅, so the opp. sides are ≅, and the quad. is a ▱ with all sides ≅ is a rhombus. **29.** 1. $\overline{AC} ≅ \overline{AC}$ (Reflexive Prop. of ≅) 2. $\overline{AC}$ bisects ∠BAD and ∠BCD. (Given) 3. ∠1 ≅ ∠2, ∠3 ≅ ∠4 (Def. of angle bisector) 4. △ABC ≅ △ADC (ASA) 5. $\overline{AB} ≅ \overline{DA}$; $\overline{BC} ≅ \overline{CD}$ (CPCTC) 6. ▱ABCD (Given) 7. $\overline{AB} ≅ \overline{CD}$ (Opp. sides of a ▱ are ≅.) 8. $\overline{AB} ≅ \overline{BC} ≅ \overline{CD} ≅ \overline{DA}$ (Transitive Prop. of ≅) 9. ABCD is a rhombus. (Def. of rhombus) **31.** In ▱ABCD, $\overline{AB} ≅ \overline{DC}$ because opp. sides of a ▱ are ≅. $\overline{AD} ≅ \overline{AD}$ by the Reflexive Prop. of ≅. Since $\overline{AC} ≅ \overline{BD}$, △BAD ≅ △CDA by SSS and ∠BAD ≅ ∠CDA by CPCTC. ∠BAD and ∠CDA are consecutive angles of a ▱, so they are supp. Therefore, both angles are rt. ∠s and the angles opp. them are rt. ∠s. So ▱ABCD is a rectangle by def. **33a.** Since ABCD is a ▱, opp. ∠s are ≅. So ∠B ≅ ∠D, therefore ∠D is a rt. angle. In a ▱, consecutive ∠s are supp. Therefore, ∠A and ∠C are each supp. to ∠D. The supp. of a rt. angle is a rt. angle, so ∠A and ∠C are rt. ∠s. Therefore, ABCD is a rectangle by def. **33b.** If one ∠ of a ▱ is a rt. angle, then the ▱ is a rectangle.

supplementary, then another pair must be also because a pair of opp. ∠s of a kite is ≅. Therefore, the opp. sides are ∥, which means the figure is a ▱ and cannot be a kite. **11b.** Yes; if 2 ≅ angles are rt. angles, they are supplementary. The other 2 angles are also supplementary. **13.** 1.5 **15.** x = 35; y = 30 **19.** $\overline{AB} ≅ \overline{AA'}$ $\overline{BA'} ≅ \overline{BA'}$, so it is a kite (unless x = 60, in which case the 4 sides are ≅ and it is a rhombus). **25a.** isosceles trapezoids **25b.** 45, 135, 135, 45 **27.** 1. Isosceles trapezoid TRAP (Given) 2. $\overline{TA} ≅ \overline{PR}$ (Diagonals of an isos. trap. are ≅.) 3. $\overline{TR} ≅ \overline{PA}$ (Given) 4. $\overline{RA} ≅ \overline{RA}$ (Reflexive Prop. of ≅) 5. △TRA ≅ △PAR (SSS) 6. ∠1 ≅ ∠2 (CPCTC)

MIXED REVIEW **29.** $\frac{3}{8}$ **31a.** $x(x + 7)$ or $x^2 + 7x$ **31b.** 78 cm² **33.** parallelogram **35.** square

Toolbox — page 469
INVESTIGATE parallelogram
CONJECTURE The quad. whose vertices are midpts. of another quad. is a ▱; yes; no.
EXTEND
• rectangle; rhombus
• The ratio of lengths of sides and perimeters is $\frac{1}{2}$; the ratio of areas is $\frac{1}{4}$; MNOP ∼ FGHE.

Lesson 9-4 — pages 473–476
ON YOUR OWN **1.** m∠1 = 77; m∠2 = 103 **3.** m∠1 = 90; m∠2 = 68 **5.** UI = 6; IT = 15; UT = 21 **7.** 12 cm, 12 cm, 21 cm, 21 cm **9a.** Isosceles trapezoid; all the large △s appear to be ≅. **9b.** 112; 68; 68 **11a.** No; if one pair of consecutive ∠s is

Toolbox — page 477
1. 4, x ≠ −3 **3.** $\frac{x-3}{x+3}$, x ≠ −3 **5.** 7w + 3 **7.** $\frac{1}{5t}$, t ≠ 0 **9.** 4x², x ≠ 3 **11.** v + 1, v ≠ −1 **13.** $\frac{3}{r}$, r ≠ 0 **15.** 15c, c ≠ −2 **17.** 15x, x ≠ 0 **19.** $\frac{3a}{2}$, a ≠ 0 **21.** $\frac{t+2}{5}$, t ≠ −3 or 2 **23.** $\frac{1}{2a + 10}$, a ≠ −5 or 5 **25.** 3y⁴ + 3y³, y ≠ −1 or 0 **27.** $\frac{3c^2 - 2c - 1}{c^2 + 1}$, c ≠ 1

Lesson 9-5 — pages 480–482
ON YOUR OWN **1.** W(0, h); Z(0, 0) **3.** W(−b, 0); Z(−b, −b) **5.** W(−r, 0); Z(0, −t) **7.** $\left(\frac{b}{2}, \frac{h}{2}\right)$, $\sqrt{b^2 + h^2}$ **9.** (−b, 0), 2b **11.** $\left(-\frac{r}{2}, -\frac{t}{2}\right)$, $\sqrt{r^2 + t^2}$ **15a.** **15b.** (−b, 0), (0, b), (b, 0), (0, −b) **15c.** b√2 **15d.** 1 and −1 **15e.** Yes, because the product of the slopes is −1. **17.** (c − a, b) **19.** (−b, 0) **21a.** (0, 0, 0), (0, 0, 2a), (0, 2a, 0), (2a, 0, 0), (0, 2a, 2a), (2a, 0, 2a), (2a, 2a, 0), (2a, 2a, 2a) **21b.** (−a, −a, −a), (−a, −a, a), (−a, a, −a), (a, −a, −a), (−a, a, a), (a, −a, a), (a, a, −a), (a, a, a) **23.**

Isosceles trapezoid; the y-axis is the ⊥ bisector of $\overline{AA'}$ and $\overline{BB'}$. In a plane, 2 lines ⊥ to a 3rd line are ∥, so $\overline{AA'} ∥ \overline{BB'}$. Also, AB = A'B'. **25a.** The diagonals of a rhombus are ⊥.

MIXED REVIEW **27.** 36√3 in.² **29.** 76 ft²

CHECKPOINT 1. $x = 51$; $y = 51$ 2. 3 3. $x = 58$; $y = 32$ 4. $x = 2$; $y = 4$ 5. The diagonals of a rhombus are $\perp$; each diagonal bisects 2 opp. angles of the rhombus.

Lesson 9-6 pages 485–487

ON YOUR OWN 3. $E(-a, 0)$, $F(-b, c)$; use the Distance Formula to find the lengths of $\overline{EG}$, $\sqrt{(b + a)^2 + c^2}$, and of $\overline{HF}$, $\sqrt{(a + b)^2 + (-c)^2}$. The lengths are $=$, so the diagonals are $=$. 5. $T(-2a, 0)$, $R(-2b, 2c)$, $D(-a - b, c)$, $E(2c, c)$, $F(a + b, c)$, $G(0, 0)$; $DE = EF = FG = GD = \sqrt{(a + b)^2 + c^2}$ 7. $K(b + a + c)$, $L(b, a + c)$, $M(b, a + c)$, $N(-b, c)$; slope of $\overline{KL}$ and slope of $\overline{MN}$ are 0. Slope of $\overline{LM}$ and slope of $\overline{NK}$ are undef. Lines with 0 slope and with undef. slope are $\perp$ to each other. Therefore, $KLMN$ is a rectangle. 11a. $\frac{b}{c}$
11b. Let a pt. on line p be (x, y). Then the equation of p is $\frac{y - 0}{x - a} = \frac{b}{c}$ or $y = \frac{b}{c}(x - a)$. 11c. $x = 0$ 11d. When $x = 0$, $y = \frac{b}{c}(x - a) = \frac{b}{c}(-a) = \frac{-ab}{c}$. So p and q intersect at $\left(0, \frac{-ab}{c}\right)$. 11e. $\frac{a}{c}$ 11f. Let a pt. on line r be (x, y). Then the equation of r is $\frac{y - 0}{x - b} = \frac{a}{c}$ or $y = \frac{a}{c}(x - b)$. 11g. $\frac{-ab}{c} = \frac{a}{c}(b - 0)$ ✔ $\frac{-ab}{c} = \frac{b}{c}(a - 0)$ ✔ 11h. $\left(0, \frac{-ab}{c}\right)$

MIXED REVIEW 13. 36% 15. The percent figure in each category is rounded to the nearest integer.

Wrap Up pages 489–491

1. $m\angle 1 = 101$; $m\angle 2 = 79$; $m\angle 3 = 101$ 2. $m\angle 1 = 71$; $m\angle 2 = 54$; $m\angle 3 = 55$ 3. $m\angle 1 = 38$; $m\angle 2 = 43$; $m\angle 3 = 99$ 4. $m\angle 1 = 52$; $m\angle 2 = 25$; $m\angle 3 = 25$ 5. E 6. $x = 2$; $y = 1$ 7. $x = 29$; $y = 28$ 8. $x = 4$; $y = 5$ 9. $m\angle 1 = 124$; $m\angle 2 = 28$; $m\angle 3 = 62$ 10. $m\angle 1 = 60$; $m\angle 2 = 90$; $m\angle 3 = 30$ 11. $m\angle 1 = 50$; $m\angle 2 = 130$ 12. $m\angle 1 = 90$; $m\angle 2 = 25$ 13. 26 in. 14. 19 ft 15. 20 cm 16. 96 ft² 18. (a, b) 19. $(-a, 0)$ 20. $(0, c)$ 21. $(a - b, c)$ 22. Sample: $A(0, 0)$, $B(b, a)$, $C(b, 0)$, $D(0, 0)$; $AC = \sqrt{a^2 + b^2}$, $BD = \sqrt{a^2 + b^2}$, so $AC = BD$, and $\overline{AC} \cong \overline{BD}$. 23. Sample: $F(0, a)$, $G(a, a)$, $H(a, 0)$, $I(0, 0)$. The slope of $\overline{FH}$ is -1. The slope of $\overline{GI}$ is 1. Since the product of the slopes is -1, $\overline{FH} \perp \overline{GI}$. 31. 6 32. 6 33. 3 34. 5

Preparing for Standardized Tests page 493

1. E 3. C 5. B 7. C 9. 140 cm²

CHAPTER 10

Lesson 10-1 pages 499–502

ON YOUR OWN 1. true 3. true 5. true 7. true 9. true 11. 1 : 360 13. no; $\frac{36}{52} = \frac{20}{30}$ 15. $JKLM \sim OPQN$; $\frac{3}{5}$ 17. No; the corres. angles are not $\cong$. 19. 6 21. 16.5 23. 7.5 25. -6 or 6 27. 3 ft by 2 ft 29. $(-4, 24)$, $(16, 24)$ 31. $x = 9$; $z = 10$ 33. $x = 20$; $y = 17.5$; $z = 7.5$ 35. No; the ratios of the corres. sides are not $=$; $\frac{17}{14} \neq \frac{25}{21}$.

39a. [graph] 39b. $JKLM \sim J'K'L'M'$ with similarity ratio 2 : 1 39c. reduction

MIXED REVIEW 45. SSS 47. SAS

Toolbox page 503

1. $t = 0.065c$ 3a. $t = 1.34n$ 3b. 14.9 gal

Lesson 10-2 pages 507–510

ON YOUR OWN 1. no 3. $\triangle ABC \sim \triangle FED$; SSS $\sim$ Thm. 5. no 7. $\triangle MGK \sim \triangle MSP$; SAS $\sim$ Thm. 9. no 11. C 13. 9 15. $12\frac{5}{6}$ 17. 8 21. 220 yd 23. 90 ft 25. 45 ft 29. 1. $\overline{BC} \parallel \overline{DF}$ (Given) 2. $\angle YBC \cong \angle YDF$ (If $\parallel$ lines, then corres. $\angle$s are $\cong$.) 3. $\angle DYF \cong \angle DYF$ (Reflexive Prop. of $\cong$) 4. $\triangle BYC \sim \triangle DYF$ (AA $\sim$ Post.) 31a. 98 m; 98 m 31b. 420 m²; 420 m² 31c. No; corres. sides need not be proportional.

MIXED REVIEW 37. $\pm 2\sqrt{5}$ 39. $\pm 2\sqrt{10}$

CHECKPOINT 1. $\triangle ABC \sim \triangle XYZ$; AA $\sim$ Post. 2. $\triangle LMN \sim \triangle RPQ$; SSS $\sim$ Thm. 3. $\triangle WST \sim \triangle GJH$; SAS $\sim$ Thm. 4. $w = 4.5$; $x = \sqrt{29.25}$ 5. 12 6. 43 ft 9 in.

Lesson 10-3 pages 514–516

ON YOUR OWN 1. JNK; KNL 3. $2\sqrt{10}$ 5. 12 7. 121 9. b 11. r, s 13. c, s 15. s 17. 20 19. $6\sqrt{3}$ 21. $(-2, 6)$, $(10, 6)$ 23. 18 mi; 24 mi 25. $x = 12$; $y = 3\sqrt{7}$; $z = 4\sqrt{7}$ 27. $x = 4$; $y = 2\sqrt{13}$; $z = 3\sqrt{13}$ 29. 3 31. 4.5 33. $5\sqrt{3}$ cm

MIXED REVIEW 37. 1979–1989 41. 7.5 mm 43. 14.5 in.

Lesson 10-4 pages 520–523

ON YOUR OWN 1. KS 3. JP 5. KM 7. JP 9. 6 11. 7.5 13. $3\frac{1}{3}$ 15. 3.6 17a. 559 ft 17b. 671 ft 19. D 21. 2.5 25. 4.5 cm; 12.5 cm 27a. If a line that intersects 2 sides of a $\triangle$ divides them proportionally, then the line is $\parallel$ to the 3rd side.

27b. Sample: [triangle diagram] Given: $\frac{QR}{RX} = \frac{QS}{SY}$ Prove: $\overline{RS} \parallel \overline{XY}$ Plan for Proof: To prove that $\overline{RS} \parallel \overline{XY}$, show that $\angle 3 \cong \angle 1$. To prove that $\angle 3 \cong \angle 1$, prove that $\triangle QRS \sim \triangle QXY$ by the SAS $\sim$ Thm. 29. yes; $\frac{15}{12} = \frac{20}{16}$ 31. yes; $\frac{45}{63} = \frac{15}{21}$ 33a. 6 33b. 25 33c. 19.5

MIXED REVIEW 37. $A'(1, 3)$, $B'(8, 0)$, $C'(-4, -2)$ 39. $A'(1, -3)$, $B'(8, 0)$, $C'(-4, 2)$ 41. 49 in.²; 28 in. 43. 24 cm²; 24 cm

Lesson 10-5 pages 527–529

ON YOUR OWN 1. $\frac{1}{2}$, $\frac{1}{4}$ 3. $\frac{2}{3}$, $\frac{4}{9}$ 5. $\frac{1}{2}$, $\frac{7}{3}$ 9. \$384 11. 2 : 1 15. 12 in. 17a. [graph] 17b. 49.5 units² 19. $\frac{8}{3}$, $\frac{64}{9}$

MIXED REVIEW 25. $\sqrt{34}$ in. 29. 135 m³; 174 m²

CHECKPOINT 1. $x = 15$; $z = 10\sqrt{3}$ 2. 7.5 3. $4\sqrt{5}$ 4. $x = 1\frac{2}{3}$; $y = 3\frac{3}{5}$ 5. $\frac{1}{2}$ 6. 2 7. 3 8. $\frac{3}{8}$ 9. D

Toolbox page 530

CONJECTURE The ratio of the surface areas of similar solids is the square of the ratio of their linear dimensions; the ratio of the volumes of similar solids is the cube of the ratio of their linear dimensions.

Lesson 10-6 pages 533–535

ON YOUR OWN 1. no; $\frac{18}{27} \neq \frac{9}{12}$ 3. yes; $\frac{4}{6} = \frac{9}{12}$ 5. E 7. $\sqrt[3]{9} : 1$ or $3 : \sqrt[3]{3}$ 9. about 1000 cm² 11. 9 : 25; 27 : 125 13. 5 : 8; 25 : 64 17. about 27,000 qt 19a. 100 times 19b. 1000 times 19c. 600 times 19d. Paul Bunyan's weight is 1000 times the weight of an average person, but his bones can only support 600 times the weight of an average person.

MIXED REVIEW 21. [graph]

Wrap Up pages 537–539

1. 4 2. 9 3. $x = 12$; $y = 15$ 4. $\triangle ABC \sim \triangle FDE$; AA $\sim$ Post. 5. no 6. $\triangle XYZ \sim \triangle JKL$; SAS $\sim$ Thm. 7. C 8. $x = 15$; $z = 12$; $z = 20$ 9. $x = 2\sqrt{21}$; $y = 4\sqrt{3}$; $z = 4\sqrt{7}$ 10. $x = 2\sqrt{3}$; $y = 6$; $z = 4\sqrt{3}$ 12. 7.5 13. 5.5 14. 37.5 15. 4 16. 19.5 17. 1 : 4 18. 27 : 64 19. 64 : 27 20. 125 : 343 22. $\frac{3}{5}$, $\frac{4}{5}$, $\frac{3}{4}$ 23. $\frac{\sqrt{2}}{2}$, $\frac{\sqrt{2}}{2}$; 1 24. $\frac{\sqrt{3}}{2}$, $\frac{1}{2}$; $\sqrt{3}$

Cumulative Review page 541

1. D 3. B 5. C 7. C

CHAPTER 11

Lesson 11-1 pages 547–549

ON YOUR OWN 1. $\frac{1}{2}$; 2 3. 1; 1 5. 74.1 7. 114.5 9. 11.2 11. 14.4 13. 32 15. 48 17. 1.6 19. 21.4 21. about 51° 23. 52 m

25a.

x	tan x°		x	tan x°
5	0.1		50	1.2
10	0.2		55	1.4
15	0.3		60	1.7
20	0.4		65	2.1
25	0.5		70	2.7
30	0.6		75	3.7
35	0.7		80	5.7
40	0.8		85	11.4
45	1			

25b. tan x° [graph] 25c. The ratio approaches 0; the ratio increases rapidly. 25d. Estimates may vary slightly. Sample: 82; 2.5; 74 27. $w = 6.7$; $x = 8.1$ 29. $w = 59$; $x = 36$ 31. 53.1 33. 33.7

MIXED REVIEW 37a. If a flag is a United States flag, then it contains the colors red, white, and blue. 37b. false; true 39a. If you live on an island, then you live in Hawaii. 39b. true; false 43. $\frac{10}{19}$, $\frac{3\sqrt{29}}{19}$ 45. $\frac{9}{15}$ or $\frac{5}{15}$; $\frac{12}{15}$ or $\frac{4}{5}$

Toolbox page 550

INVESTIGATE No; as $m\angle A$ increases, so does the ratio; 0; 1

$m\angle A$	$\frac{DE}{AE}$
10	0.17
20	0.34
30	0.5
40	0.64
50	0.77
60	0.87
70	0.94
80	0.98

CONJECTURE The values match those in the sine column; sine

EXTEND The smaller the measure of the angle, the closer DA is to AE; the values are between 0 and 1.

The greater the measure of the angle, the greater is the ratio; the values are positive and can be arbitrarily large.

$m\angle A$	$\frac{DA}{AE}$		$m\angle A$	$\frac{DE}{DA}$
10	0.98		10	0.18
20	0.94		20	0.36
30	0.87		30	0.58
40	0.77		40	0.84
50	0.64		50	1.19
60	0.5		60	1.73
70	0.34		70	2.75
80	0.17		80	5.67

Lesson 11-2 pages 554–555

ON YOUR OWN 1. $\frac{7}{25}$, $\frac{24}{25}$ 3. $\frac{1}{2}$, $\frac{\sqrt{3}}{2}$ 7. 8.3 9. 21 11. 46 13. 106.5 15. D 19a. about 1.51 AU 19b. about 5.19 AU 21. $w = 37$; $x = 7.5$ 23. $w = 59$; $x = 20.0$

MIXED REVIEW 25. $a = 90$; $b = 40$; $c = 50$ 27. $a = 90$; $b = 12.6$; $c = 3$ 29. $\angle 7$ 31. $\angle 6$ 33. 180

Lesson 11-3 pages 558–561

ON YOUR OWN 1a. angle of elevation from the submarine to the boat 1b. angle of depression from the submarine to the boat 1c. angle of elevation from the boat to the lighthouse 1d. angle of depression from the lighthouse to the boat 3. 4.8° 5. 560 ft 7. 986 m 9. 3.3 km

MIXED REVIEW 15. about 13.5% 17. 55–64 19a. 35–44 19b. 55–64; 55–64 year olds have a higher share of bluegrass sales than their share of population. 21. $(3, -2)$ 23. $(9, -7)$

CHECKPOINT 1. C 2. about 17 ft 3. about 393 m 4. 15.0 5. 61 6. 20.8

Toolbox page 562

1. $w = \frac{P - 2\ell}{2}$ 3. $b = \frac{2A}{h}$ 5. $b_2 = \frac{2A}{h} - b_1$ 7. $a = \frac{2A}{p}$ 9. $r = \sqrt{\frac{A}{\pi}}$ 11. $w = \frac{3V}{\ell h}$ 13. $b = c \cos A$ 15. $\ell = \frac{S - \pi r^2}{\pi r}$

Lesson 11-4 pages 565–567

ON YOUR OWN 1. $\langle -22, 46 \rangle$ 3. $\langle -307, -54 \rangle$ 5. 15° south of west 7. 20° west of south 9. 97 mi; 41° south of west 11. 5300 mi at 26° south of west 15. The directions of both vectors are the same. The ratio of the magnitude of the image to the magnitude of the orig. vector is k. 17. No; the description gives the direction but no magnitude. 19. No; the description gives magnitude but no direction. 21. about 54 mi/h; 22° north of east 23. about 0.22 in./h; 32° north of east 25. Vectors are $\parallel$ if they have the same or opp. directions.

MIXED REVIEW 27. Neither; you need information about at least 1 acute angle or at least 1 other side. 29. congruent; AAS 31. 12.2 m

Lesson 11-5 pages 570–572

ON YOUR OWN 1. $\langle -2, 1 \rangle$ 3. $\langle -6, 2 \rangle$ 5. $\langle -2, -9 \rangle$ 7. $\langle 1, -1 \rangle$ 9a. $\frac{2}{3}$ 11a. 15° south of west 11b. about 6.7 h or 6 h 40 min

13a. [diagram] 13b. about 173 due east

15a. [diagram] 15b. 5 at 40° south of west

17a–b. 17b. Answers may vary slightly. Sample: 134 km at 43° east of south 19. white

MIXED REVIEW 21. 452.4 cm² 23. 5542.6 m² 27. $\overline{GD}$

CHECKPOINT 1. $\vec{a}$: 6.4; $\vec{c}$: 4.5 2. $\langle -2, -9 \rangle$ 3. 304 mi/h at 9° east of south

Lesson 11-6 pages 575–577

ON YOUR OWN 1. 83.1 in.² 3. 259.8 ft² 5. 47.0 in.² 7. 2540.5 yd² 9. 27.7 m² 11. 7554.0 m² 13. 311.3 km² 15. 10.7 ft² 17a. 50 mm² 17b. 116 mm² 17c. 232 mm³ 19. 1,459,000 ft² 21. 320 ft

MIXED REVIEW 23. 5 in. 25. 8.5 m 27. 281.5 cm³; 140.7 cm²

Wrap Up pages 579–581

1. $\frac{4}{5}$, $\frac{3}{5}$, $\frac{4}{3}$ 2. $\frac{\sqrt{19}}{10}$, $\frac{9}{10}$, $\frac{\sqrt{19}}{9}$ 3. $\frac{\sqrt{3}}{2}$, $\frac{1}{2}$, $\frac{\sqrt{3}}{1}$ 4. $\frac{8}{17}$; $\frac{15}{17}$; $\frac{8}{15}$ 5. 51 6. 16.5 7. 33 8. 13.8 9. D 10. 1410 ft 11. 280 ft 13. $\langle 126, 82 \rangle$ 14. $\langle 37, -93 \rangle$

15. $\langle -22, 34 \rangle$ 16. $\langle -206, -283 \rangle$ 17. about 168 mi at 27° east of south 18. about 206 km at 14° west of south 19. about 503 mi/h at 27° north of west 20. about 175 mi/h at 31° north of west 21. Multiply each coordinate by the same positive number. 22. No; the description gives magnitude but no direction. 23. Yes; the description includes magnitude and direction. 24. No; the description gives magnitude but no direction. 25. $\langle 1, 4 \rangle$ 26. $\langle 4, -6 \rangle$ 27. $\langle 2, 0 \rangle$ 28. $\langle 1, -1 \rangle$ 29a. 5° west of south 29b. about 3 h 30. 73.5 ft² 31. 232.5 cm² 32. 80.9 in.² 33. 100.8 cm² 34. 88.4 ft² 35. 70.4 m² 37. 25π in.²; 5π in. 38. 16π cm²; 8π cm 39. 121π m²; 22π m 40. 4π ft²; 4π ft

Preparing for Standardized Tests page 583

1. D 3. C 5. A 7. E 9. C

CHAPTER 12

Lesson 12-1 pages 588–591

ON YOUR OWN 1. $(x - 2)^2 + (y + 8)^2 = 81$ 3. $(x - 0.2)^2 + (y - 1.1)^2 = 0.16$ 5. $(x + 6)^2 + (y - 3)^2 = 64$ 7. B 9. C 11. $(-7, 5)$; 4 13. $(0.3, 0)$; 0.2 15. 17.

19a. $\langle -5, 3 \rangle$ 19b. $(0, 0)$; 8 21. $x^2 + y^2 = 9$ 23. $(x - 2)^2 + (y - 2)^2 = 16$ 25. $(x + 2)^2 + (y - 3)^2 = 9$ 27. $(x + 2)^2 + (y - 6)^2 = 16$ 29. $(x - 7)^2 + (y + 2)^2 = 52$ 31. $(x - 3)^2 + (y + 2)^2 = 100$ 33a. $x^2 + y^2 = 15{,}681{,}600$ 33b. 69.1 mi 33c. 1.2 mi 33d. about 32 days 35. $(x - 5)^2 + (y - 2)^2 = 13$ 37. $(x + 3)^2 + (y + 1.5)^2 = 6.25$ 39. $(x - 2)^2 + (y + 2)^2 = 41$ 43a. $\sqrt{6}$ 43b. $(x + 1)^2 + (y - 3)^2 + (z - 2)^2 = 6$

Page 738

MIXED REVIEW 45. $\angle AEB \cong \angle DEC$ because vertical $\angle$s are. Then $\triangle ABE \cong \triangle DCE$ by AAS, and $\overline{BE} \cong \overline{CE}$, $\overline{AE} \cong \overline{DE}$ by CPCTC. $\overline{AC} \cong \overline{DB}$ by the Segment Addition Post. $\overline{BC} \cong \overline{BC}$ by Reflexive Prop. of $\cong$. Then $\triangle ABC \cong \triangle DCB$ by SSS. **47.** 512 in.³ **49.** 17°; 107° **51.** 3°; 93°

Toolbox — page 592

1. (3, 120°) **3.** (5, 315°) **5.** (2, 240°) **13.** Read the measures of the central $\angle$s for points X and Y from the graph, and subtract the measures.

Lesson 12-2 — pages 596–599

ON YOUR OWN 1. 63 **3.** 72 **5.** 13 **7.** 9 **9b.** the lines bisecting the angles formed by the axes **9c.** $y = x$, $y = -x$ **11.** D **13a.** 14.5 in. **13b.** 16.5 in. **15.** 14.2 in. **17. 1.** $\overline{BC}$ is tangent to $\odot A$ at D. (Given) **2.** $\overline{BC} \perp \overline{AD}$ (A tangent to a $\odot$ is $\perp$ to the radius drawn to the pt. of tangency.) **3.** $\overline{DB} \cong \overline{DC}$ (Given) **4.** $\overline{AD} \cong \overline{AD}$ ($\overline{AD}$ is on the $\perp$ bisector of $\overline{BC}$. (Def. of $\perp$ bisector) **5.** $\overline{AB} \cong \overline{AC}$ (A pt. on the $\perp$ bisector of a segment is equidistant from the endpts. of the segment.) **19.** They are $\cong$; $\overline{CE} \cong \overline{FE}$ and $\overline{FE} \cong \overline{DE}$ because 2 segments tangent to a $\odot$ from a pt. outside the $\odot$ are $\cong$; $\overline{CE} \cong \overline{DE}$ by Transitive Prop. of $\cong$. **21.** Blue segments are common external tangents to the sun and the moon; green segments are common internal tangents to the sun and the moon; red segments are common external tangents to the sun and Earth. **23.** 4 **25.** about 34.6 in.

MIXED REVIEW 27. $\frac{13}{17}$; $\frac{2\sqrt{30}}{17}$ **29a.** rectangle **31.** 8.1

Lesson 12-3 — pages 603–606

ON YOUR OWN 1. 6 **3.** 5 **5.** 7 **7.** 18.8 **9a.** 5.9 cm **11.** 90 **13.** about 123.9 **15.** 6 in. **17.** $8\sqrt{3}$ cm **21. 1.** $\overline{CE} \perp \overline{BD}$ (Given) (A diameter $\perp$ to a chord bisects the chord.) **3.** $\overline{CE}$ is the $\perp$ bisector of $\overline{BD}$. (Def. of $\perp$ bisector) **4.** $\overline{BF} \cong \overline{FD}$ (A point on the $\perp$ bisector of a segment is equidistant from the endpts. of the segment.) **5.** $\widehat{BC} \cong \widehat{DC}$ ($\cong$ chords have $\cong$ arcs.) **23a.** $\overline{EC}$; $\overline{ED}$; $\overline{BC}$; $\overline{BD}$ **23b.** center of the $\odot$ **23c.** A diameter $\perp$ to a chord bisects the chord and its arc; the $\perp$ bisector of a chord contains the center of the $\odot$. **25.** The thms. are not true for angles, chords, or arcs that are in noncongruent $\odot$s. **27a.** 2 **27b.** 3.5 cm and 15.5 cm

MIXED REVIEW 29. obtuse **31.** obtuse **33.** acute **35.** 80 **37.** 125

CHECKPOINT — page

1. $(x - 1.5)^2 + (y - 0.5)^2 = 2.5$ **2.** $(x - 3.5)^2 + (y - 1)^2 = 46.25$ **3.** $(x + 1.5)^2 + (y + 4)^2 = 22.25$ **4.** 76 cm **5.** 48 in. **6.** 51 m **7.** 24 **8.** 5 **9.** 8 **10b.** 3 **10c.** Kites; the sides inside the $\odot$ are $\cong$ because they are radii of the same $\odot$; the sides outside the $\odot$ are $\cong$ because they are tangent segments to a $\odot$ drawn from a pt. outside the $\odot$.

Lesson 12-4 — pages 610–613

ON YOUR OWN 1. inscribed in **3.** circumscribed about **5.** 58 **7.** $a = 218$; $b = 109$ **9.** $a = 85$; $b = 47.5$; $c = 90$ **11.** $a = 112$; $b = 124$; $c = 42$ **13. 1.** $\angle ABC$ is inscribed in $\odot O$. (Given) **2.** $m\angle ABP = \frac{1}{2}m\widehat{AP}$ and $m\angle PBC = \frac{1}{2}m\widehat{PC}$ (Inscribed Angle Thm., Case I) **3.** $m\angle ABP + m\angle PBC = \frac{1}{2}m\widehat{AP} + \frac{1}{2}m\widehat{PC}$ (Addition Prop. of $=$) **4.** $m\angle ABP + m\angle PBC = \frac{1}{2}(m\widehat{AP} + m\widehat{PC})$ (Distributive Prop.) **5.** $m\angle ABP + m\angle PBC = m\angle ABC$ (Angle Addition Post.) **6.** $m\widehat{AC} = m\widehat{AP} + m\widehat{PC}$ (Arc Addition Post.) **7.** $m\angle ABC = \frac{1}{2}m\widehat{AC}$ (Substitution) **15. 1.** $m\widehat{AD} = m\widehat{BC}$ (Given) **2.** $m\angle ABD = \frac{1}{2}m\widehat{AD}$ and $m\angle BAC = \frac{1}{2}m\widehat{BC}$ (Measure of an inscribed $\angle$ is half the measure of its intercepted arc.) **3.** $m\angle BAC = m\angle ABD$ (Substitution) **4.** $\overline{AD} \cong \overline{BC}$ ($\cong$ arcs have $\cong$ chords.) **5.** $\angle ACB \cong \angle BDA$ (2 inscribed angles that intercept the same arc are $\cong$.) **6.** $\triangle ABD \cong \triangle BAC$ (AAS) **17a.** rectangle **17b.** Opp. angles are $\cong$ and supplementary. So they are rt. angles. **19.** Draw the diameter through the given pt. Construct the line $\perp$ to the diameter through this pt. **21a.** 360 **21b.** $m\widehat{DAB} + m\widehat{BCD} = 360$. $m\angle A = \frac{1}{2}m\widehat{BCD}$ and $m\angle C = \frac{1}{2}m\widehat{DAB}$, so $m\angle A + m\angle C = \frac{1}{2} \cdot 360 = 180$. $\angle A$ and $\angle C$ are supplementary. **23.** $\angle ACB$ is inscribed in a semicircle so it is a rt. angle. Then $\overline{BC}$ is $\perp$ to radius $\overline{AC}$ and passes through its endpt. on the $\odot$. Therefore, $\overline{BC}$ is tangent to $\odot A$. **25a.** 30 **25b.** 78 **25c.** 95 **25d.** 105 **25e.** 85 **25f.** 75 **27a.** 64 **27b.** 116 **27c.** 58 **27d.** 58 **27e.** 58 **27f.** 64 **27g.** 32 **31.** 180

MIXED REVIEW 33. 5 cm **35.** 108 **37.** 130

Lesson 12-5 — pages 617–619

ON YOUR OWN 1. 46 **3.** $x = 60$; $y = 70$ **5.** $x = 100$; $y = 30$ **7.** $x = 50$; $y = 97.5$ **9a.** 160° **9b.** about 18,800 mi **11.** A **13a.** $360 - x$ **13b.** $180 - x$ **13c.** $180 - y$ **15a.** $m\angle X = 30$; $30 < m\angle Y < 180$; $0 < m\angle Z < 30$ **15b.** The ship is in safe waters if the

Page 739

measure of the angle is ≤ 30. **17.** $x = 80$; $y = 50$; $z = 90$

MIXED REVIEW 19. 35% **21.** 25–44 **23.** $\overline{HF}$; $\overline{UT}$

CHECKPOINT 1. 58 **2.** $a = 30$; $b = 42$; $c = 80$; $d = 116$ **3.** 30 **4.** $a = 140$; $b = 70$; $c = 47.5$

5. A secant extends outside the $\odot$, a chord does not.

6. D

Toolbox — page 620

INVESTIGATE The 2 products are $=$.

CONJECTURE The products of the lengths of segments formed by the intersection of 2 chords in a $\odot$ are $=$.

INVESTIGATE The 2 products are $=$.

CONJECTURE When 2 secants, such as $\overleftrightarrow{GF}$ and $\overleftrightarrow{EB}$ above, intersect at a point D outside the circle, $DG \cdot DF = DE \cdot DB$.

EXTEND The product of the lengths of the segments formed by the secant is $=$ to the square of the length of the tangent segment. When $\overleftrightarrow{DF}$ becomes tangent, pts. F and G coincide. So $DF \cdot DG = DF^2 = DG^2$.

Lesson 12-6 — pages 623–626

ON YOUR OWN 1. 11.5 **3.** 7.8 **5.** $x = 25.8$; $y = 12.4$ **7.** about 271 ft **9. 1.** $\overline{AC}$ and $\overline{BC}$ are secants of $\odot O$. (Given) **2.** $\angle CAE \cong \angle CBD$ (2 inscribed $\angle$s that intercept the same arc are $\cong$.) **3.** $\angle ACE \cong \angle DCB$ (Reflexive Prop. of $\cong$) **4.** $\triangle AEC \sim \triangle BDC$ (AA$\sim$) **5.** $\frac{EC}{DC} = \frac{AC}{BC}$ (In similar figures, corres. sides are proportional.) **6.** $BC \cdot EC = AC \cdot DC$ (Prop. of Proportions) **11.** 26.7 **13.** 14.1 **15.** 172,000 mi **17c.** The center has the greatest product of the lengths of the segments of chords passing through it. **19.** $x = 8.9$; $y = 2$ **21a.** 1.1 in. **21c.**

23a. If a tangent and a secant are drawn from a pt. outside a $\odot$, then the product of the lengths of the secant segment and its external segment $=$ the square of the length of the tangent segment. **23b.** Substitution **23c.** Distributive Prop. **23d.** Addition Prop. of $=$

MIXED REVIEW 25. 40.3

Wrap Up — pages 628–630

1. $(x - 2)^2 + (y - 5)^2 = 9$ **2.** $(x - 1)^2 + (y - 1)^2 = 5$ **3.** $(x - 9)^2 + (y + 4)^2 = 12.25$ **4.** $x^2 + (y - 1)^2 = 80$ **5.** $(x + 2)^2 + (y - 3)^2 = 85$ **6.** $(x - 10)^2 + (y - 7)^2 = 468$ **7.** E **8.** 58 in. **9.** 84 mm **10.** 9.6 cm **11.** In Ch. 11, a tangent of an angle is the ratio of the length of the opp. leg of a rt. $\triangle$ to the length of the adjacent leg. In Ch. 12, a tangent line to a $\odot$ is a line in the plane of the $\odot$ that intersects the $\odot$ at exactly 1 pt. **12.** 4.3 **13.** 19.5 **14.** 6.4 **15.** 4.5 **16.** No; the arcs have different radii so they cannot be congruent. **17.** $a = 40$; $b = 140$; $c = 90$ **18.** $a = 118$; $b = 49$; $c = 144$; $d = 98$ **19.** $a = 34$; $b = 68$ **20.** $a = 90$; $b = 90$; $c = 70$; $d = 65$ **21.** $a = 95$; $b = 85$ **22.** 37 **23.** 80 **24.** $x = 57$; $y = 44.5$; $z = 129$; $v = 51$ **25.** 9.5 **26.** 4 **27.** 17.1 **28.** 8.4

Cumulative Review — pages 632–633

1. E **3.** A **5.** E **7.** B **9.** D **11.** B **13.** B **15.** C **19.** 4 **21.** 27,475 ft²

EXTRA PRACTICE

Chapter 1 — page 634

1. 37, 42 **3.** 8, $\frac{8}{5}$ **5.** 0.0003, 0.000 03 **7.** true **9.** false **11.** false **13.** true **15.** 27 **17.** 6 **19.** 40 **21.**

23. **25.** 15 **27a.** 1.4 **27b.** (2.5, 0.5) **29a.** 19.1 **29b.** $(-0.5, 3)$ **31a.** 9.5 **31b.** (1.5, −0.5)

Chapter 2 — page 635

1. scalene, obtuse **3.** isosceles, acute **5.** 100 **7.** 65 **9.** trapezoid **11.** parallelogram **13.** Sample: $\overline{ED}$, $\overline{AE}$, $\overline{BA}$ **15.** Sample: $\overline{ED}$, $\overline{AE}$ **17.** Sample: $\angle APB$ **19.** $\angle G$ **21.** $\angle T$ **23.** $\triangle TAS$

Page 740

25.

Top / Front / Right

27.

Top / Front / Right

Chapter 3 — page 636

1. **3.** **5.** **7.**

9. E **11.** C **13.** G **15.**

17. D' = C / B' / D = C'

19. rotation **21.** translation **23a.** line, rotational, point **23b.** yes **25a.** line **25b.** yes

Chapter 4 — page 637

1. If 2 angles are $\cong$, then they are vert.; if 2 angles are not vert., then they are not $\cong$; if 2 angles are not $\cong$, then they are not vert. **3.** If a car has no doors, then it is blue; if a car is not blue, then it has doors; if a car has doors, then it is not blue. **5.** 10 **7.** 65 **9.** Assume $\triangle ABC$ is not a rt. $\triangle$. **11.** Assume lines ℓ and m are not $\parallel$. **13.** $\overline{JB}$, $\overline{BP}$, $\overline{PJ}$ **15.** $\overline{CT}$, $\overline{TA}$, $\overline{AC}$ **17.**

19. altitude **21.** angle bisector

Chapter 5 — page 638

1. 42 in.; 98 in² **3.** 10 cm; 5 cm² **5.** 15 **7.** $3\sqrt{5}$ **9.** 72 cm² **11.** $\frac{25\sqrt{3}}{4}$ mm² **13a.** 6π cm **13b.** 2π cm **15a.** 18π cm **15b.** $\frac{9\pi}{2}$ cm **17.** $\frac{49\pi}{3}$ ft² **19.** $\frac{81\pi}{8}$ cm²

Chapter 6 — page 639

1. cube **3.** cylinder **5.** 84 ft²; 108 ft² **7.** 40π in.²; 56π in.² **9.** 16 mm³ **11.** 15π m³ **13.** $\frac{500\pi}{3}$ cm³; 100π cm² **15.** $\frac{4\pi}{3}$ ft³; 4π ft² **17.** $\frac{243\pi}{2}$ m³; 81π m² **19.** 64π ft³ **21.** $(60 + 6\pi)$ in.³ **23.** $\frac{1}{5}$ **25.** $\frac{7}{24}$

Chapter 7 — page 640

1. $m\angle 1 = 134$; if $\parallel$ lines, then same-side int. $\angle$s are supplementary; $m\angle 2 = 46$, Angle Addition Post. (or, if $\parallel$ lines, then alt. int. $\angle$s are $\cong$.) **3.** $m\angle 1 = 58$; if $\parallel$ lines, then alt. int. $\angle$s are $\cong$; $m\angle 2 = 122$, Angle Addition Post. (or, if $\parallel$ lines, then same-side int. $\angle$s are supplementary.) **5.** none **7.** $c \parallel d$; if supplementary same-side int. $\angle$s, then lines are $\parallel$. **9.** $r \parallel s$; if $\cong$ corres. $\angle$s, then lines are $\parallel$. **11.** none

Page 741

13. **15.**

17. 1-pt. **19.** 2-pt.
21.
23. Sample: The measure of an exterior angle with vertex C is clearly less than $m\angle A + m\angle B$.

Since all angles are rt. angles, the quad. is a rectangle. A rectangle with all $\cong$ sides is a square.

Chapter 8 — page 641

1. $\triangle ALE \cong \triangle LAP$; SAS **3.** not possible **5.** $\triangle BOI \cong \triangle TOW$; SAS **7.** $\overline{ED} \cong \overline{RF}$ **9.** $\overline{KS} \cong \overline{PJ}$ **11.** $\overline{OS} \cong \overline{OS}$ by Reflexive Prop. of $\cong$. Since $\angle T \cong \angle E$ and $\angle TSO \cong \angle EOS$, $\triangle TSO \cong \triangle EOS$ by AAS, and $\overline{TO} \cong \overline{ES}$ by CPCTC. **13.** $\triangle QRM \cong \triangle RQS$; SSS **15.** $\triangle FAD \cong \triangle EBC$; AAS

Chapter 9 — page 642

1. $x = 12$; $y = 84$ **3.** $x = 30$; $y = 55$ **5.** yes; def. of $\square$ **7.** Yes; Triangle Angle-Sum Thm., if both pairs of opp. $\angle$s of a quad. are $\cong$, then the quad. is a $\square$. **9.** square; $m\angle 1 = 45$; $m\angle 2 = 45$ **11.** rectangle; $m\angle 1 = 116$; $m\angle 2 = 64$; $m\angle 3 = 32$; $m\angle 4 = 58$ **13.** $m\angle 1 = 110$; $m\angle 2 = 70$ **15.** $m\angle 1 = 70$; $m\angle 2 = 70$ **17.** $D(0, b)$, $S(a, 0)$ **19.** $D(-c, 0)$, $S(0, -b)$ **21.** Given: Square $DRSQ$ with K, L, M, N midpts. of $\overline{DR}$, $\overline{RS}$, $\overline{SQ}$, and $\overline{QD}$, respectively. Prove: $KLMN$ is a square.

$K(a, a)$, $L(a, -a)$, $M(-a, -a)$, and $N(-a, a)$ are midpts. of the sides of the square. $KL = LM = MN = NK = 2a$. The slopes of $\overline{KL}$ and $\overline{MN}$ are undefined. The slopes of $\overline{LM}$ and $\overline{NK}$ are 0, so adjacent sides are $\perp$ to each other.

Chapter 10 — page 643

1. 10 **3.** 2 **5.** 4.5 **7.** $\triangle QCT \sim \triangle MCP$; SAS$\sim$ **9.** not $\sim$ **11.** 14.4 **13.** $x = \sqrt{70}$; $y = \sqrt{21}$; $z = \sqrt{30}$ **15.** $x = 65$; $y = 60$; $z = 156$ **17.** $18\frac{2}{3}$ **19.** $4 : 3$; $16 : 9$ **21.** $4 : 9$; $8 : 27$ **23.** $3 : 4$; $9 : 16$

Chapter 11 — page 644

1. 5.6 **3.** 9.4 **5.** 29 **7.** 50 **9.** 653 ft **11a.** $(-49, 142)$, $(38, 47)$ **11b.** $(-11, 189)$ **13a.** $(-54, 72)$, $(-95, -33)$ **13b.** $(-149, 39)$ **15.** 30.1 ft² **17.** 43.2 cm² **19.** 31.2 ft²

Chapter 12 — page 645

1. $x^2 + y^2 = 16$ **3.** $(x - 9)^2 + (y + 3)^2 = 49$ **5.** $(x + 6)^2 + (y + 2)^2 = 13$ **7.** 65 **9.** 14.8 **13.** 5.3 **15.** $a = 154$; $b = 76$ **17.** $a = 105$; $b = 100$ **19.** $x = 193$; $y = 60.5$ **21.** 10.4 **23.** $x = 112.5$; $y = 67.5$ **25.** 42.5

SKILLS HANDBOOK

page 646

EXERCISES 1. 10 handshakes **3.** 16 regions

page 647

EXERCISES 1. 6, 8, 10 **3.** any real number between 0 and 4 **5.** 2 rolls with 36 exposures and 5 rolls with 24 exposures **7.** at least 6

page 648

EXERCISES 1. 165 toothpicks **3.** 3280 triangles

page 649

EXERCISES 1. 28 posts **3.** 30 people **5.** 25 trapezoids **7.** 101 s

page 650

EXERCISES 1. Izzy is the dog; J.T. is the canary; Arf is the goldfish; Blinky is the hamster. **3.** 14 students

page 651

EXERCISES **1.** Route 90 east, Route 128 north, Route 4 north **3.** 23 d **5.** $2000 **7.** 11.4 mi

page 652

EXERCISES **1.** 39 mm; 51 mm **3.** 3.7 cm

5.

7.

page 653

EXERCISES **1.** 0.4 **3.** 600 **5.** 1008 **7.** $1\frac{5}{16}$ **9.** 34,000
11. 4.3 **13.** 15,000 **15.** 30,000 **17.** $2\frac{1}{4}$ **19.** 0.012
21. 72 **23.** 1,080,000 **25.** 12.6 **27.** $144\frac{4}{9}$
29. about 0.72 **31.** 2419.2 **33.** 13,000,000

page 654

EXERCISES **1.** $23\frac{1}{2}$ ft to $24\frac{1}{2}$ ft **3.** $339\frac{1}{2}$ mL to $340\frac{1}{2}$ mL
5. 73.15 cm to 73.25 cm **7.** 5.35 mi to 5.45 mi
9. 8.7 cm to 9.1 cm **11.** 208 m

page 655

EXERCISES **1.** 353.6; 301; no mode **3.** $40,533;
$28,150; $18,000 **5.** Median; the mode does not
represent most of the data; the mean is significantly
affected by the single highest salary. **7.** $67\frac{6}{17}$; 67; 66
9. Yes; the mode would be 67.

page 656

EXERCISES **3.** 8 A.M.–2 P.M. **5.** No; you cannot tell how
the temp. changed between the measurements.

page 657

EXERCISES **1.** 212; 76; 29; 29; 14
3.

4-yr college	211
2-yr college	75
Tech. college	29
Work	29
Undecided/Other	14

page 658

EXERCISES **1a.** 16.6 **1b.** 15.1 **1c.** 19.4

page 659

EXERCISES **1.** −50 **3.** 15 **5.** 2 **7.** 36 **9.** −2
11. 243 **13.** −20 **15.** −4 **17.** B **19.** $2\ell + 2w$
21. $-4x - 7$ **23.** $x - 5$ **25.** $r^2 - 2r + 1$
27. $y^2 - 2y - 3$ **29.** −1 **31.** $2\pi hr^2 - 4\pi hr + 2\pi h$
33. $-x^2 - 8x - 16$

page 660

EXERCISES **1.** $3\sqrt{3}$ **3.** $5\sqrt{6}$ **5.** $2\sqrt{2}$ **7.** $\frac{\sqrt{10}}{5}$
9. $\frac{3\sqrt{2}}{4}$ **11.** $5\sqrt{10}$ **13.** $4\sqrt{14}$ **15.** $4\sqrt{10}$ **17.** $2\sqrt{29}$

page 661

EXERCISES **1.** $\frac{5}{3}$ **3.** $\frac{1}{2x}$ **5.** $\frac{6}{7}$ **7.** $\frac{5}{16}$ **9.** $\frac{3}{10}$ **11.** $\frac{r}{24}$
13. $\frac{x-3}{3x-2}$ **15.** 9 **17.** $\frac{5}{12}$ **19.** $\frac{5}{13}$ **21.** $\frac{12}{5}$ **23.** $\frac{2}{\pi}$
25. $\frac{1}{9}$

page 662

EXERCISES **1.** 17.5 **3.** −4 or 4 **5.** 3 **7.** 16.5 **9.** 78
11. 3 **13.** 26.5 **15.** 1 **17.** 12,480 km **19.** 906.25 ft²

page 663

EXERCISES **1.** 5 **3.** 3 **5.** −2 **7.** −2 **9.** $-1\frac{3}{8}$
11. $-\frac{1}{4}$ **13.** 56 **15.** −5
17. $x \geq 2$ **19.** $t \geq 4$
21. $y < -3$ **23.** $k \leq -2$

page 664

EXERCISES **1.** −2 **3.** −1 **5.** 0 **7.** undef. **9.** $\frac{1}{3}$; −1
11. no intercept; −1 **13.** 1; 1 **15.** −4; no intercept
17. 1; $-\frac{1}{2}$ **19.** −4; $2\frac{2}{9}$ **21.** undef.; $-\frac{2}{3}$; 0

page 665

EXERCISES **1.** **3.** **5.** **7.**
9. **11.**
13. **15.** **17.** **19.**

page 666

EXERCISES **1.** $w = \frac{P - 2\ell}{2}$ **3.** $r = \frac{1}{2}\sqrt{\frac{S}{\pi}} = \frac{\sqrt{\pi S}}{2\pi}$
5. $d_2 = \frac{2A}{d_1}$ **7.** $a = \frac{2A}{p}$ **9.** $h = \frac{2A}{b}$ **11.** $h = \frac{3V}{\ell w}$
13. $b = c \cos A$ **15.** $\ell = \frac{S - \pi r^2}{\pi r} = \frac{S}{\pi r} - r$
17. $B = \frac{3V}{h}$ **19.** $\ell = \frac{2S - 2B}{p}$

page 667

EXERCISES **1.** (4, −1) **3.** (4, 1) **5.** $\left(\frac{3}{4}, 1\frac{1}{4}\right)$ **7.** $\left(-\frac{1}{3}, \frac{5}{6}\right)$

Selected Answers

CHAPTER 1

LESSON 1-1

page 10 Mixed Review

41–52.

TE page 44 Lesson Quiz

1a.

b.

2a.   b.

LESSON 1-7

TE page 47 Lesson Quiz

4.

Since ∠1 and ∠2 are complements and ∠3 and ∠4 are complements, $m\angle 1 + m\angle 2 = 90$ and $m\angle 3 + m\angle 4 = 90$. By the Transitive Prop. of =, $m\angle 1 + m\angle 2 = m\angle 3 + m\angle 4$. Since $\angle 2 \cong \angle 4$, $m\angle 1 + m\angle 2 = m\angle 3 + m\angle 2$. By the Subtraction Prop. of =, $m\angle 1 = m\angle 3$ and $\angle 1 \cong \angle 3$.

CHAPTER 2

LESSON 2-2

pages 76–77 Think and Discuss

1. Sample:

No diagonal contains pts. outside the octagon.

Some diagonals contain pts. outside the octagon.

Find Out By Exploring   page 81

triangle

quadrilaterals

pentagons

hexagons

Math Toolbox   page 82

Extend

a.

b.

c.

The lines are ⊥; the product of the values of m is -1; 2 lines with equations in which the product of values of m is -1 are ⊥.

LESSON 2-3

pages 83–84 Think and Discuss

2a.

3a.

8a.

b. **c.**

b.

front   right

top

page 115 **Mixed Review**

29. Sample:

LESSON 2-7

pages 109–111 **Think and Discuss**

4a.

9a. Sample:

30. Sample:

b.

front   top   right

b. For sample in part (a):

front   top   right

TE page 115 **Lesson Quiz**

1.

right

front

pages 112–115 **On Your Own**

7a.

c. For sample in part (a):

3	1
3	1

right

front

2.

front   top   right

3.

| 1 | 2 | 3 | 2 | 1 | right
|---|---|---|---|---|

front

b.

front

right

top

25.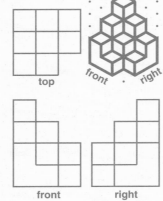

top   front   right

front   right

Chapter Assessment page 120

26.

front   right

27.

front   right

top

Additional Answers

T689

13.

CHAPTER 3

LESSON 3-3

pages 138–140   Think and Discuss

3.

page 143   Mixed Review

31.

32.

33.

34.

35.

36.

TE page 143   Lesson Quiz

1.

2.

Checkpoint   page 158

5.

Assessment   page 178

14.   Answers may vary. Sample: No; line
       m is a bisector of $\overline{UH}$ but not
       necessarily a $\perp$ bisector.

15. 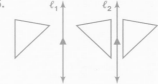   16.   17.

22.   A'   B'   C'
       $\begin{bmatrix} 8 & 12 & 20 \\ 16 & 28 & 4 \end{bmatrix}$

23.   A'   B'   C'
       $\begin{bmatrix} 0 & -1\frac{1}{2} & \frac{1}{2} \\ 0 & 1 & 3\frac{1}{2} \end{bmatrix}$

24.   A'   B'   C'
       $\begin{bmatrix} -6 & 6 & 9 \\ 6 & -6 & 12 \end{bmatrix}$

CHAPTER 4

LESSON 4-1

pages 186–187   On Your Own

20a. If coord. of a point are positive, then
      the point is in quadrant I.

  b. true; true

  c. The point is in quadrant I if and only
      if its coord. are pos.

21a. If the chemical formula of a
      substance is H_2O, then the
      substance is water.

  b. true; true

  c. A substance is water if and only if
      its chemical formula is H_2O.

22a. If a figure has rotational symmetry,
      then it has 2 lines of symmetry.

  b. true; false

23a. If the slopes of 2 nonvertical lines
      are =, then they are $\parallel$.

  b. true; true

  c. 2 nonvertical lines are $\parallel$ if and only
      if their slopes are =.

24a. If the sums of the measures of 2
      angles is 90, then the angles are
      complementary.

  b. true; true

  c. 2 angles are complementary if and
      only if the sum of their measures is
      90.

25a. If you are in Indianapolis, then you
      are in Indiana.

  b. false; true

26a. If an event is certain to occur, then
      the probability that the event will
      occur is 1.

  b. true; true

  c. The probability that an event will
      occur is 1 if and only if the event is
      certain to occur.

27a. Answers may vary. Sample: If you
      buy Tread Master Tires, then you do
      not get a flat tire.

  b. Check students' work.

28.   If a swimmer swims the fastest,
      then she wins the race; if a swimmer
      wins the race, then she swims the
      fastest.

29.   If the sum of the digits of a number
      is divisible by 3, then the number is
      divisible by 3; if a number is divis-
      ible by 3, then the sum of the digits
      of the number is divisible by 3.

32a. If a $\triangle$ is a rt. $\triangle$, then it has exactly 2
      acute angles.

b. If a △ does not have exactly 2 acute angles, then it is not a rt. △.

33a. If a polygon is regular, then all its sides are ≅.

b. If not all the sides of a polygon are ≅, the polygon is not regular.

34a. If lines have = slope, then they are ∥.

b. If lines are not ∥, they do not have = slope.

35a. If a transformation is a rotation, then it is an isometry.

b. If a transformation is not an isometry, it is not a rotation.

Find Out by Listing   page 187

There are only 2 ways all 3 boxes can be labeled incorrectly. By selecting a hat from the box labeled "1 red, 1 blue" you know which possibility is correct.

page 187   Mixed Review

36.   **37.**

38.

LESSON 4-3

pages 196–198   On Your Own

1. Answers may vary. Samples: $m\angle V = 45$ because acute angles of a rt. △ are complementary; $UT = TV$ because if 2 ∠s of a △ are ≅, the sides opposite them are ≅.

2. Answers may vary. Sample: △FED is equilateral; ∠E ≅ ∠D because base ∠s of an isosceles △ are ≅; $m\angle F = 60$ by Triangle Angle-Sum Thm.

3. *ABCD* is a rectangle; sum of the measures of angles of a quadrilateral = 360 so each angle is 90°.

---

4. Answers may vary. Sample: $m\angle DCA = m\angle A + m\angle B$; Exterior Angle Thm.

5. Answers may vary. Sample: $MP = MN$ and $NO = PO$ because if 2 ∠s of a △ are ≅, the sides opposite them are ≅.

6. Answers may vary. Samples: ∠LRO ≅ ∠QRN by Angle Addition Post.

8. Answers may vary. Sample: Both proofs list the hypothesis, the conclusion, and the reasoning. The reasoning does not depend on the form of the proof. A paragraph proof gives statements and the reasons for them in full sentences within a paragraph. In a 2-column proof, statements and reasons appear in different columns.

TE page 199   Lesson Quiz

3. Given: △EFG, with right angle ∠F. Prove: ∠E and ∠G are complementary. $m\angle F = 90$ because ∠F is a right angle. By the Triangle Angle-Sum Theorem, $m\angle E + m\angle F + m\angle G = 180$. Then, $m\angle E + 90 + m\angle G = 180$ and $m\angle E + m\angle G = 90$. So ∠E and ∠G are complementary by def.

LESSON 4-5

TE page 208   Additonal Example 2

Given: pentagon *ABCDE*

Prove: pentagon *ABCDE* has at most four acute angles.

Assume *ABCDE* has 5 acute angles. By definition, an acute angle's measure is < 90. Therefore the sum of measures of int. angles is < 450. The sum of the measures of the angles of *ABCDE* is $3(180) = 540$, which contradicts the hypothesis. So the assumption that pentagon *ABCDE* has 5 acute angles is false. Therefore, a pentagon has at most 4 acute angles.

pages 209–211   On Your Own

23. Assume $m\angle P = 90$. By def., $m\angle Q > 90$. The sum of the angle measures of △PQR is > 180. By the Triangle Angle-Sum Thm., the sum of the angle measures of a △ is 180. Therefore, the assumption is false, and an obtuse △ cannot contain a rt. angle.

24. Assume ∠B is a rt. angle. Then $m\angle B = 90$. By Isosceles Triangle Thm., $m\angle A = 90$. Then the sum of

---

the angle measures of △ABC is > 180. By the Triangle Angle-Sum Thm., the sum of angle measures of a △ is 180. Therefore, the assumption is false, and a base angle of an isosceles △ cannot be a rt. angle.

page 211   Mixed Review

32a. If a figure is a square, then it is a rhombus.

If a figure is a rhombus, then it is a square.

If a figure is a rhombus, then it is a □.

If a figure is a □, then it is a rhombus.

If a figure is a square, then it is a □.

If a figure is a □, then it is a square.

LESSON 4-7

pages 223–225   On Your Own

33a.

b.

c.

34a.

35.
side view

36.
top view

37.
side view

page 225 Mixed Review

41.

42.

Checkpoint page 225

7.

8.

LESSON 4-8

TE page 232 Lesson Quiz

1a–b.

Assessment page 238

17. Assume that the obtuse angle is not the vertex angle. Then it must be a base angle of an isosceles △. Then the 2nd base angle is ≅ to the 1st and also obtuse, because base ∠s of an isosceles △ are ≅. By def., obtuse angles measure > 90, so the sum of the angle measures of the △ is > 180. This contradicts the Triangle Angle-Sum Thm. Therefore, the obtuse angle must be at the vertex.

T692

18.

19.

20.

21.

Cumulative Review page 239

13. Sample:

CHAPTER 5

LESSON 5-7

Checkpoint page 284

10. You can (1) cut the △ in half and use the special 30°-60°-90° △ or you can (2) use the formula for the area of regular polygons. Suppose the length of each side, b, is 4.

(1) $h = \frac{\sqrt{3}}{2}b = 2\sqrt{3}$;

$A = \frac{1}{2}bh =$

$\frac{1}{2} \cdot 4 \cdot 2\sqrt{3} = 4\sqrt{3}$

(2) $a = \frac{1}{\sqrt{3}} \cdot \frac{b}{2} = \frac{\sqrt{3}}{3} \cdot \frac{4}{2} = \frac{2\sqrt{3}}{3}$;

$A = \frac{1}{2}ap = \frac{1}{2}a(3b) = 4\sqrt{3}$

CHAPTER 6

LESSON 6-1

page 302 Work Together

2b. Answers may vary. Sample: A cube is a 3-dimensional figure whose faces are 6 ≅ squares.

page 303 Think and Discuss

4. Sample:

TE page 306 Lesson Quiz

1.

2.

LESSON 6-7

pages 346–347 On Your Own

4.

$V = \frac{368}{3}\pi \text{ cm}^3$

7a.

11. An octahedron is a figure combining 2 pyramids with square bases. Find the volume of 1 pyramid; multiply the result by 2.

page 347 Mixed Review

18. Assume a base angle of an isos. △ is a rt. angle. Then the 2nd base angle is also a rt. angle by the Isos. Triangle Thm. So the sum of the measures of 3 angles of the △ is > 180. By the Triangle Angle-Sum Thm., the sum of the measures of the angles is 180. Therefore, a base angle of an isos. △ is not a rt. angle.

LESSON 6-8

Assessment page 358

10.

14. Sample: You need to know the volume of a planter to fill it with soil; you need to know the lateral area of a planter to paint its exterior sides.

Cumulative Review page 359

9.

CHAPTER 7

LESSON 7-1

TE page 369 Lesson Quiz

2a. If ∥ lines, then corres. ∠s are ≅.

b. If ∥ lines, then same-side int. ∠s are supplementary.

LESSON 7-2

TE page 372 Additional Example 1

H′ and *I′* are the images of *H* and *I* under dilation with center *G,* so △*GH′I′* is the image of △*GHI*. Then, △*GH′I′* ∼ △*GHI* because dilation is a similarity transformation. By def. of ∼ polygons, ∠*GH′I′* ≅ ∠*GHI*. If corres. ∠s are ≅, then lines are ∥, and $\overline{H'I'} \parallel \overline{HI}$.

TE page 372 Additional Example 2

∠1 and ∠2 are supplementary same-side int. ∠s, so ℓ ∥ *m*. ∠3 and ∠4 are ≅ alt. int. ∠s, so *m* ∥ *q*. Since ℓ and *q* are 2 lines ∥ to a 3rd line, ℓ ∥ *q*.

pages 373–376 On Your Own

16.

17.

18.

28.

TE page 376 Lesson Quiz

4. Since *m* ∥ *n*, *m*∠3 + *m*∠5 = 180. ∠2 ≅ ∠3, so *m*∠2 + *m*∠5 = 180. Then, ∠2 and ∠5 are supplementary same-side int. ∠s, so *p* ∥ *q*.

LESSON 7-3

pages 377–380 Think and Discuss

4.

11a–b.

12.

13.

14a.

15.

16.

26.   **27.**

28.

Checkpoint   page 383

1. If ∥ lines, then corres. ∠s are ≅.
2. If ≅ corres. ∠s, then lines are ∥.
3. If ∥ lines, then same-side int. ∠s are supplementary.
4. If ≅ alt. int. ∠s, then lines are ∥.
5. Vertical ∠s are ≅.
6. If ∥ lines, then alt. int. ∠s are ≅.
7. If ≅ corres. ∠s, then lines are ∥.
8. If ∥ lines, then corres. ∠s are ≅.

10.

11.

TE page 383   Lesson Quiz

2.

3.

Assessment   page 402

12.

16.

17.   **18.**

19. A "plane" in spherical geometry is a sphere, "lines" are great circles, and "points" are pts. on the sphere.

Check students' work for sketches.

Preparing for Standardized Tests page 403

10. The volume of the cone is $\frac{1}{3}$ the volume of the cylinder.

11. Answers may vary. Sample: The sum of the angle measures of a △ on a sphere > 180, while the sum of the angle measures of a △ in a plane = 180. An equiangular △ on a sphere can have angle measures between 60 and 180. An equiangular △ in a plane has angle measures of 60.

CHAPTER 8

LESSON 8-1

TE page 412   Lesson Quiz

3. 1. $\overline{YG}$ bisects $\overline{XZ}$ (Given) 2. $\overline{XG} \cong \overline{GZ}$ (Def. of segment bisector) 3. $\overline{YX} \cong \overline{YZ}$ (Given) 4. $\overline{YG} \cong \overline{YG}$ (Reflexive Prop. of ≅) 5. $\triangle XYG \cong \triangle ZYG$ (SSS Post.)

LESSON 8-2

TE page 415   Additional Example 2

3.

Reflexive Prop. of ≅. → △FCD ≅ △FED (AAS Thm.)

(flowchart boxes:)
$\overline{FD} \cong \overline{FD}$ — Reflexive Prop. of ≅.
$\overline{FD} \perp \overline{CE}$ — Given
$\overline{CF} \cong \overline{EF}$ — Given
$\angle CDF \cong \angle EDF$ — All rt. ∠s are ≅.
$\angle C \cong \angle E$ — Base ∠s of an isosc. △ are ≅.
$\triangle FCD \cong \triangle FED$ — AAS Thm.

LESSON 8-3

TE page 421   Additional Example 2

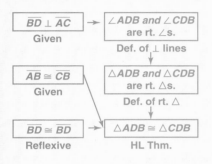

(flowchart boxes:)
$\overline{BD} \perp \overline{AC}$ — Given
$\angle ADB$ and $\angle CDB$ are rt. ∠s. — Def. of ⊥ lines
$\overline{AB} \cong \overline{CB}$ — Given
$\triangle ADB$ and $\triangle CDB$ are rt. △s. — Def. of rt. △
$\overline{BD} \cong \overline{BD}$ — Reflexive
$\triangle ADB \cong \triangle CDB$ — HL Thm.

page 425   Mixed Review

21. Angle Addition Post.

22. If ∥ lines, then alt. int. ∠s are ≅.

23. If ∥ lines, then same-side int. ∠s are supplementary.

24. If ∥ lines, then alt. int. ∠s are ≅.

25. If ∥ lines, then corres. ∠s are ≅.

26. If ∥ lines, then corres. ∠s are ≅.

Checkpoint   page 425

7a.

b. No; if 2 pairs of angles are ≅, the 3rd pair of angles is also ≅. Then the △s are ≅ by AAS or ASA.

9. If the hypotenuse and an acute angle of one right triangle are congruent to the hypotenuse and an acute angle of another right triangle, then the triangles are congruent. The HA Theorem is true. Since the right angles are congruent, the triangles are congruent by AAS.

LESSON 8-4

TE page 427   Additional Example 1

You can show $\overline{MN} \cong \overline{PO}$ if these sides are corres. parts of ≅ △s. Prove △MXN ≅ △PXO by ASA. Then use CPCTC.

TE page 427   Additional Example 2

Given: C bisects $\overline{AE}$ and $\overline{BD}$ Prove: $\overline{AB} \parallel \overline{DE}$ 1. C bisects $\overline{AE}$ and $\overline{BD}$ (Given) 2. $\overline{AC} \cong \overline{EC}$, $\overline{BC} \cong \overline{DC}$ (Def. of segment bisector) 3. $\angle ACB \cong \angle ECD$ (Vert ∠s are ≅) 4. △ACB ≅ △ECD (SAS Post.) 5. $\angle A \cong \angle E$ (CPCTC) 6. $\overline{AB} \parallel \overline{DE}$. (If ≅ alt. int. ∠s, then lines are ∥.)

TE page 427   Additional Example 3

$\overline{AC} \cong \overline{AC}$ by the Reflexive Prop. of ≅. Since $\angle D \cong \angle B$ and $\angle DAC \cong \angle BCA$, △DAC ≅ △BCA by the AAS Thm. $\overline{AB} \cong \overline{CD}$ by CPCTC.

TE page 432   Lesson Quiz

1. △PQR ≅ △TQR by SSS; $\angle PQR \cong \angle TQR$ by CPCTC

2. △FGH ≅ △FIH by ASA; $\overline{FG} \cong \overline{FI}$ by CPCTC.

3. Answers may vary. Sample: 1. $\overline{DC} \cong \overline{CE}$ (Given) 2. $\overline{DO} \cong \overline{EO}$ (All radii of a circle are ≅)
   3. $\overline{CO} \cong \overline{CO}$ (Reflexive Prop. of ≅.)
   4. △DOC ≅ △EOC (SSS Post.)
   5. $\angle DOC \cong \angle COE$ (CPCTC)
   6. $\angle DOC$ and $\angle COE$ are suppl. (Def. of supplementary ∠s) 7. $\angle DOC$ and $\angle COE$ are right ∠s (≅ supplementary ∠s are rt. ∠s.)

LESSON 8-5

page 433   Work Together

1. △AGF ≅ △BGC by SAS, ASA, AAS or HL; △DGF ≅ △DGC by AAS or HL; △ABC ≅ △BAF by SAS, ASA, or AAS; △BFC ≅ △ACF by SAS, ASA, AAS, or HL

TE page 434   Additional Example 2

1. $\overline{BA} \cong \overline{DE}$, $\overline{BE} \cong \overline{DA}$ (Given)
2. $\overline{AE} \cong \overline{AE}$ (Reflexive Prop. of ≅)
3. △BEA ≅ △DAE (SSS Post.)
4. $\angle BEA \cong \angle DAE$ (CPCTC)

TE page 434   Additional Example 3

It is given that $\angle 1 \cong \angle 2$ and $\overline{BD} \cong \overline{BE}$. $\overline{BF} \cong \overline{BF}$ by the Reflexive Prop. of ≅. △BDF ≅ △BEF by the SAS Post. and $\overline{DF} \cong \overline{EF}$ by CPCTC. Then $\angle DFA$ and $\angle EFC$ are ≅ vert. ∠s and $\angle 3 \cong \angle 4$. Therefore, △DAF ≅ △ECF by the AAS Thm.

TE page 438   Lesson Quiz

1.

1. $\angle XTZ \cong \angle WTY$, $\overline{XT} \cong \overline{WT}$, $\angle X \cong \angle W$ (Given) 2. △XTZ ≅ △WTY (ASA Post.) 3. $\overline{XZ} \cong \overline{WY}$ (CPCTC)

2.

1. $\overline{BA} \cong \overline{BD}$, $\angle A \cong \angle D$ (Given)
2. $\angle B \cong \angle B$ (Reflexive Prop of ≅)
3. △BAC ≅ △BDE (ASA Post.)
4. $\overline{AC} \cong \overline{DE}$ (CPCTC)

Cumulative Review   page 445

9.

11.

CHAPTER 9

LESSON 9-1

pages 448–450   Think and Discuss

4. Draw diagonal $\overline{BD}$. Prove △ABD ≅ △CDB by ASA and use CPCTC to prove $\angle A \cong \angle C$. Use diagonal $\overline{AC}$ to prove $\angle B \cong \angle D$.

6a. $(x + y) + (x + y) = 360$ (The sum of the measures of the ∠s of a quad. is 360.); $2(x + y) = 360$ (Distributive Property); $x + y = 180$ (Division Prop. of =)

TE page 449   Additional Example 1

1. ▱ABCD (Given) 2. $\overline{AB} \parallel \overline{DC}$, $\overline{BC} \parallel \overline{AD}$ (Def. of ▱) 3. $\angle 1 \cong \angle 4$, $\angle 3 \cong \angle 2$ (If ∥ lines, then alt. int. ∠s are ≅). 4. $\overline{AC} \cong \overline{AC}$ (Refl. Prop. of ≅) 5. △ABC ≅ △CDA (ASA Postulate) 6. $\overline{AB} \cong \overline{CD}$, $\overline{BC} \cong \overline{DA}$ (CPCTC)

TE page 449 Additional Example 2

□ABCD
Given

$\overline{AB} \parallel \overline{CD}$
Def. of □

$\overline{AB} \cong \overline{CD}$
Opp. side of □ are ≅.

∠1 ≅ ∠4 and
∠2 ≅ ∠3
If ∥ lines, then alt. int. ∠s are ≅.

△ABE ≅ △CDE
ASA Post.

$\overline{AE} \cong \overline{CE}, \overline{BE} \cong \overline{DE}$
CPCTC

$\overline{AC}$ and $\overline{BD}$ bisect each other
Def. of segment bisector

page 451–453 On Your Own

16. 1. □NGTH (Given) 2. ∠T ≅ ∠GNH (Opp. ∠s of a □ are ≅.) 3. ∠GNH ≅ ∠SNE (Vert. angles are ≅.) 4. ∠T ≅ ∠SNE (Transitive Prop. of ≅) 5. m∠T = m∠SNE (Def. of ≅ angles) 6. ∠E and ∠SNE are supplementary. (Consecutive ∠s of a □ are supplementary. See p. 449, Question 6.) 7. m∠E + m∠SNE = 180 (Def. of supplementary angles) 8. m∠E + m∠T = 180 (Substitution) 9. ∠E and ∠T are supplementary. (Def. of supplementary angles)

page 453 Mixed Review

34.

35.

36.

37.

38.

39.

TE page 453 Lesson Quiz

3. Answers may vary. Sample:
   1. □ACDF and □ABEF (Given)
   2. $\overline{AF} \parallel \overline{CD}$, $\overline{AF} \parallel \overline{BE}$, (Def. of □) 3. $\overline{CD} \parallel \overline{BE}$ (2 lines ∥ to a 3rd line are ∥)
   4. BCDE is □ (Def. of □)

LESSON 9-3

TE page 463 Additional Example 1

1. $\overline{AB} \cong \overline{AD}$ (Def. of rhombus)
2. ∠1 ≅ ∠2 (Each diag. of a rhombus bisect 2 ∠s of the rhombus.) 3. $\overline{AE} \cong \overline{AE}$ (Reflexive Prop. of ≅) 4. △ABE ≅ △ADE (SAS Post.) 5. ∠AEB ≅ ∠AED (CPCTC)
6. ∠AEB and ∠AED are rt. ∠s.
(≅ supplementary ∠s are rt. ∠s.)
7. $\overline{AC} \perp \overline{BD}$ (Def. of ⊥ lines)

LESSON 9-4

TE page 471 Additional Example 2

$\overline{AD} \parallel \overline{BC}$
Given

$\overline{AB} \cong \overline{DC}$
Given

∠ABC ≅ ∠DCB
Base ∠s of an isosc. trap. are ≅.

$\overline{BC} \cong \overline{BC}$
Reflexive Prop. of ≅.

△ABC ≅ △DCB
SAS Post.

$\overline{AC} \cong \overline{DB}$
CPCTC

LESSON 9-5

page 479 Problem Solving

$\overline{TW}$ and $\overline{UV}$ are ∥ to $\overline{OX}$ because they are midsegments of △OIX and △ORX, respectively. They are ∥ to each other, because 2 lines ∥ to a 3rd line are ∥. Similarly, $\overline{TU} \parallel \overline{VW}$. Then TUVW is a □ by def.

TE page 479 Additional Example 2

The slope of $\overline{EG}$ = −1. The slope of $\overline{FH}$ = 1. The product of the slopes is −1, so the lines are perpendicular.

pages 480–482 On Your Own

15a.

16a.   b.

26.

TE page 482 Lesson Quiz

3.

LESSON 9-6

pages 483–484 Think and Discuss

5. Answers may vary. Sample: The slope of $\overline{TV}$ is 0. The slope of $\overline{UW}$ is undefined. A line with an undefined slope is ⊥ to a line with slope 0. The diagonals of □TUVW are ⊥. Therefore, TUVW is a rhombus.

pages 485–487 On Your Own

11b. Let a pt. on line p be (x, y). Then the equation of p is $\frac{y - 0}{x - a} = \frac{b}{c}$ or $y = \frac{b}{c}(x - a)$.

d. When x = 0, $y = \frac{b}{c}(x - a) = \frac{b}{c}(-a) = \frac{-ab}{c}$. So p and q intersect at $\left(0, \frac{-ab}{c}\right)$.

f. Let a pt. on line r be (x, y). Then the equation of r is
$$\frac{y-0}{x-b} = \frac{a}{c} \text{ or } y = \frac{a}{c}(x-b).$$

g. $-\frac{ab}{c} = \frac{a}{c}(b-0)$ ✔

$-\frac{ab}{c} = \frac{b}{c}(a-0)$ ✔

page 487   Mixed Review

14. Method 1: Add the percents for the 6 age groups younger than 65. Answer: 95% Method 2: Subtract the percent for the 65-and-over group from 100%. Answer: 94% The answers don't agree because the sum for all groups is 101% instead of 100%.

TE page 487   Lesson Quiz

1. $C(0, t)$, $E(s, 0)$;
$CE = \sqrt{s^2 + t^2}$
$DF = \sqrt{s^2 + t^2}$
$CE = DF$, so $\overline{CE} \cong \overline{DF}$

2. $M(0, 0)$, $O(s + a, t)$;
$NO = \sqrt{a^2}$
$MP = \sqrt{a^2}$
$NM = \sqrt{s^2 + t^2}$
$OP = \sqrt{s^2 + t^2}$
Since NO = MP and NM = OP, opp. sides are $\cong$.

CHAPTER 11

LESSON 11-3

pages 558–560   On Your Own

13a.

b. For sample in part (a): Joelle is standing at the top of 770 ft building. She sees a famous statue at street level several blocks away. The angle of depression between the top of the building and the statue is 4°. How far is the statue from the base of the building? Answer: about 11,000 ft, or 2 mi

LESSON 11-5

page 570   Work Together

3. Answers may vary. Sample:

The magnitude of the force along the y-axis was greater.

4. Answers may vary. Sample: Have each member of the group "compete" against each other member. The person blowing along the x-axis wins if the marble stops below the line $y = x$, and the other person wins if the marble stops above $y = x$. Whoever wins the most times is the one who can exert the force with the greatest magnitude.

pages 570–572   On Your Own

9b. $\frac{2}{3}$

17a–b.

Answers may vary slightly. Sample: 134 km at 43° east of south

page 572   Mixed Review

25.

Checkpoint   page 572

4. $\vec{u} : \langle -3, -2 \rangle$, $\vec{v} : \langle -1, -4 \rangle$, $\vec{w} : \langle -4, -6 \rangle$

Preparing for Standardized Tests
page 583

10a.

b.

11.

about 0.48 in.^{2}

12.

Index

Teacher's Edition entries appear in blue type.

A

A (Angle-Angle) Similarity Postulate, 504–505, 511, 537
AAS (Angle-Angle-Side) Theorem, 416–419, 442
Acute angle, 27, 28, 29
Acute triangle, 71, 229
Addition
  of angles, 28
  of arcs, 98
  of matrices, 131
  of segments, 26
  of vectors, 568–572, 581
Addition property of equality, 46, 672
Adjacent angles, 48
Adjacent arcs, 98–101, 118
Algebra
  absolute value, 25
  coordinate plane, 9, 11, 54
  dimensional analysis, 307
  direct variation, 503
  evaluating expressions, 659
  equation of a circle, 586–588
  exercises that use, 8, 11, 17, 23, 26, 29, 30, 31, 36, 37, 47, 50, 51, 61, 63, 64, 72, 73, 89, 94, 100, 118, 120, 131, 137, 157, 189, 191, 192, 193, 206, 212, 238, 252, 255, 259, 265, 268, 272, 307, 312, 313, 320, 321, 335, 342, 346, 370, 397, 400, 402, 439, 450, 452, 458, 460, 466, 474, 476, 477, 490, 492, 499, 500, 503, 508, 509, 512, 514, 515, 520, 521, 529, 546, 548, 553, 562, 582, 592, 597, 617
  inequalities, 212, 663, 665
  linear equations, 23, 82–84, 89, 663–665
  literal equations, 562, 666
  Math Toolboxes, 11, 23, 89, 131, 212, 255, 307, 370, 439, 477, 503, 562, 592
  matrices, 131, 134
  polar coordinates, 592
  properties of equality, 46–47, 672
  properties of inequality, 212, 672
  proportions, 662
  quadratic equations, 439
  radicals, 255, 258, 660
  ratio and proportion, 103, 279, 496–498, 512, 531, 661–662
  rational expressions, 477
  sequences, 5, 648
  simplifying expressions, 659
  systems of linear equations, 14, 370, 450, 452, 466, 474, 482, 486, 487, 521, 667
Alternate exterior angles, 368
Alternate interior angles, 363–369, 372, 399
Alternative Activity(ies), 2A, 66A, 122A, 180A, 240A, 300A, 360A, 404A, 446A, 494A, 542A, 584A
Alternative Assessment. See Assessment Options.
Alternative Assessment. Teacher's Edition pages, 9, 16, 20, 23, 29, 35, 42, 50, 56, 62, 72, 80, 86, 89, 94, 99, 106, 114, 118, 129, 135, 141, 149,
155, 164, 169, 176, 186, 192, 198, 204, 210, 216, 231, 236, 247, 252, 261, 267, 272, 277, 282, 289, 295, 304, 307, 312, 320, 328, 335, 342, 346, 351, 357, 366, 374, 382, 384, 388, 394, 401, 410, 417, 421, 430, 437, 441, 443, 451, 458, 464, 471, 477, 480, 485, 491, 499, 503, 508, 520, 528, 534, 538, 545, 554, 560, 566, 570, 575, 588, 595, 603, 612, 616, 623, 630
Altitude
  of cone, 318
  of cylinder, 310
  of parallelogram, 250
  of prism, 309
  of pyramid, 316
  of rhombus, 266
  of triangle, 229–232, 237
Anemometer, 589
Angle(s)
  acute, 27, 28, 29
  adjacent, 48
  alternate exterior, 368
  alternate interior, 363–369, 372, 399
  base, 188–193, 470–471, 490
  central, 97–101
  complementary, 48, 60
  congruent, 28, 39–44, 60, 456
  consecutive, 449
  corresponding, 363–369, 371–372, 399
  defined, 26, 60
  of depression, 556–561, 580
  dihedral, 115
  of elevation, 556–561, 580
  exterior, 69–70, 75, 78–79, 117, 615
  formed by chords, secants, and tangents, 614–619, 630
  formed by tangents and chords, 610
  inscribed, 607–613, 629–630
  interior, 363
  intersecting lines and, 363–364
  linear pair, 37
  measuring, 26–31, 64, 77–79
  obtuse, 27, 28, 29
  parallel lines and, 362, 364–369, 371–376, 399
  remote interior, 69, 117
  same-side interior, 363–369, 372, 373, 399
  sides of, 26
  straight, 27
  sum of measures, 28, 68–69, 77–79, 102
  supplementary, 48, 60
  vertex, 188–193
  vertex of, 26
  vertical, 36, 48–49
Angle bisector, 34, 41–44, 61, 221–225, 227–229, 428
Angle pairs, 48–49
Angle-Angle (AA~) Similarity Postulate, 504–505, 511, 537

Angle-Angle-Side (AAS) Theorem, 416–419, 442
Angle-Side-Angle (ASA) Postulate, 414–415, 416–419, 442
Apollonius, 318
Apothem, 274, 295
Appel, Kenneth, 397
Applications. *See* Connections
Arc(s), 98–101, 118–119
  adjacent, 98–101, 118
  congruent, 281, 600–602
  intercepted, 607, 629
  length of, 281–284, 296, 671
  major, 98–101, 600
  minor, 98–101, 600
  properties of, 600–606, 629
Archimedes, 342
Area(s), 242–248, 293
  of circle, 285–290, 291, 296, 671
  of kite, 476
  of parallelogram, 249–254, 266, 294, 670
  of polygon, 243–245, 274–278, 293, 295, 670
  of rectangle, 244–248, 293, 670
  of regular polygons, 274–278, 295, 573–576, 581, 670
  of rhombus, 266, 463–464, 466–467
  of sector of a circle, 286–287
  of segment of a circle, 287
  of similar figures, 524–529, 539
  of similar solids, 531–535, 539
  of square, 243, 293, 670
  of trapezoid, 269–273, 295, 666, 670
  of triangle, 251–254, 276, 277, 294, 575–576, 577, 670
  trigonometry and, 573–577, 581
  See also Lateral areas; Surface areas
Area model, 349–352, 357
Aristarchus of Samos, 423
Arithmetic mean, 55
Art
  creative, 145, 147, 205
  exercises, 44, 94, 105, 159, 170
  graphic, 170, 191
  Native American, 137, 142, 143, 273
  See also Drawing
ASA (Angle-Side-Angle) Postulate, 414–415, 416–419, 442
Assessment
  Chapter Assessment, 63–64, 120, 178, 238, 297–298, 358, 402, 444, 492, 540, 582, 631
  Chapter Wrap Ups, 59–62, 117–119, 174–177, 234–237, 293–296, 354–357, 399–401, 441–443, 489–491, 537–539, 579–581, 628–630
  Checkpoints, 31, 52, 88, 108, 143, 158, 206, 225, 268, 284, 322, 343, 383, 425, 460, 482, 510, 529, 561, 572, 606, 619
  Cumulative Reviews, 121, 239, 359, 445, 541, 632–633
  Journal, 22, 52, 88, 101, 108, 130, 165, 206, 218, 248, 268, 314, 329, 336, 347, 383,

Acknowledgments

Cover Photos Globe and background, Bill Westheimer; concept car, Ron Kimball

Technical Illustration Fran Jarvis, Technical Illustration Manager; ANCO/Outlook

Illustration

Leo Abbett: 97 ml, 205 t, 388 b
Susan Avishai: 427
Kim Barnes: 24, 199
Tom Barrett: 186, 341 b(inset)
Judith Pinkham-Cataldo: 302 inset, 613
Jim DeLapine: 228, 289 b, 339, 340, 390 m
Kathleen Dempsey: 486
Peggy Dressel: 167 b
Howard S. Friedman: 365
Function Thru Form Inc.: 53, 134, 220 t, 303 all, 312 b, 313 t, 336, 341 t, 345 all, 346 all
Dave Garbot: 247 t, 253 t
GeoSystems Global Corporation: 127 b
Dale Glasgow & Associates: 369, 432
Kelley Hersey: 97, 509
Linda Johnson: 156 m, 157 b
Ellen Korey-Lie: 429, 572
Seymour Levy: 129 m, 150 m, 186 inset, 246, 341 b
Andrea G. Maginnis: 17 t, 30 b, 90, 137 t
Ortelius Design Inc.: 13 t, 24 inset, 270 b, 271, 395
Gary Phillips: 30 m
Lois Leonard Stock: 162 b, 164 b, 508 all, 556 all
Peter Siu: 590
Gary Torrisi: 205 t, 270 t, 352 t, 516, 558 all, 560 m, 563 all, 598 b
Gregg Valley: 224 t
Joe Veno: 4, 32

Feature Design Alan Lee Associates

Photography

Photo Research Sue McDermott

Abbreviations: JC = Jon Chomitz; FPG = Freelance Photographer's Guild; KO = Ken O'Donoghue; PR = Photo Researchers, Inc.; PH = Prentice Hall File Photo; SB = Stock Boston; SM = The Stock Market; MT = Mark Thayer; TSI = Tony Stone Images

Front matter: Page vii, David Young-Wolff/PhotoEdit; **viii,** Jerry Jacka; **ix,** Photofest; **x,** Superstock; **xi,** Tony Freeman/PhotoEdit; **xii,** Tom & Pat Leeson/DRK Photo; **xiii,** JC; **xiv,** Stephen Frisch/SB; **xv,** Geoffrey Clifford/Woodfin Camp; **xvi,** Alan and Linda Detrick/PR; **xvii,** Bob Daemmrich/SB; **xviii,** Steve Niedorf/The Image Bank.

Chapter 1: Pages 2-3, Anselm Spring/The Image Bank; **2 & 3 insets,** Used with permission of Sterling Publishing Co., Inc., 387 Park Ave. Sl, NY, NY 10016 from BEST EVER PAPER AIRPLANES by Norman Schmidt. ©1994 by Norman Schmidt. A Sterling/Tamos Book; **2 & 3 insets,** JC; **5,** David Young-Wolff/PhotoEdit; **8,** Tom Pantages; **9,** JC; **12,** Jack Newton/Masterfile; **16,** Johnny Johnson/DRK Photo; **18,** Superstock; **19,** John Gerlach/DRK Photo; **20,** JC; **21,** Will Ryan/SM; **22,** KO; **26,** Mark Bolster/International Stock Photo; **27,** JC; **29 t,** Glyn Kirk/TSI; **29 b,** Ralph Cowan/FPG; **33,** Michael Hart/FPG; **34,** JC; **36,** KO; **38,** Dan McCoy/SM; **39,** JC; **41,** JC; **44,** KO; **46,** Larry Grant/FPG; **48,** Telegraph Colour Library/FPG; **55,** Mike Agliolo/International Stock Photo; **56,** Paul Chesley/TSI; **57,** Tom Pantages.

Chapter 2: Pages 66-67, Jason Hawkes/TSI; **67 inset,** Russ Lappa; **68,** KO; **70,** Sunstar/The Picture Cube; **72,** John Coletti/The Picture Cube; **73 t,** Tom Van Sant/Geosphere Project, Santa Monica/PR; **73 bl & br,** Jerry Jacka; **76,** John Elk/SB; **78,** Richard Pasley/SB; **79 t,** KO; **79 bl,** Superstock; **79 bml,** Nawrocki Stock Photo/Picture Perfect; **79 bmr,** Jerry Jacka; **80,** Barbara Adams/FPG; **83,** Gary Brettnacher/TSI; **85,** Photo courtesy of Jacob Albert; **87 t,** B. Busco/The Image Bank; **87 b,** Frank Rossotto/SM; **90,** KO; **93,** Michael Nelson; **94,** Photograph copyright ©1996: WHITNEY MUSEUM OF AMERICAN ART, NEW YORK. Photography by Sheldan C. Collins; **96,** Courtesy of Paramount's Carowinds; **98,** Dale O'Dell/SM; **100,** David Weintraub/SB; **101,** David Weintraub/SB; **102,** NASA; **104,** Rosanne Olson/TSI; **105,** Cathlyn Melloan/TSI; **106,** Rod Planck/Tom Stack & Associates; **108,** MT; **109,** ©1996, Microsoft Corporation. Image created with SOFTIMAGE (R/3D); **110,** Barry Durand/Odyssey/Chicago; **112,** MT; **113,** Reprinted by Permission: Tribune Media Services; **115 t,** MT; **115 b,** Rick Altman/SM.

Chapter 3: Pages 122-123, MT; **123,** Bob Daemmrich/SB; **124,** KO; **126,** Frances M. Roberts; **129,** Biblioteca Ambrosiana, Milan/The Bridgeman Art Library; **130,** MAURICE HORN, THE WORLD ENCYCLOPEDIA OF COMICS (PAGE 41), reprinted with permission of Chelsea House Publishers; **132,** Photri, Inc.; **136,** Chris Michaels/FPG; **140,** NASA; **142,** Jerry Jacka; **145 l,** JC; **145 r,** Alfred Pasieka/SPL/PR; **147 bl,** Viviane Moos/SM; **147 bm,** Paul Jablonka/International Stock Photo; **147 br,** Adam Peirport/SM; **149,** KO; **152 t,** Keystone/Sygma; **152 b,** JC; **153,** PH; **154,** Frank Fornier/Contact Press Images; **155 tl,** John Kaprielian/PR; **155 tr,** Floyd Dean/FPG; **155 bl,** Michael Simpson/FPG; **155 br,** Dave Gleiter/FPG; **156,** PH; **159 t,** Tom Pantages; **160,** KO; **161,** KO; **163 l,** Russ Lappa; **163 tr,** M.A. Chappell/Animals Animals; **164 tm,** Guido Alberto Rossi/The Image Bank; **164 tr,** Courtesy of Francois Brisse; **165,** Robert Frerck/Odyssey/Chicago; **167,** Charles Gupton/TSI; **169,** Photofest; **172,** Stephen Frisch/SB; **176 l,** Patti Murray/Animals Animals; **176 m,** Russ Lappa; **178 l,** Don & Pat Valenti/DRK Photo; **178 r,** Jeff Foott/DRK Photo.

Chapter 4: Pages 180-181, Richard T. Nowitz/PR; **181,** Peter Menzel/SB; **182,** Framed. ©William Wegman 1995. 20 x 24 inches. Unique Polacolor ER photograph. Courtesy PaceWildenstein MacGill Gallery. New York; **183,** JC; **185,** ©1977 NEA, Inc.; **188,** Visuals Unlimited; **191,** Fernando Serna/Department of the Air Force; **193,** Russ Lappa, **194,** JC; **198,** John M. Roberts/SM; **199,** Corbis-Bettmann; **204,** Superstock; **207,** MT; **209 t,** Mike Penney/David Frazier Photolibrary; **209 m,** Peter Menzel/SB; **209 b,** Lynn McLaren/The Picture Cube; **211 t,** Photofest; **211 b,** PH; **213,** JC; **216,** George Holton/PR; **217,** PH; **218,** Larry Lefever/Grant Heilman Photography; **219,** JC; **220,** The Granger Collection; **223,** Mike Shirley/Picture Perfect; **224,** Martin Rogers/TSI; **225,** Globus Brothers/SM; **230,** KO; **232,** KO.

Chapter 5: Pages 240-241, John Madere/SB; **241,** Wolfgang Kaehler/Liason International; **242,** Superstock; **244,** Tony Freeman/PhotoEdit; **246,** Bill Gallery/SB; **249,** MT; **251,** Bill Horsman/SB; **254,** MT; **257,** Tom Dietrich/TSI; **260,** Robert Caputo/SB; **263,** Superstock; **264,** Nathan Bilow/Allsport; **267,** Joe Towers/SM; **270,** Terry Donnelly/TSI; **272,** William R. Sallaz/Duomo; **273 t,** Doll by Mary Tiger. Photo courtesy of the U.S. Department of the Interior, Indian Arts and Crafts Board; **273 b,** The Granger Collection; **275,** Photo courtesy of Nida-Core; **277,** G. Ross/FPG; **279,** Russ Lappa; **280,** Tony Freeman/PhotoEdit; **283 t,** CALVIN AND HOBBES ©Watterson. Dist. by UNIVERSAL PRESS SYNDICATE. Reprinted with permission. All rights reserved; **283 b,** Superstock; **286,** Gerald French/FPG; **287,** Jerry Tobias/Sharpshooters; **288,** Joe McDonald/DRK Photo; **290,** America Hurrah Archive, NYC.

Chapter 6: Pages 300-301, MT; **301,** Russ Lappa; **302,** Leigh/Stock Imagery; **304,** Sleeveless Tunic (?) with Stepped Triangles, Middle Horizon, 500-800 AD., Textile Income Purchase Fund and General Funds, Courtesy of Museum of Fine Arts, Boston; **306,** Tom & Pat Leeson/DRK Photo; **308,** KO; **311,** Greig Cranna/SB; **312,** David Young-Wolff/PhotoEdit; **313,** Scala/Art Resource; **314,** KO; **316-317,** David Sutherland/TSI; **320,** Richard Clintsman/TSI; **321 t,** KO; **321 b,** Uniphoto; **323,** KO; **326 t,** David Harp/Folio, Inc.; **326 b,** L. Kolvoord/The Image Works; **328,** Mark C. Burnett/PR; **330,** KO; **331,** Uniphoto; **334,** Uniphoto; **337,** KO; **338 l,** Mark C. Burnett/PR; **340 tl,** Mark C. Burnett/PR; **340 tml,** Richard Hutchings/PR; **340 tmr,** Tony Freeman/PhotoEdit; **340 tr,** David Young-Wolff/PhotoEdit; **340 b,** Breck Kent/Earth Scenes; **343,** KO; **344,** Don Spiro/TSI; **345,** Tom Stewart/SM; **347,** Robert Brenner/PhotoEdit; **349,** Jim Corwin/SB; **351,** Frank Fournier/SM.

Chapter 7: Pages 360-361, T. Tracy/FPG; **360 tl inset,** John Henley/SM; **360 ml inset,** Bob Daemmrich/SB; **360 bl inset,** Bill Bachman/PR; **361,** John Feingersh/SM; **363,** Charles Feil/SB; **367,** Richard Bryant/ARCAID; **368,** David Frazier/TSI; **373,** JC; **374,** JC; **375,** Paul Yandoli/SB; **376,** AP/Wide World Photos; **379 t,** Photo by Richard Cheek; **379 b,** Jock Reynolds, Installation view from Sol Lewitt: Twenty-five Years of Wall Drawings, 1968-1993, ©1993, Addison Gallery of American Art, Phillips Academy, Andover, MA; **381,** JC; **382 t,** JC; **382 b,** Andrew Brookes/TSI; **385 l,** The Granger Collection; **385 r,** Giraudon/Art Resource; **386,** Artothek; **387 l,** D & J Heaton/SB; **387 r,** Jeff Greenberg/SB; **389,** CALVIN AND HOBBES ©Watterson. Dist. by UNIVERSAL PRESS SYNDICATE. Reprinted with permission. All rights reserved; **390 tl,** Melville McLean/Portland Museum of Art; **390 tr,** Courtesy Allan Stone Gallery, New York; **390 br,** Superstock; **392,** ©AAA used by permission; **392 inset,** JC; **393,** AP/Wide World Photos; **395 tr,** Bob Krist/TSI; **395 bl,** Louis Rosendo/FPG; **395 br,** Glen Allison/TSI; **397,** JC.

Chapter 8: Pages 404-405, David Lissy/The Picture Cube; **405,** KO; **407,** Tom Alexander/TSI; **408,** MT; **409,** PH; **411,** PEANUTS reprinted by permission of United Feature Syndicate, Inc.; **415 l,** Amwell/TSI; **415 r,** Superstock; **417,** Charles Winters/PR; **419,** Charlie Westerman/Liason International; **421 l,** Lori Adamski Peek/TSI; **421 r,** Superstock; **423,** Stephen Frisch/SB; **424,** John Bechtold/International Stock Photo; **429,** Leif Skoogfors/Woodfin Camp; **434,** Jim Rudnick/SM; **435,** Miriam Nathan-Roberts; **436,** Charlie Westerman/Liason International; **438,** MT.

Chapter 9: Pages 446-447, Scott Barrow/International Stock Photo; **447,** Joy Syverson/SB; **451,** Gale Zucker/SB; **454,** KO; **457 l,** Dave Bartruff/SB; **457 r,** MT; **459,** Sepp Seitz/Woodfin Camp; **462,** Judith Larzelere; **465,** Jose Carillo/Photophile; **467,** Gabe Palmer/SM; **471,** Jan Halaska/Index Stock; **473,** Bernard Van Berg/The Image Bank; **474,** Wallace Garrison/Index Stock; **475,** PEANUTS reprinted by permission of United Feature Syndicate, Inc.; **476,** Don Smetzer/TSI; **479,** Bachman/Photo Network; **481,** Lawrence Naylor/PR; **482,** Geoffrey Clifford/Woodfin Camp; **484,** John Eastcott/Woodfin Camp; **486,** Kunio Owaki/SM.

Chapter 10: Pages 494-495, Chuck Place/The Image Bank; **495,** Russ Lappa; **497 l,** Jon Riley/TSI; **497 r,** Boden/Ledingham/Masterfile; **498 l,** Russ Lappa; **498 m,** Kathleen Campbell/TSI; **498 r,** Telegraph Colour Library/FPG; **500,** ©AAA reprinted with permission; **501,** KO; **502,** NASA; **505,** Francis Lepine/Earth Scenes; **510,** Photofest; **513,** Baron Wolman/TSI; **514 t,** Randy Wells/TSI; **514 l,** Philip & Karen Smith/TSI; **514 m,** John Chard/TSI; **514 tr,** Mulvehill/The Image Works; **518,** Chuck Kuhn/The Image Bank; **520,** William Helsel/TSI; **522,** Joe Sohm/SM; **523,** Michael Dwyer/SB; **524,** JC; **526,** Alan and Linda Detrick/PR; **528,** Bob Daemmrich/The Image Works; **531,** B. Swersey/Gamma Liason; **534,** Kevin Schafer/TSI; **535,** The Granger Collection.

Chapter 11: Pages 542-543, Jim Olive/Uniphoto; **543,** KO; **545,** Richard Steedman/SM; **547,** Courtesy of Katoomba Scenic Railway; **548,** Kaluzny/Thatcher/TSI; **552,** AGE Fotostock/First Light; **554,** Toyohiro Yamada/FPG; **557 tl,** Paul Berger/TSI; **557 tr,** Tom Carroll; **557 bl,** Bob Daemmrich/SB; **561,** Hideo Kurihara/TSI; **565,** Gary Buss/FPG; **566,** THE FAR SIDE ©1993 FARWORKS, INC/Dist. by UNIVERSAL PRESS SYNDICATE. Reprinted with permission. All rights reserved; **569,** Superstock; **570,** JC; **572,** NOAA; **574,** Guido Alberto Rossi/The Image Bank; **576,** Philip Jon Bailey/SB; **577,** Ralph Cowan/FPG.

Chapter 12: Pages 584-585, Superstock; **585,** A Joyful Scene of Spring, 1969 by Alma Thomas. From the collection of Ruth and Jacob Kainen. Photo by Gene Young; **587,** Jose Luis Pelaez/SM; **589,** Stephen J. Krasemann/PR; **590,** PEANUTS reprinted by permission of United Feature Syndicate, Inc.; **594,** Michael Rosenfeld/TSI; **597,** MT **598,** David Parker/SPL/PR; **599,** Steve Niedorf/The Image Bank; **602 l,** Robert Frerck/TSI; **602 r,** Richard Quataert/Folio, Inc.; **603,** Chad Slattery/TSI; **604,** Chad Ehlers/TSI; **611,** Chris Sorensen/SM; **613,** Nicola Goode/The Kobal Collection; **616 l,** Timothy Eagan/Woodfin Camp; **616 r,** David W. Hamilton/The Image Bank; **623,** Less Reiss/Index Stock; **626,** Telegraph Colour Library/FPG.

Flowchart information on page 158 from *Geometry and Its Applications: Symmetry & Patterns* by Nancy Crisler, ©1995, COMAP, Inc. Used with permission.

Teacher's Edition

Editorial Services Ruttle Graphics, Inc.
Design Coordination Susan Gerould/Perspectives